A TEXTBOOK OF

HISTOLOGY

By ALEXANDER A. MAXIMOW

Late Professor of Anatomy, University of Chicago

and WILLIAM BLOOM

Professor of Anatomy, University of Chicago

SIXTH EDITION

With 986 Illustrations, 257 in Color, on 580 Figures

W. B. SAUNDERS COMPANY

PHILADELPHIA AND LONDON

PREFACE TO THE SIXTH EDITION

The intent of this book now, as it was when begun twenty-six years ago by Professor Maximow, is to present a morphological and functional description of the minute structure of the human body.

As with all sciences during this quarter century, histology has undergone marked changes. When this book first appeared, morphological and biochemical endocrinology, electrical and biochemical neurology, and the histochemical and biophysical study of the submicroscopic structure of protoplasm were just entering an era of intense activity and significance.

The progressively rapid rate of increasing knowledge is producing many specialized facets of histology which are beyond the ken and competence of one person. It is accordingly a relief to me to be able to place the responsibility for some parts of this book largely on Professors P. P. H. DeBruyn, W. L. Doyle and I. Gersh. However, I have retained such final responsibility for the text as is required to promote unity, and to maintain it a textbook for medical students with the hope that it avoids becoming a series of specialized monographs.

Large sections of the book have been rewritten, and there are marked changes in content and illustrations and, in places, in point of view. Professor Doyle has written a new introductory chapter to correlate the submicroscopic, biochemical and enzymatic constitution of cells with their structure and function as determined with the optical microscope. He has also revised the discussion of renal function.

Professor DeBruyn revised and shortened the chapters on blood, connective tissue, blood formation and destruction, lymphatic system and spleen. His most important change has been to bring into the chapter on connective tissue most of the material dealing with inflammation and the macrophage system. He has also moved the discussion of the origin of connective tissue fibers to this chapter. The chapter on the thymus has been placed after that on the spleen.

Professor Gersh has written new descriptions of the endocrine glands (except the pineal). In expanding this material he has made a separate chapter for each gland. In these chapters and in those on the "target" organs he has included new illustrations showing endocrine effects. He has also revised and expanded the chapters on epithelium and glands.

To include new developments in the science I have shortened most of the chapters without deletion of essential material, particularly those on the eye, ear, male and female generative systems, nervous tissue, skin, muscle, and the digestive tract except the teeth. Few changes have been made in the descriptions of the respiratory portion of the lung (revised by Professor Loosli for the last edition) and the mammary gland. In many places, material previously in small type is now in large type.

For aid in revising the nervous tissue I am greatly indebted to Professor Patrick Wall, who made many helpful criticisms and suggestions. In response to many requests I have included several low-power photomicrographs of the central nervous system. Professor W. H. Taliaferro has revised the discussion of the physiology of the spleen. Professor F. C. McLean, as in previous editions, has contributed to the revision of the chapter on bone, and my wife has rewritten the chapter on cartilage from a more functional point of view.

There are four new colored plates by Mrs. E. Bohlman Patterson, one each in chapters I, IV, VII and XV. Seventeen photomicrographs in color are from the new atlas of von Herrath and Abramow, published by the G. Thieme Verlag. There are five new electron micrographs and several new photomicrographs by phase contrast. In addition, forty-six new photomicrographs were taken by Mr. Jean Crunelle. Abbreviations have been replaced by spelling out the labels on several of the figures, of which the most important are the two color plates showing the development of bone marrow cells.

I have been favored and assisted by suggestions, corrections and criticisms from many histologists here and abroad. In this place I cannot thank all who have contributed in this way to this revision, but among them I am particularly indebted to Professors M. Block, D. Bodian, R. G. Murray, I. Schour and J. W. Wilson.

WILLIAM BLOOM

ACKNOWLEDGMENTS FROM PAST EDITIONS

FROM THE FIRST EDITION

At the time of his death in December, 1928, Professor Maximow was writing a Text-book of Histology. This was to be based as far as possible, both as to text and figures, on human material, and the functional aspects of the structures described were to be emphasized. For this work he had collected much new material and had made many new illustrations. He had completed the sections on the male and female generative organs, the urinary tract, the organs of special sense, and epithelium. In rough manuscript he left the sections on the blood and connective tissue, the gastro-intestinal tract, the blood vascular and lymphatic systems, the spleen, the integument, and the mammary gland.

None of the chapters on the Nervous Tissue were written by Professor Maximow in their present form. His papers included some notes and drawings which were helpful in a general way as indicative of the line of treatment contemplated. There was also available the Russian text of 1918 in which the nervous tissues are treated very fully. A complete translation of these Russian chapters and the notes and drawings were placed in the hands of Professor Maximow's colleague, Professor C. Judson Herrick, and these served as the basis upon which the present text was written. . . . These chapters, accordingly, are to be regarded not as a posthumous publication, but as an entirely new formulation of the theme, the responsibility for which rests chiefly with Professor Herrick.

I am indebted to Dr. N. Hoerr for writing the description of the suprarenal bodies.

I have written the sections on the biliary and respiratory systems, the pancreas, the endocrine glands (with the exception of the suprarenals) and the introductory chapter. In all of these sections I have conformed, in general, with Professor Maximow's ideas on these subjects. In addition, I have thoroughly revised the sections on cartilage, bone and muscle, which were based on translations of parts of his Principles of Histology (Russian), and his rough manuscript on the blood vascular and lymphatic systems, the spleen, integument, mammary gland, gastro-intestinal tract, the blood, connective tissue, and the blood-forming and destroying tissues.

Throughout the work of editing and completing this book I have profited greatly by frequent consultations with Professor Bensley.

FROM THE FOURTH EDITION

The obtaining of very early implantations of chimpanzee and human ova makes it possible to include a brief description of the early stages of human placentation. Professor G. W. Bartelmez has generously contributed this new material and also a thorough revision of the rest of the chapter dealing with the female generative system.

With each revision of this book I am encouraged to face the enormous literature by the liberal help which I have received from friends and colleagues in various biological fields. I am indebted to Professor R. R. Bensley for revising the section on protoplasm, to Professor S. W. Becker for some of the changes in the chapter on the skin, to Professor E. A. Boyden for extending the description of the biliary passages, and to Professor E. M. K. Geiling for aid with the chapter on the endocrine glands. Professor S. Polyak has revised the chapters on the nervous system and the eye and has omitted some of the details of both chapters, especially of the latter. The appearance of his monograph on the retina makes it unnecessary to have the description of this structure as detailed as it was in the previous edition. Professor W. H. Taliaferro has contributed to the discussion of the macrophages and the spleen. Dr. E. Conway Mahon has helped in the revision of much of the text.

FROM THE FIFTH EDITION

Professor William L. Doyle has revised the section on protoplasm and written most of the discussion of its submicroscopic organization. Professor Clayton G. Loosli has recast the description of the respiratory portion of the lung. The chapter on bone has been rewritten in collaboration with my co-worker in this field, Professor Franklin C. McLean.

Professors Peter De Bruyn, Eugene M. K. Geiling, Ralph W. Gerard, Franklin C. McLean and William H. Taliaferro and Dr. Roy Grinker made many helpful suggestions for other topics.

The treatment of the hemopoietic tissues has been abbreviated and fairly extensive changes made in the sections on muscle and the endocrine glands. I have condensed parts of the chapter on the nervous tissue which was prepared for the last two editions by Professor Stephen Polyak. I have also rewritten much of the chapter on the female generative system. This chapter was revised in previous editions by Professor George W. Bartelmez, who contributed a description of early human placentation to the fourth edition.

WILLIAM BLOOM

CONTENTS

Contents

Contents

I. INTRODUCTION

Histology is concerned with the structural characteristics of the cells and tissues of living organisms and with the relationships of their structure to function. It involves the organization of cell types into tissues which have characteristic intercellular environments, and deals with the contributions of the various tissues to the formation of organs. Most of the basic information has been obtained by observation of living or preserved specimens with a microscope.

Although the microscope has been used for nearly 300 years for the study of minute anatomy, modern histology began with an outburst of investigation in the third and fourth decades of the nineteenth century and received its greatest impetus from Schwann's conclusion that nucleated cells are the basis of the formation of all animals and plants. His idea was received with great enthusiasm "because it gave the key to a multitude of known facts and the direction for new, planned investigations" (Henle, 1841).

The succeeding century of intensive histological investigation may be divided into several fairly distinct periods, each with different immediate aims and philosophies. But the entire history has been characterized by the desire for further knowledge of the origin and function of the parts of animals and plants as evidenced by minute structure.

As most tissues and organs are too thick to be examined directly with the microscope, the histologists of a hundred years ago examined thin membranes and scrapings and teasings of thick organs. These teasings disrupted topographic relations, and the cells soon died. With their imperfect microscopes and with the aid of only a few reagents, such as acetic acid, it seems remarkable that the histologists saw as much as they did.

The study of living and surviving cells was replaced to a large extent during the next fifty years by the investigation of details made visible in dead cells through the introduction of methods for the preservation of tissues, cutting them in thin slices and staining them with a variety of dyes. Such studies were made possible by great improvements in microscopes and microtomes and a host of "fixing" and staining methods. During this period there was accumulated a great mass of descriptive embryological, histological and histopathological data. Basic processes in the life history of the unicellular and multicellular organisms were recognized, such as their modes of reproduction, and the occurrence of growth, multiplication, differentiation and death of cells.

About the turn of the century a new period began, characterized by attempts at interpretation of structure in terms of function and by renewed interest in correlating living and dead appearances. As one of the results of

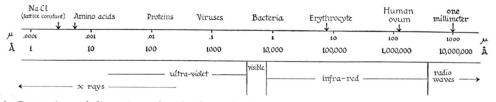

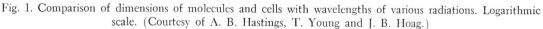

Fig. 1. Comparison of dimensions of molecules and cells with wavelengths of various radiations. Logarithmic scale. (Courtesy of A. B. Hastings, T. Young and J. B. Hoag.)

this study, a number of investigators began to look on all sectioned material as artefact and to accept as true only what could be seen in living cells. This view was soon modified, because some of the so-called artefacts of fixation have been shown to be important components of living cells. On the whole, however, the skeptical period has caused the histologist to realize that he must use all the methods of investigation, that all of them together are insufficient, and that new ones must be developed. Out of this era several significant methods of cell study developed, such as tissue culture, transplantation to foreign tissues, including the anterior chamber of the eye, the use of transparent windows in rabbit ears, and micromanipulation devices.

Today, newer methods in histology, recognizing the advances in physiology and biochemistry, are concerned with a more precise description of structure in terms of chemical composition and biochemical activities, and with the exploitation of new physical instruments capable of revealing finer structural details.

The Microscope. With the aid of an optical microscope one can distinguish objects as individual particles if they are not less than 0.2 micron apart. The resolving power of a microscope is dependent on the wavelength of the light and the light-gathering capacity (numerical aperture) of the objective. The best oil immersion objects have a numerical aperture of 1.4, but most histological work is done with lenses of numerical aperture 1.0 or less. By reducing the wavelength of light it is possible to increase the resolving power of the microscope to 0.1 micron with ultraviolet light. Particles smaller than the limit of resolution can be seen by the light reflected from them in dark-field illumination of the ultramicroscope, but it is not possible to determine their dimensions or shape precisely. From Figure 1 it can be seen that it should be possible to photograph individual molecules, provided one uses wavelengths which are sufficiently short and lenses with sufficiently high numerical apertures. As appropriate instruments are developed, the field of histology will merge more closely with that of structural chemistry. Electron beams have much shorter wavelengths than light, and magnetic lenses have been developed so that, at 100 kilovolts, a resolution of 30 angstrom units is achieved. With this resolving power the morphology of virus and protein molecules can be viewed directly on the fluorescent screen of the electron microscope or photographed.

The light microscope has also been improved by the development of phase-contrast microscopy. Most colorless structures embedded in colorless protoplasm, unless they are highly refractile, are seen indistinctly, if at all. If these structures are of different refractive index from that of protoplasm, the phase-contrast device provides differences in light intensity which reveal the structures. (See Figures 2, 3 and 11.)

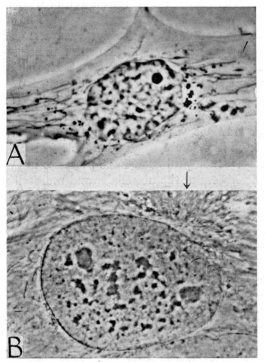

Fig. 2. Phase-contrast photomicrographs of newt cells in living culture. A, Outstretched macrophage; the largest nuclear body is the nucleolus; long mitochondria are prominent in the cytoplasm. B, Portion of fibroblast, showing nucleoli and chromatin particles in the nucleus. The arrow points to the concentration of mitochondria about the clearer cytocentrum adjacent to the nucleus. 900 ×. (Courtesy of L. Wang.)

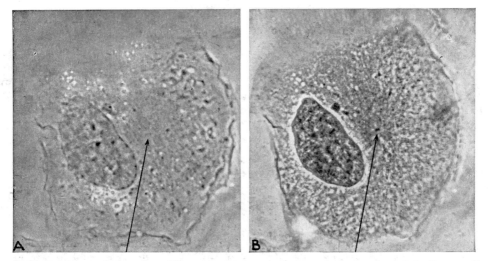

Fig. 3. Photomicrograph by phase-difference microscopy of a macrophage of newt in tissue culture. A, Before fixation; B, same cell in 95 per cent alcohol thirty four minutes after fixation in Zenker-formol. The arrows point to the centrioles. 800 ×. (After Buchsbaum.)

CELL STRUCTURE

Protoplasm. Although special techniques of tissue culture and microdissection permit the study of living tissue, the great mass of work done in both normal and pathological histology is based on preserved material which has been appropriately stained. Figure 3 demonstrates that much of the structural appearance of the living cell can be preserved by appropriate treatment. The more stable elements of cell structures are quite well preserved by a variety of procedures, and the stains hematoxylin and eosin reveal them in a manner which is easily reproducible in any laboratory. Accordingly, these procedures have become standardized for most medical teaching and pathological studies.

To appreciate the action of preservatives and stains on biological material, it is necessary to have some understanding of the nature of the living substance—protoplasm. For reasons which are not obvious, protoplasm in higher organisms characteristically occurs in the form of cells which are bounded by a so-called *plasma* or *cell membrane* and which contain a subdivision, the *nucleus*, bounded by a *nuclear membrane*; the material in which the nucleus is embedded is the *cytoplasm* (Fig. 4). The plasma membrane regulates the interchange of materials between the cell and its environment. The nature of the invisible surface membrane of the cell is still in doubt. This membrane, estimated as 100 to 200 angstrom units thick, is usually described as differentially permeable; that is, the membrane acts selectively, in unknown fashion, to permit the accumulation within the cell of some solutes and not of others. The extensive body of knowledge dealing with this topic has been thoroughly reviewed by Davson and Danielli and by Höber et al.

By microdissection it has been determined that the cell membrane is somewhat resistant and highly elastic and that, when it is destroyed at one point on a cell, a new membrane is soon formed from the cytoplasm.

Between the nucleus and the cytoplasm is another membrane, called the nuclear membrane (Fig. 4). By microdissection it has been shown that the nuclear membrane is quite tough and slightly elastic, and that, when it is punctured, the nuclear content may run out, although nuclei usually "set" as a viscous gel when they are injured. Electron micrographs of a nuclear membrane reveal a thicker structure (400 angstrom units) with the appearance of regularly arranged pores.

Taking the cytoplasm as typical protoplasm, we find that it has a consistency which may vary from that of a liquid to a rather firm gel. It presents the appearance of an optically clear (hyaline) continuous sub-

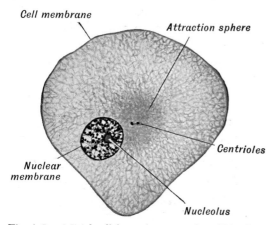

Cell membrane

Attraction sphere

Centrioles

Nuclear
membrane

Nucleolus

Fig. 4. Interstitial cell from the ovary of a rabbit. Iron-hematoxylin stain. 1300 ×. (A.A.M.)

stance in which certain visible particles are embedded. Many of these are products of cell activity, but others, such as *mitochondria* (p. 14), are to be regarded as organelles of the cell. The chemical composition of protoplasm is properly the domain of biochemistry, but certain aspects are essential to a consideration of structure.

Composition. As the cell may be considered to be an organized set of systems in dynamic equilibrium with their environments, it is not surprising that many of the common chemical elements are to be found in protoplasm. The human body has the following percentage composition on a fresh weight basis: oxygen, 65; carbon, 18; hydrogen, 10; nitrogen, 3; calcium, 2; phosphorus, 1.1; potassium, 0.35; sulfur, 0.25; sodium, 0.15; chlorine, 0.15; magnesium, 0.05; iron, 0.004. In addition to these, traces of two dozen or so other elements normally found in living organisms are vital to life. However, on the basis of the number of molecules and ions present, a table of the composition of the body would have a different aspect; thus there are 1.7 times more hydrogen atoms in the body than all the other atoms put together.

An analysis of protoplasm reveals the presence of water, inorganic ions and innumerable naturally occurring organic compounds, some of which may be broadly classed as proteins, carbohydrates, lipid substances, their combinations, their constituents and their precursors. Preeminent in the architecture of cells are the proteins.

Some proteins vary from one cell type to another and are specific for organ and species. Other proteins seem to be of common occurrence. Important constituents of nucleus and cytoplasm are the nucleoproteins (p. 7). Carbohydrates occur in animal cells as glycogen and its hydrolytic products and also combined with proteins and lipids. Intracellular fats vary from minute droplets of neutral fats in many types of cells to large accumulations in the fat cells which are specialized for the storage of these substances. Although more complex lipids such as sterols and phosphatides are widely dispersed in cells, they are only rarely demonstrated by visual means.

Protoplasm contains much potassium, little sodium, small amounts of magnesium, and even less calcium; the heavy metals are present in traces. Of the anions, bicarbonate and phosphate predominate; chloride is present in small amounts if at all, except in red blood cells. This contrasts strongly with the body fluids, in which sodium salts, especially the chloride, predominate (Figs. 5 and 30).

Extracellular and Intracellular Phases of Tissue. The chemical composition of different tissues from the same animal or of the same tissue from different animals differs widely, and it is surprising that any deductions of biological significance can be made from chemical analyses. The distribution of materials extracellularly and intracellularly has been described by Hastings as follows: Quantitative analyses of various tissues were made for water, hemoglobin, fat, total protein, collagen, elastin, chloride, bicarbonate, phosphate, magnesium, calcium, potassium and sodium. For a relatively homogeneous tissue, such as muscle, heart or liver, by expressing analytical results on a fat-free, blood-free basis, by assuming that chloride is extracellular and that its concentration in extracellular fluid is equal to that in blood plasma, save for a small correction due to the Donnan equilibrium, it is possible to calculate the following: (1) the proportions of the tissue that constitute the extracellular and intracellular phases (extracellular phase = extracellular fluid plus collagen and elastin; intracellular phase = intracellular fluid plus intracellular proteins); (2) the ionic composition of the extracellular fluid (this can be fairly completely specified); (3) the concentration of certain constituents of intracellular fluid. Further analytical studies are needed in order to complete the ionic composition of intracellular fluid.

Figure 5 is a graphic interpretation of analytical data obtained on the skeletal muscle of the dog. Concentrations in milliequivalents per kilogram of water are plotted vertically; amounts of intracellular and extracellular solids and fluids are plotted horizontally. The points of interest are (1) The extracellular solids (cross-hatched area) plus extracellular fluid (clear areas) comprise about 17 per cent of the muscle mass. (2) The extracellular fluid has an ionic composition nearly like that of blood plasma. Note that it is rich in sodium, chloride and bicarbonate, and low in potassium, calcium and magnesium. (3) The intracellular phase amounts to about 83 per cent. The water concentration of the intracellular phase is 75 per cent and remains remarkably constant. (4) The principal cations of the intracellular fluid are potassium and magnesium, and the principal anions are protein and organic phosphates. Under normal conditions the intracellular fluid contains little sodium and practically no chloride. The intracellular concentration of the bicarbonate radical is only about one third that of extracellular fluid, and from this the intracellular pH has been calculated to be about 6.8.

In view of the freedom with which potassium exchanges between extracellular and intracellular fluids, the maintenance of a thirty-fold gradient of potassium between these two fluids requires a fuller explanation than is as yet available. The opinion, recently current, that this gradient depends upon a pumplike mechanism which uses part of the energy derived from the metabolism of the cell, is now being displaced by the belief that the high concentration of potassium in the muscle fiber may be derived as a consequence

of the Donnan equilibrium plus a specific affinity between potassium and myosin. (See also page 150.)

The data for skeletal muscle are similar, though quantitatively slightly different, for

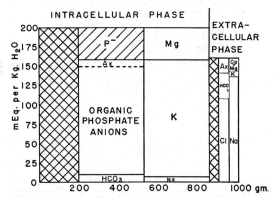

Fig. 5. Diagram of constitution of skeletal muscle. Concentrations in milliequivalents per kilogram of water are plotted vertically; amounts of intracellular and extracellular solids and fluids are plotted horizontally. The solids are represented as cross-hatched areas and the fluids as clear ones. For details, see text (p. 4, 5). (Courtesy of A. B. Hastings.)

heart muscle and liver. A similar treatment of analytical data obtained on brain and kidney is not practical, owing to their heterogeneous nature.

Chemical Architecture. It is frequently stated that protoplasm is a complex colloidal system which provides a variety of interfaces and phase boundaries at which biochemical reactions take place. But such a concept is hardly adequate in view of the degree of integration of the activities which is present in living systems. It has therefore been postulated that cells have some kind of macromolecular skeleton which provides numerous surfaces of highly specific configuration arranged as a more or less continuous phase permeated by components in true solution. If there is such a "cytoskeleton," it would have to be in dynamic equilibrium with the more fluid continuous phase. In a sense the architecture of the cell is that of a factory carrying out certain processes in connection with specialized structures, but it is a factory in which the raw materials, the machinery and the end products are continually interchanging. At one moment an amino acid molecule may be considered a potential source of food, and at another moment it may be incorporated in a protein of the metabolic machinery.

The use of isotopic tracers has led to the view that cellular structures and their chemical reaction systems are in dynamic equilibrium with an intracellular pool of metabolites composed of many small organic molecules. Thus the significance of the classical distinction betwen endogenous metabolism and exogenous metabolism disappears (Schoenheimer).

Enzymes. In the transformation from food substance to constituents of living protoplasm and in the numerous metabolic processes furnishing energy, a fundamental component of each of the mechanisms is the *enzyme* which catalyzes the reaction. Now the variety of systems which operate simultaneously in a single cell appears to be relatively large compared to the number of distinct morphological structures which we can distinguish optically. Furthermore, since in many metabolic reactions there must be a coupling between the energy-producing (*exergonic*) oxidative reactions and the energy-using (*endergonic*) synthetic processes, some sort of structural organization, such as a "cytoskeleton," is required to compartmentalize the processes. This concept of a cytoarchitecture is compatible with the observed specificity of many enzymes. Among the more important groups of enzymes are those catalyzing *oxidations, reductions, hydrolyses* and *phosphorylations*; esters are split by *esterases* and peptide bonds by *peptidases*, and so on. It may be assumed that reversal of the hydrolytic processes is frequently accompanied by (coupled to) exergonic reactions.

Owing to the remarkable specificity of many enzymes, it is not always necessary that there be a compartment for each reaction, if that were in fact possible. The oxidation of carbohydrates, for example, involves the stepwise conversion of one compound into another in a sequence of reactions each of which is catalyzed by an enzyme specific for that step. By introducing the initial compound into an appropriate solution containing three purified enzymes, one may observe that the highly specific end product of the third reaction is produced as well as if its immediate precursor had been supplied. This sequential organization of processes without benefit of any structure has been termed by Dixon "organization by specificity," and this concept is of major significance for an understanding of the physiology of protoplasm.

Several qualitative histochemical methods have demonstrated the presence of particular enzymes, notably *phosphatase*, within cells and tissues. In a few instances, quantitative studies have also been made (Figs. 236, 359). It is, however, difficult to deduce the physiological role of the enzymes from their localization in relatively high concentration (cf. Danielli). Actually, the demonstration of a spatial correlation between morphological units and chemical mechanisms involves difficulties of practical and theoretical nature. A large literature of circumstantial evidence relating the configuration of cellular structures to processes significant in particular tissues is accumulating rapidly. (See reviews by Dempsey and Wislocki; Moog.) It is also evident from the biochemical differences observed between the metabolism of tissue slices, minces and extracts that certain processes are inactivated (and others initiated) when cellular organization is disrupted. Only after suitable precautions may the structural elements be isolated in more or less intact condition for examination of their chemical mechanisms.

In multicellular animals, and more particularly in the higher forms, many cells are specialized for the execution of particular functions. These may be classified as dealing primarily with (1) the *vegetative existence* of the cell, (2) its *growth* and *reproduction*, and (3) its *special functions*. The vegetative activities of the cell, defined as the minimum of activities necessary for its continued existence, are concerned chiefly with its energy metabolism (or respiration), with the assimilation of food and the elimination of waste materials.

The processes by which energy is released

from foodstuffs and made available for the needs of the individual cell and of the organism as a whole involve the consumption of oxygen, the combustion of organic molecules, and the production of carbon dioxide and water. Oxidation occurs as the result of either the addition of oxygen to a compound or the loss of hydrogen from that compound. Cellular oxidation occurs largely as a result of dehydrogenation. In the presence of a *dehydrogenase* a molecule of foodstuff is activated in such a manner that hydrogen is transferred to a reversible oxidation-reduction system (*co-enzyme*), which becomes reduced. Hydrogen is transported from the reduced co-enzymes to other enzymes which contain iron, and, in the presence of these, it combines with oxygen. Carbon dioxide production probably occurs as the result of spontaneous or enzymatic decarboxylation of certain metabolic intermediates. Many co-enzymes are thermostable, nonprotein, organic molecules derived from vitamins. In general, it is likely that vitamins and minerals which are ingested in traces function as co-enzymes for various cellular enzymes.

By differential centrifugation of suspensions of cell fragments, one may obtain fractions which consist almost entirely of nuclei or mitochondria, or submicroscopic granules (also called microsomes) and certain other granules. By this means, mitochondria of guinea pig liver have been isolated and found to contain 65 per cent protein by dry weight and 35 per cent of fatty substances, high in phospholipids. Analyses of mitochondria of liver of other animals have given similar results. Mitochondria probably vary in composition according to the cell type in which they are found.

The relation between mitochondria and enzymes has been extensively investigated, but in only a few instances has definite quantitative evidence been presented. Most, if not all, of the cytochrome oxidase and succinic acid oxidase activity has been found to be associated with mitochondria. (See organoids, p. 13.) On the other hand, in many cells the enzymes hydrolyzing dipeptides are uniformly distributed in the cytoplasm rather than localized on visible granules. The same is true for catalase, which decomposes hydrogen peroxide. However, the enzymes amylase and a proteinase in ameba were found not to be uniformly distributed in the cytoplasm.

Numerous syntheses take place within cells. To a certain degree, as in the elaboration of proteins for the protoplasm of the individual cell, these syntheses are common to all cells, but there is also a high degree of specialization in the synthetic processes carried on within cells. The degree to which the organism as a whole can provide for its complex needs is indicated by the facts that animals can be kept alive and in excellent health with all dietary nitrogen furnished in the form of pure amino acids, and that many of the amino acids themselves can be synthesized in the body. Similarly, the animal organism can make transformations between proteins, fats and carbohydrates; indeed, it can even utilize carbon dioxide in synthesis of carbohydrate.

The end products of metabolism are chiefly carbon dioxide, water and urea. These substances diffuse readily through cell membranes, and no process, other than diffusion, is necessary for the individual cell to rid itself of these end products. In the higher animals, however, many cells are specialized for the removal of waste products from the body.

Nucleic Acids. These are of primary significance in the cell; they fall into two major categories: (1) *Desoxyribonucleic* acid (DNA) (*thymonucleic* acid) contains four nucleotides, each of which contains phosphoric acid, desoxyribose and one of the four bases—thymine, adenine, cytosine, and guanine. The proportions of nucleotides may vary, depending on the species and tissue from which the nucleic acid is derived. (2) *Ribonucleic* acid (RNA) (yeast nucleic acid) is similarly constituted with ribose as the sugar and with uracil replacing thymine. These and other nucleic acids occur naturally combined with basic proteins in the form of nucleoprotein. Despite marked variation in appearance and size of nuclei in the various cell types in mammalian species, some current work indicates that for nondividing cells the desoxyribonucleic acid content of all diploid nuclei is constant for the species. Values for a variety of mammalian species are similar, being of the order of 5×10^{-6} micrograms per nucleus (Vendrely).

Ultraviolet microscopic absorption spectroscopy, as developed by Caspersson, has provided a useful device for analysis of the distribution of nucleic acids in the nucleus and cytoplasm. Studies by this method, coupled with analytical fractionation procedures and the use of specific enzymes such as *ribonuclease* (Brachet), have gone hand in hand with advances in microbiology and genetics to indicate the chemical constitution and biochemical role of nucleoproteins in the nucleus and in the cytoplasm.

The demonstration of variations in the concentration of nucleoproteins in nucleus and cytoplasm has resulted in theories relating nucleoproteins to the synthesis of proteins. (See Caspersson.) But since we are still uncertain of the manner of formation of a simple peptide bond, any theories on the mechanism of protein synthesis must be considered tentative.

Experiments involving the quantitative analysis of nucleoproteins of tissues, notably of liver, have shown that these substances in the cytoplasm and in the nucleus exchange radioactive phosphorus with the inorganic phosphate of the cell. The turnover rate for desoxyribonucleic acid is, however, much lower than that for ribonucleic acid.

Fixed and Stained Preparations. It is the organization inherent in protoplasm which confers the attributes of life to the complex chemical machinery. To preserve the structure for microscopic examination destroys the dynamic organization and to a greater or less extent removes some of the structure and distorts the remainder. That we can recognize the preserved material at all is largely due to certain properties of the proteins which are universally present. The first step in "fixation" of protoplasm involves rendering the proteins insoluble by precipitating them. The different fixatives precipitate the proteins in aggregates having various properties and different sizes; many of them leave the lipids unaffected, but most of them remove the carbohydrates and a large part of the salts. Accordingly, to study all these constituents of a cell, various *fixation methods* must be used. Some are better than others with respect to (*a*) preservation of the cells and their constituents with a minimum of visible distortion, (*b*) speed of penetration, and (*c*) subsequent application of various stains. In general, the more acid the fixative, the more the nuclear material will be clumped; as this clumping becomes prominent after staining, there results the common belief that fixatives with picric acid or trichloracetic acid are "good" fixatives. Actually, the various fixing solutions containing neutral formalin, osmic acid and mercuric chloride, singly or in combination, are among the best for morphological purposes. Histochemical analysis of cells usually requires special fixatives.

In the Altmann-Gersh freezing-drying technique, tissues are made available for chemical study almost unaltered. The movement of crystalloids and some organic substances that

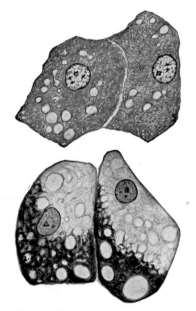

Fig. 6. Liver cells of amblystoma fixed by the Altmann-Gersh method (above) and by Zenker-formol below) and stained with hematoxylin and Best's carmine for glycogen. The glycogen is evenly distributed in the former and clumped in the latter. 400 ×. (Courtesy of I. Gersh.) (W. B.)

takes place during the application of the usual fixatives is avoided (Fig. 6). This technique has been significant in combination with micro-incineration and with ultraviolet absorption methods.

The next step in the preparation of fixed tissues for study consists in slicing them into thin layers. This is accomplished either by freezing a bit of tissue, after which it can be sectioned in a special instrument, or by infiltrating it with a solution of gelatin, paraffin, celloidin or other plastics which are later solidified so that the tissue and the embedding matrix may be sectioned together. The use of paraffin or celloidin requires that the tissue be dehydrated in solvents which remove most of the lipids. Tissues embedded in paraffin may be sectioned relatively rapidly in thin slices. Celloidin, on the other hand, disturbs the arrangement of the cells less and causes less shrinkage than does the paraffin method.

These thin slices may be stained to demonstrate the various parts of the cell and the intercellular substance. Many staining methods have been devised; a few are indispensable, but a great many are of questionable value. Although many staining reactions are primarily physical processes (see Conn), others appear to be due to chemical interactions between cellular constituents and certain dyes. The interpretations of some of these reactions are discussed by Dempsey and Wislocki.

The most commonly used staining method —hematoxylin and eosin—stains the nuclear structures dark purple or blue and practically all other structures, cells and intercellular substances varying shades of red. An exception is the blue-to-purple color of the interstitial substance of cartilage. After Zenker-formol fixation, smooth muscle stains lavender. Special staining methods are necessary to demonstrate certain cellular constituents present in the dead cell body which are not made visible by hematoxylin and eosin. Figure 7 shows that a single staining method does not suffice.

The Mallory and Mallory-azan methods stain the collagenous and reticular fibers a bright blue, most nuclei orange or deep red,

and various cell bodies red, blue, orange or purple. With hematoxylin-eosin-azure II, nuclei are blue, collagen is pink, muscle various shades of purple, and cell bodies vary from deep blue to red, depending on the cell type. After iron hematoxylin (Heidenhain), cell structures range through shades of gray to jet black, although intercellular substance is sometimes a pale yellow. Orcein and resorcin-fuchsin stain elastic fibers an orange-brown or deep purple against a pale background. In silver impregnations (Bielschowsky) reticular fibers are black and collagen fibers purplebrown. Another type of silver impregnation (Golgi) is useful for the demonstration of entire neurons.

Some of the striking differences in the effects of a few of the commonly used fixing and staining agents are shown in Figure 7, of cells from the small intestine of the guinea pig. First, it is seen that the nuclei of the cells studied supravitally consist of a sharp membrane, a prominent body called the *nucleolus*, and darkly staining granules of *chromatin* embedded in a hyaline fluid, the nuclear sap. The cells fixed in neutral formalin and Zenker-formol show much the same structures, although the latter shows more chromatin material. Absolute alcohol and the two distinctly acid fixatives (Bouin and Zenker-acetic) show nuclei with heavily clumped chromatin which stands out prominently. Second, this figure shows the differences in the effect of these fixatives on mitochondria (see p. 14). These cellular constituents are seen with difficulty in the living cell; they are obvious as blue rods and granules after supravital staining with Janus green, and are black in the cells stained with Heidenhain's iron-hematoxylin after neutral formalin and Zenker-formol fixation. But they are not visible with this stain after Bouin or Zenker-acetic fixation. Third, mitochondria are not visible after any of these fixatives followed by staining with hematoxylin and eosin.

In Figure 7 three cells were dehydrated in the frozen state and sectioned. The sections were then treated with alcohol and stained either by the periodate leucofuchsin method for insoluble carbohydrates, or by leuco-

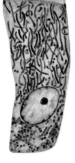

Zenker-formol
Mallory-azan

Supravital
Janus green

Supravital
unstained

Absolute alcohol
H + E

Frozen-dried
periodate-
leucofuchsin

Bouin
iron hematoxylin

10 per cent
neutral formalin
iron hématoxylin

Zenker-formol
iron hematoxylin

Zenker-acetic
iron hematoxylin

Frozen-dried
plasmal

Bouin
H + E

10 per cent
neutral formalin
H + E

Zenker-formol
H + E

Zenker-acetic
H + E

Frozen-dried
H + E

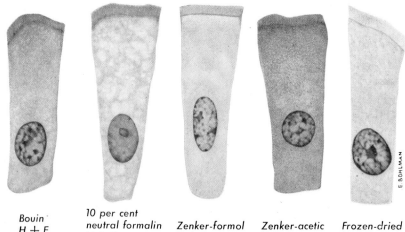

Fig. 7. Epithelial cells of small intestine of guinea pig fixed and stained in a variety of ways to emphasize the extreme importance of choice of method for the preservation, demonstration and study of cytoplasmic and nuclear structures. For explanation, see text (p. 9). 1620 ×.

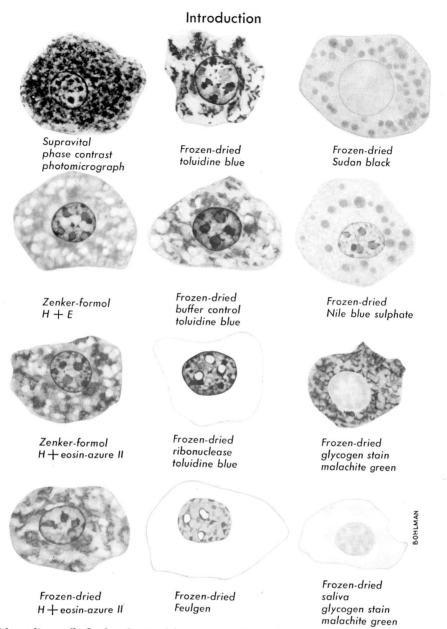

Supravital
phase contrast
photomicrograph

Frozen-dried
toluidine blue

Frozen-dried
Sudan black

Zenker-formol
H + E

Frozen-dried
buffer control
toluidine blue

Frozen-dried
Nile blue sulphate

Zenker-formol
H + eosin-azure II

Frozen-dried
ribonuclease
toluidine blue

Frozen-dried
glycogen stain
malachite green

Frozen-dried
H + eosin-azure II

Frozen-dried
Feulgen

Frozen-dried
saliva
glycogen stain
malachite green

Fig. 8. Mouse liver cells fixed and stained by a variety of cytochemical procedures to show distribution of desoxyribonucleic acid, ribonucleic acid, glycogen and lipid droplets. As these tests were all done on material fixed by freezing and drying, some of the sections are compared with similarly stained ones fixed by Zenker-formol. For further orientation, the fixed cell stained by hematoxylin and eosin and the unfixed cell photographed by phase contrast are also included. For interpretation of the tests, see page 13. 1500 ×.

fuchsin after appropriate treatment with mercuric salts for plasmal, or stained with H and E. As the striated border and the Golgi apparatus (see p. 14) are stained with periodate leucofuchsin, mucopolysaccharides are probably present in them. The plasmal reaction is believed to indicate long chain lipid aldehydes. There is some indication of stain-

ing in the Golgi zone with hematoxylin in the frozen-dried preparation.

As the cells of the intestine change their shape greatly with the extensive movements of this organ, conclusions should not be drawn from the differences in size and shape of these cells as seen in Figure 7 after the various fixing agents used. However, the im-

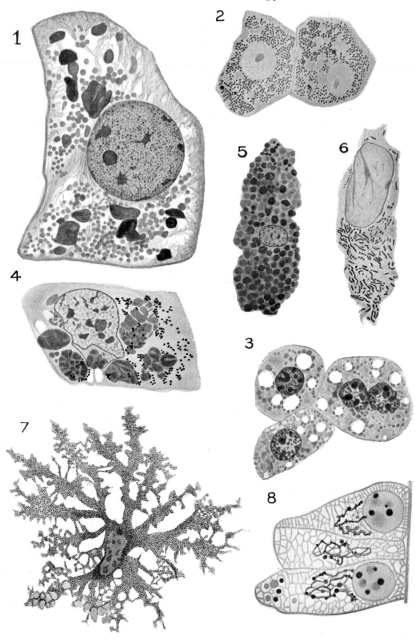

Fig. 9. Cells with various organoids and inclusions. *1*, Liver cell of axolotl, containing red-stained mito-chondria and purple-stained protein inclusions (chromophil substance). The nucleus contains an acidophil (red) nucleolus. Hematoxylin-eosin-azure. 1100 ×.

2, Liver cells of rabbit: dark green-stained protein inclusions and mitochondria (stained red). Altmann stain. 750 ×.

3, Liver cells of rat: one cell is binucleate; the clear spaces are vacuoles resulting from dissolving the fat; the red granules are glycogen. Fixed in alcohol and stained with Best's carmine. 800 ×.

4, Epithelial cell, from mouth of an axolotl embryo, containing dark pigment granules and red-stained yolk inclusions. Eosin-azure. 1200 ×.

5, Macrophage of a rat, stained intravitally with isamine blue. 1200 ×.

6, A fibroblast with rod-shaped mitochondria from a rat. 1200 ×.

pression that the cells and their nuclei are larger in the living than after histological preparation is correct.

Some of the features to be seen in fixed liver cells with special staining reactions are illustrated in Figure 8. Here the usual appearance in hematoxylin and eosin preparations after Zenker-formol fixation is shown; by addition of azure II additional basophilic regions of nucleus and cytoplasm are revealed. A frozen-dried Altmann-Gersh preparation treated with alcohol and hematoxylin-eosin-azure II should be compared with Zenker-formol and hematoxylin-eosin-azure II, since the remaining figures were fixed by this method. Toluidine blue is frequently substituted for hematoxylin-eosin-azure II to demonstrate basophil components. Those containing desoxyribonucleic acid are stained by the Feulgen method. That these are not dissolved by treatment with ribonuclease is also shown. The effect of ribonuclease is largely due to the removal of ribonucleic acid-containing elements from both nucleus and cytoplasm. Cells stained by the Feulgen method closely resemble those treated with ribonuclease and then stained for basophilic substances. Since treatment with the ribonuclease solution may have other solvent action than that due to the enzyme, a better comparison may be made with a section treated with buffer solution. However, not all nucleic acid may be demonstrated by these methods (see p. 7).

The glycogen and other carbohydrate content of such cells is shown by the periodate leucofuchsin reaction, and the effect of treatment with saliva on such preparations is also shown, the loss of red staining being due to removal of glycogen by *amylase* in the saliva. Fatty components can be demonstrated, if fat solvents including paraffin are avoided; they are colored with Sudan black and Nile blue. In the cell stained with Nile blue sulphate the blue component is nonspecific, but the salmon-pink staining occurs in fat droplets.

By the various fixation and staining methods, many structures have been described within the cell; these are artificial to the extent that the structures in fixed material are not the same as those in the living cell, nor are all the structures of the living cell still present. However, with constant fixation and staining methods, there is a constant factor of artificiality in this method of preparation. With improved methods of studying living cells, evidence has been found for the presence in the living cell of most of the important structures which had been described on the basis of fixed and stained preparations. The study of some of these relations is facilitated by phase microscopy and *vital* and *supravital staining*. In *vital staining*, certain dyes, when introduced into the living organism, will accumulate in definite parts of it, as in macrophages (Fig. 9, 5). Supravital staining results from the addition of a dye to surviving tissues, as the staining of mitochondria with Janus green B (Fig. 7).

Organoids. The basis of the cytoplasm is frequently spoken of as the *ground substance*. Embedded in it are the microscopically visible formed constituents of the cytoplasm. From studies with the optical microscope, these structures were divided into *organoids* (*organelles*) and *inclusions*. The organoids, present in practically all cells, were generally believed to be specific particles of living substance in contrast to the inclusions, which were thought of as lifeless, temporary constituents of the cell. The organoids comprise the mitochondria, the Golgi apparatus, the centrioles and fibrils; the inclusions are accumulations of proteins, fats, carbohydrates, pigments, secretory granules and crystals. The position of chromophile substance and of the submicroscopic microsomes in this classifica-

7, Chromatophore from an axolotl embryo, with pigment granules and pink-stained yolk granules. Eosin-azure. 600 ×.

8, First stage in elaboration of secretion granules (red) in the pelvic gland of *Triton taeniatus*. The granules first appear near the Golgi net (stained gray). The few granules near the free border of the lowest cell are from the preceding secretory cycle. Fixation Champy, stained with the Altmann method and aurantia. (5 and 6 are from Tschaschin, and 8 is after Nassonow.) (A.A.M.)

tion is uncertain (p. 15). With advancing knowledge of the chemistry and submicroscopic structure of protoplasm, the complete separation of all cellular constituents into either "living" or "nonliving" no longer appears as apposite as it once did. Whereas it may seem clear that a fat droplet is lifeless in the organization of the cell, it is impossible to say at what point an individual molecule of any substance becomes caught up in the organization as part of the vital machinery.

Mitochondria. These are small structures found in all animal cells. They vary from tiny spheres to short rods or filaments. They may be distinguished in unstained living cells, although their identification becomes much

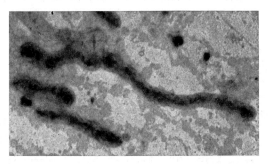

Fig. 10. Electron micrograph of mitochondria in epithelial cell of rabbit embryo in tissue culture. 10,800 ×. (Courtesy of K. Porter.)

easier through the aid of Janus green B, applied supravitally (Fig. 7). They are prominent in living cells studied by dark-field illumination and by phase microscopy (Fig. 2). In properly fixed preparations they may be stained more or less electively (Fig. 9, 2 and 6). They vary from a few to several hundred in a given cell.

Although mitochondria may perhaps participate indirectly in secretory processes, they probably are not transformed into secretion granules. Located upon mitochondria is almost the entire cell content of certain enzymes of the Krebs oxidation cycle and fatty acid oxidase. Mitochondria, by their distribution and changes in form and number, undoubtedly reflect the activity of the cell. In some cases they bear a definite relationship to the polarity of the cell (Fig. 21). They are rich in ribonucleic acid.

Internal Reticular Apparatus of Golgi. This structure consists of an irregularly arranged, interlacing network of fibrils, as seen in fixed preparations (Fig. 9). The network may be extensive or may be localized in a small part of the cell. At times it may be broken up into a large number of scattered threads. In general, it is said to be of a more or less constant type in a given kind of cell, and is usually localized about the cell center.

This network (often called the *Golgi network* or the *Golgi apparatus*) has been thought by many authors to play an important role in cellular activities, particularly those dealing with secretion. It is quite improbable, however, that the Golgi net is transformed directly into secretory vacuoles. Some writers deny the presence of a discrete apparatus such as is seen in fixed preparations.

The Golgi net contains lipids and mucoproteins and probably varies in composition from cell to cell. Experiments with the ultracentrifuge have shown that the Golgi apparatus in some cells is lighter and the mitochondria heavier than the rest of the cytoplasm.

In living cells, and occasionally in well-fixed material, clear, canal-like structures can be seen. Some authors believe that the canals are identical with the Golgi apparatus seen in fixed preparations. This has been denied by others, who claim to have demonstrated both the canals and the reticular apparatus in the same preparation. When living cells are stained with a solution of neutral red, vacuoles of dye may be seen in many of them. The canalicular apparatus in mammals does not stain with neutral red. Kirkman and Severinghaus and Hibbard give extended reviews of the literature on this organoid.

Cell Center. In most cells, usually close to the nucleus, is a condensed portion of protoplasm, called the *cell center*, or *attraction sphere*. It contains two or more small spheres which can be seen in favorable living specimens with phase microscopy (Fig. 3) and which can be demonstrated in the fixed state readily with iron hematoxylin. They are usually close together and are called the *centrioles* or the *diplosome* (Fig. 4). The Golgi apparatus is generally located around the cell center.

The cell center and its centrioles are prominent during mitosis. Occasionally, cells are found with two nuclei; these usually contain one cell center and two or more distinct diplosomes. In the relatively rare, multinucleated cells in mammals, the cell center may be large and may contain several isolated groups of centrioles. Certain cells, as those of the nervous system, do not divide; they are seldom provided with centrioles.

Fibrils. Fine fibrils develop in many cells. They are frequently thin and have been presumed by certain authors to offer stability to the cell. They have been called *tonofibrils* and are particularly characteristic in certain epithelial cells; in the skin they are believed to pass from one cell into its neighbors (Fig. 298). Tonofibrils disappear from a cell during mitosis and reappear in the daughter cells.

Very prominent are the fibrils found in nerve and muscle cells. They are one of the most characteristic features of the various types of muscle fibers. The nerve fibrils have been studied in tissue stained supravitally with methylene blue and in fixed and stained preparations. Microdissection studies suggest that they are present in the living nerve fiber, and they have been seen in living embryonic chick ganglion cells in tissue culture. They may be displaced to one side of the cell by the ultracentrifuge.

Inclusions. Proteins, Fats and Carbohydrates. The inclusions of the cell may be granules of protein material, such as the dark purple-stained granules of Figure 9, *1*, or the dark green-stained masses in *2* of the same figure. They may be of lipoid nature, as the red-stained yolk inclusions in *4* of Figure 9. In the usual histological preparations, however, the free fatty materials which were present in the cell are dissolved during the preparation of the section and thus appear as holes in the cells (Fig. 9, *3*). Much of the fat in the cell cannot be demonstrated microscopically, although it can be extracted chemically; this is called *masked* or *bound fat*.

Carbohydrates in the form of *glycogen* may be demonstrated in many cells, if the tissue is fixed in absolute alcohol, which precipitates the glycogen. Such are the red-stained granules in the liver cells shown in Figure 9, 3.

Observations on living cells in tissue culture and in tissues fixed by the Altmann-Gersh freezing method suggest that glycogen is present in solution and that the granular appearance in fixed preparations is due to its precipitation by the alcohol (Fig. 6). Glycogen has been separated as submicroscopic particles from suspensions of ground liver cells.

Crystals. Peculiar crystals, probably arising from proteins, are found in several types of cells (see Fig. 459). Their function is unknown.

Secretory Granules. In many epithelial cells various secretory granules occur. These change cyclically in the same type of cell, depending on the stage of secretory activity of the cell. In some cases the nature of these granules has been correlated with the chemical composition of the secretion, but in most cases their exact nature is not known. The secretory granules in certain cells contain antecedents of enzymes (*pro-enzymes* or *zymogen granules*). After they have left the cell, they become active enzymes. These small granules gradually progress toward the free border of the cell, where, it is claimed, they imbibe water and become vacuoles, after which they are discharged from the cell.

The origin of the secretory granules is unknown. It is unlikely that they arise through a metamorphosis either of the mitochondria or of the Golgi apparatus; nor has it been shown that they develop from nuclear material or from the chromophile substance.

Chromophile Substance. In many cells, diffuse or discrete masses of a material which stains with the same dyes as does the nuclear chromatin may be found in the cytoplasm. This material was accordingly called chromophile substance; the most prominent examples are the Nissl substance in nerve cells and the chromophile substance in the salivary glands. This material, which is apparently ribose nucleoprotein, changes greatly during the activity of the cell.

The basophilia of the cytoplasm of certain rapidly dividing cells is due to a high content of ribose nucleic acid components and is causally associated by many with protein synthesis. But some do not consider this point proved. As mentioned before, it is fruitless to categorize a substance of this sort as either organoid or inclusion.

Pigment Granules. Many cells scattered throughout the body in characteristic positions, particularly in Amphibia, contain large amounts of pigment granules, usually a melanin (Fig. 9, 7). These cells are usually called chromatophores, or melanophores, depending upon their origin.

Submicroscopic Particles. By differential centrifugation and by electron micrographic study, submicroscopic particles have been isolated as cellular constituents. They vary in size from 50 to 250 angstrom units and undoubtedly comprise a variety of materials. In the liver, some of them contain glycogen, while others are rich in ribonucleic acid. Until more is known of their chemical constitution it will not be possible to classify them more accurately.

Nucleus. Within the prominent nuclear membrane are strands or granules of material which stains deeply with basic dyes (chromatin), often connected by paler staining strands, and more or less associated spheroidal or angular nucleoli all surrounded by nuclear fluid. During cellular division (p. 17) the chromatin is condensed into readily visible discrete *chromosomes*, and the nucleoli disappear. The prominence of these elements during interphase is dependent on the synthetic activities of the cell. Chromosomes, the chromatin granules of resting cells, and the nucleoli consist of nucleic acids, basic proteins and acidic proteins in variable proportions. In a given interphase nucleus, however, the total content of desoxyribonucleic acid seems to be constant until it is doubled just prior to mitosis. The usual staining properties following basic and acid dyes or natural dyestuffs are profoundly altered by the changing proportions of acidic basic components of these nucleic acids, diamino acids, histones and acidic proteins. Consequently the basophilia to be expected of elements containing nucleic acids may not always occur;

in fact, a structure rich in ribose nucleic acid —as most nucleoli are—may be quite acidophilic in the presence of adequate amounts of appropriate proteins. The morphological changes during condensation and swelling of the chromosomes also have corresponding effects on their tinctorial and optical properties. Many of the early investigators considered that differences in staining reaction indicated structures of different origins, but in his summary of 1925 Wilson concluded that oxyphilic and basophilic reactions in both chromatin and nucleoli were due to different phases varying according to the "ratios between nucleic acid and protein components."

Nucleolus. In growing cells there are numerous examples of marked hypertrophy of nucleoli, and Heidenhain in 1907 pointed out that there was an obvious relationship between nucleolar growth and the growth of nucleus and cell body. In contrast, he was unable to find a direct relationship between these events and the formation of secretion droplets.

The role of the nucleolus, which occupied so prominent a place in the writings of Flemming, Heidenhain and Montgomery about fifty years ago, was until recently largely ignored as a result of preoccupation of cytologists with cytogenetic and mitotic phenomena.

The development of a microscope with quartz optics permitting the use of ultraviolet light brought about improved resolution, owing to the decreased wavelength of the light, and also revealed that certain nuclear structures absorbed ultraviolet light strongly. Largely under the aegis of Caspersson, the ultraviolet-absorbing properties of cell structures have been interpreted in quantitative terms. The nucleic acid content of chromatin and of nucleoli has been found in some cases to vary in relation to cell division and to cellular synthetic processes. The presence of nucleic acids is demonstrable histologically by means of their ultraviolet absorption (as measured at 2600 angstrom units) and by their basophilia. The ribose nucleic acids are differentiated from the desoxyribonucleic acids by means of the Feulgen reaction, which is positive only for the latter. The basophilia, however, as already noted, is dependent in large part on the amount and nature of the associated proteins, so that, in the presence of large amounts of basic protein, such stains (other than the Feulgen reaction) will not demonstrate nucleic acids. These studies have confirmed Wilson's conclusions and have greatly clarified our knowledge of the way in which some morphological components may undergo changes in chemical constitution. The detailed quantitative work on the nucleic acid and protein content of chromosomes, nucleoli and cytoplasm has revived interest in the significance of such changes for the physiology of the cell.

CELL DIVISION

Many of the organs of the mature mammal show relatively few cells in division; exceptions are blood-cell-forming tissues, male germinal epithelium, female organs in cyclic changes, skin and gastrointestinal epithelium. In some tissues the period between cell divisions (*interphase*) may be measured in years. The small size and the relatively large number of chromosomes in mammalian species are unfavorable for detailed observations of the processes involved. Consequently, most studies have been made on rapidly growing cells in lower forms (see Fig. 11).

The usual mode of cell division is by a process called *mitosis*. The most prominent parts in this process are played, at least at first, by the centrioles and the nucleus. Mitosis consists of four main stages: (1) *Prophase* — the centrioles separate from each other with the formation of attraction spheres around each of them while the chromatin becomes discernible as *chromosomes* whose number is constant in a given species, and is forty-eight in man (Painter). (2) *Metaphase* —the chromosomes are arranged in an equatorial plate, and each chromosome separates into two equal parts. (3) In the next stage, the *anaphase*, the halves of the chromosomes move away from each other toward the two centrioles, and, at the same time, the single centrioles in each half of the cell divide into two; this is in preparation for the next cell

division which, however, may be some time off. It may be recalled that in the resting cell there are usually at least two centrioles. At the same stage each of the apparently single chromosomes can also be seen in favorable preparations to split longitudinally preparatory to separation at the next metaphase, and this is perhaps the most striking part of the whole phenomenon. Although the mechanism of this longitudinal splitting is unknown, it is of fundamental importance with regard to some of our ideas on the mechanism of heredity. (4) Finally, in the *telophase* the two daughter nuclei begin to form. As the chromatin threads or chromosomes begin to break up into irregular bodies, nucleoli appear in each of the daughter cells. Through a progressive constriction of the cytoplasm the two daughter cells separate from each other, being attached for a time by a small acidophile body which stains black with iron hematoxylin. This is the *intermediate body* of Flemming.

Although it is not possible to distinguish individual chromosomes in interphase nuclei in vertebrate tissues, the bulk of genetic evidence and numerous examples from selected lower forms demonstrate unequivocally the continuity of individual chromosomes from one mitosis to the next. Changes in form, in degree of hydration and in nonhistone protein content of chromosomes occur at telophase; consequently the interphase nucleus may exhibit only dispersed particles of chromatin.

The mechanics of chromosome movement are imperfectly understood, and time-lapse motion picture studies give an exaggerated notion of the rates involved. The speed-up in such films is often 1000 times; it should further be noted that a speed of 10 microns per minute is about 0.1 meter per week. Although the interphase may last for hours or years, in most warm-blooded species, once division is initiated, it is usually completed in about an hour, with the prophase stages occupying most of the time. Chromosomes in metaphase are not commonly found in fixed material, since the chromosomes stay in this stage for only two to ten minutes. Chromosomes in

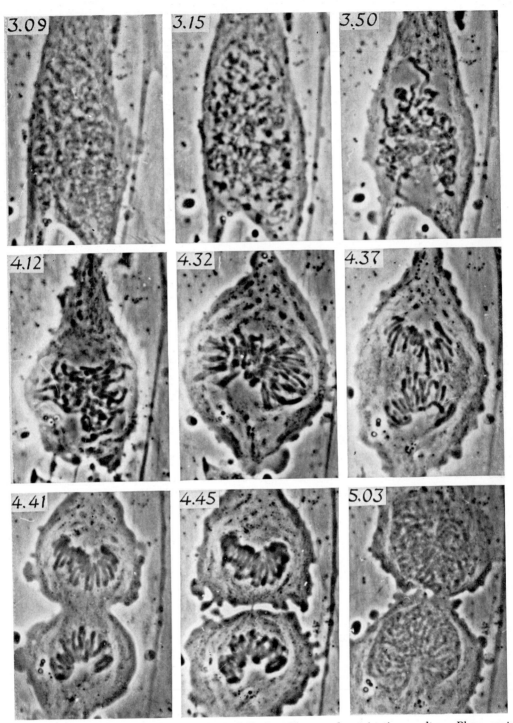

Fig. 11. Successive stages in mitosis of a spindle cell of amblystoma heart in tissue culture. Phase contrast. 785 ×. (Courtesy of L. Wang.)

anaphase are the least commonly observed because of the relatively rapid movement of the chromosomes to the poles (frequently in two or three minutes).

The cleavage of cytoplasm in animal cells usually occurs by constriction, the various inclusions and organoids of the cell body being distributed to the two daughter cells in more or less equal amounts.

In the living, interphase nucleus, the chromatin masses seem indistinct except with phase microscopy. Direct observation of dividing nuclei by ordinary microscopy shows the chromatin masses easily.

As a result of mitosis, the chromatin material, which is generally regarded as the primary carrier of the hereditary factors of the cell and of the organism, is divided equally between the two daughter nuclei; this depends primarily upon the longitudinal splitting of the chromosomes, which permits a given hereditary unit to be duplicated in each cell. The mechanism causing this division of the chromosomes—as indeed of the whole mitotic process—is unknown.

In *multipolar mitosis* there are more poles than the two which are normally present. With few exceptions, multipolar mitosis is an indication of a pathological process.

For details of the participation of the chromosomes in the mechanism of heredity, the reader is referred to general works on cytology and heredity. The mapping of the genes in the giant chromosomes of the salivary glands of Drosophila is described in the papers of Painter and of Bridges. Ultraviolet absorption studies have shown that the dark bands in these chromosomes are rich in nucleic acid, and the pale ones free of it. The bands may be clearly seen in some living cells with phase microscopy (Fig. 12). Specialized (meiotic) divisions which occur during the development of the sex cells are discussed in the chapters on the genital organs.

Amitosis. Occasionally cells are observed in the process of division with no evidence of the mitotic phases. Both nucleus and cytoplasm may be divided into two portions of unequal size or roughly equal size. In the absence of the qualitatively equal chromosomal

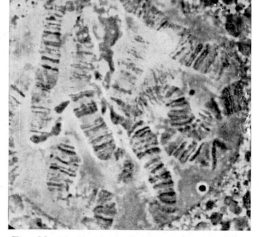

Fig. 12. Photomicrograph showing bands in living giant chromosomes in salivary gland cell of late larva of Drosophila. Preparation dissected in Ephrussi-Ringer solution. Phase difference microscopy. 980 ×. (Courtesy of J. Schultz and E. K. Patterson.)

distribution brought about by mitosis, it is doubtful that such cells can undergo subsequent divisions into normally functioning cells. Amitosis is fairly common in cells of transitory nature or degenerating cells, e.g., vertebrate decidua, embryonic envelopes.

REFERENCES

The first group of references are important source books in the fields of cytology and histology; those in the second group deal with histological techniques; while those in the third group are concerned with some of the special fields of current interest and investigation.

In searching for more information on a particular topic, the student would do well to start with the handbooks edited by von Möllendorff and by Cowdry and the manuals of Kölliker-von Ebner and Prenant, Bouin and Maillard.

I.

von Bardeleben, K., and von Eggeling, H.: Handbuch der Anatomie des Menschen. 1896-1926.

Bolk, L., Goppert, E., Kallius, E., and Lubosch, W.: Handbuch d. vergl. Anat. d. Wirbeltiere. Berlin, 1931.

Bourne, G. (editor): Cytology and Cell Physiology. Oxford, Clarendon Press, 1951.

Braus, H.: Anatomie des Menschen. Berlin, 1924.

Brachet, J.: Chemical Embryology. New York, 1950.

Cowdry, E. V. (editor): General Cytology. Chicago, 1924. Special Cytology, New York, 1932.

Clark, W. E. Le Gros: The Tissues of the Body. New York, 1939.

Dahlgren, U., and Kepner, W. A.: A Textbook of the Principles of Animal Histology. New York, 1908.

Heidenhain, M.: Plasma und Zelle. Jena, 1907-11.

von Herrath and Abramow: Atlas der normalen Histologie und mikroskopischen Anatomie des Menschen. Stuttgart, Georg Thieme Verlag, 1950.

Hertwig, G.: Die lebendige Masse. Handb. d. mikr. Anat. (v. Mollendorff), 1929, Vol. 1, Pt. I, p. 1.

Hertwig, O.: Handbuch der vergleichenden und experimentellen Entwicklungslehre der Wirbeltiere. Jena, 1901-1906.

Kölliker, T. A., and von Ebner, V.: Handbuch d. Gewebelehre des Menschen. 6th ed. Leipzig, 1889-1902.

Levi, G.: Trattato di istologia. 3rd ed. Torino, 1946.

Lison, L.: Histochimie animale. Paris, 1936.

von Möllendorff, W.: Handbuch der mikrokopischen Anatomie des Menschen. Berlin, 1927.

Morgan, T. H.: Mendelian Heredity in Relation to Cytology, In Cowdry: General Cytology. Chicago, 1924, p. 691.

Needham, J.: Biochemistry and Morphogenesis. Cambridge University Press, 1942.

Oppel, A.: Lehrbuch der vergleichenden mikroskopischen Anatomie der Wirbeltiere. Jena, 1896.

Policard, A.: Précis d'histologie physiologique. 5th ed. Paris, 1950.

Prenant, A.: Bouin, P., and Maillard, L.: Traité d'histologie. Paris, 1910, 1911.

Wassermann, F.: Die lebendige Masse. Handb. d. mikr. Anat. (v. Möllendorff), Berlin, 1929, Vol. 1, Pt. 2.

Wilson, E. B.: The Cell in Development and Heredity. 1925.

Winterstein, H.: Handbuch der vergleichenden Physiologie. Jena, 1913-1924.

II.

Bensley, R. R., and Bensley, S. H.: Handbook of Histological and Cytological Technique. Chicago, 1941.

Chambers, R.: Recent Developments of the Micro-Manipulative Technique and Its Application. J. Roy. Micro. Soc., 60:113, 1940.

Clark, E. R., and Clark, E. L.: Further Observations on Living Lymphatic Vessels in the Transparent Chamber in the Rabbit's Ear—Their Relation to the Tissue Spaces. Am. J. Anat., 52:273, 1933.

Conn, H. J.: Biological Stains: A Handbook on the Nature and Uses of the Dyes Employed in the Biological Laboratory. 5th ed., Geneva, N.Y., Biotech. Publications, 1946.

Ellinger, P.: Fluorescence Microscopy in Biology. Biol. Rev., 15:323, 1940.

Gersh, I.: Application in Pathology of the Method of Fixation by Freezing and Drying of Tissues. Bull. Int. Asso. Med. Museums, 28:179, 1948.

Hotchkiss, R. D.: A Microchemical Reaction Resulting in the Staining of Polysaccharide Structures in Fixed Tissue Preparations. Arch. Biochem., 16:131, 1948.

Knisely, M. H.: A Method of Illuminating Living Structures for Microscopic Study. Anat. Rec., 64:499, 1936.

Krause, R. P., Ehrlich, et al.: Encyklopadie der mikroskopischen Technik. Berlin and Vienna, 1926.

Lee, A. B.: Microtomists Vade-Mecum. 11th ed. (Gatenby and Cowdry). Philadelphia, 1950.

Lewis, W. H., and Lewis, M. R.: Behavior of Cells in Tissue Cultures in Cowdry: General Cytology. Chicago, 1924, p. 385.

McClung, C. E.: Handbook of Microscopical Technic. Edited by R. McL. Jones. New York, Paul B. Hoeber, Inc., 1950.

Parker, R. C.: Methods of Tissue Culture. 2d ed. New York, Paul B. Hoeber, Inc., 1950.

Peterfi, T.: Die mikrurgische Methodik. Handbuch d. biol. Arbeitsmethoden. E. Abderhalden, Abtlg. v. 479, 1924.

Policard, A.: Sur une méthode de microincinération applicable aux recherches histochimiques. Bull. Soc. chim. de France, 4th Series, 33:1551, 1923.

Romeis, B.: Taschenbuch d. mikroskopischen Technik. 15th ed. Munich, 1948.

Sanford, K. K., Earle, W. R., and Likely, G. D.: The Growth in Vitro of Single Isolated Tissue Cells. J. Nat. Cancer Inst., 9:229, 1948.

Scott, G. H.: A Critical Study and Review of the Method of Microincineration. Protoplasma, 20:133, 1933.

Wyckoff, R. W. G.: Electron Microscopy. New York, 1949.

III.

Astbury, W. T.: X-Ray Studies of the Structure of Compounds of Biological Interest. Ann. Rev. Biochem., 8:113, 1939.

Baker, J. R.: The Structure and Chemical Composition of the Golgi Element. Quart. J. Micr. Sc., 85:1, 1943.

Beams, H. W., and King, R. L.: The Effect of Ultracentrifuging upon Chick Embryonic Cells with Special Reference to the "Resting" Nucleus and the Mitotic Spindle. Biol. Buil., 71:188, 1936.

Bennett, A. H., Jupnik, H., Osterberg, H., and Richards, O. W.: Phase Microscopy. Tr. Am. Micr. Soc., 65:99, 1946.

Bensley, R. R., and Gersh, I.: Studies on Cell Structure by the Freezing-Drying Method. I. Introduction. II. Mitochondria. III. Nissl Substance. Anat. Rec., 57:205, 369, 1933.

Bensley, R. R., and Hoerr, N. L.: Studies on Cell Structure by the Freezing-Drying Method. VI. The Preparation and Properties of Mitochondria. Anat. Rec., 60:449, 1934.

Brown, G. B.: Biosynthesis of Nucleic Acids in the Mammal. Federation Proc., 9:517, 1950.

Caspersson, T. O.: Cell Growth and Cell Function. A Cytochemical Study. New York. W. W. Norton & Co. Inc., 1950.

Chambers, R.: Recent Developments of the Micromanipulative Technique and Its Application. J. Roy. Micro. Soc., 60:113, 1940.

Davson, H., and Danielli, J. F.: The Permeability of Natural Membranes. New York, Macmillan Company, 1943.

Dempsey, E. W., and Wislocki, G. B.: Histochemical Contributions to Physiology. Physiol. Rev., 26:1, 1946.

Gerard, R. W.: Unresting Cells. New York, 1940.

Gersh, I.: The Altmann Technique for Fixation by Drying while Freezing. Anat. Rec., 53:309, 1932. Recent Developments in Histochemistry. Physiol. Rev., 21:242, 1941.

Gomori, G.: Distribution of Phosphatase in the Tissues under Normal and Pathological Conditions. J. Cell. & Comp. Physiol., 17:71, 1941.

Gross, J., and Leblond, C. P.: Histological Localization of Radioactive Elements. McGill Med. J., 15: Dec. 1946.

Harrison, R. G.: Observations on the Living Developing Nerve Fiber. Proc. Soc. Exper. Biol. & Med., 4:140, 1907.

Hastings, A. B.: Harvey Lecture, 36:91, 1940.

Hibbard, H.: The Present Status of the Golgi Apparatus. Quart. Rev. Biol., 20:1, 1945.

Höber, R., and others: Physical Chemistry of Cells and Tissues. Philadelphia, Blakiston Co., 1945.

Hoerr, N. L. (editor): Frontiers in Cytochemistry. Biol. Symposia (10), Lancaster, The Jaques Cattell Press, 1943.

Hogeboom, G. H., Claude, A., and Hotchkiss, R. D.: The Distribution of Cytochrome Oxidase and Succinoxidase in the Cytoplasm of the Mammalian Liver Cell. J. Biol. Chem., 165:615, 1946.

Kirkman, H., and Severinghaus, A. E.: A Review of the Golgi Apparatus. Anat. Rec., 70:413, 557; 71:79, 1938.

Leblond, C. P.: Distribution of Periodic Acid-Reactive Carbohydrates in the Adult Rat. Am. J. Anat., 86: 1, 1950.

Mirsky, A. E., and Pollister, A. W.: The Nucleoprotamine of Trout Sperm. J. Gen. Physiol., 30:101, 1946. Chromosin, a Desoxyribose Nucleoprotein Complex of the Cell Nucleus. J. Gen. Physiol., 30: 117, 1946.

Moog, F.: The Physiological Significance of the Phosphomonoesterases. Biol. Rev., 21:41, 1946.

Painter, T. S.: A Comparative Study of the Chromosomes of Mammals. Am. Nat. 59:385, 1925.

Peters, R. A.: Perspectives in Biochemistry, edited by J. Needham and D. E. Green. Cambridge, England, 1938.

Porter, K. R., Claude, A., and Fullam, E. F.: A Study of Tissue Culture Cells by Electron Microscopy. J. Exper. Med., 81:233, 1945.

Ris, H.: Composition of Chromosomes during Mitoses and Meiosis. Symp. Quart. Biol., 12:158, 1947.

Serra, J. A.: The Parallelism between the Chemical and the Morphological Changes in the Chromosomes during Mitosis and Meiosis. Exp. Cell Res., Suppl. 1, 111, 1949.

Schmitt, F. O.: The Ultrastructure of Protoplasmic Constituents. Physiol. Rev., 19:270, 1939. Ultrastructure and the Problem of Cellular Organization. Harvey Lectures, Series 40, 249, 1944-45.

Sjostrand, F.: Über die Eigenfluoreszenz tierischer Gewebe mit besonderer Berucksichtigung der Säugetierniere. Karolinska Inst., 1944.

Sponsler, O. L.: The Structure of Protoplasm, edited by W. A. Seifriz. Monograph of Am. Soc. Plant Physiol., Ames, Iowa, 1942.

Vonwiller, P.: Microscopy with Incident Light and Its Application to Living Objects. J. Roy. Micro. Soc., 47:325, 1927.

Waugh, D. F., and Schmitt, F. O.: Investigations of the Thickness and Ultrastructure of Cellular Membranes by the Analytical Leptoscope. Cold Spring Harbor Symposia on Quantitative Biology, 8:233, 1940.

Wilson, J. W.: Cellular Tissue and the Dawn of the Cell Theory. Isis, 35:168, 1944.

II. EPITHELIUM

In the foregoing pages some of the most important visible and submicroscopic constituents of cells have been discussed. This emphasis on cells may be misleading unless it is realized that isolated cells do not occur in complex multicellular animals, except in the blood. Cells are bound together with varying amounts of intercellular substances to form *tissues* and *organs*. This applies also to the blood, the plasma of which constitutes the intercellular substance. Even in the earliest stages, when the fertilized egg divides repeatedly, the resulting cells stick together and pass through a series of complex developmental processes which take place in an orderly sequence. There is a transient phase when the early embryo consists only of simple

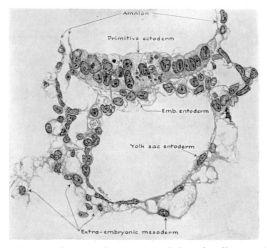

Fig. 13. Section of embryonic disk and yolk sac of human embryo of about thirteen days (Brewer). At this state there is no mesoderm between the primitive ectoderm and entoderm. (After Bloom and Bartelmez.)

epithelial layers (Fig. 13). Later, the *three primitive germ layers* give rise to *four primary tissues:* (1) epithelium—the cells are generally applied closely to one another with little cementing substance. The sheets of cells may develop into the covering of the outer and inner surfaces of the body and the glands and other structures derived from them. (2) Connective tissues—the cells are generally separated from one another to a greater or less degree by a rather rich amount of intercellular substance. From these cells are derived the blood cells and the blood cell-forming tissues, the connective tissue in its manifold varieties, cartilage and bone. These derivatives differ not only in their cell populations, but also in the nature and amount of the intercellular substance. (3) Muscle—the cells are of several varieties which are associated with movement of the skeleton and contractility in many organs, including those of the vascular system. (4) Nerve tissue—the cells are concerned primarily with rapid conduction of impulses in the integration of numerous functions. The details of these tissues will be considered in the next few chapters.

As cells are aggregated to form tissues, so these are combined and integrated in different manners to form functional structures, the organs of the body. A variety of influences come to bear on the interrelations of the tissues composing an organ—neural, endocrine, metabolic, physical and circulatory. A great part of the book is devoted to the organization of the tissues which go to form organs.

Epithelium forms the outer protecting surface of the body and all the glands, furnishes important parts of the sense organs, and lines the walls of the internal cavities, except those which develop exclusively in and from the mesenchyme, the lining epithelium of which is called *endothelium* or *mesothelium* (p. 34). The most important and general function of the epithelial tissue is its participation in the metabolism of the body through the absorption of substances from the outside medium, their modification in the body, and the elimination of other substances to the outside. All substances normally received and given off by the body must pass through the epithelium. For the performance of the secretory function, the epithelial tissue produces special structures called glands (see **Chap. XIII**).

completely separated from one another. For it has been shown by experiment that some cells from parts of each germ layer can be made to become integral parts of the other layers. However, in adult vertebrates, epithelial elements, especially of ectodermal and entodermal origin, and those of the connective tissues are morphologically independent,

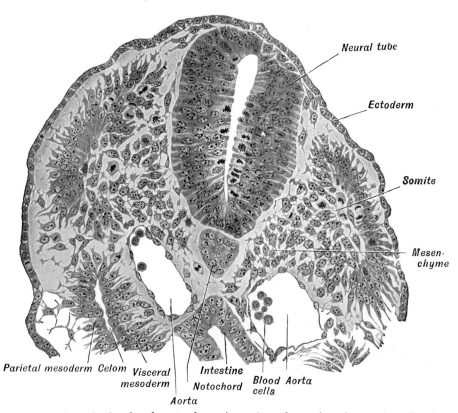

Fig. 14. Cross section through the dorsal part of a guinea pig embryo of twelve somites. Development of mesenchyme from the medial wall of a somite. 165 ×. (A.A.M.)

Histogenesis of Epithelium. Early histologists described epithelium as a layer of closely connected cells lining the cavities of the body. The term was later extended to the similar layers covering the body, and was further broadened when it was shown that the vertebrate (and most invertebrate) embryos pass through a stage during which they consist of three simple layers of cells—the embryonic germ layers called *ectoderm*, *mesoderm* and *entoderm*. While this concept has been fruitful, the derivatives of the three germ layers are no longer considered to be

and transformations between them are rare. As the embryo develops, these germ layers form the organs and tissues of the body. In some parts they persist as epithelial layers; in other parts they lose their epithelial arrangement permanently; while in still others the epithelial arrangement seems to be completely lost, but may become apparent in inflammation, tissue culture, or tumor. If the term "epithelium" is used in a purely descriptive sense, the student will often find it difficult to understand how the cells of many glands can be called epithelium. Accordingly, it might be advisable in many cases to distinguish between covering epithelium and glandular epithelium.

It is the unequal growth of these epithelial layers which produces the various organs. Some folds grow outward as evaginations, usually with a core of *mesenchyme*, the embryonic connective tissue; others grow inward as invaginations into the mesenchyme. An invagination may fuse at its mouth, severing its connection with the epithelium from which it developed, and so give rise to isolated epithelial organs surrounded by mesenchyme.

Part of the outer germ layer, or *ectoderm*, curves inward to form the *neural tube*, from which develop the elements of the brain and spinal cord. The rest of the ectoderm keeps its epithelial form and gives rise to the epidermis, the lining of the oral cavity, and parts of the sense organs.

The inner layer, the *entoderm*, furnishes the epithelial lining and the glands of the intestinal and respiratory systems.

The middle layer, or *mesoderm*, keeps its

epithelial character in the epithelium of the urinary and genital systems. The part of the mesoderm which lines the *celom*—the *peritoneal*, *pleural* and *pericardial cavities*—is histologically an epithelium, but differs in some respects from the other types of this tissue and is called *mesothelium*. A considerable part of the mesoderm is transformed into the striated muscular tissue and into the heart muscle, while another large part of it becomes the mesenchyme, which gives rise to smooth muscle and the various types of connective tissue, cartilage, bone and blood.

The *notochord,* the axial supporting structure of the embryo, probably arises from the totipotent tissue of the blastophore and behaves like a mesodermal derivative.

Experimental studies of vertebrate development, especially as carried out on amphibians and to a lesser extent on birds, show that many of the cells in these embryonic germ layers have no inherent specificity during early developmental stages. That is, if they

Parietal cell   Vessels   Cells of lamina propria

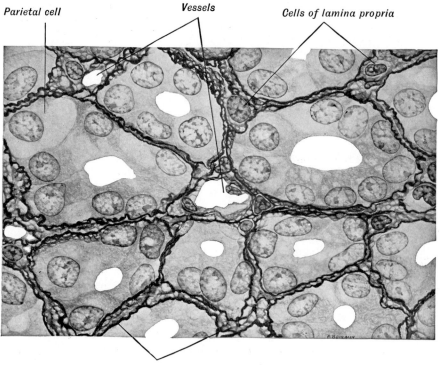

Basement membrane

Fig. 15. Basement membranes surrounding cross sections of fundic glands of human stomach. Bielschowsky stain for reticular fibers and hematoxylin. 1500 ×.

are moved from one place to another, they will often proceed to develop in conformity with their new surroundings. These and similar interesting problems of development are discussed at length by Weiss and by Child.

Basement Membrane. Between the epithelium and the underlying connective tissue there is usually a basement membrane, a condensation of the intercellular substance of the connective tissue at the surface of its contact with the epithelium. Its constitution is discussed in Chapter IV. In hematoxylin and eosin preparations the basement membrane often is hard to see, but special techniques demonstrate it readily.

Some types of epithelium seem to lack a basement membrane (thyroid gland in young animals). In the sulcus spiralis externus and in the stria vascularis of the cochlea, the epithelial cells send processes deep into the connective tissue. The original, simple, anatomical relations between epithelium and connective tissue are also completely altered in most of the endocrine glands and in the liver.

On the epithelial surface, the basement membrane at some places (skin, cornea) is provided with minute indentations into which fit corresponding, short outgrowths of the basal surface of the epithelial cells. In other places, as in the convoluted uriniferous tubules, the inner, homogeneous portion of the basement membrane has circular ridges which seem to fit into grooves on the bases of the epithelial elements.

Types of Epithelial Tissue. As different types of epithelium may arise from the same germ layer, as different germ layers may produce similar epithelial types, and as the physiological role of certain epithelia has not been determined, the various types of epithelial tissue are best classified in terms of (*a*) the shape of the epithelial cells and (*b*) their arrangement in the epithelial sheet.

Shape of Epithelial Cells. Epithelial cells in the living condition change considerably in shape if the surface they cover is subject to stretching and contraction. Stretching flattens them; contraction permits them to gain in height. In the healing of wounds, in other pathological conditions, and in tissue cultures, the form of an epithelial cell may change with its movement.

Squamous, cuboidal and columnar epithelial cells may be distinguished.

1. *Squamous Cells.* The height of the cell body is negligible in comparison with the other dimensions; the cell is a thin plate. In profile it looks like a slender rod which is usually slightly thickened in the vicinity of the nucleus (Figs. 16, 17).

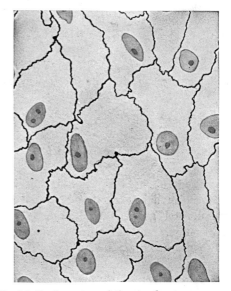

Fig. 16. Surface view of the simple squamous mesothelium of a frog's mesentery; the cell limits are stained black with silver nitrate; the nuclei are stained with picrocarmine. 390 ×.

2. *Cuboidal Cells.* The height is about equal to the width. When seen from the free surface, the cells appear as small polygons; in a section perpendicular to the surface they appear square. They are short prisms (Fig. 18).

3. *Columnar Cells.* The height greatly exceeds the width. In a section parallel to the surface the cells appear as small polygons (Figs. 19, 21, 22); in a perpendicular section, as rectangles. They are irregular tall prisms. The end directed toward the underlying tissue is often tapering and pointed, or irregularly angular and branched. Cells of a fairly regular cylindrical shape are found in the epithelium of the higher sense organs. On curved surfaces the columnar and cuboidal cells assume the shape of truncated pyramids whose thin ends are directed to either the free or the fixed surface.

Transitional forms between these three

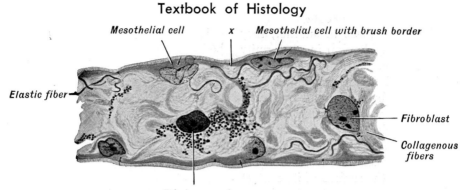

Mesothelial cell　　　*x*　　*Mesothelial cell with brush border*

Elastic fiber

Fibroblast

Collagenous fibers

Fixed macrophage

Fig. 17. Cross section of a rabbit's mesentery; *x,* cross section of cell limits. Iron-hematoxylin stain. 750 ×. (A.A.M.)

types also occur. All three forms may be provided on their free surface with motile, hair-like outgrowths called *cilia* or with a *brush border* (p. 30).

Arrangement of the Cells in Epithelial Sheets. Epithelial sheets may be classified on morphological grounds into several categories, depending on whether they consist of one or more layers and on the shapes of the cells. In the stratified epithelia only the cells of the lowest layer touch the underlying tissue. In the *pseudostratified columnar epithelium* the cells seem to be arranged in more than one layer, but all of them touch the underlying tissue (see Fig. 20).

1. *Simple Squamous Epithelium.* Thin, platelike cells are arranged in one layer on the surface of the connective tissue and adhere closely to one another by their edges. On examination from the surface, especially after the cell limits are stained with silver nitrate, a typical mosaic pattern is seen. The individual cells have regular (usually hexagonal) or irregular wavy outlines, and each contains a nucleus (Fig. 16). In perpendicular sections a thin stripe is seen, subdivided into small parts which correspond to the single cells. A given section will not pass through the nuclei of all the cells. In profile the contracted cell is a plump spindle (Fig. 17).

An epithelium of this variety is found in the human body on the inner surface of the wall of the membra-

nous labyrinth and on the inner surface of the tympanic membrane of the ear; on the parietal layer of the capsule of Bowman, and in the descending limb of the loop of Henle in the kidney; in the rete testis, and in the smallest excretory ducts of many glands.

The *mesothelium* lining the serous cavities, the *mesenchymal epithelium* lining cavities in the connective tissue, and the *endothelial* cells lining the walls of the blood and lymph vessels—all three groups being squamous cells—are also considered by many authorities to be true epithelium. However, despite the structural similarity, these elements differ in origin and developmental potencies from true epithelium (p. 34).

2. *Simple Cuboidal Epithelium.* The low prismatic cell bodies adhere to one another by their lateral surfaces. On the free surface this epithelium appears as a mosaic of small, usually hexagonal polygons; the ribbon-like cross section of the sheet is subdivided into squares (Fig. 18).

This epithelium is found in many glands, as in the thyroid, on the free surface of the ovary, on the choroid plexus, on the inner surface of the capsule of the lens, in some areas of the labyrinth, in the excretory ducts of many glands and as the pigmented epithelium of the retina. The secreting epithelium in the terminal portions of many glands can often be placed in this class, although the cells here usually have the form of truncated pyramids.

3. *Simple Columnar Epithelium.* The tall prismatic cells adhere to one another by their lateral surfaces. In sections parallel to the surface is seen a mosaic much like that in other simple epithelia (Fig. 19). In sections perpendicular to the surface the tall rectangles stand upright like fence palings. In many cases the oval nuclei are at approximately the same level.

Such an epithelium lines the surface of the digestive tract from the cardia to the anus and is also common in the excretory ducts of many glands.

4. *Simple Columnar Ciliated Epithelium.* This is like 3, except that the free surface of the cells is provided with cilia. It is found in the uterus and oviducts, in the small bronchi, in some of the nasal sinuses, and in the central canal of the spinal cord.

5. *Stratified Squamous Epithelium.* The epithelial sheet

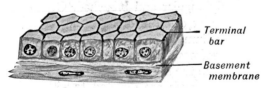

Terminal bar

Basement membrane

Fig. 18. Diagram of simple cuboidal epithelium. (Redrawn and slightly modified after Stöhr-von Möllendorff.)

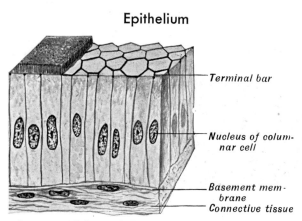

Fig. 19. Diagram of the columnar epithelium of the small intestine. The striated border has been removed in the right half to show the terminal bars. (Redrawn and slightly modified after Stöhr-von Möllendorff.)

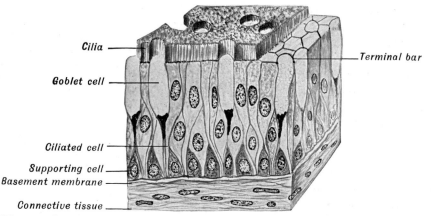

Fig. 20. Diagram of pseudostratified ciliated columnar epithelium. (Redrawn and slightly modified after Stöhr-von Möllendorff.)

is thick, and a perpendicular section shows the cells to be unequal in form (Fig. 298). The layer next to the underlying tissue consists of cuboidal or even columnar cells, sometimes with rounded upper ends, as in the cornea. Then follow a varying number of layers of more or less irregular polyhedral cells, often provided with excavations which fit the convex surfaces of their neighbors, or with long stalks attached to the basement membrane. The nearer to the free surface, the more the cells are flattened. The superficial layers consist of thin, squamous cells.

This epithelium is found in the epidermis, the mouth, esophagus, a part of the epiglottis, a part of the conjunctiva, the cornea, the vagina and a part of the female urethra.

6. **Stratified Columnar Epithelium.** The deeper layer or layers consist of small, irregularly polyhedral or fusiform cells which do not reach the free surface. The superficial cells are tall and prismatic and are not con-

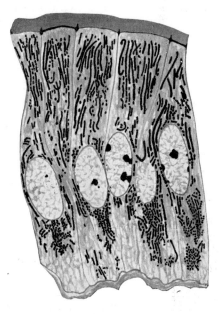

Fig. 21. Columnar epithelium from the intestine of a rat, showing striated border, terminal bars, and filamentous supranuclear, and granular infranuclear mitochondria. Iron-hematoxylin stain. 1000 ×. (A.A.M.)

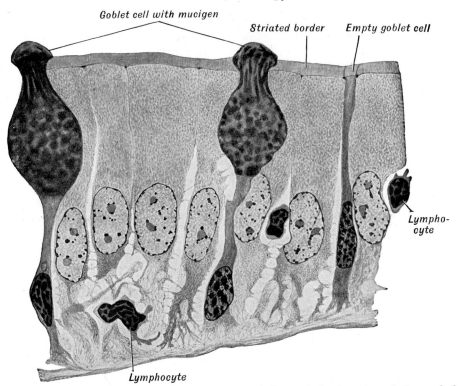

Goblet cell with mucigen   Striated border   Empty goblet cell

Lympho-
cyte

Lymphocyte

Fig. 22. Perpendicular section of the simple columnar epithelium of the intestine of the axolotl. The lateral surfaces of the epithelial cells are slightly detached from each other, and in the intercellular spaces protoplasmic bridges are seen. 750 ×. (A.A.M.)

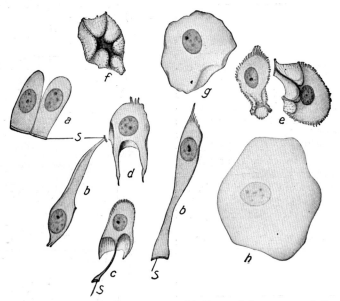

Fig. 23. Isolated cells from the stratified squamous epithelium of the cornea of the ox. *a*, Basal cells; *s*, cuticular border; *b*, club-shaped cells; *c*, cell with wing-shaped processes and with a thin stalk attached to the basement membrane; *d*, similar cell from one of the more superficial cell layers; *e*, prickle cells in profile; *f*, same in surface view; *g*, squamous cell; *h*, superficial flattened cell. 740 ×. (After Schaffer.)

nected with the underlying tissue (Fig. 446). This epithelium is rare and covers small surfaces. It is found in the fornix of the conjunctiva, in the cavernous part of the urethra, in some places in the anal mucous membrane, in the pharynx, on the epiglottis, and in the large excretory ducts of some glands. Some authors place the epithelium of the enamel organ in this group.

7. **Stratified Columnar Ciliated Epithelium.** The cells are arranged as in the preceding type, but the free surface of the superficial columnar cells is provided with cilia (Fig. 24). It is found on the upper (nasal) surface of the soft palate, in the larynx and, transiently, in the fetal esophagus.

8. **Pseudostratified Columnar Epithelium.** In the pseudostratified epithelium the nuclei are at different levels and the cells lack uniformity (Fig. 20). Some of the cells, while attached to the underlying connective tissue, may lose their connection with the free surface. These supporting cells are covered by the tall, superficial cells. In a perpendicular section the nuclei form several rows. Owing to mutual pressure, the cells may become irregular in shape and the tissue may appear to be stratified. Such an epithelium occurs in the large excretory ducts of several glands (parotid) and in the male urethra.

9. **Pseudostratified Columnar Ciliated Epithelium.** This is exactly as in 8, except that the free surface of the cells is provided with motile or nonmotile cilia (Fig. 20). It is found on the greater part of the mucous membrane of the respiratory passages, in the eustachian tube, in a part of the tympanic cavity, in the lacrimal sac and in the excretory passages of the male sexual system.

10. **Transitional Epithelium.** This was so called because it was supposed to represent a transition between the stratified squamous epithelia and the columnar epithelia. As it is found on the walls of hollow organs which are subject to great mechanical changes by contraction and stretching, its appearance varies greatly. In the contracted condition it consists of many cell layers. The deepest elements have a cuboidal or even columnar shape, then follow several layers of irregularly polyhedral cells, while the superficial layer consists of large cells with a convex free surface and excavated bevels fitting the subjacent polyhedral elements. In the stretched condition, usually only two layers can be distinguished: a superficial layer of large squamous elements over a layer of irregular cuboidal cells. Some investigators believe that the superficial cells are connected with the underlying tissue by means of thin stalks and that this epithelium is accordingly of the simple type.

The transitional epithelium is characteristic of the mucous membrane of the excretory passages of the urinary system from the renal calices to the urethra.

This classification applies only to the epithelia of the higher vertebrates. In chronic inflammatory irritations or in some neoplasms, one type of epithelium may change into another through the process of *metaplasia*. Thus the columnar bronchial epithelium may change into the stratified squamous.

Inner Structure of Epithelial Cells. The nucleus is generally single and of simple shape. In the squamous cells it is an oval disk; in the cuboidal cells it is spherical; in columnar cells it extends along the cell axis and may appear cylindrical. Epithelial cells with several nuclei sometimes occur (liver cells, parietal cells). The cell center, represented by a diplosome, is usually located above the nucleus and in columnar cells may occupy a position directly under the free surface.

Mitochondria are usually abundant. In squamous cells they surround the nucleus; in columnar cells they are arranged mainly above and below it. The longer mitochondria are usually parallel to the axis of the cell body. A *Golgi net* is always present, typically above the nucleus.

Tonofibrils are fairly common in epithelial cells. They are supposed by some to give the

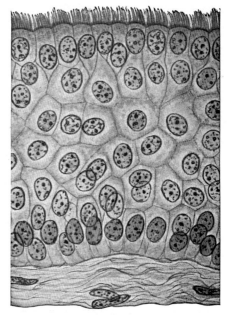

Fig. 24. Stratified columnar ciliated epithelium from the laryngeal surface of the epiglottis of a thirty-one-week human embryo. 795 ×. (After V. Patzelt, from Schaffer.)

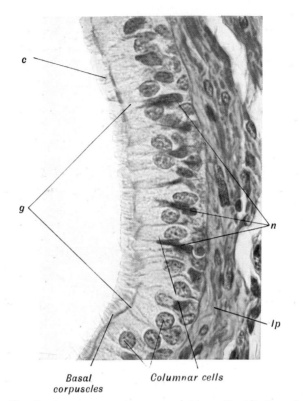

Fig. 25. Pseudostratified ciliated columnar epithelium with goblet cells (*g*) from human trachea. *c.* Cilia; *n*, nuclei of goblet cells; *lp*, lamina propria. Mallory-azan stain. 400 ×. (After von Herrath and Abramow.)

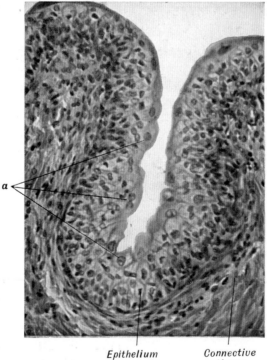

Fig. 26. Stratified epithelium of a contracted human bladder. Two of the large superficial cells (*a*) are binucleate. Photomicrograph. H + E, 240 ×. (After von Herrath and Abramow.)

soft cell body a rigid, supporting framework, while others believe them to be only tension striae in the cytoplasm. They reach an especially high development in the stratified squamous epithelium, where they form parallel or wavy bundles which pass from one cell body to another through the intercellular bridges.

A peculiarity of all epithelial cells is their *polarity*—the fact that the "proximal" side of the cell attached to the underlying tissue differs from the "distal" side, directed toward the free surface. The *cell axis*, an imaginary line connecting these two sides of the cell, is usually perpendicular to the surface of the epithelial sheet.

The polarity of epithelial cells results from their arrangement in sheets, for the two surfaces of a sheet of cells cannot have the same conditions of existence. The polarity manifests itself by the arrangement and the shape of the mitochondria at the base and at the top of glandular cells, by the unilateral position of the cytocentrum and the Golgi net, and so on. Generally, the proximal end of an epithelial cell is less differentiated and therefore more similar in the various types of epithelium, reflecting the fact that the proximal end is mainly instrumental in the reception of the nutritive material, which must always be similar. The distal part, on the contrary, is subject to manifold external influences, and in its protoplasm, above the nucleus, appear the different products of metabolism which are specific for each kind of epithelium—the secretory inclusions, the cuticular formations, and so forth.

The general structure of the epithelial elements just described presents innumerable variations due both to the special type of epithelium and to changing functional conditions. The details of these variations are described with the structure of the various organs in the chapters on special histology. All the types of inclusions mentioned in the introduction of this book may occur in and profoundly modify the structure of epithelial cells.

Free Surface of Epithelial Cells. Structures may develop on the free surface of epithelial cells by (1) specific modification of the superficial layer of protoplasm and (2) formation of membrane-like products of secretion (cuticles).

1. **Specialization of the Superficial Protoplasm.** The simplest of the first group of structures is a thin layer of condensed protoplasm on the free surface. This is not a true membrane which can be isolated. In a perpendicular section it appears on the free edge as a thin, refringent line. As an example, the superficial cells of the transitional epithelium of the urinary bladder show such a condensed cytoplasm at their free surface.

In all vertebrates the cells of the simple columnar intestinal epithelium have a distinct layer of modified protoplasm, the *striated border*, on their free surface. In a section the border shows a regular, fine, perpendicular striation. Electron microscopy fails to demonstrate a cement substance, although the rod-like processes are clearly seen (Fig. 379). Presumably, it plays an important role in the absorption of nutritive substances from the intestinal cavity.

A somewhat similar structure—a *brush border*—is found on the free surface of the epithelial cells of the main segment of the uriniferous tubules of the kidney (Fig. 437). This structure changes considerably with the functional condition of the tubules. It consists of nonmotile, hairlike outgrowths which stand upright in the fashion of a dense brush and are provided at their base with small granules. The brush border is supposed to be instrumental in the absorptive activity of the epithelium. A similar brush border has been described on the surface of the mesothelium (Fig. 17) and on the epithelium of the placental villi.

The highest structural differentiation of the free surface of the epithelium is reached in the *ciliated cells* (Fig. 24). These carry on their free surface a large number of cilia, i.e., thin, usually motile, processes. The length of the cilia in different types of epithelium varies considerably. Their substance is homogeneous, although an axial filament or a cross striation has sometimes been described. As a rule, at the base of each cilium, in the superficial layer of protoplasm is a small thickening, the *basal corpuscle*. It has a high refractive index and stains black with iron hematoxylin.

The movement of the cilia, which propels a constant stream of mucus or other liquid secretory material, consists in a rapid effective beat and a slower recovery stroke, always in one direction. The beat of each cilium begins slightly later than the beat of the one which precedes it in the direction from which movement proceeds, so that the beating moves across the ciliated surface in rapid and regular waves. If the connection between the cells in the path of the movement is severed, the

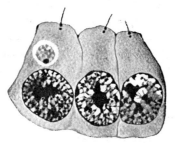

Fig. 27. Three epithelial cells with central flagella from a urinary tubule of the mesonephros of a rabbit embryo of 9.5 mm. 1500 ×. (A.A.M.)

waves in the separated areas become independent. The basis of the ciliary movement is not known; it is probably much the same as that in the muscle cell.

In the respiratory passages the ciliary movement drives the mucus toward the mouth, and with it are eliminated the particles of inhaled dust which stick to the mucous membrane. In the ductuli efferentes of the testis the ciliary movement probably helps to forward the spermia from the rete testis to the duct of the epididymis.

In the epididymis the epithelium carries long, nonmotile cilia which are supposed to help in the elimination of the secretion from the cells.

The nonmotile hairs of the epithelium of the maculae and the cristae in the inner ear serve as receptors of vibratory stimuli and transmit them to the cell body.

In the same category of structures are the *central flagella*, which have been found in many epithelial cells, especially in glandular ducts (Fig. 27) and in the mesothelial cells in the serous membranes. At its free surface the cytoplasm contains a diplosome, with

its axis standing perpendicularly. From the distal centriole an extremely thin, apparently nonmotile filament extends beyond the cell body.

2. **Cuticles.** Cuticle is generally a layer of a more or less solid substance which is secreted by and covers the free surface of an epithelial sheet. Unlike the protoplasmic crust, the cuticle is sharply delimited from the cell surface and can be detached from it. The cuticle often becomes impregnated with lime salts, chitin, and the like, and may consist of separate areas, each corresponding to one cell (tooth enamel), or it may become continuous through fusion of contiguous areas.

In the mammals the cuticles are infrequent; examples are the enamel of the teeth; the capsule of the lens; and the tectorial membrane, the lamina reticularis, and the otolithic membrane in the internal ear.

Connections between the Cells in an Epithelial Sheet. Adjacent epithelial cells cohere so tightly that relatively strong mechanical forces are necessary to separate them. This cohesion is particularly striking in the epithelium of the oral cavity and of the intestinal tract, where the movement of hard masses is unable to separate the cells from one another. It is probable that the small amount of interstitial substance acts as a plastic cement. Microdissection studies have shown that in most types of epithelium the superficial cytoplasm of the living cells contains an adhesive substance which keeps the cells together. It is possible that adjacent cells might adhere through interaction of the fibrous protein molecules in their surface membranes.

According to some, the epithelial cells are kept together by many small protoplasmic processes, running from one cell body to another and forming intercellular bridges. If the epithelial cells are isolated from one another, the broken bridges appear as short, thornlike outgrowths on the surface of the cell body. These bridges are most conspicuous in the stratified squamous epithelium of the skin, the epidermis. Here the deeper cells are separated from one another by clear, intercellular clefts filled with liquid. The intercellular bridges cross the clefts, and each shows at its middle a small thickening, the *bridge corpuscle* or *desmosome*. The tonofibrils, which reach a high grade of development in these cells, run from cell to cell through the intercellular bridges (Fig. 298).

In those epithelia which have no intercellular spaces, the lateral surfaces of the cells adhere tightly to one another and intercellular bridges cannot be seen. In the simple columnar epithelium the cells sometimes separate, and then bridges are distinct. Because this separation can be produced by the use of fixing reagents which cause shrinkage, these bridges are believed by some to be artefacts.

After the action of silver nitrate, especially in the simple squamous epithelium (or mesothelium and endothelium), the cell limits are outlined by black contours. What look to be large openings in such preparations, the "stomata" which the old histologists thought were present between the edges of the simple squamous epithelial (mesothelial or endothelial) cells, are artefacts. They are sometimes prominent as black dots along the intercellular lines.

Epithelial cells sometimes cohere intimately by means of special structures. Thus, in the convoluted uriniferous tubules the lateral surfaces of the cells are provided with alternating ridges and grooves which interdigitate with those of neighboring cells. When the limits between the cells cannot be detected, the epithelial sheet has the charac-

ter of a *syncytium*. This is found, for instance, in the epithelium of the uterine mucous membrane at the beginning of pregnancy and in some areas of the ectoderm of the embryo (trophoblast).

Terminal Bars. In various kinds of epithelium stained with iron hematoxylin, the free surfaces of the single cells are outlined by black lines different from those appearing after the action of silver nitrate. They are smoothly outlined rods of a dense cement substance which solders the edges of the cell surfaces, and are called *terminal bars* because they are supposed to close the intercellular spaces on the free surface (Fig. 28).

The terminal bars, when stained with iron hematoxylin, appear as dots if they are seen in cross section, or as short black lines if they happen to lie in the plane of the section (Fig. 28). If the free surface of the cells is provided with a cuticle, a striated or brush border, or with cilia, the bars are always located beneath these structures.

Blood Vessels and Nerve Fibers. As a rule, epithelial tissue lacks blood vessels. The nutritive liquid from the blood vessels of the underlying connective tissue reaches the epithelial elements after passing through the basement membrane and through the thin intercellular spaces between the epithelial cells. If the epithelium forms a thick layer, as in the skin, the surface of the connective tissue is usually provided with outgrowths, *papillae*, which carry blood capillaries, bulge deeply into the epithelium and probably facilitate nutrition. In a few cases (stria vascularis of the cochlea) loops of blood capillaries with thin strands of connective tissue may penetrate the epithelium. Nearly everywhere the epithelium is provided with numerous terminal branchings of nerve fibers which pierce the basement membrane and run between and even into the epithelial cells.

Extraneous Cells. Foreign cells may enter the epithelium from the connective tissue. The epithelium of the intestine is always infiltrated in special areas by a multitude of lymphocytes; these may even push aside and disfigure the epithelial cells. After they have left, the latter regain their usual form and resume their former relations. Such an infiltration reaches its highest degree in the thymus.

Regeneration of Epithelium. The epithelial layers, especially those which cover the outer surface of the body and the intestinal tract, are subject to constant mechanical and other injuries. Under physiologic conditions

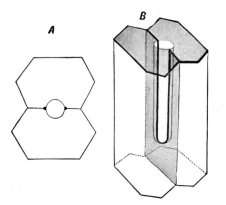

Fig. 28. Diagram of two adjacent glandular cells with a secretory capillary between them and with terminal bars: *A*, View in cross section; *B*, side view. (Redrawn after Zimmermann.)

their cells perish continuously and are shed. This is especially manifest in the epidermis, where the superficial cells are continuously undergoing a peculiar degeneration, called *cornification*. The cornified cells are constantly desquamated and are replaced by new ones which arise through the transformation of the cells of the deeper layers. In the respiratory passages, in the inner cavities of the body, and especially in most of the glands, where the epithelium is not accessible to external noxious agents, degeneration is rare.

The physiologic loss of cells in the epithelium is balanced by a corresponding regeneration. In vertebrates this is always effected through mitotic proliferation of indifferent epithelial elements. In the stratified squamous epithelium the mitoses are found mainly in the deeper columnar and polyhedral cell layers (stratum germinativum). The simple columnar epithelium of the stomach and the intestine is regenerated from special areas of proliferating undifferentiated epithelium which are located in the base of the gastric foveolae or in the crypts of Lieberkühn. In the pseudostratified and stratified columnar epithelium, dividing cells are occasionally found between the resting ones. Their round, contracted bodies usually move toward the surface. Whether the small, deeper cells connected with the underlying tissue, which were supposed to be the source of regeneration in the pseudostratified epithelium and were correspondingly called "substituting cells," really play this role seems doubtful.

In pathological conditions, as after local injuries, almost every type of epithelium in the human organism may display a considerable ability for regenerative proliferation, although the process may produce new, abnormal cell types. In tissue cultures several types of epithelium (thyroid, iris and liver) were observed to proliferate and to grow in "pure cultures" of thin sheets of flattened cells which did not change for some months. The various types of epithelium, especially those of ectodermal and entodermal origin, seem to keep their specific character even after a prolonged series of transplantations.

Although some workers have claimed that epithelial cells in tissue culture develop into fibroblasts, the evidence to date indicates that this is not true.

The proliferation in epithelial regeneration occurs only by mitotic division. Amitosis has been found in the transitional epithelium of the urinary bladder, in the mesothelium of the serous membranes and especially in tissue cultures, but it seems to result only in the formation of multinucleated cells.

In the body, excluding ciliated cells, the epithelial elements are not motile, as a rule. In the healing of wounds and in tissue cultures, however, they are seen to flatten and to display a peculiar gliding movement, by which they rapidly cover large denuded areas of connective tissue before regenerative division sets in. Occasionally, epithelial cells have even been seen to form ameboid pseudopodia. Wolbach and collaborators have shown that a deficiency of vitamin A in the diet of guinea pigs and rats results in atrophy of most of the epithelia of the body; in their place appears "a stratified keratinizing epithelium, identical in appearance in all locations, and arising from focal proliferation of basal cells." When the vitamin is supplied, the original type of epithelium appears in a few days. (See also Arey, 1936.)

Endothelium, Mesothelium and Mesenchymal Epithelium. The name *endothelium* is reserved for the simple layer of squamous cells which lines the inner surface of the wall of the blood and lymph vessels and of the heart (p. 205). In the early stages of embryonic development the endothelium arises through the flattening of mesenchymal cells (p. 93). In the later ontogenetic stages and in the adult it grows only through proliferation of its own elements and not through transformation of other connective tissue cells. On the other hand, endothelial cells can be transformed into fibroblasts.

The *mesothelium* is a simple, squamous cell layer which covers the surface of all the serous membranes (peritoneum, pericardium, pleura). Its elements have the classical structure of true squamous epithelial cells (Fig. 16). The surface of their protoplasm is provided with a thin, condensed, crustlike layer which carries, sometimes, a more or less distinct brush border (Fig. 17). The surface of the flattened, round or oval nucleus is slightly excavated, and here there is a diplosome with a typical central flagellum protruding into the serous cavity.

The prospective potencies of these elements are of double nature—epithelial and fibroblastic. In tissue cultures the mesothelium of mammals may show for a time a purely epithelial type of growth in islands and sheets of polyhedral, flattened cells. Tumors of epithelial character may develop from the mesothelium and, possibly, structures similar to uterine glands. On the other hand, in inflammation the mesothelial cells, after a period of contraction and of rounding off, finally give rise to typical fibroblasts, i.e., to connective tissue cells. The same occurs in tissue cultures. They are never transformed into ameboid phagocytes.

Mesenchymal epithelium is the simple layer of squamous cells which lines the subdural and subarachnoid spaces, the perilymphatic spaces in the inner ear and the chambers of the eyeball. (The cavities of joints are *not* lined by mesenchymal epithelium. See page 141.)

These elements seem to originate simply through flattening of common fibroblasts. The relations between the mesenchymal epithelium and the mesothelium have not been sufficiently elucidated.

REFERENCES

Arey, L. B.: Wound Healing. Physiol. Rev., *16*:327, 1936.

Chambers, R., and de Renyi, G. S.: The Structure of the Cells in Tissues as Revealed by Microdissection. I. The Physical Relationships of the Cells in Epithelia. Am. J. Anat., *35*:385, 1925.

Child, C.: Patterns of Development. Chicago, 1941.

Lucas, A. M.: Ciliated Epithelium., in Cowdry's Special Cytology. 2d ed. New York, (1), 407, 1932.

Reid, M. E.: Interrelations of Calcium and Ascorbic Acid to Cell Surfaces and Intercellular Substances and to Physiological Action. Physiol. Rev., *23*:76, 1943.

Schaffer, J.: Das Epithelgewebe, Handb. d. mikr. Anat. (v. Möllendorff). Berlin, (2), Part I, 1927.

Weiss, P.: The Chemistry and Physiology of Growth. VII. Differential Growth. Princeton University Press, 1949.

Wilbur, K. M., and Chambers, R.: Cell Movements in the Healing of Micro-wounds in Vitro. J. Exper. Zool., *91*:287, 1942.

Wolbach, S. B.: The Pathologic Changes Resulting from Vitamin Deficiency. J.A.M.A., *108*:7, 1937.

Wolbach, S. B., and Howe, P. R.: Epithelial Repair in Recovery from Vitamin A Deficiency. An Experimental Study. J. Exper. Med., *57*:511, 1933.

Worley, L. G.: Microdissection Studies of the Ciliated Epithelial Cell. J. Cell. & Comp. Physiol., *18*:187, 1941.

III. BLOOD

The embryonic connective tissue, the *mesenchyme*, gives rise to the blood, the blood vessels and the various types of connective tissue. The mesenchyme develops from the mesoderm immediately after the formation of the germ layers and soon accumulates in masses between them. The mesenchymal cells at first are irregularly stellate and connected by their processes, and their cell bodies are separated by a jelly-like, intercellular substance (Fig. 14). The cells undergo many changes to form the various blood and connective tissue cells.

There are four main types of connective tissue, all characterized by an abundant intercellular substance: (1) blood and lymph, (2) connective tissue proper, (3) cartilage, and (4) bone. In the blood and lymph the intercellular substance is liquid. In the connective tissue proper, of which there are many types, the intercellular substance always contains fibers and varies from a soft jelly to a tough fibrous mass. In cartilage the intercellular substance contains masked fibers and has a rubbery consistency. In bone the fibrous intercellular substance is impregnated with lime salts.

In the adult organism the various tissues of the connective substance cannot be sharply separated from one another in all respects. The fibers of the connective tissue proper continue into both cartilage and bone, and certain characteristic chemical substances are common to the intercellular substance in the connective tissue proper, cartilage and bone. Similarly, the cells of the blood cannot be separated from those of the connective tissue proper, since there is a constant exchange of cells between them. Certain cells of the blood and the other connective tissues may display marked differences in form and function when their environment is changed. Thus a leukocyte which seems to be inactive while in the blood may previously have been active while in the connective tissue proper and may become active again on reentering this tissue from the blood.

In the earliest stages of development the endothelial cells of the blood vessels and the blood cells arise simultaneously from the same mesenchymal elements. Moreover, the embryonic endothelium occasionally turns into blood cells. In the later stages, however, the endothelium becomes more differentiated and independent, and new vessels arise only through sprouting of preexisting ones. Thus all the vessels, including the heart, become a comprehensive specialized system, described in Chapter X. The blood vessels are always accompanied by connective tissue. However, as we shall see, some cells with the potencies of development of mesenchymal cells persist in the adult organism around the blood vessels and in the blood-cell-forming organs.

FORMED ELEMENTS OF THE BLOOD

The blood of adult vertebrates is a red liquid which circulates in a closed system of tubes, the blood vessels. Its quantity in man is estimated as about 7 per cent of the body weight. The liquid menstruum of the blood, the *plasma*, appears colorless in a thin film examined under the microscope, but varies from gray to yellow, according to species, when seen in large amounts with the naked eye. Suspended in the plasma are several kinds of formed elements: the *red corpuscles* (*erythrocytes*) *colorless corpuscles* (*white blood corpuscles* or *leukocytes*) and, in mammals, the *blood platelets.**

RED BLOOD CORPUSCLES

In the mammals the red blood corpuscles are nonmotile, highly differentiated cells which have lost their nucleus, Golgi net, mitochondria and centrioles during maturation. In the other vertebrates they retain the nucleus.

A normal adult man has about five and a woman about four and a half million erythrocytes in 1 cu. mm. of blood. Sojourn in high altitudes causes a marked increase in their number. The changes in pathological conditions are still more prominent. The erythrocytes are not always evenly distributed over the circulatory system.

The size of the erythrocytes, under normal conditions, is remarkably uniform; in man the diameter averages 7.74 microns, the thickness at the edge, 1.9 microns. According to some estimates, the erythrocytes of man have a diameter well over 8 microns, and the smaller figure given here is due to dehydration during preparation. The total surface area of all the red blood corpuscles in the human body is computed as about 3500 square meters. The specific gravity of the erythrocytes is higher than that of the plasma; the estimates vary from 1.02 to 1.08.

The red blood corpuscles are a pale, greenish yellow. This is especially marked at the periphery of the corpuscle, where the layer of the colored substance is thickest. In dense masses of erythrocytes the yellow color turns into a distinct red.

The pigment which gives the erythrocytes their color can be easily separated from the corpuscles. It then dissolves in the plasma and gives it a distinct color, while the cor-

* In an attempt to eliminate some of the hematological confusion connected with many of the names of cells now in use, a new nomenclature has been introduced in this country for the various blood cells and their precursors. For instance, in this new terminology it is proposed to supplant *erythrocyte* by *rubricyte*. Until this or another new terminology has been accepted by scientists of all nations, we shall continue to use the conventional names.

puscles become colorless, although they more or less keep their form. This process is called *hemolysis.* The pigment is *hemoglobin;* the colorless part which remains after the hemoglobin leaves is called the *stroma.* Hemoglobin and the colorless substances are present in the erythrocytes as a colloidal mixture, of which hemoglobin forms about 95 per cent of the dried weight.

The erythrocytes of the mammals are biconcave disks. In profile they have elongated bodies with rounded ends and a constricted middle part, more marked on one side than on the other.

Some investigators claim that they are shallow cups and that the biconcave form is the result of shrinkage due to an increase in the osmotic pressure of the plasma during examination. It is possible that, in the normal blood, both forms, as well as all transitions between them, are present at the same time. In the camel and the llama the erythrocytes are biconcave ovals devoid of nuclei.

The erythrocytes are extremely soft and flexible. The slightest mechanical influences distort them, but the usual form is restored as soon as the mechanical factor ceases to act. This can be seen easily during the observation of the circulating blood in living capillaries. When an erythrocyte is forced through a blood vessel of small caliber, it becomes considerably drawn out, but resumes the disk shape as soon as it enters a larger vessel. In living condition their substance appears homogeneous even with dark-field illumination. Ultracentrifuged erythrocytes are stratified into two or three layers; this indicates that they are composed of at least three substances (Beams).

Under physiological conditions the interior of the erythrocytes and the plasma are in a state of osmotic equilibrium. If the molecular concentration of the plasma is lowered through addition of water, water enters the erythrocyte. If the osmotic pressure of the plasma increases, the interior of the erythrocyte gives up water to the plasma (*crenation,* Figs. 29, X; 31). A solution of 0.9 per cent sodium chloride is isotonic with normal hu-

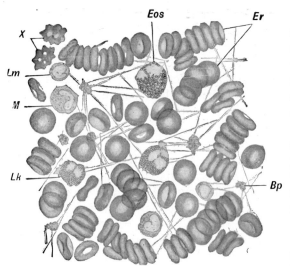

Fig. 29. Fresh preparation of human blood. *Bp*, Platelets; *Er*, erythrocytes; *Eos*, eosinophile leukocyte; *Lk*, neutrophile leukocyte; *Lm*, lymphocyte; *M*, monocyte; *X*, crenated erythrocytes. Note the strands of fibrin and rouleaux of erythrocytes. High magnification. (A.A.M.)

stream in the vessel is not too swift, the piles are seen gliding, serpent-like, through the smaller vessels. The cause of the rouleau formation is not known. Some believe that it is a display of surface tension forces which cause bodies suspended in a fluid to apply to one another by their greatest surfaces.

Irregular, persisting clumps of erythrocytes occur in the circulating blood in a variety of pathological conditions; these masses of erythrocytes, called *sludges*, have been studied extensively by Knisely and co-workers. They may cause severe local or generalized damage.

Agglutination. Various reagents, such as acid salt solutions or solutions of glucose, may cause agglutination of erythrocytes. They attract one another and assemble in small, dense groups. Agglutination of erythrocytes under the influence of *agglutinins* can occur in the circulatory system of the living organism; the resulting clusters of erythrocytes obstruct the small blood vessels and may lead to severe injuries of the tissues involved.

man plasma and therefore does not alter the size or form of the erythrocytes; it is called physiologic salt solution.

In spite of the fact that the red cells and the plasma are in a state of osmotic equilibrium, there are peculiarities of distribution of ions between them (Fig. 30). The distribution of the anions Cl^- and HCO^-_3 is readily understood as a consequence of the difference in concentration of nondiffusible protein ions (Donnan equilibrium). The mechanism by which the gradients in concentration of sodium and potassium are maintained is not yet fully understood; it is known, however, that this mechanism is dependent upon the anaerobic glycolysis which may be observed in red blood cells.

Erythrocytes have a marked tendency to adhere to one another by their broad surfaces and to assemble in long, curved columns resembling piles of coins (Fig. 29). This can be observed in a drop of fresh, undiluted blood. The piles or *rouleaux* arise at once; a slight pressure on the coverslip breaks them up. They also are formed in the living body while circulating in the blood vessels. The adhesion is so strong that, if the motion of the blood

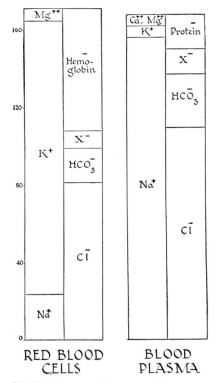

Fig. 30. Distribution of ions, in milli-equivalents per kilogram of water between red blood corpuscles and plasma. Modified after Peters and Van Slyke. (Courtesy of A. B. Hastings.)

Abnormal Erythrocyte Forms. A detailed description of abnormal forms of erythrocytes belongs to the text-books of pathology. Sometimes they occur in the blood of an apparently normal person, or are a manifestation of an accelerated formation of blood.

The erythrocyte may be unusually large or small. This phenomenon is called *anisocytosis*. The largest corpuscles are called *macrocytes*; the smallest ones, *microcytes*. If the erythrocytes acquire irregular contours, *poikilocytosis* is present. This occurs when there is a grave disturbance of hemopoiesis, as in pernicious anemia. In a special type of anemia the erythrocytes are *sickle-* or *crescent-shaped*.

The hemoglobin content may show great variations; in chlorosis each corpuscle contains an abnormally small quantity of this pigment and consequently appears paler than usual (*hypochromic*). In pernicious anemia the individual erythrocytes are abnormally rich in hemoglobin (*hyperchromic*).

The normal, mature erythrocytes in a dry smear are *acidophile*; that is, in a mixture of an acid (eosin) and a basic dye (methylene blue), such as in the Romanowsky mixture, they are stained electively with the acid dye and appear red (Fig. 32). In some cases, however, their substance will stain purple or bluish with this mixture. This condition is called *polychromia*. Polychromatic erythrocytes may occur in the human blood in various anemias. Under physiological conditions they are rarely found in the circulating blood, but are common in the bone marrow. The young forms of the erythrocytes (*erythroblasts*) also have a polychromatic protoplasm. Thus polychromia is a manifestation of immaturity of the red blood corpuscle, although it may also be found in degenerating erythrocytes. The polychromatic erythrocyte always shows a "reticulated substance" on supravital staining. It is possible that this stained network is the result of an artificial clumping of the diffused substance which causes the polychromatophilia seen with the Romanowsky stain. Protoporphyrin has been found in the blood and occurs only in the *reticulocytes* and is possibly the substance which is stained with brilliant cresyl blue in these almost mature erythrocytes. The term

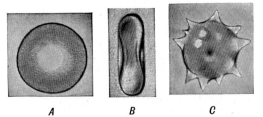

Fig. 31. Red blood corpuscle in 0.9 per cent sodium chloride solution, seen from the broad surface (*A*), in profile (*B*) and crenated (*C*). (After Broderson.)

"reticulocytes" is a poor one because of the frequent confusion with "reticular cells."

In the *basophile granulated* or "*stippled*" *erythrocytes*, with the Romanowsky stain, the substance of the erythrocytes is mottled with numerous, fine, blue granules. Stippled erythrocytes occur in the blood of embryos and of adult mammals, including man. They are found in various types of anemia, especially those of toxic nature, as in lead poisoning. In the hemopoietic organs of the adult they do not occur under physiological conditions. It is possible that the stippled condition is also a manifestation of immaturity in much the same way as the polychromia, but of an immaturity which is physiological only in the embryo; while in the adult it is an indication of an abnormal return to an embryonic type of development. The origin of the basophile granules is traced to either the nucleus of the erythroblast or to its basophile cytoplasm. It is possible that their substance is similar to the basophile substance in the polychromatic erythrocyte and differs from it only by its granular instead of diffuse distribution in the corpuscle. From this point of view the granules would be a manifestation of a degenerative change of the young erythrocytes.

Quite different from the basophile granules of the mottled erythrocytes are the peculiar granular *Howell-Jolly bodies*. These are undoubtedly remnants of the nuclear chromatin. They often occur in seemingly quite normal erythrocytes of adult and especially of embryonic mammals. They are small, sharply outlined, round or angular bodies which stain intensely with

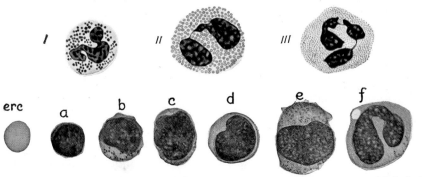

Fig. 32. *I,* Basophile leukocyte; *II,* eosinophile leukocyte; *III,* neutrophile (heterophile) leukocyte; *erc,* erythrocyte; *a, b, c, d,* lymphocytes; *e, f,* monocytes; from Romanowsky-stained, dry smears of human blood, except *I,* which is stained with thionine. (A.A.M.)

nuclear dyes, and especially with methyl green, which never stains the basophile granulation. Their number is limited to one or two in an erythrocyte.

In some pathological cases the erythrocytes contain the *rings of Cabot*. Although some believe them to be the membrane of the dissolved or extruded nucleus, Schleicher holds that they are artefacts which represent aggregated and denatured proteins of erythrocytes exposed to hemolytic agents.

Certain toxins cause the appearance of peculiar granules in the erythrocytes of the circulating blood —the *granules of Ehrlich-Heinz*. They can be stained with acid dyes in fixed smears and are products of the disintegration of hemoglobin.

Function of the Erythrocytes. The erythrocytes are carriers of oxygen. In the blood vessels of the lungs (or gills) their hemoglobin combines with oxygen and is transformed into oxyhemoglobin. In the tissues of the body where the oxygen tension is much less than in the respiratory organs, oxyhemoglobin is reduced and its oxygen is used in the metabolic processes of the cells. Hemoglobin plays an equally important part in the transport of carbon dioxide from the tissues to the lungs. As it loses oxygen it becomes a weaker acid, the diminution in its acid strength being nearly sufficient to compensate for the carbonic acid formed from the oxygen it delivers to the tissues. In the lungs, as oxygen is taken up and carbon dioxide is lost, it again becomes a stronger acid. In addition, part of the carbon dioxide carried from the tissues to the lungs is combined directly with hemoglobin in the form of hemoglobin carbamate.

COLORLESS CORPUSCLES: LEUKOCYTES, OR WHITE BLOOD CORPUSCLES

The blood of all animals contains a number of colorless corpuscles. Although the origin and morphology of these leukocytes have been studied intensively, little is known of their physiological functions.

The white blood corpuscles are more resistant to change in the surrounding medium than are the erythrocytes. In a drop of fresh blood, if desiccation is prevented, they remain alive for a considerable time and can be studied easily. Their number is far smaller than that of the erythrocytes, averaging in the normal human blood 5000 to 9000 in a cu. mm. In children the figures are higher. The number of leukocytes in the circulating blood varies at different times of the day, during digestion, in the various parts of the circulatory system and, in addition, may change rapidly under the influence of numerous conditions which are hard to control. Consequently, many of the leukocyte counts frequently have only a relative value.

The leukocytes are true cells with a nucleus and cytoplasm; they are all more or less ameboid. In fresh human blood several types can be distinguished: (1) small cells, about the size of an erythrocyte or slightly larger, with a scanty, clear, homogeneous cytoplasm and a faintly outlined, relatively large round, or indented, or irregular nucleus (*lymphocytes*); these merge by a series of transition forms into (2) slightly larger cells with an oval or indented nucleus and somewhat greater amounts of cytoplasm (*monocytes*); these cells are easily distinguishable from (3) cells with a cytoplasm filled with fine granules and a lobated nucleus (*heterophile granular leukocytes* [*neutrophile* in man]). (4) There are also a few cells with coarse, round, yellowish, brilliant granules and usually two clear spots representing the nucleus (*eosinophile granular leukocytes*). (5) Another type of leukocyte, the *basophile granular leukocyte*, is hard to identify when unstained. Thus the white blood corpuscles may be separated into two groups: (1) nongranular leukocytes, and (2) granular leukocytes. It must be emphasized that the cells, as seen in the living or in sections, are quite different from the same cells seen in dry smears, which flatten a sphere to a relatively large, thin disk. In this process many structural details are greatly changed and often distorted. For instance, the obvious nucleolus of the smaller lymphocytes is obscured in dry smears.

Nongranular or Lymphoid Leukocytes; Agranulocytes. This group contains the lymphocytes and the monocytes. As we shall see in the section on the lymphatic tissue, the largest lymphocytes do not gain access to the blood stream under normal conditions, and the large lymphocyte of the blood is the same as the medium-sized lymphocyte of the lymphatic tissue. Under abnormal conditions, large lymphocytes of lymphatic tissue appear in the blood; they are usually called *lymphoblasts*.

Lymphocytes. In human blood the lymphocytes are spherical cells 6 to 8 microns in diameter, although a few of them may be even a little larger. On the average, they are slightly larger than erythrocytes.

The characteristic feature of a small lymphocyte is a relatively large nucleus surrounded by a thin layer of cytoplasm. The nucleus is spherical; on one side it always has a more or less marked indentation. In stained preparations the chromatin forms a thick layer at the membrane and several darkly staining particles in the interior. The nucleus accordingly appears dark. The large nucleolus is invisible in stained dry smears. The cytoplasm forms a slightly larger accumulation on the indented side of the nucleus. It is homogeneous and basophile; in dry smears it stains pale blue with the Romanowsky eosin-methylene-azure mixture.

In human blood the lymphocytes form 20 to 25 per cent of the total number of colorless corpuscles.

The larger cells among the lymphocytes (Fig. 32, *b, c, d*) are relatively scarce. Their larger size is due to a slightly greater amount of cytoplasm, while the nucleus remains unchanged or is less compact.

The cytocentrum is represented by a pair of centrioles at the indentation of the nucleus (Fig. 34); it is surrounded by a small Golgi net. The mitochondria are scarce and small and have the form of small dots or short rods. They are easily stained supravitally with Janus green. Supravital staining with neutral red seldom reveals more than three to five inclusions in man. In many lymphocytes in some animals, such as the rat, a sometimes considerable number of small red vacuoles can be seen around the cytocentrum. Except for occasional small lipoid droplets, no other inclusions are found in the living, unchanged lymphocytes.

Although the lymphocytes are nongranular leukocytes, Romanowsky-stained, dry smears occasionally reveal a few round granules of different sizes and of a bright purple color in their cytoplasm. These are called *azurophile granules*. Unlike the granules of the granulocytes, they are not a constant feature of this cell type.

In the guinea pig many lymphocytes and monocytes contain a large spherical inclusion, the *Kurloff body*. In dry smears it stains in the same way as do the azurophile granules and is probably also an accumulation of a substance elaborated by the protoplasm, although it has other staining reactions which differentiate it from the azurophile granules. In living cells the Kurloff body is a homogeneous, yellowish-green body.

Fig. 33. Lymphocyte of human blood, showing mitochondria stained supravitally with Janus green. (After Cowdry.)

Fig. 34. Lymphocytes of human blood, showing cytocentrum. Iron-hemotoxylin stain. (After Weidenreich.)

Monocytes. There is much confusion as to just what a monocyte is, since the delimitation of this cell type has been obscured by the contradictory opinions of the proponents of the various theories of blood formation. When preparations of blood are examined objectively, the nongranular leukocytes are seen to consist of a series of transition forms which begins with the smaller lymphocytes and ends with larger cells of quite different appearance, the monocytes, which will be described shortly. But in the midportion of this series of transitions is a group of cells which cannot be classified as either typical lymphocytes or typical monocytes. The following description refers to the typical monocytes of the blood; a discussion of their origin is found on page 100.

The typical monocytes measure 9 to 12 microns in diameter. In dry smears, in which they are flattened and stretched, their diameter may reach 20 microns. They constitute 3 to 8 per cent of the leukocytes of the circulating blood. Their enumeration is especially difficult, because, as mentioned before, they cannot always be sharply differentiated from the larger lymphocytes of the blood.

In the typical monocytes the cytoplasm is far more abundant than in the lymphocytes, while the nucleus is relatively small. In the older monocytes the nucleus has an eccentric position, and is oval or kidney-shaped. A few monocytes have a horseshoe-shaped or deeply constricted nucleus—these are the oldest ones. The nuclear membrane is much thinner and the chromatin granules finer and more numerous than in the lymphocytes. Therefore the nucleus stains paler, especially in dry smears. One or several small nucleoli are always present, although not seen in dry smears.

The abundant cytoplasm has a pale, grayish-blue color in dry smears stained with eosin-methylene-azure. Special methods show that it contains the usual diplosome and a considerable number of mitochondria. At the periphery, near the indentation of the nucleus, is a Golgi net. Supravital staining with Janus green and neutral red reveals a spherical group of fine red vacuoles, the rosette, which surrounds the cytocentrum; its position corresponds with that of the Golgi net. The bluish-green stained mitochondria are arranged in a wreath around the rosette. The claim that this rosette is specific for monocytes is incorrect, for closely allied cell types may have neutral red rosettes (lymphocytes in the rat, plasma cells, some macrophages, some of the septal cells of the lung). The number of circulating monocytes may be increased experimentally in rabbits by infection with *L. monocytogenes* (Murray and coworkers), or by injections of the phospholipids of the tubercle bacillus (Sabin).

Monocytes are often erroneously identified with macrophages, especially in some inflammatory processes in which all the mononuclear exudate cells have been loosely spoken of as constituting a "monocytic reaction" (see p. 63).

Granular Leukocytes, or Granulocytes. In contrast to the lymphocytes and monocytes, the granulocytes always contain specific granules. These are of the same form in any given cell, but are distinctly different in various classes of granulocytes in a given species and in the homologous cells of different species. They may be relatively large or small, spherules or ovoids, or may be irregular in outline, filamentous or rod-shaped. Another general characteristic of the mature granular leukocytes is the shape of their nucleus. Instead of

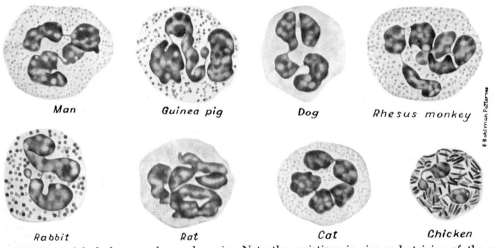

Man   Guinea pig   Dog   Rhesus monkey

Rabbit   Rat   Cat   Chicken

Fig. 35. Heterophile leukocytes of several species. Note the variations in size and staining of the granules in those species in which they are present. Wright's stain. (Courtesy of M. Block.)

being spherical and slightly indented or kidney-shaped, as in the majority of the non-granular leukocytes, the nucleus of the granulocytes is constricted into a varying number of lobes. The lobated nucleus of the mature cells gradually develops from the compact, spherical nucleus of the young forms (see Fig. 69). Although different classes of granulocytes may be identified on the basis of their nuclear form and the morphology of the cytoplasmic granules, the most convenient classification is based upon a combination of the morphology and staining reactions of the granules.

In such a classification the granulocytes fall into three general groups designated as (1) acidophile, (2) basophile, and (3) heterophile leukocytes (neutrophile in man). In the first, the granules in the cytoplasm are most often spherical or oval and are electively stained with acid dyes; in the second they are of similar form, but stain electively with basic dyes; while in the third group the granules, although constant in a particular species, differ as to form, size and staining reaction according to species (Fig. 35).

Acidophile or Eosinophile Leukocytes. The diameter of these cells, which are spherical in the fresh condition, is about 9 microns. In dry smears the size of the flattened cells is about 12 microns. Their number in the normal adult blood varies from 2 to 5 per cent of the total leukocyte count.

The nucleus usually has two oval lobes connected by a thin chromatin thread. In fixed and stained preparations, the lobes of the nucleus show a fairly dense chromatin network, but no nucleoli. A similar nucleus is found in the eosinophile leukocytes of the other mammals. In the rat and mouse it is a thick, irregular ring.

The cytoplasm forms a thin layer at the periphery of the cell. It is more distinct in moving cells, in which it sends out pseudopodia. In the interior of the cell body the cytoplasm is reduced to thin partitions between the granules and stains faintly with basic dyes. In the middle of the cell body a small area free of granules is occupied by the cytocentrum with its diplosome.

The coarse granules, in man, are spherical and are stained with acid dyes; after Romanowsky type stains they are red. Supravital staining with Janus green reveals a few mitochondria between the eosinophile granules. With the exceptions of some fishes, all vertebrates have typical eosinophile leukocytes in their blood.

Basophile Leukocytes. These cells are difficult to find in human blood, because they form only about one half of 1 per cent of the total number of leukocytes. Their size is about the same as that of the heterophile leukocytes. In a dry smear they measure 10 microns in diameter. The nucleus is elongated, often bent in the form of an **S**, and provided with two or more constrictions. The chromatin network is looser and paler than in the eosinophile leukocytes, and does not contain any nucleoli. The granules in the cytoplasm of the living cells have a low refractive index. Their substance, in man, is soluble in water; therefore, in preparations stained with the usual watery dye solutions, the granules are partly dissolved and disfigured. In dry smears or in sections of alcohol-fixed material, the cytoplasm contains round granules of different sizes, which stain a metachromatic purple with alcoholic thionine or toluidin blue. Supravital application of neutral red gives the granules a dark red color.

The solubility of the basophile granules has created considerable confusion in regard to the nature of these cells, but the use of suitable methods leaves no doubt as to their specific nature. In the guinea pig, their granules are large, oval, insoluble in water, and stain but faintly. In the dog, the granules are fine and are assembled in a small, compact group. In the cat, rat and mouse, the basophile leukocytes seem to be absent from the blood normally. In the lower vertebrates the variations are still greater.

Heterophile Leukocytes (Neutrophile in Man). This type of leukocyte is the most numerous in the blood of all vertebrates. In fresh human blood these cells can be recognized easily by their fine granulation, which is seen especially well when the cells move (Fig. 29, Lk). The size of the spherical cells

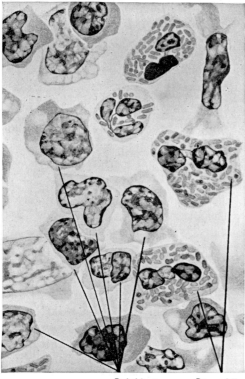

Polyblasts   Basophile
                leukocytes

Fig. 36. Basophile granular leukocytes in the local reaction of the connective tissue of a guinea pig to the injection of ventriculin 10 days previously. Hematoxylin-eosin-azure II. 2240 ×. (Courtesy of N. Plimpton; drawn by Miss E. Bohlman.)

in fresh condition is from 7 to 9 microns. In a dry smear they measure from 10 to 12 microns, and constitute 65 to 75 per cent of the total number of leukocytes.

The nucleus is highly polymorphous. It is an elongated, bent or twisted body consisting of several irregularly oval or angular lobes connected by thin chromatin threads. During ameboid motion the nucleus undergoes passive changes of its form, but the constrictions and the thickenings are constant. The number of the lobes varies from three to five and increases with the age of the cell. Under physiological conditions the majority of the cells have a three-lobed nucleus. In pathological cases these relations may change considerably. A dark chromatin network is seen in the lobes in stained sections; nucleoli are absent.

The cytoplasm has a peripheral, homogeneous layer which forms the pseudopodia.

The inner, slightly acidophile mass is full of fine granules, except for a small, clear area in the center of the cell body which contains the diplosome. In man the granules are stained with neutral dyes, and are, therefore, called neutrophile. The Romanowsky mixture gives them a purple hue. They can also be stained with acid dyes such as eosin. Supravital staining with Janus green reveals the presence of a few mitochondria. Neutral red applied supravitally gives the granules an indistinct, pale yellowish hue. Occasionally, small vacuoles and inclusions of fat or glycogen can be found between the granules.

In other mammals the granules have a variable size and staining reaction which are more or less typical for the species. In the guinea pig and rabbit the granules are stainable with either acid or basic dyes, although they show a predilection for acid dyes and, therefore, were called *pseudoeosinophils*. In some species the granules are so small that they are hardly seen with the highest powers of the microscope (see Fig. 35).

Abnormal Forms of Leukocytes. In some diseases the blood may contain degenerating leukocytes. Vacuoles, droplets of fat or lipids may appear in the protoplasm. These are well shown by the use of supravital stains. In the granular leukocytes the nucleus may undergo fragmentation into separate parts (*rhexis*) or shrinkage (*pyknosis*). Atypical and immature leukocytes enter the blood in certain diseases. (Fig. 36).

Free Macrophages of the Blood. Many investigators have described macrophages in the blood. They have a large, eccentric nucleus and a vacuolated, ameboid cytoplasm which often contains phagocytosed inclusions. In animals which have had intravenous injections of vital dyes or corpuscular matter, large quantities of these substances accumulate in the free macrophages (see p. 63). They originate in the spleen, liver and bone marrow from fixed macrophages through contraction and isolation. They are found especially in the blood of the veins and of the right heart, and the major part of them is filtered off in the capillaries of the lungs, but some may occasionally enter the general circulation.

The free macrophages appear in the blood in certain diseases, especially in those of septic nature. Their presence in the normal blood, as claimed by some authors, is doubtful, and their presence in the blood even in pathological cases is considered by some to be merely an agonal phenomenon. Confusion has been caused because many authors did not distinguish the blood macrophages from the monocytes. The cells described by some authors in leukemias and other diseases under the name of hemohistioblasts are for the most part the same free macrophages. In some cases, artificially damaged hemocytoblasts or myelocytes in dry smears have been mistaken for free macrophages or hemohistioblasts.

Functions of the Leukocytes. Little is known of the functions of the leukocytes while in the blood stream. Occasionally some of them phagocytose particulate material, such as bacteria or carbon particles. However, the function of the leukocytes is apparent when they are outside the vascular system, where they show active movement and phagocytosis; some turn into other cell types.

Movement. All leukocytes are capable of active movement, provided they have a solid substrate to move on. The movement can be observed in a drop of fresh blood protected from desiccation and kept at body temperature or, better, in tissue cultures. The movement of the leukocytes is identical in essential details with that of an ameba. The factors concerned in the movement of leukocytes are discussed by DeBruyn.

The ability of the leukocytes to move explains why they are not confined to the system of blood or lymph vessels, but may be found everywhere in the connective tissue and occasionally even in other tissues. Under physiological conditions, single leukocytes, especially lymphocytes, migrate out of the vessels into the tissue, and may return again into the blood or lymph channels. In inflammation—the reaction of a tissue to local injury—the leukocytes assemble rapidly in the blood vessels of the region and migrate in enormous numbers through the vessel walls into the tissue (see p. 63).

Chemotaxis. The migration of the leukocytes into the tissue toward the site of a local injury is believed to be caused by their chemotactic properties. In in vitro studies it is primarily the granulocytes which show chemotaxis when tested with bacterial products, products of damaged tissue and a number of carbohydrates. Although the lymphocytes do not react chemotactically to any of these substances, they and the monocytes also accumulate in great numbers in injured tissues.

Phagocytosis. The heterophile granulocytes display a marked capacity for ingesting small, discrete particles, such as cinnabar, carbon and bacteria. This action may occur within the circulating blood stream, but is distinctly more extensive in extravascular locations. Phagocytosis can be watched outside the body when living leukocytes and bacteria are brought together under suitable conditions. The phagocytosis and digestion of bacteria by the heterophile granulocytes is one of the means by which the host destroys bacteria, and the issue of some infections may depend upon the extent of phagocytosis.

The eosinophile leukocytes display phagocytosis rarely, if ever. The agranulocytes in the blood stream are seldom phagocytic, although, under suitable extravascular conditions, the monocytes, in contrast to the small lymphocytes, engulf particulate matter.

Other Properties of the Leukocytes. A positive oxydase reaction occurs in the granulocytes and in most of the monocytes. The lymphocytes do not give this reaction. Some investigators believe that lymphocytes are a source of antibodies (p. 65). The number of leukocytes in the peripheral blood can undergo variations as a result of certain pathological conditions. Certain stimuli affect one cell type more than the others. The number of eosinophils increases greatly when certain animal parasites are in the body and also during various allergic disorders. Administration of adrenocorticotropic hormone or cortisone causes a disappearance of the eosinophils from the blood, and this is used as a guide during clinical administration of these hormones. This cell type may accumulate in enormous numbers in local tissue areas, as in the mucous membranes of the respiratory passages in bronchial asthma, or about animal parasites.

The basophils increase in number in the blood stream of guinea pigs infected with *L monocytogenes*. They appear in great numbers in the inflamed area caused by the local injection of egg albumen or ventriculin in guinea pigs (Fig. 36).

Lymphocytes accumulate in small numbers about autogenous tissue grafts and in greater numbers about homoplastic tissue grafts. Heteroplastic grafts are surrounded by a large number of heterophile leukocytes and lymphocytes (Loeb).

BLOOD PLATELETS

In the circulating blood the platelets of all mammals are small, colorless corpuscles. They are round or oval, biconvex disks; when seen in profile, they look like small, plump spindles or rods. Their size is not quite uniform, the average being 3 microns. Their

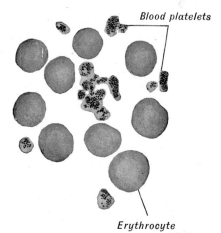

Blood platelets

Erythrocyte

Fig. 37. From a dry, Romanowsky-stained smear of human blood, showing platelets with their hyalomere and the dark, punctiform chromomere.

number varies considerably and is usually given as 250,000 in 1 cu. mm. of blood, although some authors give much higher figures. It is extremely difficult to determine the real number, because, as soon as the blood leaves the vessel, the platelets adhere to one another and to all surfaces with which they come in contact (Fig. 29).

In a fresh drop of blood the platelets at once agglutinate into small and large clusters and stick to the glass. They are the lightest elements of the blood, so that in centrifuged blood they form the uppermost white layer, lose their smooth outlines, and finally disintegrate into small groups of granules. Simultaneously, around and radiating from them, fibrils of fibrin appear in the plasma (Fig. 29).

They may be preserved for observation by

rendering the blood incoagulable through the addition of sodium citrate or heparin. Of all fixing reagents, solutions of osmic acid preserve them best. In rapidly prepared dry smears, the platelets are preserved as round corpuscles.

After fixation and staining with the Romanowsky mixture, each platelet is seen to consist of two parts. One is highly refractile and contains purple granules. This is the *chromomere.* The other is pale and homogeneous, and stains a pale blue—the *hyalomere.* The chromomere occupies a central or peripheral position. The hyalomere is often seen to send out pointed processes (Fig. 37). Sometimes the platelets contain small vacuoles.

The nature of the platelets is not known. Some older authorities believed them to be unorganized precipitates of the blood plasma. Others considered them to be products of disintegration of erythrocytes, or remnants of the nucleus or the cytocentrum of the red or white blood corpuscles.

At present the dominant opinion connects the origin of the platelets with peculiar giant cells, the *megakaryocytes,* which are found in the bone marrow of all mammals. It is claimed that pseudopodia-like excrescences become pinched off the surface of the megakaryocytes and enter the blood stream as platelets.

The changes of the platelets in a fresh drop of blood make it probable that they play a part in the coagulation of the blood. It is believed by some that they are the source of the enzymes which are necessary at least to initiate this process of clotting. However, they cannot be the only source of such enzymes, because blood plasma freed of platelets clots nevertheless. Platelets are absent from the blood of the inframammalian vertebrates. These animals have, instead, nucleated spindle cells which play a role in blood clotting, and the term "thrombocytes" should be reserved for them.

Blood Clotting. Blood, as it circulates normally in the vascular system, is a fluid tissue. Upon cessation of the circulation or upon removal of blood from the vessels, the fluidity is rapidly lost, the blood becoming a jelly-like mass. This change is termed "blood clotting" or "blood coagulation."

The physical factor involved in this change is the aggregation of a protein of the normal plasma into threads which form an interlacing network, in the small meshes of which are entangled the blood corpuscles and the aqueous menstruum.

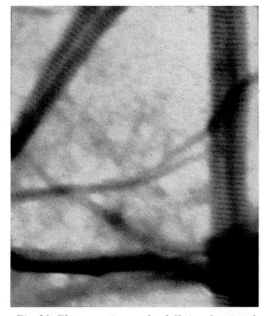

Fig. 38. Electron micrograph of fibrin, showing the periodic cross striation. 55,000 ×. (After Porter and Hawn.)

The dispersed protein of normal plasma which contributes to the formation of the network is *fibrinogen*. This, when modified physically and chemically to form the network, is known as *fibrin*. With the electron microscope it can be seen that the fibrin fibers formed from bovine fibrinogen are "cross striated." The width of these bands is about 250 angstrom units. The liquid fraction of the plasma which remains after the subtraction of fibrin is called *serum*.

Although many factors are known which modify the speed and extent of fibrin formation, and hence of blood clotting, no ultimate analysis of the phenomenon has been reached. Methods have been developed by which fibrin formation may be greatly delayed.

For the details of clotting and the chemi-

cal composition of the blood, reference should be made to a text on physiological chemistry.

LYMPH

The lymph, the liquid which fills the lymphatic vessels, is collected from all over the body and returned to the blood. The composition of the lymph arising in different organs varies markedly. There are no cells in the smallest lymph vessels, the lymph capillaries. As it passes through the lymph nodes, however, more and more cells are added to the lymph. In the thoracic duct it is a more or less opaque, sometimes pinkish liquid which contains large numbers of cells. The lymph here is similar to the plasma of the blood; it also clots, although the clot is much looser and softer. The number of cells in the lymph varies within wide limits, although their character is uniform. As a rule, besides some few erythrocytes and occasional eosinophile leukocytes, about 99 per cent of the cells are lymphocytes, of which the small lymphocytes form 80 to 85 per cent. Medium-sized and, especially, large lymphocytes are relatively rare. Cells of monocytic character occur but rarely under physiological conditions; the same is true of larger cells of the macrophage type. Under pathological or experimental conditions, including tissue cultures of lymph, the cellular aspect of the lymph changes rapidly, and numerous macrophages develop from the lymphocytes.

REFERENCES

The student will find detailed discussions of the cells of the blood in Downey's Handbook of Hematology. New York, 1938.

Beams, H. W., and Hines, E. B.: Stratification of the Rat Erythrocyte by Ultracentrifuging. Anat. Rec., 90:155, 1944.

Bunting, C. H.: The Granular Leukocytes, in Cowdry's Special Cytology. 2d ed. New York, (2), 683, 1932.

Conway, E. A.: Reaction of Lymphatic Tissue in Early Stages of B. *monocytogenes* Infection. Arch. Path., 25:200, 1938.

Dobriner, K., and Rhoads, C. P.: The Porphyrins in Health and Disease. Physiol. Rev., 20:416, 1940.

DeBruyn, P. P. H.: Theories of Ameboid Motion. Quart. Rev. Biol., 22:1, 1947.

Hawn, C. van Z., and Porter, K. R.: The Fine Structure of Clots Formed from Purified Bovine Fibrinogen and Thrombin: A Study with the Electron Microscope. J. Exper. Med., 86:285, 1947.

Jordan, H. E.: The Origin and Significance of the Megakaryocytes of the Lungs. Anat. Rec., 77:91, 1940.

Knisely, M. H., Bloch, E. H., Eliot, T. S., and Warner, L.: Sludged Blood. Science, 106:431, 1947.

Maximow, A.: The Lymphocytes and Plasma Cells, in Cowdry's Special Cytology. 2d ed. New York, (2), 601, 1932.

McCutcheon, M.: Chemotaxis in Leukocytes. Physiol. Rev., 26:319, 1946.

Merrell, M., Gellhorn, A., and Flexner, L. B.: Studies on Rates of Exchange of Substances between the Blood and Extravascular Fluid. II. The Exchange of Sodium in the Guinea Pig. J. Biol. Chem., 153: 83, 1944.

Pappenheim, A.: Morphologische Hämatologie (1 and 2). Leipzig, 1919.

Porter, K. R., and Hawn, C. van Z.: Sequences in the Formation of Clots from Purified Bovine Fibrinogen and Thrombin: A Study with the Electron Microscope. J. Exper. Med., 90:225, 1949.

Quick, A. J.: The Anticoagulants Effective in Vivo with Special Reference to Heparin and Dicumarol. Physiol. Rev., 24:297, 1944.

Rebuck, J. W., and Woods, Helen L.: Electron Microscope Studies of Blood Cells. Blood, J. Hematol., 3:175, 1948.

Sabin, F. R., Smithburn, K. C., and Thomas, R. M.: Cellular Reactions to Wax-like Materials from Acid-fast Bacteria. J. Exper. Med., 62:751, 1935.

Schleicher, E. M.: The Origin and Nature of the Cabot Ring Bodies of Erythrocytes. J. Lab. & Clin. Med., 27:983, 1942.

Sturgis, C. C., and Bethell, F. H.: Quantitative and Qualitative Variations in Normal Leukocytes. Physiol. Rev., 23:279, 1943.

Weidenreich, F.: Die Leucocyten und verwandte Zellformen. Wiesbaden, 1911.

Waugh, D. F.: The Ultrastructure of the Envelope of Mammalian Erythrocytes. Ann. New York Acad. Sc., 50:835, 1950.

IV. THE CONNECTIVE TISSUE PROPER

The connective tissue proper always contains fibers in its intercellular substance. As this substance and the cells present numerous variations, this type of tissue may be subdivided into numerous categories. The classification is difficult and inexact, for the different categories are linked by transitional forms. Even in the adult organism one type of connective tissue may be directly transformed into another.

The fibrous components of the connective tissue of the body are in general irregularly arranged. Depending on whether the fibers are loosely woven or densely packed, we speak of *loose connective tissue* or *dense connective tissue*. The fibers have a regular arrangement in tendons, fibrous membranes and in the connective tissue lamellae of some organs; these are therefore called *regular connective tissues*. In addition, there are a number of types of connective tissues with special properties: *mucous connective tissue, elastic tissue, reticular tissue, adipose tissue, pigment tissue*, the specialized connective tissue (lamina propria) of the intestinal and uterine mucous membranes, and the interstitial connective tissue of lung, testis and ovary. All are modifications of the basic loose connective tissue.

LOOSE CONNECTIVE TISSUE

The loose connective tissue develops from the mesenchyme which remains after all the other types of the connective tissue have been formed. It contains almost all the cellular and intercellular elements (or their precursors) which occur in the other kinds of connective tissue, and serves as a prototype of the connective tissue in general. It is a whitish, sticky mass, which fills out the spaces between the organs and penetrates with the blood vessels into the interior of the organs.

Where the organs are separated from one another it is stretched between them in thin membranes and threads, and is easily torn during dissection. Like a collapsed sponge, it contains innumerable potential cavities which can be easily filled artificially with liquids or air. These are the "cells" of the old anatomists, who are responsible for the name "areolar tissue" sometimes used.

Intercellular Substance. The intercellular substance forms the main mass of the tissue; three parts can be distinguished in it: (1) the collagenous or white fibers, (2) the elastic or yellow fibers, and (3) the amorphous ground substance. In addition, there are reticular fibers which occur at the boundary of the connective tissue and other structures.

Collagenous Fibers. All types of connective tissue show collagenous fibers as their most characteristic element. In the loose tissue these are long, straight or wavy threads or ribbons of 1 to 12 microns in thickness. They run in all directions (Fig. 46), and their ends cannot be found. They are colorless and show longitudinal striation, while in cross section they seem granular. This microscopic appearance results from the fact that the fibers consist of parallel fibrils, 0.3 to 0.5 micron in thickness, held together by a cementing substance, presumably a protein, since it is digested by trypsin. On the surface of the fiber the cement substance forms a thin membrane. The fibrils are thought not to branch, but the fibers branch in many places.

The collagenous fibers are flexible, but offer a great resistance to a pulling force. The breaking point of human collagenous fibers (tendon) is reached with a force of several hundred kg./cm.^{2}, and their elongation at this point is only a few per cent. In polarized light, collagenous fibers show positive uniaxial form and also crystalline birefringence.

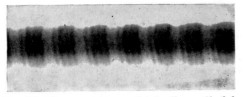

Fig. 39. Electron micrograph of collagen fibril from tendon of rat tail. Phosphotungstic acid stain. 110,000 ×. (After Schmitt, Hall and Jakus.)

The *form birefringence* indicates the presence of submicroscopic, elongate structures oriented in the direction of the fiber axis and made visible as fibrils by the electron microscope. The presence of *crystalline birefringence* reflects the fact that inside these fibrils a finer structure is present of molecular dimensions and with a regular periodic pattern. This is in accordance with the findings based on x-ray diffraction methods, according to which the fibrils consist of long polypeptide chains running predominantly in the direction of the fiber axis. In the electron microscope the fibrils are cross striated; the distance between the bands is 644 angstrom units on the average. When stained with phosphotungstic acid, each striation is resolved in a series of smaller bands (Fig. 39).

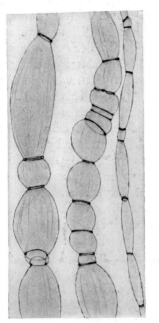

Fig. 40. Swelling of collagenous fibers, from the loose connective tissue of a rabbit, on the addition of 0.5 per cent formic acid. 185 ×. (A.A.M.)

In boiling water the collagenous substance dissolves and yields a solution of animal glue or gelatin. In weak acids and alkalies the collagenous fibers swell. Pepsin in acid solution digests the collagenous bundles, but they resist alkaline trypsin solution.

A typical reaction is obtained with dilute formic acid (Fig. 40). This causes the bundles to swell considerably, lose their longitudinal striation, and become transparent; in many places these swollen bundles are constricted transversely or obliquely. No satisfactory explanation of this phenomenon has been given. Concentrated acids and alkalies destroy collagenous fibers. Collagen gives an insoluble product with salts of heavy metals and with tannic acid. Collagenous fibers have no specific staining reactions; however, acid aniline dyes, as, for instance, the acid fuchsin of van Gieson's stain or the aniline blue in Mallory's mixture, stain the bundles sharply, especially after mordants. Collagen may present physical and chemical differences in various parts of the body and in different species of animals.

Elastic Fibers. In the loose connective tissue, elastic fibers are scarce. They are long and run in various directions; they appear as brilliant, highly refractive cylindrical threads or flat ribbons, much thinner than the collagenous fibers. In contrast to the latter, the elastic fibers are not fibrillar, but are usually homogeneous, although the larger fibers may stain more deeply at their periphery; they branch and anastomose freely and form a loose network (Fig. 46). If the tissue is fixed in its natural position, the elastic fibers are straight, while in teased preparations they often appear wavy or spiral. When assembled in large numbers, they have a yellowish color on macroscopic examination.

Elastic fibers yield easily to stretching. The breaking point occurs when they are stretched to about 150 per cent of their original length. For this a force of only 20 to 30 kg./cm.^{2} is necessary. When released after stretching, elastic fibers return practically entirely to their former length. Elastic fibers at most show only weak positive birefringence, but become strongly birefringent on stretching.

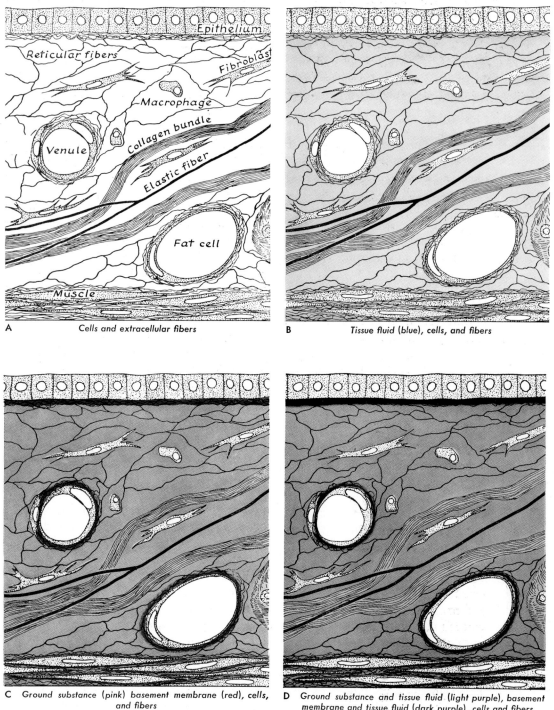

A   Cells and extracellular fibers

B   Tissue fluid (blue), cells, and fibers

C   Ground substance (pink) basement membrane (red), cells, and fibers

E. Bohlman Patterson

D   Ground substance and tissue fluid (light purple), basement membrane and tissue fluid (dark purple), cells and fibers

Fig. 41. Diagram of relations of cells, tissue fluid, amorphous substance and connective tissue fibers. A, Cells and extracellular fibers. B, Tissue fluid (blue), cells and fibers. C, Ground substance (pink), basement membrane (red), cells and fibers. D, Ground substance and tissue fluid (light purple), basement membrane and tissue fluid (dark purple), cells and fibers. (Drawn by E. Bohlman Patterson; after Gersh.)

This is caused by an orientation of the submicroscopic components in the direction of the fiber axis.

The characteristic constituent of the elastic fiber, *elastin*, is an albuminoid and may vary slightly in its qualities according to its origin. It is highly resistant to boiling water, acids and alkalies, and through the action of alkalies it can be isolated from the other constituents of the tissue. Elastin is slowly digested by both pepsin and trypsin. Unlike the collagenous fibers, elastic fibers can be stained fairly electively (orcein or resorcin fuchsin). According to Gross, elastic fibers show a coiled structure in electron micrographs.

Amorphous Ground Substance. Collagenous, reticular and elastic fibers and the cells of connective tissue are embedded in a homogeneous material, the ground substance. Its consistency varies from fluid to gel-like. It may be stained metachromatically (purple with toluidine blue) and reacts as if it were a polysaccharide-containing protein, a glycoprotein. At least two polysaccharides have been identified in loose connective tissue. The viscosity of such compounds is markedly affected by spreading factors, of which the most notable is hyaluronidase. When the ground substance surrounds certain structures (muscle, capillaries), or is at the base of certain epithelial structures, it is so modified that, together with the enclosed reticular fibers, it forms the basement membrane. It is highly probable that the components of the ground substance are structurally organized on a submicroscopic level, and that changes in this submicroscopic organization are correlated with changes in consistency. Alterations in the ground substance have been described with age, activity, and in certain pathological conditions. It is presumably the ground substance which appears to be affected by hormones such as relaxin, *adrenocorticotropic hormone* and *cortisone*. The whole range of activities influenced by the state of the ground substance is not yet known, but it appears to be implicated in diffusion of nutrients in extracellular spaces, capillary permeability, growth of certain organs and tumors, cartilage, bone formation and resorption, and calcification. Associated with changes in the nature of the ground substance are certain connective tissue cells (fibroblasts and possibly others) containing granules which appear to be precursors of the ground substance polysaccharides. In some conditions macrophages appear to phagocytose ground substance.

The ground substance is believed to be derived from connective tissue cells. It differs thus from the *tissue fluid* which originates from the plasma. The tissue fluid constitutes the medium by which nutrients and waste products are exchanged between the circulating blood and the cells of tissues and organs.

Reticular Fibers. In certain places in the loose connective tissue are networks of highly branched, reticular fibers. The methods generally used for the demonstration of collagenous fibers do not stain them distinctly; besides, they are too thin to be seen easily among other elements of the tissue. They are, however, electively impregnated with silver by modified Bielschowsky methods, after which they appear as black, sharply drawn nets. Hence the name argyrophile fibers.

They occur where connective tissue is adjacent to other tissues. In the basement membrane they form a dense network separating the epithelium from the connective tissue (Figs. 15, 371). Similar networks are formed around blood vessels, particularly capillaries, muscle fibers, nerve fibers, fat cells and in the respiratory portions of the lung. Reticular fibers are continuous with collagenous fibers, and there is a gradual transition of one into the other. Microdissection studies have shown reticular fibers to be inelastic. Like the collagenous fibers, they resist digestion by trypsin in an alkaline medium, but, unlike them, do not swell on the addition of dilute organic acids. Their submicroscopic structure needs further study. Some consider the argyrophile fibers to be immature collagenous fibers and call them "precollagenous" fibers. The idea of the immature nature of the reticular fibers agrees well with the fact that they are usually found in those places in the connective tissue where undifferentiated cells of mesenchymal nature are assembled (see Chap. V).

Origin of Fibers. Practically all investigators believe that connective tissue fibers arise between the cells through a condensation or tend far into the intercellular substance. The finest of the developing fibrils are shown by the electron microscope to have the characteristic cross striation of collagen and to be apparently extracellular (Fig. 43). The first

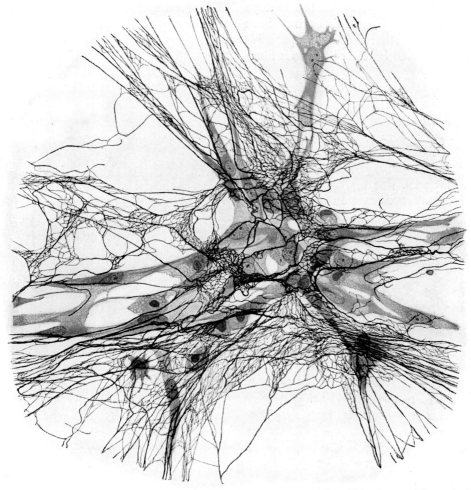

Fig. 42. Development of reticular fibers in a twenty-day culture of adult rabbit thymus. The reticular fibers stain black. Bielschowsky-Foot and Mallory-Azan stains. 900 ×. (A.A.M.)

crystallization of an intercellular substance secreted by the cells.

The process of collagen formation is identical in principle in the body of an embryo, in young scar tissue and in a tissue culture; the silver impregnation methods give a clear insight into the morphology of this process. Delicate networks of branching and anastomosing argyrophile fibrils appear on the surface and between the fibroblasts (Fig. 42). The fibrils may follow the outlines of the cell bodies and their processes, but they also ex-

networks increase in number and thickness, and then are rearranged into parallel, wavy bundles which continue into the argyrophile networks. The bundles of fibrils increase in thickness and finally lose the ability to be impregnated with silver (Fig. 44). Instead, they begin to stain with the methods for collagenous fibers (Mallory, van Gieson) and, like them, resist digestion by pancreatin in an alkaline medium. The final arrangement and direction of the collagenous bundles are probably influenced by mechanical forces.

Connective tissue fibers do not develop in scorbutic guinea pigs, and they appear rapidly when such animals are given vitamin C. Extracellular phosphatase is present in large amounts in the developing collagen of a scar.

The elastic fibers appear in the embryo much later. Their histogenesis has not been adequately studied, but it is highly probable that the facts found for the collagenous fibers will be equally applicable to them.

Cellular Elements. The loose connective tissue contains the following cell types: fibroblasts, undifferentiated cells, macrophages (histiocytes) and a varying, but much smaller, number of lymphoid wandering cells, mast cells, eosinophils, plasma cells, pigment cells and fat cells.

Fibroblasts. These common connective tis-

sue cells are generally believed to be instrumental in the elaboration of the intercellular fibers. The fibroblasts are long, flat elements which in profile appear as slender spindles. Their elongated or star-shaped body sends out several spear-shaped processes which end with one or several points. These cell bodies

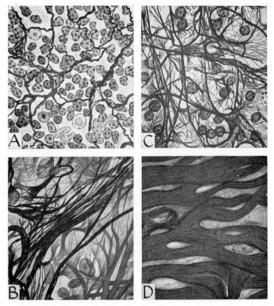

Fig. 43. Electron micrograph of a formation of collagen fibers which developed from an explant of chick embryo skin during nine days in culture. Only broader compound strands would be visible with the light microscope. Compare with Figure 44. 19,600 ×. (After Porter and Vanamee.)

Fig. 44. Four stages in development in tissue culture of collagenous fibers from reticular tissue of rabbit lymph node: A, section of normal lymph node showing cells and reticular fibers (black); B, after five days in vitro the reticular fibers (black) contrast with newly formed collagenous fibers (gray); C, the reticular fibers are branching and much more numerous after four days in vitro; D, after six days in culture there are only thick bundles of collagenous fibers. Bielschowsky-Foot and Mallory-Azan stains. About 500 ×. (After McKinney.)

Fig. 45. Electron micrograph of gold-shadowed, minute connective tissue fibrils developing in culture of chick embryo skin. Note the distinct cross banding with the characteristic spacing of collagen. 25,000 ×. (After Porter and Vanamee.)

are easily demonstrable with iron hematoxylin, but are hard to see in hematoxylin and eosin preparations (Fig. 46). The cells are usually adjacent to the surface of the collagenous bundles. The large, oval nucleus has a delicate, sometimes slightly folded, outline and contains dustlike chromatin particles and one or more large nucleoli. Near the nucleus are a diplosome and a Golgi net. The mitochondria appear as slender rods which are scarce in the processes, but more numerous near the nucleus and around the cytocentrum. Tonofibrils (fibroglia fibers) run along the inner surface of the cell.

The cytoplasm of the fibroblast rarely contains inclusions except occasional, small, fat droplets and usually remains colorless when neutral red is applied supravitally (Fig. 47). In inflammation and tissue cultures, however, it contains a number of small neutral red vacuoles.

The majority opinion holds that fibroblasts are differentiated cells which do not give rise to other types of free cells of the connective substance. There is good evidence, however, that they can develop into bone cells and some indication that they become slightly phagocytic on intense stimulation.

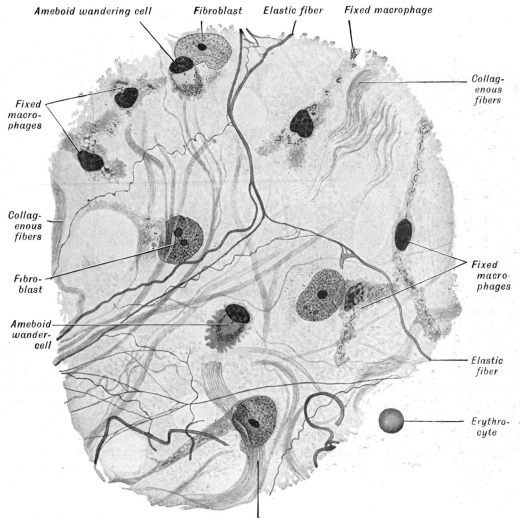

Fig. 46. Section through slightly edematous, subcutaneous, loose connective tissue from the thigh of a man. Iron-hematoxylin stain. 950 ×. (A.A.M.)

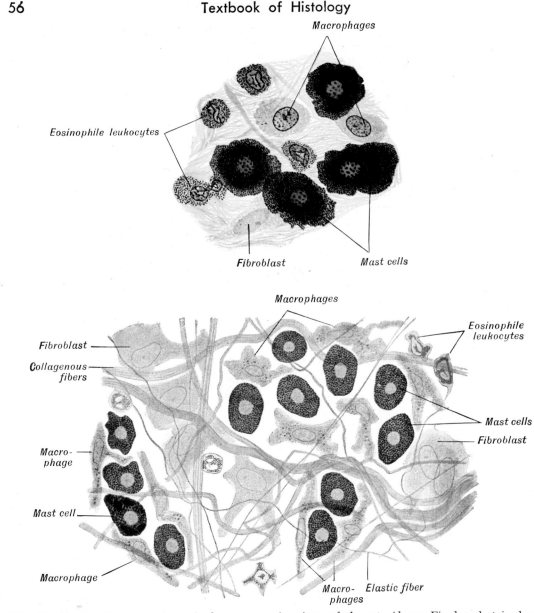

Macrophages

Eosinophile leukocytes

Fibroblast

Mast cells

Macrophages

Fibroblast

Collagenous fibers

Eosinophile leukocytes

Mast cells

Fibroblast

Macro-phage

Mast cell

Macrophage

Macro-phages

Elastic fiber

Fig. 47. The two figures are from the loose connective tissue of the rat. Above: Fixed and stained with hematoxylin-eosin-azure. 600 ×. Below: Stained supravitally with neutral red. 800 ×. (A.A.M.)

Not all the relations of fibroblasts to mesenchymal and reticular cells have been determined.

Each fibroblast is an independent cellular element. In inflamed tissue and in tissue cultures it moves with a gliding motion which does not affect the outer form of the cell body. Ameboid pseudopodia are never observed.

Undifferentiated (Mesenchymal) Cells. Many investigators believe with Marchand that some outstretched connective tissue cells persist in the adult organism with the potencies of mesenchymal cells. They are often smaller than the fibroblasts, but have the same general appearance; in the loose connective tissue they are usually arranged along the blood vessels, particularly along the capillaries (Fig. 48). The conviction that they are not common fibroblasts, but are undifferentiated cells is gathered from numerous observations which show that, under the influence of certain stimuli—as in tissue cultures, inflammation, and the effects of injection of blood toxins—they may develop into new cell types. They probably have much the same properties as the *primitive reticular* cells of the blood-forming tissues and of the free lymphoid stem cells. (See page 75 and Figure 89.)

darker than in the fibroblasts. The cytoplasm has distinct, ragged outlines and stains darkly (Fig. 46). Near the nucleus there is a distinct diplosome and a Golgi net; the mitochondria are short rods or granules and are assembled mainly around the cytocentrum. The cytoplasm usually contains a number of small vacuoles which stain supravitally with neutral

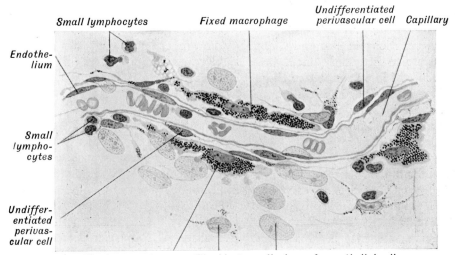

Fig. 48. Stretch preparation of omentum of a rabbit vitally stained with lithium carmine. Hematoxylin stain. 500 ×. (A.A.M.)

Macrophages (Histiocytes). In the loose connective tissue the number of macrophages varies according to the region of the body and the animal species. On the average they seem to be almost as numerous as the fibroblasts, which they outnumber in the richly vascular areas. They are scattered singly among the fibroblasts or are assembled in small groups. The macrophages in the normal loose connective tissue are usually outstretched resting cells, but in inflammation they round up and become actively motile, *free macrophages.*

In form the outstretched macrophages vary from flat, rounded or oval cells to elongated, spindle-shaped elements which sometimes have branched processes. Ameboid movements are not seen under physiological conditions. The nucleus is smaller than that of the fibroblast, has a heavy, slightly folded membrane, and is irregular, oval or kidney-shaped. It contains no large nucleoli; the chromatin particles are coarser and stain

red (Fig. 47). These cells are able to ingest many types of particulate matter and store electively certain electronegative, acid aniline dyes in colloidal solution, such as trypan blue and lithium carmine. After repeated injections, the dye inclusions become numerous and large, and the tissue develops a distinct, macroscopic color. As the fibroblasts store little or none of the dye, this method allows a precise identification of the macrophages. The most intense storage is obtained where the concentrated dye solution has immediate access to the cells, as in a subcutaneous injection. The vital storage of acid dyes has been looked upon as a phagocytosis of ultramicroscopic particles.

In the loose connective tissue of mammals, under physiological conditions, transitional forms between macrophages and fibroblasts and between lymphoid wandering cells and macrophages are rare. But in inflamed tissue the sharp limits between the cells are effaced in certain stages (p. 63). The distinction between these different cell types may also be difficult in the lower vertebrates.

The macrophages of the loose connective tissue have also been called *clasmatocytes, rhagiocrine cells, histiocytes, resting wandering cells,* and many other names. The macrophages along the blood vessels, together with the perivascular undifferentiated cells, have also been called *adventitial cells.*

Lymphoid Wandering Cells. These cells present marked variations in size and shape (Fig. 46), and are so irregularly distributed that large stretches of loose connective tissue may be devoid of them. The smallest have a round, large, darkly-staining nucleus and a scanty, basophile cytoplasm which contains few or no inclusions after supravital staining with neutral red. Such cells resemble the lymphocytes of the blood in every respect.

Many of the wandering cells appear to be monocytes and, among other properties, display a neutral red rosette. The largest cells, which normally are rare, may be 12 microns or more in diameter and have an eccentric, kidney-shaped nucleus and a highly ameboid cytoplasm containing various inclusions when stained supravitally with neutral red (p. 41). Such elements are structurally identical with the small *polyblasts* of inflammation, in which a continuous series of gradual transitions can be found between all these cell types (p. 63).

Although the lymphoid cells are identical with the nongranular leukocytes of the blood, many of them originated in the embryonic mesenchyme and stayed there. These cells can always enter the circulation. There is no reason for distinguishing hematogenous and histogenous cells among them; they all have the same potencies.

Mast Cells. Mast cells have been found, often in groups about the blood vessels, in the connective tissue of most vertebrates. Their cytoplasm is filled with granules which stain metachromatically with basic aniline dyes; with methylene blue or thionine the granules have a purple color. Neutral red stains them supravitally a dark, brick red

(Fig. 47). The granules in most species are soluble in aqueous fixatives.

In the rat and mouse the mast cells are large and polyhedral; in other mammals, including man, they are smaller, irregularly oval or flattened cells. Slow amebism can be observed occasionally. The relatively small nucleus is inconspicuous. In the neighborhood of the nucleus is a diplosome.

In mammals the mast cells of the connective tissue and the basophile leukocytes of the blood are independent cell types, despite similar staining properties of their granules. There is an accumulating mass of evidence that the mast cells elaborate an *anticoagulant,* identical with or much like *heparin.* This is based on the similarity of staining reactions and on experiments which show a parallelism between the mast cell content of certain organs and extractible, blood-clotting inhibiting substance.

Eosinophile Cells. In man these cells are occasionally found in the interstitial connective tissue of some glands, particularly the mammary gland, and of the lung, and in the omentum. Under certain pathological conditions they may accumulate in the connective tissue in large numbers. They are numerous in the loose connective tissue of the rat, mouse and guinea pig (Fig. 47).

Excluding the connective tissue of the intestinal mucosa, where special conditions prevail, the eosinophile cells of the connective tissue are eosinophile leukocytes which have migrated from the blood vessels and have settled in the tissue.

The nucleus in these cells always has the typical, polymorphous character of the mature eosinophile leukocyte of the respective species. Thus, in the rat or mouse it is a thick ring. Round, compact nuclei, as well as mitoses, which are typical for the young forms of the eosinophile leukocytes, do not occur in the connective tissue.

Plasma Cells. In the common connective tissues, plasma cells are extremely rare, although they occur frequently in the serous membranes and in the lymphatic tissue. They may be only as large as a small lymphocyte,

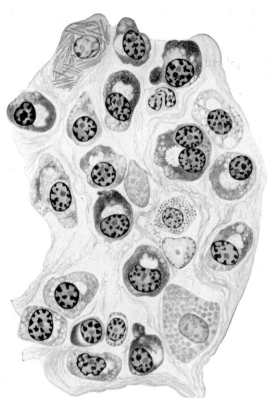

Fig. 49. Plasma cells from connective tissue near human tonsil. There are transitions from small lymphocytes to plasma cells. Several of the latter contain globular or crystalloid inclusions. Hematoxylin-eosin-azure. (A.A.M.).

or may be two or three times that size (Fig. 49). Their form is spherical or often flattened. In the living cell the spherical or polygonal body has a glassy, homogeneous appearance. Slow movements can sometimes be observed.

The nucleus is small, round or slightly oval, and has an eccentric position. In its interior and at the membrane, coarse, darkly staining, regularly distributed chromatin particles are seen. Binucleate cells occur, but mitoses are exceedingly rare.

The homogeneous cytoplasm is strongly basophile and forms a broad layer in the cell body. The middle of the cell is occupied by a round, pale area adjacent to the nucleus; this area is the cytocentrum with its diplosome. Scattered around the cytocentrum are mitochondria and a varying number of vac-

uoles, which stain supravitally with neutral red. These occupy the site of the Golgi net in fixed preparations.

In most of the foci of plasma cells, all transitions from small lymphocytes to fully developed plasma cells can be found, and the process of change has been followed in tissue cultures. The transformation of large lymphocytes (hemocytoblasts) into plasma cells has also been observed.

The plasma cells seem unable to change into any other cell type (except possibly into inflammatory macrophages); they are specifically differentiated elements which finally degenerate. During degeneration, large spherical drops or crystals of a peculiar, acidophile substance frequently accumulate in the cell body. When the cytoplasm disintegrates, these inclusions are set free and remain between the other elements of the tissue as *Russell's bodies*.

Pigment Cells. In the loose connective tissue of the mammals, pigment cells are rare; they occur more frequently in the dense connective tissue of the skin. They are elongated cells with short, irregular outgrowths; the cytoplasm contains small granules of *melanin*. The pigmented cells in the superficial layers of the derma are believed by many to be merely connective tissue phagocytes which receive their pigment from the epithelium; they may be called *dermal chromatophores*. Pigment cells containing melanin which they themselves have elaborated occur in the

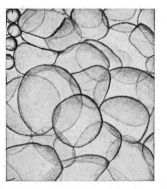

Fig. 50. Fresh preparation of a human fat lobule, showing fat cells and smaller, extracellular fat drops (more highly refractile). 160 ×. (After Schaffer.)

derma in the sacral region of the newborn of the Mongolian race. These cells had best be called *dermal melanoblasts*, to distinguish them from the *epidermal melanoblasts* (see Chap. XX). Melanoblasts are found in most mammals in the pia mater of the ventral surface of the medulla oblongata. A large number of them are assembled in the pigment tissue of the choroid of the eye, where they are flattened and have broad, lobated processes.

The pigment granules in the melanophores in hypophysectomized frogs retract about the nucleus. After the injection of extracts of the pars intermedia of the hypophysis and exposure of the frogs to sunlight, the pigment granules extend rapidly throughout the processes of these cells.

The pigment cells arise early in development from neural crest cells in amphibians (DuShane) and birds. Their origin in mammals is not as clear.

Fat Cells. Small droplets of neutral fat may occur in any cell of the connective tissue. There are, however, cells with a special fat-storing function; only these should be termed "fat cells." They are found scattered singly or in groups in the loose connective tissue, especially along the blood vessels. When they accumulate in large numbers and crowd out the other cells, the tissue is transformed into *adipose tissue*.

A living fat cell is a large, brilliant, spherical body. Every mature fat cell contains only one large drop of neutral fat, which can be stained black with osmic acid or orange with Sudan III. The cytoplasm is reduced to a thin membrane which surrounds the drop; it is thickened in that part which contains the flattened nucleus with its central mass of

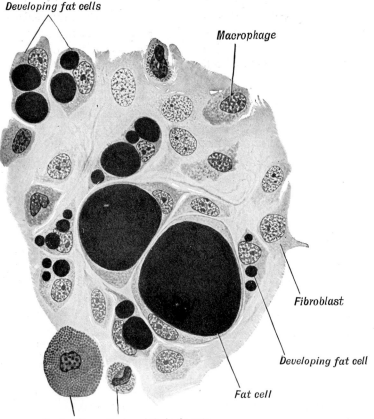

Fig. 51. Several fat cells from the subcutaneous, loose connective tissue of a rat. The fat has been stained black by the osmic acid of the fixation fluid. About 1000 ×. (A.A.M.)

chromatin. The individual fat cells are surrounded by a network of argyrophile fibers. In the brown fat tissue (interscapular gland) the cells, as a rule, contain not one large, but several small fat droplets.

New fat cells may develop at any time in the connective tissue of the adult organism, and fully developed fat cells may lose their fat when the organism does not receive sufficient nutritive material. In tissue cultures of

same series of transitional forms can be observed in the reverse sequence. The question of the exact nature of the cells into which the fat cells are transformed when they lose their fat is unsettled. They do not always resemble fibroblasts, but may remain, as in serous atrophy, as sharply outlined, spherical or oval elements. This has been confirmed by studies on living cells in chambers in the rabbit's ear (Clark and Clark).

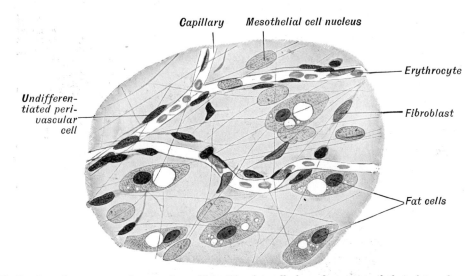

Fig. 52. Portion of omentum of a starving rabbit. The fat cells have lost most of their fat and appear with much cytoplasm. 375 ×. (A.A.M.)

adult loose connective tissue and in ear chambers in living rabbits, the development of fat cells from fibroblast-like cells has been observed. It is possible that, when new fat cells develop in the adult, they arise from the undifferentiated mesenchymal cells. This would agree with the fact that new fat cells—as in the embryo—always appear along the small blood vessels, which are accompanied by cells of undifferentiated mesenchymal nature.

The first step in the formation of a fat cell is the appearance of a few small droplets of fat in the cytoplasm. These increase in size and gradually fuse. Simultaneously, the cell body swells, the processes are withdrawn, and the cell becomes spherical. As the fat drop increases in size, the cytoplasm is reduced to a thin membrane, while the nucleus is compressed and flattened. Mitoses are not found in fat cells. When the fat cell loses its fat, the

The fat enters and leaves the cell in the invisible form of its soluble components. The idea that small droplets of fat (hemoconia) may penetrate the membrane and fuse with the large fat drop has not been confirmed.

Functions of the Loose Connective Tissue. The loose connective tissue is the medium supporting and surrounding the elements of the other tissues. It serves as packing material and fills out the spaces between the organs, and its flexible collagenous fibers allow a more or less distinct movement of the connected parts in relation to one another. This is its mechanical function.

In addition, this tissue plays an important role in the nutrition of the elements of other tissues which are embedded in it. The part each cell type takes in this function is unknown. But it is clear that all substances which the cells of the other tissues receive

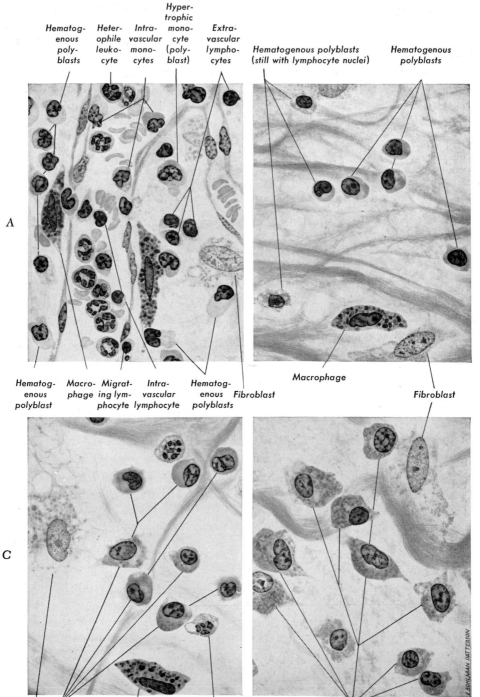

Fig. 53. Four stages in the early inflammatory reaction caused in the connective tissue of a rat by the local injection of trypan blue. A, At six hours, B, at eight hours, C, at twenty-four hours, D, at thirty-two hours after injection. These figures show the migration of lymphocytes and monocytes into the connective tissue and their rapid transformation into large, dye-storing macrophages by thirty-two hours. See text (p. 63). Hematoxylin-eosin-azure II. 700 ×.

from the blood, and all the products of metabolism and water which they turn over to the blood and lymph, must pass through a layer of connective tissue. It has been claimed that some of the cells of this tissue have an endocrine function, but the evidence supporting this view is not convincing.

Inflammation. Of great importance is the role the loose (and dense) connective tissue plays as the arena of the local reactive process called inflammation. Even under physiological conditions, endogenous noxious substances may appear in various places in the body. Some of them have to be neutralized or destroyed by the elements of the connective tissue; this process has been termed "physiological inflammation." Exogenous stimuli which cause a pathological inflammation call forth a much more intense local reaction which manifests itself in a series of complicated phenomena in which local elements of the connective tissue as well as cells and liquid from the blood participate. The results of this local reaction are the destruction, digestion and absorption of the foreign noxious substances and the reparation of the damage caused by them.

In inflamed connective tissue, leukocytes migrate from the vessels into the tissue at the very beginning of the process. The heterophile leukocytes soon degenerate. The mononuclear blood cells (lymphocytes and monocytes) hypertrophy in a couple of days after the onset of inflammation and transform into large phagocytic elements, the hematogenous macrophages. In these early stages of inflammation, all transition forms from lymphocytes and monocytes to hematogenous macrophages can be seen. Another source of phagocytic elements is the macrophages already present in the connective tissue. A number of them turn into free macrophages (histogenous macrophages). There are thus in the field of inflammation a variety of mononuclear cells of different origin, called *inflammatory mononuclear cells* or *polyblasts*. There is some evidence that the fibroblasts can also turn into macrophages, but this transformation is denied by most investigators. In inflammation the endothelial

cells of blood vessels swell and may divide mitotically, but they do not turn into leukocytes or macrophages. During the first two days of inflammation, the polyblasts from hematogenous origin can still be distinguished from those of local origin because of their smaller size. But they continue to grow, so that after this time the polyblasts of local and of hematogous origin can no longer be distinguished.

In tuberculous lesions some polyblasts become changed into the epithelioid cells of the tubercle. The polyblasts may form, through fusion, giant cells of the foreign body or the tuberculous type. In the later course of the inflammatory process the fibroblasts proliferate. The polyblasts scattered among the fibroblasts settle down as resting macrophages; in still later stages, some become fibroblasts. The fibroblasts form collagen in the process of scar formation.

Tissue Cultures. Essentially the same cellular transformations occur in tissue cultures. The lymphocytes and monocytes of the circulating blood (Fig. 54) and the lymphocytes of the lymph and lymphatic tissue develop rapidly into macrophages. If the nutritive medium contains a vital dye, the hypertrophied lymphocytes and monocytes store it in granular form. In older cultures the transformation proceeds further; the cells proliferate mitotically and turn into fibroblasts which form large sheets of connective tissue in which the development of argyrophile and collagenous fibers has been observed. In tissue cultures, as in inflammation, the fibroblasts proliferate, but fail to change into other cell types.

THE SYSTEM OF MACROPHAGES
(Reticulo-Endothelium)

In discussing inflammation it was pointed out that the macrophages of the tissue and those which developed from blood cells play the main role in disposing of local noxious agents. Generalized noxious stimuli are taken care of by similar cells scattered in the various connective tissue all over the body. Like the macrophages of the loose connective tissue, they have the ability to take up particulate matter, including bacteria, and to store foreign substances brought to them in colloidal solution. These cells form the *system of macrophages*, consisting largely of the macrophages of the loose connective tissue (already discussed) the phagocytic reticular cells of the lymphatic tissue, myeloid tissue and

of names has been applied. Because Metchnikoff, who called them *macrophages*, was the first to recognize that they belong to a single physiological system and to see clearly their defensive function in inflammation and in immunity, the term *macrophage system* is

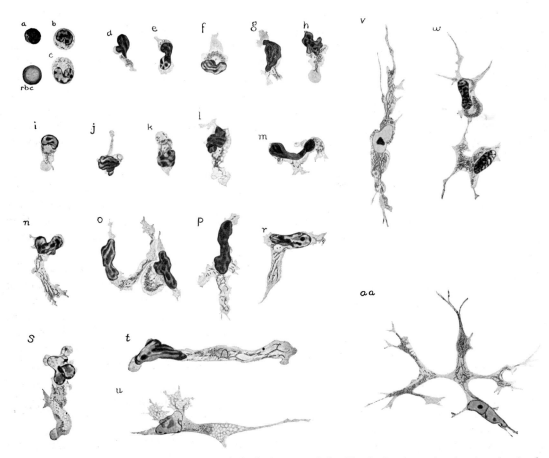

Fig. 54. Cells from sections of cultures of the leukocytes of the blood of guinea pig, showing the development of lymphocytes and monocytes into macrophages (polyblasts). *a* and *b*, Lymphocytes and, *c*, monocyte from centrifuged blood; *d* and *e*, ameboid lymphocytes and *f*, ameboid monocyte, from a three-hour culture; *g* to *k*, from a ten-hour culture; *l* to *r*, from a twenty-five-hour culture; *s* to *u*, from a two-day culture; *v*, *w*, from a five-day culture; *w* is in mitosis; *aa*, macrophage from twelve-day culture. Note mitochondria in all cells; iron-hematoxylin stain. 750 ×. (A.A.M.)

spleen, the Kupffer cells in the sinusoids of the liver, lining cells of the sinusoids in the adrenal gland and hypophysis, certain perivascular cells and the "dust" cells of the lung.

All these phagocytes, although dissimilar under physiological conditions, react similarly in response to the same noxious stimuli. This observation led to the idea that they constitute a single class of cells, to which a variety

probably the most appropriate for this collection of cells. So defined, the macrophage system is essentially the same as the "reticuloendothelial system" of Aschoff.

As mentioned earlier, the most easily controlled criterion for deciding whether a cell of the connective tissue or blood is a macrophage is whether the cell will accumulate a colloidal dye from solutions so weak that the other elements of the connective tissue do not take up appreciable amounts of it. In animals which have had repeated injections of adequate doses of a vital dye, and in general infections, large numbers of free macrophages are mobilized in the spleen, liver and bone marrow.

In tissue cultures, macrophages take up water by *pinocytosis* (W. Lewis). In the spleen and liver they phagocytose worn-out or damaged erythrocytes, with the result that iron-containing pigment may accumulate in their cytoplasm. Fat and lipoid inclusions are common. Dust and other materials entering the lungs are removed by the "dust cells." Foreign particulate material in the blood stream is removed by the macrophages in the liver, spleen and bone marrow, where they come in contact with the blood. Similarly, foreign particulate material in the lymph stream is removed by the macrophages of the lymph nodes. Foreign materials are gradually destroyed, at least in part, through intracellular digestion; in this way the organism gets rid of some of the foreign substance. Macrophages while filled with a foreign substance are less capable of performing other functions.

Although it is widely believed that macrophages produce *antibodies*, there is considerable evidence that both macrophages and lymphoid cells are involved. In the so-called plasma cell theories, antibodies are supposed to be formed chiefly by lymphoid cells transitional between the fixed reticular cells and the mature plasma cells. These transitional cells have been variously termed: large lymphocytes, acute splenic tumor cells, myeloblasts, lymphoblastic plasma cells, developing immature plasma cells, macrohistiocytes and basophile macrophages (Taliaferro, 1949).

In considering the source and behavior of macrophages in defense, it must be pointed out that they cannot be sharply separated from the lymphoid cells. It seems that in all defense reactions some new macrophages arise locally from the division of preexisting macrophages or by the assumption of phagocytic activity by cells having mesenchymal potencies. In the loose connective tissue the latter are the outstretched, undifferentiated perivascular mesenchymal cells; in the hematopoietic tissues they are the primitive reticular cells. In addition, many new macrophages arise from the hypertrophy and development of lymphocytes and monocytes. In the loose connective tissue these are hematogenous; in the spleen and other reticular tissue they represent lymphocytes which proliferate under the stimulus of the noxious agent. To signalize the fact that macrophages may develop homoplastically from macrophages and heteroplastically from lymphoid cells (and primitive reticular cells), Taliaferro and Mulligan proposed the term "lymphoid-macrophage system" to include both macrophages and all macrophage precursors.

Some believe that macrophages do not constitute a specific cell lineage, but represent a functional transformation of many different types of cells. The question whether the macrophages have hemopoietic potencies is discussed on page 103.

Tissue of the Serous Membranes. The serous membranes (the *peritoneum*, the *pleura* and the *pericardium*) are thin layers of loose connective tissue covered by a layer of mesothelium. When the membranes are folded, as the omentum or the mesentery, both free surfaces are covered with mesothelium. The serous cavities always contain a small amount of serous liquid, the *serous exudate*. The cells floating in it originate from the serous membrane.

All the elements of the loose connective tissue are found in the serous membranes, where they are arranged in a thin layer. The mesentery contains a loose network of collagenous and elastic fibers, scattered fibroblasts, macrophages, mast cells and a varying number of fat cells along the blood vessels.

Physiologically, the most important and, histologically, the most interesting part of the serous membranes in mammals is the omentum. In places the membrane is pierced by innumerable holes and is thus reduced to a fine lacelike net formed by collagenous bundles covered by mesothelial cells. Such areas have few or no vessels.

In those areas of the omentum which are

not provided with holes, undifferentiated cells occur along the vessels, and macrophages are numerous. There are also many small lymphocytes and plasma cells and, occasionally, eosinophile leukocytes and mast cells. The number of lymphocytes and plasma cells varies considerably in different animals.

Free Cells of the Serous Exudate. Normally, the amount of serous exudate is small, but in pathological conditions it may increase enormously. The exudate contains a number of freely floating cells. Among them the following can be distinguished:

1. Free macrophages which originate in the

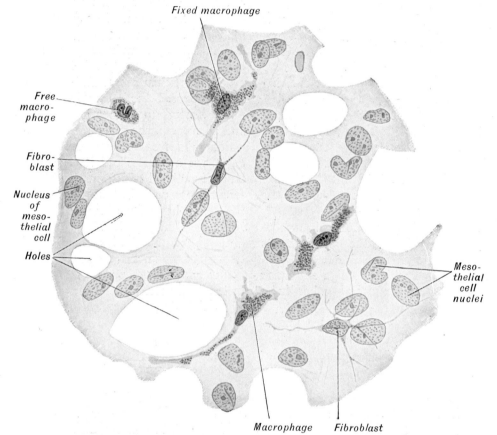

Fixed macrophage

Free macrophage

Fibroblast

Nucleus of mesothelial cell

Holes

Mesothelial cell nuclei

Macrophage   Fibroblast

Fig. 55. Stretch preparation of a thin part of the omentum of a rabbit injected with lithium carmine. 375 ×. (A.A.M.)

In certain areas the macrophages are accumulated in especially dense masses. Such macroscopically visible areas are often arranged along the blood vessels as small or large, round or oval patches, called *milky spots*. These may or may not contain blood vessels, and are sometimes also found in the netlike part of the omentum. They are characteristic in the omentum of the rabbit. In the serous membrane which lines the pleural cavities there are cellular areas much like the milky spots of the omentum.

milky spots of the omentum and migrate into the cavity. They correspond with those polyblasts of the inflammatory exudate which originate from the local macrophages.

2. Desquamated mesothelial cells which keep their squamous form or become spherical with small, budlike protuberances. The nucleus usually contains a heavily staining nucleolus. In inflammation and tissue culture they develop into fibroblasts.

3. Small lymphocytes, the vast majority of which have migrated from the blood vessels

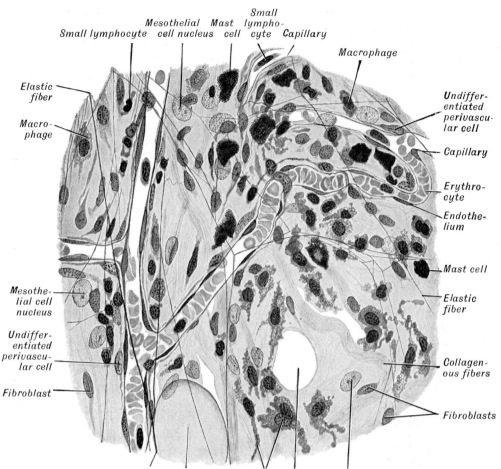

Fig. 56. Stretch preparation of human omentum. Hematoxylin-eosin-azure stain. 450 ×. (A.A.M.)

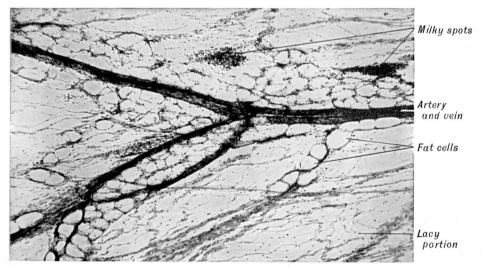

Fig. 57. Photomicrograph of stretch preparation of omentum of *Macacus rhesus*. Hematoxylin-eosin-azure II.
55 ×.

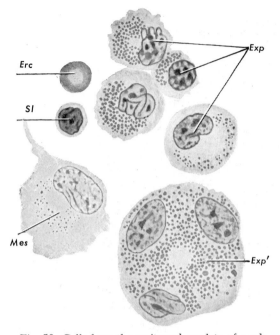

Fig. 58. Cells from the peritoneal exudate of a rabbit which had several intravenous injections of lithium carmine. *Mes*, Desquamated mesothelial cell; *Sl*, small lymphocyte; *Exp*, carmine-storing exudate polyblasts; *Exp'*, exudate polyblast with three nuclei; *Erc*, erythrocyte. Moist fixed smear. Note carmine granules (dark gray). Hematoxylin stain. 1000 ×. (A.A.M.)

of the omentum. A few may have developed through proliferation of the undifferentiated mesenchymal cells of the omentum. In inflammatory exudates, transitions from lymphocytes to large macrophages can be found in great numbers.

4. Eosinophile leukocytes of hematogenous origin occur in some animals (guinea pig).

5. Free connective tissue mast cells occur in the rat and mouse.

6. In pathological inflammatory exudates there are great numbers of heterophile leukocytes from the blood.

THE DENSE CONNECTIVE TISSUE

This tissue is found mainly in the derma of the skin and the submucous layer of the intestinal and parts of the urinary tracts. Its constitution in the derma is typical. The elements are the same as in the loose variety, but the collagenous bundles are thicker and are woven into a compact feltwork. They are accompanied by many elastic networks. All the fibers from the derma continue directly into those of the loose, subcutaneous tissue, where their arrangement is correspondingly looser. There is less amorphous ground substance in the dense connective tissue. Between the two kinds of fibers and the amorphous cement substance are the cells; these are much more difficult to identify than in the loose tissue. The macrophages are easily recognized in vitally stained animals. Along the small vessels there are always many inconspicuous nuclei which probably belong to undifferentiated mesenchymal cells.

THE REGULAR CONNECTIVE TISSUE

The constituents of the regular connective tissue, especially the collagenous bundles, are arranged according to a definite plan. The particular arrangement reflects the mechanical requirements of the particular tissue, whether a tendon, a fibrillated membrane or lamellated connective tissue.

Tendons. Here the fibers form a flexible tissue which offers great resistance to a pulling force. Macroscopically, the tissue has a distinct fibrous structure and a characteristic, shining, white appearance.

The chief constituents of the tendon are thick, closely packed, parallel, collagenous bundles, in structure the same as those in the loose connective tissue. They show a distinct longitudinal striation and in many places fuse with one another at acute angles. In cross section they appear as finely dotted areas, usually separated from one another by broken, angular lines, although often continuing into one another. Fine elastic networks have been described between the collagenous bundles.

The fibroblasts are the only cells present; they are arranged in long, parallel rows in the spaces between the parallel collagenous bundles. The cell bodies are rectangular, triangular or trapezoid when seen from their surface, and rod-shaped when seen in profile. Their cytoplasm stains darkly with basic dyes and contains a clear attraction sphere adjacent to the single, round nucleus. Although the limits between the successive cells in a row are distinct, the lateral limits of the cells

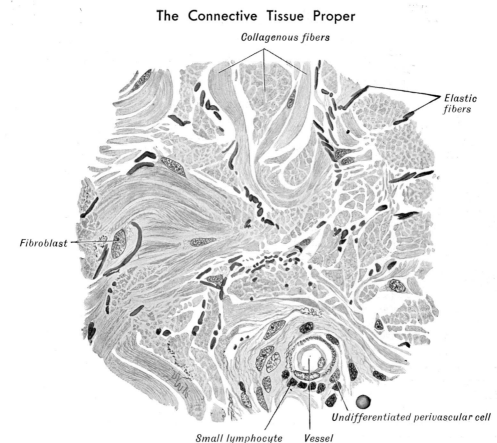

Collagenous fibers

Elastic fibers

Fibroblast

Undifferentiated perivascular cell

Small lymphocyte   *Vessel*

Fig. 59. Section of derma of man: dense, irregularly arranged connective tissue. Orcein and hematoxylin stains. 500 ×. (A.A.M.)

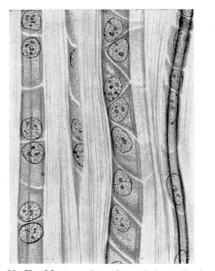

Fig. 60. Freshly teased tendon of the tail of a rat, stained with methylene blue. The rows of tendon cells run between the collagenous bundles. 380 ×. (A.A.M.)

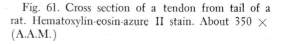

Tendon cell

Bundles of collagenous fibers

Fig. 61. Cross section of a tendon from tail of a rat. Hematoxylin-eosin-azure II stain. About 350 × (A.A.M.)

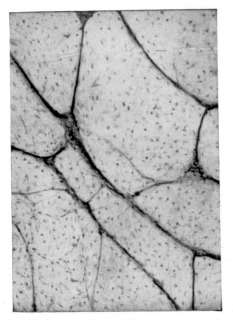

Fig. 62. Cross section of a human tendon, showing the separation of the tendon bundles by loose connective tissue, which stains dark. Hematoxylin-eosin-azure II stain. Photomicrograph. About 120 ×.

are indistinct, because here the cytoplasm continues into a thin membrane. Sometimes it can be followed in the transverse direction to another cell row. In a stained cross section of a tendon the cells appear as dark, star-shaped figures between the collagenous bundles. A tendon consists of a varying number of small tendon bundles bound by loose connective tissue into larger bundles.

The *ligaments* are similar to the tendons, except that the elements are less regularly arranged.

Fibrous Membranes. The tissues of this group form membranes which surround various organs. On examination with the naked eye they show, in the fasciae, aponeuroses and tendinous center of the diaphragm, a parallel fibrillation, and are white and shiny like the tendons. In other situations the fibrillation is less regular, and the tissue is opaque and white—perichondrium, periosteum, dura mater, sclera, capsules of some organs and the tunica albuginea of the testis. In the cornea of the eye the tissue is transparent.

In the fasciae and aponeuroses the col-

lagenous bundles and fibroblasts are arranged regularly in sheets. In each sheet the fibers follow a parallel and often slightly wavy course. In the different sheets the direction may be the same or it may vary. The fibers often pass from one sheet into another; therefore a clear isolation of the sheets is seldom possible. Between the collagenous bundles, fine networks of elastic fibers are usual. The cells correspond to the tendon cells and adapt themselves to the spaces between the collagenous bundles.

In the fibrous membranes with somewhat less regularly arranged elements (periosteum, sclera, and the like), a section perpendicular to the surface shows layers of collagenous bundles cut in the longitudinal, oblique or transverse directions, and cells which are irregular, flat or fusiform. In these tissues there are always gradual transitions to places where the elements have a quite irregular, dense arrangement. There is also no sharp distinction between them and the surrounding loose connective tissue.

Lamellated Connective Tissue. The lamellated connective tissue is found where small organs or parts of organs, usually of cylindrical shape, need thin and soft, but re-

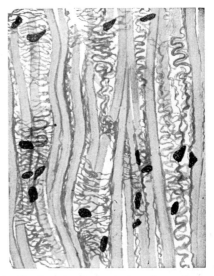

Fig. 63. Longitudinal section from ligamentum nuchae of an ox. The thick, elastic fibers form most of the tissue. Between them are dark fibroblast nuclei and wavy collagenous fibers. Eosin-azure stain. 300 ×. (A.A.M.)

sistant, protective sheaths. It may be looked upon as a condensation of the loose connective tissue on the surface of these cylindrical structures. The elements cannot be sharply separated from those of the loose connective tissue.

Lamellated connective tissue is found outside the basement membrane in the wall of the seminiferous tubules in the testis; in the perineurium, which ensheathes the bundles of nerve fibers in a nerve trunk; and in the outer capsule of some sensory nerve endings, especially the corpuscles of Pacini. In a cross section through any of these structures, the periphery is found to be surrounded by a number of concentric, sometimes dotted lines between which are thin, rod-shaped nuclei. The lines are cross sections of thin lamellae, parallel or irregularly arranged collagenous fibers in an amorphous cement substance. These lamellae also contain elastic networks and reticular fibers. The surface of the lamellae is covered with a layer of flattened, endothelium-like fibroblasts, whose outlines can be made distinct by the use of silver nitrate. Macrophages are also present.

CONNECTIVE TISSUE WITH SPECIAL PROPERTIES

Mucous Connective Tissue. This tissue is found in many parts of the embryo, as under the skin, and is a form of the loose connective tissue. The classical object for its study is *Wharton's jelly* of the *umbilical cord* of the human fetus. The cells are large, stellate fibroblasts whose processes often are in contact with those of neighboring cells. A few macrophages and lymphoid wandering cells are also present. The intercellular substance is soft, jelly-like and homogeneous in fresh condition; when fixed, it contains granules and fibrillar precipitates. It gives the reaction for mucin and contains thin, collagenous fibers which increase in number with the age of the fetus.

In the walls of large arteries (p. 212) the spaces between the elastic membranes and the cells are filled with a mucoid intercellular substance, which stains metachromatically because of the presence of chondroitin sulfuric acid.

Elastic Tissue. Some parts of the body have an elastic tissue which yields easily to a pulling force, but regains its original length as soon as the tension is released. Here the elastic fibers predominate, and the tissue has a yellow color macroscopically. It may appear in the form of strands of parallel fibers, as in the ligamenta flava of the vertebrae, in the true vocal cords, in the ligamentum stylohyoideum, the ligamentum suspensorium penis, and in the tendons of the smooth muscle of the trachea. In these situations the elastic fibers are thick, refringent, and round or flattened; they branch frequently and fuse with one another at acute angles, as in a stretched fishing net. In cross sections the angular or round areas representing the fibers form small groups; the spaces between the elastic fibers are filled with a delicate feltwork of collagenous fibers and a few fibroblasts.

The elastic tissue forms membranes in the walls of hollow organs upon which a changing pressure acts from within, as in the largest arteries, in some parts of the heart, in the trachea and bronchi.

In the large arteries the structural unit of the elastic tissue is a *fenestrated membrane*, a lamella of *elastin* of variable thickness provided with many irregular openings (Fig. 215). The fenestrated membranes are arranged in many layers around the cavity of the organ and are connected with one another by oblique, ribbon-like branches. The spaces between the lamellae contain a mucoid amorphous mass and smooth muscular cells with irregular outlines. It is impossible to distinguish sharply between the fibrous elastic networks and the fenestrated elastic membranes.

Reticular Tissue. The fibrous elements of some types of connective tissues are *reticular fibers*. These occur in the lymphatic tissue, myeloid tissue, spleen, and in the wall of the sinusoids of the liver. The cell types which are usually associated with the fibers of this reticulum are the primitive reticular cells and phagocytic reticular cells or macrophages. There are many transitions from the first cell

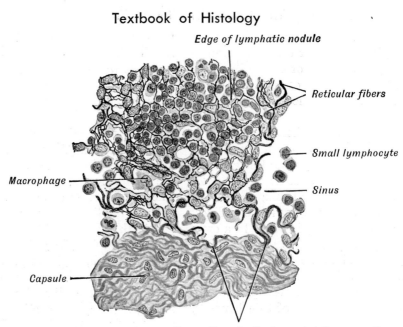

Edge of lymphatic nodule

Reticular fibers

Small lymphocyte

Macrophage

Sinus

Capsule

Connection of reticular and collagenous fibers

Fig. 64. Portion of cortex and capsule of human mesenteric lymph node. Bielschowsky stain. 500 ×. (A.A.M.)

type into the latter. In the meshes of this fibrous and cellular reticulum are free cells, varying in type and number, depending on the type and functional state of the tissue. This tissue is discussed at length in Chapter V.

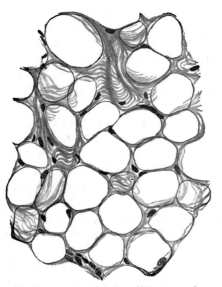

Fig. 65. Portion of a lobule of fat tissue from the subcutaneous tissue of man. The fat has been dissolved in preparing the section. About 200 ×. (A.A.M.)

Adipose Tissue. The fat cells are closely packed and form the bulk of this tissue. In the narrow spaces between them, compressed fibroblasts, numerous lymphoid cells and mast cells are scattered. Collagenous fibers and elastic networks run in all directions between the fat cells. The argyrophile fibers are well developed, especially along the blood vessels, and form a netlike basket around each fat cell. The fat tissue always contains a rich network of blood capillaries. The fully developed fat tissue usually is more or less distinctly divided into lobules of varying size and shape, separated by partitions of fibrous connective tissue.

The most important function of the fat tissue is the storing of neutral fat. Since it consists of a multitude of closely packed liquid fat drops, the fat tissue forms soft and elastic pads between the various organs of the body.

The *brown fat tissue* must be distinguished from the common or white fat tissue. In rats and other rodents it is highly developed and forms yellowish, lobated masses in certain parts of the body—between the scapulae, on the neck, in the mediastinum, in the inguinal region, and elsewhere. Macroscopically, it suggests a gland, and so was called *interscapular* or *hibernating gland*. The latter name was given because this tissue was believed to play a peculiar role during hibernation. The brown fat contains a pigment which gives the tissue its color. The fat cells are assembled in groups separated by thin networks of collagenous or reticular fibers and numerous capillaries. The microscopic structure suggests an endocrine gland. While the common fat tissue loses or accumulates neutral fat with changes in the nutritional condition of the animal, these factors do not seem to affect the brown fat tissue. It has been claimed that the brown fat loses its lipids after hypophysectomy and that these changes can be prevented by injection of adrenocorticotropic hormone.

In adult man and other mammals the two kinds of fat tissue cannot be distinguished clearly. The morphological interrelationships between the two and the function of the brown fat tissue require further study.

Pigment Tissue. In the tunica suprachoroidea and in the lamina fusca of the sclerae of the eye, the majority of the cells in the loose connective tissue are melanophores. Such a tissue can be termed "pigment tissue." It is described in the chapter on the Eye.

Connective Tissue (Lamina Propria) of the Intestinal and Uterine Mucous Membranes, the Interstitial Connective Tissue of the Lung, Testis, Ovary. The connective tissue which surrounds and supports the epithelial

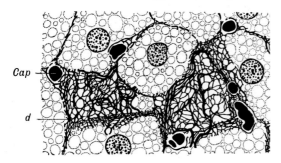

Fig. 66. Brown fat tissue from "hibernating gland" of white rat. *Cap*, Capillary; *d*, intercellular fibrous network. Impregnation method of Hortega. 900 ×. (After Nageotte and Guyon.)

elements in these organs acquires a specifically differentiated structure. It is described in the chapters which deal with these organs.

REFERENCES

Astbury, W. T., and Bell, F. O.: Molecular Structure of the Collagen Fibres. Nature, 145:421, 1940.

Clark, E. R., and Clark, E. L.: Microscopic Studies of the New Formation of Fat in Living Adult Rabbits. Am. J. Anat., 67:255, 1940.

Creditor, M. C., Bevans, M., Mundy, W. L., and Ragan, C.: Effect of ACTH on Wound Healing in Humans. Proc. Soc. Exper. Biol. & Med., 73:245, 1950.

Cunningham, R.: The Changes in the Omentum of the Rabbit during Mild Irritations, with Especial Reference to the Specificity of the Mesothelium. Bull. Johns Hopkins Hosp., 33:257, 1922.

DuShane, G. P.: The Development of Pigment Cells in Vertebrates. Special Publ. New York Acad. Sc., 4:1, 1948.

Ehrich, W. E., Harris, T. N., and Mertens, E.: The Absence of Antibody in the Macrophages during Maximum Antibody Formation. J. Exp. Med., 83: 373, 1946.

Evans, H. M., and Scott, K. J.: On the Differential Reaction to Vital Dyes Exhibited by the Two Great Groups of Connective Tissue Cells. Carnegie Contrib. Embryol. No. 47, 1, 1921.

Fawcett, D. W., and Jones, I. C.: The Effects of Hypophysectomy, Adrenalectomy and of Thiouracil Feeding on the Cytology of Brown Adipose Tissue. Endocrinology, 45;609, 1949.

Foot, N. C.: Studies on Endothelial Reactions. X. On the Origin of the Pulmonary "Dust Cell." Am. J. Path., 3:413, 1927.

Gersh, I., and Catchpole, H. R.: The Organization of Ground Substance and Basement Membrane and Its Significance in Tissue Injury, Disease and Growth. Am. J. Anat., 85:457, 1949.

Kolouch, F., Jr.: The Lymphocyte in Acute Inflammation. Am. J. Path., 15:413, 1939.

Mall, F. P.: On the Development of the Connective Tissues from the Connective Tissue Syncytium. Am. J. Anat., 1:329, 1902.

Marchand, F.: Der Prozess der Wundheilung. Deutsche Chirurgie (v. Bermann u. v. Bruns) Lief, 16, Stuttgart, 1901. Die örtliche reaktiven Vorgänge (Lehre von der Entziendung). Handb. d. allg. Pathol. (Krehl u. Marchand), Leipzig, (4), Pt. 1, 78, 1924.

Maximow, A.: Ueber die Zellformen des lockeren Bindegewebes. Arch. f. mikrosk.-Anat., 67:680, 1906. The Morphology of the Mesenchymal Reactions. Arch. Path., 4:557, 1927. Bindegewebe und blutbildende Gewebe. Handb. d. mikrosk.-Anat. d. Menschen (v. Möllendorff), (2), 232, Berlin, Pt.

I, 1927. The Macrophages or Histiocytes, in Cowdry's Special Cytology. 2d ed. New York, (2), 709, 1932.

Menkin, V.: Dynamics of Inflammation. Exper. Biol. Monographs, New York, 1940.

Plenk, H.: Ueber argyrophile Fasern (Gitterfasern) und ihre Bildungszellen. Ergebn. d. Anat. u. Entwick., 27:302, 1927.

Porter, K., and Vanamee, P.: Observations on the Formation of Connective Tissue Fibers. Proc. Soc. Exper. Biol. & Med., 71:513, 1949.

Ranvier, L.: Traité technique d'histologie. Paris, 1875. Des clasmatocytes. Arch. d'Anat. micro., 3:123, 1900.

Sabin, F., Doan, C., and Cunningham, R.: Discrimination of Two Types of Phagocytic Cells in the Connective Tissues by the Supravital Technique. Contrib. to Embryol., Carnegie Inst., Wash., 16: 125, 1925.

Schmitt, F. O.: Tissue Structure: Polarization Optical Analysis. Medical Physics, 2:1128, 1950.

Schmitt, F. O., Hall, C. E., and Jakus, M. A.: The Ultrastructure of Protoplasmic Fibrils. Biol. Symposia, 10:261, 1943.

Taliaferro, W. H.: The Cellular Basis of Immunity. Ann. Rev. Microbiology, 3:159, 1949.

Webb, R. L., and Simer, P. H.: The Relation of Lymph Vessels to Omental Milk Spots. Anat. Rec., 83:437, 1942.

Wells, H. G.: Adipose Tissue, A Neglected Subject. J.A.M.A., 114:2177, 1940.

Wolbach, S. B.: Controlled Formation of Collagen and Reticulum. A Study of the Source of Intercellular Substance in Recovery from Experimental Scorbutus. Am. J. Path., 9: Suppl., 689, 1933.

Wolbach, S. B., and Howe, P. R.: Intercellular Substances in Experimental Scorbutus. Arch. Path., 1: 1, 1926.

V. BLOOD CELL FORMATION AND DESTRUCTION

The short-lived blood corpuscles are kept at a constant number in the blood by the continuous formation of new cells. Under normal conditions, blood cells are regenerated only within the lymphatic and the myeloid tissues and organs (*hemopoietic* organs and tissues). The process of their formation is called *hemopoiesis*.

The cells of the circulating blood may be divided into two groups, according to their origin. To the first group belong the lymphocytes (and probably the monocytes), which originate in the lymphatic tissue and are called *lymphoid elements*. The second group consists of the erythrocytes and the granular leukocytes; these originate in the myeloid tissue and are the *myeloid elements*. But this separation of myeloid and lymphatic tissue is not absolute; for it is effaced in certain abnormal conditions in postnatal mammals, and, in the early embryonic stages of the mammals as well as through life in most of the lower vertebrates, there is no such separation.

All the blood cell-forming tissues of adult mammals have the same fundamental structure—a fibrous and cellular stroma in the meshes of which hemopoiesis takes place. This framework is composed of reticular fibers and cells.

The reticular fibers are accompanied or sheathed by a thin layer of protoplasm in which are scattered pale oval nuclei. These *primitive reticular cells* often show no cell limits. They are not active phagocytes and only rarely contain a few granules of waste pigment; they do not store appreciable amounts of vital dyes (Fig. 68). Like the mesenchymal cells of the embryo, they are endowed with the ability to turn into all types of blood and connective tissue cells.

From these *primitive reticular cells* there are many transitions to larger cells which are active phagocytes, called *phagocytic reticular cells* or *fixed macrophages*. These have an abundant cytoplasm and a large pale nucleus. Most of them are stellate or spindle-shaped and adhere to the reticular fibers. They may contain debris of dead cells, foreign materials, engulfed erythrocytes in various stages of disintegration and, in vitally stained animals, numerous large dye granules. In fresh preparations stained supravitally with neutral red, the inclusions and vacuoles of the macrophages stain deeply. The fixed macrophages may become *free macrophages*.

LYMPHATIC TISSUE

In mammals the lymphatic tissue forms distinctly outlined organs, the *lymph nodes*, which are arranged along the course of the lymph vessels. It is present in small amounts in the bone marrow and in large amounts in the *spleen*, where it may undergo specific modifications depending on the peculiar type of blood circulation in this organ (see Chap. XII). In addition, lymphatic tissue is scattered in the mucous membranes of the alimentary canal and of the respiratory passages, in the conjunctiva and elsewhere. The *hemal nodes* are described on page 235. The *thymus*, which has a number of features in common with lymphatic tissue, is described in Chapter XIII.

Two microscopic constituents can be distinguished in the lymphatic tissue: (1) a spongelike framework or stroma and (2) free cells in the meshes of the stroma. These constituents are present in different proportions in various parts of the lymphatic tissue, so that we may distinguish (*a*) *loose lymphatic tissue*, consisting predominantly of stroma; (*b*) *dense lymphatic tissue*, in which the free cells predominate; and (*c*) *nodular lymphatic tissue*, especially dense accumulations of free cells within the loose or dense lymphatic tissue. Under various physiological and pathological conditions, each of these types of tissue may turn into either of the others (p. 78).

The loose lymphatic tissue, as found in the lymph nodes, forms sinuses or pathways for the lymph which flows through the organ. Unlike the lymph vessels, which have a free lumen and a wall of their own, the sinuses are merely portions of the lymphatic tissue which are especially loose in structure (see Chap. XI).

Stroma. The framework of lymphatic tissue is made up of (1) reticular fibers and (2) reticular cells (Fig. 67).

Fibers. The fibers are of the reticular type and are best shown by the silver impregna-

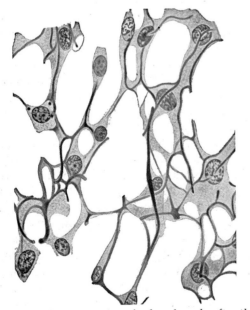

Fig. 67. From a section of a lymph node after the lymphocytes have been removed, showing the network of reticular cells and their intimate relations with the reticular fibers. Mallory-azan stain. (Redrawn after Heidenhain.)

tion method. At the periphery of the nodules the framework is dense and the meshes small, while the stroma within the nodules is loose, with thin fibers; in the loose tissue of the sinuses the large meshes are composed of coarse fibers (Fig. 72). Along the walls of all the blood vessels the reticulum is condensed.

Cells. The cells of the stroma are the primitive reticular cells and the phagocytic reticular cells or fixed macrophages. The primitive reticular cells of the lymphatic tissue have the ability to develop into phagocytes and lymphocytes, as well as into myelocytes in ectopic myelopoiesis (p. 98). Under certain conditions the fixed macrophages may become free macrophages anywhere in the lymphatic tissue; they are especially numerous in the sinuses. When the lymph contains foreign substances, such as lithium carmine or bacteria, the number of free macrophages greatly increases.

The fixed and free macrophages of the lymphatic tissue correspond closely with those of the loose connective tissue (p. 57). In the lymphatic tissue they increase by division and by development from primitive reticular cells.

The macrophages which help form the walls of the sinuses, and which are attached to the fibers passing through the cavity of these spaces, are often flattened and resemble endothelial cells (Fig. 68). For this reason they have been called endothelium, but, as the ability to store vital dyes and to transform into free macrophages has not been proved to be present in the endothelium of the common blood or lymph vessels, the term is not justified. The flattened form of these macrophages is an adaptation to their position on the wall of the channels through which the lymph flows. The term *littoral* or *lining cells* of the system of macrophages is perhaps the best to use.

The lymphatic tissue does not contain fibroblasts (except along the arteries and veins and in the trabeculae of the lymphatic organs), although, in inflammation and in cultures of this tissue, fibroblasts develop from the primitive reticular cells and from the macrophages.

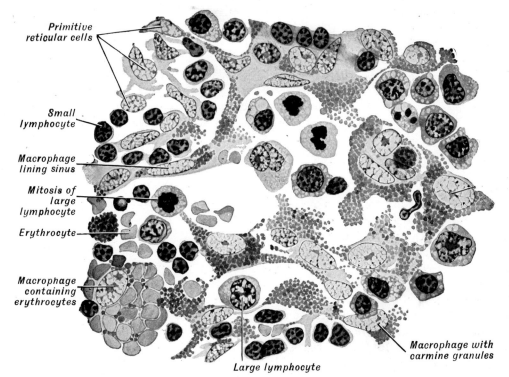

Primitive
reticular cells

Small
lymphocyte

Macrophage
lining sinus

Mitosis of
large
lymphocyte

Erythrocyte

Macrophage
containing
erythrocytes

Macrophage with
carmine granules

Large lymphocyte

Fig. 68. Medullary sinus of mesenteric lymph node of a rabbit which had repeated intravenous injections of lithium carmine. Hematoxylin-eosin-azure stain. 950 ×. (A.A.M.)

Free Cells. The meshes of the fibrous and cellular reticulum contain free cells. In dense lymphatic tissue and in the nodules the free cells are so densely crowded that the nuclei of the primitive reticular cells can be seen among them only in thin sections. The free cells are much less numerous in the meshes of the sinuses; here they float in the lymph which passes slowly through the channels. Except for the free macrophages described earlier, the free cells are all *lymphocytes*.

In the lymphatic tissue can be distinguished several types of lymphocytes: (1) The *small lymphocytes* form the vast majority (Fig. 69) (see Chap. III). The *medium-sized lymphocytes* are scattered everywhere among the small lymphocytes, but in a much smaller number. They are slightly larger than the small variety, and the nucleus is clearer and contains less chromatin; one or two nucleoli are prominent, and there is more cytoplasm. These cells divide mitotically. (3) *Large lymphocytes, macrolymphocytes,* are scattered singly among the other lymphocytes and measure up to 15 microns in diameter, al-

though occasional ones may measure 20 microns or more when rounded. They occur everywhere, even in the sinuses, but are more numerous in the lymphatic nodules, their number varying with the functional condition of the lymphatic tissue. Often, especially in human lymph nodes, they may be absent. Their cytoplasm forms a broad layer around the nucleus and is strongly basophile, presumably due to ribosenucleic acid. It may contain a few vacuoles at the indentation of the nucleus; the hemispherical cytocentrum with a diplosome is surrounded by a Golgi net. There are more rod-shaped mitochondria than in the smaller forms, and they are arranged around the cytocentrum. The large, usually kidney-shaped nucleus occupies a slightly eccentric position, with the excavation directed toward the large accumulation of cytoplasm. The nuclear membrane is coarsely outlined; the chromatin particles are widely scattered in a large quantity of clear nuclear sap. Always there are one or more large irregularly shaped nucleoli. The large lymphocytes are found dividing by mitosis.

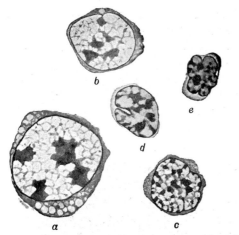

Fig. 69. Lymphocytes from a human lymph node. *a*, Large, *b*, *c*, medium-sized, and *d*, *e*, small lymphocytes. Hematoxylin-eosin-azure stain. 1500 ×. (A.A.M.)

These three types of lymphocytes are connected with one another by an uninterrupted series of transitional forms. In the small lymphocytes mitoses are extremely rare under normal conditions, the main source of the lymphocytes of the blood being the medium-sized lymphocyte.

Under suitable conditions the small lymphocyte may hypertrophy into a larger one and regain the ability to divide. This transformation probably occurs but rarely in the lymphatic tissue. The small lymphocytes of the blood can hypertrophy in tissue culture within a day into typical large lymphocytes.

Plasma cells are of common occurrence in the lymphatic tissue, especially in the medullary cords of the lymph nodes; their number is subject to marked variation, particularly under pathological conditions. In some animals (rat, mouse) plasma cells are especially numerous. Sometimes, eosinophile leukocytes are found in the lymphatic tissue. Heterophile granulocytes are a sign of an inflammatory lesion. Young forms of granulocytes (myelocytes) are found only in *extramedullary myelopoiesis* (p. 98). Mast cells are often found scattered along the fibers of the reticulum; monocytes usually do not occur.

Development of Lymphocytes. In the postnatal mammals most lymphocytes arise by mitosis of preexisting lymphocytes within the lymphatic tissue. This occurs mainly in the nodular, but also to some extent in the diffuse and loose lymphatic tissue. The mother cell is usually a medium-sized lymphocyte, although dividing large lymphocytes are not uncommon. In some instances it has been possible to trace lymphocytes to their origin in primitive reticular cells—a source probably active only when the preexisting lymphocytes are unable, by their mitoses, to fill the demand for lymphocytes (see p. 90).

Lymphatic Nodules. The lymphatic nodules are especially dense accumulations of lymphocytes embedded in a relatively scanty cellular and fibrous reticulum, and are usually the expression of some stage of lymphocytopoietic activity focused at a small area in the lymphatic tissue. The nodules appear and disappear, or pass through a series of cyclic changes during which an intense new formation of lymphocytes proceeds through proliferation of preexisting lymphocytes and to a lesser extent through transformation of the primitive reticular cells.

In its fully developed form, a nodule consists of a central portion and a peripheral zone, sometimes called *corona*. The central portion of a nodule which is actively producing lymphocytes is called the *germinal center* (Figs. 70 and 71). This germinal center may attain a diameter of 1 mm. It often has a small artery supplying it with blood. This central area in such a nodule appears paler than the surrounding mass of small lymphocytes with their dark nuclei, for the majority of its cells are medium-sized lymphocytes. They contain more mitotic figures than do the medium-sized lymphocytes in loose and dense lymphatic tissue. Scattered among them are a few large lymphocytes and all transitions between them. A few small lymphocytes also are found. Among the lymphocytes of an actively lymphocytopoietic nodule are scattered primitive reticular cells with indistinct cytoplasm (Fig. 71). These also show occasional mitoses. Macrophages with phagocytosed inclusions are distributed along the capillaries in the nodule.

At the end of a proliferative phase, mitosis ceases in the germinal center, which gradually becomes depleted of lymphocytes. Such an *inactive center* contains reticular cells, macrophages and a few lymphocytes. In certain pathological conditions, such as diphtheria, burns and severe bacterial and plasmodial infections, the central portion may have a similar appearance, although there are usually more active macrophages in these conditions.

Such central areas have been described as *"reaction centers."* Some of the stages of their development are much like the "inactive centers."

The *peripheral zone* or *corona* appears in sections darker than the central portion of the nodule, for the majority of its cells are densely crowded small lymphocytes with

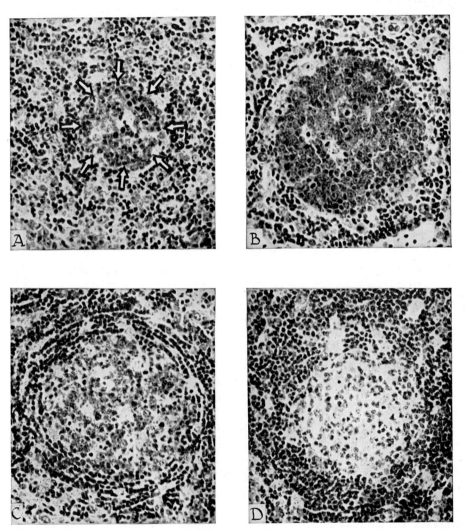

Fig. 70. Photomicrographs showing four nodules at different stages of development in mesenteric lymph node of guinea pigs, five days after injection of *B. monocytogenes*. A, Small new "bare" germinal center consisting of dividing medium-sized lymphocytes. Its margins are indicated by the arrowheads. B, Later stage in the development of a nodule. This "bare" germinal center contains twenty-seven mitoses in medium-sized lymphocytes. C, Corona of densely packed small lymphocytes has been formed around the germinal center, which is actively lymphopoietic and contains fifteen mitoses in medium-sized lymphocytes. This is the type of nodule which is often regarded as typical, consisting of an outer dark-staining zone and a lighter central area. D, Nodule with inactive center. It has a pale-staining central portion consisting mainly of reticular cells, free macrophages and a few scattered lymphocytes. This nodule with its center depleted of lymphocytes resembles the "reaction center" type. Hematoxylin-eosin-azure II. 300 ×. (After Conway.)

their dark nuclei. These small lymphocytes are frequently seen arranged in concentric layers.

In a stage of complete rest the lymphatic nodule consists mainly of small lymphocytes, so compactly arranged that the nodule stands out as a dense, darkly-stained area in the dif-

formation or through mitoses of the primitive reticular cells (Figs. 70, 79). Such a small isolated mass of densely packed medium-sized lymphocytes is in every respect similar to a germinal center. Because of the absence of a corona of small lymphocytes, it may be described as a *"bare" germinal center.* Many of

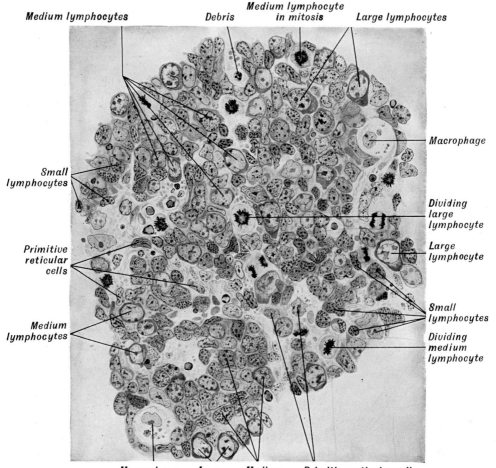

Fig. 71. Portion of actively lymphocytopoietic nodule of human lymph node. Hematoxylin-eosin-azure II. (A.A.M.)

fuse lymphatic tissue. New nodules may develop anywhere in the loose or dense lymphatic tissue. Indeed, they may even develop in a preexisting nodule. These new areas of lymphocytopoiesis start with the appearance of many, rapidly repeated mitoses in medium-sized lymphocytes. In some instances these have been shown to arise as free cells, with a narrow rim of cytoplasm by individual trans-

the medium-sized lymphocytes become large lymphocytes, and some of the primitive reticular cells become macrophages. The bare germinal center increases in size because of the continued mitoses of the medium-sized lymphocytes. The growth pressure may cause development of a corona of densely packed small lymphocytes, depending on the density of the surrounding lymphatic tissue.

As a lymphocyte-forming nodule becomes inactive, mitoses become less numerous, and the last divisions of the medium-sized cells give rise to small lymphocytes; some of the latter may originate from shrinkage of the larger cells. Plasma cells also appear. The decrease of the growth pressure effaces the sharp boundary line between the center and the periphery of the nodule, which then becomes uniform in appearance and composition.

New Formation of Lymphatic Tissue. New foci of lymphatic tissue and even lymph nodes can develop in any part of the loose connective tissue in the adult organism. When this happens, the lymphocytes and the elements of the stroma develop from the ubiquitous undifferentiated elements of the adult connective tissue (p. 56). When the lymphatic tissue involutes and disappears, the lymphocytes degenerate or wander away, while the reticular cells seem to be transformed into fat cells.

Function of the Lymphatic Tissue. The most conspicuous function of the lymphatic tissue is the production of lymphocytes. The lymphocytes which are newly formed in the lymph nodes—the vast majority of them are the small variety—migrate into the sinuses and are carried away by the lymph stream into the lymphatics and the thoracic duct, and hence into the blood. In addition, numbers of small lymphocytes migrate directly from the lymphatic tissue into the blood through the endothelium of the venous capillaries. In extramedullary myelopoiesis the lymphatic tissue can also become the source of granulocytes (see p. 98).

In the early stages of infection of rabbits and guinea pigs with *B. monocytogenes* the lymphocytes of the lymph nodes, and occasionally even of the nodules, turn into monocytes. Lymphoid hyperplasia in malaria was found by Taliaferro and Mulligan (1937) to have a functional significance in malarial immunity, in that it builds up a mesenchymal reserve from which new macrophages are formed (p. 65). The other functions of the lymphatic tissue are concerned mainly with its macrophages and will be discussed with the structure of the lymph nodes and spleen. Evidence is accumulating that lymphocytes are rich in specific immune bodies and that the delivery of lymphocytes to the circulation is, in part, under control of the adrenal cortex and of the pars distalis of the hypophysis. The source of antibodies has not been determined, and the significance of the antibody content of lymphocytes awaits clarification.

The marked atrophy of lymphoid tissues which results from the action of a variety of noxious agents (part of the "alarm reaction" of Selye) is believed to result from the liberation of adrenal cortical hormones; it does not occur if the adrenal cortex is removed.

Some authors deny the importance of the nodules for the regeneration of the lymphocytes, believing them to be only centers of reaction of the lymphatic tissue to various toxic agents. As proof, they point to the degeneration of lymphocytes and reticular cells as evidenced by the nuclear debris in the macrophages of the centers, in intoxications, burns, inflammatory lesions and in certain infectious diseases. It is true that cellular debris occurs in the center of the nodule (Fig. 71). This is, however, no evidence that the center of the nodule is exclusively a site of cell destruction, since lymphocytes continue to proliferate (see mitoses in lymphocytes in Figure 71) and the germinal center can increase in size, while debris is present. Just as in all areas of rapid new formation of cells, some of the newly formed cells degenerate (see nervous system, Fig. 197, Testis, p. 461), so do a number of the newly formed lymphocytes degenerate in the germinal center.

The lymphocytes are among the most sensitive cells in the body to ionizing radiations and certain toxins (mustard gas); the reticular cells are among the most resistant.

Embryonic lymphatic tissue has nodules which are dense masses of small lymphocytes, lacking pale-staining central areas. It is claimed that guinea pigs which have been reared for sixty days on sterile media do not show centers in the nodules (Glimstedt).

Lymphatic Tissue in the Lower Vertebrates. In the lower vertebrates, although

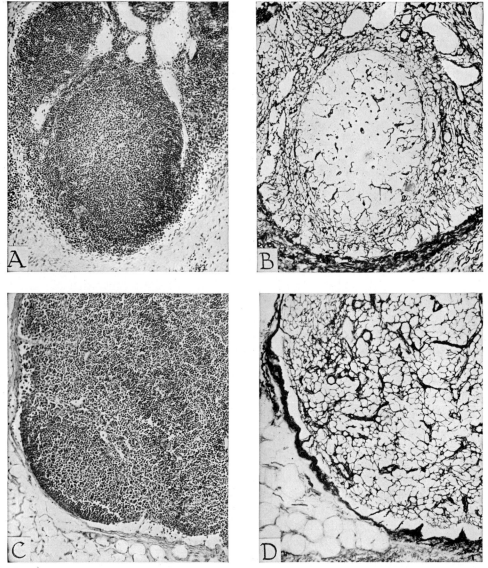

Fig. 72. A and B, photomicrographs from sections of the same block of mesenteric lymph node of rabbit, thirty-six hours after injection of B. *monocytogenes*; C and D, from a block of mesenteric lymph node of rabbit, forty-eight hours after injection of the same bacterium. When nodular lymphatic tissue (A) becomes diffuse lymphatic tissue (C), the reticular-fiber framework, characteristic of the nodules (B), is lost (D). In all sections the subcapsular sinus is prominent. A and C stained with hematoxylin; B and D impregnated for reticular fibers by the Foot method. 107 ×. (After Conway.)

lymphocytes are plentiful, their regeneration is not localized in special lymphatic organs, but occurs in many places in the connective tissue; in fact, lymph nodes are usually absent. The most important difference in comparison with the mammals is that the lymphatic tissue is not sharply separated from the myeloid tissue.

MYELOID TISSUE. THE BONE MARROW

Of the several kinds of bone marrow which differ macroscopically, the two most important varieties are the *red* and the *yellow*, or *fatty*, bone marrow. Only the red marrow, which consists of myeloid tissue, plays a role in hemopoiesis, producing the red blood cells and the granulocytes. In the embryo and the newborn, red marrow only is found in the bone cavities. With progressing age the red marrow is gradually replaced by the yellow marrow with its fat cells. In the normal adult, red marrow is found in the vertebrae, the ribs, the sternum, the *diploë* of the bones of the skull, and in the proximal epiphyses

acquires a gray "pyoid" character. Figure 80 shows the effect of raising the temperature of fatty marrow.

The myeloid tissue, like the lymphatic, consists of (1) the spongelike framework or stroma which is intimately connected with the blood vessels and (2) the free cells in the meshes of the stroma.

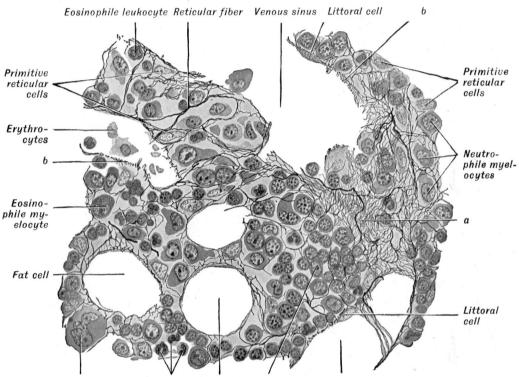

Fig. 73. Bone marrow from upper epiphysis of a femur of a child of six years. The fibrous network of the wall of a vessel is seen from the surface at *a* and in cross section at *b*. Bielschowsky stain. 500 ×. (A.A.M.)

of the femur and humerus. Bone marrow forms 2 to 3 per cent of the body weight.

No sharp limit can be drawn between the two kinds of bone marrow. After considerable losses of blood or in the anemias, the fatty bone marrow is replaced to a greater or less extent by red marrow. After prolonged starvation or in some wasting diseases the bone marrow loses its blood cells, and the fat acquires a peculiar gelatinous appearance; it is then called gelatinous or "mucous" bone marrow. In myeloid leukemia the red bone marrow becomes rich in granulocytes and

Stroma. As in the lymphatic tissue, the stroma consists of primitive and phagocytic reticular cells attached to the argyrophile fibers (Figs. 67, 73). The network of cells and fibers is looser and its meshes are larger than in the lymphatic tissue. Particulate matter and vital dyes injected into the blood are taken up rapidly by the fixed macrophages of the bone marrow.

Circulation in the bone marrow is characterized by the presence of many large vessels, called *sinusoids*, through the walls of which innumerable cells pass into the blood stream.

The sinusoids are lined by flattened, fixed macrophages (littoral cells), like those forming the walls of the lymph node sinuses. These dye-storing and phagocytosing cells have indistinct limits and are in direct connection with similar cells of the stroma. They can round off and appear as free macrophages in the blood of the sinusoids. The manner in which the arteries connect with the sinusoids needs further study.

The stroma of the myeloid tissue is distinguished by the constant presence of fat cells. These are scattered singly in the red marrow (Fig. 73), but in the yellow bone marrow they crowd out practically all the other cells; between them remain (besides the blood vessels and reticular fibers) only scattered fixed macrophages and primitive reticular cells. The latter are probably the main source of the new blood cells when the yellow bone marrow is transformed into red marrow. Small accumulations of lymphatic tissue with nodules occur regularly in the bone marrow, but lymph vessels have not been found

Free Cells. In contrast to the free cells of the lymphatic tissue, those of the myeloid tissue are extremely varied in form and are scattered irregularly throughout the tissue. The vast majority of them are immature myeloid elements.

MATURE MYELOID ELEMENTS

Mature, non-nucleated erythrocytes, and the three types of granular leukocytes as they occur in the circulating blood, are found everywhere between the other cells. Thus the tissue which produces these elements always contains a ready supply of them and in case of need can forward large quantities at once into the blood (Fig. 74).

IMMATURE MYELOID ELEMENTS

The other free cells in the bone marrow are *hemocytoblasts* (*free stem cells*); *erythroblasts*—the precursors of the red blood corpuscles; *myelocytes*—the precursors of the three principal types of granular leukocytes; and *megakaryocytes*.

Hemocytoblasts. The myeloid tissue of all adult mammals contains ameboid, nongranular, basophile cells of lymphoid nature. They vary in size, the largest measuring 15 microns, and are scattered singly or in groups of two or four. Their structure corresponds exactly to that of the lymphocytes. They are the free stem cells of all other myeloid elements. A suitable name for them is *hemocytoblast*. The small cells of this type are connected with the larger ones by a complete series of transitional forms. According to the unitarian theory of hemopoiesis, both lymphocytes and hemocytoblasts have identical developmental potencies (page 97).

Erythroblasts. The young forms of the red blood corpuscles are spherical cells with spherical nuclei and are called erythroblasts. In living cells their cytoplasm is homogeneous, and of a yellow color which intensifies as the cells develop into erythrocytes. Supravital staining with neutral red produces red precipitates in their cytoplasm. Erythroblasts never show ameboid motion. In fixed and stained sections they show mitochondria, a Golgi net and a cytocentrum. The round nucleus of the erythroblasts always presents a checker-board distribution of angular particles of chromatin. The nucleoli gradually involute. The number of mitotic divisions in the cell lineage is not known. The changes in the erythroblasts as they develop into erythrocytes are clearly shown in Figures 75, 76.

The erythroblasts closest to the stem cell are called *basophile erythroblasts*, because of the intense basophilia of their protoplasm; it is deeper than that of the hemocytoblasts. An intermediate cell (*proerythroblast*) has been described.

The erythroblasts of the next youngest generation have a small amount of hemoglobin. (Some authors call them *megaloblasts*, a misleading term because it was first used for the erythroblasts of pernicious anemia, which are of different nature—see Jones.) After fixation and staining with the Romanowsky mixture (eosin-methylene-azure) the cytoplasm varies from a purplish-blue to lilac or gray. These erythroblasts are, therefore, called *polychro-*

matophile. This staining reaction is due to the appearance of pink-staining hemoglobin in the basophile cytoplasm of the erythroblast, which stains blue.

The polychromatophile erythroblasts divide mitotically. Some of them remain in the

cytes. The small round nucleus contains a dense accumulation of angular chromatin particles and stains very dark. After an unknown number of mitotic divisions, the nucleus is condensed to a darkly staining body. Each mature normoblast loses its pyknotic

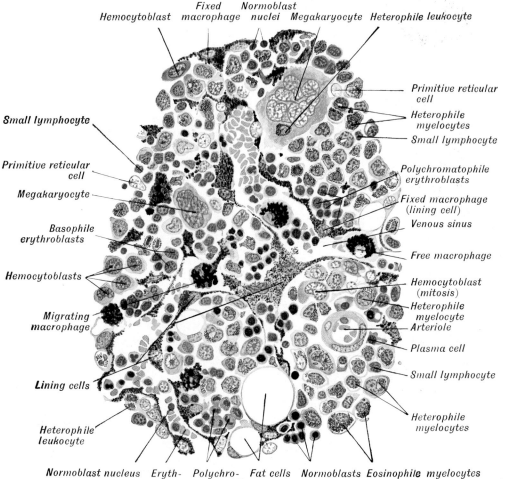

Fig. 74. Section of bone marrow of rabbit which had injections of lithium carmine and India ink. Hematoxylin-eosin-azure II. 460 ×. (A.A.M.)

tissue in a resting condition for future use. In the others the amount of hemoglobin increases while the basophilia of the cytoplasm diminishes; in this way *normoblasts* arise in which the cytoplasm stains a bright pink with the Romanowsky mixture. Normoblasts are smaller than polychromatophile erythroblasts and only slightly larger than mature erythro-

nucleus and is transformed into a red blood corpuscle. Some investigators hold that the nucleus is lost by *karyolysis*, but most believe this occurs by *extrusion*.

Myelocytes. Besides the erythroblasts, the young forms of the three types of leukocytes (heterophile, eosinophile and basophile) are common cell types of the myeloid tissue. The

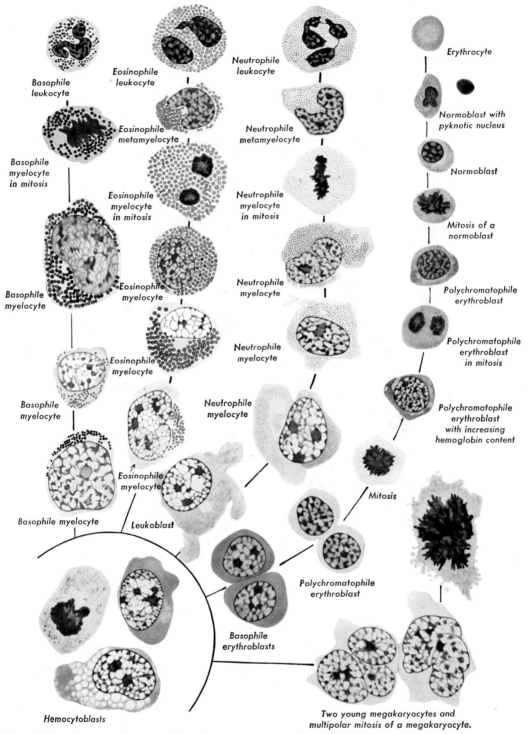

Fig. 75. Development of the myeloid elements of human bone marrow from a common lymphoid stem cell as seen in sections stained with hematoxylin-eosin-azure II. The basophile myelocytes were fixed in absolute alcohol and stained with alcoholic thionine. The mature cells are from dry smears of human blood stained with May-Grünwald-Giemsa, except the basophile leukocyte, which is stained with alcoholic thionine. 1500 ×. (A.A.M.)

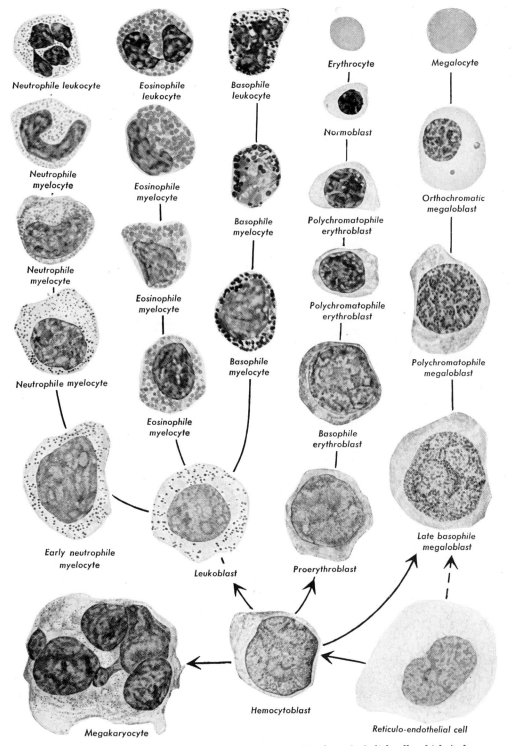

Neutrophile leukocyte

Eosinophile leukocyte

Basophile leukocyte

Erythrocyte

Megalocyte

Neutrophile myelocyte

Eosinophile myelocyte

Normoblast

Neutrophile myelocyte

Eosinophile myelocyte

Basophile myelocyte

Polychromatophile erythroblast

Orthochromatic megaloblast

Neutrophile myelocyte

Eosinophile myelocyte

Polychromatophile erythroblast

Neutrophile myelocyte

Basophile myelocyte

Polychromatophile megaloblast

Eosinophile myelocyte

Basophile erythroblast

Early neutrophile myelocyte

Leukoblast

Proerythroblast

Late basophile megaloblast

Hemocytoblast

Megakaryocyte

Reticulo-endothelial cell

Fig. 76. Cells from human bone marrow dry smears, except reticulo-endothelial cell, which is from a smear of human embryonic liver. Note differences in size of cells and in nuclear structure of the erythroblast and megaloblast series (of pernicious anemia). Slides of O. P. Jones. May-Grünwald-Giemsa stain. 1350 ×. (Drawn by Miss Esther Bohlman.)

myelocytes of each of the three types are provided with their characteristic granulation and cannot be transformed into myelocytes of another type or into elements of another kind. They have a compact, round or kidney-shaped nucleus, and proliferate intensely by mitotic division. Some of their progeny remain unchanged, while others undergo progressive maturation. Finally, each cell is transformed individually into a mature polymorphonuclear granular leukocyte. These details are clearly shown in Figures 75 and 76, which also illustrate the differences resulting from the use of the two technics.

Myelocytes with Heterophile Granules (Neutrophile Myelocytes of Man). The heterophile myelocytes are larger than the mature heterophile leukocytes. In the youngest generation, sometimes called *promyelocyte*, the oval or kidney-shaped nucleus contains a loose chromatin network and several nucleoli. At the indentation of the nucleus there is a distinct cytocentrum. The ameboid cytoplasm is slightly basophile, although it often shows acidophile areas. The specific granules are scarce and usually are confined to the periphery of the cytocentrum and to the acidophile areas in the cell body. In dry smears the promyelocytes contain, in addition to the heterophile granules, azurophile granules which later disappear.

The promyelocytes often show mitosis. In the following generation, the cytoplasm of the heterophile myelocytes becomes diffusely acidophile, while the specific granules increase in number and fill the whole cell body, except for the cytocentrum. The chromatin network of the nucleus becomes coarser and stains darker, and the nucleoli become indistinct. Mitoses are common; during division the granules are evenly distributed among the daughter cells and continue to increase in numbers as the latter grow. Some of the heterophile myelocytes are small and have a dark nucleus; these are called *micromyelocytes*.

After an unknown number of mitoses, a generation of heterophile myelocytes appears which does not divide. The nucleus in these cells shows a beginning polymorphism and has the shape of a horseshoe. Such cells are called *metamyelocytes*; each of them matures by progressive constriction of the horseshoe-shaped nucleus into a mature heterophile leukocyte.

Myelocytes with Eosinophile Granules. Less numerous than the heterophile myelocytes are the myelocytes with eosinophile granules, which undergo in general the same changes. Among them also different generations can be distinguished. They all have a slightly basophile protoplasm. The eosinophile promyelocytes contain a small number of specific granules which do not stain alike. The youngest among them show a distinct basophilia and stain bluish with eosin-azure; from these there are all transitions to mature, purely eosinophile granules. Mitoses are common in the eosinophile myelocytes, especially in the large ones. The horseshoe-shaped nucleus of the metamyelocytes becomes constricted, often into two lobes in the mature leukocytes.

Myelocytes with Basophile Granules. These are much scarcer than the heterophile myelocytes and are difficult to study because their granules, in man, are easily soluble in water.

For the most part the basophile myelocytes are small cells with a paler nucleus than the other myelocytes. The protoplasm contains a widely varying number of specific, basophile, metachromatic granules of unequal size.

Megakaryocytes. These giants cells with a polymorphous nucleus are characteristic of the mammalian bone marrow, where they are scattered evenly among the other elements. Some of them have a diameter as large as 40 microns. The form of the cell body is spherical, but its surface is often provided with irregularly shaped processes.

The nucleus is deeply constricted in many places; the lobes bulge at the periphery, while their central parts are interconnected by short, branched stalks. The interior of the nucleus shows a chromatin network and indistinct nucleoli. In the living cell the abundant cytoplasm is homogeneous and contains many groups of centrioles scattered in the furrows of the nuclear surface. Mitochondria and a Golgi net have also been described.

With special fixation and staining, fine, azurophile granules are seen distributed in the cell body in large quantities, sometimes in small dense groups. The presumed role of the megakaryocytes in the production of platelets is discussed on page 46.

In every normal bone marrow many megakaryocytes are found degenerating (Fig. 77), while there are frequent signs of their new formation from hemocytoblasts. The first stage is hypertrophy of the nucleus, which then becomes constricted in several places. Then follows a series of peculiar mitotic divisions which concern only the nucleus. The centrioles divide into several groups, and a complex spindle with several poles arises. The chromosomes are arranged in several equatorial planes and give rise to several daughter nuclei. There is no constriction of the cytoplasm, and the daughter nuclei at once fuse into a new, larger nucleus. After an interval a new mitosis with still more centers occurs, the daughter nuclei again fuse in the telophase, and the quantity of chromatin and the number of the centrioles again increase. The number of mitoses is not known. Sooner or later the cell degenerates; the giant nucleus shrinks, the cytoplasm disintegrates, and the final result is a naked, shrunken, nuclear remnant. Such degenerated nuclei often find their way into the sinusoids of the marrow and are carried with the blood into the right heart and thence into the capillaries of the lungs, where they remain and probably undergo autolysis. Under pathological conditions this embolism of the lung vessels by megakaryocytes may occur on a large scale; in fact, not only degenerating nuclei, but even whole cells with unchanged protoplasm may be found obstructing the pulmonary capillaries. Howell finds megakaryocytes and extensive platelet formation in the pulmonary vessels of the dog. (See also Jordan, 1940.)

Plasma Cells. Plasma cells constitute 1 to 3 per cent of the hematopoietic cells of normal human marrow. They are found primarily within the reticular fiber sheath of the terminal portions of the arterial capillaries, but also occur as isolated cells or in small foci throughout the marrow. In certain diseases

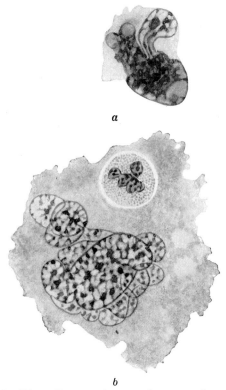

Fig. 77. *a*, Degenerating megakaryocyte; *b*, megakaryocyte containing a neutrophile leukocyte; both from human bone marrow. 1500 ×. (A.A.M.)

the level of globulins in the plasma seems to vary with the number of plasma cells in the marrow.

Monocytes. Many hematologists believe that monocytes are formed in the myeloid tissue. Under normal conditions they are found only in the lumen of the venous sinusoids. The origin of these cells is discussed on page 100.

Homoplastic and Heteroplastic Hemopoiesis. Under physiological conditions the needs of the adult organism for myeloid blood elements are usually supplied by *homoplastic hemopoiesis*—the production of mature cells by young elements of the same type. But not all the young forms reach maturity; some of them remain unused in the tissue. Whenever the requirements of the body for erythrocytes or leukocytes are greatly increased, homoplastic hemopoiesis does not suffice, and new *erythroblasts* and *myelocytes develop from stem cells.* This is called *heter-*

oplastic hemopoiesis, which also applies to the development of free stem cells from fixed ones.

In this process, when a hemocytoblast divides, either its daughter cells remain in the tissue as hemocytoblasts or one of its latent potencies develops and both daughter cells become erythroblasts or myelocytes. Transi-

main undifferentiated. But under physiological conditions it is rare for primitive reticular cells to become hemocytoblasts in the bone marrow. The mitoses of the myelocytes and erythroblasts—and occasionally of hemocytoblasts—usually are sufficient. Pathological stimuli sometimes facilitate the new formation of hemocytoblasts from the primitive

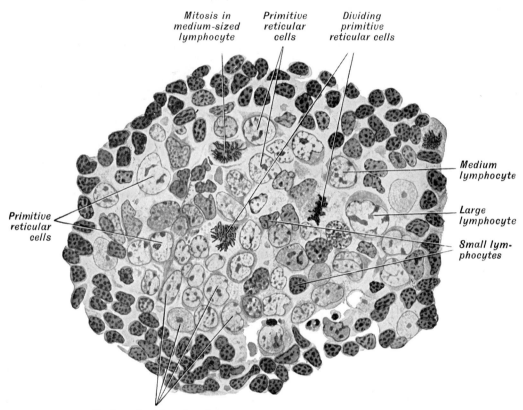

Fig. 78. Heteroplastic development of lymphocytes from primitive reticular cells in a human lymph node. Hematoxylin-eosin-azure II. 750 ×. (A.A.M.)

tional cells between the hemocytoblasts and early myelocytes have been described under the name of *leukoblasts* (Figs. 75, 76). Their structural differences are so insignificant that to recognize these elements as a separate cell type seems unwarranted.

In the embryo the hemocytoblasts of the bone marrow which produce the myeloid forms originate from outstretched mesenchymal cells. In the adult the same process may occur. It has been explained that some of the cellular elements of the reticulum always re-

reticular cells (Fig. 79). As described on page 78), heteroplastic development of lymphocytes may also occur (Fig. 78).

Entry of Myeloid Elements into the Blood. Because the myeloid elements arise outside the blood stream, it is obvious that the newly formed mature myeloid cells must pass through the walls of the blood vessels to enter the circulation. The thin-walled venous sinusoids make this possible. Through them easily pass, not only the ameboid mature granular leukocytes, but also the nonmotile erythrocytes. When these are ready for circulation, they slip through the membrane into the blood stream in the lumen of the sinusoid. The mechanism of this phenomenon is probably regulated by changes in the permeability of the vessel walls and in the surface energy.

The claim that red blood corpuscles in the adult, normal man are formed intravascularly

of the bone marrow. In most general or severe local infections the heterophile granulocytopoietic apparatus is stimulated, and the percentage of myelocytes of this type increases greatly. In typhoid fever or in agranulocytic angina the heterophile myelocytes decrease in number. Whenever there is an increased need of erythrocytes or when the erythrocytes are destroyed in large quantities,

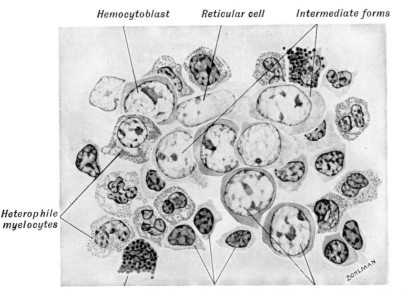

Fig. 79. Section of human bone marrow from a case of polycythemia vera, showing stages in development of primitive reticular cells into hemocytoblasts and basophile erythroblasts. Zenker-formol and hematoxylin-eosin-azure II. From a preparation of C. Huggins. 1380 ×.

is based on unconvincing evidence. In the embryonic mammalian liver and bone marrow the red blood cells develop extravascularly, while in the yolk sac they are preponderantly of intravascular origin.

Functions of the Myeloid Tissue. The main function of the bone marrow seems to be the production of myeloid elements for the blood. The macrophages of the bone marrow also function like the macrophages in other tissues (see p. 63).

The cellular composition of the blood is intimately connected with the condition of the bone marrow. Under physiological conditions the relative numbers of the different cells in the bone marrow, as in the blood, vary only a little. But all general pathological processes immediately affect the composition

they and their precursors predominate in the myeloid tissue. That temperature plays some role in the control of hemopoiesis in the marrow is shown by the fact that the fatty marrow of the tail bones of a rat becomes hematopoietic when the temperature of the bone is raised to that of the body, as by placing it in the body (Fig. 80).

The production of erythrocytes depends in part on an *anti-anemic factor* which is stored in the liver. This factor probably is the result of the interaction of a substance in the gastric juice (*intrinsic factor* of Castle) with some substance in the diet (*extrinsic factor*). The absence of the anti-anemic factor results in pernicious anemia, which can be treated successfully by the administration of liver or gastric extract or vitamin B_{12}.

The erythroblasts are about as sensitive to ionizing radiations as the hemocytoblasts (lymphocytes). The myelocytes are more resistant and the megakaryocytes much more so, while the reticular cells are extremely resistant.

Destruction of Blood Corpuscles. Both the red and the white corpuscles constantly perish in large numbers, even under normal conditions. With the aid of isotopes it has been

spleen to the bone marrow has not been described.

In addition, a constant disintegration of erythrocytes into hemoglobin-stained fragments in the circulation itself is thought to be an important factor, the fragments being taken up by the macrophages in various regions of the body. In certain pathological conditions when the erythrocytes degenerate in large quantities, erythrophagocytosis in the

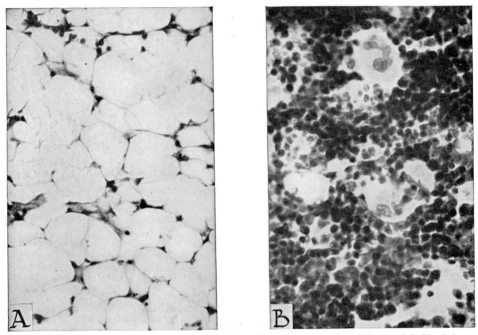

Fig. 80. A tail loop was constructed in a twenty-three-day rat by skinning the distal half of the tail and inserting it surgically in the peritoneal cavity, where it was kept for 125 days. The section on the left (A) is from the cool outside loop and shows fatty bone marrow; that on the right (B) shows hemopoietic marrow from the warm region of the tail in the abdominal cavity. 500 ×. (Courtesy of C. Huggins.)

shown that the life span of a human erythrocyte is about 120 days. The manner and site of the physiological destruction and final disposal of the erythrocytes have not been completely elucidated. It has long been known that there is destruction of red blood cells by the phagocytes of the spleen, liver and bone marrow. The hemoglobin of the ingested erythrocytes is broken into hematin and globin. The first is further split into bilirubin, which is excreted with the bile, and into iron, which is retained, especially by the spleen, and utilized for the formation of new erythrocytes. How this iron is transferred from the

spleen is greatly increased, and the macrophages contain large amounts of hemosiderin and waste pigment. In these disturbances, other organs, especially the liver with its Kupffer cells, may also take part in the destruction of the erythrocytes.

The presence of degenerating leukocytes in the circulating blood, although often described, has never been confirmed conclusively. Destruction of granular leukocytes through phagocytosis by the Kupffer cells in the liver has been observed. Large numbers of lymphocytes may degenerate in the very place where they are formed in the lymphatic tissue. In addition, the organism always loses lymphocytes through migration into the cavity of the intestine.

EMBRYONIC DEVELOPMENT OF BLOOD AND CONNECTIVE TISSUE

The manner in which blood cells develop in embryonic and postnatal animals is one of the most controversial subjects in histology. In our opinion, the following presentation is the most accurate, although some hematologists do not agree. Downey's *Handbook of Hematology* contains extended discussions of the subject.

Blood is formed in practically the same manner in all embryonic mammals. Beginning hemopoiesis is the same in almost all situations, and consists in the rounding up of outstretched mesenchymal cells into free basophile cells, which in turn give rise to all types of blood cells. The first site of this process is the wall of the yolk sac, succeeded by the body mesenchyme, liver, bone marrow, spleen, and lymph nodes. In the yolk sac most of the *primitive stem cells* become *primitive red blood corpuscles*, which serve as oxygen carriers until they are replaced by the permanent erythrocytes. The remaining stem cells give rise to the *definitive* or *permanent red blood cells*, *granulocytes* and *megakaryocytes*. In all other situations in which blood formation occurs, the process is the same except that primitive erythroblasts are not formed.

In all areas of embryonic blood formation the free stem cells are morphologically the same as the various-sized lymphocytes (or hemocytoblasts) of the adult. Even in the primordia of the lymphatic tissue large numbers of erythrocytes, myelocytes and megakaryocytes are formed. It is only in the late embryonic stages that an apparent division of blood-forming tissues into myeloid and lymphatic takes place, and this division seems to hold for most of the normal adult life. Under abnormal conditions, however, the myeloid potencies of the cells of the lymphatic and loose connective tissues may become apparent even in the adult mammalian organism. *Blood formation in the embryo*

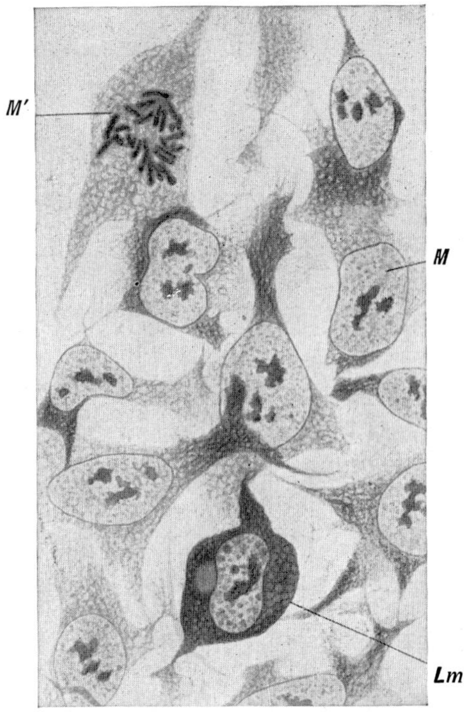

Fig. 81. Mesenchyme from head of a rabbit embryo of nine and three-quarter days. Development of large lymphoid wandering cell (*Lm*) from mesenchymal cells (*M* and *M'*). Eosin-azure stain. 1025 ×. (A.A.M.)

thus takes place through the development of a hemopoietic tissue whose constituent cells are qualitatively the same, but which vary quantitatively in the successive locations in which this process takes place.

Origin of Mesenchyme. The mesenchyme arises from the mesoderm through the isolation from this layer of cells, which become distributed singly and in groups in the spaces between the three germinal layers. The sclerotomes are an especially abundant source of the mesenchyme. Some mesenchymal cells also arise from the surface of the parietal mesoderm facing the ectoderm, from the surface of the visceral mesoderm facing the entoderm, and from the lateral layer of the somites, the skin plate.

Yolk Sac. In early human ova irregular strands of primitive mesodermal cells traverse the small chorionic "cavity." As fluid accumulates in the blastocyst, these strands cover the surfaces of the chorionic, amniotic and yolk sac vesicles. As the embryo develops, the yolk sac becomes larger and its mesoderm assumes a more typical epithelium-like arrangement. This yolk sac mesoderm is apparently the source of the yolk sac mesenchyme, which then develops hematopoietically as in other mammals. The mesenchyme between the

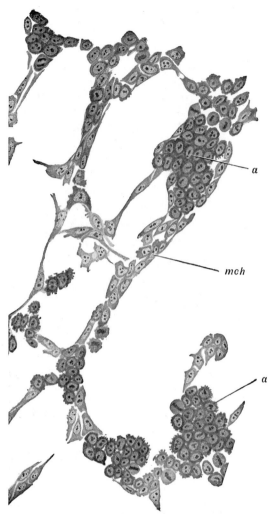

Fig. 82. Stretch preparation of the wall of the yolk sac of a guinea-pig embryo of thirteen days. Development of blood islands, (*a*,) from the cells of the peripheral, mesenchymal mesoblasts (*mch*). Eosin-azure stain. 220 ×. (A.A.M.)

splanchnopleure and the entoderm gives rise to groups of spherical basophile cells (the *blood islands*) connected with one another by strands of elongated cells (Fig. 82). The peripheral cells of the islands and those of the strands become transformed into endothelial tubes. The endothelium secretes the blood plasma, which fills the tubes. In this way the first blood vessels, the yolk sac vessels, arise. The round cells of the islands are the first blood cells. In the first stages of development, the endothelial cells of the blood vessels in the area vasculosa are often seen to swell, and become free in the lumen as additional primitive blood cells (Fig. 83).

The first blood elements are hemocytoblasts. They are free mesenchymal cells and are usually called *primitive blood cells* (Fig. 83). Almost immediately after

their formation most of them elaborate hemoglobin and become *primitive erythroblasts* (Fig. 84). They accumulate large quantities of hemoglobin and finally cease dividing, although the nucleus remains in the cell. Such older forms are called *primitive erythrocytes*; they serve the growing embryo as oxygen carriers, but finally die out. They do not form definitive erythrocytes. A few of the primitive blood cells remain unchanged as ameboid basophile hemocytoblasts. The intravascular hemocytoblasts at these early stages sometimes form atypical megakaryocytes. Free phagocytes arise from the primitive endothelial cells and are shed into the lumen. These are the first macrophages of the embryo; they engulf degenerating blood cells. In the human yolk sac vessels, the hemocytoblasts later produce a few secondary erythroblasts (Fig. 85) identical with those in adult bone marrow.

The primitive wandering cells (hemocytoblasts) in the mesenchyme outside the yolk sac vessels produce a few heterophile and eosinophile granulocytes. The hemopoietic activity of the yolk sac in man continues but a short time, and the organ soon atrophies. When the yolk sac of the rat is transplanted to the anterior chamber of the eye, the hemocytoblasts produce great numbers of myelocytes instead of primitive erythroblasts (Block).

Body Mesenchyme. In the diffuse mesenchyme of the body, wandering cells of hemocytoblastic and macrophage appearance occasionally give rise to small extravascular groups of myelocytes and erythrocytes; most of these degenerate. The hemopoietic activity of the wandering cells in the diffuse mesenchyme soon subsides, but these same elements in the specialized blood-forming areas of the mesenchyme are the source of a most intense hemopoiesis.

Vascular Endothelium. In early embryonic stages the endothelium of the blood vessels is identical in its potencies with the common mesenchymal cells. Thus, in the yolk sac vessels and in the caudal portion of the aorta, the endothelial cells form clusters of hemocytoblasts. The endothelium of the vessels of the embryonic liver, bone marrow and spleen may take part for a short time in the production of hemocytoblasts. Later, this endothelium becomes the littoral cells of the macrophage system which either have lost or do not use their hemopoietic powers in the adult organism. In all the other vessels the endothelium loses its hemopoietic potency early (Chap. X).

Liver. The liver, the second blood-forming organ of the embryo, develops as a network of branching epithelial strands from the epithelium of the intestine. Large, thin-walled blood vessels are located in the meshes of this network from the very beginning. Between this endothelium and the epithelium are thin layers of mesenchyme which give rise to hemocytoblasts. They proliferate hemopoietically. The liver cells are soon outnumbered by the dense masses of extravascular definitive erythroblasts; a few megakaryocytes and myelocytes are also present.

The erythroblasts produce mature erythrocytes which

slip through the walls of the sinusoids and enter the general circulation. The endothelium of these vessels is transformed into a layer of macrophages which become the Kupffer cells of the adult. Toward the end of gestation the hemopoietic activity of the liver gradually subsides, so that only small foci of erythroblasts can be found in the liver of the newborn. These, too, soon disappear.

while the others develop into macrophages and fat cells. Argyrophile fibrils develop about them. The primitive endothelium of the vessels becomes the littoral macrophages in later stages.

Lymphatic Organs. The lymph nodes arise along the course of the lymphatics or in the walls of the primitive lymph sacs in relatively late stages of embryonic development. Here again, in circumscribed areas of

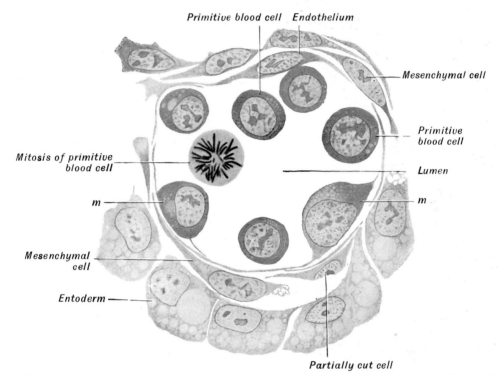

Fig. 83. Cross section of a vessel of the area vasculosa of a rabbit embryo of eight and one-half days (five somites). *m*, Rounding off of endothelial cells and their transformation into primitive blood cells. Eosin-azure stain. 1000 ×. (A.A.M.)

Bone Marrow. The third hemopoietic organ of the mammalian embryo is the bone marrow. The myeloid tissue develops from the primitive bone marrow, the mesenchyme which resorbs the cartilage in the bones of endochondral origin and fills the spaces between the bone trabeculae of the endochondral or periosteal bone. Here again, the process is the same in principle as in the diffuse mesenchyme of the body and in the liver. Some of the fixed mesenchymal cells become wandering cells of hemocytoblastic or macrophage type. These proliferate and form dense, extravascular clusters of erythroblasts, groups of myelocytes of the three different types, and megakaryocytes. Soon, especially in the older regions, as in the diaphyses of the long bones, a solid mass of myeloid tissue develops. Of the original fixed mesenchymal elements, only a few stellate cells remain between the meshes of the young blood cells; some of them remain as the primitive reticular cells of the stroma of the bone marrow,

the diffuse mesenchyme, many fixed mesenchymal cells are transformed into wandering cells. As in the other blood-forming organs, cells of hemocytoblastic and free macrophage types can be distinguished (Fig. 238). Wandering cells of the small lymphocyte type, rarely found in the bone marrow, now appear in large numbers. The number of large and small lymphocytes increases, in part, through continued mobilization of new, fixed mesenchymal cells, but mainly through intense mitotic proliferation of the free lymphocytes. The fixed mesenchymal cells which remain between the free cells become the cellular components of the reticular stroma, and in later stages elaborate argyrophile fibrils.

The lymphatic tissue in the embryo always contains many heterophile and eosinophile myelocytes and a few megakaryocytes and erythroblasts; these develop from the same wandering cells from which the small lymphocytes arise. Thus in the embryo of the mam-

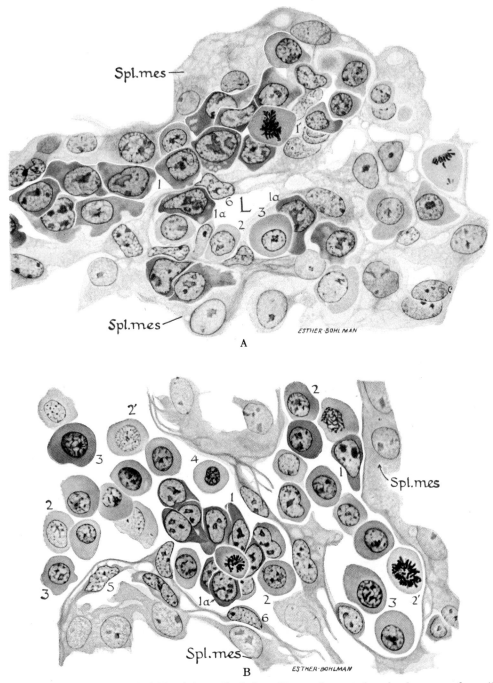

Fig. 84. Two sections through folds of the wall of the yolk sac of twenty-four-day human embryo (H1516 Univ. Chicago Emb. Coll.). A, Early stage of hematopoiesis, consisting of proliferating extravascular hemo-cytoblasts (1, 1′); L, Lumen of a small vessel containing a few primitive polychromatophile erythroblasts. B, Later stage of hematopoiesis showing transformation of hemocytoblasts (1) into primitive basophile eryth-roblasts (1a), primitive polychromatophile erythroblasts (2, 3) and primitive erythrocytes (4); 5, mesenchymal cells; 6, endothelium; Spl. mes, splanchnic mesothelium. Hematoxylin-eosin-azure II. 1100 ×. (From Bloom and Bartelmez: Am. J. Anat., 67: No. 1, July, 1940.)

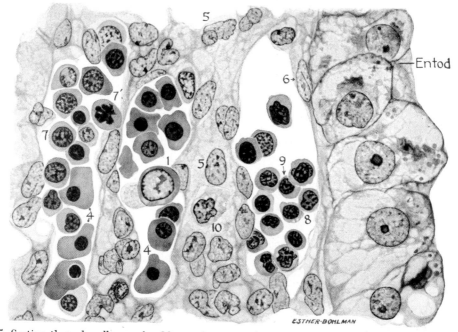

Fig. 85. Section through yolk sac of a 20-mm. human embryo. In addition to circulating primitive erythrocytes, there are two foci of developing polychromatophile definitive erythroblasts. *1*, Hemocytoblast; *4*, primitive erythrocytes; *5*, mesenchymal cells; *7* and *8*, early and late definitive polychromatophile erythroblasts with one in mitosis at *7'*; *9* normoblast; *10*, lymphoid wandering cell. Hematoxylin-eosin-azure II. 1100 ×. (From Bloom and Bartelmez: Am. J. Anat., 67: No. 1, July, 1940.)

mals the myeloid and the lymphoid elements are not sharply separated from each other.

In the *spleen* the lymphocytes develop in much the same way as in the lymph nodes, although more erythrocytes and other myeloid cells are formed. Some myelocytes also develop from the lymphoid wandering cells in the embryonic thymus.

Loose Connective Tissue. When connective tissue fibers appear in the mesenchyme, this tissue becomes the connective tissue. The exact moment when a mesenchymal cell changes into a fibroblast has not been determined, because there is no appreciable change in structure. In fact, in all regions of the body some fixed mesenchymal cells remain undifferentiated, mainly along the capillaries.

At the later embryonic stages the vast majority of the wandering cells in the connective tissue are macrophages; hemocytoblasts are rare except in the primordia of the lymphatic organs and the bone marrow.

Many of the wandering cells persist as such in the adult connective tissue. Most of them, however, become fixed macrophages. The primitive wandering cells also give rise to mast cells, which then proliferate mitotically.

The appearance of the primordia of the white and of the brown fat tissue is closely connected with the development of networks of blood vessels. The fibrillar intercellular substance of the connective tissue around the growing capillaries undergoes a peculiar dissolution, and the mesenchymal cells in these areas

proliferate and form loose, cellular networks. Although some consider such accumulations of cells as specific, primitive fat organs, it is more probable that these elements are common mesenchymal cells, which accumulate fat droplets and become fat cells. In the primordia of the brown fat tissue, stellate cells assume a polyhedral form, and the accumulated fat droplets fail to fuse.

POTENCIES OF DEVELOPMENT OF THE LYMPHOID STEM CELLS OF THE LYMPHATIC AND MYELOID TISSUES

Nearly all hematologists agree that the various myeloid elements of the bone marrow develop through proliferation and differentiation from a basophile free stem cell—designated here as the hemocytoblast. In the lymphatic tissue the small lymphocytes develop from young forms of larger size which have exactly the same structure as the hemocytoblasts in the bone marrow. *The question arises whether the lymphoid cells in both tissues have identical or different developmental potencies.* If they are identical, then all blood elements of the adult originate from one common stem cell which may appropriately be called the hemocytoblast (the "unitarian theory" of hemopoiesis). If, on the contrary, the large lymphoid cells of the lymphatic and of the myeloid tissues differ in their potencies, then each of these two tissues has a specific stem cell, and one of these could be called the *lymphoblast*, the other the *myeloblast* ("dualistic" theory of hemopoiesis). The "trialistic" theory holds that the monocytes, too, have a distinct stem cell. There are many variations of each of these theories.

The sum of all the facts speaks more in favor of the unitarian than of either of the pluralistic theories. Structural differences between the lymphoblasts and myeloblasts are

In Lower Vertebrates. The boundary between myeloid and lymphoid tissue is completely effaced in the lower vertebrates. The developing lymphoid and myeloid elements are everywhere mixed with each other.

In Embryonic Development. In all hematopoietic foci in the mammalian embryo both lymphoid and myeloid elements arise from the same lymphoid wandering cell (see Embryonic Development of Blood and Connective Tissue, p. 93).

In Tissue Cultures. If a fragment of a lymph node of an adult rabbit is cultivated

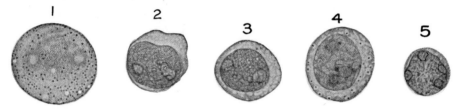

Fig. 86. *1*, Myeloblast with azure granules from normal human bone marrow; *2*, myeloblast from the blood in chronic myeloid leukemia; *3, 4*, lymphoblasts from the blood in chronic lymphatic leukemia; *5*, lymphoblast from the blood in subacute lymphatic leukemia. (Cells 2 to 5 are from pathological human blood.) May-Grünwald-Giemsa-stained dry smears. (After Downey.)

not constantly present, and all the various morphological criteria for separating them which have been proposed, such as detailed structure of the nucleus, number of nucleoli (Fig. 86), mitochondria, supravital staining, oxidase and peroxidase reaction, are unreliable. Lymphocytes and myeloblasts have the same type of movement in tissue culture (DeBruyn). In fact, the stem cells which appear in the blood in leukemia are now frequently called "blasts" by most clinical hematologists until changes in the blood picture or in the clinical course of the disease permit the classification into myeloid or lymphatic type.

Much confusion is due to the fact that many hematological theories rest almost exclusively on studies of the peripheral blood of man in health and disease. The unitarian theory, however, is based on comparative and experimental histogenetic studies of blood and connective tissues in both embryonic and adult animals and is in agreement with results obtained from studies on *inflammation, extramedullary hematopoiesis* and *tissue cultures*.

in a medium containing bone marrow extract, the large lymphocytes (lymphoblasts or hemocytoblasts) may differentiate into myelocytes and megakaryocytes. Lymphocytes of the thoracic duct of ascaris-immunized rabbits have also been observed to develop into heterophile leukocytes in cultures containing bone marrow extract and ascaris extract (Fig. 87). The myeloblasts of the blood in myeloblastic leukemia develop into macrophages and fibroblasts in tissue culture, just as do the lymphocytes of lymphatic leukemia under the same conditions. The claim that myeloblasts can produce only myelocytes and erythroblasts is thus refuted. These experiments also refute the so-called "trialistic theories" of blood formation, for, in these cultures, both myeloblasts and lymphocytes often pass through a monocyte stage before becoming macrophages.

Extramedullary Myelopoiesis. Under physiological conditions in adult mammals, and especially in man, the formation of the myeloid elements is confined to the bone marrow. In various abnormal conditions *ex-*

tramedullary or *ectopic myelopoiesis* or *myeloid metaplasia* is of common occurrence.

Local myelopoiesis has been observed in the sclerotic aortic wall, in the adrenal and in other places; it develops after ligation of the renal artery and vein of the adult rabbit. More generalized extramedullary myelopoie-

that the myelocytes and erythroblasts in extramedullary myelopoiesis originate in several different ways: (1) Sometimes the first myeloid elements appear in the lumen of the venous capillaries, where they originate from lymphoid cells which circulate in the blood. From the viewpoint of the unitarian theory

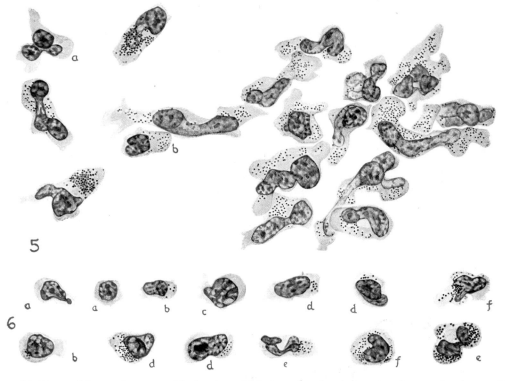

Fig. 87. Heterophile myelocytes and leukocytes which have developed from lymphocytes in tissue culture. The thoracic duct lymph of a rabbit immunized to ascaris extract was cultured with connective tissue in plasma and bone marrow and ascaris extracts. Cell *5a* is an unchanged lymphocyte; *5b* is an early myelocyte with a lymphocytic nucleus. The cells of 6 show stages in the development of lymphocytes *a, c* into myelocytes *b, d, e, f*. Hematoxylin-eosin-azure II. 1490 ×. (Drawn by Miss E. Bohlman, after Bloom, 1937. Courtesy of Wistar Press.)

sis occurs in various parts of the body in leukemia and certain intoxications and infections. It can be produced through repeated bleeding or chronic poisoning with blood-destroying substances. As a rule, the spleen is the first organ affected. Later the liver, the lymph nodes, the adrenal and other organs become involved. Nearly always, it is the heterophile and eosinophile myelocytes which first appear in the new place; megakaryocytes come later, and finally erythroblasts develop.

Experimental investigations have shown

the latter are identical with lymphocytes. The newly formed myeloid elements may pass through the wall of the vessels into the tissue, where they continue to proliferate. (2) In the lymphoid organs, including the spleen, the free basophile cells of the tissue, the lymphocytes, are often the source of the myeloid elements; this process even occurs in the germinal centers where medium-sized and small lymphocytes transform directly into myelocytes. (3) In still other cases the first myelocytes may develop directly from undifferentiated perivascular cells or primitive reticular cells with or without passing through a hemocytoblast stage (p. 90).

Origin of the Monocyte. The questions of the origin and nature of the monocyte are among the most debated problems in morphological hematology. Some believe the monocyte to develop from specific monoblasts in the bone marrow, but the morphological specificity of the precursors has not been proved. Myeloblasts from the blood in myeloblastic leukemia pass through monocyte-like stages as they develop into macrophages in tissue culture. Most of the recent investigations indicate that endothelium does not furnish ameboid cells in the adult mammal.

The monocytes of the blood do not store vital dyes, as do the macrophages, both large and small. It is clear, however, that the monocytes, as they develop into macrophages, soon take on the ability to store vital dyes. While it is possible that monocytes may develop directly from the reticular cells of the blood-forming organs, such a process has never been demonstrated.

The unitarian hematologists consider the lymphocytes to be the source of monocytes. They point out that in blood smears of most animals it is impossible to separate all the monocytes as a cell type distinct from lymphocytes. In the rat and, to some extent, the monkey, supravital staining with neutral red and Janus green shows the monocytes to be connected with the common small lymphocytes by a complete series of transitional forms. Similar transition forms between lymphocytoid and monocytoid wandering cells are to be found in the loose connective tissue. In inflammation the hematogenous lymphocytes and monocytes rapidly become ameboid phagocytic elements (polyblasts). In this progressive development the lymphocytes often pass through a transitory state in which they cannot be distinguished from monocytes and, among other characteristics, have a typical neutral red rosette. In cultures of normal and leukemic blood leukocytes, as well as of lymphocytes of rabbit lymph, the small lymphocytes change into monocytoid cells and then into large macrophages and

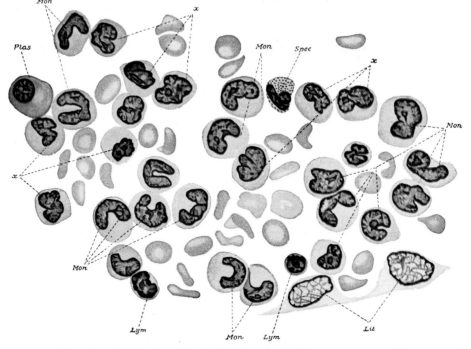

Fig. 88. Section through a splenic sinus of a rabbit infected with *L. monocytogenes*: *Mon*, monocytes; *Lym*, lymphocytes; *x*, transitions from lymphocytes to monocytes; *Plas*, plasma cell; *Lit*, lining (littoral) cells; *Spec*, heterophile leukocyte. Hematoxylin-eosin-azure stain. 1200 ×. (After Bloom.)

finally into fibroblasts. In rabbits in which an extensive monocytosis has been produced, as by *B. monocytogenes*, the monocytes develop by individual hypertrophy from the common smaller lymphocytes. In none of this experimental material is there any evidence for the existence of a specific monoblast different from a lymphocyte (hemocytoblast).

The majority of the facts support the idea that monocytes are lymphocytes, that is, hemocytoblasts, which have developed somewhat in the phagocytic direction. The main site of this transformation is the blood in the venous sinusoids of the spleen, liver and bone marrow, where transitional forms between lymphocytes and monocytes are common, especially in experimentally produced monocytoses (Fig. 88).

GENETIC INTERRELATIONSHIPS AND POTENCIES OF THE CELLS OF THE BLOOD AND LYMPH, THE CONNECTIVE TISSUE AND ENDOTHELIUM

From a general histological point of view, three large groups of cells can be distinguished in the connective tissue and the blood: (1) fixed, highly specialized elements. As fibroblasts they produce collagen; as endothelium, they line blood channels; and as chondrocytes and osteocytes, they form the cells of cartilage and bone. (2) Fixed or free cells which phagocytose, store vital dyes and other colloidal substances, and play important roles in the general metabolism and especially in the "defense" reactions. These are the *macrophages*. (3) Free cells which circulate in the blood or are scattered throughout the connective tissue. These are the *hemocytes*; among them are to be distinguished: (*a*) the hemocytoblasts (lymphocytes) which serve as stem cells for (*b*) granulocytes, monocytes, erythrocytes and megakaryocytes.

The relations between all these cells are not clearly observable under physiological conditions. Under pathological or experimental conditions, when there is an increased destruction of cells and a corresponding intense new formation, the genetic relationships may be analyzed more easily. Three

processes especially favor such analysis: (1) the changes in the tissue in the local "defense" reaction, that is, in inflammation; (2) the reactions of tissue in culture; and (3) extramedullary myelopoiesis.

It is clear from such studies that the various-sized lymphocytes (hemocytoblasts) are all endowed with hemopoietic, phagocytic and fibrocytic potencies. The lymphocytes are free, mesenchymal cells which are scattered everywhere in the tissues of the adult body and circulate in the blood and lymph. Under normal conditions they keep the appearance of lymphocytes, but, in response to certain pathological stimuli, they may become granulocytes, erythroblasts, macrophages, and so on. They may be looked upon as an easily movable mesenchymal reserve.

It has been shown that fixed cells with unrestricted mesenchymal potencies are present in the connective tissues of the adult mammals. According to various investigators, these are fibroblasts or endothelial cells or fixed macrophages. But the most convincing evidence indicates that the original mesenchymal potencies are retained by cells scattered in the loose connective tissue along the blood vessels, by the primitive reticular cells of the hemopoietic tissues, and by some cells lining the venous sinuses of the liver.

Undifferentiated Fixed Cells; Primitive Reticular Cells. In the lymphatic and myeloid tissue the development of fixed and free macrophages from the primitive reticular cells can be observed in the body and in cultures of these tissues. Lymphoid cells, hemocytoblasts, also originate from the same source, particularly in the germinal centers. In the omentum the new formation of fixed macrophages from perivascular, undifferentiated cells has been described. In extramedullary myelopoiesis the myelocytes can often be traced directly to perivascular, fixed cells. If foreign substances, especially foreign proteins, are introduced into the organism, the macrophage system which has to dispose of them shows an increase in the size and number of its cells all over the body.

The question, which cells of the connective tissue represent undifferentiated elements, is

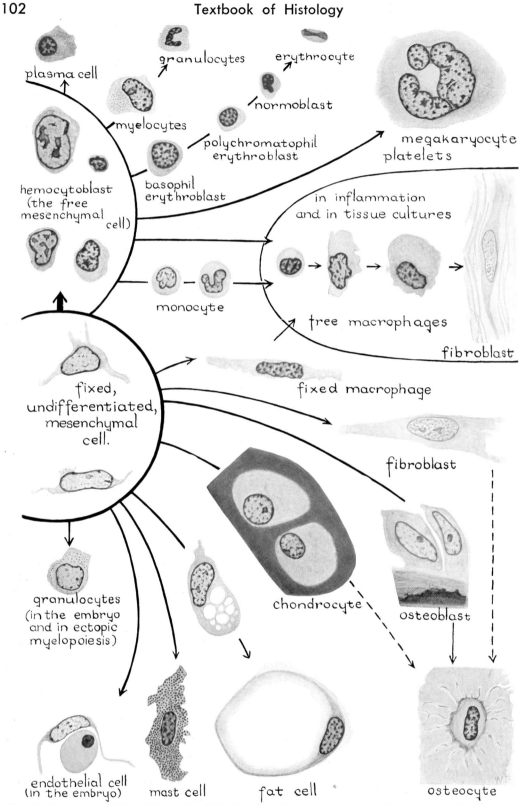

Fig. 89. Interrelationships of the cells of the blood and connective tissues of mammals. All cells are from human tissues. The dotted lines indicate unusual transformations. The lymphocytes are included with the hemocytoblasts. Hematoxylin-eosin-azure II. 720 ×. (W. B.)

answered in different ways by various authors. A few investigators believe that, under the influence of external stimuli, all fibroblasts can produce any other cell type of the blood and connective tissue. This has not been confirmed. According to another opinion, macrophages of every kind are endowed with full mesenchymal potencies.

But the histogenesis of the lymphocytes of the lymphatic tissue shows that the lymphocytes arise, not from the fixed macrophages, but from the primitive reticular cells, which are also the source of the fixed macrophages. The same is true for the development of myelocytes in extramedullary myelopoiesis in the lymph nodes. The question is undecided whether a fixed macrophage (phagocytic reticular cell) can cease its phagocytic activity and become a primitive reticular cell again, with all the potentialities of this cell type.

REFERENCES

The most important source book in English is Downey's Handbook of Hematology, New York, 1938.

Awrorow, P. P., and Timofejewsky, A. D.: Kultivierungsversuche von leukämischen Blute. Virchows Arch., 184:216, 1914.

Bjørneboe, M., Gormsen, H., and Lundquist, F.: Further Experimental Studies on the Rôle of the Plasma Cells as Antibody Producers. J. Immunol., 55:121, 1947.

Block, M.: An Experimental Analysis of Hematopoiesis in the Rat Yolk Sac. Anat. Rec., 96:289, 1946.

Bloom, W.: The Origin and Nature of the Monocyte. Folia Haematol., 37:1, 1928. Mammalian Lymph in Tissue Culture. From Lymphocyte to Fibroblast. Arch. f. exp. Zellforsch., 5:269, 1928.

Bloom, M. A., and Bloom, W.: The Radiosensitivity of Erythroblasts. J. Lab. & Clin. Med., 32:654, 1947.

Bloom, M. L., and Wislocki, G. B.: The Localization of Lipids in Human Blood and Bone Marrow Cells. Blood, J. Hematology, 5:79, 1950.

Conway, E. A.: Cyclic Changes in Lymphatic Nodules in the Rat. Anat. Rec., 67:487, 1937. Reaction of Lymphatic Tissue in Early Stages of *Bacterium monocytogenes* Infection. Arch. Path., 25:200, 1938.

Custer, R. P.: Atlas of the Blood and Bone Marrow. Philadelphia, W. B. Saunders Company, 1949.

Danchakoff, V.: Origin of the Blood Cells. Development of the Hematopoietic Organs and Regeneration of the Blood Cells from the Standpoint of the Monophyletic School. Anat. Rec., 10:397, 1916.

Doan, C. A.: Capillaries of Bone Marrow. Bull. Johns Hopkins Hosp., 33:222, 1922. Current Views on the Origin and Maturation of the Cells of the Blood. J. Lab. & Clin. Med., 17:887, 1932.

Dougherty, T. F., and White, A.: An Evaluation of Alterations Produced in Lymphoid Tissue by Pituitary-Adrenal Cortical Secretion. J. Lab. & Clin. Med., 32:584, 1947.

Downey, H.: The Myeloblast—Its Occurrence under Normal and Pathologic Conditions, and Its Relations to Lymphocytes and Other Blood Cells. Folia Haematol., Archiv., 34:65, 145, 1927.

Drinker, C. K., Drinker, K. R., and Lund, C. C.: The Circulation in the Mammalian Bone Marrow. Am. J. Physiol., 62:1, 1922.

Hall, B. E., and Watkins, C. H.: Experience with Pteroylglutamic (Synthetic Folic) Acid in the Treatment of Pernicious Anemia. J. Lab. & Clin. Med., 32:622, 1947.

Hamre, C. J.: Hematopoiesis in the Bone Marrow of Rats Recovering from Nutritional Anemia. J. Lab. & Clin. Med., 32:756, 1947.

Jolly, J.: Traité technique d'hématologie. Paris, 1923.

Jones, O. P.: Morphologic, Physiologic, Chemical and Biologic Distinction of Megaloblasts. Arch. Path., 35:752, 1943.

Jordan, H. E.: The Relation of Lymphoid Tissue to the Process of Blood Production in Avian Bone Marrow. Am. J. Anat., 59:249, 1936.

Kindred, J. E.: A Quantitative Study of the Hemopoietic Organs of Young Adult Albino Rats. Am. J. Anat., 71:207, 1942.

Latta, J. and Henderson, J. W.: The Hemopoietic Disturbances Induced in the Albino Rat by Insulin Administration. Folia Haematol., 57:206, 1937.

Maximow, A.: Bindegewebe und blutbildende Gewebe. Handb. d. mikr. Anat. (v. Möllendorff), (2), Pt. 1, Berlin, 1927.

Osgood, E. E., and Seaman, A. J.: The Cellular Composition of Normal Bone Marrow as Obtained by Sternal Puncture. Physiol. Rev., 24:46, 1944.

Reinhardt, W. O.: Growth of Lymph Nodes, Thymus and Spleen, and Output of Thoracic Duct Lymphocytes in the Normal Rat. Anat. Rec., 94:197, 1946.

Sabin, F. R.: Bone Marrow, in Cowdry's Special Cytology. 2d ed. New York, (1), 505, 1932.

Schultze, M. O.: Metallic Elements and Blood Formation. Physiol. Rev., 20:37, 1940.

Schwind, J. L.: The Supravital Method in the Study of the Cytology of Blood and Marrow Cells. Blood, 5:597, 1950.

Taliaferro, W. H., and Mulligan, H. W.: The Histopathology of Malaria, with Special Reference to the Function and Origin of the Macrophages in Defence. Indian Med. Res. Memoirs, No. 29, 1, 1937.

Thorell, B.: The Relation of the Synthesis of Hemoglobin to the Cellular Growth during Normal and

Certain Pathological Conditions. Acta Path., 25: 54, 1948.

Weidenreich, F.: Die Leucocyten und verwandte Zellformen. Wiesbaden, 1911.

Wislocki, G. B., and Dempsey, E. W.: Observations on the Chemical Cytology of Normal Blood and Hemopoietic Tissues. Anat. Rec., 96:249, 1946.

Yoffey, J. M.: The Mammalian Lymphocyte. Biol. Rev., 25:314, 1950.

VI. CARTILAGE

Cartilage, a specialized, fibrous connective tissue, forms most of the temporary skeleton of the embryo, provides a model in which most bones develop, and is an important part of their growth mechanism. It persists in adult mammals as parts of joints, and in the respiratory passages and the ears. The intercellular component of cartilage predominates over the cells, which occupy special cavities within it. Because of differences in their intercellular substance, several types of cartilage may be distinguished; of these, the important are the hyaline, elastic, and fibrous varieties. Hyaline cartilage is the most widespread and the most characteristic, the others being modifications of it. Blood vessels supplying other tissues occasionally pass through cartilage, but it has none of its own. With the exception of its naked surfaces in joint cavities, cartilage is always covered externally by a firmly attached layer of dense connective tissue—the *perichondrium*.

Hyaline or Glasslike Cartilage. In adult mammals hyaline cartilage is found on the ventral ends of the ribs, on the surfaces of bones within joints, and in the respiratory passages. It is much more widespread in the embryo. It is a flexible and somewhat elastic, semitransparent mass with an opalescent bluish tint, similar to that of frosted glass.

Cells of Cartilage (Chondrocytes). The cells of hyaline cartilage are usually spherical, although there are many exceptions. Thus, in the layers of the cartilage under the perichondrium or under the free joint surface, the cells are flattened in a plane parallel with the surface and, in the lower layers, are hemispherical or angular because of mutual pressure. On the border between cartilage and perichondrium there are intermediate

forms between cartilage cells and ordinary fibroblasts.

The body of the cartilage cell completely fills the cavity which it occupies in the interstitial substance. In adult, higher vertebrates, the cartilage cells rarely have processes, and, since they are not connected with the wall of the cavity, they may drop out if the cavity is opened. Occasionally in the cartilage of

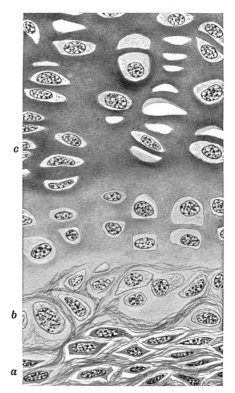

Fig. 90. Hyaline cartilage from xiphoid process of rat. *a,* Transition layer adjacent to perichondrium; *b,* continuation of collagenous fibers from perichondrium into interstitial substance of cartilage; *c,* columns of isogenous groups of cartilage cells, some of which have fallen out of the cavities. Eosin-azure stain. 750 ×. (A.A.M.)

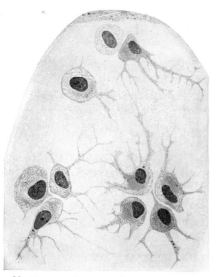

Fig. 91. Groups of cells with long, branching, anastomosing processes in the homogeneous interstitial substance of a cartilage of *Sepia officinalis*. 330 ×. (A.A.M.)

surrounded by a solid interstitial substance, they divide several times in rapid succession. In this way individual cells give rise to closely adherent groups, imprisoned in the intercellular matrix. As these groups arise by division of one cell, they are called *isogenous*.

Interstitial Substance. When the cells are closely packed, the interstitial substance appears, in section, as a framework of thin cross beams surrounding the cartilage cavities. But more often it appears as a solid mass in which separate cells and groups of cells are dispersed at some distance from one another. In fresh condition and after ordinary fixation, the substance seems to be homogeneous, because the index of refraction of its collagenous fibers and the binding material which covers them is the same. However, the layers adjacent to the cell cavities and forming their walls are always distinguishable by their greater refractility, by their somewhat different staining

the joints of higher vertebrates, and frequently in lower vertebrates and in early embryonic stages, the cytoplasm may extend into processes which enter the interstitial tissue (Fig. 91); the cells correspond in this respect with those of ordinary connective tissue.

The cytoplasm of the cartilage cells contains long mitochondria, vacuoles, fat droplets and variable amounts of glycogen. The vacuoles in the peripheral portion of the cell body frequently are so large as to distend the cell like a bubble. Around the nucleus a cytocentrum with centrioles and a Golgi net can be distinguished. The nucleus contains one or several spherical nucleoli. Mitotic figures are practically never found in cartilage cells in the mature organism. In the cartilage of the adult the cells are usually gathered into compact groups. These may be irregularly placed, rounded, or stretched into small columns of flattened cells. In growing bones the cartilage cells form characteristic columns before they are invaded by advancing bone (Fig. 113). Within the groups the interstitial substance may be compressed into thin bands between the separate cells or may even be absent. This distribution of the cartilage cells is the result of their multiplication during the last stages of development. After they are

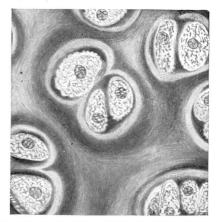

Fig. 92. Hyaline cartilage of a calf. 400 ×. (Redrawn and modified after R. Krause.)

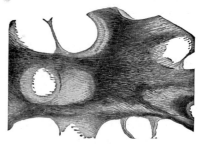

Fig. 93. Portion of tracheal cartilage of guinea pig from which all constituents except the collagenous fibers have been removed by digestion with trypsin. (Redrawn after Ruppricht.)

reactions and, sometimes, by their concentric striation. They enclose the cartilage cells and are called *cartilage capsules*. The capsules belong to the intercellular substance, being its youngest layers and those nearest to the cells.

Despite its amorphous appearance, the interstitial substance is thoroughly permeated by thin fibrils which either form a dense feltwork running in all directions, or gather into definitely oriented bundles. The collagenous fibers can be demonstrated with the silver impregnation methods or by digesting the tissue with trypsin, which does not affect the fibers. The collagen from cartilage seems to be much the same chemically as that from the loose connective tissue.

The interstitial substance of hyaline cartilage is markedly basophile, owing to its content of *chondromucoid*, a glycoprotein which, on hydrolysis, yields the sulfonated polysaccharide, *chondroitin sulfate*.

The intercellular substance immediately surrounding the capsules is often especially basophile, presumably owing to a concentration of chondromucoid in these areas or to a change in its condition. Based on chemical studies of bovine nasal cartilage, Partridge has reported cartilage matrix to be composed almost exclusively of two major components, proteins of the collagen group and chondroitin sulfate.

Using the same methods that were applied to the analysis of muscle (see p. 5), a first attempt has recently been reported at a histochemical characterization of the inorganic and organic composition of the cellular and extracellular compartments of hyaline cartilage (Eichelberger and co-workers). From calculations of analyses of a typical specimen of articular cartilage, it appears that about one-third is intracellular phase and about two-thirds extracellular. The intracellular phase consists of one-third protoplasmic solids and two-thirds water. About one-quarter of the extracellular phase is made up of solids, of which about two-thirds are connective tissue components and one-third chondroitin sulfate. Water constitutes about three-quarters of the extracellular phase, and is associated with the connective tissue and chondroitin sulfate components and with the ultrafiltrate derived from plasma.

Because cartilage is devoid of blood vessels and forms large, compact masses, the nutritive fluid from the blood vessels in the perichondrium must pass through the interstitial substance, often for considerable distances, to reach the cells. A system of liquid-conducting canalicules, described as passing from one cell capsule to another, was considered a possible means for transferring substances through cartilage. It is now believed that these canalicules are artefacts. Direct observation of the action of a nontoxic stain upon living cartilage shows that the dye is quickly and evenly absorbed by the interstitial substance. In probably the same manner, the interstitial substance is permeated in the living condition by the tissue fluids from the perichondrium.

Elastic Cartilage. In mammals this variety of cartilage is found in the external ear, the walls of the external auditory and eustachian tubes, the epiglottis, and in parts of the corniculate and cuneiform cartilages. It differs from hyaline cartilage macroscopically by its yellowish color and by its greater opacity, flexibility and elasticity.

Its cells are similar to those of hyaline cartilage; they are of the same rounded shape, are also surrounded by capsules, and are scattered singly or in isogenous groups of two or three cells. The interstitial substance differs from that of hyaline cartilage by being penetrated in all directions by frequently branching fibers, which give all the tests for elastin. They form a network which is often so dense that the amorphous substance filling its loops is obscured; sometimes the network is especially dense at the periphery of the cells. In the layers beneath the perichondrium, the feltwork of the elastic fibers is looser. The elastic fibers of the cartilage continue into those of the perichondrium.

Fibrocartilage. Fibrocartilage occurs as indistinctly outlined, small accumulations in a few places in the bodies of mammals. It is found in the intervertebral disks, certain articular cartilages, in the symphysis pubis, in the ligamentum teres femoris, in the places

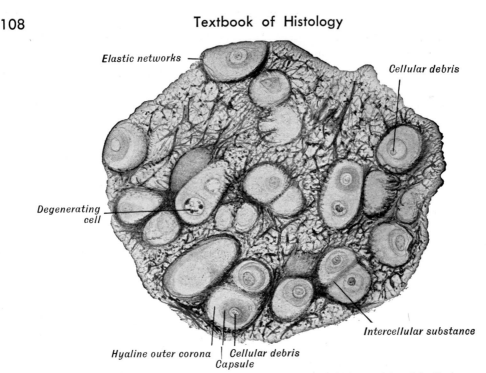

Fig. 94. Elastic cartilage of human ear. Orcein stain. 380 ×. (After Schaffer.)

of attachment of certain tendons to bones. Here, again, the tissue contains typical cartilage cells with homogeneous capsules which lie either singly or in pairs, and sometimes in larger groups extended lengthwise. The interstitial substance contains thick, compact, collagenous bundles, parallel with one another and separated only by narrow clefts into which are squeezed the encapsulated cells. Usually little is seen of the amorphous interstitial substance.

Fibrocartilage is closely associated with the dense connective tissue of the capsules and ligaments of joints. It is a transitional form between cartilage and connective tissue, and this gradual transformation can be observed, in the embryonic histogenesis as well as in the adult organism, wherever there is fibrocartilage. Thus, in the intervertebral disks, the hyaline cartilage connected with the vertebrae shows distinct collagenous fibers in the apparently homogeneous interstitial substance. Then these fibers collect into thick bundles which almost entirely displace the homogeneous substance, while the cartilage cells retain their spherical form and their capsules. Finally, this typical fibrocartilage goes over into connective tissue, the cells of which are provided with processes and are devoid of capsules.

Other Varieties of Cartilage and Chondroid Tissue. There is a transitory phase in the embryonic development of hyaline cartilage when it is composed of closely adjacent vesicular cells, provided with thin capsules, and with collagenous fibers in its interstitial substance. In this undeveloped condition the cartilage may remain throughout life in certain parts of the body of higher organisms. It occurs often in lower vertebrates (fishes, amphibians; as in the sesamoid cartilage of the tendon of Achilles in frogs) and is still more common in invertebrates. Such tissue has been called *pseudocartilage, fibrohyaline tissue, vesicular supporting tissue* or *chondroid tissue*. This tissue serves as a mechanical support for other parts of the body.

The tissue composing the *notochord* of vertebrates has a similar structure. Here, there is a shaft of variable thickness which consists of large, closely packed vesicular cells distended with fluid and with an elastic membrane. The notochordal tissue has a different embryological origin from that of the cartilage and of the other connective tissues.

Histogenesis of Cartilage. In those parts of the embryo where cartilage will develop, the mesenchyme cells round up and the spaces between them become smaller. In most cases, at early stages in the formation of cartilage, collagenous fibrils are present in the intercellular substance. This acidophilic material becomes enclosed by the basophile intercellular substance characteristic of cartilage, which stains metachromatically (purple) with methylene azure. It is probably a secretion of the cells and masks the collagenous fibrils embedded in it.

The cells enclosed by the interstitial substance soon acquire the distinctiveness of cartilage cells. They accumulate large amounts of fluid in vacuoles in their cytoplasm and become spherical or, through mutual compression, polyhedral. Mitoses may be observed among them for a long period; during the constriction of the cytoplasm in such a division, a new partition of interstitial substance quickly develops and separates the two daughter cells. Some cells atrophy, become compressed between neighboring cells, and eventually disappear.

With the gradual increase of the interstitial substance, there appears a thin, shining layer—the capsule—along the line of its contact with the cytoplasm of the cartilage cells. This structure becomes progressively thicker, developing in the same manner as the rest of the interstitial tissue, of which it represents the youngest layers. The multiplication of the cells by mitosis and the increase in mass of the intercellular substance are called *interstitial growth*.

The mesenchyme surrounding the cartilage primordium forms a special layer, the *perichondrium*, which merges gradually with the cartilage on one side and the adjacent connective tissue on the other. Throughout embryonic life there is a constant transformation of layers of this connective tissue into cartilage. Here the acidophile collagenous fibers of the dense connective tissue of the perichondrium are arranged in flat bundles; these are gradually covered with the basophile, cartilaginous ground substance. At the same time the fibroblasts of the connective tissue lose their spindle shape, change into spherical cells, and thus are transformed directly into cartilage cells surrounded by capsules. This process is called *appositional growth*; it probably contributes more to the mass of the cartilage than does the interstitial growth. The ability of the perichondrium to form cartilage persists, although latent, in the adult organism.

Most of the hyaline cartilage of the embryonic

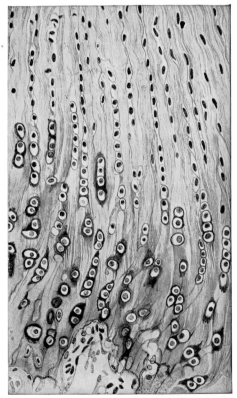

Fig. 95. Low-power drawing of insertion of tendon into the tibia of a rat. Note the direct transformation of rows of tendon cells (top) into cartilage cells surrounded by deeply staining cartilaginous matrix. Hematoxylin-eosin-azure II. From a preparation of F. C. McLean. (Drawn by Miss A. Nixon.)

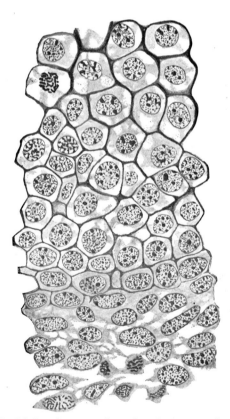

Fig. 96. Development of cartilage from mesenchyme in a 15-mm. guinea pig embryo. The mesenchyme (below) gradually merges into the protochondral tissue with interstitial substance (above). Note mitoses. 750 ×. (A.A.M.)

skeleton is later replaced by bone (Chap. VII). Some cartilages are completely absorbed, as is the case with Meckel's cartilage.

At the site of the future elastic cartilage in the embryo, there is at first connective tissue containing fibroblasts and wavy fibrillar bundles which do not give characteristic reactions for either collagen or elastin. These indifferent fibers apparently are partly transformed into elastic fibers. The cells acquire capsules and become cartilage elements. On the surface of the elastic cartilage there is also a perichondrium which also initiates appositional growth of the cartilage during embryonic life.

Fibrocartilage develops in much the same way as ordinary connective tissue. In the beginning there are typical fibroblasts separated by a large amount of fibrillar substance. Then these cells become round, are surrounded by capsules, and are directly transformed into cartilage cells. The interstitial substance becomes infiltrated only slightly, if at all, with the basophile, amorphous, binding mass.

Regeneration of Cartilage. After a wound or excision of a portion of living hyaline cartilage in adult mammals, an independent regeneration of the cartilage does not take place, according to most observers. In the injured area only necrotic and atrophic changes can be seen in the cells. The defect is soon filled by newly formed connective tissue, which grows in from the perichondrium or nearest fascia. Then the fibroblasts of this granulation tissue become round, produce capsules around themselves, and may become transformed into new cartilage cells. Meanwhile, the fibrillar, interstitial substance of the scar tissue becomes homogeneous and gives rise to new interstitial substance in the same manner as in the embryonic development of cartilage. Accordingly, in adult organisms, new cartilage tissue is formed by metaplasia of the loose connective tissue.

Such a metaplasia sometimes takes place in connective tissue under the influence of simple mechanical forces acting from the outside, such as pressure, particularly when combined with friction. It is claimed that the presence of cartilage on the joint surfaces of bones is related to the constant mechanical influences to which a normal joint is subjected during its function. When these mechanical conditions disappear, as happens in dislocation of bones, the cartilage often undergoes dedifferentiation. On the other hand, cartilage is laid down in the primordia of the joint surfaces in the embryo at a time when there are probably no mechanical forces acting on the joint.

Regressive Changes in Cartilage. Calcification, the most important regressive change in cartilage, precedes and is closely related to one type of bone development (intracartilaginous ossification). The cartilage cells become arranged in groups as in a vertebra, or in more or less irregular columns separated by wide, parallel bands of interstitial tissue, as in the epiphysis of a long bone. In proceeding from the zone where cartilage cells are multiplying toward the area where bone formation will occur, one finds the cartilage cells becoming larger and their glycogen content rising greatly (zone of hypertrophic cartilage cells). This zone also contains much alkaline phosphatase, whose function here is not clear. Still closer to the zone of ossification, the matrix becomes calcified and the cartilage cells lose their glycogen. Minute granules of calcium phosphate and carbonate are deposited in the interstitial substance, primarily in the vicinity of the cells. As these become larger and merge, the cartilage becomes opaque, hard and brittle. The great majority of the cells degenerate as vascular connective tissue invades the calcified cartilage preceding the formation of bone. Those few cartilage cells

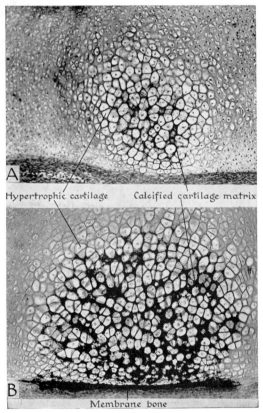

Fig. 97. Two stages in the calcification of the cartilage model of the calcaneus in rats; A, two days and, B, four days after birth. The calcium salts appear black because of the silver nitrate stain. Undecalcified preparations stained with von Kossa's method and H+E, 75 ×. (After Bloom and Bloom.)

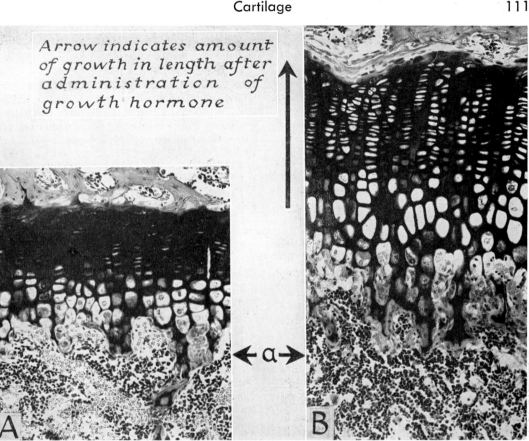

Fig. 98. Photomicrographs of proximal metaphysis of tibias of young rats to show effects of growth hormone. A, Atrophic cartilage of hypophysectomized rat; B, hypertrophy and growth of cartilage with new bone formation in hypophysectomized rat after injection for four days with purified growth hormone. a, Tip of spongiosa. Zenker-formol, H+E. 165 ×.

which do not perish probably turn into cells of bone. The process of ossification is described in Chapter VII. In man, ossification may take place in certain cartilages of the larynx as early as twenty years of age.

Hyaline cartilage may undergo the so-called *asbestos transformation*. Within the homogeneous intercellular substance, parallel fibers are deposited which have nothing in common with collagenous fibers. They do not swell in acetic acid, but dissolve in boiling water and in low concentrations of alkalies. They give the tissue a silky, glossy appearance similar to that of asbestos; they spread over wide areas and may lead to a softening of the tissue and even to the formation of spaces in it. It has been reported that new cartilage may develop in these spaces. In elastic as well as in hyaline cartilage, calcification and asbestos transformation may take place with advancing age.

Histophysiological Remarks. Cartilage in joints has the remarkable property of sustaining great weight and at the same time allow-

ing the bones which carry this weight to move easily and smoothly against one another. In other places, such as the ear and the respiratory passages, cartilage serves as a pliable yet resistant framework which prevents the collapse of the passages. Finally, cartilage in many bones makes possible their growth in length, and is important in determining their size and shape.

Far from being an inert tissue, cartilage, through its participation in the growth of bones, is a fairly delicate indicator of metabolic disturbances. It reflects *nutritional deficiencies*, especially in protein, minerals or vitamins. For example, the width of the epiphyseal cartilage plate diminishes rapidly when a young rat is placed on a protein-deficient diet. In the absence of vitamin D or in a deficiency in calcium and phosphorus from an otherwise adequate diet, the cartilage continues to proliferate for some time, unchecked by calcification or by erosion by the vascular connective tissue.

The participation of cartilage in the growth in length of bones is in part under control of several hormones, the most important being the *growth hormone*. Hypophysectomy in young rats leads to a thinning of the cartilage plate, with cessation of mitosis and a decrease in number and especially in size of its cells. After a short time the cartilage fails to be eroded, with consequent cessation of growth of the bone. When growth hormone is injected into such animals, the cartilage undergoes a striking metamorphosis, and within a few days resembles that of a normal, young, growing animal, and the bone again resumes its growth. The response of the cartilage varies with the dose level and has been used to assay extracts containing the hormone. Long-continued administration of the hormone produces giant rats, this being made possible in part by growth of cartilage after it would normally have ceased growing. Further, the injection of the hormone into old rats in which cartilage proliferation has stopped can to some extent reactivate its growth, with subsequent increase in size of bones. When growth of cartilage has been retarded by removal of the thyroid from rats shortly after birth, it can be stimulated to renewed activity by administering *thyroxin*. Mechanical injury to the cartilage may result in localized disturbance of growth. Lesions produced in the cartilage by x-rays or other high energy radiations frequently result in a marked stunting of growth. Although much has been learned of the relation of the cells of cartilage to other mesenchymal cells, the interstitial substance is less well understood. Its mode of formation, even its physical state, the organization of its polysaccharides, and the mechanism of calcification are all fundamental problems which need further study.

REFERENCES

Becks, H., Asling, C. W., Simpson, M. E., Li, Choh Hao, and Evans, H. M.: The Growth of Hypophysectomized Female Rats following Chronic Treatment with Pure Pituitary Growth Hormone. III. Skeletal Changes: Tibia, Metacarpal, Costochondral Junction and Caudal Vertebrae. Growth, 13: 175, 1949.

Benninghoff, A.: Der funktionelle Bau des Hyalinknorpels. Ergeb. der Anat. u. Entwick., 26:1, 1925.

Clark, E. R., and Clark, E. L.: Microscopic Observations on New Formation of Cartilage and Bone in the Living Mammal. Am. J. Anat., 70:167, 1942.

Eichelberger, L., Brower, T. D., and Rosa, M.: The Distribution of Water, Electrolytes, Nitrogen and Chondroitin Sulphate in Hyaline Cartilages. Am. J. Physiol., 166:328, 1951.

Fell, H. B.: Chondrogenesis in Cultures of Endosteum. Proc. Roy. Soc., London, s. B, 112:417, 1933.

Follis, R. H., and Berthrong, M.: Histochemical Studies on Cartilage and Bone. I. The Normal Pattern. Bull. Johns Hopkins Hosp., 85:281, 1949.

Glücksmann, A.: Studies on Bone Mechanics in Vitro. II. The Role of Tension and Pressure in Chondrogenesis. Anat. Rec., 73:39, 1939.

Greenspan, F. S., Li, Choh Hao, Simpson, M. E., and Evans, H. M.: Bioassay of Hypophyseal Growth Hormone: The Tibia Test. Endocrinology, 45:455, 1949.

Ham, A. W.: Cartilage and Bone, in Cowdry's Special Cytology. 2d ed. New York, (2), 979, 1932.

Landacre, F. L., and Warren, J. H.: The Origin of Cartilage from Ectoderm in the Urodeles. Anat. Rec., 14:42, 1918.

Montagna, W.: Glycogen and Lipids in Human Cartilage, with Some Cytochemical Observations on the Cartilage of the Dog, Cat, and Rabbit. Anat. Rec., 103:77, 1949.

Murray, P. D. F.: The Physiology of Supporting Tissue. Ann. Rev. Physiol., 9:103, 1947.

Partridge, S. M.: The Chemistry of Connective Tissues. I. The State of Combination of Chondroitin Sulphate in Cartilage. Biochem. J., 43:387, 1948.

Pirie, A.: Mucoitin Sulphuric Acid, Chondroitin Sulphuric Acid, Hyaluronic Acid and Heparin. (Proc. Biochem. Soc.) Biochem. J., 40:XI, 1946.

Schaffer, J.: Die Stützgewebe. Handb. d. mikr. Anat. d. Menschen (v. Möllendorff), (2), Part 2, 1, 1930.

Sheehan, J. F.: A Cytological Study of the Cartilage Cells of Developing Long-Bones of the Rat, with Special Reference to the Golgi Apparatus, Mitochondria, Neutral-Red Bodies and Lipid Inclusions. J. Morphol., 82:151, 1948.

Streeter, G. L.: Developmental Horizons in Human Embryos (Fourth Issue). A Review of the Histogenesis of Cartilage and Bone. Carnegie Institution of Washington, Publ. 583, Contributions to Embry., 33:149, 1949.

Weiss, P., and Amprino, R.: The Effect of Mechanical Stress on the Differentiation of Scleral Cartilage in Vitro and in the Embryo. Growth, 4:245, 1940.

VII. BONE

Bone is a hard, specialized connective tissue, with a calcified collagenous intercellular substance. It performs a mechanical function in forming the *skeletal support of the body*; it protects the vital organs of the cranial and thoracic cavities and lodges the bone marrow. Its structure, even to minute details, is beautifully adapted to the performance of its supporting function with the least expenditure of material and with the least weight. As a second important function, related to its impregnation with minerals, bone serves as a store for calcium, and thus plays a part in the meeting of the immediate needs of the organism for this element.

Despite its passive character, low metabolic rate and great content of inorganic material, bone is a plastic tissue and is highly sensitive to alterations of its normal mechanical function. Thus disuse is followed by *atrophy*, in this case associated with a loss of substance; while increased use is accompanied by *hypertrophy*, with an increase in the mass of the bone. Owing to the ability of the bone to undergo internal reconstruction in response to external stimuli, it may to some extent be modified at will by surgical and experimental procedures.

Macroscopically, mammalian bone is either *spongy* (*cancellous*) or *compact* in structure. Spongy bone consists of intercrossing and connecting osseous bars of varying thickness and shapes. These branch, unite with one another, and partially surround intercommunicating spaces filled with bone marrow, by their arrangement giving the skeleton a maximum rigidity and resistance to changes in shape. Compact bone appears as a continuous hard mass in which spaces can be distinguished only with the aid of the microscope. No sharp boundary can be drawn between the two types of bone tissue; they are merely different arrangements of the same histological elements. Moreover, practically every bone contains both types of osseous tissue.

In typical long bones (femur and humerus) the *diaphysis* (shaft) consists of compact bone and contains in its center a voluminous, cylindrical, bone marrow cavity. The *epiphysis* (at the end of the shaft) consists of spongy bone with a thin, peripheral cortex of compact bone. The cavities of this spongy bone are, in the adult animal, direct continuations of the bone marrow cavity of the diaphysis. In the growing animal the epiphysis and diaphysis are separated by the *epiphyseal cartilage* plate, which is united with the diaphysis by columns of spongy bone, often called the *metaphysis*. The epiphyseal cartilage, together with the spongy bone of the metaphysis, forms a *growth apparatus*, within which growth in length of the long bones occurs.

In the flat bones of the skull, the compact substance forms a relatively thick layer on both surfaces, between which there is a layer of spongy bone of varying thickness (*diploë*). The short and irregular bones usually are of spongy substance covered with a layer of compact bone.

All bones are covered with a modified connective tissue, called *periosteum*; a somewhat similar tissue, the *endosteum*, lines the marrow spaces, including those in spongy bone.

Bone develops through a transformation of connective tissue (*intramembranous ossification*) or by a replacement of cartilage (*intracartilaginous* or *endochondral ossification*) or through a combination of these processes. The formation of bone tissue takes place by apposition, new bone being laid down upon connective tissue, upon cartilage matrix, or upon bone itself. As a bone grows in size it undergoes *internal reconstruction*, which continues throughout the life of the animal, although at a greatly reduced rate in adults. As a result of the reconstruction during growth, mature bone acquires a complex structure.

Microscopically, by far the greater part of the mass of bone is made up of layers (*lamellae*) of calcified *interstitial substance* or *bone matrix*; the arrangement of the lamellae differs in spongy and in compact bone. By appropriate methods the lamellae are found to be fibrillar in structure. Embedded within the interstitial substance are *lacunae* (cavities), completely filled with bone cells (*osteocytes*). In the walls of the lacunae are fine apertures, from which arise numerous thin

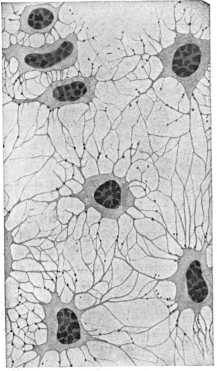

Fig. 99. Thin, transparent membrane bone of a white mouse, stained supravitally with methylene blue, in glycerin. The interstitial substance appears homogeneous; the angular osteocytes with their nuclei fill the cavities. From the cells arise anastomosing processes which lie in the canalicules and in cross section appear as dots. 1040 ×. (A.A.M.)

canals, the *bone canalicules*, which penetrate the hard interstitial substance in all directions. They branch abundantly and anastomose with one another in a sort of network, connecting all the lacunae into a system of cavities. On the surfaces of bone, and much more numerous during the active development and growth of the skeleton, are *osteoblasts* and *osteoclasts*, associated respectively with the apposition and the reconstruction of bone. The contribution of the cellular elements of bone to its total mass is small.

Cells of Bone. Osteoblasts, osteocytes and osteoclasts, peculiar to bone, are closely interrelated, in that transformations from one to another of the three cells are frequently observed.

The *osteoblast*, associated with the formation of osseous tissue, appears on the surface of bone which is undergoing growth and development. These cells are frequently present in a continuous layer, suggesting a cuboidal epithelium (Fig. 102) and are found in this location as long as active growth occurs. The body of the osteoblast has a diameter of 15 to 20 microns. The nucleus is large, and there is usually one fairly large nucleolus. The cytoplasm of the osteoblast stains intensely with basic aniline dyes, suggesting the presence of ribose nucleic acid. This, together with the presence of *phosphatase* in these cells, suggests that the cells are concerned with the synthesis of the proteins of the bone matrix. The cytoplasm also contains numerous threadlike mitochondria; near the nucleus is a pale-staining attraction sphere with a diplosome and a Golgi net. Spherical, cytoplasmic granules 0.3 to 0.6 micron in diameter have been demonstrated in many osteoblasts in sections of frozen-dried bones stained with the periodate-leuco-fuchsin method (Heller). There is evidence that the number of cells containing these granules as well as their number in each cell is greater when new bone is being formed. The osteoblasts are often connected with one another by thin cytoplasmic processes.

The *osteocyte* is frequently, perhaps usually, an osteoblast which has become embedded within the bone matrix (Fig. 99). It has a faintly basophile cytoplasm, containing a few mitochondria and a small Golgi net. It is uncertain whether it contains a cytocentrum and centrioles. When stained supravitally with neutral red, it contains neutral red vacuoles, especially in young bone. Fat droplets and glycogen have been demonstrated in the cytoplasm, which also contains periodate-leucofuchsin-stainable granules indistinguishable from those in osteoblasts. The oval nucleus is large and filled with large chromatin particles and one or more nucleoli. In general, the appearance of the osteocytes suggests that of a somewhat shrunken fibroblast with a darker nucleus. Cells with two nuclei occur; mitoses have not been described in osteocytes.

The shape of the lacunae in which the osteocytes lie is usually flat and oval, resembling that of a melon seed. They range in size from 22 to 52 microns in length, 6 to 14 microns in width, and 4 to 9 microns in thickness. On the surface of the cell bodies are many fine projections which enter the corresponding apertures in the walls of the lacunae. In the early stages of development of bone in mammals, thin cytoplasmic processes penetrate the bone canalicules so that the bone cells are directly connected. How far these cytoplasmic processes extend into the bone canalicules in adult mammals has not been determined.

The *osteoclast* is a multinucleated giant cell, varying greatly in size and in the number of nuclei. These cells are derived from the stromal cells of the marrow; at times they arise by the fusion of a number of osteoblasts, and they may also include osteocytes liberated from bone by resorption. Their pale-staining cytoplasm is often foamy; they frequently have branching processes with serrated edges (Fig. 102). The numerous nuclei are poor in chromatin, and each has a prominent, although small, nucleolus.

Interstitial Substance. The apparently homogeneous interstitial substance of fresh bone contains masked fibers, called *osteocollagenous fibers* (*ossein*), similar to the collagenous fibers of loose connective tissue. By silver impregnation and other special methods it can be shown that the individual fibrils are often connected into small bundles 3 to 5 microns thick; they are united by an amorphous binding substance. It is in this organic binding substance that the mineral constituents of bone are laid down. The glycoprotein component of this amorphous substance in fully formed bone is barely stainable with the periodate-leucofuchsin procedure. It becomes more vividly stained when bone is being deposited or resorbed rapidly, or when present as rachitic osteoid. During bone formation and destruction, it is significant that a

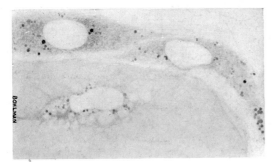

Fig. 100. Margin of a spicule of bone from a young rat; frozen-dried, undecalcified and stained with periodic acid-leucofuchsin. The cytoplasm of the osteocyte and two osteoblasts contains granules; the nuclei do not stain, and the matrix stains feebly. 3000 ×. (After Heller.)

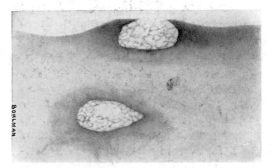

Fig. 101. Edge of a spicule of bone from a rat, six hours after injection of 1000 units of parathyroid extract. The dark-staining matrix around the osteocyte in the center and at the margin of the spicule indicates bone resorption. The upper osteocyte is partially liberated from the matrix. Cytoplasmic granules are absent. Frozen-dried, undecalcified, periodic acid-leucofuchsin stain. 3000 ×. (After Heller.)

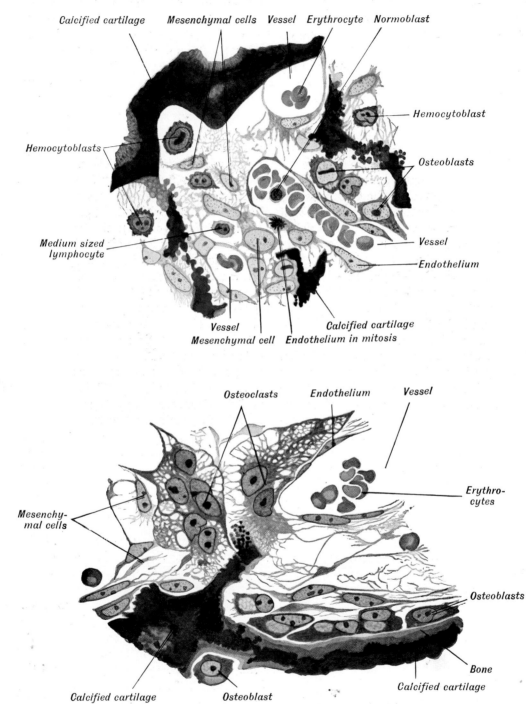

Fig. 102. Two areas from sections of bone marrow cavity near the zone of endochondral ossification of the humerus of a human embryo of 70 mm. Hematoxylin-eosin-azure stain. About 700 ×. (A.A.M.)

method which does not demonstrate phosphate or carbonate in apatite crystals will show much reactive phosphate and carbonate in just those areas of bone matrix which stain vividly with periodate-leucofuchsin.

A specialized, thin layer of the interstitial substance directly adjoins the lacunae and the canalicules and forms a sort of capsule for them. It differs from the rest of the in-

in the poorly calcified bone of *rickets* and *osteomalacia*. Bone salt consists essentially (Hendricks and Hill) of submicroscopic crystals of *hydroxyapatite* $[Ca_3(PO_4)_2]_3 \cdot Ca(OH)_2$ or the closely related hydrated tricalcium phosphate. From x-ray spectograms the *apatite* lattice has been determined. Certain ions such as radium or fluoride are sometimes found substituted in the lattice.

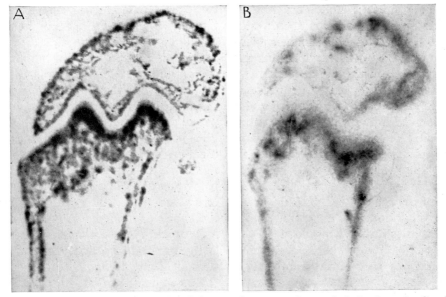

Fig. 103. Autoradiographs of distal ends of femur of rats to show relatively sharp localization of an α-emitting element (plutonium) in A, and the more indefinite localization of a long range β emitter (P³²) in B. Both sections of undecalcified bones after fixation in alcohol. About 10 ×. (With the permission of the Atomic Energy Commission.)

terstitial mass in that it lacks fibrils, and by not dissolving when heated in a solution of strong alkali.

Chemical Composition of the Interstitial Substance. The hard interstitial substance is chemically similar in different types of animals. Besides water, the amount of which varies greatly and which is abundant in the bones of young animals, the interstitial substance consists of two main components: the organic framework, and inorganic salts. Of compact bone, the inorganic part, or *bone ash*, chiefly the *bone salt*, attains a maximum of approximately 65 per cent of the dry, fat-free weight in adult life. In developing bone, especially in the embryo, this proportion is lower, and may be as low as 30 to 35 per cent

The mineral of bone, however, includes other cations, notably magnesium and sodium and considerable amounts of the anions carbonate and citrate. These substances are at present believed to be present on the surfaces of the crystals rather than as substituents within the crystal lattice. Owing to the small size of the crystals, the surfaces available are large per unit of mass. Study of the turnover of the inorganic substances in bone is greatly aided by the use of radioactive isotopes (Fig. 103). Certain radioactive substances accumulate in bone and may cause severe damage to the bone tissue.

The organic portion of compact bone, amounting to 35 per cent or more, is made up chiefly of *bone collagen* or *ossein*; only a small fraction of the dry weight is contributed by the bone cells. The organic framework yields gelatin when boiled.

A weak acid removes the inorganic salts, leaving the original appearance and microscopic structure. If a bone be ignited, only the inorganic constituents remain; a bone so treated becomes brittle, although it retains its external form and, to a certain degree, its microscopic structure.

Architecture of Bone. Bones are formed of two types of tissue, both found in nearly every bone. The cortex of a bone is commonly compact osseous tissue, while cancellous, or spongy, bone is found in the medulla. Spongy bone is simple in structure, but varied in form. It consists of tubes, plates and bars, forming a network especially fitted for definite mechanical functions in individual bones; the parts are usually arranged in those directions which correspond with the lines of maximum pressure or tension. The trabeculae of the spongy substance are made up of a varying number of closely adjoining bone plates, or lamellae. Embedded in the interstitial substance are the lacunae, containing osteocytes and intercommunicating with each other through a network of canalicules.

In the compact substance, the lamellae are regularly arranged, in a manner closely connected with the distribution of the blood vessels which nourish the bone. The compact substance of the diaphysis of any long bone is penetrated by numerous cylindrical, branching and anastomosing canals. These are the *haversian canals*; they contain blood vessels with a small amount of connective tissue. They communicate by the *canals of Volkmann* with the external surface of the bone and with the bone-marrow cavity. It is by the haversian canals and their related structures that the internal structure of compact bone differs from that of spongy bone.

Haversian Systems. The haversian system is the unit of structure of compact bone. It is an irregularly cylindrical, branching and anastomosing structure, with thick walls and a narrow lumen, the haversian canal. The canals are generally from 22 to 110 microns in diameter; they are surrounded by concentrically arranged plates or lamellae of bone, of which there may be from four to twenty in a single system, each from 3 to 7 microns in thickness. The haversian systems are directed mainly in the long axis of the bone, so that in cross section the canals appear as round openings and the lamellae are ring-shaped, while in longitudinal sections the canals appear as long slits (Fig. 104). In addition to the canals and lamellae, the haversian systems include large numbers of lacunae, each containing an osteocyte, and of canalicules, forming a network branching out from the canals and intercommunicating with each other and with the lacunae. The broad surfaces of the lacunae are circumferentially placed in the lamellae.

A haversian canal carries one or more, usually two, blood vessels. These are for the most part capillaries and postcapillary venules, lying in close association with the loose connective tissue which fills the remainder of the canal; occasionally an arteriole is found in a canal. The canalicules of the haversian systems are extravascular, their function presumably being to promote the diffusion of the tissue fluids required for the maintenance of the osteocytes and of the interstitial substance of the bone. In a typical haversian system (Fig. 105) canalicules branch out from the canal and form a network which includes the lacunae. The canalicules, for the most part, are directed radially, forming the channels of communication between the canal and the successive lamellae of the haversian system and their lacunae, and circumferentially and longitudinally, providing for intercommunication between the lacunae of the same lamella. The radially arranged canalicules communicate with the broad surfaces of the lacunae; the circumferential and longitudinal canalicules project from the thin edges of the lacunae. In the outermost lamella of a haversian system the external canalicules loop back into the system; intercommunication between the canalicules of adjacent systems is the exception rather than the rule.

In cross sections of a haversian system,

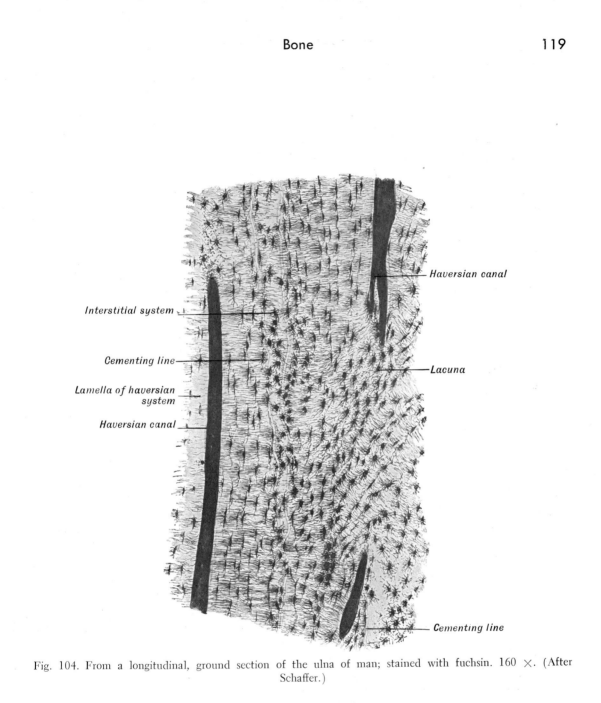

Fig. 104. From a longitudinal, ground section of the ulna of man; stained with fuchsin. 160 ×. (After Schaffer.)

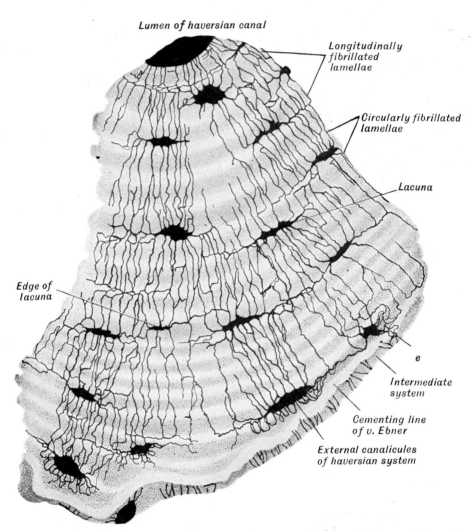

Lumen of haversian canal

Longitudinally fibrillated lamellae

Circularly fibrillated lamellae

Lacuna

Edge of lacuna

e

Intermediate system

Cementing line of v. Ebner

External canalicules of haversian system

Fig. 105. Sector of a cross section of a haversian system of a macerated human hip bone. The cavities and canalicules are filled with a dye: *e*, connection of canalicules of the haversian system with those of an intermediate system. 520 ×. (A.A.M.)

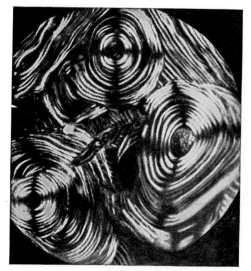

Fig. 106. Cross section of human hip bone in polarized light. The cross sections of three haversian systems are seen as bright Maltese crosses. 130 ×. (Redrawn after Gebhardt.)

stained for connective tissue fibers, are seen lamellae which are alternately longitudinally and circularly fibrillated. The alternation of perfectly longitudinal and circular lamellae, however, occurs rarely. More frequently this arrangement is only approximated, and the fibrils in all the lamellae run spirally to the axis of the canal. These spirals in adjacent plates cross at various angles and are sometimes perpendicular to one another. The direction of the fibrils within the plates of a haversian system is shown diagramatically in Figure 107. The alternation in the direction of fibrillation in the lamellae causes the optic phenomena seen in cross sections of the systems in polarized light (Fig. 106).

Structure of Compact Bone. Compact bone, e.g., the shaft of a long bone, is made up chiefly of large numbers of haversian systems. The irregular angular spaces between these systems are filled with the *interstitial* or *ground lamellae* (Fig. 108). Most of these are the remains of haversian systems which were only partly destroyed during the internal reconstruction of the bone (p. 127). On the external surface of the compact substance, and on the internal surface which forms the wall of the marrow cavity (Fig. 108) are the

basic or *circumferential lamellae:* these vary in number and are arranged, as the name implies, in the circumference of the bone. Penetrating these lamellae, and opening on the free surface of the bone or in the marrow cavity, are the *canals of Volkmann,* within which are the blood vessels communicating with those of the haversian canals. They differ in appearance from the haversian canals in that they are not surrounded by concentrically arranged plates, and usually contain larger blood vessels. Haversian canals frequently communicate with the marrow; such intercommunication is also carried out through the canals of Volkmann: in the periosteum, blood vessels communicating with haversian canals are carried solely by the canals of Volkmann.

Sharpey's Fibers. Compact bone also contains *Sharpey's* or *perforating fibers;* these are collagenous bundles of varying thickness passing from the periosteum through the systems of lamellae in different directions, independently of the ossein fibrils, lacunae and

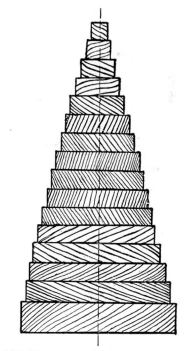

Fig. 107. Diagram of the direction of the fibrils in successive plates of a haversian system. (Redrawn and slightly modified from Gebhardt.)

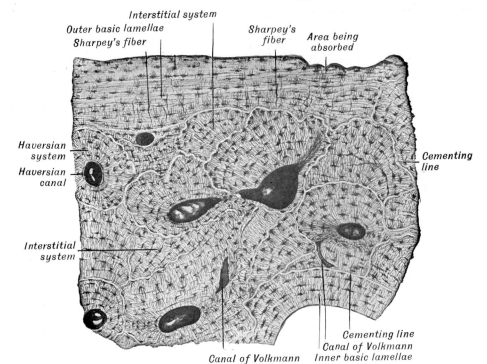

Fig. 108. Ground portion of a human metacarpal bone. Stained with fuchsin, mounted in Canada balsam. 160 ×. (After Schaffer.)

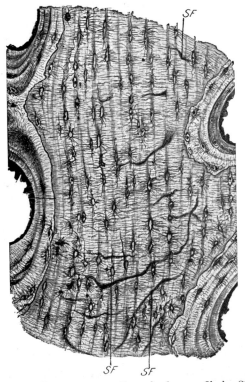

Fig. 109. From a cross section of a human fibula. SF, Sharpey's fibers. 160 ×. (After Schaffer.)

canalicules (Fig. 109, *SF*). They are found in those places where, during the formation of a new bone plate, thick collagenous bundles of the surrounding connective tissue become surrounded by bone. When uncalcified, they occupy irregular, fairly wide canals in the compact bone substance. When calcified, they appear in sections as prominent, irregular stripes or spots against the background of interstitial substance.

Sharpey's fibers are encountered in the external basic and in the interstitial layers which develop by periosteal ossification. They are not found in the haversian and internal basic systems. Their number depends on the type of bone and varies greatly; they may appear singly or, as in some of the bones of the skull, in large numbers. They may be so numerous as to displace much of the interstitial substance and to compress and deform the lacunae (see Weidenreich, 1930).

In addition to Sharpey's fibers, it is said that *elastic fibers* also penetrate the bone from the periosteum, and are to be found together with or independently of the collagenous bundles; their occurrence in bone is also denied.

Periosteum, Bone Marrow, and Endosteum. Except where it is joined to articular cartilage, bone is covered by the *periosteum*, a special, dense connective tissue layer. The attachment is tight on most of the surface of short bones, at the epiphyses of long bones, and where tendons and muscles are attached. This close connection depends mainly on the continuation of dense collagenous bundles from the periosteum into the bone as Sharpey's fibers. At such places, too, large blood vessels and nerves enter the bone. Where the periosteum is loosely connected, there are only a few, thin, collagenous bundles, and attachment to the bone is largely maintained by small blood vessels.

The periosteum in adults consists of two layers, not sharply defined. The external layer is a network of dense connective tissue containing blood vessels. The deep layer, adjacent to the bone, sometimes called the *cambium layer,* by a fancied analogy with the wood-forming zone of trees, is composed of more loosely arranged collagenous bundles; some of these change direction and enter the bone as Sharpey's fibers. The deep layer also contains spindle-shaped connective tissue cells and a network of thin elastic fibers. Blood vessels from the external layer enter the deep layer and pass through the canals of Volkmann to the haversian canals.

In the adult organism the periosteum has no osteogenic function under normal conditions and does not contain osteoblasts. If the bone is fractured, however, the bone-forming potentialities are activated, and osteoblasts reappear in the deepest layer of the periosteum (p. 133).

The *endosteum* is a thin connective tissue layer lining the walls of the bone cavities, which are usually filled with bone marrow. It resembles the periosteum in some respects, and is the condensed peripheral layer of the stroma of the bone marrow where it is in contact with bone. All the cavities of bone, including the marrow spaces within spongy bone, are lined with endosteum after osteoblasts are no longer recognizable; that lining the compact bone of the shaft, however, is more prominent. The endosteum has both osteogenic and hematopoietic potencies.

HISTOGENESIS OF BONE

Bone always develops by a transformation of embryonic or adult connective tissue into a calcified connective tissue. In embryonic life and in postnatal development, bone arises *de novo* in a relatively small number of areas, and growth of bone thereafter is by extension or apposition. Similarly, in the healing of fractures, the bony callus grows by extension from the fractured bone, although not, as a rule, from within the fracture gap. Occasionally, and in certain special circumstances, bone may arise within tissues not connected with the osseous system, and from connective tissue not ordinarily manifesting osteogenic potencies, in which case the process is called *ectopic, heterotopic* or *metaplastic ossification.*

In embryonic life the greater part of the skeleton is formed by ossification in *cartilage models* of the bones, and growth in length of these bones continues after birth by a similar process of erosion of cartilage and deposition of bone, generally upon a framework of cartilage matrix. This process is called *intracartilaginous* or *endochondral ossification,* in contrast with simple *intramembranous ossification,* in which bone is formed from connective tissue without intervening stages of cartilage formation and destruction.

Intramembranous Ossification. This process can be studied favorably in the developing bones of the calvarium. The place of origin of the first bone within the embryonic connective tissue is determined, to a large extent, by the course of the blood vessels. Bone first appears between and at equal distance from two neighboring blood vessels, and only later spreads toward the vessels. In an area where bone will develop, the connective tissue cells are connected with one another by their processes, and delicate bundles of collagenous fibrils run in all directions between them. The tissue is rather loose, and between its cells and fibrils is a semifluid, amorphous substance.

The first signs of bone development in such places are thin bars of dense intercellular substance which run between the cells; they soon become wider and thicker, and often unite with one another to form a network in whose meshes the cells remain.

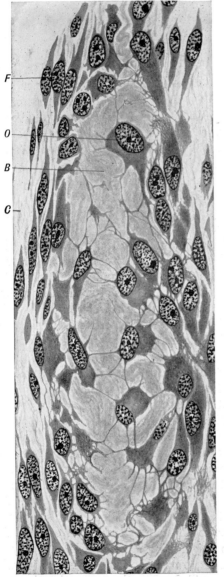

Fig. 110. Beginning intramembranous bone formation in the skull of an embryo cat of 5.5 cm. *F*, Ordinary connective tissue cells (fibroblasts); *C*, collagenous interstitial substance; *B*, homogeneous, thickened collagenous fibers which become the interstitial bone substance; *O*, connective tissue cells, with processes, which become osteoblasts and later bone cells. Eosin-azure stain. 520 ×. (A.A.M.)

Simultaneously, the cells increase in size and become polyhedral while retaining their numerous processes which are connected with those of the adjacent elements, by which time they become recognizable as osteoblasts (Fig. 110, *O*) or as osteocytes. Singly or in groups, the cells become surrounded by the dense interstitial substance, which gradually crowds out the amorphous, semifluid intercellular material (Fig. 110, *B*). Fibrils passing out of the newly formed bone substance continue into those of the surrounding tissue (Fig. 110, *C*). The interstitial substance is explained as a secretion or as a transformation of the protoplasm of its cells; the same explanations are offered for the formation of the interstitial substance in all connective tissue.

When a certain stage in the transformation of the interstitial substance is reached, the tissue becomes calcifiable, bone salt is deposited in it, and it is now known as bone. The property of calcifiability is presumably conferred upon the transformed connective tissue by the osteoblasts. Osteoblasts arise in the early embryo by direct transformation from mesenchymal cells; similarly, they may arise in the adult from fibroblasts and reticular cells.

Soon after the initial stages of formation of bone from connective tissue, there are signs of organization; osteoblasts appear on the surface of developing bone in a continuous layer (Fig. 111). Between their lateral surfaces remain spaces through which fibrils pass into the bone from the surrounding connective tissue. To these are added new fibrils formed by the osteoblasts, presumably making up the bulk of the fibrillar structure of the new bone.

Through the activity of the osteoblasts the bone increases in thickness. Successive layers are added, by apposition, to the fibrillar mass which is being calcified while the osteoblasts remain on the exterior surface (Fig. 112). As the bone becomes thicker, some of the osteoblasts which lie on the surface are included, one by one, within its substance; they are the first bone cells or osteocytes, and they lie in the lacunae. They are formed directly from those osteoblasts which have become surrounded by the calcified interstitial substance which they have produced; the possibility of direct transformation of a mesenchymal cell into an osteocyte is not excluded. Most of the osteoblasts continue at the periphery and, with the gradual thickening of the layers of the interstitial substance, move away from those cells which remain in the lacunae. The osteoblasts maintain a continuous layer on the surface of the plate. As some of them become included in the bone as osteocytes, or as more are required for the formation of bone,

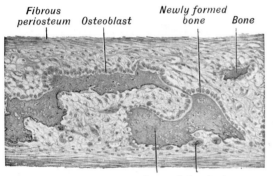

Fig. 111. Cross section through primordium of the parietal bone of a four-months' embryo. 100 ×. (After Schaffer.)

new osteoblasts are formed by the transformation of cells from the surrounding connective tissue. Mitotic division seldom occurs among osteoblasts themselves.

Osteoblasts are connected with one another by processes, and osteocytes are osteoblasts included within the ossifying substance; this explains how the processes of osteocytes penetrate the interstitial bone substance and connect the neighboring cells (compare Figs. 99 and 110). During the transformation of osteoblasts into osteocytes the cytoplasm of the latter even forms a number of new processes. In a mature osteocyte only a few mitochondria remain; these are near the nucleus.

Bone which develops within the connective tissue has a spongy character for a long period. It consists of irregular plates and bars which branch and unite with one another, their fibrils becoming more regularly arranged

as the plates thicken. The spaces between the plates are filled with connective tissue rich in blood vessels and dividing cells; this tissue is gradually transformed into myeloid tissue. The connective tissue surrounding a growing mass of spongy bone remains on its surface and gives rise to the periosteum. The osteoblasts which have remained on the surfaces

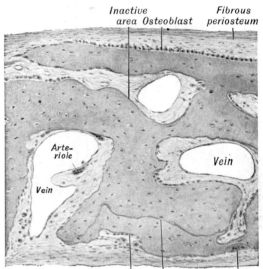

Fig. 112. Analogous section of a six-months' embryo. 100 ×. (After Schaffer.)

of the bone during its active development assume a fibroblast-like appearance, and remain as the deepest layers of the periosteum and endosteum; their osteogenic potencies are recognizable only when they are again called upon to form bone, in which circumstances they again assume the morphological characteristics of osteoblasts.

Intracartilaginous Ossification. In the process of intracartilaginous bone formation, the hyaline cartilage undergoes degenerative changes, is eroded by capillaries accompanied by osteogenic cells, and is replaced by bone which develops in the same manner as in intramembranous ossification. This process is most favorably studied in the zone of endochondral ossification, which is continuous with the epiphyseal cartilage plates of the long bones (Fig. 113), and in which endochondral ossification continues until growth in length of the long bones is complete. In

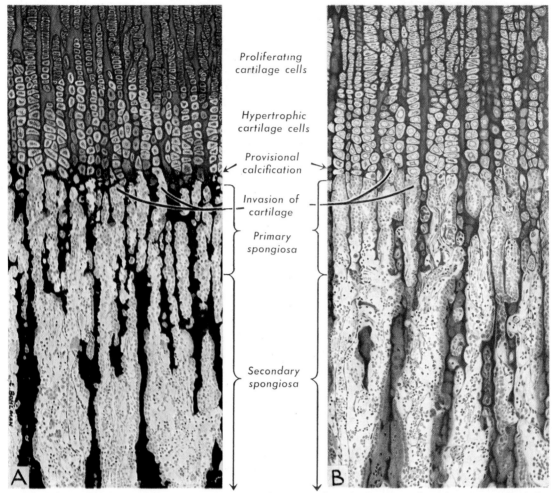

Fig. 113. Endochrondral ossification in longitudinal sections through the zone of epiphyseal growth of the distal end of the radius of a puppy. A, Neutral formalin fixation; no decalcification. Von Kóssa and H–E stain. All deposits of bone salt are stained black; thus bone and calcified cartilage matrix stain alike. B, Zenker-formol fixation. Decalcified. Hematoxylin-eosin-azure II stain. Persisting cores of cartilage matrix in trabeculae of bone take a deep blue or purple stain, while bone stains red. It is impossible to tell where calcium deposits had been. 95 ×.

this zone cartilage cells multiply from mother cells and form columns of flattened cells, instead of the irregular isogenous groups found in masses of hyaline cartilage. The cells in a column are separated by thin capsules; adjacent columns are separated by wide, parallel bands of interstitial substance.

Nearer the zone of ossification, the flat cells in the columns develop small, and then larger, vacuoles in their peripheral cytoplasm, causing the cells to swell. The nuclei also swell and lose most of their chromatin, and the cells degenerate. The matrix adjacent to

these *vesicular* or *hypertrophic* cartilage cells becomes calcifiable, presumably under the influence of the cells. If there are adequate concentrations of calcium and phosphate in the blood plasma, the matrix then calcifies, especially the broad bands separating adjacent columns of cartilage cells; this forms the zone of *provisional* or *preliminary calcification*, which bridges and gives rigidity to the gap between hyaline cartilage and spongy bone.

The next stage in intracartilaginous ossification is due to the activity of the connective tissue and blood vessels of the bone marrow.

Loops of blood vessels with accompanying connective tissue penetrate the cartilage. The interstitial substance separating the cartilage cells in the columns is dissolved in unknown fashion, and the distended cartilage cells are opened up, so that they are penetrated by the vascular connective tissue. In this way communicating canals arise, whose irregular walls are formed by the deeply staining and calcified cartilage matrix. The canals are filled with blood vessels and loose connective tissue; they lengthen as new capsules are opened up. Most of the vesicular cartilage cells perish during penetration of their capsules by the capillaries; a few of them may survive and become osteoblasts.

The process just described is dependent, for its orderly progress, upon the formation of the zone of provisional calcification, which advances just ahead of the penetration of the cartilage by capillaries and removal of the cartilage cells. If calcification in the cartilage matrix fails, owing to a deficiency of bone minerals, cartilage removal ceases; if multiplication of cartilage cells in columns continues, as is usually the case, the epiphyseal cartilage plate increases greatly in thickness. This, together with the appearance of uncalcified osteoid tissue in excessive amounts, constitutes the histological picture characteristic of *rickets* (Fig. 121).

When the vascular connective tissue penetrates the capsules, those connective tissue cells touching the cartilage matrix turn into a layer of osteoblasts. Then, between the osteoblasts and the cartilage matrix, the latter of which remains as a scaffolding upon which new bone is deposited, a thin, new layer of tissue appears, gradually thickens, and surrounds the contours of the cartilage bars (Fig. 102). This tissue is calcifiable when it is laid down and, under favorable conditions, begins to calcify as it is deposited, and thus acquires the characteristics of osseous tissue, or bone. An intermediate stage of uncalcified osseous tissue, or *osteoid*, is not a necessary step in the formation of bone, but there may be a lag in calcification, even under physiological conditions, owing to a local failure in the supply or transport of bone mineral.

When this failure becomes general, and osteoid tissue appears in excess, the condition is known as *rickets* or *osteomalacia* (p. 139). The calcification of new bone is best demonstrated in undecalcified sections, in which the bone salt is positively stained.

From this point, bone is formed by the osteoblasts just as in intramembranous bone formation. In quite the same fashion, the layers of the interstitial substance become thicker and surround isolated osteoblasts, transforming them into osteocytes. The spongy endochondral bone at this time consists of various-sized trabeculae, covered by osteoblasts, with a few osteoclasts, and containing the remains of cartilage matrix in their interior. The latter serve to differentiate bone formed by endochondral ossification from that arising by the intramembranous process alone. The wide spaces between the plates are filled with hematopoietic bone marrow.

Internal Reconstruction of Bone. Bones developing in cartilage increase in length by endochondral ossification and radially by the deposition of new periosteal bone. The process of increase in size is complicated by the necessity of weight bearing throughout the whole period of growth, requiring continuous internal reconstruction of the growing bones. The final result is an increase in strength, as well as size, of the bones, together with the provision of the large cavities lodging the bone marrow.

With the first appearance of bone, wherever formed, a destructive process also appears, generally associated with the presence of osteoclasts (p. 115). The relation of the osteoclasts to the resorption or dissolution of bone is uncertain. It is commonly believed that they produce a substance which dissolves the bone, but there is no direct evidence to support this belief. Osteoclasts are usually, but not always, seen where bone is dissolving, and are frequently found in deep grooves, *Howship's lacunae*, which have the appearance of having been eroded in the bone. Or an osteoclast may surround the free edge of the end of a trabecula of bone undergoing dissolution. The possibility that the osteoclast has a phagocytic function seems slight. Both organic matrix and inorganic bone salt are resorbed simultaneously, but neither cellular debris nor bone salt can be demonstrated in the osteoclasts, although, in certain circumstances, both appear in the macrophages of the bone marrow.

When resorption of bone ceases in a particular location, the osteoclasts disappear, most of them becoming either osteoblasts or reticular cells, depending upon whether new

Formation of Haversian Systems. In parts of the skeleton spongy bone becomes transformed into compact bone. In the irregular, communicating cavities of the spongy bone, filled with bone marrow, the amount of marrow between the spicules of bone decreases as the osteoblasts covering the bone produce layer after layer of concentric bone plates or lamellae. This process continues until all that remains of the former marrow cavity is a comparatively narrow canal containing the

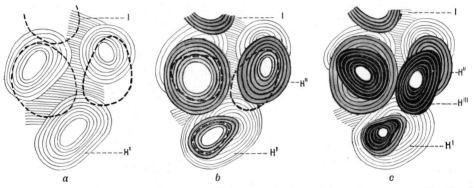

Fig. 114. Diagram showing stages in formation of three generations of haversian systems, H', H'', H'''; I, interstitial lamellae. (Slightly modified after Prenant.)

formation of bone is to follow. Osteoclasts are rarely seen to degenerate. This reconstruction of bone is coordinated with the local mechanical conditions. The direct causes determining whether adjacent cells in a growing bone become either osteoblasts or osteoclasts are unknown.

A greatly diminished rate of reconstruction of bone, the "physiological turnover," continues throughout adult life, and is associated with the maintenance of the level of calcium in the plasma. In fact, calcium can be made available to the blood from bones only by destruction of osseous tissue; simple decalcification of bone by solution of its minerals in the body fluids (*halisteresis*) in all probability does not occur. When, in adult life, the skeleton is called upon to furnish large amounts of calcium, as in pregnancy, the turnover of bone may be greatly accelerated. If, in these circumstances, there is not sufficient calcium in the diet to calcify the new osseous tissue formed, the condition known as *osteomalacia* (*adult rickets*) follows.

blood vessels surrounded by little of the bone marrow. In this manner, systems of concentric bone lamellae, called *primitive haversian systems*, are formed.

Then, at some places, the bone substance begins to dissolve, a process which may include parts or all of the newly formed primitive haversian systems as well as the periosteal bone, and which is associated with the presence of osteoclasts. Wide cylindrical cavities filled with blood vessels and with embryonic bone marrow are formed anew. Then the destruction of bone ceases, the activity of the osteoblasts begins, and concentric systems are once more laid down on the walls of the cavities. These are the haversian systems of the second generation. The dissolution may be renewed in adjacent areas of the bone, to be followed by the formation of haversian systems of the third generation (Figs. 114, 115). Haversian systems are always formed by apposition of bone on the inner surfaces of lamellae of bone surrounding blood vessels; this results in a progressive decrease in the size of the haversian canals, and in an increase in the compactness of the bone.

This process of destruction and construction continues actively until the bones approach adult size, after which reconstruction continues throughout life, but at a sharply

Development of Bones as a Whole. Most of the bones of the skeleton are first laid down in the embryo in hyaline cartilage; this group includes all the bones of the thorax, the limbs, the greater part of the bones of the skull, and the hyoid bone. The ossification

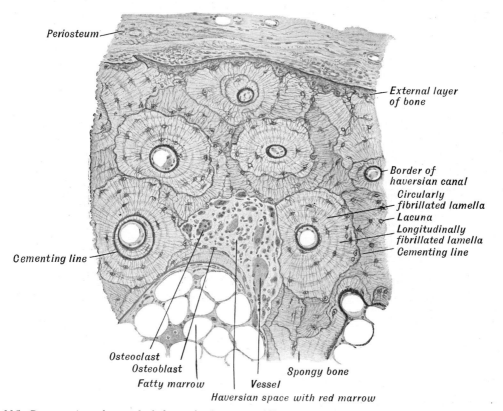

Fig. 115. Cross section of second phalanx of a human middle finger, showing replacement of spongy bone by compact bone. 110 ×. (After Schaffer.)

reduced intensity. It is upon this reconstruction that the complicated structure of the mature compact substance with its haversian and intermediate systems depends. As a bone increases in thickness, the periosteum and the endosteum lay down successive layers of *basic* or *circumferential lamellae* on the surfaces of the bone. During reconstruction of the bone these lamellae also undergo destruction and replacement by haversian systems. The intermediate systems, then, include the remains of these lamellae, of which those of periosteal origin contain Sharpey's fibers, and portions of former, partially destroyed haversian systems of various generations.

of these cartilage models proceeds typically in the long bones of the limbs.

The external shape of the cartilage model suggests in general the future bone; in it a diaphysis, with an epiphysis at each end, may be distinguished early. Externally, the cartilage model is covered by a perichondrium of closely packed, embryonic connective tissue cells. Bone formation begins within a ring-shaped area surrounding the center of the diaphysis. The perichondrium is called the periosteum as soon as it begins to form bone, and the process is accordingly called "periosteal ossification," and is of the intramembranous type (p. 123). The cells of the

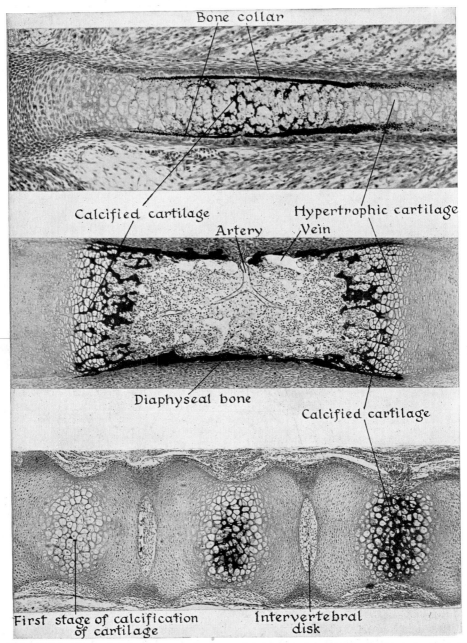

Fig. 116. Photomicrographs showing several stages of bone formation in developing rats. From formalin fixed, undecalcified sections stained with silver nitrate to show bone salt (black). Upper figure is a longitudinal section through second rib of eighteen-day rat embryo; calcification of the periosteal bone collar is further advanced than that of the cartilage. Middle figure is a section of metatarsal of four-day rat, in which ossification is proceeding toward the epiphyses; the hyertrophic cartilage is not completely calcified. Lower figure shows three stages in calcification of vertebrae in twenty-day rat embryo. 117 ×, 63×, and 57 × respectively. (Bloom and Bloom.)

perichondrium adjoining the cartilage increase in size and become osteoblasts. Between them appear thin and later thicker bone lamellae with bone cells (Fig. 116). These lamellae form a bone ring, the *periosteal bone band* or *collar*, which surrounds the middle of the diaphysis of the cartilage. This band is a spongy bone network, through whose meshes the connective tissue of the periosteum continues in direct contact with the cartilage.

Before or shortly after the bone collar appears, the cartilage tissue inside the diaphysis changes markedly; the cells swell into vesicles, and the interstitial substance between them becomes thinner (Fig. 116) and calcified. Through the spaces in the periosteal band the connective tissue of the periosteum, together with the blood vessels, penetrates the transformed cartilage at one or several places (Figs. 117, 118). The capsules of the vesicular cartilage cells are quickly opened for a long distance (p. 125), and become filled with embryonic bone marrow with its thin-walled blood vessels. In this manner a cavity with irregular walls is formed in the cartilage of the interior of the diaphysis in the area surrounded by the periosteal band (Figs. 116, 119). This constitutes the *primary bone marrow cavity*, filled with embryonic bone marrow. The periosteal collar performs an important function by bridging the gap which would otherwise result from the formation of this cavity; it is the primitive shaft of the bone. Scattered between the elements of the marrow are angular remains of calcified cartilage. Some of the cells of the embryonic marrow become osteoblasts, which come in contact with these cartilaginous remains and surround them with layers of bone. Some of the cartilage cells also become osteoblasts. In other places osteoclasts are formed where the newly formed bone is being resorbed (Fig. 118).

With the continued growth of cartilage in the epiphyses, the entire cartilage model increases in size. The mass of the periosteal as well as of the endochondral bone in the diaphysis also grows progressively. The periosteal bone band widens toward the epiph-

yses, and is demarcated from the spongy endochondral bone by a thin, refractile line. The endochondral bone may also be distinguished by the remains of deeply staining cartilage matrix within its trabeculae. At a much later period, in man usually during the first few years of postnatal life, *ossification centers* appear in the epiphyses, until then formed of hyaline cartilage, and the process of endochondral ossification is repeated in these areas.

The epiphyseal cartilage plates (see p. 113) between the epiphyses and the diaphysis are temporary formations which serve for the growth in length of the bone. Multiplication of cartilage cells, arranged in columns, occurs from the epiphyseal aspect of the disk, removal of mature or hypertrophic cells from the diaphyseal aspect. Under normal conditions of growth these two processes balance one another, and the disk remains at approximately constant thickness. Growth in length results from the fact that the cartilage cells continually grow away from the shaft, being replaced by bone as they recede; the net effect is an increase in length of the shaft. When proliferation of the cartilage ceases, at the end of the period of growth, the cartilage plates or disks are entirely replaced by bone (*closure of epiphyses*), the epiphyses unite with the diaphysis, and longitudinal growth of the bone is no longer possible (Fig. 119).

The contribution of each of the two epiphyses of a long bone to its growth may differ markedly; growth in length of the femur takes place mainly at the distal epiphysis.

As the growing bone advances into and replaces the cartilage, the cartilage matrix separating the columns of cartilage cells becomes covered with osseous tissue, forming the mass of spongy bone called the metaphysis. This bone normally undergoes extensive reorganization and thinning out as the growth process passes it by. Two parts of it become recognizable, the *primary* and *secondary spongiosa*, being differentiated by the fact that the secondary spongiosa has undergone reconstruction. As a part of this reconstruction, the tips of trabeculae of the spongiosa are continually undergoing resorption, with the result that the spongiosa tends to remain constant in length. The total picture in the growth zone, then, is that of an epiphyseal cartilage disk, a zone of provisional calcification, within which cartilage cells are being opened and gradually toward the epiphyses. Inside the central portion of the diaphysis, and extending toward the epiphyses, an extensive dissolution of bone begins, which is not compensated by a corresponding formation of new bone. In this manner the *definitive bone*

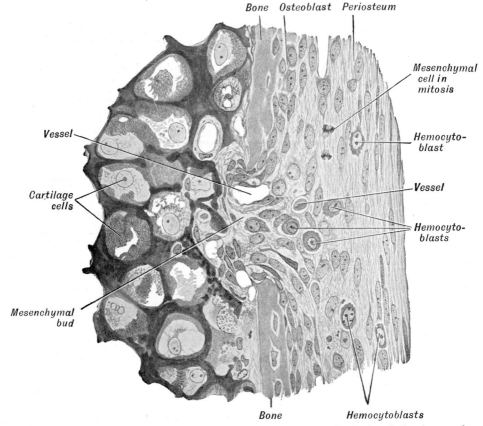

Fig. 117. Part of longitudinal section through the middle of the diaphysis of the femur of a 25-mm. human embryo. Mesenchyme with vessels entering calcified cartilage through an opening in the periosteal bone collar. Eosin-azure stain. 560 ×. (A.A.M.)

destroyed, and a zone of spongy bone. All these zones remain at approximately constant dimensions, while the shaft of the bone increases in length, owing to the fact that the proliferating structures, the growth apparatus, constantly grow away from the diaphysis.

At first the only bone formed is of the spongy type, of periosteal and endochondral origin. Then the internal reconstruction begins in the periosteal bone and leads to the development of compact bone. In the diaphysis it finally forms a thick layer, which tapers

marrow cavity arises. In a completed bone it occupies the entire diaphysis and continues into the spaces of the spongy substance toward the epiphyses.

In short bones developing in cartilage, a central point of endochondral ossification appears and progresses from the center to the periphery. This continues until only a thin cartilage layer remains. When the cartilage no longer regenerates and is completely used up, the surrounding layer of connective tissue becomes the periosteum, and begins to deposit upon the exterior of the endochondral spongy bone a layer of periosteal bone of varying thickness. This later becomes compact bone.

In flat bones which develop in cartilage (scapula), periosteal ossification is followed by endochondral bone formation, just as in pact substance through internal reconstruction. In the central layers, dissolution outstrips the formation of new bone, so that in the course of time there is formed a spongy substance with wide bone marrow spaces—diploë.

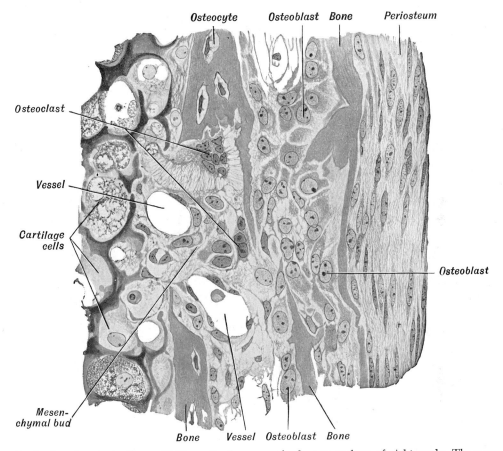

Fig. 118. Similar place as in Figure 117 from the humerus of a human embryo of eight weeks. The process of ossification has advanced slightly farther than in that figure. Eosin-azure stain. 560 ×. (A.A.M.)

the long bones. The bones of the calvarium, the sides of the skull and almost all the facial bones develop directly from connective tissue. In a limited region of this tissue a small center of spongy bone is formed. Its lamellae develop radially from this point of ossification in one place; such a growing bone consists of a solid mass in its interior and thin, bony rays at its periphery. The layers of connective tissue which cover the surfaces differentiate into periosteum and increase the thickness of the bone by apposition. The peripheral layers of the bone become com-

The lower jaw is an example of a special mode of ossification, for its model, although formed in the embryo of cartilage (*Meckel's cartilage*), does not undergo ossification, but simply serves as a surface for the deposition of bone by connective tissue. The cartilage is later resorbed.

Repair of Bone. After a fracture there are first the usual reactions of any tissue to severe injury, including hemorrhage and organization of the clot by ordinary granulation tissue, the *procallus*. The granulation tissue becomes dense connective tissue, and car-

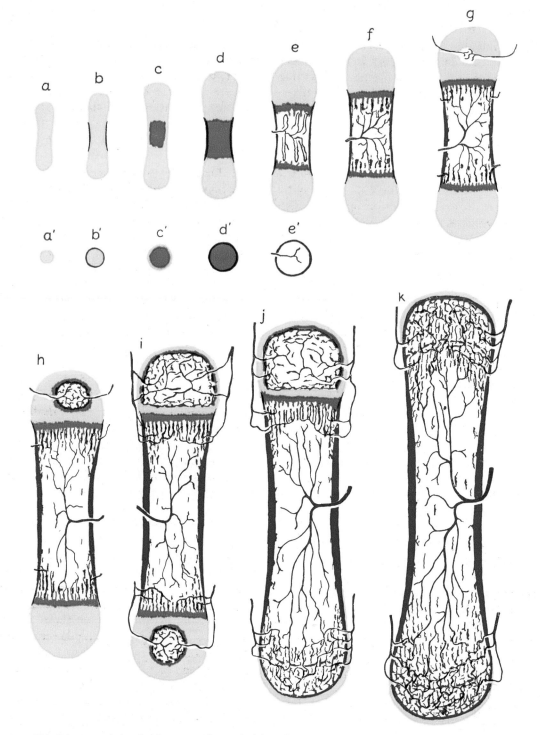

Fig. 119. Diagram of the development of a typical long bone as shown in longitudinal sections. *Pale green,* cartilage; *purple,* calcified cartilage; *blue,* bone; *red,* arteries. *a', b', c', d', e',* cross sections through the centers of *a, b, c, d, e* respectively. *a,* Cartilage model; *b,* appearance of the periosteal bone collar before the development of calcified cartilage, *c,* or after it, *d; e,* vascular mesenchyme has entered the calcified cartilage matrix and divided it into two zones of ossification, *f; g,* blood vessels and mesenchyme enter upper epiphyseal cartilage; *h,* epiphyseal ossification center develops and grows larger; *i,* ossification center develops in lower epiphyseal cartilage; *j,* the lower and *k,* the upper epiphyseal cartilages disappear as the bone ceases to grow in length, and the bone marrow cavity is continuous throughout the length of the bone. After the disappearance of the cartilage plates at the zones of ossification, the blood vessels of the diaphysis, metaphysis and epiphysis intercommunicate.

tilage and fibrocartilage develop within it, forming the *fibrocartilaginous callus*, which fills the gap between the ends of the fragments. The new bone, which will ultimately unite the fragments, begins to form at some distance from the fracture line, originating from the deeper layers of the periosteum and endosteum, and invading the fibrocartilaginous callus at its periphery (Bast, Sullivan and Geist). It extends centripetally, replacing the tissues of the callus with new bone, the *bony callus*, which is calcifiable as it is laid down and, under favorable conditions, calcifies as it is formed. Ossification of the callus, then, like intracartilaginous bone formation, is essentially a process of replacement of the earlier tissue by bone, only enough of the first tissue remaining to furnish a framework for the deposition of the new bone. *Bony union* of the fracture is accomplished when the new spongy bone, invading the callus from the periosteum of the two fragments of bone, makes contact and unites. After this there is reorganization, with resorption of excess bone, and internal reconstruction, resulting finally in bridging the gap with compact bone. The fate of the cells of the fibrocartilaginous callus needs further study.

Ectopic Ossification. In the processes already described bone has been formed from connective tissue, with the transformation of fibroblasts and reticular cells into osteoblasts, osteocytes and osteoclasts; the return of these cells to fibroblasts and reticular cells has also been described. All the processes described have in common the fact that bone has developed only in connection with the osseous system—the skeleton. The influences under which ordinary connective tissue gives rise to bone in the embryo are but little understood, but it is clear that previously undifferentiated connective tissue cells are capable of transformation to the cells characteristic of bone.

It would also appear that, once cells have exhibited osteogenic potencies, these potencies are readily evoked for an indeterminate period after the cells have returned to an indifferent morphological state. Thus, in the healing of fractures, cells in the deepest layers of the periosteum and endosteum, under the stimulus of trauma, reassume the form of osteoblasts and once again are actively engaged in osteogenesis. Moreover, cells grown from bone in tissue culture, and having lost the morphological characteristics of osteoblasts, once again form bone when implanted into the anterior chamber of the eye (Fig. 120).

Furthermore, under certain conditions bone may be formed spontaneously from connective tissue not in association with the skeleton. This ectopic ossification has been described in such diverse locations as the pelvis of the kidney, in the walls of arteries, in the eyes, in muscles and in tendons. From this it may be inferred that many types of connective tissue have latent osteogenic potencies, which are exhibited only rarely away from the skeletal system. This conclusion is supported by experimental production of bone in connective tissue after ligation of the renal artery and vein (Sacerdotti and Frattin), after transplantation of bladder epithelium (Huggins), and after the injection of alcoholic extracts of bone into muscle (Levander, Annersten, Lacroix). In the latter case there is evidence (Heinen) that alcohol alone frequently induces osteogenesis in muscle, and that it shares this ability with other irritating substances.

Many attempts have been made to utilize the osteogenetic potencies of periosteum and bone by transplanting these tissues to areas in which it is desired that new bone be formed; the modern "bone-bank," which supplies fragments of bone preserved by freezing or by other means, is the fruit of these efforts. While, as noted before, certain cells with osteogenetic potencies may form bone when transplanted to a favorable environment, and while there is little question that autogenous grafts of fresh bone or periosteum in laboratory mammals may survive and form new bone, it seems clear that homogenous grafts of preserved bone do not give rise to new bone. Such grafts do, however, favor the induction of new bone formation by the cells of the host.

Reticular cells within the orbit of advancing bone, e.g., in the formation of medullary

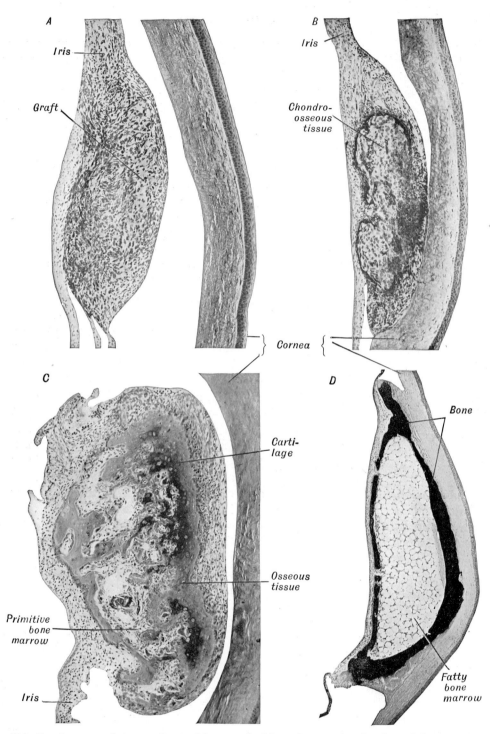

Fig. 120. Development of tissue cultures of bone grafted into the anterior chamber of the eye. Fragments of tibiae of twelve-day rats were cultured in rat plasma and embryo extract. The outgrowths were removed after four days *in vitro* and transplanted to the iris of normal rats. These outgrowths contained no bone or cartilage. A, After one and one-half days in the eye there was no cartilage or bone. B, After two and one-half days in the eye, chondro-osseous tissue developed from the culture. C, After six days in the eye, much bone and cartilage and some marrow appeared. D, After four months, a "bone" with central fatty marrow developed. A, B, C, Zenker-formol, hematoxylin-eosin-azure II. Photomicrographs, 80 ×. D, Formalin fixation, silver nitrate-hematoxylin-eosin. Photomicrograph, 32 ×. (Courtesy of J. H. Heinen.)

bone in birds (p. 137), perhaps by a somewhat similar process of induction, assume the form of osteoblasts before they actually join in the process of osteogenesis. This observation, together with those upon the behavior of bone grafts just cited, suggests that the presence of bone itself may be an important aid in activating osteogenetic potencies. There is thus histological evidence in favor of *induction* of formation of bone, although attempts to isolate a specific *inductor* substance have so far given equivocal results.

Histophysiological Remarks. The mechanism of the deposition of calcium in bone is still incompletely understood. At least two factors, local and humoral, are involved. The humoral factor is related to the supply of minerals in the fluids of the body, and to the solubilities of the difficultly soluble salts of calcium and phosphate; it may be defined in terms of the concentrations of these substances in the blood. But the local factor, which determines the occurrence and specific localization of the deposition of bone salt, when adequate concentrations of calcium and of phosphate are present in the blood, is not understood.

When calcification fails in growing animals or young children, the osseous tissue continues to grow, but the new uncalcified, but calcifiable, tissue is known as *osteoid*. This failure of calcification to keep pace with growth is known as *rickets*, and is usually associated with a diminished concentration of phosphate in the blood plasma. The preventive and curative action of *sunlight* and of *vitamin D* in rickets is generally attributed to increased absorption of calcium and phosphate from the gastro-intestinal tract. That rickets is not due to failure in the local mechanism is shown by the fact that the cartilage matrix of rachitic bone calcifies readily, either *in vivo* or *in vitro*, when the surrounding medium is supplied with the necessary minerals in adequate concentrations (Fig. 121). *Phosphatase* is present in osteoblasts, but not in osteoid tissue; the staining reactions of these cells also indicate that they are rich in ribosenucleic acid. It is suggested that these sub-

stances are associated with the formation of the bone matrix by osteoblasts, rather than with calcification.

The interstitial substance of bone acts as a store for calcium, there being a constant interchange of this substance between the blood and the bones, with the result that the calcium ion concentration in the plasma remains approximately constant. Calcium, when once laid down in the form of bone salt, can be made available to the blood only by destruction of osseous tissue, including its organic matrix, chiefly from the spongy bone near the epiphyses of the long bones. The rate of the resorptive process is regulated by the *parathyroid hormone*, which has no effect upon the deposition or calcification of bone.

In birds, an entire new system of *medullary bone*, produced chiefly by an outgrowth from the endosteal lining of the shafts of the long bones, is formed during the egg-laying cycle, or may be induced by the administration of *estrogens*, and serves to accumulate calcium to be used in the formation of the egg shell. When the egg shell is being calcified, calcium is made available by destruction of the medullary bone, including its organic matrix; osteoclasts are prominent during this resorptive stage. Mice react to the administration of estrogens in much the same way as do birds; endosteal bone formation has not been reported in rats, in which estrogens have the effect of inhibiting the normal resorption of the spongiosa during growth by endochondral ossification. This latter effect results in a greatly elongated and dense spongiosa, containing cores of deeply stained cartilage matrix, thus resembling the findings in *marble bone disease*.

The growth of bone is markedly influenced by the *growth hormone* of the anterior pituitary. Hypophysectomy results in cessation of endochondral ossification; administration of growth hormone reinitiates growth, and, if continued for a sufficiently long time, may result in *gigantism*. The *thyroid glands* influence the growth of bone, but not specifically.

The experiments of Barnicot and of Chang with grafts of parathyroid gland to bone show that this organ secretes a hormone which causes a resorption of bone by direct action on this tissue.

In *hyperparathyroidism*, bone is extensively resorbed, and is replaced by fibrous tissue containing large numbers of osteoclasts; this resembles the pathological picture of *osteitis fibrosa* (*von Recklinghausen's disease*). When large doses of parathyroid hormone are given to animals, changes in the

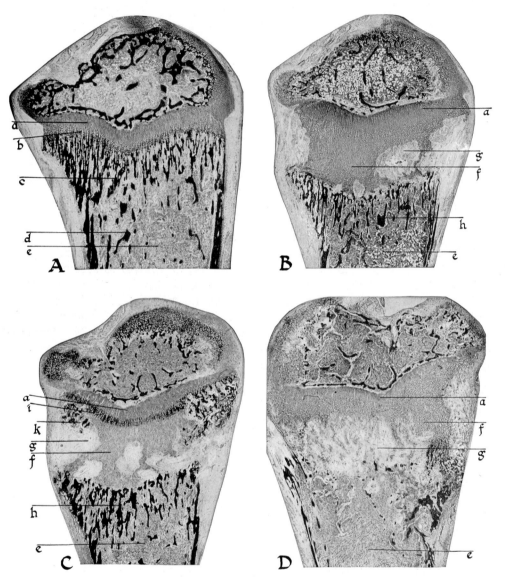

Fig. 121. Head of tibia in experimental rickets in rats. All sections from undecalcified bones stained with silver nitrate to show calcification, and counterstained with H and E. All rats weaned to experimental diet at twenty-one days. A, Normal control, aged thirty-one days, Bills' stock diet. B, Littermate of A, aged thirty-one days, same diet plus 2 per cent $BeCO_3$. C, Age fifty-seven days, stock diet plus 1 per cent $BeCO_3$, given daily intraperitoneal injections of sodium phosphates for last seven days. Note calcified cartilage matrix and beginning healing. D, Age sixty-two days, rickets due to high calcium, low phosphate diet (Steenbock-Black). *a*, Proliferating cartilage; *b*, zone of provisional calcification; *c*, trabeculae of primary spongiosa; *d*, secondary spongiosa; *e*, bone marrow; *f*, hypertrophic cartilage; *g*, osteoid tissue; *h*, trabeculae calcified before onset of rickets; *i*, calcification preparatory to healing; *k*, healing with calcification of new bone. Photomicrographs, 15 ×. (Courtesy of F. C. McLean.)

bones are profound. Within a few hours many osteoblasts die, although the majority change into fibroblasts or osteoclasts or become phagocytic. There is widespread necrosis of the elements of the bone marrow and, blasts, and new bone, formed intramembranously, replaces the fibrous tissue (Fig. 122).

In long-standing deficiency of calcium and of vitamin D, especially when aggravated by pregnancy, the bones of adults contain much

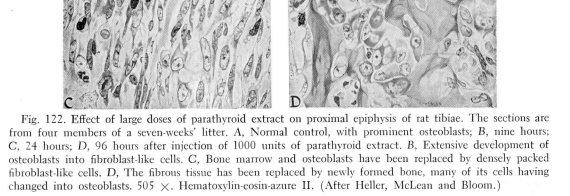

Fig. 122. Effect of large doses of parathyroid extract on proximal epiphysis of rat tibiae. The sections are from four members of a seven-weeks' litter. A, Normal control, with prominent osteoblasts; B, nine hours; C, 24 hours; D, 96 hours after injection of 1000 units of parathyroid extract. B, Extensive development of osteoblasts into fibroblast-like cells. C, Bone marrow and osteoblasts have been replaced by densely packed fibroblast-like cells. D, The fibrous tissue has been replaced by newly formed bone, many of its cells having changed into osteoblasts. 505 ×. Hematoxylin-eosin-azure II. (After Heller, McLean and Bloom.)

at least in certain species, of the osteocytes. The calcium-containing trabeculae are rapidly resorbed and replaced by fibrous tissue. Salts of calcium have not been demonstrated within the osteoclasts, but have been found extracellularly as well as in the macrophages of the marrow. Recovery occurs when large numbers of osteoblasts develop from fibro- uncalcified osteoid tissue, and their mineral content is greatly diminished—a condition known as *osteomalacia (adult rickets)*. The diminution in calcium content is due to failure of calcification of new bone formed in the turnover of this tissue, rather than to simple decalcification of previously calcified bone. In osteomalacia, and in the form of rickets induced experimentally by deprivation of calcium, the parathyroid glands are enlarged; they are much less affected in the rickets associated with deficiency of phosphate.

In *osteoporosis*, a term generally understood to mean an increase in the relative size of the haversian canals with a corresponding decrease in the mass of the compact bone substance, the total mineral content of the bones is diminished. It has not been shown that the mineral content of the bone sub-

the relative sizes of the spinal cord and the vertebrae. Excessive administration of vitamin A accelerates remodelling of bone (Wolbach).

JOINTS AND SYNOVIAL MEMBRANES

Bones are joined to one another by connective tissue structures which permit varying degrees of movement between the adjoining bones. Such structures are called joints or articulations. These present extreme variations in character which depend primarily

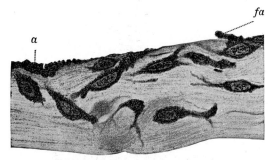

Fig. 123. Hip joint of man; the synovial membrane has relatively few cells; between them are collagenous fibers. *a*, swollen cellular process on the surface; *fa*, processes projecting freely above the surface. (After Hammar.)

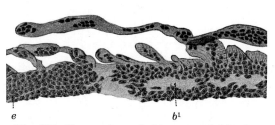

Fig. 124. Free surface of thin synovial fold from which villi protrude. b^1, Superficial connective tissue; *e*, cells arranged in an epithelial-like fashion. (After Hammar.)

stance itself is lessened in this condition, which occurs in elderly people, and more especially in women after the menopause. In *Paget's disease*, little understood, the bones are both thickened and softened, resorption and apposition of bone occurring simultaneously. In this condition the blood calcium and the parathyroid glands are normal.

Deficiency of *vitamin C* leads to profound changes in tissues of mesenchymal origin, producing the condition known as *scurvy* (*scorbutus*), which has been characterized as an inability of the supporting tissue to produce and maintain intercellular substance. In bone this results in destruction of the collagen of the matrix, with extensive reparative proliferation of fibroblasts. Deficiency of *vitamin A* results in a diminution in the rate of growth of the skeleton, without a corresponding retardation of growth of the central nervous system. The resulting damage to the central nervous system is regarded as mechanical, owing chiefly to the discrepancy in

upon the type of bones which are joined and the varying degrees of motion permitted by the articulation. Thus, in some cases, as in the skull, the joints are immovable, and the connected bones are separated only by a thin connective tissue layer, the sutural ligament. Other joints are slightly movable, such as the intervertebral articulations. Here the succeeding vertebrae are joined to one another by dense fibrous tissue and cartilage. Still other bones are freely movable upon one another, and here the bones are completely separated by cartilage and fibrous capsules.

Joints in which there is little or no movement are called *synarthroses*. There are three types of these: If the connection between the bones is of bone, it is a *synostosis*; if of cartilage, a *synchondrosis*; and if of connective tissue, a *syndesmosis*. Joints which permit free movement of the bones are called *diarthroses*.

In the diarthrodial joints there is a cavity. Because this was thought by some to have a continuous lining of flattened, epithelium-like cells, the tissue was called "mesenchymal epithelium." However, the walls of the joint cavities are composed of a dense connective tissue whose cells are irregularly distributed and seldom suggest epithelium in arrangement. Occasionally, small amounts of cartilage and all transitions between the cartilage cells and the joint or synovial cells can be found.

The articular surface of the bones is covered with hyaline cartilage. Where the opposing cartilages touch, they are not covered with dense connective tissue, but at their bases a small area of perichondrium is reflected backward into the membrane of the joint capsule. At this point there are many cartilage cells extending into the synovial membrane. As is true of most of the cartilage of the body, the articular cartilages contain no blood vessels; it is generally believed that they are nourished by osmosis from the surrounding tissues. The articular cartilages are intimately adherent to a layer of compact bone which lacks haversian systems and has large lacunae, said to be free of canalicules.

Most of the joint capsules are composed of two fairly distinct layers. The external consists of dense fibrous tissue and is called the *fibrous layer*. The inner is the *synovial layer*, which is more cellular and is thought to secrete the viscid, colorless liquid of the joint cavity. However, the joint membrane exhibits many variations in structure. The synovial layer is sometimes thrown into marked folds which may project for surprising distances into the cavity. The larger of these folds frequently contain vessels. In other cases the two layers appear fused, or the synovial layer may rest directly on muscle or fatty tissue or periosteum. It has been suggested that the synovia be classified according to the tissues on which they lie: that is, loose connective, dense fibrous, or adipose tissue.

Synovial membranes which rest on loose connective tissue usually cover those parts of the joints which are not subjected to strain or pressure. As a rule they have a definite surface layer, separated from the underlying tissue of the joint by loose connective tissue.

The surface layer consists of collagenous fibers interspersed with fibroblasts whose processes may extend for long distances, although sometimes the cells are rounded. The fibroblasts do not form a complete covering

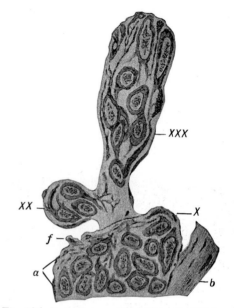

Fig. 125. End of branching villus. X, Thicker portion of the villus, where many of the cells are of epithelioid appearance and their processes (*a*) are more superficial than the cell bodies; *b*, less cellular connective tissue cord; XX and XXX, small, secondary villi with branching cells; *f*, wartlike protuberance of the surface containing a cell process. (After Hammar.)

for the interstitial collagenous substance; those cells on the surface have unusually long processes. The collagenous fibers are either irregularly arranged or may be oriented along the main lines of stress. In addition to the fibroblasts, there are a few macrophages, leukocytes and lymphoid wandering cells. In addition to blood vessels, the loose connective tissue contains many lymphatics.

The fibrous synovial membrane covers the interarticular ligaments and tendons and lines those parts of the joints which are subject to strain. It consists of dense connective tissue; the surface zone is slightly more cellular than the rest. Some of the fibroblasts have capsules. When unusual pressure is applied to the synovial membrane, fibrocartilage develops.

The adipose type of synovial membrane

covers the fat pads which project into the joint cavities. The synovial membrane in this case usually consists of a single layer of cells resting on a thin layer of connective tissue.

The fibroblasts of the synovial membrane rarely show mitoses. They may occasionally contain one or two vacuoles. There are no vacuoles within them which stain with neutral red. Mitochondria and a Golgi net have been demonstrated in them.

Folds of the synovial membrane may be either temporary formations which depend on the position of the joint, or they may form permanent *villi* which project into the joint cavity. Some of these villi have a broad base and a rather short stalk, while others may be thin and long. The larger folds contain blood vessels, lymphatics and occasionally lobules of adipose tissue. There is an increase in the size and number of the villi with age. New islets of cartilage are formed in them, mainly by metaplasia of the synovial fibroblasts.

Blood vessels probably do not lie free on the surface of the synovial membrane. There are two plexuses of lymphatics, as a rule, within the synovial membranes, a superficial and a deep plexus. The nerves which accompany the blood vessels end in the layer beneath the surface in terminal arborizations or endbulbs or plates. Pacinian corpuscles are always present.

When injured, the synovial membrane reacts like any other connective tissue by the formation of granulation tissue, and after some weeks may be completely regenerated. The synovial fluid is normally small in amount and seems to be a dialysate of blood to which have been added small amounts of mucin and a very few cells, chiefly lymphocytes, monocytes and macrophages.

REFERENCES

Barnicot, N. A.: The Local Action of the Parathyroid and Other Tissues on Bone in Intracerebral Grafts. J. Anat., 82:233, 1948.

Bast, T. H., Sullivan, W. E., and Geist, F. D.: The Repair of Bone. Am. J. Anat., 31:255, 1925.

Bauer, W., Ropes, M. W., and Waine, H.: The Physiology of Articular Structures. Physiol. Rev., 20:272, 1940.

Bloom, W., Bloom, M. A., and McLean, F. C.: Calcification and Ossification. Medullary Bone Changes in the Reproductive Cycle of Female Pigeons. Anat. Rec., 81:443, 1941.

Chang, Hwei-ya: Grafts of Parathyroid and Other Tissues to Bone. Anat. Rec., 111:23, 1951.

Dantschakoff, W.: Ueber die Entwicklung des Knoch-enmarks bei den Vögeln und über dessen Veränderungen bei Blutentziehungen und Ernährungsstörungen. Arch. mikrosk.-Anat., 74:855, 1909.

Dodds, G. S.: Osteoclasts and Cartilage Removal in Endochondral Ossification of Certain Mammals. Am. J. Anat., 50:97, 1932.

Fell, H. B.: Osteogenesis in Vitro. Archiv. f. exper. Zellforsch., 11:245, 1931.

Fell, H. B., and Robison, R.: The Development and Phosphatase Activity in Vivo and in Vitro of the Mandibular Skeletal Tissue of the Embryonic Fowl. Biochem. J., 24:1905, 1930.

Gebhardt, F.: Ueber funktionell wichtigen Anordnungsweise der gröbere und feineren Bauelemente des Wirbeltierknochens. Arch. f. Entwick., 11, 12, 20:1901, 1906.

Giblin, N., and Alley, A.: Studies in Skull Growth. Coronal Suture Fixation. Anat. Rec., 88:143, 1944.

Glücksmann, A.: Studies on Bone Mechanics in Vitro. II. The Rôle of Tension and Pressure in Chondrogenesis. Anat. Rec., 73:39, 1939.

Ham, A. W.: Cartilage and Bone. Special Cytology (Cowdry) 2d ed., New York, 1932, p. 981.

Hancox, N. M.: The Osteoclast. Biol. Rev., 24:448, 1949.

Heinen, J. H., Dabbs, G. H., and Mason, H. A.: The Experimental Production of Ectopic Cartilage and Bone in the Muscles of Rabbits. J. Bone & Joint Surg., 31:765, 1949.

Heller, M.: Ground Substance, Bone Salts, and Cellular Activity in Bone Formation and Destruction, Am. J. Anat. (in press).

Heller, M., McLean, F. C., and Bloom, W.: Cellular Transformations in Mammalian Bones Induced by Parathyroid Extract. Am. J. Anat., 87:315, 1950.

Hendricks, S. B., and Hill, W. L.: The Nature of Bone and Phosphate Rock. Proc. Nat. Acad. Sci., Geophysics, 36:731, 1950.

Huggins, C.: The Composition of Bone and the Function of the Bone Cell. Physiol. Rev., 17:119, 1937.

Key, J. A.: The Synovial Membrane of Joints and Bursae, in Cowdry's Special Cytology. 2d ed. New York, 1932, Vol. 2, p. 1053.

Kirby Smith, H. T.: Bone Growth Studies. A Miniature Bone Fracture Observed Microscopically in a Transparent Chamber Introduced in the Rabbit's Ear. Am. J. Anat., 53:337, 1933.

Lacroix, P.: L'organisation des os. Liège, 1949.

Maximow, A.: Untersuchungen über Blut und Bindegewebe. III. Die embryonale Histogenese des Knochenmarks der Säugetiere. Arch. f. mikr.-Anat., 76:1, 1910.

McLean, F. C., and Bloom, W.: Calcification and Ossification. Calcification in Normal Growing Bone. Anat. Rec., 78:333, 1940.

Murray, P. D. F.: Bones. A Study of the Development and Structure of the Vertebrate Skeleton. Cambridge, 1936.

Petersen, H.: Die Organe des Skeletsystems, in v. Möllendorff's Handbuch der mikroskopischen Anatomie des Menschen. Berlin, 1930, Vol. 2, Pt. 2, p. 521.

Ruth, E. B.: Bone Studies. I. Fibrillar Structure of Adult Human Bone. Am. J. Anat., 80:35, 1947.

Sigurdson, L. A.: The Structure and Function of Articular Synovial Membranes. J. Bone & Joint Surg., 12:1, 1930.

Urist, M. R., and Johnson, R. W.: Calcification and Ossification. IV. The Healing of Fractures in Man under Clinical Conditions. J. Bone & Joint Surg., 25:375, 1943.

Urist, M. R., and McLean, F. C.: Calcification and Ossification. I. Calcification in the Callus in Healing Fractures in Normal Rats. Jour. Bone & Joint Surg., 23:1, 1941.

Weidenreich, F.: Das Knochengewebe, in Möllendorff's Handbuch der mikroskopischen Anatomie des Menschen. Berlin, 1930, Vol. 2, Pt. 2, p. 391.

Weinmann, J. P., and Sicher, H.: Bone and Bones. Fundamentals of Bone Biology. St. Louis, 1947.

Wolbach, S. B.: Vitamin A Deficiency and Excess in Relation to Skeletal Growth. Proc. Inst. Med. Chicago, 16:118, 1946.

Wolbach, S. B., and Howe, P. R.: Intercellular Substances in Experimental Scorbutus. Arch. Path., 1: 1, 1926.

VIII. MUSCULAR TISSUE

The muscular tissue performs mechanical work by contracting, that is, by a shortening and thickening of its constituents. The contracting muscle cells regulate the position and movements of the various parts of the body with respect to one another. In the hollow viscera, ducts and blood vascular system the muscles propel the body liquids and excretions from place to place. Muscle cells are always elongated in the direction of the contraction, and are usually grouped into bundles which sometimes reach a considerable length.

The vertebrates have two distinct types of muscle: *smooth muscle* and *striated muscle*, connected by many intermediate forms. As a rule, smooth muscles contract independently of voluntary control, while the striated muscles are subject to voluntary control. *Cardiac muscle*, although striated, is involuntary and contracts automatically and rhythmically.

SMOOTH MUSCULAR TISSUE

Smooth muscle shows a close relationship to the ordinary connective tissue and is found primarily in the internal organs. In man it forms the contractile portions of the wall of the digestive tract from the middle of the esophagus to the internal sphincter of the anus, of the ducts of the glands connected with the intestine, of the respiratory passages from the trachea to the alveolar ducts, and of the urinary and genital ducts. The walls of the arteries and veins and some of the larger lymphatics also consist to a considerable extent of smooth muscle. It is scattered in varying amounts in the connective tissue of the skin, in the capsule and trabeculae of the spleen, and in the connective tissue of certain sensory organs, such as the eye. Peculiar smooth muscle cells are often closely connected with the epithelial tissue of the dermal and salivary glands (see p. 145).

Smooth Muscle Cells or Fibers. When a bit of fresh smooth muscle is examined under the microscope, the muscle cells (i.e., fibers) appear as long, spindle-shaped bodies which are thickened in the middle and become narrow toward their pointed ends (Fig. 126). Occasionally, the cells are branched or star-shaped.

The smooth muscle cells may reach a

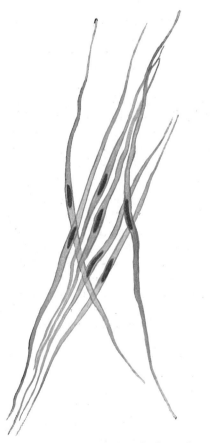

Fig. 126. Isolated smooth muscle cells from the wall of the stomach of a cat. 220 ×. (A.A.M.)

length of 0.5 mm. in the pregnant human uterus, while their average length in the intestine of man is 0.2 mm., with a thickness of 6 microns. The smallest smooth muscle cells occur in the small blood vessels, where they are 15 to 20 microns in length.

The nucleus, as seen in cross sections, is slightly eccentric and occupies the middle, widest portion of the cell body. It is elongated in the long axis of the cell, and has an oval or cylindrical form with pointed or rounded ends. It contains several nucleoli and a pale chromatin net which lies along the internal surface of the nuclear membrane. During the contraction of the cell the nucleus becomes folded on its lateral surface or markedly twisted. In general, the size of the nucleus increases with the size of the cell. Close to the nucleus, in a small indentation of its membrane, is a diplosome without an attraction sphere.

Smooth muscle cells do not have a distinct membrane which corresponds to the sarcolemma of the striated muscles (p. 148). The cytoplasm of smooth muscle cells in the living condition and sometimes after fixation and staining appears homogeneous. But some threads, the *myofibrils*, can always be made visible by maceration in nitric or trichloracetic acid. After this treatment the individual fibrils become visible as parallel threads running the length of the cell (Fig. 127).

The fibrils are homogeneous and lack the alternating sections characteristic of striated muscles. The fibrils are doubly refractile. The *border* or *external fibrils* are coarse and thick and stain deeply. In a cross section through a smooth muscle cell, they appear as sharply stained dots near the edge of the cytoplasm. The internal fibrils are thinner, measuring 0.3 micron. The number of fibrils in the smooth muscle cell varies, and in some cases the border fibrils may be few in number or absent.

It is generally believed that the fibrils represent the contractile elements of the smooth muscle cell. The actomysin of smooth muscle is similar to that of striated muscle (see p. 148). The substance between the fibrils is called *sarcoplasm*; it usually accumulates in

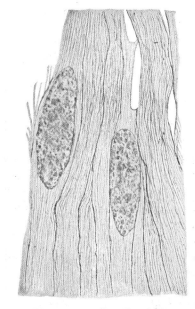

Fig. 127. Smooth muscle cells of the intestine of *Triton vulgaris;* the myofibrils are distinct. Biondi stain. 1430 ×. (After Levi.)

small amounts at both ends of the nucleus. Most of the cell body is occupied by fibrils so closely associated that sarcoplasm cannot be noticed between them. Mitochondria, a Golgi net and sometimes glycogen granules have been described in the sarcoplasm.

Contact of Smooth Muscle Cells with One Another. In many places in the body, but particularly in the skin, smooth muscle fibers are scattered singly or in small groups in the ordinary connective tissue. Here they are closely welded to the collagenous bundles and are often surrounded by thin elastic fibers. During contraction they throw the tissue into fine folds and wrinkles; this can be well seen in the skin of the mammary papillae or the scrotum. Sometimes several parallel fibers unite to form a small cylindrical bundle whose ends are covered by elastic fibers. An example is the smooth muscles connected with the hairs.

In other cases the smooth muscle fibers are arranged parallel to one another in one plane where they form a layer of varying thickness, as in small arteries. Here, because of the small lumen, each fiber bends sharply to surround the vessel. In the walls of certain large hollow organs, such as the intestine, bladder and

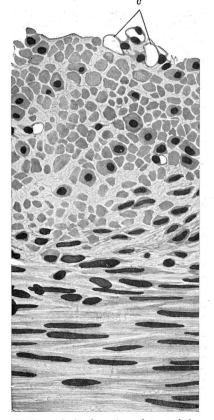

Fig. 128. Longitudinal section of part of the muscularis externa of intestine of a dog; external longitudinal layer (below), cross section of internal layer (above); c, blood capillaries. 530 ×. (A.A.M.)

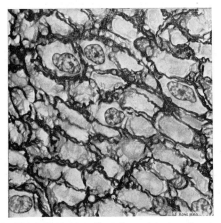

Fig. 129. Cross section through smooth muscle from human intestine, stained with the Bielschowsky silver method for reticular fibers and hematoxylin. The fibers form continuous networks about each of the muscle cells. Few of the cells have their nuclei in the plane of the section. 1875 ×. (Drawn by Miss E. Bohlman.)

uterus, the smooth muscle cells are arranged in layers or bundles. The direction of the fibers is the same in each layer, while it varies in different layers or bundles. Thus, in the intestine the internal layer of the muscularis externa consists of circularly arranged fibers forming a close spiral, while the external layer is composed of longitudinally arranged fibers forming a long spiral (see Fig. 128 and Chap. XXIV).

The cells are so arranged that the thick middle portion of one cell is opposite the thin ends of adjacent cells. Consequently, in cross sections through a smooth muscle bundle, some of the cells have nuclei in the plane of the section, and some do not.

The connective tissue fibers outside the muscle cells continue into the spaces between them and bind them into the bundles. Between the thicker bundles and layers of smooth muscles, loose connective tissue is present in small amounts. It contains fibroblasts and wandering cells, collagenous and elastic fibers, and a thick network of blood vessels and nerves. But connective tissue cells do not occur in the narrow slitlike spaces between the individual smooth muscle cells; here there are only a few thin, collagenous bundles and dense networks of reticular and elastic fibers.

The reticular fibers branch irregularly and pass longitudinally and transversely between the bodies of the smooth muscle cells. They can be stained with Mallory's aniline blue method and still more sharply with the silver impregnation methods. They form a regular system of supporting and binding material which forms a *sheath* about each muscle cell (Fig. 129). A characteristic of smooth muscle all over the body is the intimate association it bears with elastic fibers. This is so extensive that some authors consider them as forming a "myo-elastic" tissue. These elastic fibers are continuous with those of the surrounding loose connective tissue.

In smooth muscles, the pull of each contracting cell is first transmitted to the surrounding sheath of reticular fibers which continue directly into those of the surrounding connective tissue. This arrangement permits the force of the contraction of the entire layer of the smooth muscle to be uniformly transmitted to the surrounding parts, as in the narrowing of the lumen of blood vessels or in peristalsis of the intestine.

STRIATED MUSCULAR TISSUE

Muscle Fibers. The muscles attached to the skeleton of mammals consist of striated muscular tissue. In a teased preparation of fresh striated muscle, the tissue appears to consist of long cylindrical *muscle fibers*. These are large, multinucleated cells. As a result of teasing, only torn and broken sections of the fibers are seen, and the normal ends of the fibers are seldom found. When their undamaged ends are seen, however, the gradual tapering of the fibers toward a point is clearly visible. In other cases the end of the fiber appears rounded or notched; such an appearance is particularly frequent at the union of the muscle with a tendon.

Although the fibers are usually close to one another, they are entirely independent. Occasional anastomoses have been described between them. In nontapering muscles, such as the sartorius, the fibers apparently continue without interruption through the entire muscle, so that their length is equal to that of the muscle (Lockhart and Brandt). It is generally believed that in most muscles the fibers are usually shorter than the muscle; in this case, one end may be connected with a tendon, while the other end terminates among other fibers, or both ends may be free in the muscle. This statement should be subjected to further investigation. The thickness of the fibers fluctuates from 10 to 100 microns or more; apparently it depends, not on the length of the fiber, but on the type of animal and the particular muscle. In a given animal the more primitive muscles, such as those of the eye, are thinner. Fibers of varying caliber may be found in the same muscle. The thickness of the fibers increases with the age of the organism as well as under the influence of strenuous muscular activity.

Even in teased preparations of fresh muscle, the complex structure of the striated fibers is seen readily (Fig. 131). The freshly

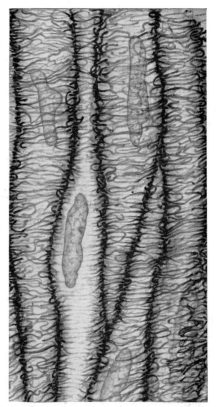

Fig. 130. Longitudinal section through smooth muscle of human intestine, stained with Bielschowsky silver method for reticular fibers and hematoxylin. 1875 ×. (Drawn by Miss E. Bohlman.)

teased fiber is usually slightly yellow and striated in both the longitudinal and transverse directions. These striations depend on the fact that the fibers consist of two parts: (1) a protoplasmic mass, the *sarcoplasm*, and (2) thin cross-striated fibrils, *myofibrils*, which are present in large numbers parallel to one another in the sarcoplasm.

The transverse striation is due to the fact that each myofibril consists of *disks* or sections which alternate regularly along its length. The corresponding disks of adjacent fibrils are usually arranged at the same level in the fiber.

The nuclei are seen in a fresh preparation of striated fibers, particularly after staining. Their great number corresponds with the large size of the fibers (Fig. 131).

The chief solid mass of the muscle fibers consists of several proteins, of which the most

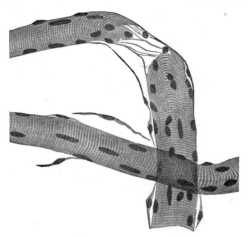

Fig. 131. Two striated muscle fibers of man, in a teased preparation, with stained nuclei. The upper fiber is crushed in its middle, and here the sarcolemma is seen. Between the fibers are several spindle-shaped connective tissue cells. 250 ×. (A.A.M.)

important are *myogen* and *myosin* combined with *actin*. Striated muscle contains more myogen and less myosin and one tenth as much nucleoprotein as smooth muscle. The fibers also contain carbohydrates, fats, lipids, and a pigment *myoglobin*, which is closely related to hemoglobin. Cytochrome, which consists of several hemochromogens, is also present. The fibers contain various metabolic intermediaries such as lactic acid, creatin-phosphate, hexosephosphate.

Sarcolemma. The striated fibers are covered with the *sarcolemma*, a thin (1 micron), structureless membrane which completely invests the fiber and follows its changes in form during contraction. In teased fresh preparations it can be seen as a transparent

film where the fiber has been torn or crushed (Fig. 131). It is probably a product of the cytoplasm of the muscle cell, although some consider it a product of the connective tissue surrounding the muscle fibers. Several authors have described a fibrillar structure in it, which they compare with the basement membrane. The chemical reactions of the sarcolemma differ, however, from those of collagen and elastin. Moreover, electron micrographs have so far failed to demonstrate any structure comparable to that of connective tissue fibers (Pease and Baker).

Myofibrils. In longitudinal sections through muscle fibers or in preparations where they have separated into individual fibrils, the latter appear as long, parallel threads (Fig. 132), which do not branch. The thickness of the fibrils fluctuates, but they are not larger than 1 to 2 microns in ordinary preparations, and some authors have given 0.2 micon as the lower limit.

Hall, Jakus and Schmitt found that in electron micrographs the myofibrils are composed of bundles of myosin filaments ranging from 50 to 250 angstrom units in width and extending in relatively parallel straight lines for indefinite lengths in the fibrils.

Myofibrils are distributed evenly or in compact bundles in the cytoplasm, the spaces between the fibrils being occupied by sarcoplasm. In cross section the separate fibrils appear as fine dots. When the fibrils are packed in bundles, the latter are separated by sarcoplasm, forming fields of Cohnheim (Fig. 136).

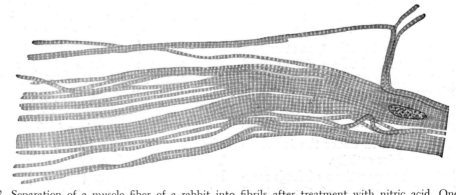

Fig. 132. Separation of a muscle fiber of a rabbit into fibrils after treatment with nitric acid. One nucleus is seen within a spindle-shaped accumulation of sarcoplasm. 530 ×. (A.A.M.)

Structure of the Myofibrils. The appearance of the striated muscle fiber depends on whether it is at rest, contracted, or passively stretched. The myofibril is composed of two main types of substance which alternaate regularly along its length. They are short cylinders and are called disks. One type is markedly refractile and appears dark and shining; it stains intensely with iron hematoxylin and, since it is doubly refractile, or *anisotropic*, in living cells as well as after fixation, had best be designated A disk (also called Q). The anisotropism of the A disks is due to their content of *actomyosin*.

Alternating with the A disks are *isotropic* (singly refractile) or I disks (J in German). It is claimed that these disks appear isotropic because the positive birefringence of their actomyosin is cancelled by a negatively birefringent component. With the usual stains the I disks remain colorless. In resting fibrils the A and I disks are approximately the same height. When the fibers are passively stretched, the I disk appears taller than the A disk.

There are other disks in the myofibril; the most important of these is the Z or *intermediate disk*, which is doubly refractile and occupies the middle of the I disk. Unlike the A and the I disks, the Z disk is not confined to the myofibril, but passes through the entire diameter of the fiber. During contraction the center of the A disk appears paler than the rest and is called Hensen's disk, within which a thin middle stripe indicated by the letter M may be seen. The N disk may be seen at times within the I disk between the Z and A disks.

The electron micrographs of Hall, Jakus and Schmitt show that the Z disks are not collagenous (as some had believed), and that the I as well as the A disks consist of myosin filaments. These are apparently the contractile units.

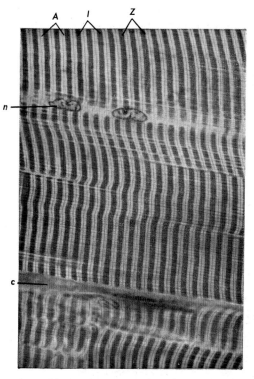

Fig. 133. Section of an infrahyoid muscle of man, showing characteristic cross striations with A, I and Z disks. *n*, Nucleus; *c*, endomysium. Photomicrograph. Mallory-azan stain. 1125 ×. (After von Herrath and Abramow.)

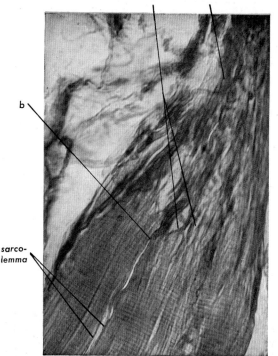

Fig. 134. Section from human tongue, showing connection of striated muscle and its tendon. The fibrils of the tendon apparently are connected with myofibrils at (*a*) and with sarcolemma at (*b*) (but see text, p. 152). Photomicrograph. Mallory-azan stain. 500 ×. (After von Herrath and Abramow.)

M   Z   M   Z

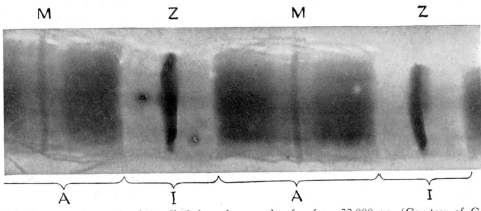

A   I   A   I

Fig. 135. Electron micrograph of myofibril from leg muscle of a frog. 32,000 ×. (Courtesy of C. Hall, M. Jakus, and F. Schmitt.)

The amount of substance included between two Z disks is called a *sarcomere*. This has been considered to be the structural and functional muscular unit (Fig. 135).

According to studies made with the older histochemical methods and with the aid of micro-incineration (Scott), it is believed that there is a concentration of potassium in the A disks. Gersh claims that potassium, phosphate and carbonate are uniformly distributed in the muscle cells. Potassium is thirty times, and phosphate at least eight times, as concentrated in the muscle cells as in the interstitial tissue.

In the invertebrates, especially in insects, many other disks may be seen in striated muscle.

Sarcoplasm. The cytoplasm of the muscle fiber which fills the spaces between the myofibrils is called sarcoplasm. The sarcoplasm accumulates constantly around the nuclei, especially at their ends. It is also present in small islands about the terminal endings of the motor nerves.

Variations in the Amount of Sarcoplasm. It is customary to distinguish striated muscle fibers rich in sarcoplasm from those poor in sarcoplasm. In certain vertebrates, as the rabbit, one can even recognize two types of muscles with the naked eye; one appears red and the other white. Under the microscope the fibers of the first type are seen to be rich, and those of the second type poor, in sarcoplasm. In the pale fibers the fibrils are small and regularly arranged. In the fibers of red muscles the longitudinal striation is more prominent and the transverse striation is somewhat irregular. The red fibers contain many fat granules and

have a "muddy" appearance. The nuclei of the red fibers occupy a more central position in the fiber and are rarely found at the periphery. As a rule, the red granular fibers in the lower vertebrates are confined to the most important muscles, while in the higher animals only the least active muscles are white. The red pigment is usually found in those muscles which contract repeatedly and over long periods of time. The "twitch" is longer in red muscles, which are more easily "tetanized." Those muscles which contract slowly are red, but not all red muscles contract slowly. The pigments which give these fibers their red color are probably muscle hemoglobin and cytochrome.

In the rabbit each type of fiber is generally gathered into separate muscles which show certain physiological differences. In the majority of animals, including man, both types of fibers enter into the composition of all the muscles; according to the type of muscle, one or the other type of fibers predominates.

Organoids and Inclusions. The sarcoplasm of many striated muscle fibers contains fat droplets, pigment and lipoid granules, and glycogen. In addition to these inclusions, the sarcoplasm contains mitochondria and particles called sarcosomes. The latter occur in both the I and the A disks, and their exact nature is undecided. As the sarcosomes and mitochondria have been demonstrated in preparations made with different techniques, the question is unsettled as to possible interrelationships between them. The fat inclusions diminish or disappear in starvation. In fixed preparations, glycogen appears as granules of irregular shape and size between the myofibrils. The sarcoplasm also contains a small Golgi net, frequently at each pole of the nucleus.

Nucleus. The nuclei of striated muscle fibers are rounded, oval, or elongated in the direction of the long axis of the fiber. Their size varies considerably. Their number fluctuates within wide limits, since it depends on the length of the fiber. The nuclei are always numerous, and in fibers several centimeters long they number several hundred.

The position of the nucleus varies according to the species of animal and the type of muscle. In the muscles of the lower vertebrates, and in many of the red muscles of mammals, the nuclei are scattered through the entire fiber. In the great majority of striated muscles of mammals, the nuclei are in the layer of sarcoplasm immediately beneath the sarcolemma.

Union of Striated Muscle Fibers with One Another to Form Muscles. Muscles are formed of parallel muscle fibers held together by connective tissue. The arrangement of muscle fibers within the muscle is clearly seen in cross sections and is similar to the structure of tendons. Like the collagenous bundles in tendons, so the muscle fibers here combine to form the *primary bundles*; several primary bundles combine to form *secondary bundles*; *tertiary bundles* are formed by the secondary ones, and so on. Large bundles and layers of interstitial connective tissue at the periphery of the muscles, the *epimysium*, project into the spaces between the bundles of muscular

fibers as the *perimysium*. They consist of irregularly arranged collagenous, reticular and elastic fibers, and many varieties of connective tissue cells, including fat cells. These thick layers branch and send thin layers between the smaller bundles (Fig. 138).

Between the separate muscle fibers inside the primary muscle bundles, the *endomysium* consists, as in smooth muscles, of thin fibrous networks which form capsules for the fibers. The endomysium also contains fibroblasts and fixed macrophages. The latter play an important role as phagocytes in inflammation of the muscle.

The number of elastic fibers in the interstitial connective tissue varies with the type of muscle and is probably closely connected

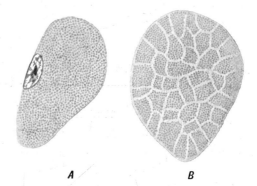

Fig. 136. Cross section of two striated muscle fibers of a rabbit. A, Uniform distribution of fibrils; B, Cohnheim's fields. 1000 ×. (Redrawn after Szymonowicz.)

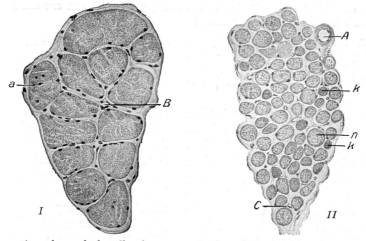

Fig. 137. Cross section of muscle bundles from two muscles of the same man. I, Gastrocnemius muscle; a, fiber with central nuclei; B, Blood vessel. II, Ocular muscle; n, normal fiber with Cohnheim's fields; k, dense portion of fiber; A, artery; C, capillary. Both figures 110 ×. (After Schaffer.)

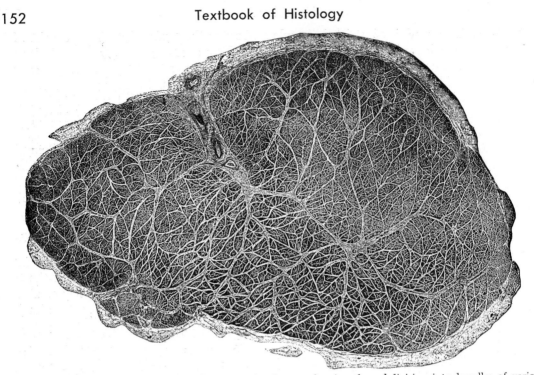

Fig. 138. Cross section through the sartorius muscle of man, showing the subdivision into bundles of various sizes of connective tissue. 4 ×. (Photograph by Müller, from Heidenhain.)

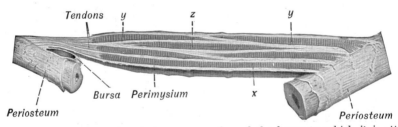

Fig. 139. Diagram showing connections between a muscle and the bones to which it is attached. Muscle fiber, x, begins and ends in tendons attached to the bones; y, terminates at one end in the muscle; z, terminates at both ends in the muscle. (After Braus.)

with its functional peculiarities. They are extremely abundant in the eye muscles and in muscles which attach to soft parts (muscles of the tongue and face).

Where a muscle is attached to a tendon there is a close union of the muscle fibers with the collagenous bundles of the tendon. The collagenous bundles of the perimysium pass directly over into those of the tendon; the sarcolemma covering the rounded, cone-shaped ends of the muscle fiber is fused with the ends of the collagenous bundles. The cone-shaped ends of the muscle fiber fit into grooves in the tendon. The connection of the sarcolemma with the collagenous bundles

is much more rigid than with the substance of the muscle fiber itself; for, if a fresh muscle is put into hot water, the contents of the muscle fiber at the ends separate from the sarcolemma.

Several authors have claimed that, besides the union of the sarcolemma with the tendon, there is a direct continuation of the myofibrils of the muscle fiber into the collagenous fibrils of the tendon. The transverse striation of the myofibrils disappears at such places. This conception has been denied by other investigators, who claim that the collagenous fibrils of the tendon only *appear* to continue into the myofibrils. The problem requires investigation with new methods and should be amenable to solution by electron microscopy.

Blood Vessels and Nerves. The blood vessels of skeletal muscle tissue (particularly red muscles) are abundant; capillaries which directly enlace separate fibers form a dense network with meshes stretched along the length of the fiber (Fig. 140). The short sides of these meshes sometimes appear as swollen spindles.

Lymphatics have been found in certain muscles within the layers of the perimysium and around the blood vessels.

The main nerve supply of the skeletal muscles is from the myelineated cerebrospinal afferent and efferent nerves.

CARDIAC MUSCULAR TISSUE

The heart of all vertebrates is composed of a network of peculiar striated muscle fibers. It contracts rhythmically and automatically. Its structure differs in several respects from that of skeletal striated muscles.

In a section of mammalian cardiac muscle, parallel to the surface of the heart, one can see that the fibers form networks with narrow meshes stretched in one main direction. In cross section the fibers appear as rounded or irregular areas of various sizes. Free endings can be found in cardiac muscle fibers only in teased, macerated preparations taken from the region of the atrioventricular openings and from the papillary muscles.

The cardiac muscle fibers consist of (1) nuclei, (2) myofibrils, (3) sarcoplasm, (4) a sarcolemma, according to some authors, and (5) intercalated disks.

Nuclei. The nuclei in cardiac muscle fibers, in contrast to those of striated muscle, are always arranged in the interior, usually in the axial part, of the fiber. They are scattered in the network of the fibers at various distances from one another. Their shape is oval, and their internal structure shows nothing peculiarly different from that of the nuclei of skeletal muscle fibers (Fig. 141).

Myofibrils. The myofibrils are similar to those of ordinary striated fibers, and are composed of the same types of disks, A, I, Z, and the like. Transversely, they are connected by the continuations of the Z disks passing through the sarcoplasm.

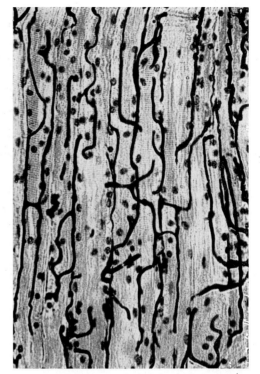

Fig. 140. Photomicrograph of striated muscle of monkey injected with India ink to show pattern of small blood vessels. Note arrangement of capillaries parallel to muscle fibers and transverse branches. 250 ×.

The fibrils in the cardiac muscle pass uninterruptedly along the length of the fiber, so that their free ends are not seen. The cross-striated fibers here, too, are gathered into bundles or columns. The individual fibrils have been seen in living tissue cultures (Hogue, 1937).

Sarcoplasm. The sarcoplasm in the cardiac muscle fibers is usually rather abundant; hence the longitudinal striation is well pronounced. In the nuclear areas it forms elongated accumulations devoid of fibrils; the swollen middle portion of these accumulations contains the nucleus, and tapers gradually to the ends (Fig. 141). Mitochondria are scattered in the sarcoplasm. In the spindle-shaped accumulations which surround the nuclei there are also fat droplets, a poorly developed Golgi net and pigment granules which increase with age.

Sarcolemma. The free surface of the cardiac muscle fibers is provided with a thin

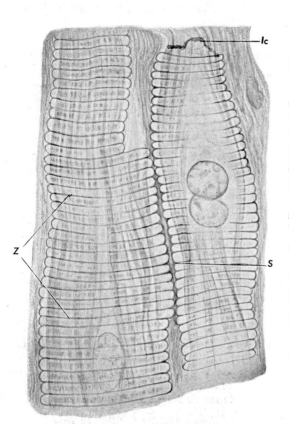

Fig. 141. Section of human cardiac muscle fibers, showing connection between the Z disks (Z) and the sarcolemma (S); Ic, intercalated disk. Mallory-Azan stain. 1400 ×. (Drawn by Miss Agnes Nixon.)

sheath which is well seen in sections as a sharp line. It is not so easily isolated as the sarcolemma of striated skeletal muscle. It may be selectively stained with certain dyes, and the Z disks are attached to it in the same way as to the sarcolemma of skeletal muscles (Fig. 142, S). The origin of this sheath is not clear; some authors regard it as a condensation of sarcoplasm, others as a product of the interstitial connective tissue. Well-pronounced, interstitial connective tissue areas are found only in the cardiac muscle of adult mammals.

Intercalated Disks. For a long time the attention of investigators has been attracted by short lines called *intercalated disks*, oriented transversely to the long axis of the fibers. The height of the stripes is somewhat less than that of a sarcomere; but, like a sarcomere, the intercalated disks are practically always bounded on both sides by the Z plates. Where the fibers branch, intercalated disks are sometimes found which are cone-shaped in sections (Fig. 142).

The substance of the intercalated disks stains sharply with various dyes. Under high magnification it appears to consist of vertical rods whose ends are directly fused with the myofibrils approaching the disk from both sides. The myofibrils are believed to pass uninterruptedly through the intercalated disks.

The physiological significance of the intercalated disks is unknown. It is certain that

Fig. 142. Section of human cardiac muscle, showing intercalated disks. Sublimate fixation; stained in thiazin red and toluidin blue. About 450 ×. (Slightly modified after M. Heidenhain.)

they are not the result of an agonal, abnormal contraction followed by shrinkage, as was thought by some authors. It is not probable that these disks represent areas where the cardiac fibers are able to grow in length, that is, where the new formation of sarcomeres is possible. According to another opinion, these areas act as fine, elastic interstitial tendons. The intercalated disks have also been considered to be altered Z disks which divide the network of cardiac muscle fibers into cell territories.

These areas consist of a number of branched processes separated from one another in the longitudinal direction by intercalated disks. The number of nuclei in each segment is rather constant for each type of animal; it is usually one to two in man and may be as great as thirty-two in the pig. It was therefore supposed that cardiac muscle is composed of independent muscle cells and that the intercalated disks are the cell boundaries. But most authors do not believe that these disks are cell membranes. They point out that the fibrils pass uninterruptedly through the intercalated disks from one segment into the next. They have also shown that in each segment there is at least one place where it is not separated by an intercalated disk from the adjacent segment and that consequently both segments are connected by anastomoses.

The intercalated disks appear comparatively late in the development of the cardiac muscle, and their number gradually increases with age, independently of cell multiplication. The disks are, therefore, a sign of secondary, incomplete division of the entire mass of cardiac muscle into separate territories or segments. According to most authors, cardiac muscle represents a syncytial, multinucleated mass of reticularly arranged protoplasmic bars in which contractile fibrils pass independently of cell territories.

It has been clearly shown in tissue culture that two heart muscle cells, which are not completely separated by a distinct cell membrane and which seem to have a partially continuous protoplasm and common fibrils, may beat with independent rhythms (Fig. 143). This observation offers a fairly strong argument in favor of the view that the cardiac muscle cells are independent cells. It shows, at least, that an apparent syncytium can break down into separate cells. Although the cardiac muscle cells may have a certain degree of morphological continuity, they are obviously discontinuous functionally—otherwise it is difficult to see how the two cells shown in Figure 143 could beat with different rhythms.

Purkinje Fibers. Fibers of the Impulse-Conducting System. Under the endocardium which lines the internal surface of the heart, particularly of the interventricular septum, there is a net of atypical muscle fibers, called "Purkinje fibers" after the man who discovered them.

It is now established that, just as in the ordinary cardiac muscle, the Purkinje fibers form a continuous, sarcoplasmic network. It appears to be divided into separate sections because of the extremely irregular arrangement of the continuous bundles of striated fibrils; these pass mainly in the peripheral portions of the fibers. These are also provided with intercalated disks. Large amounts of sarcoplasm are accumulated about the nuclei. The sarcoplasm of the fibers of Purkinje often has a large amount of glycogen, particularly in children. In many places a gradual passage

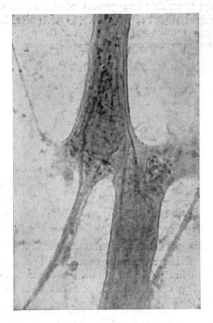

Fig. 143. Two cells from a seven-day culture of the heart of a four-day chick embryo. The two cells were beating with different rhythms. Two smooth fibrils continue from one cell into the other. There is no distinct cell membrane separating the two cells. The dark granules are mitochondria. Stained with Janus green and fixed with iodine. 1450 ×. (Courtesy of W. H. Lewis.)

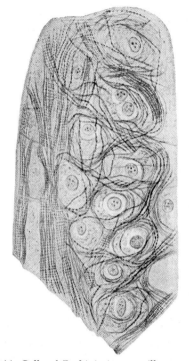

Fig. 144. Cells of Purkinje in a papillary muscle of a sheep; concentric arrangement of the myofibrils in the peripheral part of the cells. 475 ×. (After Levi.)

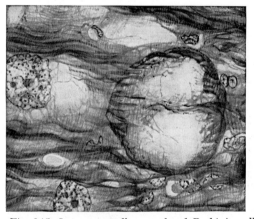

Fig. 145. Large, centrally vacuolated Purkinje cells of human heart. The myofibrils are concentrated at the periphery of the cells. 950 ×. (Drawn by Miss E. Bohlman.)

of these Purkinje fibers into ordinary cardiac fibers can be noticed.

The coordinated contractions of separate parts of the cardiac muscle depend on the presence of a mechanism for conducting the stimuli for contraction. The fibers of Purkinje form part of this mechanism. Nerves may also participate in the conduction of the contractile impulse (see p. 161).

The sino-atrial and atrio-ventricular nodes have the same structure as the Purkinje fibers.

Connective Tissue and Blood Vessels of Cardiac Muscle. Loose connective tissue is found in the slitlike spaces of the cardiac muscle. The muscle fibers are everywhere surrounded by dense, basket-like networks of blood capillaries. These arise from the coronary arteries and are collected in the cardiac veins.

Histogenesis of Smooth Muscle. Smooth muscle cells arise from the mesenchyme. In those places where a layer of smooth muscle will later develop, the mesenchymal cells begin to stretch out, the nuclei become elongated, and thick fibrils appear in the cytoplasm. They probably do not develop from the mitochondria. The thick myofibrils, at least in the beginning, apparently run continuously through a whole series of cells; later they split into thin myofibrils. In blood vessels, which at first consist only of endothelium, mesenchyme cells become arranged at regular intervals along the outside of the tube. They stretch out transversely, multiply by mitosis, and then produce myofibrils within their cytoplasm. Then the edges of these *myoblasts* come in contact with one another, and a continuous layer of smooth muscle is produced.

The reticular fibers between the muscle cells are probably produced by the same cells which become muscle fibers—the developing smooth muscle cells function as both myoblasts and fibroblasts. The smooth muscle elements (myo-epithelial cells, p. 339) in certain glands arise from the epithelium from which the glandular elements arise.

It is claimed that some of the new smooth muscle cells which develop in the uterus during pregnancy arise from the undifferentiated connective tissue cells in this tissue as well as from lymphocytes which wander into the myometrium. In a virgin rabbit uterus after injection of the female sex hormone there is mitotic proliferation of the smooth muscle cells.

Histogenesis of Striated Muscle Tissue. The striated muscular tissue arises in vertebrates from the mesoderm and in particular from its somites, except in the head, where it develops directly from mesenchyme. Those cells which give rise to the muscle tissue are called *myoblasts*. Within the myotome they are regular and cylindrical, but soon they stretch, become spindle-shaped and arrange themselves into parallel bundles. At the same time they multiply rapidly by mitosis.

There are several explanations of how the large, multinucleated, skeletal muscle fibers arise from the myoblasts: (1) Each muscular fiber is a syncytium resulting from fusion of many separate cells. (2) Each myoblast grows markedly in length, and the rapid multiplication of the nuclei by mitosis (and perhaps later by amitosis) is not accompanied by division of protoplasm, so that a multinuclear cell is produced. (3) Both methods of development occur. A final decision of this question must be left to future investigations.

In the spindle-shaped myoblasts, thin threads appear, which in the beginning are quite homogeneous, but which later acquire thickenings at equal distances along their entire length; these are the precursors of the A disks. After this a second series of thickenings appears, halfway between the first; these are the forerunners of the Z disks. After this the thin regions of the threads between the thickenings develop into iso-

tropic disks. At first the myofibrils are separated from one another; they connect up secondarily through continuous membranes, the Z disks.

Practically all investigators believe that the continued increase in the number of myofibrils is accomplished by longitudinal splitting. This problem should be studied with the modern techniques which can be applied to submicroscopic structures. Although many hold that mitochondria give rise to myofibrils, this idea is probably incorrect. The mitochondria remain in the sarcoplasm between the fibrillar columns and accumulate around the nuclei. The fibrils occupy the peripheral part of the fiber.

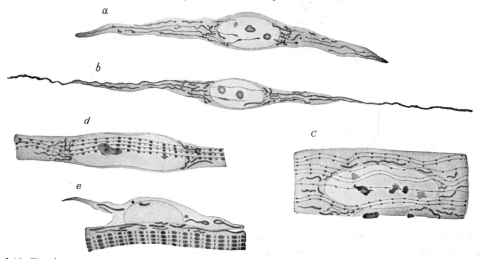

Fig. 146. Development of myofibrils within the myoblasts of a chick embryo. *a*, Myoblast of 64-hour embryo; *b*, myoblast of 76-hour embryo; *c*, middle portion of the myoblast with nucleus from a 124-hour embryo, showing the first appearance of segmentation of the myofibrils; *d* and *e*, later stages. (Redrawn after Duesberg.)

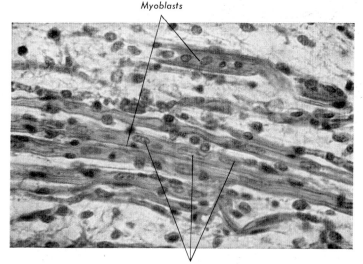

Fig. 147. Myoblasts in a muscle of the lower jaw of an eleven-week embryo. The myoblasts contain rows of centrally placed nuclei and a longitudinal fibrillation, but lack cross striations. Photomicrograph. H + E. 500 ×. (After von Herrath and Abramow.)

In the further development of the muscular tissue the separate fibers increase in thickness and length, and their number increases through transformation of new myoblasts, and later by a longitudinal splitting of existing fibers. The increase in number of fibers in the sartorius muscle stops when the human embryo is 130 to 170 mm. long. The future growth of the muscle depends only on the continued increase in the size of the fibers already present. However, it is also claimed that splitting of fibers and the continued new forma-

tion of fibers from undifferentiated elements occur in newborn mammals.

The sarcolemma appears at the surface of the embryonic muscle fibers at comparatively late stages. The nuclei, during the gradual growth of the muscle fiber, increase in number by mitosis and, in later stages, perhaps by amitosis. In mammals the nuclei at first are in the center, and the fibrils occupy the periphery of the fiber. In later stages the nuclei move toward the periphery, so that the central parts become occupied by fibrillar columns.

Contractility begins in the embryonic muscular elements about the time or shortly before the first myofibrils arise in their protoplasm. This contractility, at first slight and slow, gradually increases with the increase in number of myofibrils and their arrangement in bundles. The appearance of voluntary movements is connected with the development of the nervous motor tracts which lead from the spinal cord to the myotomes.

During the embryonic histogenesis of the striated muscle tissue, degenerative processes accompany the phenomena of progressive character. These sometimes include a considerable portion of the muscle fibers and may lead to their complete destruction.

Histogenesis of Cardiac Muscular Tissue. Cardiac muscle in the embryo forms from the splanchnopleure adjoining the endothelium of the heart primordium. At first a layer of loosely connected cuboidal cells, this part of the splanchnopleure becomes stratified. Its star-shaped cells anastomose with one another by processes which gradually thicken, forming a syncytium of protoplasmic shafts. The nuclei, scattered in the syncytium, multiply energetically by mitosis. The cytoplasm con-

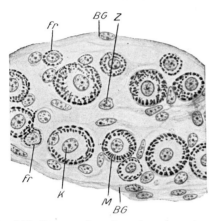

Fig. 148. Cross section through embryonic muscle bundle of a sheep. BG, Cells of the primordium of the perimysium; fr, muscle fibers in cross section with a single layer of primitive fibrils; K, nucleus in the axial sarcoplasm; M, primitive muscle fibers; Z, connective tissue cell. 740 ×. (After Schaffer.)

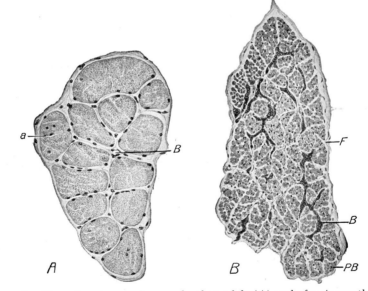

Fig. 149. Cross section through gastrocnemius muscle of an adult (A) and of a six-month fetus (B). Notice the difference in thickness of the fibers. a, Fiber with central nuclei; B, blood vessel; PB, primary bundle, the number of whose fibers corresponds to those in Figure A; F, connective tissue. 110 ×. (After Schaffer.)

tains many rod-shaped mitochondria, often in groups. The development of myofibrils proceeds here as in striated muscle. Homogeneous fine threads appear in the cytoplasm and run for long distances independently of cell territories. Then swellings appear at regular distances along these threads; they are the primordia of the A disks and are immediately followed by a second series of swellings—the Z disk primordia. As in striated muscle, the myofibrils are believed to increase by splitting longitudinally. Later the protoplasmic shafts with their fibrils become more and more separated from one another at various places. Interstitial connective tissue penetrates the spaces between the splitting and separating portions of the syncytium.

The *Purkinje fibers* develop from the same primary syncytium as the cardiac muscle fibers. They soon become distinguishable from the remaining myocardiac mass as thick protoplasmic shafts, swollen about the nuclei; they lie directly under the endocardium. A few myofibrils are irregularly distributed at their periphery.

Toward the end of the embryonic period, cardiac muscular tissue is well differentiated. But how it grows to form the mature organ is not yet clear. It is clear that the nuclei increase at first by mitosis and later perhaps by amitosis. The manner in which the fibers of the myocardium increase in number is unknown, although it has been supposed that this happens by longitudinal splitting of the existing fibers.

Regeneration of Smooth Muscle. In the vicinity of injured regions in the walls of the intestine or stomach, mitosis has been observed in the smooth muscle cells. But this capacity for regeneration is small, and great defects in smooth muscle heal by scar formation. Whether smooth muscle cells in the adult organism may be formed anew from fibroblasts has not been established; it is practically certain that they may develop from the perivascular embryonic cells of the adult (p. 56).

Regeneration of Striated Muscle. During intensive activity, the skeletal muscles increase in volume by enlargement of the existing fibers through an increase in the sarcoplasm, and not of the fibrils.

The regenerative capacity of the striated muscular tissue of higher vertebrates is usually insignificant and does not always lead to the formation of functioning fibers. After destruction of muscle fibers, regeneration always starts from existing fibers. The most successful regeneration takes place when the nuclei with the surrounding sarcoplasm remain

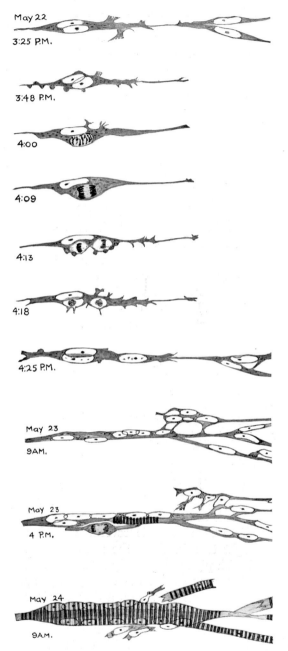

Fig. 150. Differentiation of myoblasts into cross-striated muscle fibers as seen in living regenerating zone, following removal of the tip of a tadpole's tail. One of a pair of closely associated myoblasts was watched throughout its nuclear division. The next day many nuclei were present. At 4 P.M. the first faint cross striations were visible. The following day many cross striations were in evidence in all fibers. (Redrawn after Speidel.)

alive. These become separate cells called *sarcoblasts* or *myoblasts*. The ends of the fibers become thicker and grow out toward the place of injury as muscular buds. The sarcoblasts hypertrophy, multiply, digest the degenerating fibers, and fuse in groups. Inside the old sarcolemma they form new fibers in which striated fibrils appear. In such a regenerative process, the sarcoblasts or myoblasts can be easily distinguished in vitally stained animals from the macrophages which have penetrated the fiber (see Speidel, 1938). It has been claimed that muscle cells turn into macrophages under the influence of choline in tissue cultures. A large defect in the muscular tissue is replaced by a connective tissue scar. Connection with motor nerve fibers is necessary for the existence of skeletal muscular tissue as well as for its successful regeneration. For details of the atrophy of muscle after section of the nerves, see Tower.

Regenerative Capacity of Cardiac Muscle. In various pathological conditions in the adult organism, an increase in volume of the cardiac muscle may take place. This probably depends in part on the increase in thickness and length of the existing fibers and in part on continued splitting of the muscular network, as in its normal development.

The regenerative capacity of cardiac muscle tissue is insignificant, and healing takes place by the formation of scar tissue. The large cells of the Aschoff nodules in the myocardium in rheumatic fever are no longer thought to arise from the muscle fibers. A yellowish pigment, possibly an abnormal metabolite, accumulates in smooth, cardiac and skeletal muscle of rats on a diet deficient in vitamin E.

Morphological Changes during Contraction of Muscle Fibers. If a bit of fresh smooth muscle is stimulated by an electric current, each spindle-shaped cell shortens and becomes thicker. In the spontaneous contraction of smooth muscle, sarcoplasm flows to a central point which thickens while the nucleus and the mitochondria move passively. No fibrils can be seen in such living cells. When living smooth muscle is fixed, some cells are often fixed in contraction, while adjacent cells are in relaxation. In such preparations, nodes of contraction may be seen over a small portion of the cell, and sometimes only a few fibrils (Fig. 151). Double refraction of the fibrils appears only in these contracted places, while the internodal portions are isotropic.

The ability of striated muscle fibers to contract and relax rapidly cannot depend on the transverse striation of the fibrils, since cardiac muscle cells in culture may lose their cross striations and continue to contract rapidly.

In contracting, the striated muscle fiber, as well as the entire muscle, may shorten to as little as one tenth of its original length. Its thickness increases greatly, and its volume decreases only by 0.05 per cent. In warm-blooded animals the contraction wave is so long and rapid that the entire striated muscle shortens at once. Numerous nerve endings scattered along their length permit all the fibers of a muscle to contract simultaneously.

When a living muscle is teased under the microscope, its fibers are seen to contract for a long time. On fixation, the entire fiber may contract, or agonal, local contraction waves may become fixed. One can thus follow all the steps in the change from resting, thin, cylindrical fibers into the condition of maximal contraction when they are thick and spheroidal. In such fixed preparations the fibrils thicken and the disks become wider and thinner; indeed, the I disk may become so thin that it disappears completely. When the shortening of the fibrils of the fiber reaches 50 per cent or more, a *reversal of striation* takes place. This is the appearance

Fig. 151. Smooth muscle cell from the stomach of a sparrow, showing six short contraction bands. (Redrawn after Soli, from Maximow.)

of thick, dark, transverse stripes in place of the Z disk. According to some, this is because the darkly stained substance of the A disk spreads in both directions from the middle disk M, penetrates the I disk, and closely approaches the Z disk. However, during these changes the double refraction of the A disk retains its location and only flattens and widens, although the disk itself no longer stains, and loses its definite boundaries. In the return to the resting stage, these changes are repeated in the reverse order.

The main part of contraction has as its morphological substrate the A and I disks. The M and especially the Z disks apparently do not take an active part in contraction. These transverse, elastic partitions attached to the sarcolemma are believed to support the fiber by interferring with the shifting of fibrils in relation to one another. The sarcoplasm must take part in the nutrition of myofibrils, since it completely surrounds them. It probably plays an important role in conducting excitation through the muscle fiber.

Mechanism of Muscular Contraction. The mechanism of the contraction of muscle is partially known. The evidence from studies with x-rays and double refraction indicates that there is a definite molecular orientation, especially of stretched-out protein molecules, in parallel chains. It is believed that, during contraction, owing to chemical changes at the side groups of the proteins, these chains crumple and shorten in the longitudinal direction; the reverse change takes place in relaxation (see Astbury). Chemical analyses of contracting muscle have shown that its carbohydrate breaks down into lactic acid; its combined phosphates also break down, and one of the nucleotides becomes deaminized. On the basis of ultraviolet absorption spectra of striated muscle, Caspersson and Thorell claim that the main part of the adenine derivatives (adenylic and adenyl-pyrophosphoric acids) in resting muscle are localized in the I disks, and that most of the myosin is in A disks. They suggest that, as a result of chemical processes taking place in the I disks, energy is transferred to the A disks, which are the seat of the contractile ele-

ments. The electron microscope studies by Schmidt and his co-workers indicate that the myosin filaments extend throughout the length of the sarcomere.

Participation of Nerves in Muscular Contraction. All muscles are under more or less continuous nervous stimulation whose nature varies with the type of muscle and its nervous connections. Smooth and cardiac muscle are under autonomic nervous control and contain autonomic nerve cells. The striated skeletal muscles receive their motor impulses from the central nervous system by way of craniospinal nerves. They probably do not receive additional innervation from the autonomic system.

When a skeletal muscle, preferably of a cold-blooded animal to avoid the effect of cooling, is removed from the body and its attached nerve is stimulated by a single electric shock, the muscle contracts quickly and relaxes almost immediately. This process is called a "twitch." When the nerve is stimulated by a rapid series of shocks, the muscle remains contracted, and the condition is called "tetanus." The muscles are in this condition when executing any voluntary movements. In the body, change in the position of any of its parts depends on a constant series of nervous impulses mediated by the myelinated efferent nerves. These cause a beautifully coordinated series of contractions and relaxations of the antagonistic muscles involved.

In addition to this neuromuscular mechanism which controls the movements of the limbs and other parts, and is based on typical reflex arcs (p. 189), there is another mechanism which controls the position of the limbs in space. This involves a series of unconscious, involuntary proprioceptive reflexes from the muscles themselves (see p. 179) from pressure organs, the labyrinths, eyes, and so forth. These are mediated through the central nervous system by myelinated nerve fibers and probably affect the same muscles as those involved in the voluntary movements. The impulses responsible for this "tone" are carried by the same nerves that carry the voluntary impulses. This is clearly shown when a nerve bundle was dissected until only one fiber was left undivided. When stimulated, this nerve fiber caused the muscle to contract; when not stimulated, it still carried sufficient impulses to maintain the tone of the muscle. Thus it appears highly probable that tone in skeletal muscle depends on the contraction of a few fibers. The normal stimulus for tone is probably in part the stretch put on the fibers as a result of the position the members of the body occupy after all movements. Those voluntary muscles which normally oppose the pull of gravity show tonus except during deep sleep and general anesthesia.

Between the extremes of skeletal and smooth muscle is the fairly quick contraction of cardiac muscle. In addition, it contracts rhythmically and does not develop fatigue—its rest periods are slightly longer than its periods of contraction. It is not under voluntary control. Its rhythmical activity is an intrinsic characteristic of the muscle, for in embryos the heart contracts for several days before any nerves have reached it. Moreover, in tissue cultures of embryonic heart muscle, individual muscle cells which have wandered into the plasma beat with characteristic rhythms. Indeed, two apparently connected cells may have individual rhythms.

Microdissection studies by de Renyi and Hogue (1938) show that in embryonic chick cardiac muscle cells in culture both myofibrils and sarcoplasm contract synchronously; but when the sarcoplasm is paralyzed by the injection of certain reagents, the myofibrils continue to be active.

REFERENCES

Astbury, W. T., Perry, S. V., Reed, R., and Spark, L.: An Electron Microscope and X-ray Study of Actin. Biochimica et Biophysica Acta, 1:379, 1947.

Beams, H. W., Evans, T. C., Janney, C. D., and Baker, W. W.: Electron Microscope Studies on the Structure of Cardiac Muscle. Anat. Rec., 105:59, 1949.

Carr, R. W.: Muscle-Tendon Attachment in the Striated Muscle of the Fetal Pig; Demonstration of the Sarcolemma by Electric Stimulation. Am. J. Anat., 99:1, 1931.

Caspersson, T., and Thorell, B.: The Localization of the Adenylic Acids in Striated Muscle Fibers. Acta Physiol. Scandinav., 4:97, 1942.

Cohn, A. E.: Cardiac Muscle, in Cowdry's Special Cytology. 2d ed. New York, 1932, Vol. 2, p. 1127.

Fenn, W. O. (ed): Muscle. Biol. Symposia, 3:1941.

Fischer, E.: Vertebrate Smooth Muscle. Physiol. Rev., 24:467, 1944.

Gasser, H. S.: Contracture of Skeletal Muscle. Physiol. Rev., 10:35, 1930.

Gersh, I.: Improved Histochemical Methods for Chloride, Phosphate-Carbonate and Potassium Applied to Skeletal Muscle. Anat. Rec., 70:311, 1938.

Goss, C. M.: The Attachment of Skeletal Muscle Fibers. Am. J. Anat., 74:259, 1944; First Contractions of the Heart without Cytological Differentiation. Anat. Rec., 76:19, 1940.

Hall, C. E., Jakus, M. A., and Schmitt, F. O.: An Investigation of Cross Striations and Myosin Filaments in Muscle. Biol. Bull., 90:32, 1946.

Hartz, P. H.: Proliferation of Muscle Cells in the Myometrium of the Nonpregnant Uterus. Arch. Path., 39:323, 1945.

Heidenhain, M.: Plasma und Zelle. Jena, 1911.

Hogue, M. J.: Studies of Heart Muscle in Tissue Cultures. Anat. Rec., 67:521, 1937.

Jordan, H. E.: The Structural Changes in Striped Muscle during Contraction. Physiol. Rev., 13:301, 1933.

Lewis, W. H., and Lewis, M. R.: Cultivation of Embryonic Heart Muscle. Contrib. to Embryol., Carnegie Inst., 1926.

Lockhart, R. D., and Brandt, W.: Notes upon Length of Striated Muscle Fibre. J. Anat., 72:470, 1938.

Mason, K. E., and Emmel, A. F.: Vitamin E and Muscle Pigment in the Rat. Anat. Rec., 92:33, 1945.

Meigs, E. B.: Striated and Smooth Muscle, in Cowdry's Special Cytology. 2d ed., New York, 1932, Vol. 2, p. 1087.

Nicholas, J. S.: Development of Contractility. Proc. Am. Philosophical Soc., 94:175, 1950.

Pease, D. C., and Baker, R. F.: The Fine Structure of Mammalian Skeletal Muscle. Am. J. Anat., 84:175, 1949.

Policard, A., and Baud, A.: Sur l'histologie inframicroscopique de la fibre musculaire striée. Bull. d'Histologie Appliquee, 27:121, 1950.

Renaut, J., and Maillard, J.: Le myocarde. Rev. gén. d'histologie, 1905.

Roskin, G., and Volzhina, N.: Investigation of the Smooth Muscle Cell and Its Fibrils with the Aid of Microsurgical Technique. C. Rend. Acad. Sci. URSS, 49:447, 1945.

Sacks, J.: Changing Concepts of the Chemistry of Muscular Contraction. Physiol. Rev., 21:217, 1941.

Schmitt, F. O.: Morphology in Muscle and Nerve Physiology. Biochimica et Biophysica Acta, 4:68, 1950.

Scott, G. H., and Packer, D. M.: An Electron Microscope Study of Magnesium and Calcium in Striated Muscle. Anat. Rec., 74:31, 1939.

Truex, R. C., and Copenhaver, W. M.: Histology of the Moderator Band in Man and Other Mammals, with Special Reference to the Conduction System. Am. J. Anat., 80:173, 1947.

IX. THE NERVOUS TISSUE

The entire mass of nervous tissue in the body forms the nervous system. The essential function of this tissue is to receive stimuli from the environment, to transform them into nervous excitations and to transmit them to the nervous centers, where they are reorganized to call forth appropriate responses. By these means the individual adjusts to the events of the world in which it lives and so coordinates the functions of its organs that they maintain the integrity of the body. The nervous system also includes the specific apparatus of all conscious experience. It is the dominant mechanism for the regulation of behavior and the maintenance of unity of the personality.

In the brain and spinal cord, the *central nervous system*, nervous impulses from all parts of the body come together and are integrated with other nervous impulses resulting from stimuli coming from outside the body. The *peripheral nervous system* is made up of all nerve tissue outside the brain and spinal cord and serves to interconnect all other tissues with the central nervous system. In this way, all parts of the organism are integrated by a central clearing house which controls the activity of the organism as a biological entity.

The function of the nervous system is based on two fundamental properties of living substance. The first is the ability to react to various physical and chemical agents. The second is the ability to transmit the excitations thus elicited from one locality to another. The first property is called *irritability*; the second, *conductivity*.

The nervous system of the higher organisms evolved from these primitive properties of living substance in lowly forms. In the Metazoa certain cells developed the properties of irritability and conductivity to a high degree, forming a rudimentary nervous system. By further specialization some of the nerve cells evolved the capacity to react to special kinds of exogenous energy. These cells, with the corresponding accessory structures distributed throughout the body or near its surface, produced three sensory systems: the *exteroceptive system*, concerned with receiving impulses from the surface of the body; the *interoceptive system*, responsive to impulses from the internal organs; and the *proprioceptive*, receiving excitations from the muscles, tendons and joints. Other nerve cells became connected with the peripheral *effector organs*, as the muscles and glands, forming the *neuromotor* and *secretory systems*. Still other nerve cells, mostly collected in a large, central mass, assumed the role of *correlators* or *integrators*. These receive, select, combine, distribute, inhibit or otherwise modify the excitations arriving from the receptive surfaces or from the inner organs, and finally influence properly the peripheral effectors.

The cells within the nervous system which carry out its special functions are called nerve cells or *neurons*. Their numbers, although enormous, are exceeded by other cells which serve to maintain the unusual shapes of the neurons and the physical integrity of the tissue, and also supply its nutritional and biochemical requirements. The cells not specifically concerned with conduction of nervous impulses are the *neuroglia cells* and the cells of the rich vascular plexus which pervades the central nervous system.

The neurons have a body made up of a nucleus and surrounding cytoplasm (*perikaryon*) which expands into a number of processes (Fig. 152). These usually comprise several short *dendrites* and only one *axis cylinder,* or *axon,* which may have a great length (Fig. 153).

The size, shape and other peculiarities of the body, and the number and mode of branching of the processes, vary, producing countless varieties of nerve cells. It has been assumed that with the morphological diversity there goes some sort of functional specialization. The neurons are related anatomically and functionally by their expansions which are in contact with other nerve cells, or with epithelial, muscular or glandular

cells. The point of contact of two nerve cells, called a *synapse,* transmits functional influence from one cell to another in one direction only (p. 187). Nearly every nerve cell has many synapses with other cells. If the nervous system were organized as a syncytium without inner boundaries, the impulses would spread in all parts without restraint. The evidence—morphological, physiological and pathological—indicates that the nervous system is built of countless individual cells that are structurally and functionally independent to a greater or lesser degree.

MINUTE STRUCTURE OF THE NEURON

The nerve cell or neuron has a body containing a nucleus and threadlike processes or expansions. Often the mass of the cytoplasm in the processes is much greater than that in the cell body. The superficial zone of the cytoplasm appears to be of somewhat different character from that of the core of the cell body and evidently plays an important role in the transmission of the nervous excitations.

Nucleus. The globular nucleus is relatively large, though it varies with the volume of the cell body and apparently fluctuates with phases of life or activity of the cell. The usual position of the nucleus is in the center of the body. A nuclear membrane is always present. The linin framework is prominent but sparse. Characteristically, there is one relatively large oxyphile nucleolus; rarely are there several nucleoli. The basichromatin is scanty, and the nuclei of the nerve cells appear as pale vesicles when stained with basic dyes.

Body or Perikaryon. The cytoplasm that constitutes the body of a nerve cell is differentiated into several structures: (1) neurofibrils, (2) interfibrillar substance, (3) chromophile substance or Nissl's bodies, (4) mitochondria, (5) internal reticular apparatus of Golgi, (6) centrosome, and (7) various inclusions. Special methods must be used to demonstrate most of these structures, although neurofibrils and mitochondria have been seen in fresh cells.

Neurofibrils. The *neurofibrils* are best developed in large neurons, but their presence

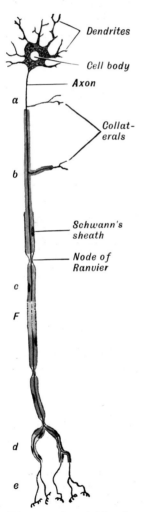

Fig. 152. Diagram of a peripheral motor neuron. *a,* Naked axon; *b,* axon invested only with myelin; *c,* axon covered with both myelin and Schwann's membrane; *F,* broken lines indicating great extent of the fiber; *d,* the axis cylinder, covered only with Schwann's sheath and its nuclei; *e,* the naked axis cylinder ending.

has been demonstrated in almost every variety of nerve cell. They appear as homogeneous threads, embedded in a more liquid protoplasm (Fig. 156). The neurofibrils are distributed as a complicated network throughout the cell body, and spread into all processes, where they can be followed into the

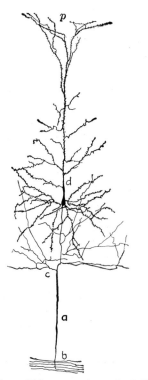

Fig. 153. Pyramidal neuron (type I of Golgi) from cerebral cortex of rabbit. The axon gives off numerous collateral branches close to the cell body and then enters the white substance, within which it extends for a long distance. Only a small part of the axon is included in the drawing. *a*, Axon; *b*, white substance; *c*, collateral branches of axon; *d*, ascending or apical dendrite; *p*, its terminal branches at the outer surface of brain. (After Ramón y Cajal.)

vestigators, the neurofibrils are confined to the territories of their respective neurons (see Bartelmez and Hoerr; Bodian; and Fig. 190).

The Neuroplasm. The *neuroplasm* is the undifferentiated part of the cytoplasm of the nerve cells wherein the neurofibrils are embedded. Neuroplasm in the processes is called interfibrillar substance; in the axis cylinder it is called axoplasm. In fresh condition the axoplasm appears homogeneous; in the dark field it contains scattered bright granules.

Chromophile Substance. The *chromophile substance*, or *Nissl's bodies* (Figs. 155, 158, 189, 201), are conspicuous structures of the nerve cells and show important changes in some pathological conditions. They are in-

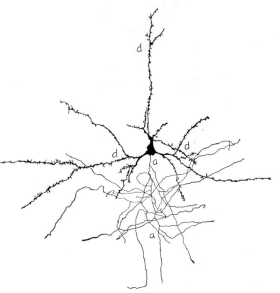

Fig. 154. Neuron of type II from cerebral cortex of cat. The entire neuron is included in the drawing. *a*, Axon whose branches terminate close to the cell body; *d*, dendrites. (After Kölliker.)

finest terminal ramifications (Figs. 174, 175, 190). It is possible that the neurofibrils seen with the optical microscope are aggregates of minute axon-filaments, 100 to 200 angstrom units thick, which have been found with the electron microscope (O. F. Schmitt).

The function of the neurofibrils is not clear. In the opinion of some, they are the substrate for the transmission of the nervous excitations; others consider them to be merely supporting structures. According to most in-

visible in living or fresh material, and are best shown by staining with toluidin blue or thionine or other basic aniline dyes. Thus treated, the granules appear intensively stained, much like the chromatin of the nucleus; the intervening channels are filled with the neurofibrils, which remain unstained (compare Figs. 155 and 156).

The physiological significance of the chromophile substance is undetermined. It is absent from certain neurons and from the

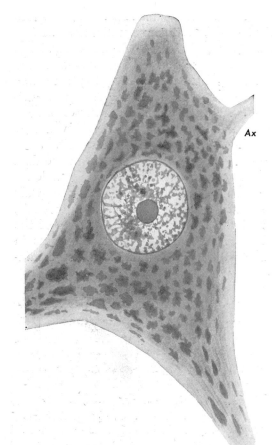

cell body or to the axis cylinder anywhere along its course, and is called *chromatolysis* (Fig. 201); the process that brings it about, if caused by injury to the axon, is called Nissl's reaction or primary irritation of the nerve cell (p. 196).

The study of this substance with the freezing-drying method favors the view that it is not distributed homogeneously in the living cell (Fig. 158). With the aid of ultraviolet microscopy and the use of ribonuclease, it has been shown that ribose nucleoprotein is one of the main constituents of the Nissl substance. Treatment of the sections with ribonuclease results in the loss of stainability with basic dyes, although the protein structure of the Nissl bodies is left intact. Some believe in a nucleolar origin of this material.

Golgi Apparatus. The *intracellular reticular apparatus of Golgi* (Fig. 159) is present in all nerve cells and appears as a network of black, irregular, wavy threads and bands, coarser than the neurofibrillar network. The form varies considerably in different types of neurons.

It is necessary to point out the difference between this intracellular reticular structure and another network, the *pericellular net of Cajal and Golgi*. The latter surrounds the body of the nerve cell from outside; it is essentially of neuroglial origin and is, therefore, not part of the neuron.

Mitochondria. The rodlike or filamentous *mitochondria* are scattered everywhere between the Nissl's granules and neurofibrils (Fig. 160). They can be demonstrated in many fresh nerve cells by supravital staining. Their number varies from a few to many.

Fig. 155. Motor cell from the gray substance of the ventral horn of the spinal cord of a cat, showing granular chromophile substance. Ax, Axon hillock. 670 ×. (A.A.M.)

axis cylinders. Possibly it represents reserve material easily utilizable during the activity of the nerve cell—a view supported by the marked changes observed in the chromophile granules under varying physiological and pathological conditions.

The chromophile granules are distributed in the entire cell body except in its most peripheral layer and the zone immediately adjacent to the nucleus. They are also present in the dendrites, but absent from the axon and its origin from the cell body, the axon-hillock. The form, size and distribution of the chromophile granules vary in the extreme, appearing in as many patterns as there are varieties of nerve cells. As a rule they are coarser and more abundant in large cells, especially motor ones, and scarce and fine in small cells. Under different physiological conditions, such as rest and fatigue, the granules change their aspect. In pathological processes they may disappear. Their disappearance may be the consequence either of direct injury to the

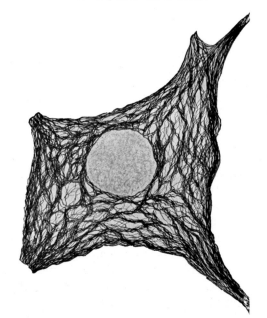

Fig. 156. Motor cell of the ventral gray column of spinal cord of rabbit; the net of neurofibrils in the perikaryon continues into the processes; the nucleus appears as a pale disk. Bielschowsky method. 500 ×. (A.A.M.)

Centrosome. The *centrosome* is a spherical structure characteristic of the immature, multiplying nerve cells during the early stages of embryonic development. In fully developed, static, adult neurons, especially of the vertebrates, a typical centrosome is rarely seen. Most of the structures so designated have another significance.

Inclusions. Besides the structures mentioned, there are inclusions in the nerve cells which are less widespread and less constant. Bright *vacuoles* have been described in the fresh nerve cells of lower animals. *Pigment granules* are frequently encountered. The coarse, dark-brown or almost black granules are undoubtedly melanin and are found in certain cells only, in the substantia nigra of the midbrain, in the locus coeruleus in the floor of the fourth ventricle, in the dorsal vagus nucleus, and in the spinal and sympathetic ganglia. Its physiological significance is unknown. More frequent, especially in man, are fine lipochrome granules of yellowish color. They are probably a product of normal activity which remains within the protoplasm in a useless although noninjurious capacity. In favor of this view is the gradual increase in the amount of the pigment with advancing age. *Fatty substances* are encountered in the form of inclusions in the protoplasm of the nerve cells, either as reserve material or as a product of normal or pathological metabolism. *Glycogen* is found in the ependyma, choroid plexus and nerve cells of the embryonic, but not in a demonstrable quantity in the adult, nervous tissue. *Iron-containing granules* are found in the nerve cells of the substantia nigra, the globus pallidus and elsewhere. Their number increases as the tissue grows older.

Processes or Expansions. The processes or expansions of the nerve cells are their most remarkable characteristics. In almost every one of the many varieties of neurons there are two kinds of processes: the dendrites, and the axis cylinder.

The *dendrites,* or the *protoplasmic processes* (Fig. 152), are direct expansions of the body. Nissl's chromophile granules and mitochondria are found in the thicker portions of the dendrites (Figs. 155, 158, 160). A neuron usually has several main dendrites; more rarely there is only one (Fig. 555). At the point where the dendrites emerge from the cell body they are thick, rapidly becoming slender toward their ends. Each dendrite usually divides into primary, secondary, tertiary and more branchlets. These are of the most varying shapes and sizes, distributed in the most diverse ways, but they are typical for each variety of neuron. As seen in Golgi preparations, the surface of many dendrites

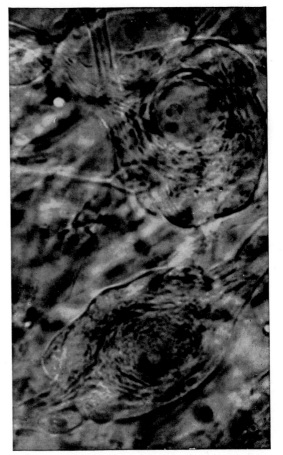

Fig. 157. Two bipolar cells of a ganglion from an eight-day chick embryo cultivated *in vitro* for seven days. Unretouched photograph of the living cells showing neurofibrils. 1650 ×. (After Weiss and Wang, 1937; courtesy of The Wistar Press.)

is covered with a great number of minute, thorny "spines," also called "gemmules," giving the dendrites the appearance of a test-tube brush. These "spines" and other similar terminal twigs often serve as synaptic organs. In the majority of the neurons the dendrites are short and are confined to the immediate vicinity of the cell body. The number, length and arrangement of the terminal twigs of the dendrites vary in the extreme, and are not directly dependent upon the size of the perikaryon. The pattern and the size of the dendrites are characteristic for each variety of neuron.

The dendrites, through their synapses with the axon endings of functionally related neu-ons, receive nervous impulses from other neurons. A minority of synapses end directly on the cell body itself.

The *axis cylinder* or *axon* differs considerably from the dendrites. While there are usually several dendrites, there is only one axis cylinder to each neuron (*a* in Fig. 152). This process often arises from a small conical elevation on the cell body, devoid of Nissl's granules, called axon-hillock (Fig. 155). The axon does not contain Nissl's granules and usually is thinner and much longer than the dendrites of the same neuron. The axon gradually decreases in diameter as the distance from the cell body increases.

Along its considerable course the axis cylinder may or may not emit collateral branchlets (Fig. 152). The chief arborization, however, is at the end of the main branch and is called *axon ending* (also *telodendron*) (*e* in Fig. 152; Fig. 555). It is composed of primary, secondary and other branches and buds varying greatly in number, shape and distribution. Often its branches are assembled into baskets that surround the body of the related neuron, or they twist around the dendrites of the latter. In simpler cases one or two twigs of an axon ending just touch the surface of a dendrite or the body of another related neuron (Figs. 191, 557).

The axon normally receives nervous excitations from its own cell body, and thus indirectly from its dendrites. Occasionally, an axon may arise from a principal dendrite rather than from the cell body. In such instances there may be direct conduction from dendrite to axon of the same cell (as in the second S—ganglion cell from the left in Fig. 557). The axon transmits the excitation through its ending to other neurons or to effector cells, as muscle fibers or glandular cells. There are as many modes or types of axon endings as there are varieties of neurons (Figs. 191, 557). Moreover, the same axis cylinder may terminate in several different ways and be synaptically connected with several different neurons (Fig. 557).

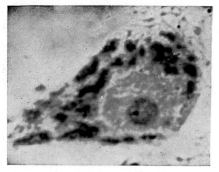

Fig. 158. High-power photomicrograph of anterior horn nerve cell of spinal cord of rabbit, fixed by the freezing-drying method, untreated, undenatured, and stained with toluidin blue. (After Bensley and Gersh.)

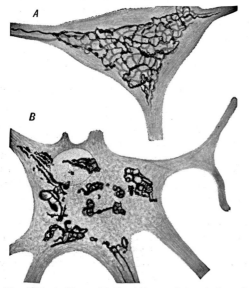

Fig. 159. A, Normal cell of the nucleus of the sublingual nerve of rabbit, showing the intracellular reticular apparatus; B, similar cell four days after cutting the nerve. (Redrawn after Marcora.)

Some exceptions to these features characterizing dendrites and axons are encountered, as in the peripheral sensory neurons of the spinal ganglia (Fig. 161). In these the afferent fiber in the adult has the histological and conducting properties of an axon, although it normally conducts impulses toward its cell body in the same way as dendrites of other neurons.

A recent development in our knowledge of nerve cells is the concept that the nerve cell body is continuously forming new cytoplasm that flows continuously down the nerve cell processes, perhaps at about 1 mm. per day. According to Weiss and Hiscoe, "the perpetual growth of the neuron presumably serves to replace katabolized protoplasmic systems, especially proteins, which cannot be synthesized in the peripheral cytoplasm."

Forms and Varieties of Neurons. Depending on the number, length, thickness, and mode of branching of the processes, and also on the shape, size and position of the cell body, and on the synaptic relationships, an infinite number of types of neurons can be distinguished in the nervous system. In general, the neurons may have axis cylinders of considerable length that leave the place of their origin in the gray substance and traverse the so-called "white or fibrous mass," or become peripheral nerve fibers, and terminate at some

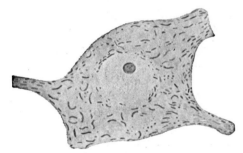

Fig. 160. Nerve cell body of a rabbit, showing mitochondria. (Redrawn after Schirokogorow.)

Fig. 161. Collection of cells from the ganglion of the trigeminus of embryonic guinea pig, to illustrate stages in the transformation of bipolar neuroblasts into unipolar ganglion cells. (After van Gehuchten.)

distance in another locality. Such are termed *Golgi type I* neuron with the long axon (Figs. 153; 556, *m, n, o, p, s*). To this type belong all the peripheral nerves and neurons whose axis cylinders form long fiber tracts of the brain and spinal cord. In other neurons the axis cylinder is relatively short and does not leave the confines of the gray substance where its body lies. These represent *Golgi type II* neuron with the short axon (Figs. 154; 556, *c, d, e, f, h, l, i*). Such neurons are especially numerous in the cerebral and cerebellar cortex and in the retina.

The shape of the cell bodies is variable; it may be spherical, oval, piriform, spindle-shaped or polyhedral. The shape is determined by the mechanical pressure of surrounding structures, by the number, size and place of origin of the processes, by the internal organization of the cell, but above all by the requirements of function. The absolute size of the neurons likewise

varies between extreme limits, from midgets to those of giant size.

The *unipolar neurons* are the nerve cells that have a single process, the axon. They do not have dendritic processes. In the central nervous system such neurons are rare, except in early embryonic stage (Figs. 199, 200). In the *bipolar neurons* each cell has one main dendrite and one axis cylinder projecting from opposite ends of the fusiform body. Typical bipolars are found in the retina (Figs. 554, 556), in the vestibular and cochlear ganglions, and in the olfactory nasal epithelium. In vertebrate embryos all neurons of the craniospinal ganglia are at first bipolar (Figs. 157, 198); during further development they undergo changes (Fig. 161), resulting in the peculiar forms to be described. The single process shown by most of these cells does not represent a simple axon; because of this these elements may be called pseudo-unipolar (Fig. 162).

In the multipolar neurons, representing by far the great majority of neurons, the shape is determined by the number and arrangement of their dendrites (Fig. 152). The *star-shaped neurons* are the motor cells of the ventral gray columns or anterior horns of the spinal cord (Figs. 155, 159). The *pyramidal neurons* (Figs. 153, 189, 201) are one of the characteristic elements of the cerebral cortex. In these a thick, trunk-like dendrite projects from the upper end of the cell body, and, in its vertical course, reaches the superficial layers, where it splits into a tassel, the so-called "apical dendrite." Other dendrites arise from the lower end of the body—the basal dendrites. The axis cylinder emerges from the base and passes into the subcortical white mass.

Of remarkable shape are Purkinje's cells in the cerebellar cortex. In these, from the upper end of the body arise two thick, rapidly dividing dendrites covered with a multitude of tiny "spines." The large dendritic tree-top is confined to a narrow zone; it resembles a richly arborized fan oriented across the longitudinal axis of one of the cerebellar convolutions and vertical to its surface. The axis cylinder enters the white subcortical mass.

Many more varieties are found both in the cerebral and cerebellar cortex and elsewhere, among which are conspicuous diminutive *granule cells*, especially characteristic of the receptive sensory areas, as the striate area (visual), the region around the central sulcus (part of the sensory-motor cortex) and of the transverse temporal convolutions in the Sylvian fossa (auditory). In these the few short dendrites radiate in all directions, while the axis cylinder and its branches are also confined to the immediate neighborhood of the cell. This variety exemplifies neuron type II of Golgi with the short axon. To the same type belong also many other neurons, as the asteriform and basket cells in the cerebellar cortex and the horizontal cells in the retina (Fig. 556, *c*).

Of special interest are the ganglion cells of the root ganglia of the cranial and spinal nerves (Figs. 161,

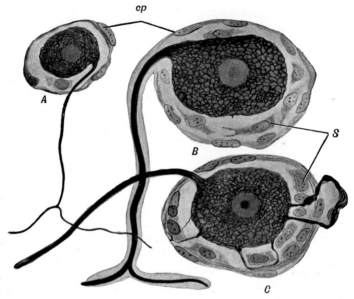

Fig. 162. Three cells from the nodose ganglion of the vagus nerve of man, A and B, with two T-shaped dividing processes: *cp*, capsule; *S*, satellites; cell *C* has looped processes. (Redrawn after Ramón y Cajal.)

162). These are mostly pseudo-unipolar. From the globular or pear-shaped body a single process arises which divides like the letter T into a peripheral or dendritic branch that becomes the axon of a peripheral sensory nerve fiber, and into a central or axonic branch which is the axon of a sensory posterior root fiber that terminates in the central nervous system. Although unipolar, these neurons are physiologically bipolar. The initial single expansion and both central and peripheral branches are enveloped in myelin and Schwann's sheaths. The body of each cell is enveloped by two cellular capsules. The inner is made up of small, flat, epithelium-like satellites or Schwann's cells continuous with similar cells enveloping the peripheral processes. The outer capsule is formed by a special modification of the interstitial connective tissue, with a thin, structureless membrane as an inner layer. A dense capillary network is present in the capsule of each cell. The capsule is made up of collagenous fibers and fibroblasts arranged concentrically. It extends along the cellular process, becoming continuous with the endoneurium of the nerve fiber.

The few examples described give an incomplete picture of the wealth of the varieties of neurons. Many more have been discovered by numerous investigators, especially by Ramón y Cajal and his pupils, but probably many more remain unknown. It is apparent that each ganglion or cortical area is composed of a multitude of varieties of neurons differing from place to place, and occurring side by side.

THE NERVE FIBER

The nerve fiber, in the conventional sense (Fig. 163), is the axis cylinder or axon of a nerve cell with its enveloping neurolemmal and myelin sheaths (if the latter is also present). In the fresh condition the nerve fiber appears as a homogeneous, shiny and slightly yellowish tube with thick walls. Various histological techniques reveal in its center a continuous smooth gray stripe, the axis cylinder, wrapped in one or two sheaths (Fig. 163). In cross sections the unstained myelinated nerve fibers appear as small or large circles with sharp outlines formed by the highly refractive neurolemmal sheaths, and with darker spots in their centers which are the axis cylinders (Figs. 169, 171). The myelin sheaths in untreated preparations remain invisible. The appearance of the various constituents of the nerve fiber differs according to the technique applied: the vital methylene-blue and the various silver methods stain the axis cylinder blue, brown or black; Weigert's and similar methods stain the myelin sheath alone.

Axis Cylinder. The axis cylinder, or axon, is a thin thread of fairly uniform thickness and smooth appearance. In the periphery, at fairly regular intervals, at the nodes of Ranvier (p. 172), it is thinner than between them.

The fresh axis cylinder appears homogeneous. However, when it is treated with selective methods (vital methylene blue, methods of Cajal or Bielschowsky, observation of living tissue cultures), the presence of *neurofibrils* and of the undifferentiated axoplasm is revealed. Each neurofibril is directly continuous with the neurofibrillar network of the cell body. There are no Nissl granules in the axis cylinders. Some have reported the presence of mitochondria in the axon near its origin on the cell body.

is composed of *Schwann's cells*, that, like the links of a chain, follow one another along every peripheral nerve fiber from its beginning, at the spinal root or in some ganglion, almost to its peripheral termination. Each Schwann's cell, with its flat and oval nucleus surrounded by protoplasm containing a Golgi net and mitochondria, envelops a segment of axis cylinder (Figs. 163, 164). In myelinated nerve fibers the consecutive segments are separated from one another by a *node of*

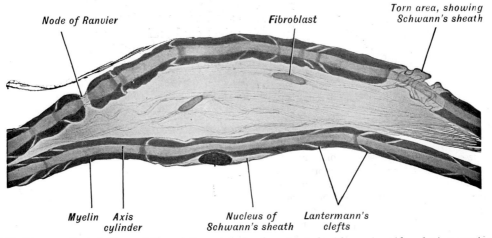

Fig. 163. Two myelinated fibers of the sciatic nerve of a frog; treated with osmic acid and picrocarmine and teased. 330 ×. (A.A.M.)

The axis cylinder conducts nervous impulses from the body of a neuron, and thus from its receptive dendrites, to some effector organ, a muscle or a gland. In the process of conduction the myelin sheath or cell membrane act as insulators. The axis cylinder carries the nervous influences to distant regions of the body—as from the cells of the cerebral cortex to the cells of the anterior horns of the spinal cord, and, as the peripheral neuron, from these to the various muscles, and other tissues.

Schwann's Sheath, or Neurolemma.* This is a delicate, transparent, tubelike membrane which, in the peripheral nerve fibers, envelops the axis cylinder (Figs. 152, 163, 164). In those nerve fibers that also have a myelin sheath the neurolemma is the outermost. It

---

* Prof. F. T. Lewis pointed out to me the historical correctness of "neurolemma" (not "neurilemma").— W. B.

Ranvier, where the adjoining segments merge (Fig. 163). The neurolemma does not belong to the connective tissue, but is a membrane similar to sarcolemma. It occasionally contains granular inclusions of complex lipids which increase greatly with advancing age and even more so in pathological conditions.

Like the neurons, Schwann's cells are of ectodermal origin. They can be considered the "peripheral neurolgalia" that have left the central nervous system and have become adapted to the special conditions of the peripheral nervous system (Harrison). As the peripheral axons grow, embryonic cells of Schwann follow them, enveloping one segment after another, and freely migrate from branch to branch or from axon to axon, until they form the complete neurolemmal sheaths (Speidel).

Schwann's cells are indispensable for the life and function of the axons of the periph-

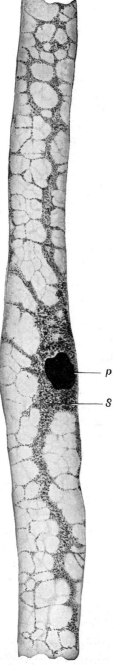

Fig. 164. Nerve fiber from the cauda equina of a cat. S, Large Schwann's cell, with its nucleus, p, and granular protoplasm. (After Nemiloff.)

mains continuous with the cell body of the neuron, and spreads along the bridges formed by Schwann's cells (p. 199). In tissue cultures, Schwann's cells may transform into macrophages.

Myelin Sheath. Nerve fibers which have a myelin sheath are called myelinated or medullated nerve fibers (Fig. 163). In fresh, unstained nerve fibers, myelin forms a glistening envelope around the axis cylinders. It is this property of myelin that is responsible for the white color of the fiber masses of the brain, called white substance, and of parts of the spinal cord and numerous peripheral nerves.

Schmitt, Bear and Palmer, on the basis of x-ray diffraction patterns, describe the myelin sheath as "being composed of concentrically wrapped layers of mixed lipides alternating with thin, possibly unimolecular, layers of neurokeratinogenic protein material. Within the layers the lipide molecules are oriented with paraffin chains extending radially and with polar groups in the aqueous interfaces, loosely bonded to those of the protein. . . . The specific structure of the sheath is relatively insensitive to the action of temperature, electrolytes, and detergents." This view of the structure of the myelin sheath is supported by studies with the electron microscope which show its lamellar structure (Fernandez-Moran).

In contrast to the continuous neurolemma, the myelin sheath of a nerve fiber is completely interrupted at fairly regular intervals by circular *nodes of Ranvier* and is thus divided into cylindrical segments. These are shorter in the terminal portion of the fiber. The length varies in different nerve fibers and in different animals from 50 to 1000 microns. The thicker the fiber, the longer are the segments. Each segment consists of one neurolemmal cell of Schwann. The protoplasm of the cell is seen with some stains as a complex net of thick and thin trabeculae pervading the entire myelin sheath as far as the axis cylinder. Whether these trabeculae merge into a distinct envelope, the axolemma of Mauthner, separating the axon from the myelin sheath, is not certain. If the peripheral

eral nerve fibers. They probably are important in the metabolism of the axon. In the process of regeneration the newly built axon always grows out of the central stump, which renerve fiber gives off collateral branches, this always takes place at a Ranvier's node. (Fig. 152).

In fixed preparations of the peripheral nerves the myelin of each segment is interrupted by oblique partitions, the *incisions* or *clefts of Schmidt-Lantermann,* several to each Schwann's segment (Fig. 163). The clefts have been seen in teased fresh nerves of rats. Many nerve fibers in the brain and spinal cord, especially those that form the white subcortical substance, have myelin sheaths but lack the neurolemma, for which is substituted neuroglia, particularly the oligo-dendroglia (Figs. 166, 186). Both Ranvier's nodes and Schmidt-Lantermann's clefts seem to be absent in the brain and spinal cord.

The question of the *origin of myelin* has been variously answered. Some think that it is the product of Schwann's neurolemmal cells (in the peripheral nervous system), or of the neuroglial cells (in the brain and spinal cord). Others consider that the myelin is the product of the axis cylinder and is, therefore, a part of the neuron itself. However, certain observations, such as the fact that the bodies of cells of the spiral ganglion of the acoustic nerve are enveloped by myelin husks whose structure resembles neuroglial husks elsewhere, are difficult to reconcile with the latter opinion. In any case, there is little doubt that the neurolemma and the neuroglia are indispensable for the formation of myelin (p. 195). Likewise, in pathological processes, whenever a neuron and its axis cylinder are affected, both the neurolemmal and the myelin sheaths undergo reactive changes; in the central nervous system the neuroglial cells react in addition to the myelin sheaths (p. 196).

The myelinated nerve fibers are characteristic of the vertebrate nervous system. In lower animals they are rarely present. During ontogenesis the myelin appears relatively late, and the *process of myelinization* ends only some time after birth. Different fiber systems or tracts of the brain and spinal cord become myelinated at different times (Flechsig).

Numerous, mostly thin, axis cylinders in the peripheral nervous system, especially in the sympathetic, have only a neurolemmal sheath, the myelin being absent. These are gray and are difficult to demonstrate with ordinary techniques. They can be seen more easily when stained with the vital methylene-blue method or with silver. These unmyelinated nerve fibers are known as *C fibers* (Figs.

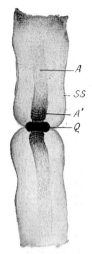

Fig. 165. Silvered, myelinated nerve fiber from sciatic nerve of a frog, showing a cross of Ranvier. *Q*, Cross plate (cementing ring), *A′*, spiny bracelet of Nageotte; *A*, axis cylinder; *SS*, neurolemma. 740 ×. (After Schaffer.)

167, 168). However, studies with polarized light indicate that many apparently naked fibers may have traces of myelin.

The probable function of the myelin sheath is to improve the insulation of the axis cylinder against the loss of nervous current traversing it during its activity, as compared with the naked axon wrapped only in the neurolemmal sheath. Precisely how the insulation is achieved, and what chemical and physical interactions take place between the axon and the various sheaths during the active nervous process and in the exchange of nutritive materials, are unknown.

Physiological Properties of the Nerve Fiber. The nerve fiber is essentially a highly irritable conductor. Along it the dynamic nervous excitation propagates in waves at a relatively high speed (up to 150 meters per

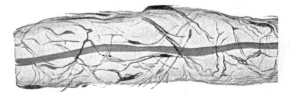

Fig. 166. Myelinated nerve fiber from ventral column of the white matter of the spinal cord of a cat; the axis cylinder is surrounded by a myelin sheath enveloped by neuroglia fibers. (Redrawn after Paladino.)

Fig. 167. Unmyelinated sympathetic nerve fibers of cat, teased and stained with hematin. (Redrawn after Ramón y Cajal.)

second), faster in myelinated than in naked axons. During the conduction of excitation the activity of one portion of the axon serves as a stimulus activating the next portion, and so on. As the nerve fiber becomes active, it changes its electric potential, the outside of each active portion becoming negative relative to resting portions. Action currents then flow between active and resting regions. When artificially stimulated, the nerve fiber increases its metabolism. The electrical changes in active nerves and the accompanying chemical reactions are discussed in detail in textbooks of physiology.

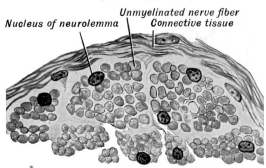

Nucleus of neurolemma   *Unmyelinated nerve fiber*
                                 Connective tissue

Fig. 168. Cross section of a sympathetic nerve of ox. (Redrawn after Ramón y Cajal.)

The following features are characteristic of the activity of the nerve fiber or axis cylinder: (1) Like all living substance, it has *irritability*, the ability to respond to various stimulating agents, and *conductivity*, the ability to transmit impulses from point to point. (2) To act as a transmitter, the nerve fiber must be anatomically continuous and physiologically in an appropriate condition. (3) After the passing of the impulse the fiber remains for a short time unexcitable ("refractory period"). (4) The axon can conduct an impulse with equal ease in the normal direction and in the opposite, *antidromic*, direction. (5) The impulse normally remains confined to the stimulated axon, spreading only along it and its branches to the synapses. (6) The impulse traveling along an axon can be weak-

ened temporarily or blocked by the local action of heat, cold, pressure, electric current and by many drugs (anesthetics, narcotics). (7) Any stimulation intense enough to cause the axon to respond calls forth the maximum discharge of which the axon is capable ("all or nothing law").

The properties of simple nervous conductors, as listed, differ profoundly in several respects from those of the synaptic gray nervous substance of the brain, the spinal cord and the ganglia, as discussed on page 193.

Nerve Fibers as Constituents of Peripheral Nerves, Brain and Spinal Cord. In their peripheral course outside the central nervous system, both myelinated and unmyelinated nerve fibers are bound into bundles by connective tissue, forming peripheral *nerve trunks* and their branches (Figs. 168–171). While most of the nerve fibers are myelinated, they are characteristically white and glistening in appearance. The *white matter* of the brain, the various bundles of the brain stem, the core of the cerebellum and the white columns of the spinal cord, consist mainly of nerve fibers; here there are few, if any, nerve cells. The *gray matter*, found in both the cerebral and cerebellar cortex, in the basal ganglia of the brain, in the numerous nuclei of the brain stem, in the gray columns of the spinal cord, in the peripheral ganglia and in the retina of the eyes, is chiefly composed of the bodies of numerous nerve cells, their dendrites, and the initial and terminal unmyelinated portions of axis cylinders. The nerve fibers of some sympathetic nerves are mostly unmyelinated gray fibers. Both white and gray matter contain neuroglia and blood vessels, although these elements are more abundant in the gray matter. In certain regions of the central nervous system the constituents of both white and gray substance are mixed in various degrees, as along the sides of the thalamus, in the subthalamus and

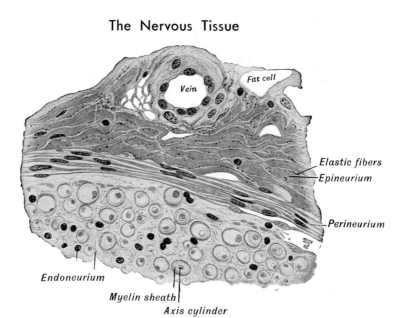

Fig. 169. Portion of cross section through a branch of the median nerve of man. 380 ×. (After Schaffer.)

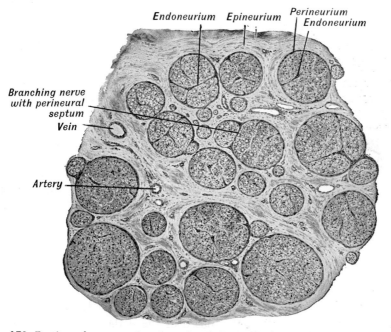

Fig. 170. Portion of cross section through sciatic nerve of a newborn. 42 ×. (After Schaffer.)

hypothalamus, in the tegmentum of the brain stem and at the junction of the anterior and posterior gray horns of the spinal cord. Such regions are called *reticular formations*.

The *peripheral nerves* are composed of fascicles of nerve fibers of varying thickness (1, 2 and up to 30 microns), held together by connective tissue. The outer layer of the latter, the *epineurium* (Figs. 169, 170), is made up of connective tissue cells and of collagenous fibers, mainly arranged longitudinally. Fat cells may also be found here. Each of the smaller fascicles of a nerve is in turn enclosed in a membrane of dense, concentric layers of connective tissue called *perineurium* (Figs. 169, 170). From this, fine longitudinally arranged strands of collagenous fibers, fibroblasts and fixed macrophages pass into

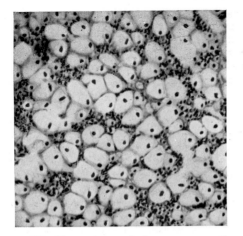

Fig. 171. Photomicrograph from a cross section of human medial cutaneous nerve, prepared by Davenport's reduced silver method and kindly furnished by S. W. Ranson. 450 ×.

the spaces between the individual nerve fibers; this is the *endoneurium*. Where the nerve trunks divide into branches, the connective tissue sheaths become thinner. The smaller branches show no epineurium, and here the perineurium cannot be distinguished from the endoneurium, being reduced to a thin, transparent, fibrillated membrane covered with flat connective tissue cells resembling endothelial cells whose outlines can be demonstrated with silver. From this membrane filaments extend to wrap around each nerve fiber, thus forming the delicate *endoneural* or *connective tissue sheath of Key and Retzius,* a network of elastic fibers attached

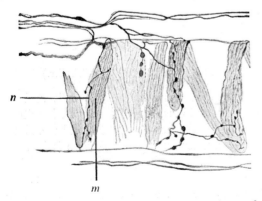

Fig. 172. Nerve endings (*n*) on the smooth muscle cells (*m*) of an artery from the vascular membrane of a rabbit's eye. (Redrawn after Retzius.)

to the neurolemmal sheath of Schwann. This sheath is also known as the sheath of Henle, although he called it neurilemma. Blood vessels are embedded in the epineurium and perineurium and in the thicker layers of endoneurium.

It has become customary to classify nerve fibers according to their diameter, since the speed of impulse transmission and size of the action potential vary with the square root of the diameter. Fiber diameters cover a wide and continuous spectrum from large myelinated to small unmyelinated fibers. It is found in peripheral nerve that fibers are collected into three distinct diameter groups. The large A group, conducting impulses at 15 to 100 meters per second, contains motor and some sensory fibers. The B group conducts at 3 to 14 meters per second and contains mainly visceral sensory fibers. The C group consists of unmyelinated fibers, conducting at 0.5 to 2 meters per second, and carries autonomic and some sensory impulses.

The following rule on the *functional characteristics of the nerve fibers* holds good: the motor nerve fibers of the skeletal muscles are thick and heavily myelinated; those of the smooth visceral muscles are thin and lightly myelinated or without myelin; those of tactile sensibility are of medium size and moderately myelinated; those of pain and taste are thinner, with less myelin or none at all; and those of the olfactory nerve are always unmyelinated. Such histologically defined fiber aggregates are therefore functional systems: tactile, gustatory, somatic motor, visceral motor, and so forth.

A particularly clear segregation of functionally different nerve fibers is found in the *spinal roots.* In general, each segmental spinal nerve contains in its ventral roots coarse, heavily myelinated somatic motor fibers for skeletal muscles and thinner, more lightly myelinated or naked visceral motor fibers for the sympathetic nervous system. Its dorsal roots contain cutaneous fibers of several types, as those of deep sensibility, proprioceptive fibers from muscles and tendons, and afferent fibers of visceral sensibility from the sympathetic system. More than half of the dorsal root fibers are naked axons, and most of these are distributed with the cutaneous rami. The relative number of myelinated and unmyelinated fibers varies widely in different spinal segments and in the same segment of different mammalian species. In the mixed trunks peripheral to the spinal ganglia, the fibers of the motor and sensory roots mingle, and to those are added sympathetic fibers from the communicant rami (Figs. 169, 171). The myelinated fibers of various sizes are readily identified by the clear zones of unstained myelin surrounding the darkly stained axis cylinders. The unmyelinated fibers tend to assemble in small fascicles. Some of these are sensory fibers from the spinal ganglia; others are postganglionic sympathetic fibers.

In the *central nervous system*, in the brain and spinal cord, numerous nerve fibers are also segregated into functional systems. Such are especially the afferent and efferent pathways (cortico-spinal, cortico-nigral, spino-cerebellar, spino-thalamic and many other fiber tracts). Each of these has a special function, partly well known, partly still obscure.

Peripheral Nerve Endings. Each peripheral nerve fiber, be it sensory, motor or secretory, sooner or later terminates in some peripheral organ with one or several terminal arborizations. Some nerve fibers spread as free endings among the non-nervous tissue cells; others are attached to these by means of complicated structures. The nerve fibers ending as *receptors* are homologues of dendrites; those with *motor* or *secretory* endings are homologues of axis cylinders, and their terminations are equivalent to axon endings. In general, the structure of the nerve endings is adapted to increase the surface of contact between the neuron and its related non-nervous element. The chemical-physical changes which mediate the transfer of the various "sensory" stimuli from, or of the efferent impulses to, a peripheral non-nervous organ have been the subject of intense investigation (see p. 187). According to the tissue, three groups of nerve terminations can be distinguished: (1) endings in muscle, (2) endings in epithelium, and (3) endings in connective tissue.

Nerve Endings in Smooth and Cardiac Muscle. These belong to the unmyelinated type of fibers. From complicated plexuses, thin nerve fibers are given off that eventually come in contact with the surface of the muscle cells. Some of these, the sympathetic *motor endings* (Figs. 172, 173), terminate here by means of one, two or more terminal swellings. Possibly, some even penetrate the substance of the muscle fibers. The *visceral sensory fibers* spread in the connective tissue between the smooth muscle bundles, or are in contact with the muscle fibers themselves. In the cardiac muscle the tissue is permeated by a multitude of thin fibers passing between the muscle trabeculae, on whose surface they form varicosities.

Terminations of the Myelinated Somatic Motor Nerve Fibers on Striated Muscles (Motor Plates). These have a more complex structure (Figs. 174, 175). As the nerve fiber approaches the muscle fiber, it loses its myelin sheath. The connective tissue membrane of Key and Retzius with its nuclei extends over the surface of the sarcolemma and disappears. The neurolemma, according to some, also terminates abruptly in the sarcolemma, while, according to others, it may run for a short distance within the plate. At the junction of the nerve and muscle fibers the sarcoplasm forms a mass that varies in form and size beneath the sarcolemma. This is the *motor plate*. It receives the naked axis cylinder, which here breaks up into a number of terminal ramifications. The deep layer of the motor plate adjacent to the contractile substance is its *sole*. Here muscle nuclei may be found in large numbers. The ramifications of the axis cylinder are accompanied by small, dark nuclei interpreted as those of neurolemmal cells. The terminal arborization of the axis cylinder in a motor plate is beneath the sarcolemma (hypolemmal), and not over it (epilemmal).

The so-called "accessory motor nerve fibers" probably are somatic sensory fibers, if not collateral branches of the somatic motor fibers. It is unlikely that they are of sympathetic origin and responsible for the tonus of the skeletal muscles, as has been claimed. On the other hand, the muscles are permeated by a rich sympathetic plexus related solely to the blood vessels and connective tissue. The nature of the so-called "peri-

Nerve endings

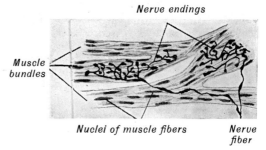

Muscle bundles

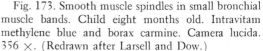

Nuclei of muscle fibers   *Nerve fiber*

Fig. 173. Smooth muscle spindles in small bronchial muscle bands. Child eight months old. Intravitam methylene blue and borax carmine. Camera lucida. 356 ×. (Redrawn after Larsell and Dow.)

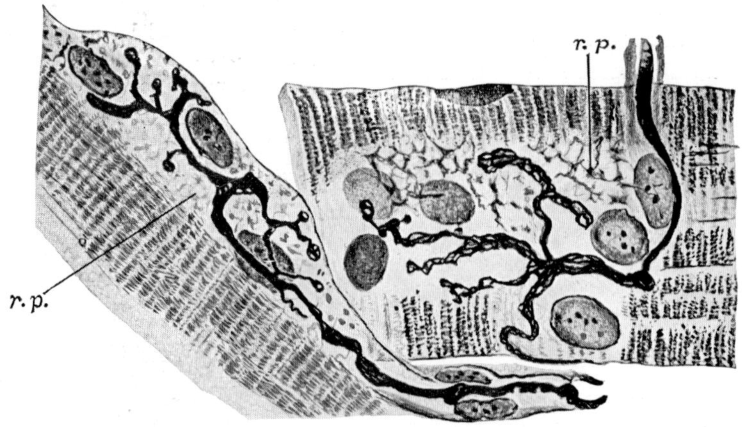

Fig. 174. Motor end plate from tongue of rabbit, showing the "periterminal net" (*r. p.*) of the end plate. (Redrawn after Ramón y Cajal.)

Fig. 175. Sensory nerve ending enveloping a fiber of an ocular muscle. (Redrawn after Dogiel.)

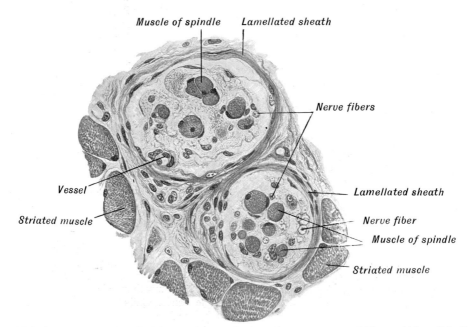

Fig. 176. Cross section of a double muscle spindle from human tongue. 380 ×. (After Schaffer.)

terminal net" in the muscle plate (Fig. 174) is obscure. It is considered an artefact by some.

Sensory Nerve Endings in Striated Muscles. These are always present in considerable numbers. Some are located in the muscular tissue, others on tendons or at musculo-tendon junctions. Some terminations are simple, others complex. The interstitial terminations are distributed in the connective tissue; the epilemmal terminations are in close contact with the muscle fibers, but, in contrast with the motor plates, remain on the surface of the sarcolemma. The interstitial terminations may be simple naked branches of the axis cylinders or encapsulated structures. The epilemmal endings likewise may be simple: one or more tortuous axis cylinders, after shedding their myelin sheath at approximately the middle of a muscle fiber, envelop the sarcolemma by continuous circular and spiral twists. Their varicose twigs terminate with nodular swellings (Fig. 175). More complicated are the *neuromuscular spindles*, found in higher vertebrates only (Figs. 176, 177). They are narrow, long (0.75 to 7 mm. or more) structures slightly thickened in the middle, arranged lengthwise with the bundles of ordinary muscle fibers, and present mainly at the junction of muscles with tendons. Each spindle consists of one or several long striated muscle fibers. They are enveloped by a connective tissue capsule. Each spindle is supplied by thin motor nerves that terminate at the muscle fibers of the spindle with typical motor plates. These motor nerve fibers have been shown to affect the sensitivity of the sensory endings on the muscle spindle. In addition, the spindle is approached by one or more thick sensory nerve fibers. Their axis cylinders, covered with a thin layer of Schwann's cytoplasm and nuclei, wind around the intracapsular portion of the axial muscle fibers and are in close contact with the sarcolemma, forming spirals (Fig. 177). The muscle fibers of the spindles are distinguished by their thinness, abundant sarcoplasm and their peripheral nuclei; in this they resemble the so-called "red muscle fibers."

Sensory Nerve Endings in Tendons. These are of several kinds, and are also either simple or encapsulated. In simple forms the naked nerve fibers and their branches spread over the surface of the somewhat changed tendon fibers in small treelike figures of different forms (Fig. 178). The composite forms, such as the neurotendinal spindles, the organs of Golgi, resemble the neuromuscular spindles and are always found at the very border of the muscular tissue.

The physiological significance of the muscular and

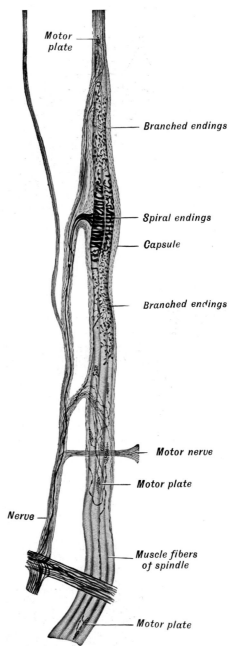

Fig. 177. Neuromuscular spindle of a cat, showing nerve endings. (Redrawn after Ruffini.)

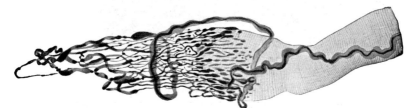

Fig. 178. Sensory nervous apparatus, consisting of palisade-like terminal branches, located at the junction of a muscle fiber with a tendon. (Redrawn after Dogiel.)

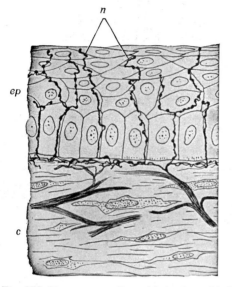

Fig. 179. Free nerve endings (*n*) in the epithelium (*ep*) of rabbit cornea; *c*, connective tissue of the corneal substance proper. Impregnation with gold chloride. (Redrawn after Ramón y Cajal.)

tendinous sensory apparatus probably is their responsiveness to various peripheral stimuli of general character, giving sensations of pain, pressure, and particularly of "muscle sense."

Nerve Endings in Epithelial Tissue. These are of both receptor and effector type. Histologically, they can be distinguished only in rare instances. The terminations in the epithelial layers of the skin and mucous membranes are regarded as sensory receptors, those in the epithelial glands partly as secretory, partly as sensory. The terminations of the cochlear and vestibular nerves are undoubtedly sensory in their function. The *nervous terminations in glands* (lacrimal, salivary, kidneys, and so on) are all unmyelinated sympathetic fibers forming dense nets on the outer surface of the basement membrane, with branches penetrating the latter and often forming a second network on its inner surface. They end between the glandular cells as thin varicose threads.

Free Sensory Epithelial Endings. These are found in the epithelium of the cornea (Fig. 179), epithelium of the mucous membrane of the respiratory passages, skin, and oral cavity, and are especially abundant in places which have a well-developed sensitiveness. In the epidermis these branches do not penetrate farther than the granular layer.

Nerve Endings in Connective Tissue. These are numerous and of many forms, particularly in the derma, under the epithelium and mesothelium of the mucous

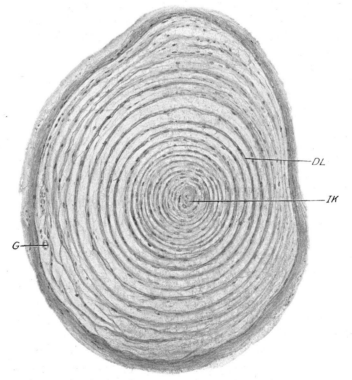

Fig. 180. Cross section of corpuscle of Vater-Pacini, from derma of the sole of a human foot. *DL*, Lamellae; *G*, blood vessel between superficial lamellae; *IK*, inner bulb. 110 ×. (After Schaffer.)

and serous membranes, around the joints, in the endocardium and elsewhere. The terminations of the somatic cerebrospinal nerve fibers in the connective tissue are either free or encapsulated endings, or are
connected with special tactile cells of epithelial origin.
More complex endings are in the skin and hypodermis,
in mucous and serous membranes, endocardium, cornea, sclera, periosteum and elsewhere. *Nonencapsulated nerve glomeruli* are frequent in the papillary
layer of the skin, in the connective tissue of the mucous membranes as that of the urinary bladder, in the
pericardium and endocardium, periosteum, and so
forth. In these the terminal branches of the nerve
fibers form spherical or elongated structures resembling
glomeruli.

Encapsulated Terminal Sensory Apparatus. In these
there is a special connective tissue capsule of varying
thickness surrounding the actual nerve endings. The
capsule attains its greatest thickness in the *corpuscles
of Vater-Pacini* (Fig. 180). Terminations of this type
are found in the deeper layers of the skin, under the
mucous membranes, in the conjunctiva, cornea, heart,
mesentery, pancreas, and in loose connective tissue in
general. The size of these structures is considerable (1
to 4 by 2 mm.), and they are white. Each corpuscle is
supplied with one or more thick myelinated fibers
which lose their myelin. Their sheaths of Schwann
and of Key-Retzius are continuous with the capsule.
Of the same type are the so-called *genital corpuscles*
found in the skin of the external genital organs and
of the nipple. *Meissner's corpuscles* (Fig. 181) are
found in the connective tissue of the skin of the palms,
soles and tips of the fingers and toes. They are elongated, pear-shaped or elliptical formations with rounded ends, located in the cutaneous papillae, with the
long axis vertical to the surface. Their size varies (40 to
100 by 30 to 60 microns). The *corpuscles of Golgi-
Mazzoni* or *the terminal bulbs of Krause* are similar
in structure to the corpuscles of Vater-Pacini, but are
smaller in size and simpler in construction. (On terminations of the dendrites and axis cylinders in the
brain and spinal cord, see p. 187.)

AUTONOMIC NERVOUS SYSTEM

The autonomic nervous system is composed of numerous small ganglia, some of
which are arranged in two chains along the
spinal column, and more of which are scattered among other tissues of the body, all
being connected by an intricate system of
nerve fibers. The autonomic nervous system
consists of the *parasympathetic* (*craniosacral*) and *sympathetic* (*thoracolumbar*) out-
flows.

The sympathetic trunks and the ganglia
contained within them, the *vertebral ganglia*,
are the chief avenues of communication be-

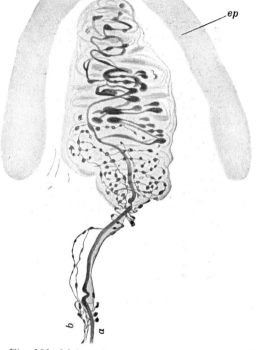

Fig. 181. Meissner's corpuscle of a dermal papilla
of a human finger. *a*, Thick and, *b*, thin myelinated
fiber; *ep*, epithelium. Methylene blue. (Redrawn after
Dogiel.)

tween the central nervous system and the
outlying sympathetic ganglionic plexuses.
Each sympathetic trunk contains ganglia at
the level of exit of most of the spinal nerves.
The *communicating branches* (rami communicantes) pass between the trunk and the
spinal nerves in these regions.

All the neurons of the central and the
peripheral systems primarily concerned with
the regulation of visceral activities form the
autonomic portion of the *visceral nervous
system*. Neurons which lie wholly within the
sympathetic system may exercise a local regulatory control over the viscera to which they
are related. These local adjusters are under
modification by the visceral centers of the
spinal cord and brain.

On the sensory or afferent side of the reflex
arcs, all neurons whose peripheral processes
extend from the viscera through the communicating branches to the spinal ganglia are

not autonomic, but belong to the somatic nervous system.

The visceral sensory neurons cannot be readily distinguished from the somatic sensory or craniospinal elements, with which they are mingled in the spinal ganglia, except by following their peripheral fibers outward into the communicating branches.

The bodies of the *visceral motor neurons* of the spinal nerves are segregated in the "intermedio-lateral gray column" of the

mostly unmyelinated *postganglionic fibers*—transmit the impulse to visceral muscles or glands.

The *communicating branches* (Fig. 182) are the paths of connection between the spinal nerves and their adjusting centers in the spinal cord on one hand, and the local visceral adjusting mechanisms on the other. The white branches contain myelinated fibers of the sensory and of the preganglionic efferent neurons, while the gray contain un-

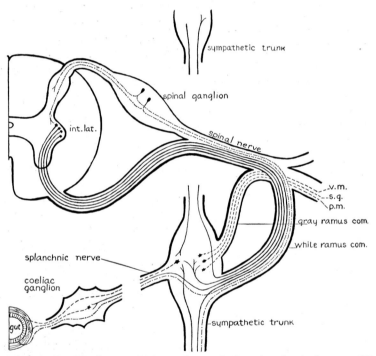

Fig. 182. Diagram of relations of sympathetic trunk to spinal cord and spinal nerves. Visceral sensory fibers are drawn in dot-and-dash lines, preganglionic fibers in continuous lines, and postganglionic fibers in broken lines. For clearness the rami communicantes are drawn farther separated from the spinal ganglion than natural. *Int. lat.*, Intermediolateral gray column of the spinal cord, axons of whose cells form preganglionic fibers; *p.m.*, pilomotor postganglionic fiber; *s.g.*, postganglionic fiber for sweat glands; *v.m.*, vasomotor postganglionic fiber. (From Herrick's Introduction to Neurology.)

spinal cord (Fig. 182, *int. lat.*). Their axons pass out of the cord into the ventral roots and through the white communicating branches, to end either in a vertebral ganglion of the sympathetic trunk or in one of the outlying ganglionic plexuses (a prevertebral ganglion). These axons, *preganglionic fibers*, with thin or no myelin sheaths, always terminate in a sympathetic ganglion. Here they effect synaptic junction with secondary visceral motor neurons, whose axons—the

myelinated axons of the postganglionic efferent neurons which carry visceral efferent nervous impulses from the sympathetic ganglia to the spinal nerves. Among the latter are the *vasomotor fibers* going chiefly to arterial muscles, the *pilomotor fibers* to the small muscles of the hair follicles, and the *sudomotor fibers* to the sweat glands. Other postganglionic fibers go to the viscera in the sympathetic nerves, like the splanchnic nerves, where they are mingled with the myelinated axons of the preganglionic and visceral sensory neurons.

The *autonomic system* can be subdivided into three sections on an anatomical basis. However, the distinction frequently made between the sympathetic and parasympathetic systems as functionally antagonistic systems on the basis of different reactions to certain drugs no longer holds.

1. *The cranial autonomic (cranial parasympathetic system)* includes the preganglionic neurons whose axons enter the oculomotor, facial (chorda tympani), glossopharyngeal, vagus and accessory nerves, and also the postganglionic neurons of the peripheral ganglia in the head and trunk. 2. *The sacral autonomic (sacral parasympathetic system)* includes the preganglionic neurons whose axons emerge in the ventral roots of the second to the fourth sacral spinal nerves, and also the related postganglionic neurons of their peripheral sympathetic ganglia. 3. *The thoracolumbar autonomic (sympathetic system)* includes preganglionic neurons whose cell bodies lie in the intermediolateral gray columns of the thoracolumbar portion of the spinal cord and whose axons emerge in the ventral roots of the thoracic and the first three or four lumbar nerves, and the related postganglionic neurons.

Autonomic Nerve Cells. The cell bodies of the preganglionic visceral efferent neurons are small, spindle-shaped elements in the intermediolateral gray column.

The postganglionic neurons of the craniosacral visceral nervous system lie, as a rule, close to the viscera innervated. The preganglionic fibers, accordingly, are relatively long—as in the vagus nerve—and the postganglionic fibers are short. On the other hand, most of the synapses of the thoracolumbar system are in the ganglia of the sympathetic chains or trunks; therefore their postganglionic fibers are relatively longer.

The nervous elements of the sympathetic ganglia are generally small and have such diverse shapes and structure that some maintain that no morphological classification is practicable. The cells are generally multipolar, with the dendrites and axon sometimes being clearly distinguishable, in other cases showing no obvious difference. Preganglionic fibers often synapse with the dendrites of the ganglion cell in dense glomeruli. For a typical example see the description of the postganglionic neurons of the intestine (p. 383).

The cell body may be surrounded by a capsule of satellite cells, which, like those of the craniospinal ganglia, are ectodermal elements related to the cells of Schwann in the nerve sheaths. In the outlying sympathetic ganglia these capsules may be absent, but the cells of Schwann accompany the peripheral sympathetic fibers everywhere.

NEUROGLIA

The term "neuroglia" is applied to the following interstitial tissues: the *ependyma* which lines the ventricles of the brain and spinal cord, *neuroglial cells* and their expansions or "fibers" which bind together the neurons in the central nervous system and in the retina, and the *satellite* or *capsular cells* of the peripheral ganglia. The *cells of Schwann* of the peripheral nerves may be considered equivalent to peripheral neuroglia.

Ependyma. In the early embryonic stages of the brain and spinal cord the wall of the neural tube is a simple epithelium (Fig. 197). Certain thin, non-nervous parts of the brain retain this structure throughout adult life, as the epithelial layer of the chorioid plexus (Fig. 204). In most other parts of the neural tube, the wall is greatly thickened by the differentiation and multiplication within it of neurons and neuroglial elements. The lining of the inner surface of the wall enclosing the ventricular cavities always retains an epithelial character (Fig. 183). This lining membrane, the adult ependyma, is composed of

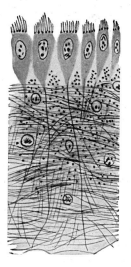

Fig. 183. Neuroglia from the ependymal layer of the fourth ventricle (tuberculum acusticum) of a cat, with ciliated ependymal cells. (After Rubaschkin.)

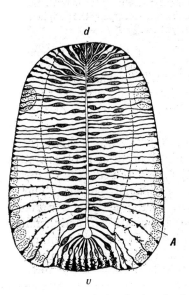

Fig. 184. Cross section of neural tube of a three-day chick embryo. Spongioblasts stain black; neuroblasts between them are unstained. *v*, Ventral side; *d*, dorsal side; A, region of future anterior column of the white substance. Method of Golgi. (Redrawn after Ramón y Cajal.)

the inner ends of the persisting epithelial cells, with their nuclei and some of their cytoplasm, and such derivatives of the primitive embryonic epithelium as remain in connection with it.

The embryonic ependyma is ciliated, and in some parts of the ventricular lining the cilia may persist in adult life. In the mature brain, their broad bases taper to long, threadlike processes that may branch and that are lost among other elements of the brain (Fig. 183). In a few places, where the nervous wall is thin, as in the ventral fissure of the spinal cord, some ependymal cells span the entire distance between the ventricular and external surfaces (Fig. 185). All of them do so in the early embryonic stages (Fig. 184). In these cases the ependymal cells form a dense *internal limiting membrane* at the ventricular end.

At the external surface under the *pia mater* the ependymal threads and bars expand into pedicles which fuse into a thin, smooth and dense membrane, the *external limiting membrane* of the central nervous system (Figs. 184, 185). Similar membranes are formed around the blood vessels (Figs. 186, 187). In most parts of the adult human brain and spinal cord, with the increase in the thickness of the wall, the ependymal threads are stretched between the internal and external limiting membranes beyond the breaking point. Finally the ependymal threads lose contact with the opposite face of the wall, remaining connected with their own ependymal cells (Fig. 185).

Neuroglia Proper or "Glia." In any section of the central nervous system prepared by

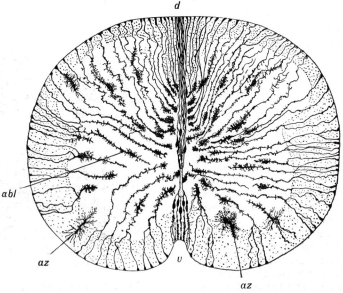

Fig. 185. Cross section of spinal cord of newborn mouse. *v*, Ventral side; *d*, dorsal side; *abl*, astroblasts moving away from the central canal; they are transformed into stellate neuroglia cells (astrocytes), *az*. Method of Golgi. (Redrawn after Ramón y Cajal.)

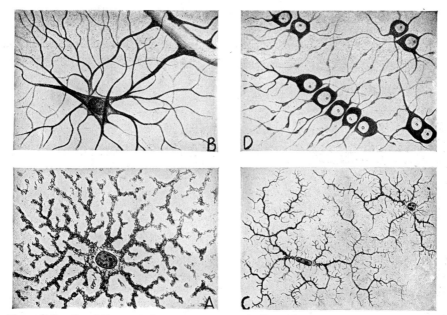

Fig. 186. Neuroglial cells of the central nervous system. A, Protoplasmic astrocyte; B, fibrous astrocyte; C, microglia; D, oligodendroglia. (After Río-Hortega.)

ordinary histological methods, small nuclei are seen scattered among the nerve cells and their processes (Figs. 189, 201). The cytoplasm and long processes of these neuroglial elements are revealed by special histological technique.

Three types of neuroglia are distinguished: *astrocytes*, *oligodendrocytes*, and *microglia*. The first two are undoubtedly of ectodermal origin, as are the nerve cells proper. The third, or microglia, according to Río-Hortega, originates from mesodermal cells of the pia mater which migrate into the central nervous system along the blood vessels. His opinion is not accepted by all.

The *astrocytes*, termed also "astroglia," "macroglia" or "spider cells," are of two varieties. The first is the *protoplasmic astrocyte* with nucleus larger than in oligodendrocytes and microglia, and with relatively abundant granular cytoplasm and numerous, rather thick plasmatic expansions (Fig. 186). Many of their processes are attached to the blood vessels and to the pia mater by means of expanded pedicles. In other cases, the body of the cell lies directly on the wall of the blood vessel or on the inner surface of the pia. Some of the smaller cells of this variety lie close to the bodies of the neurons and are called *satellite cells*. The other variety is the *fibrous astrocyte* (Fig. 186), distinguished from the first by long, relatively thin, smooth, and little branched expansions. Embedded

within the cytoplasm of their bodies and expansions are fibrillar structures or *neuroglial fibers* (Fig. 188). These cells also are often attached to the blood vessels by means of their processes. The protoplasmic astrocytes are found chiefly in the gray substance, the fibrous astrocytes in the white substance of the brain insinuated between the fascicles of nerve fibers. Mixed or *plasmato-fibrous astrocytes* are occasionally encountered at the boundary between the gray and white sub-

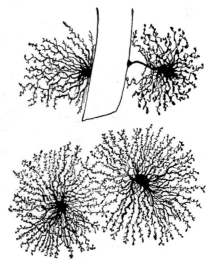

Fig. 187. Short-rayed astrocytes from the gray matter of the brain of an adult man; the two upper ones are connected with the walls of a blood vessel by their processes. Golgi method. (After Ramón y Cajal.)

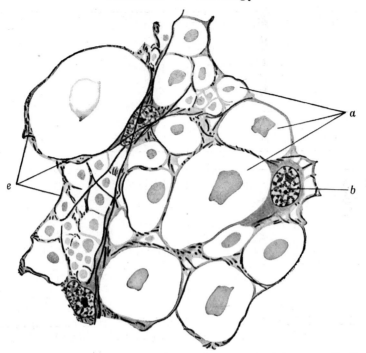

Fig. 188. Cross section of white matter of spinal cord of a cat stained for neuroglia fibers. *a*, Nerve fibers of different calibers, with a centrally located axis cylinder and with a wide, pale myelin sheath; *b*, neuroglia cell; *c*, neuroglia fibers. Weigert method. 1000 ×. (A.A.M.)

stance; those of their processes that spread into the gray substance have a protoplasmic character, while those that pass into the white substance are fibrous.

The *oligodendrocytes*, also called "oligodendroglia" and "oligoglia" (Fig. 186), are closely akin to the astrocytes, which they resemble in most respects. They are smaller and have smaller nuclei, although there are

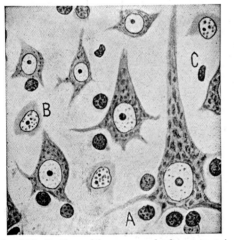

Fig. 189. Portion of human cerebral cortex stained by Nissl's method. A, Naked nuclei of oligodendroglia cells; B, protoplasmic astrocyte; C, nucleus of microglia cell. In addition, large and small pyramidal neurons. (After del Río-Hortega.)

many transitional forms. The name is derived from the fact that their few and slender processes have few branches. The processes rarely if ever form footlike expansions on blood vessels, and no true neuroglial fibers are related to them. They seem to be in an especially intimate relationship with the nerve fibers along which they are frequently found in rows or columns. Because of this they are regarded as the central homologue of the neurolemmal cells of Schwann. In the gray substance those oligodendrocytes that adjoin the nerve cells proper are called "satellites" (Fig. 189, A).

In the *microglia* or Hortega's cells (Fig. 186, C), the nucleus is small but deeply stained and surrounded by scanty protoplasm. The few expansions are rather short and, unlike the more or less straight expansions of the astrocytes, are twisted in various ways. Also, the processes and the body do not appear smooth, but are covered with a considerable number of tiny pointed twigs or "spines." The microglial cells are scattered everywhere throughout the brain and spinal cord.

The neuroglia of the adult central nervous system develops from the primitive spongioblasts of the embryo (Fig. 196), and is of ectodermal origin. An exception is the microglia, which possibly is mesodermal. In the mature brain and spinal cord the neuroglial tissue as a whole forms an extremely complicated supporting framework of cells and their expansions, with a multitude of passages, in which the nerve cells proper or neurons and their processes are suspended. Like the nerve cells, the supporting neuroglial cells do not form an actual syncytium (as assumed by some), but they, too, retain a certain degree of individuality, although apparently less than do the neurons, since the adjoining neuroglial cells form virtually a sealed honeycomb. In the chambers of this honeycomb the nerve cells and their expansions are individually encapsulated and thus separated or insulated from one another (Fig. 188). Only at the points of the synapses are the neuroglial barriers broken, and only here is a direct contact between the neurons possible.

The neuroglia appears also to be an important mediator for the normal metabolism of the nervous elements proper, although little is known in this respect. More is known about the activity of the neuroglia in pathological processes. Whenever the neurons are affected by a local or distant pathological process, the surrounding neuroglial elements always react in some way. They are actively involved in the degeneration and regeneration of the nerve fibers, in vascular disorders, in various infectious processes, and are the chief source of tumors of the central nervous system. In particular, the microglial cells assume a great variety of forms, with active migration and phagocytosis. They probably play a role in the metabolism of the nerve cells, and phagocytose disintegrating nervous elements (p. 199).

SYNAPSE AND THE INTERRELATIONSHIPS OF NEURONS

Essentially, the nervous system is composed of complex chains of neurons so arranged as to permit the passage of nervous impulses from one neuron to other neurons in the central nervous system and from the non-nervous to the nervous organs, and vice versa.

What the basis of functional polarization at the synapse, leading to irreciprocal conduction across it, may be is not certain. There is much coordinated physiological and anatomical evidence, however, that this may be in part a matter of geometric relations. A small fiber, for example, may be able to excite a large one, while the reverse is impossible.

A great mass of physiological and morphological data makes it seem certain that the two sides of the synaptic membrane are dissimilar in their minute structural organization and in their functional properties. Of particular interest here are the giant terminal feet or "club endings" measuring up to 7 microns across (Fig. 190); Bartelmez, Bartelmez and Hoerr, and Bodian). In each of these, neurofibrils terminate close to the synaptic boundary with button-like swellings and do not pass into the related neuron.

The number of synapses on a neuron may vary from only a few to as many as 1800 on the body of a single motor neuron. The forms of the synapses vary in the extreme (Fig. 190). Usually they are tiny swellings at the ends of the axon endings. Or the twigs form bouquets or loose baskets, and the like, adhering to the body or dendrites of another nerve cell. Each variety of neuron is distinguished by its own form of synaptic terminations, some having endings of several kinds. Neurons that have no direct or even indirect synaptic relationship with one another are independent of one another. Bodian (1942) has an excellent review on the "Cytological Aspects of Synaptic Function."

The unity of the nervous system as a complex whole is maintained by the countless synaptic connections among its constituent cells, and perhaps also by operation of potential fields and electric currents flowing between cell groups. However, in those viscera which always act *in toto* and in which there is no minute territorial delimitation of function, the nerve cells or their expansions perhaps undergo such intimate connections with one another as practically to abolish most visible boundaries such as are found in the other parts of the nervous system. This problem needs further investigation.

The conception of the structure of the nervous system just sketched forms the almost universally held *neuron doctrine*. It maintains that each mature nerve cell represents a cellular unit capable, in given circumstances, of independent existence. The processes of a nerve cell are dependent on the body with its nucleus; when cut off, they die, although peripheral processes may regenerate from the perikaryon (p. 197). The body and nucleus of the nerve cell are the trophic center of the whole neuron. If a nerve cell suffers irreparable injury, adjoining nerve cells are not necessarily affected.

Various theories based on chemical and electrical changes observed in nerves have been advanced to explain the transmission of the nervous impulse from one neuron to another or to another effector ending. It should be pointed out that much of the controversy over the neuron doctrine was due to the assumption that crude histological methods can give evidence on such delicate cytological structures as the synapses in the central nervous system and the relationships of peripheral nerves to end organs. As finer methods are developed, we shall be able more adequately to analyze the submicroscopic structure of neurons and their synapses, for there is much physical and chemical evidence that a thin outer layer (100 to 200 angstrom units) of the nerve cell and its processes is a critical zone in the transmission of the impulse.

practically all neurons are connected with several or many other neurons. With the aid of the Golgi impregnation and other methods, several different types of relationships between neurons have been shown to be present. These vary from extremely complex

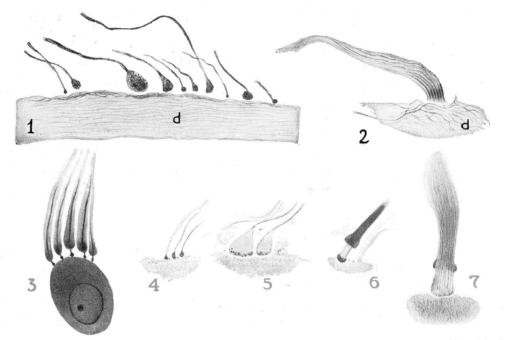

Fig. 190. Types of nerve fiber endings in the vertebrate central nervous system. *1*, End-feet of Held of unmyelinated nerve fibers ending on dendrite of another neuron (*d*). *2*, Club ending of Bartelmez which ends abruptly on dendrite of another neuron (*d*). *3*, Fine myelinated fibers ending on nerve cell by means of tiny "end-feet." *4*, Similar endings of unmyelinated fibers on dendrite of another nerve cell. *5*, Large "end-feet" on dendrite of another nerve cell. Note red-stained granular mitochondria at terminal surfaces of the "end-feet." *6*, *7*, Clublike endings of myelinated fibers ending on dendrites of other cells. Neurofibrils in dendrite of *7* are cut transversely and appear as fine dots. *1* and *2* stained for neurofibrils with reduced silver. *3* to *7* fixed by injecting Zenker-formol into blood vessels of living animal; silver followed by Mallory-azan stain. All from the brain of the goldfish. 1440 ×. (After Bodian, 1937; Courtesy of Wistar Press. Drawn by Miss Agnes Nixon.)

Examples of Interrelationships of Neurons. Except in the primate retina, where one-to-one synapses are found (Fig. 191),

relationships involving the processes of hundreds of cells to relatively simple configurations. It will suffice here to give examples of a few extreme categories. For instance, attached to the body and dendrites of many large motor cells of the anterior gray columns of the spinal cord are many hundreds of synaptic buttons of axon endings of neurons in the cerebral cortex, medullary nuclei and elsewhere in the spinal cord. The spinal motor cells serve, accordingly, as the *final common pathway* where the nervous impulses from a variety of sources are trans-

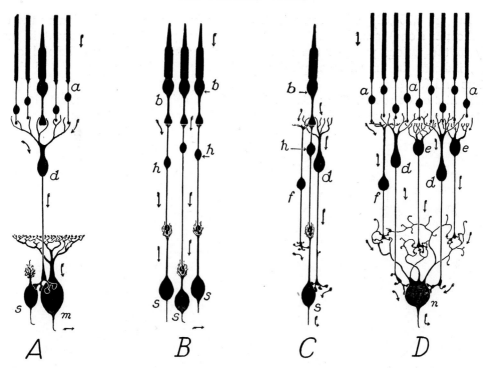

Fig. 191. Several types of synaptic relationships of neurons. A, *d*-Bipolar neuron serving as a common pathway for both rods and cones (*a*); B, isolated conduction or one-to-one relationship of neurons (*b-h-s*); C, a single excitation (in *b*) is transferred to each of the three related neuron varieties (*d, f, h*); D, excitations from a number of rods (*a*) pass through intermediary neurons (*d, e, f*) to a single large neuron (*n*). Examples from the primate retina (see Fig. 557). (Courtesy of S. Polyak.)

mitted to effector organs. A clear instance of this is found in the giant Mauthner's cells in the medulla oblongata of fishes (Fig. 190). In the retina, the *d*-bipolars serve as a common pathway for impulses from both rods and cones (Fig. 191, A). The reverse arrangement is shown in Figure 191, C, where one retinal cone is in contact with three neurons (*d, f, h*).

In the frequent arrangement in which a few neurons are related to a large group of neurons, the reaction is not commensurate with the initial stimulus, but is determined by the number and kinds of reacting neurons, often arranged in internuncial chains effecting inhibition or facilitation of the impulse (Lorente de Nó). Thus, in a spinal reflex arc (Fig. 192) the excitation of a few peripheral sensory elements may activate a great number of motor neurons, and the total response or effect may exceed many times the energy that initiated it. Another example is the ex-

citation of a few photoreceptor cells of the retina and the subsequent turning of the eyes and head toward the source of the stimulus.

These glimpses of the exceedingly intricate interconnections between neurons, coupled with their enormous numbers (it is estimated

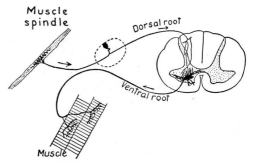

Fig. 192. Diagram illustrating simple spinal reflex arc consisting of a sensory neuron connected with a receptor ending and a motor neuron connected with a muscle. Physiological connection between the two neurons is effected within the spinal cord. (Modified from van Gehuchten.)

that there are 9,200,000,000 neurons in the cerebral cortex alone), and their extreme variability in the various parts of the nervous system, indicate the extreme complexity of structure and function.

White Matter Conducts, Gray Matter Integrates Impulses. The details of the ex-

tremely complex organization of the central nervous system must be sought in manuals of neurology. But it may be helpful to include here a few photomicrographs of three different parts of the nervous system. Figure 193 of the spinal cord emphasizes the external position of the great masses of myelinated

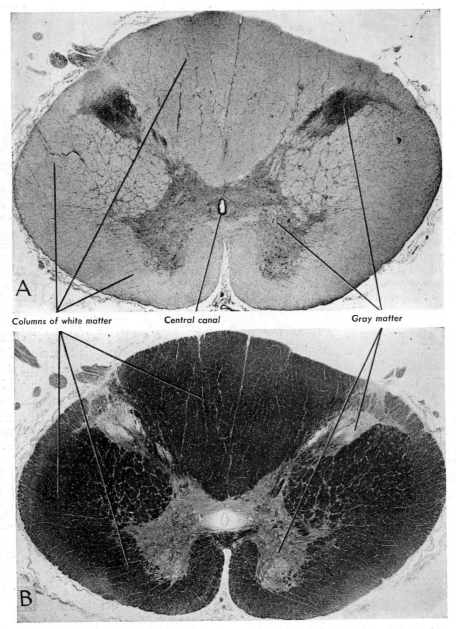

Columns of white matter   Central canal   Gray matter

Fig. 193. Sections through human, upper cervical spinal cord stained with thionine (A) to show cells, and with the Weigert-Weil method (B) to show myelinated fibers. Note the external arrangement of the fibers (white matter) and the central, cruciate area containing the cell bodies (gray matter). The ventral surface is below. A portion of the dorsal root is seen in the upper left. 12 ×. (Courtesy of P. Bailey.)

fibers with the relatively small amount of gray substance with nerve cell bodies. Figures 194 and 195 show the gray matter outside the white in cerebral cortex and cerebellum. The white matter of the brain, the numerous tracts of the brain stem and spinal cord, and practically all peripheral nerves, are chiefly or entirely made up of myelinated or unmyelinated axis cylinders. These parts serve, accordingly, to transmit nervous excitations from the viscera to the central nervous system, or vice versa, or from one part of the brain or cord to other parts. There is no evidence that

any essential modification of the passing excitations occurs in the fibrous parts.

In the regions composed chiefly of nerve cells, unmyelinated and some myelinated nerve fibers, in the nerve centers which constitute the so-called "gray matter" (cerebral and cerebellar cortex, various subcortical nuclei, gray columns of the spinal cord, peripheral ganglia), the situation is reversed. Here innumerable reciprocal contacts between the various types of neurons make possible an endless variety of mutual influences. It is here that the centralizing, selecting, combining,

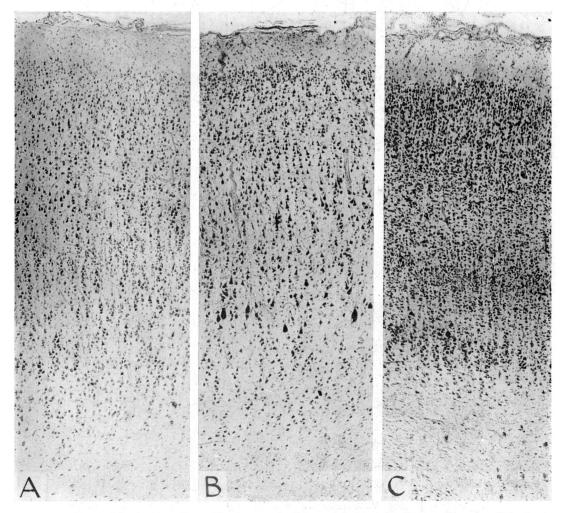

Fig. 194. Sections from three areas of human cerebral cortex, showing distribution of nerve cell bodies in the temporal eulaminate (associational) cortex (A), precentral agranular cortex (motor area) (B) and occipital koniocortex (striate visual cortex) (C). Much stress has been laid on minute differences in lamination of the nerve cells and fibers in these and other areas of the cortex, but there is now a tendency toward minimizing some of these differences. 53 ×. (Courtesy of P. Bailey.)

dividing and intensifying of incoming impulses is performed and the resulting impulses sent back to the peripheral organs of execution. A preparation of such an area shows the bodies of the cells arranged in a certain order, usually in layers. The space between the cellular layers, and also between the individual cells, is filled with innumerable axis cylinders and dendrites, and also with neuroglia and blood vessels. The nervous expansions usually are without myelin sheaths,

which accounts for the gray appearance of these parts in fresh condition.

When stained with routine methods, the nervous plexiform substance between the cell bodies has a dotted aspect, and was often called *neuropil*. Where the separation of cellular elements from the plexiform substance is complete (as in the molecular layer of the cerebellar cortex, in the plexiform layer of the cerebral cortex, and in the retina) certain layers are composed almost exclusively of the

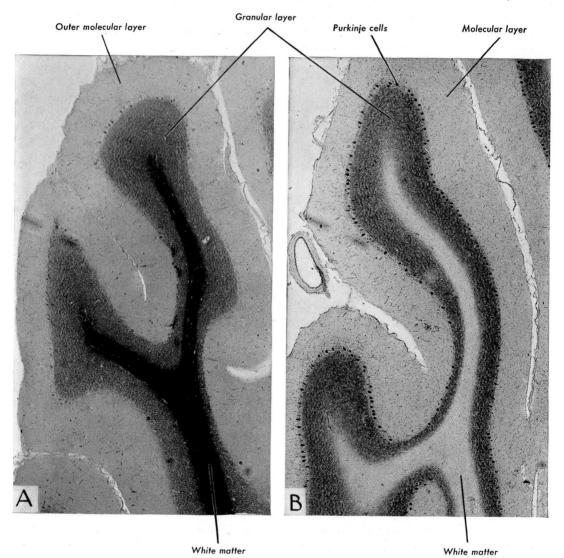

Fig. 195. Sections of human cerebellar folia stained with Weigert-Weil (A) for myelinated fibers and with thionine for cells (B). Note the central disposition of the white matter with its myelinated fibers, which stain black with Weigert-Weil and pale with thionine, the outer molecular layer (pale gray) with scattered neurons and the large Purkinje cells, and the intermediate or granular layer composed of cells and fibers. 32 ×. (Courtesy of P. Bailey.)

naked expansions of the neurons and of the neuroglia. Since, in these layers, huge numbers of synaptic contacts take place, they can be called *synaptic fields* (layers 5 and 7, Figs. 531, 556) (cf. Herrick, 1934).

The pattern of the cell and fiber arrangement in the gray nervous substance varies much in detail from place to place. Every subcortical nucleus, peripheral ganglion, and locality of the cerebral cortex has architectural features of its own. Thus the cortex in the precentral convolution of the primate brain, which coincides with the so-called *motor area*, differs from that of the postcentral convolution, where the combined *somatosensory function* is represented, or from any other portion of the cerebral cortex. One of the most characteristic cortical areas is along the calcarine fissure of the occipital lobe which corresponds with the *visual center* (area striata). Another, in the Sylvian fossa, is the *auditory center*. Careful attempts to correlate cytoarchitectonic and functional findings have, however, failed up to the present time. Some functions of the central nervous apparatus are territorially well localized, whereas others are properties of large volumes of tissue.

The gray nervous substance differs profoundly from the simple nerve fibers or axons in several respects. Although most reflexes are transmitted over several intercalated neurons, a diagrammatically oversimplified reflex arc may serve as an example. It can be conceived to be composed of a sensory (afferent) and a motor (efferent) neuron connected in the nervous center, together with the corresponding peripheral receptor and effector (Fig. 192). Such a mechanism is functionally characterized by the following: (1) It fatigues rapidly in contrast to the simple nerve fibers, which are exhausted slowly—or never as the myelinated fibers. (2) The reflex is blocked in the center by a fraction of the amount of a drug which suffices to block the peripheral nerve fiber. (3) The direction of the excitation is always from the sensory fiber to the motor or secretory fiber, indicating the functional polarity of the gray substance, termed irreversibility or irreciprocal conduction. (4)

The response varies greatly with respect to the latent period and the intensity, depending on various conditions of the central nervous system itself; this is termed "variability." (5) The latent period is much longer than in the nerve fiber, and there may be an after-discharge; that is, the response may continue for some time after the stimulus ceases. (6) Whereas one or a few stimuli may have no effect, an effect may result from numerous stimuli applied in sequence, which indicates summation. (7) Certain nerves are capable of slowing down or stopping the reflex response induced by the stimulation of other nerves, an effect interpreted as inhibition. (8) The rhythm of the response in a reflex is usually slower than that of the applied stimulus. (Sherrington; for further details see Gerard, 1931.)

Little is known of the mechanism underlying these phenomena. Some features may be due to difference in size, number of contacts and minute structure and organization of the various types of synaptic junctions and dendrite trees.

Electric Manifestations of the Brain. Considerable attention has been paid to two kinds of electric activity of the cortical gray substance. The spontaneous potentials manifest themselves by automatic rhythmic "beats" even in the absence of outside impulses; the other, the evoked potentials, often likewise rhythmic, arise only when a peripheral sensory organ is stimulated or a motor action initiated. These potential changes often have some characteristic local features limited to a particular architectural area. The subcortical pathways, various nuclei, the spinal cord and even the peripheral ganglia may show a like activity.

It would thus seem that the normal cerebral cortex is in a state of constant activity, irrespective of the stimuli from the peripheral sense organs. This is paralleled by its high metabolism, which, for oxygen, has been shown to be twenty-five times as great as in muscle or peripheral nerve. A great deal of automatic rhythmic activity seems to be inherent even in single neurons or agglomerations of these (Gerard, 1941). The brain activity seems, therefore, to be the result of the interplay of the central autonomous forces and the excitations coming from the peripheral organs. When a particular peripheral sense organ (e.g., eye) is stimulated, the electrical reaction is primarily in the afferent pathway (optic nerve, tract, radiation in the case of the eye) and in the particular cortical field of projection (area striata).

DEVELOPMENT OF THE NEURONS AND OF THE NERVOUS TISSUE

The neurons of the nervous system develop from embryonic ectoderm; an exception is the peripheral olfactory neurons, which develop from the sensory epithelium of the nasal sacs. Likewise of ectodermal origin are the neuroglial cells (with the probable exception of microglia), the neurolemmal cells of the peripheral nerves and the satellite cells of the peripheral ganglia— and apparently also certain elements of the meninges.

In early embryonic stages the future central nervous system separates by folding from the primitive ectoderm to form the *neural tube*. Next, other cells detach from the neural tube to form cellular bands between the neural tube and the ectoderm that later becomes epidermis. These bands, the *neural crests*, soon become segmented, the precursors of the cranial and spinal ganglia, and probably the autonomic ganglia. The epithelium that forms the neural tube is gradually differentiated into *spongioblasts*, which will become the ependyma and neuroglia, and *neuroblasts*, the future neurons. In a similar way some cells of the neural crests become peripheral neurons; others, satellite cells; still others, neurolemmal cells. These ectodermal tissues are at first sharply separated from the surrounding mesenchyme, from which the meninges and the connective tissue of the central nervous system and of the ganglia are derived. The intimate association of the nervous and the connective tissues found in the adult is achieved only gradually.

The sensory neurons of the craniospinal nerves arise from the cells which remain in the vicinity of the original neural crests where they form ganglia of these nerves. The peripheral (dendritic) processes of these

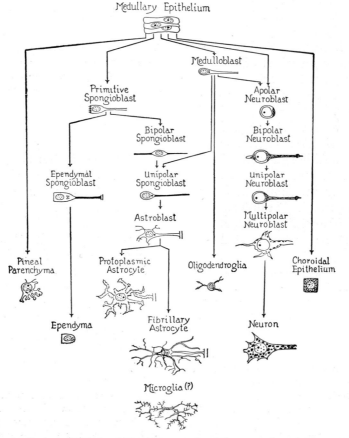

Fig. 196. Diagram, partly hypothetical, of the histogenesis of the central nervous system. Especially hypothetical are the medulloblasts, yet their existence seems to be necessary to explain the histogenesis of the nervous system, its malformations, and its tumors. (After Bailey.)

cells grow outward and become the axis cylinders of the sensory nerve fibers. Their central processes enter the central nervous system as dorsal roots. The cell bodies of the peripheral motor and visceral neurons remain within the brain or spinal cord, their axons form the motor roots of the peripheral nerves and terminate in the muscles or in the visceral ganglia. Some of the indifferent cells leave the central nervous system and migrate into various parts of the body, where they become sympathetic or visceral ganglia. The steps by which the various cells of the central nervous system are derived from the primitive undifferentiated epithelium of the neural tube are illustrated in Figures 191, 196.

As soon as the immature neurons of the neural tube and crest can be distinguished from other cells, they are called *neuroblasts* (Fig. 198). Those of the spinal ganglia (o) send their axons through the dorsal roots (B) into the spinal cord; those in the ventral part of the neural tube (e) send their axons through the ventral

roots (A) outward toward the muscles and viscera; those in the dorsal part of the neural tube (a) become correlation neurons of the spinal cord. The protoplasm of the growing axons shows ameboid movements and insinuates itself between the other tissue elements by a positive outgrowth. At its advancing tip there is a bulbous enlargement, called "growth cone" (Fig. 200), from which slender, spinelike projections are thrust between obstructing cells and fibers (a few such are seen in Fig. 198, d, h, i).

The knowledge of the development of the neurons expounded above is based chiefly upon the study of the fixed and stained material by His, Ramón y Cajal, Lenhossék, Neal, et al., and was confirmed in all essential points by Harrison's observations on living nervous tissue. This was amplified by Speidel's studies of the growing nerves in the transparent tail of the living frog tadpole. These observations showed that the axons of the unipolar neuroblasts grow into the intercellular spaces as slender, naked protoplasmic strands (Figs. 199, 200). Nor do they form a true syncytium, but each pursues its separate course, although secondary anastomoses between peripheral naked axons are the rule.

From the observations of Speidel it is clear that in the peripheral nerve fibers all newly formed nerve sprouts are at first devoid of neurolemmal and myelin sheaths. Next they are joined by Schwann's cells, but remain unmyelinated. The earliest myelin appears near the nucleus of the sheath cells, from which locality it spreads proximally and distally.

The forces that in the course of phylogeny and ontogeny have brought about the complex nervous tissue of

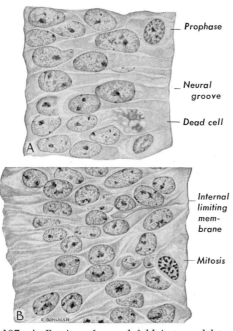

Fig. 197. A, Portion of neural fold just caudal to the posterior neuropore of an eighteen-somite human embryo (about twenty-four days old). It is a pseudostratified epithelium with cell boundaries clearly defined. The internal limiting membrane is developing, but the external one has not appeared. As in most rapidly growing tissues, there is an occasional degenerating cell. 845 ×. B, Part of lateral wall of neural tube in the region of the medulla oblongata from a twenty-six-somite human embryo (about four weeks old). The cells are much longer and more irregular than in A, but it is occasionally possible to follow one through the entire thickness of the wall. Cell boundaries indicate that the original epithelial condition persists. Both external and internal limiting membranes are present. 845 ×. (Courtesy of G. W. Bartelmez.)

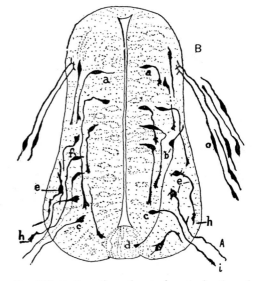

Fig. 198. Section through spinal cord of a three-day chick. A, Anterior and, B, posterior roots; a, b, c, etc., neuroblasts whose axons frequently end in swellings (d, h, i); o, spinal ganglion cells whose processes have penetrated the spinal cord. Golgi method. (Redrawn after Ramón y Cajal.)

vertebrates are unknown. Some saw in *mechanical factors* the chief cause directing the growth of the neuroblasts and their expansions. Others thought that in addition the various peripheral tissues secrete substances which exert *chemotactic influences* upon the sensitive growing buds of the axons, a process called *neurotropism*. In the central nervous system a similar force is believed to attract the dendrites and the bodies of the neurons toward the points whence this force emanates.

The concept of *neurobiotaxis* assumes the driving force to be a difference in electric potential between the dendrites and the axis cylinder. In this theory a neuron, or a group of them, is attracted by the axis cylinders and endings of other related neurons, this attraction being at first expressed by the shortening of the dendrites and later by the migration of the bodies in the direction of the source whence their stimuli come.

The role of *purely mechanical factors*, of the oriented ultra-structure (micellar orientation and aggregation), as the guide along whose channels the developing axis cylinders spread, has lately been experimentally tested, and the importance of the chemotactic, electrical and electromagnetic factors has been questioned. No effect of a galvanic or faradic current has been seen upon

either the rate or the direction of the growth of nerves in the living vertebrate.

The ultimate causes are not known which determine the orientation of the ultramicroscopic micellar units in the media wherein the nervous processes expand, and induce the selecting of particular micellar pathways by particular axons. Although most attention has been directed to problems of outgrowing fibers, it now seems likely (Weiss, Sperry and others) that the periphery can affect the central connections after contact has been established between outgrowing fibers and the periphery.

DEGENERATION AND REGENERATION OF THE NERVOUS TISSUE

The neuroglia of the adult central nervous system and the cells of Schwann and allied elements of the peripheral system are less specialized than the neurons. In certain circumstances they are capable of rapid proliferation. This occurs in certain tumors (gliomas), in scar tissue, in various other pathological conditions, and in a special form during the process of regeneration of peripheral nerve fibers.

Mammalian nerve cells, on the contrary, as soon as they reach that early stage of differentiation when they can be recognized as neuroblasts, appear to lose the power of multiplication. If any neurons are destroyed, they are not replaced.

Though mature neurons cannot proliferate, they show visible changes in the course of normal physiological activity and in various pathological conditions. The change in size and shape is particularly manifest in the following instances: (1) transplantation or explantation of nerve cells, (2) pathological or operative destruction of portions of the central nervous system, and (3) after injury to peripheral nerves.

The chromophile substance of Nissl is especially sensitive to both artificial stimulation and normal fatigue. In nervous elements which were highly active or were in some way impaired, the chromophile substance partly disintegrates into granules distributed throughout the cytoplasm and partly dissolves. This phenomenon is called *chromatolysis* or *tigrolysis* (Fig. 201). The Nissl substance may even disappear completely in con-

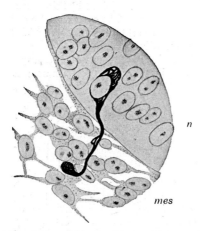

Fig. 199. Axon of a neuroblast with neurofibrils extending from the neural tube (*n*) into the surrounding mesenchyme (*mes*). (Redrawn after Hoven.)

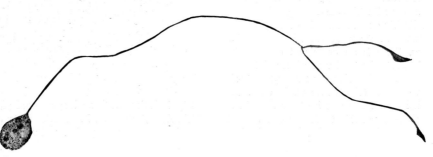

Fig. 200. Isolated unipolar neuroblast with a forked process, from a part of the neural tube of *Rana palustris* explanted in a drop of lymph of *Rana pipiens* two days previously. 350 ×. (Redrawn after Harrison.)

sequence of extreme fatigue or exhaustion. After a period of rest this substance again accumulates and the cell assumes its original appearance. If too high a degree of fatigue is produced, complete degeneration and death of the neuron may result.

Accompanying chromatolysis may be an increase in the volume of the cell due to an increased water content of both nucleus and cytoplasm. With the advance of exhaustion of the cell, a decrease in its volume is evident; the cytoplasm becomes vacuolated, and finally the cell perishes. During intense activity the neurofibrils likewise increase in number and become thinner and paler staining. During hibernation they diminish in number, and become thicker and more deeply stained.

The comportment of chromophile substance in fatigue and in various pathological conditions has been much studied. Most of these changes take the form of chromatolysis, with considerable variety in detail. The most complete observations concern the change in the cell body after its axon is severed. This is the so-called *primary reaction of Nissl*, the *axon reaction* or the *retrograde cell degeneration*. The cell body grows larger, chromatolysis is observed, the nucleus migrates to one side of the body, and the nuclear membrane shrivels. The reaction may be more or less severe, depending on the variety of the neuron, the nature of the injury, the distance from the cell body at which the axon was cut, and the degree of regeneration, if any, which follows the injury. When the axon is not destroyed completely, so that the remaining part may still perform some function, and when regeneration occurs, the injured neuron may make a complete recovery. In more severe injury the changes in the cell body are more rapid and continue until degeneration is complete and the cell dies. In the brain the neurons probably always degenerate and disappear completely whenever their axis cylinders are interrupted. The axis cylinder exhibits immediate

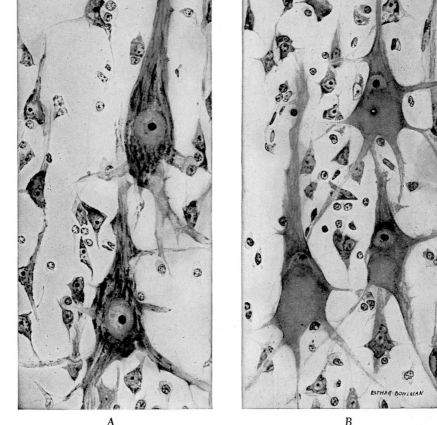

A   B

Fig. 201. A, Normal cells of motor cortex of macaque; B, chromatolysis in similar cells after hemisection of the cervical spinal cord. Stained after Nissl-Lenhossék. (Courtesy of S. Polyak.)

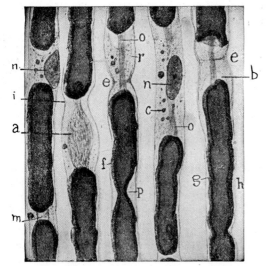

Fig. 202. Fibers of the peripheral stump twenty-four hours after section of a nerve of a rabbit. *a*, Widening of the axon next to a constriction (*i*); *b*, vacuole of the constriction; *c*, spherules of Erholz; *e*, cementing disk; *f*, incisure of Schmidt-Lantermann; *g*, infundibulum of incisure; *m*, protoplasmic bridges formed at the level of the incisures; *n*, nuclei; *o*, subsistent axon in the protoplasm of Schwann's cells; *r*, protoplasm accumulated next to the disks of Ranvier. (After Ramón y Cajal.)

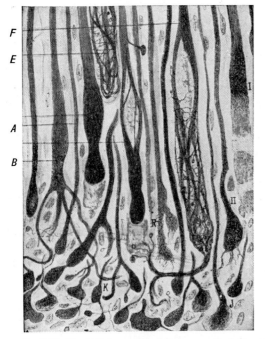

Fig. 203. Central stump of sciatic nerve of adult cat, two days after the section. A, Nonmedullated fiber; B, medullated axon ending in terminal branches; E, F, structures of Perroncito. (After Ramón y Cajal.)

changes in form and structure after subjection to drugs, heat, cold, starvation, and after mechanical injury.

It is difficult and frequently impossible in normal material to follow the axons of some particular group of nerve cells as they make their devious ways through the central or peripheral nervous system, mingled with other fibers. If some of these fibers are severed by accident or disease, or if they are cut in an experiment, the cell bodies from which the injured fibers arise will show chromatolysis. On the other hand, the myelinated fibers which have been separated from their cell bodies, or whose cells have been destroyed, degenerate. During the period of from one to twelve weeks or more after the injury, before the degenerating myelin is resorbed, it can be specifically stained by a *method devised by Marchi*. Since the altered myelin stains black in contrast to the unstained myelin of the uninjured fibers, the course of the injured fibers distal to the injury can be accurately followed. These two methods—Nissl's method of retrograde chromatolysis and the method of Marchi—are extensively used in the investigation of the fiber tracts of the brain and the spinal cord. Fine fibers can be studied during early stages of degeneration by following their structural changes in silver-stained preparations.

Table 1. Table of Changes in Peripheral Nerve after Section

DAYS AFTER SECTION	
0– 3	Slight structural changes; chromatolysis
3– 8	Impulse transmission fails; myelin fragments; enzyme content decreases
8–32	Destruction of myelin with changes of fat chemistry
32–	Connective tissue changes
8–10	Regeneration starts from central stump, and new fibers grow out at the rate of about 1.5 mm. per day
35–	Myelinization of new fibers begins

When a nerve trunk is severed, the peripheral or distal portion soon loses its glossy white aspect and becomes dull and gray. The central or proximal portion remaining continuous with the cell bodies apparently does not change much. Artificial stimulation of the peripheral portion three or four days after the operation fails to produce a contraction of the muscles which it supplies, if it contains motor fibers. However, stimulation of the central portion, if it be a sensory or mixed nerve, produces the usual pain sensations and more or less widespread motor reflexes. Microscopic examination shows that the immediate result of the operation is a primary degenerative change which involves the ends of both the central and peripheral portions for a short distance. This is *traumatic degeneration*. But the changes in the whole length of the peripheral portion depend upon a different process. This is called *secondary* or *wallerian degeneration* of the nerve fiber (Fig. 202). It affects the entire length of the peripheral portion of the nerve, including its terminal apparatus.

In wallerian degeneration those parts of the severed peripheral fiber which are organic parts of the neuron, and hence trophically dependent upon its cell body, undergo complete degeneration. However, if conditions are favorable for regeneration, they may be restored to perfect function. This applies to the axis cylinder, and to the myelin sheath if present. On the other hand, the sheath of Schwann, being trophically independent of the neuron, survives and is reorganized with the active proliferation of nuclei and the growth of cytoplasm. It assists in the regeneration of the axon. It is possible to induce degeneration of peripheral axons by vitamin B deficiency without seriously altering the myelin sheath (E. Clark).

The axis cylinder of the peripheral stump always perishes. But in many cases there is ultimately a complete *regeneration* of this degenerated portion of the nerve and its terminal apparatus (Fig. 203). This regenerative process always proceeds from the end of the central stump. It progresses much slower than the rapidly occurring wallerian degeneration. It is accomplished relatively easily and quickly when the two severed ends of the nerve are immediately brought into close contact with each other. If the ends have been widely separated, the regenerative process may require a long time or may never take place. It occurs much more rapidly and successfully in a young person than in an old one.

The nonmyelinated fibers also undergo a secondary degeneration peripheral to the injury. Here, too, the axis cylinder disintegrates, and its fragments are absorbed by the protoplasm of Schwann's sheath. This process differs from that in the myelinated fibers only by the absence of the myelin sheath.

The degenerative processes cannot be sharply separated from those of regeneration, for the entire response of the neuron to injury seems to be reparative from the start. It is now definitely established that the regeneration can be carried through to completion only by the outgrowth of nerve fibers from the uninjured axons of the central stump. Büngner's strands of Schwann's cells do not develop axons of their own, but are penetrated by new axons growing from the central stump of the nerve.

CONNECTIVE TISSUE, CHOROID PLEXUS, VENTRICLES, AND MENINGES OF THE CENTRAL NERVOUS SYSTEM

In addition to the neurons and the supporting neuroglia, both of ectodermal origin, the brain and the spinal cord everywhere contain blood vessels derived from mesenchyme. The membranes enveloping the brain and spinal cord are likewise composed chiefly of connective tissue. There are three such membranes. The outermost, the dura mater or pachymeninx, is dense and firm. Both the inner membranes, the innermost or the pia mater and the one next to it, the arachnoid membrane, are composed of much looser connective tissue and are called leptomeninges. The dura and arachnoid membranes are separated by the subdural space; the space between the outer layer of arachnoid and pia is called subarachnoid. Both spaces contain loosely arranged connective tissue and are filled with cerebrospinal fluid.

Dura Mater. The relation of the dura to the surrounding bones differs in the spinal cord and in the brain. In the vertebral canal the inner surface is lined by its own periosteum, and within this a separate cylindrical dural membrane loosely encloses the cord. There is a rather wide epidural space between the periosteum and the dura which contains much loose connective and fatty tissue with many veins. The dura is firmly connected to the spinal cord on each side by a series of denticulate ligaments. The inner surface of the spinal dura is lined with squamous cells. Its collagenous bundles run for the most part longitudinally, and the elastic nets are less prominent than in the cerebral dura.

The dura mater of the brain at the beginning of its embryonic development also has two layers, but in the adult these are more or less closely joined. Both consist of loose connective tissue with elongated fibroblasts. The outer layer adheres to the skull rather loosely except at the sutures and the base of the skull. It serves as periosteum, is looser and richer in cells than the inner layer, and contains many blood vessels; its thick collagenous fibers are arranged in bundles. The inner layer is thinner, with finer fibers forming an almost continuous sheet. Its fibers run from in front and below backward and upward, thus with orientation opposite to those of the outer layer. These fibers are so arranged as to equalize tensions and pressures within the cranial cavity. The inner surface of the dura is smooth and covered with a layer of squamous mesothelial cells.

Arachnoid. In the brain and spinal cord the leptomeninges are similar in structure.

The arachnoid is a thin, netlike membrane devoid of blood vessels, resembling the transparent parts of the omentum. Its outer surface is smooth, but from its inner surface run a multitude of thin, branching threads and ribbon-like strands, attached to the pia. The tissue on macroscopic examination has a cob-web-like appearance. The arachnoid membrane bridges over the sulci and the fissures on the surface of the brain and the spinal cord, forming subarachnoid spaces of various extent within these sulci.

Pia Mater. This inner membrane is a thin connective tissue net that closely adheres to the surface of the brain and the spinal cord. It contains a large number of blood vessels from which most of the blood of the underlying nervous tissue is derived. Attached to the pia are the inner fibrous strands of the arachnoid, and these two membranes are so intimately related that their histological structure can best be described together. In fact, these two membranes are often treated as one, the *pia-arachnoid.*

The main elements of both the arachnoid and the pia are interlacing collagenous bundles surrounded by fine elastic networks. In the spinal pia an outer longitudinal and an inner circular layer can be distinguished. Among the cells are fibroblasts and fixed macrophages; these are especially numerous in the pia along the blood vessels. They correspond in their general histological properties to the macrophages of the other parts of the body. They store vital dyes injected directly in the subarachnoid space. In inflammation, especially in tuberculous meningitis, they are transformed into large, free macrophages or epithelioid cells. In man they often contain, even under apparently physiological conditions, considerable amounts of a yellow pigment that sometimes reacts positively to tests for iron. When vital dyes are injected intravenously into a living animal, the macrophages of the leptomeninges store only small quantities of them; at the same time, the tissues of the central nervous system (except the choroid plexus) remain practically colorless, at least in adult animals. Thus the walls of the blood vessels of the leptomeninges seem to be an unsurmountable barrier for some of the vital dyes that have entered the general circulation. In young animals given intravenous dye injections, however, there can be found a distinct, although small, storage of the dye in the nerve cells in different places of the brain stem, so that the apparent impermeability of the walls of the blood vessels develops gradually.

Along the blood vessels of the pia mater are scattered single mast cells and small groups of lymphocytes. In certain pathological conditions the latter increase enormously in number and may become transformed into plasma cells. The tissue of the leptomeninges, especially along the blood vessels of the pia, also contains many embryonic mesenchymal elements. In the pia mater, particularly on the ventral surface of the medulla oblongata, a varying number of melanoblasts can be found.

The outer and the inner surfaces of the arachnoid, the trabeculae, and the outer surface of the pia are lined with a layer of squamous mesenchymal epithelial cells. Whereas some investigators describe their rounding off, mobilization and transformation into free macrophages under the influence of inflammatory stimuli, others trace the origin of macrophages exclusively to fixed macrophages. This question requires further study.

During development of the meninges two zones may be distinguished: an outer zone of condensation of mesenchyme which gives rise to periosteum, dura, and membranous arachnoid; and an inner zone which becomes pia. Between these two zones the mesenchyme remains loose and later forms spongy tissue permeating the subarachnoid spaces.

In lower vertebrates the mesenchyme of the head is formed of cells derived in part from the entoderm (mesentoderm) and in part from the ectodermal neural crest (mesectoderm). Both types of mesenchyme have been shown to participate in the formation of the meninges. Working with amphibians and birds, Burr and others have transplanted portions of the early neural tube with and without the neural crest into foreign tissue. In subsequent development the transplants with the neural crest acquire typical pia mater containing cells of neural crest origin, while those lacking the neural crest show an atypical and defective pia.

If the mammalian pia mater likewise contains elements derived from both mesectoderm and mesentoderm, then it is uncertain whether the microglia, which is said to migrate into the brain from the pia mater, is ultimately of ectodermal or entodermal origin. It has been suggested, moreover, that this twofold origin of the elements of the leptomeninges explains some peculiarities of meningeal tumors.

Nerves of the Meninges. The dura and pia are richly supplied with nerves. All vessels of the pia and of the choroid plexus are surrounded by extensive nervous plexuses in the adventitia, from which fine fibrils penetrate the media. These nerves have their origin in the carotid and vertebral plexuses and in certain cranial nerves, and belong to the sympathetic system. Some fibers seem to emerge directly from various places of the brain. Sensory, nonencapsulated nerve terminations, and even single nerve cells, are also present on the adventitia of the blood vessels.

The cerebral dura contains, besides the nerves of the vessels, numerous sensory nerve endings in its connective tissue. The connective tissue of the cerebral pia contains extensive nervous plexuses. They are especially abundant in the tela choroidea of the third ventricle.

The fibers end either in large, pear-shaped or bulbous swellings or in skeins and convolutions similar to those of the corpuscles of Meissner. In the spinal pia the vessels receive their nerves from the plexuses following the larger blood vessels to the cord. Afferent nerve endings are also present, but are very unevenly distributed.

Both myelinated and unmyelinated nerve fibers accompany the blood vessels into the substance of the spinal cord and the brain, ending on the muscle cells of the vessels. These come from similar nerves of the pial vessels, and the two nervous plexuses are continuous.

Choroid Plexus. There are four places where the wall of the brain retains its embryonic character as a thin, non-nervous epithelium. This part of the brain wall is the lamina epithelialis. The pia mater which covers it is extremely vascular and otherwise modified to form a choroid plexus. The lamina epithelialis is closely joined to the choroid plexus, and the whole is called tela choroidea or, less exactly, choroid plexus.

These choroid plexuses are found in the roof of the third and fourth ventricles, and in a part of the wall of the two lateral ventricles. In each case the tela choroidea is much folded and invaginated into the ventricle, so that the free surface exposed to the ventricular fluid is large, with branching tufts of tortuous vessels and a rich capillary net.

The epithelium early acquires a peculiar structure, different from that of the ependymal cells lining the ventricles. In embryonic stages it contains glycogen and

carries cilia. In the adult its cells are cuboidal and are arranged in a single, regular layer. Each contains a large, round nucleus and a varying number of rod-shaped and granular mitochondria. Common inclusions are large, transparent vacuoles in the distal part of the cell, or large, usually single, fat droplets. On the free surface some have a brushlike border and, in the guinea pig, long, motile cilia. In animals repeatedly injected intravenously with vital dyes, such as trypan blue, the epithelium of the choroid plexus stores large amounts of the dye in granular form. In the perivascular connective tissue core of the plexus are many fixed macrophages which store large amounts of dye in contrast to those of the leptomeninges.

Blood Vessels of the Central Nervous System. The arteries reach the spinal cord with the ventral and dorsal nerve roots (anterior and posterior radicular arteries) and form a dense arterial network in the spinal pia mater. Here several longitudinal arterial pathways can be distinguished (spinal arterial tracts). The most important among them is the anterior arterial tract; it gives off a multitude of small branches (central arteries) which enter the ventral medial fissure and penetrate to the right and left into the medial part of the anterior gray columns. They supply the major part of the gray substance with blood. Numerous smaller branches of the pial arterial net, the peripheral arteries, penetrate the white substance of the cord along its entire circumference. The capillary nets in the white substance are loose and have meshes which are drawn out longitudinally. The capillaries of the gray substance are much more numerous and dense. The course of the veins does not correspond with that of the arteries. Numerous venous branches emerge from the periphery of the cord and from the ventral median fissure and form a diffuse plexus in the pia; this is especially promi-

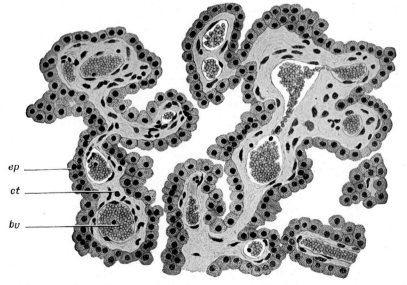

Fig. 204. Choroid plexus of the fourth ventricle from man. *ep*, Epithelium; *ct*, connective tissue; *bv*, blood vessels. 190 ×.

nent on the dorsal surface of the cord. From this plexus the blood is led away by veins accompanying the ventral and dorsal roots.

The arterial supply of the brain is derived almost entirely from the carotids and the large arteries at its base, chiefly the basilar artery and the circle of Willis. Most of the arteries from these large vessels pass upward in the pia mater, from which smaller vessels dip into the brain substance. These vessels, after penetrating the brain, were commonly supposed to be end arteries, with no appreciable amount of anastomosis from one to another; this problem requires further study in mammals.

As in the spinal cord, the capillary net in the cerebral white matter is relatively meager, with elongated meshes; in the gray matter the net has a closer mesh. It is assumed that the density of capillaries is a crude indication of the rate of metabolism of the tissue supplied by it. On this assumption, it is clear that the metabolism of the gray substance is much more active than that of the white.

The linear extent of capillaries per unit volume of brain substance has been measured by Craigie in a number of representative parts of the central nervous substance in various animals. He finds, for instance, in the rat that parts of both white and gray matter differ in vascularity, all the gray being more vascular than the white. The motor nuclei are less vascular than the sensory nuclei and correlation centers. In the cerebral cortex the fourth layer of Brodmann is more vascular than the other layers, and the supragranular layers tend to be more vascular than the infragranular layers. The parietal area is more vascular than the others, and the vascularity of the cerebellar cortex is about the same as that of the cerebral cortex taken as a whole. In studying the postnatal development of this vascular pattern, it was concluded that the richness of the capillary supply is directly related to functional activity, and that the metabolism involved in the latter requires a greater blood supply than does the metabolism of growth.

There are no lymphatics in the central nervous system. Blood fluids which pass out from the capillaries seep through the tissue and are not collected in lymphatic vessels, as in most other parts of the body. The blood vessels that penetrate from the pia mater are surrounded by perivascular spaces which open freely at the brain surface into the subarachnoid spaces. Thus the cerebrospinal fluid, derived from the blood, is drained from the brain tissue outward toward the meninges without at any time being enclosed in definite lymphatic vessels.

Ventricles. The central nervous system begins its development as a neural tube with a wide cavity throughout its length, and it preserves its character as a hollow organ throughout life. The ventricle of the spinal cord, or central canal, in the adult is minute, or it may be obliterated. It does not seem to perform any important function. But in the normal adult the ventricular cavities of the brain always form a continuous channel for flow of cerebrospinal fluid throughout its length. If any part of this channel is occluded by disease so as to prevent free circulation of its fluids, an increased intracerebral pressure develops, with resulting hydrocephalus or other serious pathological consequences.

The ventricular cavity is dilated in four regions: the two lateral ventricles in the cerebral hemispheres, the third ventricle in the thalamic region, and the fourth ventricle in the medulla oblongata and pons. Choroid plexuses develop in these four regions, and most of the ventricular fluid is derived from the blood vessels of these plexuses.

Meningeal Spaces. Between the dura mater and the arachnoid, the subdural space is comparable to a serous cavity. It contains a minimum of fluid and in reality is scarcely more than a potential space. Between the outer sheet of arachnoid and the pia, the subarachnoid space is traversed by cobwebby connective tissue trabeculae. It is independent of the subdural space and contains a large amount of fluid. At the summits of the convolutions it is narrow, but in the sulci it is wide and deep. The subarachnoid space is especially wide throughout the length of the spinal cord. In the brain it is greatly enlarged in a few places termed "cisterns," where the arachnoid is widely separated from the pia and the trabeculae are rare or absent. The most important of the cisterns lies above the medulla oblongata and below the posterior border of the cerebellum (cisterna cerebellomedullaris, or cisterna magna). The fourth ventricle communicates with this cistern through three openings in the tela choroidea: a medial foramen of Magendie—recently questioned by Meulen—and the two lateral foramina of Luschka.

Cerebrospinal Fluid. The central nervous system is surrounded on all sides by cerebrospinal fluid; it is suspended in it as in a water-bed. This fluid protects it from concussions and mechanical injuries and is of importance for its metabolism. The subarachnoid spaces are in free communication, so that cerebrospinal fluid may pass through them from end to end of the central nervous system. The amount of the fluid is variable, estimated as 80 to 100 cc., or even as much as 150 cc. It is limpid and slightly viscous and has a low specific gravity (1.004 to 1.008). It contains traces of proteins, small quantities of inorganic salt and dextrose, and few lymphocytes (about two or three, and not more than ten in 1 cu. mm.). It resembles the aqueous humor of the eye more closely than any other liquid of the body.

The cerebrospinal fluid is constantly renewed. It circulates slowly through the brain ventricles and through the meshes of the subarachnoid spaces. If these spaces are opened to the outside by injury (subarachnoid fistula), large amounts of fluid steadily drain off—200 cc. or more in a day. The sources of this fluid are primarily the blood vessels of the choroid plexus, the pia mater, and the brain substance. From the brain substance the flow is outward into the subarachnoid spaces; from the choroid plexus it is inward into the ventricles. Fluid may be added to the ventricles in a few other places, notably in the area postrema at the lower end of the fourth ventricle. The ependymal surfaces in general do not seem to discharge fluid into the ventricles. On the other hand, the absorption of fluid from the ventricles into neighboring veins takes place through the ventricular walls. The plexuses are wholly secretory, not resorptive, in function. They are the chief source of the cerebrospinal fluid. The chief channel of discharge of ventricular fluid outward into the subarachnoid spaces is through specially modified localities of the membranous roof of the fourth ventricle.

The flow of ventricular fluid normally passes from the lateral ventricles of the cerebral hemispheres, where it is derived chiefly from the lateral choroid plexuses, through the foramina of Monro into the third ventricle. Here fluid is added from the choroid plexus, and the augmented flow passes through the aqueduct of Sylvius into the fourth ventricle, where more fluid is added from the choroid plexus. From the fourth ventricle the fluid passes into the cerebellomedullary cistern, and from here it diffuses in all directions through the subarachnoid spaces. Some of it apparently gets into the extracranial lymphatics by way of the perineural spaces within the sheaths of the cranial nerve roots, part reaching the nasal cavity along the perineural sheaths of the olfactory nerve filaments. Around the spinal nerve roots there is an arrangement of the dural veins and sinuses adapted for the passage of cerebrospinal fluid directly into the venous blood, rather than into the lymphatic vessels. A small part of the cerebrospinal fluid enters the lymphatics or the veins by the routes just mentioned. Most of it passes directly into the big endocranial venous sinuses through the arachnoid villi.

Arachnoid Villi. The large endocranial venous sinuses are entirely enclosed by massive walls of dura mater except in definite places, chiefly in the sagittal sinus of the falx, where the dura is perforated by numerous protrusions of the arachnoid membrane, through each of which a finger-like evagination of the arachnoid mesothelium is thrust into the lumen of the sinus. This is the arachnoid villus. Its cavity, which contains a small amount of loose arachnoid tissue, is in free communication with the subarachnoid spaces, so that here the fluid of these spaces is separated from the blood of the sinus only by the thin mesothelial membrane.

These villi have been found in dogs, cats, monkeys, human infants, and adults. In man, with advancing age, they are enlarged and in this condition have long been known as Pacchionian corpuscles (granulations).

The arachnoid villi provide the main pathway for the outflow of cerebrospinal fluid directly into the venous circulation. This flow is rapid. Dyes and other chemicals injected into the subarachnoid spaces can be detected in the blood stream in ten to thirty seconds, and only after thirty minutes can they be found in the lymphatics.

REFERENCES

Adrian, E. D.: The Mechanism of Nervous Action. Philadelphia, University of Pennsylvania Press, 1933.

Ariëns Kappers, C. U., Huber, G. C., and Crosby, E. C.: The Comparative Anatomy of the Nervous System of Vertebrates, Including Man. New York, 1936, 2 vols.

Bartelmez, G. W., and Hoerr, N. L.: The Vestibular Club Endings in Ameiurus. Further Evidence on the Morphology of the Synapse. J. Comp. Neur., 57:401, 1933.

Bensley, S. H.: Cytological Studies of the Reaction of Myelinated Nerve Fibers to Section of the Nerve. Anat. Rec., 90:1, 1944.

Bethe, A., Bergmann, G., Embden, G., and Ellinger, A.: Handbuch der Norm. u. Pathol. Physiologie. Berlin, 1927–31, vols. 1, 9, 10, 11, 12.

Bishop, G. H.: Neural Mechanisms of Cutaneous Sense. Physiol. Rev., 26:77, 1946.

Bodian, D.: Nucleic Acid in Nerve-Cell Regeneration. Symposia Soc. Exp. Biol., 163, 1947.

Boeke, J.: The Sympathetic Endoformation, Its Synaptology, the Interstitial Cells, the Periterminal Network, and Its Bearing on the Neurone Theory. Discussion and Critique. Acta Anat., 8:18, 1949.

Child, G. M.: Physiological Foundations of Behavior. New York, 1924.

Eccles, J. C.: An Electrical Hypothesis of Synaptic and Neuromuscular Transmission. Ann. New York Acad. Sc., 47:429, 1946.

Economo, C.: The Cytoarchitectonics of the Human Cerebral Cortex. Oxford, 1929.

Fernándex-Morán, H.: Sheath and Axon Structures in the Internode Portion of Vertebrate Myelinated Nerve Fibres. Exper. Cell Res., 1:309, 1950.

Fulton, J. F.: Physiology of the Nervous System. New York, 1949.

Gasser, H. S., et al.: Symposium on the Synapse. J. Neurophysiol., 2:361, 1939.

Gerard, R. W.: Intercellular Electric Fields and Brain Function. Schweiz. med. Wchenschr., 12:555, 1941.

Gerard, R. W.: Nerve Conduction in Relation to Nerve Structure, Quart. Rev. Biol., 6:59, 1931.

Gersh, I., and Bodian, D.: Some Chemical Mechanisms in Chromatolysis. J. Cell. Comp. Physiol., 21: 253, 1943.

Haggar, R. A., and Barr, M. L.: Quantitative Data on the Size of Synaptic End-Bulbs in the Cat's Spinal Cord; With a Note on the Preparation of Cell Models. J. Comp. Neur., 93:17, 1950.

Hanström, B.: Vergleichende Anatomie des Nervensystems der wirbellosen Tiere. Berlin, 1928.

Hard, W. L., and Lassek, A. M.: The Pyramidal Tract. Effect of Maximal Injury on Acid Phosphatase Content in Neurons of Cats. J. Neurophysiol., 9:121, 1946.

Harrison, R. G.: Observations of the Living Developing Nerve Fiber. Anat. Rec., 1:116, 1908; The Outgrowth of the Nerve Fiber as a Mode of Protoplasmic Movement. J. Exper. Zool., 9:787, 1910; Neuroblast versus Sheath Cell in the Development of Peripheral Nerves. J. Comp. Neur., 37:123, 1924.

Heidenhain, M.: Plasma und Zelle, in Bardeleben's Handb. d. Anatomie des Menschen, Vol. 8, (2), 1911.

Herrick, C. J.: Neurological Foundation of Animal Behavior. New York, 1924; Brains of Rats and Men. Chicago, 1926; The Thinking Machine. Chicago, 1929; An Introduction to Neurology. Philadelphia and London, 1931; J. Comp. Neur., 59:93, 239, 1934.

Hines, M.: Studies in the Innervation of Skeletal Muscle. J. Comp. Neur., 56:105, 1932.

Hinsey, J.: The Innervation of Skeletal Muscle. Physiol. Rev., 14:514, 1934.

Hoerr, N. L.: Cytological Studies by Altmann-Gersh Freezing-drying Method. III. The Pre-existence of Neurofibrillae and Their Disposition in the Nerve Fiber. IV. The Structure of the Myelin Sheath of Nerve Fibers. Anat. Rec., 66:81, 91, 1936.

Hydén, H.: Protein Metabolism in the Nerve Cell during Growth and Function. Acta Physiol. Scandinav., 6: Suppl. 17, 1943.

Kuntz, A.: The Autonomic Nervous System. Philadelphia, 1929.

Langley, J. N.: The Autonomic Nervous System. Cambridge, 1921.

Lillie, R. S.: Protoplasmic Action and Nervous Action. Chicago, 1932.

Lorente de Nó, R.: Transmission of Impulses through Cranial Motor Nuclei. J. Neurophysiol., 2:402, 1939.

McCulloch, W. S.: The Functional Organization of the Cerebral Cortex. Physiol. Rev., 24:390, 1944.

Miner, R. W. (ed.): The Physico-chemical Mechanism of Nerve Activity. Ann. New York Acad. Sc., 47:375, 1946.

Nonidez, J. F.: The Nervous "Terminal Reticulum," a Critique. Anat. Anz., 82:348, 1936; 84:1, 315, 1937.

Patek, P. R.: The Perivascular Spaces of the Mammalian Brain. Anat. Rec., 88:1, 1944.

Penfield, W.: Cytology and Cellular Pathology of the Nervous System. New York, 2 vols.; Neuroglia, Ibid., 2:423, 1932.

Polyak, S.: The Main Afferent Fiber Systems. Berkeley, 1932; The Retina. Chicago, 1941.

Ramón y Cajal, S.: Histologie du système nerveux de l'homme et des vertébrés. Paris, 1909–11; Degeneration and Regeneration of the Nervous System. Oxford, 1928; Les preuves objectives de l'unité anatomique des cellules nerveuses. Travaux Lab. Invest. Biol. Madrid, 29:1, 1934.

Ranson, S. W., and Clark, S. L.: The Anatomy of the Nervous System. Philadelphia, W. B. Saunders Company, 1947.

Rasmussen, A. T.: The Principal Nervous Pathways. New York, 1941.

Rényi, G. S. de: The Physical Properties of the Living Axis Cylinder in the Myelinated Nerve Fiber of the Frog. J. Comp. Neur., 47:405, 1929. III. Observa-

tion on the Sheaths of Myelinated Nerve Fibers of the Frog. Ibid., 48:293, 1929.

Río-Hortega, P. del: Microglia, in Penfield's Cytology, etc., 2:481, 1932.

Sanders, F. K.: Special Senses, Cutaneous Sensation. Ann. Rev. Physiol., 9:553, 1947.

Sauer, F. C.: Mitosis in the Neural Tube. J. Comp. Neur., 62:377, 1935.

Sawyer, C. H.: Cholinesterases in Degenerating and Regenerating Peripheral Nerves. Am. J. Physiol., 146:246, 1946.

Scharrer, E.: The Blood Vessels of the Nervous Tissue. Quart. Rev. Biol., 19:308, 1944.

Schmitt, F. O.: The Structure of the Axon Filaments of the Giant Nerve Fibers of Loligo and Myxicola. J. Exp. Zool., 113:499, 1950.

Schmitt, F. O., Bear, R. S., and Palmer, K. J.: X-ray Diffraction Studies on the Structure of the Nerve Myelin Sheath. J. Cell. Comp. Physiol., 18:31, 1941.

Sherrington, C. S.: The Integrative Action of the Nervous System. New York, 1906.

Speidel, C. C.: Adjustments of Nerve Endings. The Harvey Lectures, Series 36, 126, 1940–41.

Speidel, C. C.: Studies of Living Nerves. VII. Growth Adjustments of Cutaneous Terminal Arborizations. J. Comp. Neur., 76:57, 1942.

Speidel, C. C.: Studies of Living Nerves. J. Exper. Zool., 61:279, 1932; Am. J. Anat., 52:1, 1933; J. Comp. Neur., 61:1, 1935.

Sperry, R. W.: Neuronal Specificity, Genetic Neurology (Weiss), 232. The University of Chicago Press, 1950.

Thomas, G. A.: Quantitative Histology of Wallerian Degeneration. II. Nuclear Population in Two Nerves of Different Fibre Spectrum. J. Anat., 82:135, 1948.

Tower, S. S.: Atrophy and Degeneration in the Muscle Spindle, Brain, 55:77, 1932.

Weed, L. H.: Certain Anatomical and Physiological Aspects of the Meninges and Cerebrospinal Fluid. Brain, 58:383, 1935.

Weiss, P.: Genetic Neurology. Problems of the Development, Growth, and Regeneration of the Nervous System and Its Functions. University of Chicago Press, 1950.

Weiss, P., and Hiscoe, H. B.: Experiments on the Mechanism of Nerve Growth. J. Exp. Zool., 107:315, 1948.

Windle, W., and Clark, S. L.: Observations on the Histology of the Synapse. J. Comp. Neur., 46:153, 1928.

Wislocki, G. B., and Singer, M.: The Basophilic and Metachromatic Staining of Myelin Sheaths and Its Possible Association with a Sulfatide. J. Comp. Neur., 92:71, 1950.

Woollard, H. H., and Harpman, J. A.: Discontinuity in the Nervous System of Coelenterates. J. Anat., 73:559, 1939.

Young, J. Z.: Functional Repair of Nervous Tissue. Physiol. Rev., 22:318, 1942.

X. THE BLOOD VASCULAR SYSTEM

Multicellular organisms require a mechanism to distribute nutritive materials, oxygen and hormones to the various parts of the body and to collect the products of metabolism from the whole body and transmit them to the excretory organs. In the vertebrates this function is carried out by the vascular system. It consists of tubelike vessels, the *arteries, capillaries* and *veins,* and the central motor apparatus, the *heart,* which maintains a constant circulation of the blood by its contractions. The arteries lead from the heart to the capillaries, the veins from the latter to the heart. Lymphatic vessels are described in Chapter XI.

The circulation of the blood in a living animal may be studied directly in a thin vascular membrane, such as the web of a frog's tongue, the wing of a bat or the special chambers inserted in the ear of a rabbit (Sandison, 1932). The vessels of thicker organs may be studied with the aid of illuminated glass or quartz rods (Knisely, 1936).

CAPILLARIES

The main component of the wall of a capillary is the endothelium; this is the characteristic structure in every vessel, including the heart. In the living animal it is usually possible to distinguish the endothelial nuclei scattered along the outlines of the capillaries. After fixation and staining, the wall of the capillaries stands out clearly as a thin, homogeneous membrane, within which the endothelial nuclei are located at various distances from one another.

The endothelial cells are structurally similar to fibroblasts. The elongated or oval nucleus is flattened, sometimes curved with the lumen of the vessel, and contains fine, dustlike chromatin particles similar to those in the nucleus of the fibroblast; it lacks, however, the large nucleoli. Its membrane often shows longitudinal folds. These slight differences are rapidly effaced when the endothelial cells turn into fibroblasts.

The flat endothelial cells are usually stretched along the axis of the capillary and have tapering ends. In the wider capillaries they are shorter and broader. In the lung their outlines are irregularly scalloped. In capillaries of medium width, only two curved cells surround the lumen. In wider capillaries the aperture may be surrounded by a greater number of cells, while in narrow ones a single endothelial cell may form the wall of the tube.

The caliber of the capillaries in various parts of the body of a given animal varies within narrow limits and is closely related to the size of the red blood corpuscles. In man it averages about 8 microns. Patent thin capillaries, through which only blood plasma circulates, probably are not present, although great numbers of the capillaries are collapsed when the organ or tissue is in a resting condition. When the organs begin to function actively, these collapsed capillaries open up, and blood circulates through them. In sections of tissues fixed in the usual manner, the capillaries appear narrower than in the living animal, while artificially injected capillaries are often distended beyond their normal limits.

In the majority of capillaries it is possible to show by the injection of silver nitrate that their walls consist of separate endothelial cells whose boundaries stand out as sharply stained black lines; each cell contains a single nucleus (Fig. 205). In such preparations the cell boundaries are frequently covered with angular, dark spots. They were originally thought to be openings in the walls of the capillaries between the endothelial cells, the so-called *stigmata* or *stomata*; they are now known to be artefacts. In the living frog intravascularly injected India ink particles were

Fig. 205. Capillary from the mesentery of frog. Boundaries of the endothelial cells are stained black with silver nitrate. 350 ×. (Redrawn after Ranvier.)

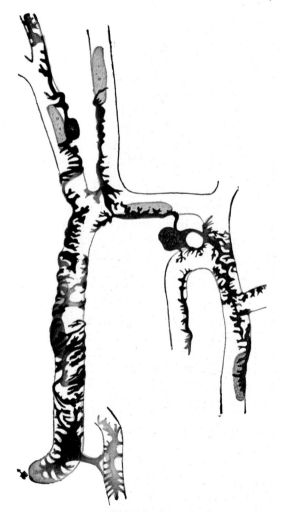

Fig. 206. Arterial capillaries from the heart of a forty-three-year old man. Four polymorphous perivascular cells continue into those of the capillaries. The arrow points toward the artery. Chrome-silver impregnation. 1000 ×. (Redrawn after Zimmermann.)

seen to accumulate first in the cementing lines.

The capillaries originate from the embryonic connective tissue. As they penetrate everywhere between the elements of various organs and tissues, they are accompanied along their entire course by connective tissue cells and layers of thin, collagenous or reticular fibers, which closely adjoin the endothelium in most places. The network of reticular fibers forms a thin membranous sheath around the capillaries and separates them from the elements of the other tissues.

The connective tissue which accompanies the capillaries is sometimes called *perithelium*. This is an indefinite term which includes several types of cells; because of its indefiniteness, it should be discarded. The usual capillaries are accompanied by fixed macrophages, cells of probably undifferentiated mesenchymal nature, and a few scattered nerve cells which can be identified only through the use of special histological methods. The pericapillary mesenchymal cells are beautifully demonstrable in the serous membranes (Fig. 48). In certain instances the pericapillary cells are of quite different nature. Thus, along the capillaries of the nictitating membrane of the frog's eye are peculiar cells with long, branching processes which surround the capillary wall (Rouget cells). These cells have been seen to contract under electric stimulation. Hence, in this membrane, these cells may be considered to be of the nature of smooth muscle cells. The Rouget cells round up, but do not contract when prodded, and lack the birefringent myofibrils characteristic of smooth muscle. Studies made on living blood vessels in chambers inserted in the rabbit's ear indicate that capillary contractility in the mammals does not depend on the Rouget cells (Clark). Microdissection studies have shown that the endothelial cells may contract after direct mechanical stimulation.

The fluid part of the blood reaches the elements of the tissues only by passing through the endothelial protoplasm of the capillaries. Leukocytes pass through the wall by their ameboid movement, in which they push apart the processes of the endothelial cells, or pass through the protoplasm of these cells and form temporary openings which close immediately after their passage.

The capillaries connect the terminal branches of arteries and the beginnings of the veins. They always form extensive networks by their frequent branchings and anastomoses; these networks thoroughly penetrate the various tissues which they nourish. In most instances the meshes of the capillary network, adjusting themselves to the available free spaces between the elements of the tissues, have a polygonal shape and are of approximately equal size in all planes (Fig. 207).

It is obvious that, if the tissue consists of a thin membrane, its capillary network will be arranged in the same plane. If the tissue elements are all elongated and lie parallel to one another, as in nerves, tendons

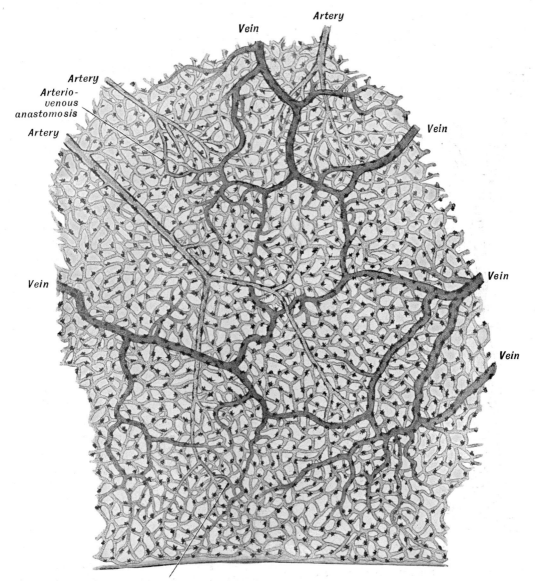

Fig. 207. Network of blood vessels in the web of a frog, showing the connection of arteries and veins with the capillary network and direct connections between arterioles and venules. Many chromatophores are scattered along the capillaries. Medium magnification. (A.A.M.)

or muscles, the capillaries between them form a network with elongated meshes, often with right angular meshes in some of the muscles (Fig. 140).

The higher the metabolism of the organ, the denser is its network, and vice versa. In the pulmonary alveoli the meshes are somewhat less than the diameter of the capillary tubes themselves. The capillary networks are dense in various glands, in the mucous membrane of the intestinal tract, and elsewhere. In the gray matter of the central nervous system the vascular network is considerably denser than it is in the white matter, which consists only of nerve fibers. In tendons the capillaries are scarce, while in adipose tissue they are abundant.

The transitions between arteries and capillaries and between capillaries and veins are gradual. This applies to the structure of the wall as well as to the caliber of the vessel. However, capillaries are often found which project directly from small arteries before a complete ramification of the latter has taken place;

similarly, accessory capillaries frequently enter directly into a well-developed small vein.

In following the ramifications of an artery in the direction of the flow of the blood, only that part of the wall of the vessel which has entirely lost its muscular elements and consists only of endothelium should be called a capillary (Fig. 208, x). The first stretches of the capillary network are ordinarily called the *arterial capillaries*; they are usually a little wider than the main mass of the network. Where the veins are formed from the capillary network, the capillary tubes again become gradually wider and at the same time less numerous—these are the so-called *venous capillaries*, which not infrequently have a considerable diameter. The appearance of the first smooth muscle cells or of denser collagenous fibers in their walls indicates the beginning of a small vein. The concept of arterial and venous capillaries is rather indefinite, and it is often impossible to distinguish them by the width of their apertures from ordinary capillaries.

In the capillaries of the intestinal villi, part of those in the renal glomeruli, hyaloid membrane of the frog's eye and the majority of developing embryonic capillaries, it has not been possible to demonstrate the outlines of separate endothelial cells. Accordingly, in these places the endothelium is thought to be a continuous, protoplasmic membrane.

Sinusoids. In certain organs there is another type of connection between arteries and veins. These are called "sinusoids" and are structurally quite different from the capillaries. The capillaries have a constant bore and a complete endothelial lining in which the cell boundaries are clearly demonstrable in most cases by treatment with silver nitrate. The sinusoids, on the contrary, have irregular, tortuous walls which vary from 5 to 30 microns or more in diameter in fixed material. Their walls are not formed by a continuous layer of endothelial cells, as in the capillaries, but by irregularly scattered phagocytic and nonphagocytic cells. The ordinary capillary endothelial cells do not store vital dyes or phagocytose bacteria as do the phagocytes of the sinusoids. The outlines of the cell bodies in the sinusoids are not demonstrable in most instances by treatment with silver nitrate. The sinusoids are accompanied by a dense, membranous network of reticular fibrils. The sinusoids probably represent a primitive type of capillary. In the adult mammalian body, sinusoids occur in the blood-

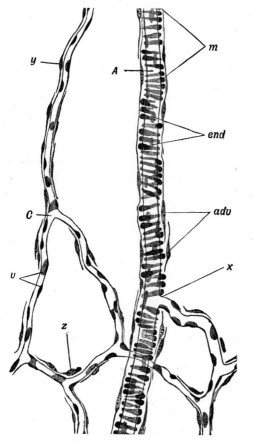

Fig. 208. Small artery, A, and capillaries, C, from mesentery of a rabbit; *m*, muscle cells in the media; *adv*, adventitia; *x*, origin of a capillary from the artery; *y*, pericyte; *z*, perivascular (adventitial) histiocyte; *end*, *v*, endothelial nuclei. 187 ×. (A. A. M.)

forming tissues, the liver and certain endocrine glands.

The concept that phagocytosis by cells lining vessels depends on a sluggish circulation should be dropped. Studies of the living circulation show that the rate of flow varies considerably in all capillaries (and sinuses) and that it often ceases for hours in many vessels which are not sinuses. But phagocytosis and dye storage by the common endothelial cells in these vessels, as in muscle and in the glomeruli, have not been reported.

ARTERIES

The blood is carried from the heart to the capillary networks of the tissues and organs of the body by arteries. These are tubes which begin with the aorta and pulmonary artery on the left and right sides of the heart, respectively, and then split into smaller branches. The caliber of the arteries gradually decreases as they recede from the heart, while the sum of the diameters of the lumens of all the branches of these arteries increases greatly the further they are from the heart. The lining of the walls of all the arteries consists of the same kind of endothelium as is found in the capillaries. But external to the endothelium in the arteries, other elements can be distinguished which cause the strength, rigidity and complexity of the arterial walls. All these qualities decrease progressively in passing from the larger arteries which originate in the heart to the capillaries. Besides the endothelium, the arteries are composed of: (1) fibroblasts and collagenous fibers, (2) bands and networks of elastic fibers, and (3) smooth muscle cells. The arterial walls are abundantly provided with nerves, and in the large arteries small blood and lymphatic vessels are present.

The wall of the largest arteries (such as the aorta) differs from the wall of arteries of medium caliber (such as the radial artery) by its absolute thickness and by its structure. In the aorta the middle layer of the vessel is distinctly yellow, because of the predominance of elastic elements; in the second instance it is red-gray because of smooth muscles. The arteries of *elastic type* are of large caliber and include the aorta, innominate, subclavian, the beginning of the common carotid, and the pulmonary arteries; these are also called the *conducting arteries*. The arteries of *muscular type* (the *distributing arteries*) include the majority of the arteries; they continue from the afore-mentioned large vessels close to the heart and extend to the unnamed arteries which are difficult to distinguish with the naked eye. The smallest arteries, 0.3 mm. in diameter or smaller, are usually grouped in a separate class and are called *arterioles*. In the transition between the arterioles and the capillaries some authors distinguish *precapillary arterioles*—an ill-defined concept. The peculiarities in the structure of the different types of arteries are reflected in their physiological significance.

In the walls of every artery, three layers can be distinguished: (1) the inner coat, *tunica intima* or *interna*, whose elements are oriented mainly longitudinally; (2) the intermediate coat, *tunica media*, most of the elements of which are directed circularly. This is the thickest layer of the wall, and its character determines the type of artery. (3) The external coat, *tunica adventitia* or *externa*, most of the elements of which run parallel to the long axis of the vessel. The elements of this tunic gradually merge with those of the surrounding loose connective tissue which accompanies every blood vessel. The boundary between the tunica intima and tunica media is formed by the *internal elastic membrane*, which is particularly noticeable in arteries of medium caliber. Between the tunica media and the tunica adventitia, an external elastic membrane can be distinguished in most cases.

Small Arteries—Arterioles. The *tunica intima* consists only of endothelium and the internal elastic membrane (Fig. 209). In cross section the elastica interna usually appears as a thin, bright line just beneath the endothelial nuclei. It is markedly scalloped in sections, because the agonal contraction of the muscle fibers throws it into longitudinal folds.

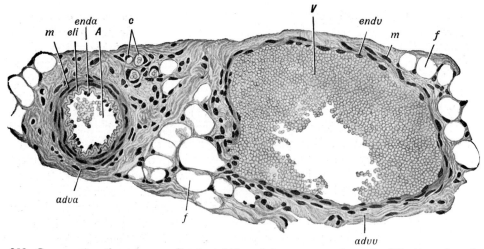

Fig. 209. Cross section through a small artery (A) and its accompanying vein (V) from the submucosa of a human intestine. *adva* and *advv*, Adventitia of the artery and vein; *c*, cross sections of capillaries; *enda* and *endv*, endothelium of the artery and vein; *eli*, elastica interna; *m*, muscle cells of the media; *f*, fat cells in the loose connective tissue. 187 ×. (A.A.M.)

The *tunica media* of small arteries consists of smooth muscle cells, 15 to 20 microns in length. They are always oriented transversely to the length of the vessel, and are bent with the curvature of the arterial wall. The number of layers of muscle cells depends on the caliber of the artery.

The *tunica adventitia* approximately equals the tunica media in thickness; it is a layer of loose connective tissue with longitudinally oriented, collagenous and elastic fibers, and a

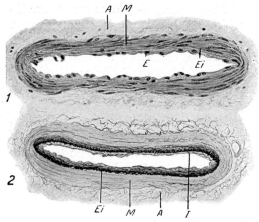

Fig. 210. Cross section of central artery of human retina. *1*, Stained with H + E, *2*, stained with orcein; A, adventitia; E, endothelium; Ei, internal elastic membrane; I, intima; M, muscular layer. 160 ×. (After Schaffer.)

few fibroblasts. It merges with the surrounding connective tissue. The small arteries lack a definite external elastic membrane.

When these small arteries merge into capillaries, the endothelium remains uninterrupted and unchanged, while the internal elastic membrane becomes progressively thinner and disappears when the vessel has a diameter of 62 microns. The spindle-shaped muscle cells disappear when the caliber of the blood vessel decreases to that of the capillary. The tunica adventitia loses its elastic fibers, which are replaced by networks of reticular fibers and the perivascular cells of the capillaries.

Arteries of Medium Caliber or of Muscular Type. This group comprises most of the arteries. The *tunica intima* is lined by the endothelium, which is continuous with that of the arteries of small caliber. Beneath the endothelium in the smaller arteries of this group is the internal elastic membrane. In larger vessels, collagenous and elastic fibers and a few fibroblasts lie beneath the endothelium.

The *internal elastic membrane* is well developed. In cross section it appears homogeneous and bright; because of agonal contraction of the tunica media it is typically scalloped (Fig. 211). In large blood vessels it

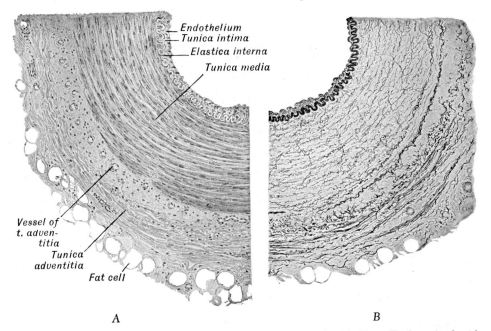

Endothelium
Tunica intima
Elastica interna
Tunica media

Vessel of
t. adven-
titia
Tunica
adventitia
Fat cell

A   B

Fig. 211. Two cross sections of volar digital artery of man; A, stained with H + E; B, stained with orcein to show elastic tissue. 80 ×. (Slightly modified after Schaffer.)

is a thick, "fenestrated" elastic membrane provided with a number of irregular, rounded or oval openings (Fig. 215). In many arteries the elastica is split into two or more layers (Fig. 212, I).

The *tunica media* of arteries of muscular type consists almost exclusively of smooth muscle cells arranged in concentric layers. Thin reticular fiber membranes can be demonstrated to form sheaths for the individual muscle cells. Thin elastic fiber networks with wide meshes course circularly in the tunica media and continue into the external and internal elastic membranes (Fig. 212, G).

The *tunica adventitia* of arteries of the muscular type is sometimes thicker than the tunica media. It consists of loose connective tissue whose collagenous and elastic fibers pass predominantly in the longitudinal or tangential directions. The elastic layer immediately adjacent to the smooth muscles stands out as a well-defined, perforated membrane, the external elastic membrane. The tunica adventitia passes over into the surrounding connective tissue without sharp boundaries. Owing to this loose consistency of its external

layers, the tunica adventitia permits the arteries to move within certain limits and allows the constant changes in the size of the lumen; it also limits the amount of shortening of the arteries which takes place after they are cut.

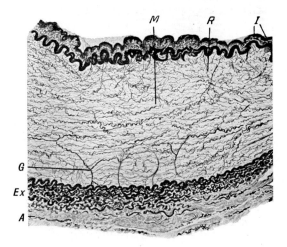

M   R   I

G
Ex
A

Fig. 212. Portion of cross section of mesenteric artery of man. A, Adventitia; Ex, external elastic layer; G, branching elastic fibers; I, elastica of the intima, which is here split into two layers; M, tunica media; R, radial elastic fibers. Orcein stain. 110 ×. (After Schaffer.)

Arteries of Large Caliber or of Elastic Type. The resistant, elastic wall of these blood vessels (such as the aorta) is much thinner, in comparison with the size of their lumen, than that of the vessels of the preceding group.

Tunica Intima. The tunica intima in an adult man is rather thick (127 microns) (Fig. 213, *I*). The endothelium differs from the endothelium in smaller arteries by the fact that the cells are not elongated, but have an oval or polygonal form. The layer directly beneath the endothelium is normally thin. It

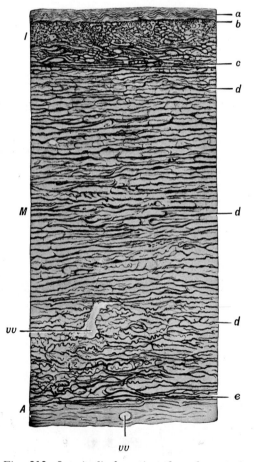

Fig. 213. Longitudinal section through posterior wall of human descending aorta. Elastic tissue is black —the other elements are not shown clearly. *I,* Intima; *M,* media; *A,* adventitia; *a,* subendothelial layer; from *b* to *c,* the longitudinally striated layer, which becomes a fenestrated membrane at *c; d,* fenestrated elastic membrane; *e,* the last membrane, elastica externa, on the boundary between adventitia and media; *vv,* vasa vasorum. Elastic fiber stain. 85 ×. (After Kölliker-von Ebner.)

consists of a few thin interlacing fibers and fibroblasts. A few wandering cells may normally be present. The next layer consists of many branching elastic fibers which fuse in places into a more or less well-pronounced, striated membrane. Between these fibers are a few collagenous fibers, fibroblasts and small bundles of smooth muscle cells. Externally, this layer of elastic fibers passes into a fenestrated elastic membrane, which by its location corresponds with the internal elastic membrane. But it does not differ from the many similar membranes which follow toward the exterior and form the tunica media of the aorta. Thus, the tunica intima in the largest blood vessels is but poorly delimited from the tunica media.

Tunica Media. The tunica media consists mainly of elastic tissue (Fig. 213, *M*). In the human aorta it appears in the form of fifty to sixty-five concentric "fenestrated" elastic membranes, 2.5 microns thick, between which the interspaces measure 6 to 18 microns. The neighboring membranes are frequently connected with one another by elastic fibers or bands.

In the spaces between two adjacent elastic membranes are thin layers of connective tissue with thin collagenous and elastic fibers, fibroblasts and smooth muscle cells (Fig. 216). The latter, particularly in the inner layers of the tunica media of the aorta, are flattened, branched elements with irregular outlines and serrated edges; they have characteristic, rodlike nuclei. Most of them are arranged circularly. These smooth muscle cells are closely surrounded by collagenous fibers which bind them to the elastic membranes. Between these various structures is an appreciable amount of basophile amorphous ground substance which stains like mucus with certain dyes. The basophilia of this ground substance is believed to be due to the presence of chondroitin sulphuric acid.

Tunica Adventitia. The tunica adventitia in arteries of large caliber is relatively thin. It cannot be sharply distinguished from the surrounding connective tissue. The most external of the fenestrated membranes of the tunica media serves as an external elastic membrane, from which numerous elastic

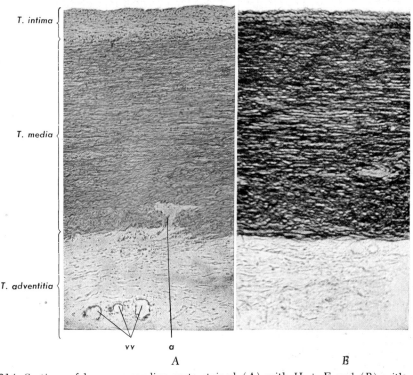

T. intima

T. media

T. adventitia

vv a

A B

Fig. 214. Sections of human ascending aorta stained (A) with H + E and (B) with resorcin-fuchsin for elastic fibers. Vasa vasorum (vv) penetrate the tunica media at a. Photomicrographs. About 50 ×. (After von Herrath and Abramow.)

fibers project. There is a gradual transition from the tunica adventitia into the surrounding loose connective tissue with its fat cells.

Connection between Arteries of Different Types. As one type of artery goes over into another without marked boundaries, it is sometimes difficult to classify an artery as of a given type. Some arteries of rather small caliber (popliteal, tibial) have walls which suggest large arteries, while some large arteries (external iliac) have walls like those of medium-sized arteries. The change of an artery of elastic type into an artery of muscular type usually takes place gradually, so that the intermediate regions are often designated *arteries of mixed type.* Such are the external carotid, axillary, and common iliac arteries. In their middle tunics are islands of smooth muscle fibers which interrupt the elastic membranes in many places.

Where arteries of mixed or elastic type pass suddenly into arteries of the muscular type, short transition regions occur; these are called *arteries of hybrid type,* and are found in the visceral arteries which arise from the abdominal aorta (Fig. 212). In them, for a varying distance, the tunica media may consist of two different layers—the internal is muscular and the external is composed of typical elastic membranes.

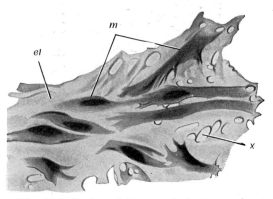

Fig. 215. Portion of fenestrated elastic membrane from aorta of a calf; *el,* Elastic substance; *x,* openings; *m,* smooth muscle cells adherent to the membrane. 250 ×. (Redrawn after Prenant.)

Special Types of Arteries. In the tunica media of the arteries of the lower limbs, the muscular tissue is more highly developed than in the arteries of the upper limbs.

The *arteries of the skull,* which are protected from external pressure or tension, have a thin wall and a well-developed elastica interna. In the tunica media the elastic fibers are almost entirely absent.

The *umbilical artery* has an atypical, special structure. Its intima consists only of endothelium and lacks an internal elastic layer. The tunica media contains a small number of elastic fibers and two thick, muscular layers which are sharply separated from each other. The inner layer is composed of longitudinally directed fibers; in many places these form longitudinal protrusions into both the lumen and the outer circular muscular layer. The extra-abdominal portion of the umbilical artery is provided with numerous oval swellings; in these regions the wall becomes thin and consists almost exclusively of circularly arranged muscles.

The various organs show differences in their arteries. These are described in the following chapters.

Physiological Significance of the Structure of Arteries. As the movement of the blood in the arteries is caused by the contractions of the heart, it is rhythmically interrupted. If the walls of the arteries were inflexible, the flow of blood in their terminal branches would also be irregular. But the walls of the largest vessels near the heart are composed of an elastic, easily expanding tissue, and only a part of the force of contraction (systole)

immediately advances the blood. The remainder of the force of the contraction expands the large elastic arteries and is accumulated as potential energy in the increased elastic tension of the arterial wall. With the closure of the aortic and pulmonary valves, this tension becomes transformed into kinetic energy which moves the blood forward while the ventricles are at rest (diastole). At the beginning of the arterial system the flow of blood is irregular; it becomes more and more continuous in the direction of the terminal ramifications.

The arteries of elastic type can be regarded as regulating the general blood circulation, while the muscular arteries, by contracting or relaxing, decrease or increase the supply of arterial blood in any region of the body. These contractions and dilatations of the muscular arteries are regulated by the *vasoconstrictor* and *vasodilator nerves* of the autonomic nervous system which terminate in the smooth muscles.

The muscular tissue of the arterial walls is normally somewhat contracted; this is the basis of the tone of the vessels. The degree of tone fluctuates continuously.

Changes in the Arteries with Age. The arterial blood vessels reach their mature form

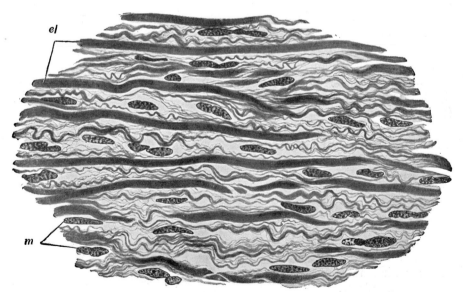

Fig. 216. Cross section from media of aorta of a five-year-old boy. *el,* Cross sections of fenestrated elastic membranes, between which are fine collagenous fibers; *m,* smooth muscle nuclei. Orcein and hematoxylin. 500 ×. (A.A.M.)

only in adult life. During the fourth month of embryonic life in man, the arteries acquire their three main layers. From this time the wall of the vessels changes gradually, so that the intima of the aorta, for example, becomes complete only at about thirty years of age. The arterial system, with the heart, is always active mechanically and seems to wear out more than any other system of organs. Indeed, the final differentiation of the structure of the wall frequently cannot be sharply separated from the regressive changes which develop gradually with age and lead to *arteriosclerosis*. Some authors view this process as a physiological, others as a pathological, progression. In general, arteriosclerosis is a pathological process when its intensity in a given vessel is beyond the norm for this vessel at a particular age. The arteries of elastic type, particularly the aorta, show much greater changes with age than do the arteries of muscular type. The small arteries hardly participate in this process under physiological conditions.

In the aorta of a four months' human embryo, the intima consists only of the endothelium and of one rather thick, elastic membrane—the elastica interna. The media consists of several layers of circular smooth muscles, between which are flat networks of elastic fibers. The adventitia is thicker than the media and consists of embryonic connective tissue.

At the end of embryonic life the internal elastic membrane becomes thicker, while the flat networks of elastic fibers in the media turn into thick elastic membranes. The muscular elements have increased slightly in number, but are still inconspicuous. The adventitia by this time has become smaller.

After birth the number and thickness of the elastic membranes in the media of the aorta gradually increase. They are much like the elastica interna now. Between the endothelium and the elastica interna in the intima, an elastic muscular layer appears. It arises in part by a splitting of the elastica interna and in part by the new formation of collagenous and elastic fibers, and gradually increases in thickness. At about the age of

twenty-five, these layers are completley differentiated.

The medium-sized muscular arteries, such as the brachial, even in the middle of embryonic life, have an intima composed of an endothelium and an elastica interna, a media of circular smooth muscles, and an adventitia. The last has a pronounced elastica externa surrounded by a connective tissue layer rich in elastic fibers. Toward the end of the embryonic period the greatly thickened media consists only of circular muscles bounded by the external and internal elastic membranes. After birth, in the arteries of muscular type, in addition to the thickening of the wall as a whole, a connective tissue layer gradually develops between the endothelium and the elastica interna.

The wearing out of a large vessel, such as the aorta, is shown mainly in an irregular thickening of the tunica intima. Later on, fat infiltrates the interstitial substance, and the degenerative processes begin. In the tunica media, the elastin of the fenestrated membrane may transform into the nonelastic *elacin*. In the medium-sized arteries of muscular type, the main change is a calcification within the tunica media, although the intima frequently thickens through a splitting of the elastica interna and the new formation of collagenous and elastic fibers.

VEINS

The blood is carried from the capillary networks toward the heart by the veins. In progressing toward the heart, the caliber of the veins gradually increases, while the wall becomes thicker. The veins usually accompany their corresponding arteries. As the caliber of an artery is always less than that of the corresponding vein or veins, the venous system has a much greater capacity than the arterial (Fig. 209). The wall of the veins is always thinner, softer and less elastic than that of the arteries. Hence in sections the veins, if empty, are collapsed, and their lumen is irregular and slitlike.

One can frequently distinguish three types of veins: those of small, medium-sized, and large calibers. This subdivision is often unsat-

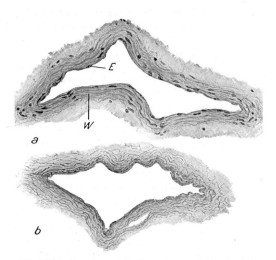

Fig. 217. Cross section through central vein of human retina. *a*, Stained with H + E; *b*, with acid orcein. E, Endothelium; W, connective tissue wall whose fine elastic fibers are visible in *b*. 160 ×. (After Schaffer.)

certain veins these coats, particularly the tunica media, cannot be distinguished. The muscular and elastic tissue is much more poorly developed in the veins than in the arteries, while the connective tissue is much more prominent in the veins.

Veins of Small Caliber. When several capillaries unite, they first form a tube about 20 microns in diameter. This consists of a layer of endothelium surrounded by a thin layer of longitudinally directed collagenous fibers and fibroblasts (Fig. 217). When the caliber has increased to about 45 microns, partially differentiated, smooth muscle cells appear between the endothelium and the connective tissue. These cells are at first located at some distance from one another; they later become arranged closer and closer together. In veins with a diameter of 200 microns these elements form a continuous layer and have a typical, long, spindle shape. In still larger veins thin networks of elastic fibers appear. In them the tunica intima consists only of endothelium, while one or several layers of smooth muscle cells form the media. The tunica adventitia consists of scattered fibroblasts and thin elastic and collagenous fibers; most of them run longitudinally, and some enter the spaces between the muscle cells of the tunica media.

isfactory, for the caliber and structure of the wall cannot always be correlated. Individual veins show much greater variations than do the arteries, and the same vein may show great differences in different parts.

Most authors distinguish three layers in the walls of the veins: tunica intima, tunica media, and tunica adventitia. But their boundaries are frequently indistinct, and in

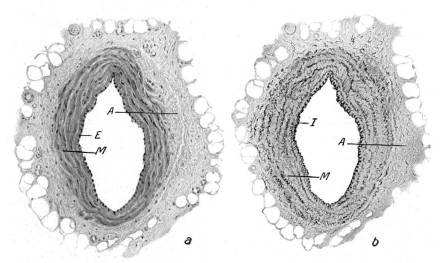

Fig. 218. Cross section through common digital vein of a man. Stained with H + E (*a*) and with acid orcein (*b*); A, adventitia; E, endothelium; I, internal elastic membrane; M, muscular coat. 80 ×. (After Schaffer.)

Veins of Medium Caliber. The veins of medium caliber (2 to 9 mm.) include the cutaneous and deeper veins of the extremities up to the brachial and the popliteal, and the veins of the viscera and head with the exception of the main trunks. In the *tunica intima* of these veins the endothelial cells are irregular polygons. Sometimes the tunica intima also contains an inconspicuous connective tissue layer with a few cells and thin elastic fibers. Externally, it is sometimes bounded by a network of elastic fibers. As it is frequently feebly developed, some authors consider the inner and middle coats as forming one layer.

The *tunica media* is much thinner than in the arteries, and consists mainly of circular smooth muscle fibers separated by many longitudinal collagenous fibers and a few fibroblasts (Fig. 218).

The *tunica adventitia* is usually much thicker than the media and consists of loose connective tissue with thick, longitudinal, collagenous bundles, and elastic networks. It often contains in the layers adjacent to the media a number of longitudinal smooth muscle bundles.

Veins of Large Caliber. The *tunica intima* has the same structure as in the medium-sized veins. In some of the larger trunks its connective tissue layer is of considerable thickness (45 to 68 microns).

The *tunica media*, in general, is poorly developed and is sometimes absent. Its structure is the same as in the veins of medium caliber. The *tunica adventitia* composes the greater part of the venous wall and is usually several times as thick as the tunica media (Fig. 219). It consists of loose connective tissue containing thick elastic fibers and mainly longitudinal collagenous fibers. In the layer adjacent to the tunica media or, if the latter is absent, to the tunica intima, the tunica adventitia contains prominent longitudinal layers of smooth muscles and elastic networks. This is the structure of the inferior vena cava and the portal, splenic, superior mesenteric, external iliac, renal and azygos veins.

Special Types of Veins. There are longitudinal or tangential smooth muscle fibers in the subendothelial connective tissue layer of the tunica intima of the iliac, femoral, popliteal, saphenous, cephalic, basilar, median, umbilical and other veins. In certain veins the longitudinal orientation is also noticed in the innermost muscular layers of the tunica media.

In a considerable portion of the inferior vena cava, the tunica media is absent and the well-developed longitudinal muscle bundles of the tunica adventitia are directly adjacent to the intima. In the pulmonary veins the media is well developed with circular muscles and is like an artery in this respect. Smooth muscles are particularly prominent in all the layers of the walls of the veins in a pregnant uterus.

Certain veins are entirely devoid of smooth muscle tissue and consequently of a tunica media. In this group belong the veins of the maternal part of the placenta, of the spinal pia mater, of the retina, of bones, the sinuses of the dura mater, the majority of the cerebral veins, the veins of the nail bed and of the trabeculae of the spleen. The last two are simply channels lined by endothelium with a fibrous connective tissue covering.

The adventitia of the vena cava and particularly of the pulmonary vein is provided for a considerable distance with a layer of cardiac muscle fibers arranged in a ring with a few longitudinal fibers where these vessels enter the heart. In the rat, the pulmonary veins up to their radicles contain much cardiac muscle in the tunica media.

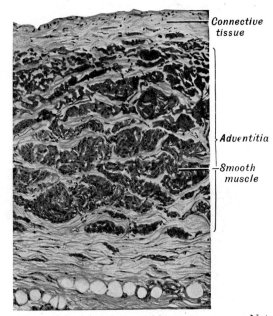

Fig. 219. Low-power view of human vena cava. Note the muscular adventitia. (Drawn by E. Bohlman.)

Valves of the Veins. Many veins of medium caliber, particularly those of the extremities, are provided with valves which prevent the blood from flowing away from the heart. These are semilunar pockets on the internal surface of the wall and are directed with their free edges in the direction of the blood flow. In man they are usually arranged in pairs, one opposite the other, distal to the branches entering the veins. Between the valves and the wall of the veins there is the so-called *sinus of the valve*; in this place the wall of the blood vessel is usually distended and thin.

The valve is a thin, connective tissue membrane; on the side toward the lumen of the vessel, it contains a thick network of elastic fibers continuous with those of the tunica intima of the vein (Fig. 220). The wall of the vein is thinner in the region of the sinus; here its intimal and medial tunics contain only longitudinal smooth muscles; these do not enter into the substance of the valve in man (Fig. 220).

Both surfaces of the valve are covered by endothelium which is reflected from the internal surface of the intima. The endothelial cells lining the surface toward the lumen of the vessel are elongated in the axis of the vessel; those which line the valves facing the sinus are elongated transversely.

Blood Vessels of Blood Vessels (Vasa Vasorum). The walls of all artries and veins with a caliber greater than 1 mm. are provided with their own blood vessels, the vasa vasorum. These originate from the adjacent small arteries and form a dense capillary network in the adventitia. In even the larger arteries they do not penetrate further than the external layers of the media (Fig. 213, *vv*). In the veins, however, they are in general more abundant and may even penetrate up to the intima; the veins of these blood vessels often open into the lumen of the vessels which they drain. Networks of thin-walled, frequently wide lymphatics have been proved to be present in all the larger arteries and veins. They connect with the *perivascular lymphatics* and, according to some authors, may even be traced into the media. The blood vessels in the central nervous system are surrounded by perivascular lymphatic spaces bounded externally by a limiting membrane of neuroglia.

Nerves of Blood Vessels. All the blood vessels, particularly the arteries, are well supplied with nerves. These are of two types, vasomotor and receptor or sensory nerves (see p. 177).

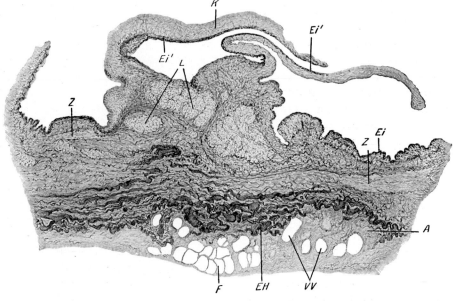

Fig. 220. From cross section of femoral vein of man. The section passes through the origin of a valve. A, Adventitia with its elastic membrane, EH; Ei, elastic fiber network in the intima; Ei', the same on the inner surface of the valve leaflet; F, fat cells; K, leaflet of the valve; L, longitudinal muscles at the base of the valve; VV, vasa vasorum; Z, circular muscle bundles in the media. Acid orcein stain. 70 ×. (After Schaffer.)

Other Connections between Arteries and Veins. As a general rule, a capillary network connects the terminal ramifications between the arteries and veins, and the transition occurs gradually. In many organs and tissues, however, modifications of this vascular plan are adapted to the peculiar functions of the particular tissues.

In certain cases an artery or vein may ramify into a number of capillaries, which are then collected into larger vessels of the original type, i.e., an artery or vein. An example of this is found in the arteries which form the glomeruli of the kidney; the afferent artery suddenly breaks up into a mass of twisting capillaries which coalesce to form the efferent artery. The portal vein of the mammalian liver arises from the capillary networks of the abdominal viscera, enters the liver, and separates into a network of sinusoids. They penetrate the organ and are then gathered into the hepatic vein. This is a "portal" system.

Arteriovenous Anastomoses. The terminal ramifications of arteries are connected with veins, not only by capillaries, but also by direct arteriovenous anastomoses in many parts of the body. As the lumen of these anastomoses changes within wide limits and is often closed, the anastomoses are probably a mechanism for the local regulation of blood circulation and pressure. In addition to these simple direct communications, Masson has described highly organized connections between arteries and veins which occur as part of a specific organ, the *glomus*, found in the nailbed, the pads of the fingers and toes, ears, hands and feet. The afferent arteriole enters the connective tissue capsule of the glomus, loses its internal elastic membrane, and develops a heavy epithelioid muscle coat and narrow lumen. This arteriovenous anastomosis of the glomus may be branched and convoluted, and is richly innervated by sympathetic and myelinated nerves. The anastomosis empties into a short, thin-walled vein with a wide lumen which drains into a periglomic vein and then into the ordinary veins of the skin.

In addition to helping regulate the flow of blood in the extremities, it is claimed that the glomus is concerned with temperature regulation and conservation of heat.

A special place in the blood vascular system is occupied by the cavernous tissue of erectile organs (see Chap. XXIX).

Coccygeal Body. This organ, erroneously included in the paraganglia, does not contain

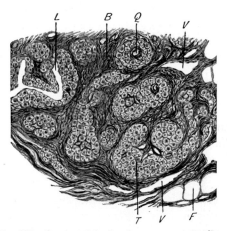

Fig. 221. Coccygeal body of man: portion of a cross section. *B*, Connective tissue; *F*, fat cells; *L*, vessel in longitudinal, *Q*, in cross, and, *T*, in tangential sections; *V*, veins. Mallory's aniline blue stain. 110 ×. (After Schaffer.)

chromaffin cells. It is situated in front of the apex of the coccyx and measures 2.5 mm. in diameter. It consists of numerous arteriovenous anastomoses embedded in a dense fibrous matrix. The smooth muscle cells have undergone extensive "epithelioid" change. An internal secretion has not been demonstrated in this organ.

THE HEART

The heart, a thick, muscular, rhythmically contracting portion of the vascular system, is a roughly conical organ. It lies in the pericardial cavity within the mediastinum. It is about 12 cm. long, 9 cm. wide, and 6 cm. in its anteroposterior diameter. It consists of four main chambers: a right and left *atrium* and a right and left *ventricle*. The superior and inferior venae cavae bring the venous blood from the body to the right atrium, whence it passes to the right ventricle. From here the blood is forced through the lungs, where it is aerated and brought to the left atrium. It then passes to the left ventricle and is distributed throughout the body by the aorta and its branches. The atria are separated from the ventricles by the tricuspid and mitral valves on the right and left sides. The pulmonary artery and the aorta are separated from the right and left ventricles, respectively, by the semilunar valves.

The wall of the heart, in both the atria and the ventricles, consists of three main layers: (1) the internal, or *encodardium*; (2) the intermediate, or *myocardium*; (3) the external, or *epicardium*. The internal layer is in immediate contact with the blood; the myocardium is the contractile layer; and the epicardium is the visceral layer of the *pericardium*, a serous membrane which forms the pericardial sac in which the heart lies.

Most authors believe that the endocardium is homologous with the tunica intima of the blood vessels, the myocardium with the tunica media, and the epicardium with the tunica adventitia.

Endocardium. The endocardium is lined with ordinary endothelium which is continuous with that of the blood vessels entering and leaving the heart. This endothelium consists of rounded or polygonal cells. In most places, directly under the endothelium, there is a thin *subendothelial layer*; it contains collagenous and a few elastic fibers and fibroblasts. External to this layer is a thick layer of connective tissue which composes the main mass of the endocardium and contains great numbers of elastic elements (Fig. 222, G). In the left atrium these elastic fibers pass into a typical, fenestrated elastic membrane. Bundles of smooth muscle fibers are found in varying numbers in this layer, particularly on the interventricular septum (Fig. 222, L).

A *subendocardial layer* (Fig. 222, I), absent from the papillary muscles and the chordae tendineae, consists of loose connective tissue which binds the endocardium and the myocardium together and is directly continuous with the interstitial tissue of the latter. It contains blood vessels, nerves, and branches of the conduction system of the heart. In the spaces between the muscular bundles of the atria, the connective tissue of the endocardium continues into that of the epicardium, and the elastic networks of both layers intermingle.

Myocardium. The minute structure of the cardiac muscle has been described on page 153. In the embryos of the higher vertebrates the myocardial fibers form a spongy network. In the adult stage, however, they are bound by connective tissue into a compact mass. This condensation of the myocardium progresses from the epicardium toward the endocardium. Many embryonic muscular bars remain in a more or less isolated condition on the internal surface of the wall of the ventricular cavities. These bars are covered with endocardium and are called "trabeculae carneae."

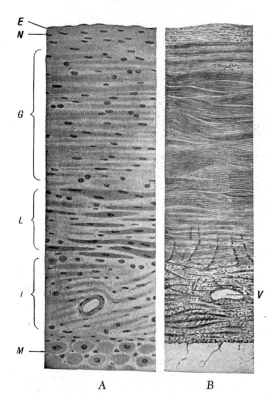

Fig. 222. Cross section through left atrium of a man; A, stained with H+E; B, after orcein. E, Endothelium; N, subendothelial layer; G, inner layer, and, L, outer layer with smooth muscle fibers of the endocardium; I, subendocardial layer; M, myocardium; V, blood vessel. 200 ×. (Redrawn after Favaro.)

Elastic elements are scarce in the myocardium of the ventricles of adult mammals, except in the tunica adventitia of the larger blood vessels of these chambers. In the myocardium of the atria, however, there are networks of elastic fibers which run everywhere between the muscle fibers and are directly connected with similar networks in the endocardium and epicardium. They are also continuous with the elastic networks in the walls of the large veins. A large part of the interstitial connective tissue of the cardiac muscle consists of extensive networks of reticular fibrils.

Epicardium. The epicardium is covered on its free surface by a single layer of mesothelial cells. Beneath the mesothelium is a thin layer of connective tissue with flat networks of elastic fibers, blood vessels and many

ton (Poirier, Tandler). It has a complicated form and consists mainly of dense connective tissue; its main parts are the *septum membranaceum*, the *trigona fibrosa*, and the *annuli fibrosi* of the atrioventricular and the arterial foramina.

In man the fibrous rings consist mainly of dense connective tissue which contains some fat and thin elastic fibers. The structure of the septum membranaceum suggests that of an aponeurosis, with its more regular distribution of collagenous bundles in layers. The connective tissue of the trigona fibrosa contains islands of chondroid tissue. The cells of the latter are globular as in cartilage, al-

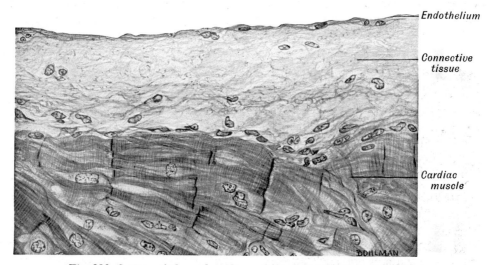

Fig. 223. Section of the endocardium of the ventricle of man. 265 ×.

nervous elements. About the adventitia of the coronary vessels there is a loose layer of considerable thickness which contains much adipose tissue.

The parietal layer of the pericardium is a serous membrane of the usual type—a flat layer of connective tissue which contains elastic networks, collagenous fibers, fibroblasts, fixed macrophages and a covering layer of mesothelial cells. Removal of the parietal pericardium in cats results in thickening of the epicardium and enlargement of the heart.

Cardiac Skeleton. The central supporting structure of the heart, to which most of the muscle fibers are attached and with which the valves are connected, is the cardiac skele-

though they lack true capsules. The interstitial substance stains deeply with basic aniline dyes and hematoxylin, and is penetrated by collagenous fibers and practically no elastic fibers. In aged persons the tissue of the cardiac skeleton may in places become calcified and sometimes even ossified.

There are important differences in the histological structure of the cardiac skeleton among different animals, and even in persons of different ages. In some cases it is a simple, dense connective tissue with a few elastic fibers and is directly continuous with the interstitial tissue of the myocardium; in some cases it approaches cartilage in its structure (horse and pig); in the dog it forms true hyaline cartilage, and contains bone in the ox. These tissue types may be located in islands side by side; one type may merge into another.

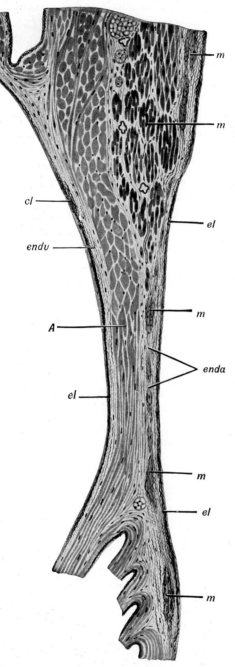

Fig. 224. Cross section through mitral valve of man. Atrial surface on the right, ventricular on the left. In the upper left-hand corner is the attachment of the aortic valve; on the left, below, is the passage of chordae tendineae into the valve. A, Dense tissue plate; *enda*, endocardium from the atrial, and, *endv*, from the ventricular side; *el*, elastic fibers; *m*, myocardium. Low magnification. (After Sato.)

Cardiac Valves. *Atrioventricular Valves.* These consist of a plate of connective tissue which begins at the annulus fibrosus and is reinforced by ligamentous threads. It is covered on the atrial and ventricular sides by a layer of endocardium. At the free edge of the valve these three layers blend.

The ground plate consists mainly of dense chondroid tissue with small, spindle-shaped or rounded cells and a basophile, fibrillated, interstitial substance. The endocardial layer is thicker on the atrial side. Here the subendothelial layer has a small amount of chondroid tissue and rests upon a connective tissue layer which contains many elastic fiber networks and some smooth muscles. In the vicinity of the annulus fibrosus the subendocardial layer is quite loose, and the musculature of the atrium penetrates far into it. On the ventricular side the endocardial layer has a similar structure, but is much thinner. In many places the chordae tendineae enter it, and at the base of the valves are some muscle fibers from the ventricle.

Aortic and Pulmonic Valves. The aortic and pulmonic valves have the same general structure as the atrioventricular valves. In the middle of the valve are plates of chondroid tissue with collagenous and thin elastic fibers. At the root of the valve these all continue into the annulus fibrosus of the arterial foramen, and at the middle of the free edge they form the noduli Arantii.

On the arterial side this plate is covered with a thick, uneven endocardium consisting of (1) connective tissue with coarse, collagenous bundles (Fig. 225, III *a*) and a few elastic fibers; (2) a thin subendothelial layer with an elastic network and a peripheral endothelium (Fig. 225, III *b*). On the ventricular side the central plate (Fig. 225, II) is covered with a thick endocardium composed of (1) a connective tissue layer with longitudinal collagenous and elastic fibers (Fig. 225, I *c*) and (2) two connective tissue layers not sharply outlined from each other; one of these contains longitudinal (Fig. 225, I *a*) and the other transverse (Fig. 225, I *b*) elastic fibers; the covering is endothelium. There is here also a dense network of particularly thick elastic fibers which suggest the elastica interna of arteries.

Impulse-Conducting System. In the vertebrate embryo and in the adult lower vertebrates, the heart is a bent tube whose contractile walls are dilated and constricted in several places. The tube consists of four portions which lie behind one another in the caudocranial direction: (1) sinus venosus, (2) atrium, (3) ventricle, (4) conus arteriosus. Patten and Kramer studied living chick embryos and noted that the heart develops by "progressive fusion of paired primordia, ventricular end first, then atrium, and last of all sinus." As each part forms, it begins to beat and controls the rate of contraction of the parts previously laid down. Thus the regular activity of a primitive vertebrate heart is based on (1) the origin of the stimulus in a definite area of the organ, and (2) the transmission of this stimulus to the following portions.

In the adult mammalian heart, too, the motor impulse arises in that part of the heart which develops from the embryonic sinus venosus, that is, where the superior vena cava enters the right atrium. There is a specialized mechanism by which the contraction spreads to the atria and then to the ventricles.

Beginning with the sinus node and extending up to the papillary muscles and the other portions of the myocardium of the ventricles, there is a continuous tract of atypical muscles (the Purkinje fibers, p. 155), the *sinoventricular system*. This system serves for the origin and transmission of the contractile impulse. This conduction system is accompanied by many nerves which also play a part in carrying the contractile impulse. The usual descriptions picture the Purkinje fibers as arising at the sinus node, spreading over the atria, concentrating at the atrioventricular node, and passing by one main bundle (the atrioventricular bundle) to the ventricles, where they again branch out over the whole inner surface of these cavities. This description is but partially correct. The atypical fibers of the conduction system do appear in these positions; in addition, however, they pass from the atria to the ventricles by several other routes which have not been studied as thoroughly as the atrioventricular bundle.

This system of conduction fibers, even up to the terminal ramifications in the ventricles, is covered with a connective tissue membrane which separates it from the remaining muscular mass of the heart.

At the boundary between the right atrium and the superior vena cava, in the region of the sulcus terminalis, is the sino-atrial node, 1 cm. in length and 3 to 5 mm. in width. Although not sharply outlined, it can be seen with the naked eye. It consists of a dense network of twisted Purkinje fibers.

The atrioventricular node is a flat, white structure about 6 mm. long and 2 to 3 mm. wide; it is located in the posterior lower part of the interatrial septum under the posterior aortic valve. The node consists of Purkinje fibers, which form a tangled dense network whose meshes are filled with connective tissue. These fibers pass into (or between) the usual myocardial fibers, so that the boundary of the node is indistinct over much of its periphery. Toward the ventricles the substance of the node contracts abruptly into a shaft about 1 cm. long, the atrioventricular bundle. It is located in the dense connective tissue of the trigonum fibrosum dextrum and continues into the septum membranaceum, where it divides into two branches.

The first branch, a cylindrical bundle 1 to 2 mm. thick, runs downward along the posterior circumference of the membranous septum and is located in part directly under the endocardium of the right ventricle. It proceeds along the interventricular septum and splits into many branches which spread along the entire internal surface of the right ventricle and along the papillary muscles of the trabeculae carneae and disappear in the substance of the myocardium.

The left branch is a wide, flat band which comes forward under the endocardium of the left ventricle in the upper portion of the interventricular septum, under the anterior edge of the posterior cusps of the aortic valve. It divides into two main branches at the border between the upper and middle thirds of the septum; then it separates, as in the right ventricle, into numerous, anastomosing thin threads which are lost to view in the myocardium.

Blood Vessels of the Heart. The blood supply to the heart is carried by the coronary arteries, usually two in number, which arise in the aortic sinuses. They are

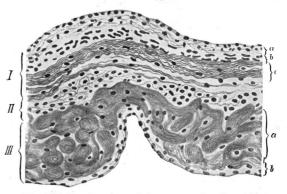

Fig. 225. Section through human aortic valve. Above is the ventricular surface; below is the lumen of the aorta. Elastic fibers unstained. See text (p. 222) for detailed explanation. (Redrawn from Mönckeberg.)

distributed to the capillaries of the myocardium. The blood from the capillaries is collected by the cardiac veins, most of which empty by way of the coronary sinus into the right atrium. A few small cardiac veins empty directly into the right atrium.

In the coronary arteries of the human heart, the tunica media, which is limited on both sides by the usual internal and external elastic membranes, is divided by a thick fenestrated membrane into an inner and an external layer.

In ordinary preparations it is difficult to see blood vessels in the cardiac valves. Most authorities now believe that normal valves are practically devoid of vessels and that those which have been demonstrated are the result of chronic inflammatory processes (endocarditis).

There are a few vessels in the chordae tendineae; they run for the most part under the endothelium and arise from the vessels of the papillary muscles.

The sinoventricular system and, particularly, both its nodes are abundantly supplied with blood from special, rather constant branches of the coronary arteries.

Lymphatic Vessels of the Heart. Three groups of lymphatic vessels are described in the heart: (1) large lymphatic vessels which lie in the grooves of the heart together with the blood vessels; they are connected with the lymphatic nodes beneath the loop of the aorta and at the bifurcation of the trachea; (2) the lymphatic vessels of the epicardial connective tissue; and (3) lymphatic vessels of the myocardium and the endocardium.

In the subepicardial connective tissue ordinary flat networks of lymphatic capillaries may be demonstrated easily. These are connected with large efferent lymphatic capillaries and vessels.

Within the subendothelial connective tissue there is an even larger network of typical lymphatic capil-

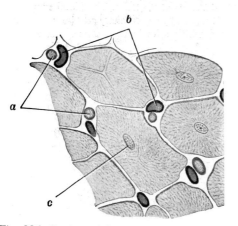

Fig. 226. Section of human myocardium, perpendicular to the muscle fibers, showing injected blood vascular capillaries, a, and lymphatic capillaries, b; c, nucleus of muscle fiber. High magnification. (Redrawn after Bock.)

laries; the larger vessels have valves. Lymphatic capillaries have been described in the atrioventricular and semilunar valves.

This lymphatic network in the endocardium was formerly often confused with the netlike ramifications of the sinoventricular system, for both structures may be demonstrated by the same injection method. But the conducting system forms much wider meshes, and its cross bars are thicker and coarser.

The myocardium is penetrated by an abundant lymphatic network, which is everywhere connected with the subendocardial one and also continues into the pericardial network. Each muscular fiber is surrounded by several lymphatic capillaries longitudinally oriented along its surface. These are connected by means of cross and tangential anastomoses and closely adjoin the blood vessel capillaries, which follow approximately the same direction.

Nerves of the Heart. The numerous nerves of the heart belong in part to the vagus nerve and in part to the sympathetic nerves. For a detailed description, see Kuntz (1929).

Some nerve endings in the heart are apparently of effector type, while other endings are of receptor or sensory character. The nerve endings in the myocardium have been described (p. 177). Nonidez has given detailed descriptions of the nerve endings in the large arteries, near the heart, which are affected by changes in pressure in these vessels.

Carotid and Aortic Bodies. These structures have until recently been erroneously included with the paraganglia. They do not contain chromaffin cells and have not been shown to have an internal secretion. The carotid and aortic bodies are similar in structure and presumably in function.

The carotid bodies are flattened, inconspicuous structures at the bifurcation of each common carotid artery. They contain irregular masses of pale-staining epithelial-like cells with pale nuclei closely applied to the endothelium of sinuses. The epithelioid cells are richly supplied with nerve endings apparently specialized to receive chemical stimuli (hence the name *chemoceptors*) indicating a fall in pH, a rise in carbon dioxide and a decrease in oxygen of the circulating blood. Hollinshead found a degranulation of the epithelioid cells when the oxygen tension was reduced to lethal levels. He believes that the granules "are directly concerned with the initiation of chemoreceptor reflexes." The specific nerves from the carotid body reach the central nervous system by the sinus branch of the glossopharyngeal nerve.

The aortic body on the right side lies between the angle of the subclavian and the carotid, while on the left it is found above the aorta mesial to the origin of the subclavian, in each case occurring where the aortic nerve reaches the externa of the artery on which it ends (Nonidez). The structure of these bodies is identical with that of the carotid bodies.

The carotid body arises from the mesenchyme of

the third branchial cleft artery and from the glosso-pharyngeal nerve. It is believed that the aortic bodies have a similar origin from the fourth branchial cleft artery and the vagus nerve.

The impulses from the aortic bodies are carried by the aortic nerve (depressor nerve of the vagus).

Chromaffin Cells. In the connective tissue between the aorta and pulmonary artery, approximately at the level of the semilunar valves, and also within the sub-epicardial connective tissue in the sulcus coronarius, mainly along the left coronary artery, small islands of chromaffin cells, similar to the elements of the medullary substance of the suprarenal glands, are scattered (p. 300). They are in close connection with nerve networks and ganglion cells. They are more highly developed in the newborn than in adults.

Histogenesis of the Blood Vessels and of the Heart. *Blood Vessels.* The blood vessels and the heart first appear as a layer of endothelial cells. In mammals the first vessels are laid down in the area vasculosa, where they develop from the mesenchymal cells (p. 93). In the organism proper the blood vessels and the heart appear later; at first they are devoid of blood cells and are empty.

In the spaces between the germ layers, groups of mesenchymal cells flatten around spaces filled with fluid which are thus surrounded by a thin endothelial wall. In this way, in given places in the body, the primordia of the heart and the main blood vessels, such as the aorta, cardinal and umbilical veins, and so forth, are laid down. Then, these at first independent primordia rapidly unite with one another and with the vessels of the area vasculosa, after which the blood circulation is established. The endothelial cells in these first stages are merely mesenchymal cells adjusted to the new and special function of bounding the blood vessel lumen. The idea that the vascular system in the embryo proper arises as an ingrowth of vessels from the area vasculosa has been rejected by most observers. (See articles by McClure, Sabin, Clark.)

After the closed blood vascular system has developed and the circulation begun, new blood vessels always arise by "budding" from pre-existing blood vessels.

The new formation of blood vessels by budding may be studied in sections of young embryos or in the living condition in the margin of the tail in larval amphibians, the mesentery of newborn mammals, or the thin layer of inflamed tissue which grows in between two cover slips introduced under the skin of an animal (Fig. 228). A method has been devised for the continued observation of such chambers in the living rabbit for weeks and even months (Clark, Sandison).

In the process of budding, a protrusion appears on the wall of the capillary and is directed into the surrounding tissues. From the beginning it often appears to be a simple, hollow expansion of the endothelial wall; in other cases it is at first a solid accumulation of endothelial cytoplasm. This *vascular bud* or sprout enlarges, elongates, and assumes many shapes. Most frequently it appears as a pointed cylinder. It always becomes hollow and thus represents a local outpouching of the blood vessel into which blood cells penetrate.

An endothelial bud may encounter another bud and fuse with its end, or its lateral wall may come in contact with another bud or with another capillary. A lumen appears within the fused endothelial protoplasm and unites the two capillaries. In this way a new mesh is formed in the capillary network, and blood begins to circulate in it. Later, new buds may arise from the newly formed vessels.

The developing vascular buds are often accompanied by undifferentiated cells, phagocytes and fibroblasts, stretched parallel to the long axis of the buds; sometimes there are also wandering cells.

The most probable explanation for the cause of the capillary bud is that the increase of metabolism within the tissue causes an increase in circulation of substances through the endothelium and thereby induces the growth of the endothelium in the direction of this current.

Arteries and veins of all types are always laid down at first as ordinary capillaries. The primary endothelial tube expands and thickens as new elements, uniting with the outside of the wall, differentiate in several directions. These elements originate from the surrounding mesenchyme in the embryo, and form cells with mesenchymal potencies along the capillaries in the adult. They play an important part in the new formation of arteries and veins from capillaries, as well as in the formation of large vessels from smaller ones in the development of a "collateral circulation" of the blood.

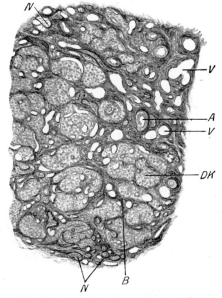

Fig. 227. Cross section through part of a carotid body of a man. A, Artery; B, connective tissue; DK, cords of epithelioid cells; N, nerves; V, veins. Mallory's aniline blue stain. 42 ×. (After Schaffer.)

The mesenchymal cells outside the endothelium become young smooth muscle cells, and myofibrils differentiate in their cytoplasm. Soon more layers of smooth muscle fibers join in the first layer; these arise in part by multiplication of the smooth muscle cells and in part by the addition of new mesenchymal cells. In addition, networks of reticular fibers appear and form sheaths around the smooth muscle cells.

The factors which cause the larger arteries and veins to develop into more or less constant shapes in definite places and in definite directions are not completely solved. It is probable that in the earliest embryonic stages the formation of the vessels takes place through forces of heredity, while in the later stages the shape and growth of the blood vessels are determined by local mechanical and chemical stimuli.

The Heart. The heart at the beginning of the circulation is a tube with a double wall: the internal, endothelial layer from which the endocardium develops, and the external, myo-epicardial. The latter consists of several layers of cells with indistinctly outlined boundaries. In the beginning (human embryo of 3 mm.

length) the distance between the two layers of the wall is rather great and is filled with a gelatinous, intercellular substance, which is penetrated by long, protoplasmic processes passing from the endothelium to the myo-epicardial layer.

In a human embryo 3.5 mm. in length, beginning with the sinus venosus and passing over to the atrium and the ventricle, this mucoid tissue disappears, and the endothelium closely adjoins the myocardial layer. But in the vicinity of the opening which connects the atrium with the ventricle and in the bulbus, this tissue remains. In this way, cushion-like thickenings of the endocardium are formed; they consist of a mucoid connective tissue. The myocardium differentiates at the same time into an external peripheral layer of flat cells, the primordium of the serous membrane of the epicardium, and into the internal, thicker layer of irregular cells united into a syncytium by intercellular bridges. The histological differentiation of the developing cardiac muscle from the syncytial layer located between the endocardium and epicardium has been described in the section on Cardiac Muscular Tissue.

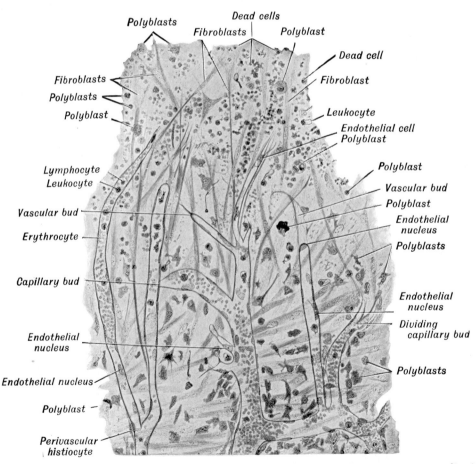

Fig. 228. Young connective tissue with budding vessels growing into the space between two cover slips inserted twenty days previously into the subcutaneous connective tissue of a rabbit. (A.A.M.)

The endocardial, cushion-like thickenings play an important role in the formation of partitions which separate the primary single cavity of the heart into compartments, and are particularly important in the formation of valves.

In the earlier stages of development the myocardium is continuous from the atria to the ventricles. But later, from the epicardium, along the course of the atrioventrciular ridge, a transverse band of embryonic connective tissue develops which completely encircles the heart. It cuts into the myocardium from the exterior and separates entirely the muscle of the atria from that of the ventricles, save for the connection between them due to the atypical fibers of the conduction system.

REFERENCES

Aagard, O. C.: Les vaisseaux lymphatiques lu cœur chez l'homme et chez quelques mammifères. Copenhagen and Paris, 1924.

Abell, R. G., and Page, I. H.: The Reaction of Peripheral Blood Vessels to Angiotonin, Renin, and other Pressor Agents. J. Exper. Med., 75:305, 1942.

Benninghoff, A.: Blutgefässe und Herz. Handb. d. mikr. Anat. (v. Möllendorff), 1930, Vol. 6, pt. 1, p. 1.

Boyd, J. D.: The Development of the Human Carotid Body. Contrib. Embryoi., Carnegie Inst. Washnigton, 152:3, 1937.

Chambers, R., and Zweifach, B. W.: Capillary Endothelial Cement in Relation to Permeability. J. Cell. & Comp. Physiol., 15:255, 1940.

Clark, E. R.: Growth and Development of Blood Vessels and Lymphatics. Ann. Int. Med., 9:1043, 1936; Arteriovenous Anastomoses. Physiol. Rev., 18:229, 1938.

Clark, E. R., and Clark, E. L.: Microscopic Observations on the Extra-endothelial Cells of Living Mammalian Blood Vessels. Am. J. Anat., 66:1, 1940.

Gregg, D. E.: The Coronary Circulation. Physiol. Rev., 26:28, 1946.

Goss, C. M.: The Physiology of the Embryonic Mammalian Heart before Circulation. Am. J. Physiol., 137:146, 1942.

Harper, W. F.: The Blood Supply of Human Heart Valves. Brit. M. J., 2:305, 1941.

Hollinshead, W. H.: Effects of Anoxia upon Carotid Body Morphology. Anat. Rec., 92:255, 1945.

Knisely, M. H., Bloch, E. H., and Warner, Louise: Selective Phagocytosis. I. Microscopic Observations Concerning the Regulation of the Blood Flow through the Liver and Other Organs and the Mechanism and Rate of Phagocytic Removal of Particles from the Blood. Det Kongelige Danske Videnskabernes Selskab, Biol. Skrifter, 4:2, 1948.

Kuntz, A.: The Autonomic Nervous System. Philadelphia, 1929.

Lutz, B. R., Fulton, G. P., and Akers, R. P.: The Neuromotor Mechanism of the Small Blood Vessels in Membranes of the Frog (Rana pipiens) and the Hamster (Mesocricetus auratus) with Reference to the Normal and Pathological Conditions of Blood Flow. Exper. Med. & Surg., 8:258, 1950.

McClure, C.: The Endothelial Problem. Anat. Rec., 22:219, 1921.

Nonidez, J. F.: Identification of the Receptor Areas in the Venae Cavae and Pulmonary Veins Which Initiate Reflex Cardiac Acceleration (Bainbridge's Reflex). Am. J. Anat., 61:203, 1937; The Aortic (Depressor) Nerve and Its Associated Epithelioid Body, the Glomus Aorticum. Am. J. Anat., 57:259, 1935.

Patten, B. M., and Kramer, T. C.: The Initiation of Contraction in the Embryonic Chick Heart. Am. J. Anat., 53:349, 1933.

Sabin, F. R.: Studies on the Origin of Blood Vessels and of Red Blood Corpuscles as Seen in the Living Blastoderm of Chicks during the Second Day of Incubation. Contrib. Embryol. Carnegie Inst., 9:213, 1920.

Sandison, J. C.: Contraction of Blood Vessels and Observations on the Circulation in the Transparent Chamber in the Rabbit's Ear. Anat. Rec., 54:105, 1932.

Schmidt, C. F., and Comroe, J. H., Jr.: Functions of the Carotid and Aortic Bodies. Physiol. Rev., 20:115, 1940.

Vimtrup, Bj.: Beiträge zur Anatomie der Capillaren. I. Ueber contractile Elemente in der Gefässwand der Blutcapillaren. Zeitschr. f. Anat. und Entwicklungs., 65:150, 1922.

Weidenreich, F.: Allgemeine Morphologie des Gefässsystems. Handb. d. vergleich. Anat., 6:375, 1933.

Zimmermann, K. W.: Der feinere Bau der Blutkapillaren. Zeit. f. Anat. u. Entwicklungs., 68:29, 1923.

Zweifach, B. W.: A Micro-manipulative Study of Blood Capillaries. Anat. Rec., 59:83, 1934.

XI. THE LYMPHATIC SYSTEM

An exchange of nutritive materials and oxygen proceeds continuously between the blood within the capillaries and the tissue juice bathing the cells of the various tissues. Most of the waste products of metabolism are returned from the tissues to the capillaries and capillary veins. In the vertebrates the vessels of the closed lymphatic system return some of the tissue fluids to the general circulation by a roundabout route.

The lymphatic system is composed of *lymphatic vessels* and *organs*. The smallest vessels, the *lymphatic capillaries*, are thin-walled, blindly ending tubes which form a dense network in most of the tissues of the body. They collect tissue juice which is called lymph as soon as it enters these capillaries. The lymphatic capillaries unite to form larger vessels, the largest of which empty into veins. The lymphatic system thus differs from the blood vascular system in that it is not a closed vascular ring. The lymphatic organs are located along the course of the lymphatic vessels and contribute various-sized lymphocytes to the lymph passing through them. The lymph of the finest lymphatic radicles is almost devoid of cells.

Connected with the lymphatic system are the serous cavities, the spaces surrounding the meninges, the chambers of the eye, Tenon's cavity around the eyeball, the cavity of the internal ear, the ventricles of the brain, and the central canal of the spinal cord. The liquids in these cavities are different from the lymph and have a different physiological significance, although the liquid in the serous cavities is much like lymph. Nevertheless, injected colloidal solutions and particulate matter may penetrate from these cavities into the lymphatic vessels, and vice versa.

LYMPHATIC CAPILLARIES AND VESSELS

Lymphatic capillaries are thin-walled, tubular structures of slightly greater caliber than blood capillaries. Unlike the latter, which usually have a regular cylindrical form, they have irregular shapes and are constricted in some places and dilated in others. They branch abundantly and anastomose freely with one another. Dilatations occur frequently where several capillaries join. The lymphatic networks are often located beside networks of blood capillaries, but are always independent of them. As a general rule, the lymphatic networks are farther from the surface of the skin or mucous membranes than the blood capillary networks .

Further, the lymphatic networks are distinguished from the blood capillaries by ending blindly in rounded or swollen ends. This is best seen in the mucous membrane of the small intestine, where a network of lymphatic capillaries or a single, blindly ending vessel, the *central lacteal*, extends in the lamina propria up to the end of the villus (Fig. 229). The lymphatic capillaries form expanded net-

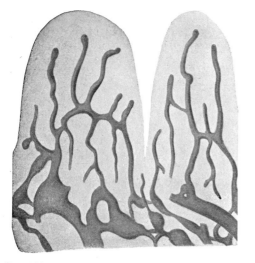

Fig. 229. Lymphatic capillaries (lacteals) filled with Berlin blue in the villi of the intestine of a rat. (Redrawn after Ranvier.)

works of considerable size around the solitary and aggregated lymphatic nodules of the intestine, and in the thyroid and mammary glands.

The wall of the lymphatic capillaries is formed by a single layer of flat endothelial cells; these are slightly larger and thinner and a few tangential smooth muscles, and several thin elastic fibers. The tunica adventitia is the thickest layer and consists of interlacing collagenous and elastic fibers, and smooth muscle bundles. The elastic fibers of the tunica adventitia continue into those of the surrounding connective tissue.

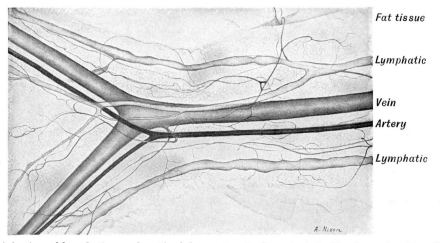

Fat tissue

Lymphatic

Vein

Artery

Lymphatic

Fig. 230. Vital injection of lymphatic vessels with alpha-azurine F. G. and of the blood vessels with colloidal mercuric sulfide. Mesentery of rabbit. About 20 ×.

than those of the blood capillaries. Hence, in sections of collapsed lymphatic capillaries, only the endothelial nuclei can be seen, and these cannot be distinguished from the nuclei of the surrounding fibroblasts. The lymphatic capillaries abut directly against the surrounding tissues and are not provided with a layer of pericytes like the blood capillaries.

The lymph passes from these capillary networks into lymphatic vessels which have slightly thicker walls and valves. They are covered at first by thin, collagenous bundles, elastic fibers and a few smooth muscle cells, arranged tangentially or transversely to the vessel. Those lymphatic vessels with a diameter greater than 0.2 mm. have thicker walls in which three layers, corresponding to the inner, medial, and adventitial coats of arteries and veins, can be distinguished. The boundaries between these layers are often indistinct, so that the division is somewhat artificial. The tunica intima consists of endothelium and a thin layer of longitudinal, interlacing elastic fibers. The tunica media is composed of several layers of mainly circular

Valves. The valves of the lymphatic vessels always occur in pairs; they are placed on opposite sides of the vessel, and their free edges point in the direction of the lymph flow. The valves are frequently unable to withstand the pressure of a retrograde injection.

As in the veins, the valves of the lymphatic vessels are folds of the tunica intima. They have a thin connective tissue base and are covered on both sides by a layer of endothelium continuous with that of the rest of the vessel. Although valves are not present in all lymphatic vessels, when they occur, they are usually much closer together than those in the veins. Above each pair of valves, the lymphatic vessel is more or less distinctly expanded, and the wall in these places has several prominent layers of smooth muscles in its media. It is believed by some that the contractions of these muscles may help move the lymph along the vessel.

Large Lymphatic Vessels. Thoracic Duct. The lymphatic vessels unite with other similar vessels and become larger and larger, while

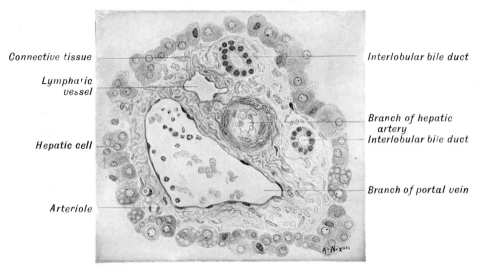

Fig. 231. Section of periportal area of a human liver. 480 ×.

their walls become thicker. They form networks which often surround blood vessels. This is very marked about the mesenteric vessels of some mammals.

Finally, all the lymphatics come together and form two main trunks—the right lymphatic duct, and the thoracic duct. The former is the smaller; it carries the lymph from the upper right portion of the body and usually opens into the right innominate vein, where it arises from the right internal jugular and subclavian veins. The thoracic duct carries the lymph from all the remaining parts of the body (including the digestive system) and opens into the point of junction of the left internal jugular and subclavian veins. Both ducts are provided with valves where they enter the veins.

The wall of the thoracic duct differs from that of the great veins by the greater development of the muscles in the tunica media, by a less distinct division into three layers, and, particularly, by the great irregularity in the structure of adjacent portions.

The tunica intima consists of the endothelial lining and several thin layers of collagenous and elastic fibers; the latter condense into a layer similar to an internal elastic membrane near the junction with the tunica media. The transverse smooth muscle bundles in the tunica media are penetrated by elastic fibers coming from the elastica interna. The tunica adventitia is composed of longitudinal collagenous fibers, interlacing elastic fibers, and a few longitudinal smooth muscle

bundles. The tunica adventitia gradually merges into the surrounding loose connective tissue.

Blood Vessels of Lymphatics. The wall of the thoracic duct is provided with many blood vessels which extend into the outer layer of the middle tunic; these vessels are similar to the vasa vasorum of the larger blood vessels. The narrow, thin-walled lymphatic vessels are often accompanied by a small artery and a vein which run parallel to it. Capillaries arise from them and encircle the lymphatic vessel or form regular networks on its surface.

Nerves of Lymphatics. Both the large thoracic duct and the smaller lymphatic vessels are abundantly supplied with nerves. In both adventitial and medial coats some of the fibers terminate in sensory endings. The other fibers are motor nerves for the smooth muscles, as in the blood vessels.

Passage of Lymph from the Tissues into the Lymphatics. Investigation with the aid of injection methods has shown that the lumen of lymphatics does not communicate directly with the "tissue spaces." The so-called "stomata" seen in silver nitrate preparations are undoubtedly artefacts. As the lymphatics form a closed, endothelium-lined system of tubes, the tissue juice must pass through the endothelial cytoplasm to reach the lumen of the lymphatics. In inflammation the permeability of the local lymphatics to certain dyes is increased.

LYMPHATIC ORGANS

Closely connected with the lymphatic vessels are collections of *lymphatic tissue* aggregated into the *lymphatic organs*. The lymphatic tissue has been discussed in Chapter V. The tonsils and the solitary and aggregate follicles of the intestine are described in Chapter XII. Here only the lymph nodes will be considered.

LYMPH NODES

The lymph nodes are large accumulations of lymphatic tissue organized as a definite lymphatic organ. They are always located along the course of lymphatic vessels, whose contents pass through the nodes on their way to the thoracic and the right lymphatic ducts. Lymph nodes are scattered in large numbers, usually in groups, throughout the prevertebral region, in the mesentery, and in the loose connective tissue of the inner surfaces of joints, such as the axilla, groin, and elsewhere. They are flat, well-defined bodies varying from 1 to 25 mm. in diameter. Their form is rounded or kidney-shaped, and their surface is somewhat rough. Usually there is a slight indentation, the *hilus,* on one side of the node, where blood vessels enter and leave the organ. Lymphatic vessels enter the node at many places over its convex surface; they leave it only at the hilus.

Framework. The lymph node is covered by a *capsule* of dense collagenous fibers with a few fibroblasts and, particularly on its inner surface, networks of thin elastic fibers. A few smooth muscle cells are also found in the capsule about the points of entry and exit of the afferent and efferent lymph vessels. At the *hilus* the capsule is greatly thickened. *Trabeculae* of dense collagenous connective tissue arise from the capsule and penetrate the organ. Towards the hilus they become highly branched and finally fuse with the collagenous tissue of the hilus. Near the capsule, they divide the interior of the lymph node into roughly round areas, sometimes called ampullae or alveoli. As the trabeculae are frequently interrupted, adjacent ampullae connect with each other. The capsule, the

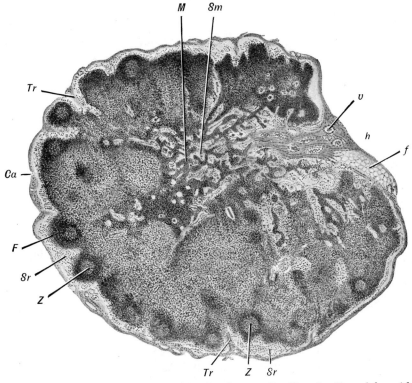

Fig. 232. Section through small jugular lymph node of man. *Ca,* Capsule; *F,* nodules with their centers *Z; f,* fat tissue; *h,* hilus; *M,* medullary cord; *Sm,* medullary and, *Sr,* subcapsular sinus; *Tr,* trabeculae; *v,* blood vessel. 18 ×. (Redrawn and slightly modified from Sobotta.)

hilus and the trabeculae constitute the collagenous framework of the lymph node. Suspended within this collagenous framework is the *reticular framework*. The reticular fibers are frequently continuous with fibers of the collagenous framework. The reticular fibers penetrate all parts of the node and form a

stroma are the free cells, mostly lymphocytes of various sizes. Plasma cells often occur, especially in the rat. A few hematogenous eosinophile leukocytes can be found in most lymph nodes. The sinuses, particularly of the medulla, contain free macrophages, even under normal conditions. Usually there are

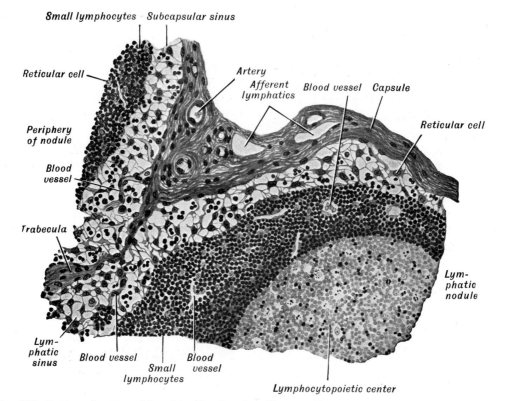

Fig. 233. Portion of cortex of lymph node of a dog. Hematoxylin-eosin-azure stain. 187 ×. (A.A.M.)

network of varying density in different locations. The loosely meshed areas constitute the sinuses, through which the lymph percolates. Such loosely meshed areas occur under the capsule and along the trabeculae, where they are called subcapsular or trabecular sinuses respectively. The *cellular stroma* of the lymph node is made up of the primitive reticular cells and the dye-storing fixed macrophages. These are associated with the reticular fibers. It is generally believed that the primitive reticular cells or the fixed macrophages (or both) form the reticular fibers, since typical fibroblasts are found only in the collagenous framework. In the meshes of the

fewer free cells in the sinuses than in the tissue, since the cells are swept away by the flowing lymph.

Cortex and Medulla. The sectioned surface of a lymph node under low magnification shows the organ divided into an outer cortical and an inner medullary part. The difference in appearance between the cortex and medulla consists mainly in differences in arrangement of the lymphatic tissue in the two zones. The cortex occupies the surface of the organ, with the exception of the hilus, and consists primarily of dense lymphatic tissue which continues into the medulla as medullary cords. As mentioned before, a rim of loose lymphatic tissue is present under the capsule and bordering the trabeculae. The cortex contains lymphatic nodules about 1 mm. in diameter. The nodules are temporary structures (see p. 78), expressing the cytogenetic and defense functions of the lymphatic tissue, which depend on age, condition

larger. With advancing age they become less conspicuous and smaller, and in old age and in various diseases may disappear. The medulla consists of the same cytological constituents as the cortex. It is not sharply separated from the cortex and usually occupies the inner portion of the node radiating from

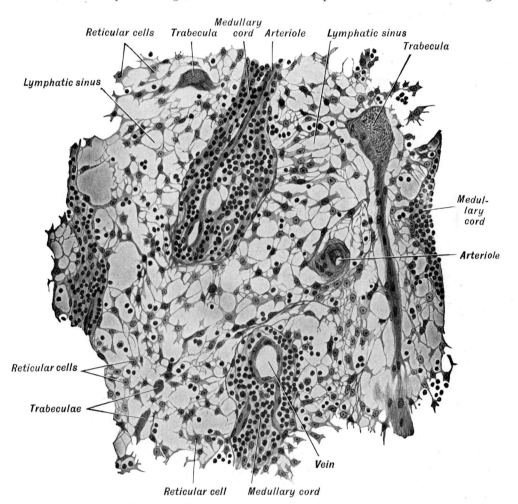

Fig. 234. Portion of medulla of a dog's lymph node. Hematoxylin-eosin-azure stain. 187 ×. (A.A.M.)

or nutrition of the organism, and the like. They may develop and disappear, to reappear again at the same or another place. The number and size of the nodules fluctuate remarkably. In the embryo and in the first months after birth they lack the central "germinal" or "reactive" areas. With the growth and development of the organism these centers appear and then become more numerous and

the hilus. The medullary cords are dense lymphatic tissue and rarely contain nodules. The cords branch and anastomose freely with one another. Near the hilus they terminate with free ends, or, more frequently, they form loops which continue into other cords. The cords are accompanied and surrounded by the medullary sinuses, which separate them from the trabeculae and are continuations and amplifications of the cortical sinuses. The substance of the sinuses is also composed of lymphatic tissue, but its meshes are so wide that they constitute relatively broad channels for the passage of lymph.

walls are not continuous, and are formed of reticular cells and fixed macrophages supported by the reticular fibers. As a continuous stream of lymph flows through the sinuses, lymphocytes are swept into the ef-

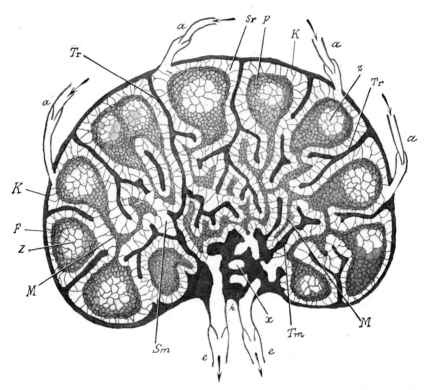

Fig. 235. Diagram of lymph node. a, Afferent and, e, efferent lymphatic vessels with valves; the arrows indicate the direction of lymph flow; F, cortical tissue; K, capsule; M, medullary cords; Sm, medullary and, Sr, cortical sinuses; Tm, medullary trabeculae, continuous with those of the cortex; Tr, trabeculae originating in the capsule and dividing the cortex into ampullae; x, lymphatic vessels in the dense connective tissue of the hilum; h; Z, nodules.

Lymphatic Vessels and Sinuses. The vessels which supply lymph to the node (vasa afferentia) are provided with valves which open toward the node (Fig. 235). These afferent vessels approach the convex surface of the node, pierce its capsule and open into the subcapsular sinus. From here the lymph passes through the looser parts of the lymphatic tissue, the sinuses, of both the cortex and medulla, and then into the efferent lymphatic vessels at the hilus.

Unlike the tubular, endothelium-lined blood vascular and lymphatic *vessels*, the lymphatic *sinuses* are irregular, tortuous spaces within the lymphatic tissue. Their

ferent lymphatic vessels, and new lymphocytes enter the sinuses by their own ameboid movement.

The sinuses of the medullary substance at first pass over into a network of twisted tubes, which penetrate the thickened portion of the capsule at the hilus and then continue into the efferent vessels, which lead the lymph away. These are wider and less numerous than the afferent vessels; they are provided with valves which open away from the node. The arrangement of the valves in the afferent and efferent vessels thus permits a flow of lymph in only one direction through the node.

The margins of the endothelial cells in the lymphatic vessels can be outlined by treatment with silver nitrate. The outlines of the reticular cells which form the walls of the lymphatic sinuses may sometimes be demonstrated by this means when they are so closely packed as to simulate endothelial cells. In all cases their reticular nature is easily recognizable.

Variations in Structure of Lymph Nodes. The described arrangement of the constituents of a typical lymphatic node is realized in but few instances, for the lymph nodes show great variations in structure, depending on the animal species as well as the location of the node. But none of these deviations affects the fundamental structure.

In large nodes the trabeculae are prominent; in small nodes they are thin and frequently interrupted, so that they may be absent for long stretches. The nodes deep in the body, as in the peritoneal cavity, are also distinguished by the poor development of their trabeculae as contrasted with the more peripheral nodes.

In some cases a hilus may be absent, while in others it may be so highly developed that its connective tissue may penetrate far into the node and divide it completely. In the ox the trabecular system is so well developed that the ampullae of the cortex are completely separated from one another. When the trabecular system is poorly developed, as in man, the nodules of the cortical substance and the sinuses may lose their sharp outlines and often fuse into a continuous, diffuse mass of lymphatic tissue, in which there are occasional looser strips or passages along which the lymph flows. Such areas, when filled with macrophages, have been called "interfollicular tissue." The term should be discarded, since the only tissue in the node is lymphatic tissue.

The relative amounts of cortical and medullary substance and their mutual arrangement fluctuate within wide limits. The nodes of the abdominal cavity are especially rich in medullary substance. In those cases in which the cortical substance predominates, the nodules may be arranged in several layers. Sometimes the cortical substance may surround the medulla completely, while in other cases the medullary substance may be adjacent to the capsule for long distances. In some cases the medulla and cortex may accumulate at opposite poles of the node, while in the pig the cortical substance with its nodules is collected in the central portion of the node, and the medullary cords with their wide sinuses may occupy only small portions of the periphery.

Blood Vessels. Almost all the blood vessels destined for the lymph node enter it through the hilus; only occasionally small ones enter through the capsule. The larger arterial and venous branches pass along the trabeculae, while the smaller ones pass along the axis of the medullary cords toward the cortex. The capillaries form particularly dense networks in the peripheral layers of the medullary cords and of the nodules. In the latter they form radially arranged meshes. In the cortex, they have a thickened endothelium, so that in cross section they often appear as though lined by cuboidal epithelium. Large numbers of small lymphocytes are present and pass through this endothelium into the blood.

Nerves. Nerves enter the hilus of the node with the blood vessels forming perivascular networks. In the trabeculae and in the medullary cords, independent nervous networks may be noticed. But in the nodules nerves are present only along the vessels and are probably of vasomotor type.

Hemal Nodes. Even in normal lymph nodes varying numbers of erythrocytes are found; these have either entered the lymph from the afferent vessels or have come from the blood vessels of the node. Some of them pass with lymph into the efferent vessels, but most of them are engulfed by the fixed macrophages. Some nodes, however, are characterized by their great content of erythrocytes; macroscopically, such organs are called *hemal nodes*. They are most numerous and well defined in the ruminants (sheep); they probably do not occur in man.

They vary from the size of a hardly noticeable granule to that of a pea or larger, and are scattered near large blood vessels in the retropleural and retroperitoneal tisues along the vertebral column from the neck to the pelvic inlet. They are also found near the kidneys and spleen, where they are believed by some to be accessory spleens.

Each node is covered by a dense capsule loosely connected with the surrounding tissue. At the hilus a small artery and a large vein enter and leave. The nodes are devoid of lymphatics.

The hemal node is a mass of lymphatic tissue, separated from the capsule by a sinus filled with blood. The lymphatic tissue is often penetrated by sinuses originating from the peripheral sinus and emptying into the "central" sinuses. All are filled with blood. A connection between the blood-containing sinuses and branches of arteries or veins has not been demonstrated.

The hemal nodes are "filters" of lymphatic tissue, situated in the course of blood vessels, and their structure is closer to that of the spleen than of lymph nodes. In the pig a special type of hemolymphatic node occupies a position halfway between the ordinary lymph node and the typical hemal node. It has blood as well as lymphatic vessels, and the contents of both types of vessels mix in the sinuses. It is possible that even in adult animals a simple lymph node may change into a hemal node, and vice versa. The functions of the hemal nodes are probably like those of the spleen.

Function of Lymphatic Nodes. Although they share this function with all the other accumulations of lymphatic tissue in the body, they are the most active structures for the formation of the lymphocytes. The stimuli for lymphocyte production are probably brought to the lymph nodes by both lymphatic and arterial vessels. Although great numbers of lymphocytes are produced in certain infections, the lymphatic leukemias and in some intoxications—such as diphtheria—the actual stimuli for lymphocytopoiesis in these conditions, as well as in physiological states, are unknown. As the lymph nodes are composed essentially of lymphocytes and phagocytes, it is obvious that their man functions depend on these cells. The functions of these cells are discussed in Chapters IV and V.

In some pathological conditions, *extramedullary myelopoiesis* occurs, and the nodes become the site of formation of granular leukocytes.

Because of the phagocytic activity of the reticular cells, particularly in the sinuses, the nodes serve as filters in which various particles, arising locally or brought with the lymph from other regions of the body, are taken up and often destroyed. Even in normal conditions, erythrophagocytosis can be seen in the sinuses of lymph nodes. This process is much more prominent when great numbers of erythrocytes are brought to the nodes as a result of hemorrhage into the nearby tissues. Particles of coal dust inhaled into the lungs finally enter the bronchial lymph nodes, where they are taken up by the reticular cells and often accumulate in such

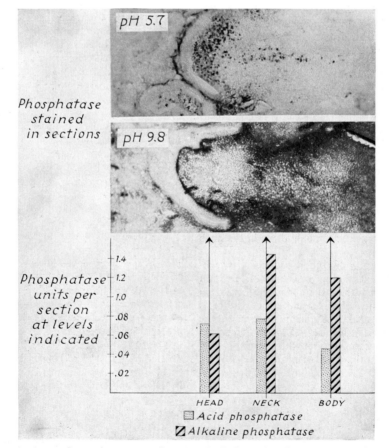

Fig. 236. Quantitative analyses of amounts of acid and alkaline phosphatase were made on sections taken at the levels indicated in rabbit appendix. The qualitative distribution of the enzymes in the lymphatic tissue is shown in the photomicrographs made with the methods of Gomori. (After Doyle.)

quantities that the organ becomes black. Pathogenic bacteria brought to the lymph nodes are frequently ingested and sometimes destroyed by the macrophages. Just like all the other tissues and organs containing many macrophages and lymphoid cells, the lymph nodes probably elaborate *antibodies*.

Histogenetic Remarks. In the mammalian embryo the lymphatic system is laid down much later than the blood vascular system. The lymphatic vessels arise first, and the lymphatic organs develop in connection with them somewhat later.

Lymphatic Vessels. Although there are many unsettled details in the question of the mode of development of the lymphatic system, most observers believe that the primordia of the lymphatic sacs and vessels arise independently of the veins, although often close to them, as isolated small clefts in the mesenchyme, which are filled with tissue fluid and surrounded by mesenchymal cells. The latter, owing to the pressure exerted by the fluid, acquire a flattened appearance and the character of endothelium. These spaces gradually fuse, forming in certain places large cavities, the *lymphatic sacs*, as well as vessels of more or less cylindrical shape. The sacs later communicate with the adjacent veins.

The vessels elongate rapidly in all directions owing to a continued addition of new cavities arising in the mesenchyme. The presence of blood in the early lymphatic vessels is explained as being due in part to a flow of blood from the veins and in part to the appearance of local hemopoietic islands in the mesenchyme together with the lymph sacs. These blood cells become included in the latter and are carried with the lymph into the veins.

After a certain stage the further development of the lymphatic system takes place mainly by budding of the endothelium of existing lymphatic vessels. These outgrowths may be observed directly in the tail of living amphibian larvae and in chambers in the rab-

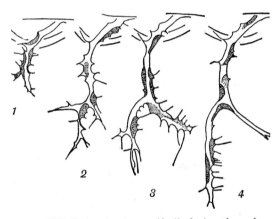

Fig. 237. Successive stages (*1–4*) during three days of growth of bud of a lymphatic capillary of frog tadpole. 180 ×. (Redrawn after E. R. Clark.)

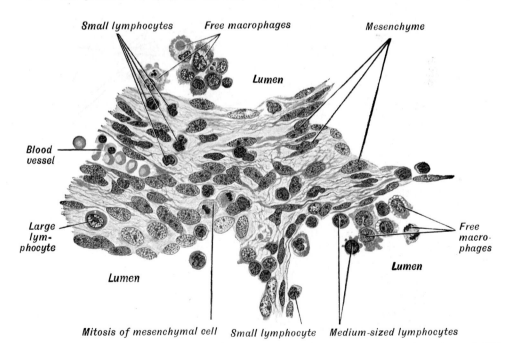

Fig. 238. Primordium of lymph node in the wall of cervical lymph sac of a human embryo of 37 mm. Lumen of the sac is divided into cavernous spaces by partitions of mesenchyme. Eosin-azure stain. About 400 ×. (A.A.M.)

bit's ear. They agree closely with the outgrowths from blood vessels (p. 225).

As in the blood vascular system, the developing lymphatic system does not retain all the parts laid down in the beginning; its constituents continue to change and become reconstructed. The main parts of the primary lymphatic system, the *sacs*, spread irregularly in various directions, and change their form; they develop in part into networks of lymphatic vessels and in part into complexes of lymphatic nodes. The student is referred to Zimmermann's monograph for the latest survey of the field.

Valves. Valves appear in the lymphatic vessels several weeks before they develop in the blood vessels. They appear first in the lymphatics near the jugular sacs and the upper part of the thoracic duct, then in the lymph vessels of the appendages, and finally in the remainder of the thoracic duct. They consist of a connective tissue base and a covering of endothelium.

Lymphatic Nodes. The development of the lymph nodes begins after the formation of the primary lymphatic vascular system. The earliest or primary nodes develop by a transformation of the lymphatic sacs. Each sac disappears as such and separates into a group of connected networks of lymphatic vessels which become nodes of various sizes; portions of the primary cisterna chyli and of the jugular sacs remain as cavities. As the sacs are at first the centers of development of the lymphatic vessels in a given region of the body, so in the future all the lymph collected from that region is finally carried into the corresponding group of deep primary nodes, as the deep jugular nodes, retroperitoneal, and so on. The secondary nodes, such as the peripheral, the inguinal, and the like, appear later along the course of lymphatic vessels; many smaller nodes are apparently formed after birth.

The transformation into a primary node is carried out by an invagination, into the lumen of the sac, of the surrounding mesenchyme, which grows through the sac in thick or thin bars. The mesenchyme forming the bars or partitions between the cavities at first does not contain wandering cells.

According to the newer investigations, the lymphatic sinuses arise as irregular, blind and anastomosing spaces, lined from the beginning by flattened mesenchymal cells, and only later do they come in contact with the endothelium-lined afferent and efferent vessels.

The primary node is a common primordium for the lymphatic tissue of the cortex and medulla, from which the medullary substance arises first. The true cortical substance appears much later as the medullary cords on the periphery of the node gradually develop club-shaped thickenings which bulge into the marginal sinus. The development of the lymphatic nodules is completed late, in the majority of cases after birth.

The lymphocytes develop *in situ* by the isolation and rounding up of mesenchymal elements and later through their own multiplication. They accumulate mainly in the marginal sinus and are carried away by the lymph stream. Among these cells, at first the small ones always predominate, but large lymphocytes and macrophages also occur. Granulocytes and megakaryocytes appear temporarily with the lymphocytes, but soon disappear. The mesenchymal elements, which did not transform into lymphoid cells, either remain as undifferentiated elements (primitive reticular cells) or give rise to the fixed macrophages of the stroma. Fibers appear rather late in the stroma of lymphatic tissue.

Regenerative Capacity of Lymphatic System. When the adult human body is incised or otherwise injured, lymphatic vessels, and sometimes lymphatic organs, are injured. Regeneration of the vessels begins in the lymphatic capillaries and proceeds by vascular budding. In some cases, however, for reasons not known, regeneration of the lymphatic vessels does not take place.

The tissue of the lymphatic nodes responds to local injury at first by the rounding up of reticular cells and their transformation into macrophages, which multiply by mitosis. The lymphocytes, which at first are unchanged, then begin to multiply and hypertrophy into polyblasts. But this attempt at regeneration is limited, and healing is usually brought about by the development of ordinary scar tissue.

After excision in young rabbits, lymph nodes may regenerate from local cells. With advancing age the regenerative ability decreases markedly.

REFERENCES

Clark, E. R., and Clark, E. L.: Further Observations on Living Lymphatic Vessels in the Transparent Chamber in the Rabbit's Ear—Their Relation to the Tissue Spaces. Am. J. Anat., 52:263, 1933.

Conway, E. A.: Cyclic Changes in Lymphatic Nodules. Anat. Rec., 69:487, 1937.

Downey, H.: The Structure and Origin of the Lymph Sinuses of Mammalian Lymph Nodes and Their Relations to Endothelium and Reticulum. Haematologica, 3:31, 1922.

Downey's Handbook of Hematology. New York, 1938.

Doyle, W. L.: The Distribution of Phosphatases in the Rabbit Appendix after X-irradiation. Am. J. Anat., 87:79, 1950.

Drinker, C. K., and Yoffey, J. M.: Lymphatics, Lymph, and Lymphoid Tissue. Their Physiological and Clinical Significance. Cambridge, Mass., 1941.

Furuta, W. J.: An Experimental Study of Lymph Node Regeneration in Rabbits. Am. J. Anat., 80:437, 1947.

Hellman, T.: Lymphgefässe, Lymphknötchen und

Lymphknoten. Handb. d. mikr. Anat. (v. Möllendorff), 1930, Vol. 6, Pt. 1, p. 233.

Johnson, V., and Freeman, W.: The Adaptive Value of Absorption of Fats into the Lymphatics. Am. J. Physiol., *124*:466, 1938.

Kampmeier, O.: The Genetic History of the Valves in the Lymphatic System of Man. Am. J. Anat., *40*: 413, 1928.

Latta, J.: The Histogenesis of Dense Lymphatic Tissue of the Intestine (Lepus): A Contribution to the Knowledge of the Development of Lymphatic Tissue and Blood-cell Formation. Am. J. Anat., *20*: 159, 1921.

McClure, C. W. F.: The Endothelial Problem. Am. J. Anat., 22:219, 1921.

McMaster, P. D., and others: Lymph. Ann. New York Acad. Sc., *46*:679, 1946.

Recklinghausen, F. v.: Das Lymphgefässsystem. Stricker's Handb. d. Lehre von den Geweben, 1871, Vol. 1, p. 214.

Webb, R. L., and Nicoll, P. A.: Behavior of Lymphatic Vessels in the Living Bat. Anat. Rec., 88: 351, 1944.

Zimmermann, A. A.: Origin and Development of the Lymphatic System in the Opossum. University of Illinois Press, (3), 7, 1940.

XII. THE SPLEEN

The spleen, one of the blood-forming and destroying organs, plays important roles in the metabolism and defense mechanisms of the body. It is the largest mass of lymphatic tissue in the body. But unlike the other collections of this tissue which are interposed in the lymph stream, the spleen is inserted in the blood stream. Owing to a peculiar type of blood vessel which allows the circulating blood to come into close contact with the macrophages of this organ, the spleen acts in many respects as a filter for the blood; this property becomes greatly accentuated in immune reactions.

The spleen, much like the lymph node, has a collagenous framework within which is suspended a reticular framework. As in the lymph node, the collagenous framework consists of a *capsule*, thickened at the hilus of the organ, where it is attached to folds of the peritoneum and where arteries enter and veins leave the viscus. Branching and anastomosing continuations of the capsule, called *trabeculae*, penetrate the organ and form part of its framework.

The reticular framework fills the spaces between the capsule, hilus and trabeculae and forms, together with the cells present, the splenic tissue. This is composed of typical lymphatic tissue (*white pulp*) and an atypical lymphatic tissue (*red pulp*). The red pulp is a pastelike, dark red mass which can be scraped from the cut surface of the organ. On a freshly sectioned surface of the spleen the white pulp is seen as irregular long or rounded gray areas, 0.2 to 0.7 mm. in diameter, scattered throughout the red pulp. These white areas are often called malpighian bodies, after the anatomist who first described them. They consist of diffuse and nodular lymphatic tissue, which varies considerably in its finer structure from time to time. It is inadvisable to use the term "malpighian body," since it has been interpreted to mean different structures by various histologists.

The structure of the spleen and the relations between the red and white pulp depend on the distribution of the blood vessels, and changes markedly in certain infections, intoxications and disturbances in blood cell formation (anemias, leukemia). The arteries are closely connected with the white pulp and the veins with the red pulp.

Capsule and Trabeculae. The capsule and the trabeculae of the spleen consist of dense connective tissue and a few smooth muscle cells. The collagenous fibers of the trabeculae are continuous with the reticular fibers of the pulp. Elastic fibers form a network between the collagenous bundles. In man, the network of the thickest elastic fibers is located in the deep layers of the capsule. The external surface of the capsule is covered by a layer of flattened mesothelium which is part of the peritoneum.

In the trabeculae the elastic fibers are more numerous than in the capsule and sometimes replace most of the collagenous fibers. Muscle fibers are present in small groups (in man) or in long cords. The slow rhythmical changes in the volume of the organ are due to the smooth muscle in the capsule and trabeculae (in those species in which smooth muscle is prominent) and to the vascularly controlled changes in the amount of blood in the organ

White Pulp. The white pulp (lymphatic tissue) forms a sheath about the arteries. The stroma is a network of reticular fibers closely joined to the primitive reticular cells and phagocytic reticular cells or fixed macrophages (p. 76). As in all lymphatic tissue, the meshes of the framework are filled with free lymphocytes of various sizes, distributed to form diffuse and nodular lymphatic tissue. In the center of the lymphatic nodules of the spleen (Fig. 239) (see p 78), as in the tinuously and reflect the reaction of the lymphatic tissue to various generalized stimuli. The lymphatic tissue of the spleen undergoes the same changes described on pages 78 to 81 for the lymphatic tissue in gen-

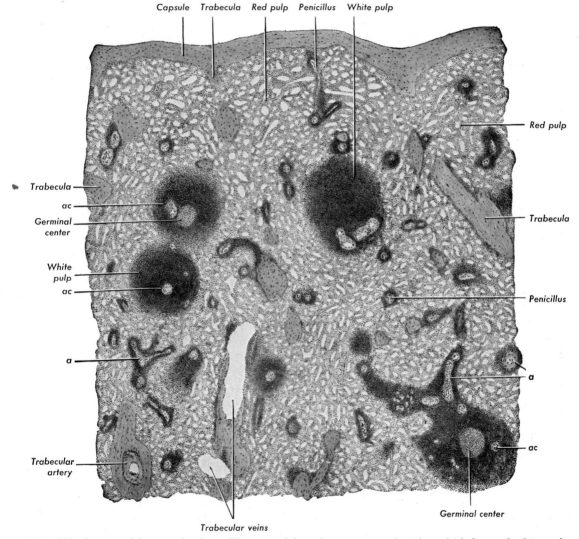

Fig. 239 Section of lumen of spleen. The arterial branches are covered with a thick layer of white pulp (lymphatic tissue) at *ac* and a thin layer at *a*. 32 × (A.A.M)

nodules of lymph nodes, the framework consists of thin, scattered threads, while at the periphery it is coarser and much denser. A few elastic fibers are interspersed among the reticular fibers of the white pulp close to the artery and its capillaries.

The absolute and relative amounts of dense and nodular lymphatic tissue vary con-

eral. That is, diffuse lymphatic tissue may become nodular, and vice versa. The centers of the nodules undergo the same cyclic changes as described on page 79. The volume and number of the nodules decrease progressively with age. In myeloid leukemia the red pulp is greatly increased in amount (besides changing qualitatively), while the white pulp almost disappears. In lymphatic leukemia, on the contrary, the white pulp hypertrophies and the red pulp atrophies. The amount of lymphatic tissue is said to diminish during starvation. Lymphocytopoietic centers in the nodules appear and disappear in connection with the general condition of the organism. In the young they are numerous, while in the aged they are usually absent (especially in man). "Reaction centers" are common in certain infections and intoxications.

between the white and red pulp, it is evident that the fibers of the former continue into those of the latter. The collagenous fibers of the trabeculae continue directly into the reticular fibers of the red pulp. The fibrous stroma of the latter is accompanied by fixed macrophages and primitive reticular cells.

In the meshes of this framework are many lymphocytes, free macrophages and all the elements of the circulating blood. The nongranular leukocytes are the most numerous of

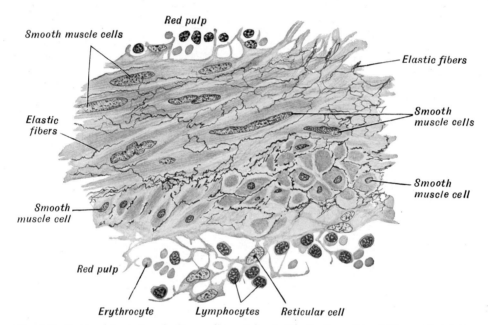

Fig. 240. Portion of a trabecula from spleen of a cat. Elastic fiber stain. 750 ×. (A.A.M.)

Red Pulp. This tissue consists of the "venous sinuses" and the tissue filling the spaces between them, the "splenic" or "Billroth cords." The venous sinuses will be discussed in the section on the veins of the spleen, of which they form an integral part. The splenic cords form a spongy network. Their tissue is a modified lymphatic tissue which merges gradually into the tissue of the white pulp. Outside the latter, there is a band of tissue looser than the white pulp and containing some erythrocytes, but devoid of venous sinuses. It constitutes the so-called "marginal zone" of the periarterial lymphatic tissue.

A framework of reticular fibers forms the foundation of the red pulp. At the boundary

these free cells. Among them small, medium-sized and large lymphocytes and monocytes are present in great numbers, intermingled without order. The various types of lymphocytes which arise in the white pulp spread by ameboid movement throughout the red pulp, where they continue to multiply.

The free macrophages are similar to those of the lymphatic tissue and are in close genetic relation with the fixed macrophages. They are round or irregularly shaped cells with large vesicular nuclei and much cytoplasm, which often contains engulfed particles, mainly erythrocytes in different stages of digestion, and yellow and brown granules, some of which give an iron reaction (Fig.

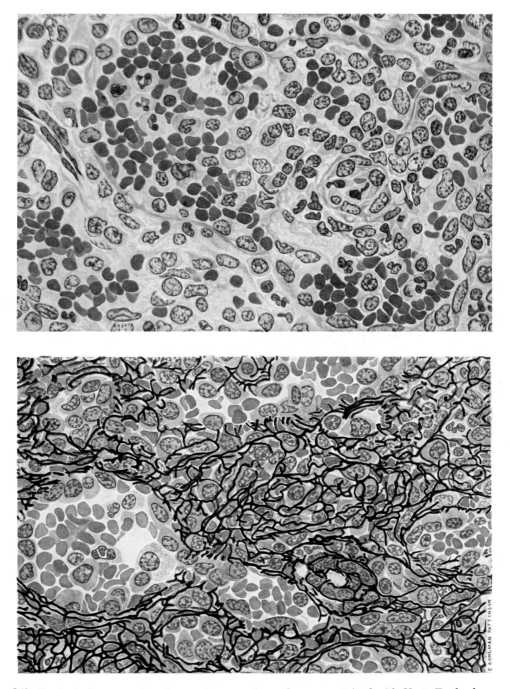

Fig. 241. Portions of two sections from a human spleen, the upper stained with H + E, the lower with H + E after the Bielschowsky impregnation method for reticular fibers. 600 ×.

244). Free macrophages can sometimes be found in blood filling the venous sinuses.

In many mammals (mouse, guinea pig and hedgehog) and in human embryos the red pulp of the spleen contains varying sized groups of myelocytes, erythroblasts, megakaryocytes and plasma cells.

In infections, in some of the anemias and leukemias, in poisoning with certain blood-destroying agents, and in local inflammations of the organ, the splenic tissue undergoes a *myeloid metaplasia* (p. 98). Myelocytes, megakaryocytes and erythroblasts develop within the red pulp; only myelocytes have been described as arising in the germinal centers. This indicates that both white and red pulp are composed primarily of the same lymphatic tissue, which also has myeloid potencies. The myeloid elements may develop from typical lymphocytes as well as from primitive reticular cells. The old idea of an "antagonism" between the red and white pulp is obviously untenable. The *red pulp is merely a modified lymphatic tissue heavily infiltrated with all the cells of the circulating blood.*

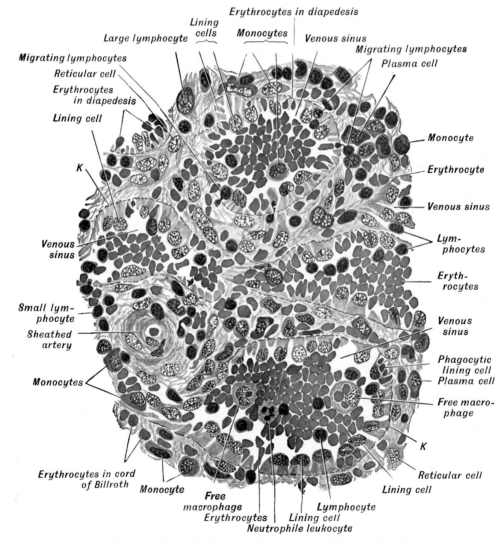

Fig. 242. Red pulp of a human spleen. *K*, Condensed cytoplasm of lining cells. Eosin-azure stain. 750 ×. (A.A.M.)

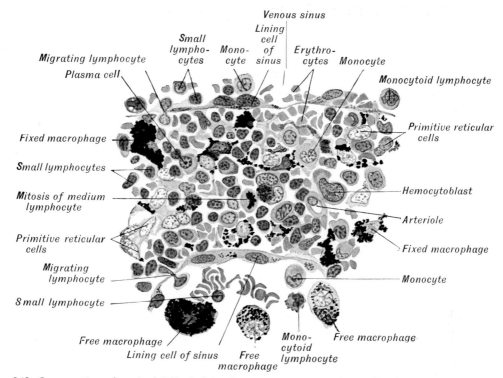

Fig. 243. Cross section of cord of Billroth lying between two venous sinuses from spleen of a rabbit injected with lithium carmine and India ink. Hematoxylin-eosin-azure II. 460 ×. (A.A.M.)

Arteries. The branches of the splenic artery enter the hilum and pass along the trabeculae, with which they branch repeatedly, becoming smaller in caliber. They are muscular arteries of medium caliber and have a loose tunica adventitia surrounded by the dense connective tissue of the trabeculae.

When the arterial branches have reached a diameter of approximately 0.2 mm., they leave the trabeculae (Fig. 245). At this place the tunica adventitia is replaced by a cylindrical sheath of lymphatic tissue (the white pulp) which accompanies the arteries almost to the point where they break up into capillaries. In many places along the course of the arteries the lymphatic sheath contains lymphatic nodules. The artery, although called "central artery," practically never passes through the nodules.

Throughout its course within the white pulp, the artery gives off numerous capillaries which supply the lymphatic tissue of the sheath. The endothelial wall of these capillaries is supported externally by a thick network of reticular fibers. These arterial capillaries pass into the red pulp. Their terminations are uncertain (p. 248).

The small arteries in the white pulp continue to branch and become thinner; on reaching a caliber of 40 to 50 microns they leave the lymphatic tissue and enter the red pulp. Here they branch into small, straight vessels called *penicilli*, which show three successive parts. The first portion is the longest (0.6 to 0.7 mm.) and is called the *artery of the pulp*, which rapidly becomes narrow and divides (the caliber now is about 10 microns). Each branch (0.15 to 0.25 mm. long) is provided with a characteristic spindle-shaped thickening of its wall, the *Schweigger-Seidel sheath*, but has a narrow lumen (6 to 8 microns)—the so-called *sheathed artery*; this portion may ramify into two or three branches. These—forming the third portion —are the shortest (60 to 90 microns with a lumen up to 10 microns) and represented simple arterial capillaries (Fig. 245), which either do not divide or split into only two branches. Their terminations are unknown and will be discussed after the veins have been described.

The artery of the pulp has a tunica media consisting of one layer of smooth muscles surrounded by a thin, discontinuous envelope of lymphatic tissue which contains a few elastic fibers. In man the Schweigger-Seidel sheaths are only slightly developed. The tunica media is lost, so that the sheath is external to the endothelium (Fig. 246). The sheath is a compact mass of concentrically arranged, elongated nuclei (probably reticular cells) and longitudinal fibers which continue into the reticular fibers of the red pulp. The arterial capillaries consist of the endothelium, supported externally by a few longitudinal fibers and elongated cells.

In the dog, hedgehog and pig, and in the lower vertebrates, the sheaths are thick, oval bodies; they may be seen in the red pulp with low magnification. Red corpuscles are always present in large or small numbers inside the sheath.

Veins. The veins of the spleen begin as networks of *venous sinuses* which penetrate all the red pulp and are especially numerous outside the marginal zone surrounding the white pulp. These vessels are called *sinuses* because they have a wide (12 to 40 microns) irregular lumen whose size varies with the amount of blood in the organ. The sinuses, even when moderately expanded, occupy more space than the splenic cords between them.

Unlike the veins, the walls of the venous sinuses do not contain common vascular endothelium, but are lined by long narrow cells arranged parallel to the long axis of the vessel. The middle of each of these rod-shaped cells is distended by a nucleus. These lining cells are fixed macrophages identical in origin and properties with those of the adjacent splenic

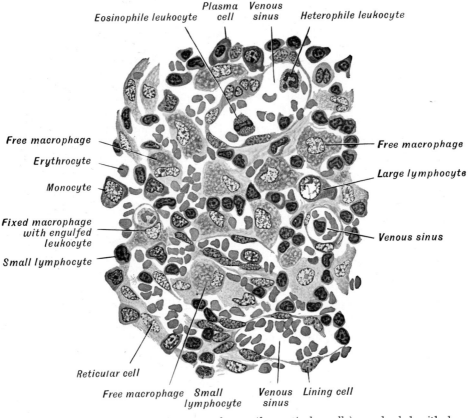

Fig. 244. Red pulp of rabbit spleen. The macrophages (free reticular cells) are loaded with hemosiderin granules. Eosin-azure stain. 750 ×. (A.A.M.)

cords, although normally less actively phagocytic than the fixed macrophages of the cords.

Outside the rod-shaped cells, the wall of
the sinus is supported by a system of circular,
occasionally branching, reticular fibers which
continue into the reticular fibers of the
splenic cords. The outer surface of the rod-
shaped cells has grooves into which the reticular fibers fit. The sinus wall is thus a network of longitudinal, rod-shaped fixed macrophages and circular reticular fibers. Some
hold that the meshes of this framework are
closed by a thin, homogeneous membrane or
by the edges of the phagocytes. Others claim
that the presence of such a membrane has
not been clearly proved and that the wall of
the venous sinuses of the spleen is perforated

by many permanent openings. The solution
of this problem will do much to solve the
riddle of the blood circulation in the spleen.

The venous sinuses empty into the veins
of the pulp, whose wall consists of endothelium supported externally by a condensed
stroma of the red pulp and a few elastic
fibers. These pulp veins coalesce to form the
veins of the trabeculae. These vessels consist
only of endothelium supported by the connective tissue of the trabeculae. The trabecular veins form the splenic veins, which leave
the organ at the hilum and empty into the
portal vein.

Union of the Arteries with the Veins. In
almost all the other organs of the body the
connection between the arterial and venous

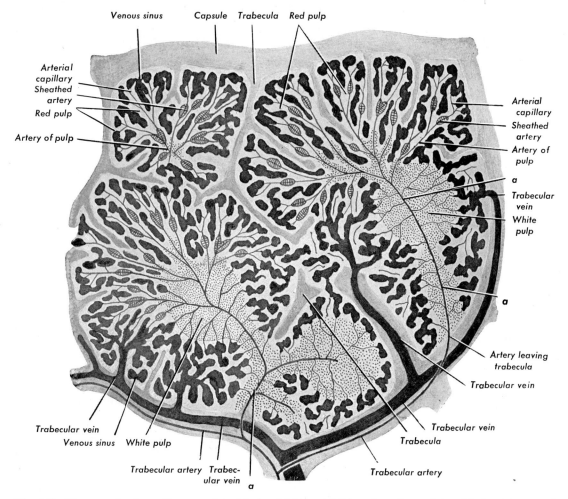

Fig. 245. Diagram of spleen. Two complete lobules (right and left) and portions of two lobules (above and
below) are shown. *a*, Artery surrounded by lymphatic tissue (white pulp).

systems is accomplished by a direct passage of the arterial capillaries into the venous, in which the endothelium retains its continuity and the vascular lumen is completely closed. In the spleen, however, the connection is different, and its details are still subject to dispute. There are three main theories as to how blood gets from the arteries to the many erythrocytes scattered irregularly between the fixed cells in the splenic cords. As there is no evidence of erythropoiesis in the cords, the conclusion is that the red blood cells have come from the circulating blood through gaps in the vascular connection between the arterioles and the venous sinuses. Those who maintain that the circulation is

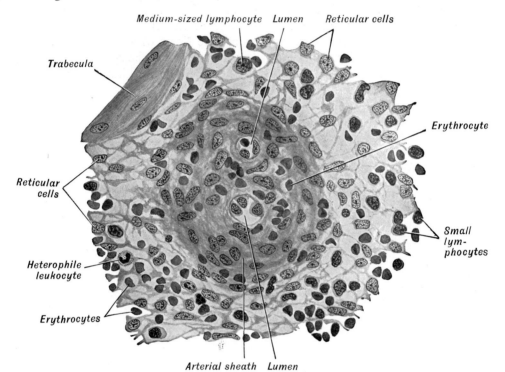

Fig. 246. Cross section of sheathed artery which has divided into two lumens. Spleen of a dog. Eosin-azure stain. 500 ×. (A.A.M.)

venous sinuses: (1) The arterial capillaries open directly into the spaces between the reticular cells of the splenic cords, and the blood gradually filters into the venous sinuses —the "open" circulation theory. (2) The arterial capillaries communicate directly with the lumen of the venous sinuses—the "closed" circulation theory. (3) The compromise view holds that both types of circulation are present at the same time. One of the latest aspects of this theory is that a "closed" circulation in a contracted spleen may become an "open" circulation when the organ is distended (Fig. 248).

The opposing theories are based on the following observations: (1) There are always "closed" hold that the number of erythrocytes in the splenic cords is much smaller than it should be if the arterial capillaries opened directly into the pulp. They point out that if the capillaries were open, the red pulp should be completely filled with blood, as in hemorrhages in the spleen.

2. When the splenic arteries are injected, even at low pressures with stained fluids, India ink or avian erythrocytes, the foreign materials readily gain access to the spaces between the fixed cells of the splenic cords, particularly in the red pulp about the white pulp. Only later do they reach the venous sinuses. When the splenic vein is injected, the venous sinuses and the meshes of the

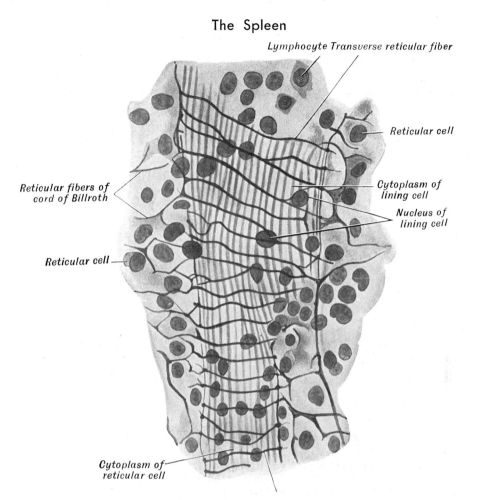

Fig. 247. Wall of a venous sinus from monkey spleen, seen from the surface. (Redrawn after Mollier.)

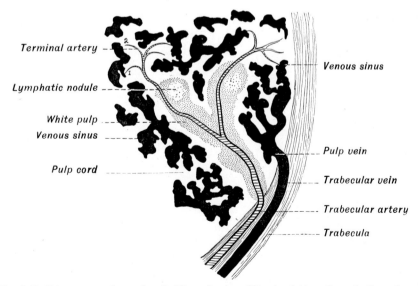

Fig. 248. Diagram to show closed (*1*) and open (*2*) circulation through the spleen.

stroma can be filled easily, but the arteries cannot.

Those who hold for a closed circulation believe that this injection of the red pulp by foreign materials is artificial and results from the rupture of the delicate vascular walls.

3. In every freshly fixed spleen, granulocytes, lymphocytes with greatly constricted nuclei, and erythrocytes can be found passing

is a marked intermittence of circulation, there is extensive filtering of the liquid portion of the blood from the sinuses into the cords of Billroth, and diapedesis of erythrocytes from the sinuses may occur normally and especially during death of the animal. These conclusions are contradicted by another group, which find that the circulation is open, that is, without preformed connec-

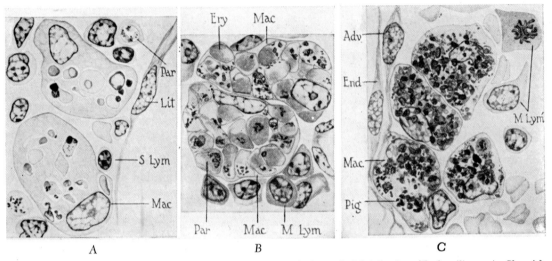

Fig. 249. Sections of spleens of monkeys at different stages in malarial infection (*P. brasilianum*). Sluggish phagocytosis by macrophages during acute rise in the infection (A), intense phagocytosis of parasitized erythrocytes during the crisis (B), and accumulation of malarial pigment and debris of erythrocytes in the macrophages two days after the crisis (C); *Adv*, adventitial cell; *End*, endothelium of a venule; *Ery*, erythrocyte; *Lit*, lining cell of sinus; *Mac*, macrophage; *M Lym*, medium lymphocyte; *Par*, parasite; *Pig*, pigment; *S Lym*, small lymphocyte. Hematoxylin-eosin-azure II. 970 ×. (After Taliaferro and Cannon.)

through the walls of the venous sinuses. It is difficult to reconcile this finding with either the "closed" or the "open" circulation theories, for these views hold that there are open connections between the sinuses and the arterial terminals or the meshes of the cords of Billroth, respectively. It is of course possible that such pictures are artefacts due to the collapse of the spleen after it is incised before being fixed.

The problem of circulation in the spleen would seem to be an ideal one for solution by direct observation of the living organ. Unfortunately, the technique available for this is difficult, and the few reports made with it are contradictory. According to one group, the circulation in the spleen is closed, there

tions between the arterial and venous systems, so that the blood from the terminals of the arterial tree passes between the reticular cells (fixed macrophages) of the cords of Billroth and finds its way through openings into the sinuses. According to these observations, erythrocytes may be stored in the spaces between the reticular cells, and it is here that the separation of the blood cells from the plasma occurs. The channels in the cords of Billroth vary from time to time with the degree of engorgement of that part of the organ, so that a channel which previously had been a tortuous passage between reticular cells may appear as a direct communication to the lumen of a venous sinus when the spleen is contracted. From the foregoing it is obvious that the manner of connection of arterioles and venules in the spleen requires further investigation.

If the splenic veins are tied for a few moments, the splenic artery ligated and the entire organ fixed and sectioned, one can easily trace columns of erythrocytes from the meshes of the cords of Billroth into the venous sinuses. The pictures seen in spleens prepared by this old method correspond more with those seen in the living organ than do the usual preparations made by cutting thin slices from the fresh organ before fixation.

Lymphatic Vessels and Nerves. In man, lymphatic vessels are poorly developed and are found only in the capsule of the spleen and in the thickest trabeculae, particularly those in the vicinity of the hilus. In some mammals true lymphatic vessels follow the arteries of the white pulp to the hilus. Nervous networks, which originate from the celiac plexus and which consist almost entirely of nonmedullated fibers, accompany the splenic artery and penetrate into the hilus of the spleen. In the sheep and ox these nerves form trunks of considerable thickness. The nerve bundles follow mainly the ramifications of the arteries and form networks which can be followed up to the central arteries of the white pulp and even along the branches of the penicilli. The terminal branches usually end with button-like thickenings in the smooth muscles of the arteries and of the trabeculae. Apparently many branches penetrate into the red as well as the white pulp, but their endings here are not definitely established.

Functions of the Spleen. The spleen is closely related to the lymphatic and hemal nodes and the bone marrow, and is an important hemopoietic organ. Lymphocytes are produced in it, mainly in the white pulp and in particular in its nodules. From the white pulp they migrate into the red pulp, where some of them are thought by certain authors to become monocytes. Lymphocytes and monocytes actively enter the venous sinuses through the reticular wall.

Although in the embryo the spleen is a hemopoietic organ of some importance, the red corpuscles of the splenic tissue of the *normal adult man* are never formed in the white or the red pulp. In certain mammals (but not in man) a few myelocytes and erythroblasts are found normally in the red pulp.

In pathological cases, especially in *myeloid leukemia*, the red pulp of the spleen undergoes *myeloid metaplasia*. In this case a large number of erythroblasts, megakaryocytes and myelocytes appear in the tissue, so that the red pulp acquires a structure similar to that of red bone marrow.

After the removal of the spleen the number of lymphocytes in the blood increases (lymphocytosis); this is explained by an excessive compensation on the part of lymph nodes. Then, there is an increase in the number of eosinophile leukocytes. Both phenomena soon disappear.

The spleen also acts as a store for red blood cells. From time to time large numbers of them are retained in the red pulp and then given up to the blood stream as they are needed in the circulation.

The destruction of erythrocytes occurs in the spleen, with a varying intensity in different species, for they are phagocytosed by the macrophages in the splenic cords and sometimes by those lining the sinuses. Disintegrating erythrocytes and granules of hemosiderin are often found in the cytoplasm of these phagocytes. After poisoning with substances which destroy the red blood cells (pyrogallol), the red pulp becomes filled with large macrophages containing the debris of erythrocytes. The destruction of erythrocytes also proceeds extracellularly, for particles of disintegrating erythrocytes may be encountered among the cells of the red pulp (p. 92). After splenectomy the erythrolytic function is carried out by the macrophages of the bone marrow, lymph nodes and liver.

Closely connected with erythrocyte destruction by the spleen is its function in iron metabolism. The iron-containing component of hemoglobin is freed from the disintegrating erythrocytes and stored in the reticular cells of the spleen. This accumulated iron is again utilized in the formation of hemoglobin.

Probably correlated with these phagocytic functions is the great importance of the

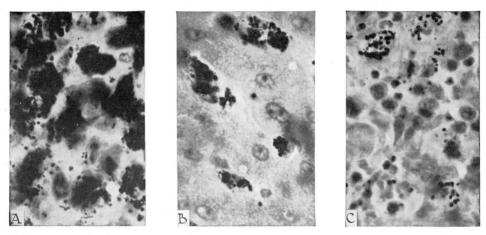

Fig. 250. Sections of spleen (A), liver (B) and bone marrow (C) of monkey infected with malaria (*P. knowlesi*). Phagocytosis of the black malarial pigment is most marked in the spleen. The Kupffer cells in the liver are also heavily laden with pigment. Phagocytosis is less prominent in the bone marrow. Photomicrographs. 830 ×. (After Taliaferro and Mulligan.)

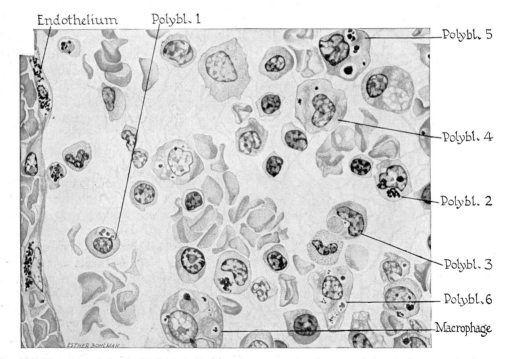

Fig. 251. Transitional forms (*Polybl. 1–5*), showing progressive hypertrophy and phagocytosis, from nongranular leukocytes to macrophage. From spleen of monkey (*Silenus rhesus*) killed nine days after infection with malaria (*P. knowlesi*) and three days after the parasites appeared in the peripheral blood. *Polybl. 1* has a small lymphocyte nucleus with an increase in cytoplasm. *Polybl. 5* has a medium-sized lymphocyte nucleus. The endothelium of the trabecular vein (actually a pulp vein) is phagocytic. Hematoxylin-eosin-azure II. 1400 ×. (After Taliaferro and Mulligan.)

spleen in the production of antibodies and in the defense of the organism against various infections, especially those which are generalized enough to be in the blood stream. The liver and bone marrow, which contain macrophages similarly strategically placed for contact with substances in the blood, share these functions. Of these three organs, the macrophages of the spleen are generally most active, those of the liver next and those of the bone marrow least. The direct function of the macrophages in defense is well exemplified during a blood infection such as malaria. Here, from the onset of the infection, parasites are filtered out in the spleen, liver and, to a less extent, bone marrow, and are eventually phagocytosed by the macrophages of these organs. Then, as acquired immunity develops, they are filtered out and phagocytosed so much more rapidly that they not only become exceedingly scarce, but superinfection is prevented. This acquired immunity is dependent on an increased number of macrophages, particularly in the spleen, and a much greater individual activity of the macrophages in all three organs. It seems probable that the increase in individual phagocytic activity in acquired immunity is associated with an opsonic antibody. Whenever the malarial infection persists, a pronounced hyperplasia of several types of cells of the spleen occurs. Mitotic division is most pronounced in the medium lymphocytes, to a less extent in the large lymphocytes and reticular cells, and to a slight degree in the functional macrophages. This type of proliferation has been termed "mesenchymal activation" and is frequently associated with pronounced splenomegaly. A similar activation has been noted in infections other than malaria in which the exact causal agent is unknown and in which direct phagocytic activity can accordingly not be observed, and during immunization with noninfectious antigens. In malaria the functional significance of the activation is largely that of producing increased numbers of macrophages. Taliaferro and Mulligan (1937) showed that in malaria numerous lymphocytes can be found in all stages of development into functional macro-

phages and that hyperplasia of the reticular cells (fixed macrophages) is insufficient to describe the cellular mechanism involved in immunity.

In many animals, splenectomy is often followed by a recrudescence of a latent or low grade infection, as is strikingly exemplified by Bartonella infections of rats, piroplasms of dogs and sheep and malaria of monkeys. Similarly, splenectomy often temporarily depresses antibody formation. This effect is greatly enhanced if combined with so-called "blockade" by the intravenous injection of colloidal dyes or particular matter.

Recent work by the Taliaferros (1951) indicates the relative importance of the spleen in forming antibody after intravenous anti-

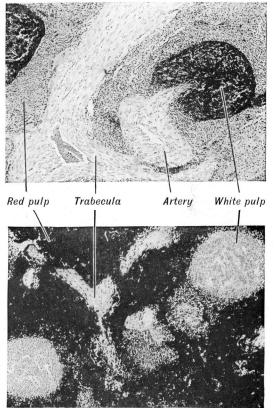

Red pulp   *Trabecula*   *Artery*   *White pulp*

Fig. 252. Photomicrographs of sections of spleen of a dog, showing distribution of alkaline phosphatase as the black-stained material in the white pulp of the upper figure and of acid phosphatase as the black-stained material in the red pulp of the lower figure. The thick trabeculae are characteristic of the dog's spleen. 30 ×. (Courtesy of G. Gomori.)

gen injections. Two days after a single small injection of antigen, serum antibody accumulates rapidly and is derived mainly from the spleen for the first week. Since the spleen then abruptly stops forming antibody, that present in the serum undergoes metabolic decay (as do all serum proteins) until a level is reached which represents the continuing low grade production from nonsplenic sources. Serum antibody arises more slowly in nonsplenic sources, but, since it continues to be produced longer, may be greater in total amount than that produced during the first week by the spleen. After more intense immunization by multiple injections of antigen, the production of antibody increases in both the spleen and nonsplenic sites, but increases markedly in the latter.

As macrophages in contact with the blood stream are not restricted to the spleen, it is not surprising that the effects of splenectomy largely disappear as the splenic functions are assumed by the macrophages of other organs, particularly the liver and bone marrow. This makes improbable the view of a few authors that the spleen has peculiar powers of defense in addition to those referable to its content of macrophages and lymphoid cells.

When the lipids in the blood are increased in amount, the reticular cells of the spleen, like the other macrophages of the body, have the capacity to remove the lipids from the blood and to store them. During this process these macrophages increase greatly in size, are filled with lipoid droplets and acquire a foamy appearance; this is observed in man in diabetic lipemia and in lipoid histiocytosis (Niemann-Pick disease), and in the experimental hypercholesterolemia of rabbits.

The spleen is thought by some to regulate the formation and destruction of erythrocytes by the production of a hormone which decreases the erythropoietic capacity of the bone marrow. Others think that a hormone is produced by the spleen which inhibits the formation of leukocytes in the other hematopoietic organs. Shielding of the spleen during total body irradiation with x-rays greatly enhances the resistance of mice and accelerates regeneration of bone marrow.

During digestion, the spleen increases in size. The reason for this is not known. Relations between the spleen and the various glands of internal secretion have not been established.

Histogenesis and Regeneration of the Spleen. The primodium of the spleen appears, in human embryos of 8 to 9 mm., as a small thickening of the dorsal mesentery, consisting of a closely aggregated mass of energetically multiplying mesenchymal elements.

The mesenchymal cells which compose this first primordium of the spleen multiply independently by mitosis, and the primordium grows. It has been supposed that it also increases in size by apposition of new cells from the mesothelium of the body cavity covering the primordium. After the embryo (pig) has reached a length of 15 mm., it receives no more cells from the mesothelium.

The elements of the primary mesenchymal primordium differentiate in two directions. Some remain connected with one another by means of processes and form the reticular framework of the white as well as of the red pulp. Some of the mesenchymal elements soon become isolated from the rest and become free cells, located in the meshes of the framework. At first they all have the character of basophile wandering elements—lymphocytes. Later on, they give origin to red corpuscles, granular myelocytes and leukocytes, and megakaryocytes, as well as to more lymphocytes. In the lower vertebrates up to the urodele amphibians, this erythropoietic function is retained throughout life in the spleen; in the higher vertebrates the myeloid function stops sooner or later and is replaced by an erythrolytic function, although the formation of lymphocytes persists throughout life.

In mammals (pig) the mesenchymal primordium contains a capillary vascular network connected with the afferent arteries and efferent veins. Meanwhile, irregular spaces, the precursors of the venous sinuses, appear (embryo pigs of 4 to 6 cm.) and become connected, in 6- to 7-cm. embryos, with the afferent and efferent vessels.

The tissue of the embryonic mammalian spleen has at first a myeloid character and cannot be compared with either the red or white pulp. At the end of fetal life (in the rat) the adventitia of the arteries begins to be infiltrated with large numbers of lymphocytes, and in this manner the white pulp originates; typical lymphatic nodules are found after birth. Simultaneously, the myeloid elements which had reached their maximum development three weeks after birth (in the rat) begin to disappear gradually, and the tissue of the spleen located between the accumulations of white pulp may be then called the red pulp.

When the spleen is removed, its functions are taken over by other organs, and the formation of a new spleen has never been observed, although a compensatory hypertrophy of the so-called "accessory spleens" has been described. Local injuries and wounds of the spleen are accompanied by a temporary myeloid metaplasia of the red pulp and heal with a simple scar. In the amphibians, particularly in larval stages, a certain degree of regeneration is possible, while in birds the spleen shows marked regenerative powers.

REFERENCES

Cannon, P. R., and McClelland, P. H.: The Reticuloendothelial System in Infectious Anemia of Albino Rats. Arch. Path. & Lab. Med., 7:787, 1929.

Hartmann, A.: Die Milz. Handb. d. mikr. Anat. (v. Möllendorff, 1930, Vol. 6, Pt. 1, p. 397.

Jacobson, L. O., Marks, E. K., Robson, M. J., Gaston, E., and Zirkle, R. E.: The Effect of Spleen Protection on Mortality following X-Irradiation. J. Lab. & Clin. Med., 34:1538, 1949.

Klemperer, P.: The Spleen. Downey's Handbook of Hematology. New York, 1938.

Knisely, M. H.: Spleen Studies. I. Microscopic Observations of the Circulatory System of Living Unstimulated Mammalian Spleens. Anat. Rec., 65:23, 1936.

Kyes, P.: The Spleen, in Cowdry's Special Cytology. 2d ed. New York, (1), 529, 1932.

MacKenzie, D. W., Jr., Whipple, A. O., and Wintersteiner, M. P.: Studies on the Microscopic Anatomy and Physiology of Living Transilluminated Mammalian Spleens. Am. J. Anat., 68:397, 1941.

Mall, F. P.: On the Circulation through the Pulp of the Dog's Spleen. Am. J. Anat., 2:315, 1903.

Mollier, S.: Ueber den Bau der Kapillaren der Milzvene (Milzsinus). Arch. f. mikr. Anat., 76:1910, 1911.

Peck, H. M., and Hoerr, N. L.: The Intermediary Circulation in the Red Pulp of the Mouse Spleen. Anat. Rec., 109:447, 1951.

Robinson, W.: The Vascular Mechanism of the Spleen, Am. Jour. Path., 2:341, 1926.

Snook, T.: A Comparative Study of the Vascular Arrangements in Mammalian Spleens. Am. J. Anat., 87:31, 1950.

Solnitzky, O.: The Schweigger-Seidel Sheath (Ellipsoid) of the Spleen. Anat. Rec., 69:55, 1937.

Taliaferro, W. H., and Mulligan, H. W.: The Histopathology of Malaria, with Special Reference to the Function and Origin of the Macrophages in Defence. Indian Med. Res. Memoir, No. 29, Supplement to Ind. Jour. Med. Res., 1937.

Taliaferro, W. H., and Taliaferro, L. G.: The Role of the Spleen in Hemolysin Production in Rabbits Receiving Multiple Antigen Injections. J. Infect. Dis. 89:143, 1951.

Thiel, G. A., and Downey, H.: The Development of the Mammalian Spleen, with Special Reference to Its Hematopoietic Activity. Am. J. Anat., 28:279, 1921.

Weidenreich, F.: Das Gefässsystem der Milz des Menschen. Arch. f. mikr. Anat., 58:247, 1901.

XIII. THYMUS

In man the thymus is an unpaired organ situated in the anterior mediastinum, in close connection with the pericardium and the great veins at the base of the heart. The thymus presents marked variations in its structure which depend on the age and con-

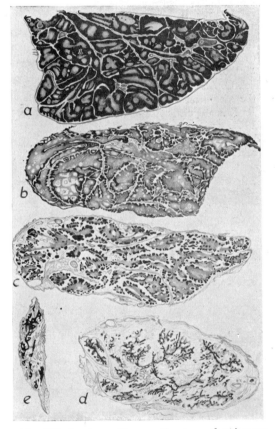

Fig. 253. Sections of human thymuses, showing age and accidental involution. *a*, From a newborn (15-gm. gland); *b*, from a 7-year-old boy (35-gm. gland); *c*, from a seventeen-year-old boy (35.2-gm. gland), showing beginning age involution; *d*, from a seventeen-year-old boy (8.8-gm. gland), high grade accidental involution; the dark parenchyma is surrounded by fat and connective tissue; *e*, from a seventeen-year-old boy, (1.65-gm. gland), extensive accidental involution. (Redrawn and slightly modified after Hammer, 1906).

dition of the organism as a whole. The organ is closely related to lymphatic tissue, but its specific function other than the production of lymphocytes is unknown, although it has been the subject of much experimentation.

In relation to body weight, the thymus is largest during embryonic life and in childhood up to the period of puberty. After this it begins to involute—a process which proceeds gradually and continuously throughout life under normal conditions. This change in its structure is spoken of as *age involution*. During the course of infectious and cachectic diseases the normal slow involution may be greatly accelerated. This is called *accidental involution* and explains many of the contradictory reports on the size of the thymus, since the organ did not have a chance to regenerate in those persons who died as a result of severe infections. At birth the thymus weighs 12 to 15 gm. This increases to about 30 to 40 gm. at puberty, after which it begins to decrease in weight, so that at sixty years it weighs only 10 to 15 gm.

The thymus consists of two main lobes, one on each side of the median line, which are closely joined by connective tissue, but are not actually fused. Each of these lobes is divided into a number of macroscopic lobules varying from 0.5 to 2 mm. in diameter. The lobules are separated from one another by the interlobular connective tissue and are divided into a darkly staining, peripheral cortical area and an inner, lighter staining, medullary portion (Fig. 253). With the study of serial sections one can trace a continuity of the medullary tissue from one lobule to another. That is, the medulla consists of a central stalk from which arise projections of medullary tissue; these are almost completely surrounded by a zone of cortical tissue.

The difference between the cortex and medulla is the fact that the cortex consists mainly of densely packed small lymphocytes with their dark nuclei and in between them only a relatively few reticular cells, with pale-staining nuclei. In the medulla it is the reverse. As one proceeds from the cortex toward the medulla, the number of lymphocytes packed around them. However, in the medulla, where the lymphocytes are less numerous, it can be seen that the reticular cells form a network with its meshes filled with lymphocytes. Most of the reticular cells are of endodermal origin, although there are a few reticular cells of mesenchymal origin around the blood vessels.

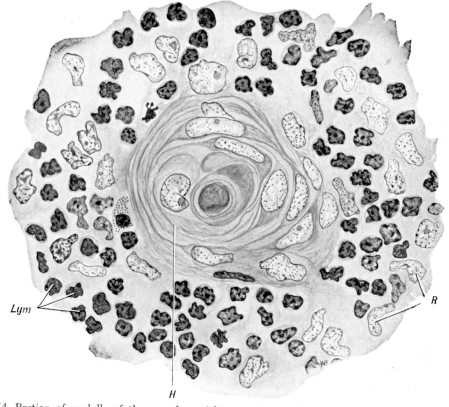

Fig. 254. Portion of medulla of thymus of an eight-year-old boy. *H*, Hassall's body; *R*, epithelial reticular cells; *Lym*, lymphocytes; an eosinophile myelocyte is just outside the left-hand margin of the Hassall's body. Eosin-azure stain. 970 ×. (W. B.)

drops rather abruptly, but there is no sharp line of demarcation between the two zones. The medulla is more vascular than the cortex.

Cells. As mentioned, the cells of the thymus are lymphocytes and reticular cells. The reticular cells are elongated and have pale, round or oval nuclei. In most cases their nuclear membrane is smooth; the nucleus contains a few small chromatin particles and one or two small nucleoli. In the cortex it is difficult to follow the outlines of the cytoplasm, since the surrounding lymphocytes are closely

In the embryo the epithelial nature of many of the reticular cells is quite obvious (Fig. 256); but as the organ becomes more and more heavily infiltrated with lymphocytes, these epithelial cells become flattened, and it is difficult to distinguish them from the nuclei of connective tissue reticular cells. A peculiarity of the thymic cellular reticulum is the fact that in vitally stained animals these cells in the thymus do not take up any of the dyestuff, while in certain diseases of malnutrition in infants, these reticular cells store large quantities of iron and fat, and in lipoid histiocytosis (Niemann-Pick disease) they become swollen with lipoid droplets. In experimental accidental involution the epithelial cells become loaded with dead lymphocytes.

phologically identical with the small lymphocytes in the lymph node and other lymphatic tissues. Some of them are identical with medium-sized and large lymphocytes. Some authors deny their lymphocytic nature and call them *thymocytes*, believing that they

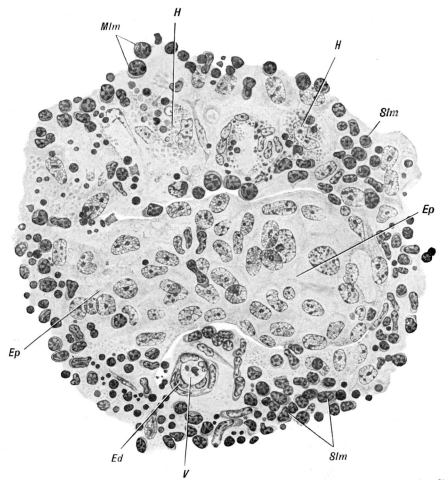

Fig. 255. Tissue culture of adult rabbit thymus, 24 hours *in vitro*, in a medium containing lithium carmine. The epithelial reticulum is contracting into a solid epithelial island (*Ep*); *Ed*, endothelium; *H*, macrophages with carmine granules and cellular debris; *Mlm*, medium-sized lymphocytes; *Slm*, small lymphocytes; *V*, vessel. 870 ×. (After Popoff.)

The epithelial nature of the great mass of reticular cells become prominent when the lymphocytes have been destroyed by x-ray and the epithelium begins to develop. It becomes even more prominent in transplants and tissue cultures of the thymus (Fig. 255). Certain tumors of clearly epithelial nature arise in this gland.

The lymphocytes of the thymus are mor-

have an epithelial origin. However, most workers agree that they arise from the mesenchyme and are lymphocytes which have wandered into the epithelium (see p. 260). In addition, these small cells show the same susceptibility to x-ray injury as do ordinary lymphocytes. Both are cytolyzed by sera obtained by the injection of thymus cells into rats, and both show the same type of ameboid motion and ability to transform into macrophages. Transplants of the thymus consist only of epithelium if lymphocytes are prevented from migrating into them by mechanical means. Further, the transformation of the small thymocytes into plasma cells and great masses of epithelial reticular cells do not contain any of these fibers. Further study of the fiber content of the organ, particularly during involution, is necessary.

Hassall's Bodies. The medulla contains the bodies of Hassall, which are characteristic

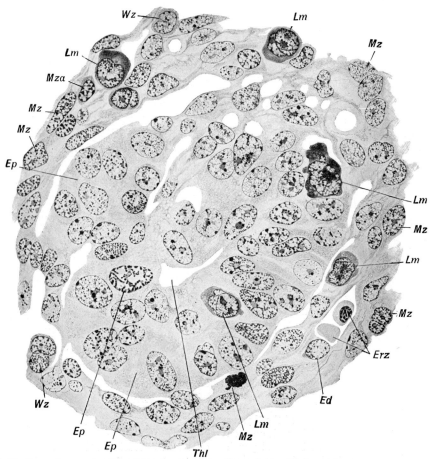

Fig. 256. Portion of cross section through the right thymus of a 14.5-mm. rabbit embryo. The organ appears as an epithelial island (*Ep*) surrounded by mesenchyme (*Mz*); *Ed*, endothelium of a vessel containing a nucleated erythrocyte (*Erz*); lymphocytes (*Lm*) originate from the mesenchyme and wander into the epithelium; *Thl*, lumen of the thymus; *Wz*, histioid wandering cell. 900 ×. (A.A.M.)

eosinophile myelocytes is generally admitted. The mitochondria have the same appearance in both types of cells.

In addition to lymphocytes and reticular cells, eosinophile myelocytes and plasma cells occur not infrequently in the medulla. Exceptionally, the thymus may contain lymphatic nodules.

Fibers. Most of the reticular fibers are concentrated around the blood vessels, and the of the thymus. They are rounded acidophile structures which vary from 30 to over 100 microns in diameter. They are composed of concentrically arranged cells, many of which show evidences of degeneration and hyalinization. Reticular cells are connected at one or more places with the periphery of each Hassall's body. The cells of the central part of a Hassall's body may degenerate completely, so that small cysts may develop in the center.

In other cases calcium may be deposited in them.

Involution of the Thymus. The description of a clear-cut separation of the thymus into cortex and medulla obtains normally in the later embryonic periods and in childhood. Normally, involution begins as a gradual thinning out of the lymphoid cells of the cortex; at about four years the epithelial reticular cells become compressed, and the area occupied by them is gradually replaced by adipose tissue, which is thought to arise in the interlobular connective tissue. The medulla begins to atrophy at puberty. This process continues throughout life. The last elements to be replaced are the Hassall's bodies, but even in very old persons there are scattered Hassall's bodies surrounded by a few reticular cells and lymphocytes. This process of normal or age involution may be complicated by the rapid changes of "accidental involution" (Fig. 253).

Vessels and Nerves. The arteries supplying the thymus arise from the internal mammary and the inferior thyroid arteries and are first distributed to the cortical tissue. Large venules arise in the medulla and combine into larger veins which empty into the left innominate and thyroid veins. The lymphatics run mainly in the interlobular connective tissue and empty into the anterior mediastinal and tracheobronchial lymph nodes. The thymus receives a few branches from the vagus and sympathetic nerves; these are probably mainly of vasomotor nature.

Histogenesis. In man the primordium of the thymus is an outgrowth of the third branchial pouch on each side of the median line; the fourth branchial pouch often gives rise to some thymic tissue. It has a cleft-like lumen (Fig. 256) and a wall of several layers of cylindrical epithelium (Fig. 256). The surrounding mesenchyme, in the earliest stages, contains many lymphoid cells which arise from mesenchyme cells. The epithelial bud proliferates, the lumen disappears, and anastomosing strands extend into the mesenchyme. The future lobules arise at the ends of these branches.

In an embryo of about 20 mm., small thymocytes appear. A few authors derive them from the epithelial cells, but most believe that the thymocytes develop from the inwandering of lymphoid cells. Some of them are large, others are small, and there are numerous transitions between the two. The number of lymphocytes increases greatly, partly from inwandering and in part through their own proliferation. The small lymphocyte type gradually predominates. The epithelium is converted into a reticular cell mass whose meshes are occupied by the lymphocytes and are penetrated here and there by blood vessels.

The definitive medulla arises late in the main stem and deeper portions of the lobules by hypertrophy of the epithelium, while most of the lymphocytes move from these areas or degenerate. Later, the Hassall's bodies arise.

In later stages of embryonic life some of the lymphocytes turn into granulocytes, but much larger numbers wander into the blood and lymph streams. The thymus in the embryo is thus a blood-forming tissue even though few or no erythrocytes are produced in it. The embryonic thymus bears some points of similarity to the embryonic liver: in both organs the epithelial cells are separated by mesenchymal cells and lymphocytes. In both organs the lymphocytes produce granulocytes, although in the liver they produce vast numbers of erythrocytes.

Most investigators ascribe the regeneration of the small thymocytes in transplants of the gland to immigration of lymphocytes (see Jolly, 1932).

Function of the Thymus. The functions of the thymus are unknown, except for its ability to form lymphocytes and a few plasma cells and myelocytes. But the change from a large organ in the embryo, infancy and childhood into a gradually disappearing organ with the development of sexual maturity has led many authors to ascribe an endocrine function to this gland.

Purified adrenocorticotropic hormone causes a striking reduction in weight and size of the thymus in male rats. Repeated injections of horse gonadotrophic hormone cause atrophy of the thymus, but this does not occur in castrated rats. On the contrary, castration causes hyperplasia of the involuted gland in the rat. Selye has found that fasting, toxins and morphine cause a rapid atrophy of the thymus and enlargement of the adrenal cortex in rats, and that atrophy of the thymus does not take place in adrenalectomized rats; hypophysectomy hastens thymic atrophy. The claims that the injection of extracts of the thymus into parent rats causes a precocious growth of their progeny which is cumulative in succeeding generations and that thymectomy causes a retardation in growth of the progeny have not been substantiated.

REFERENCES

Grégoire, Ch.: Recherches sur la symbiose lymphoépithéliale au niveau du thymus de mammifère. Arch. de Biol., 46:717, 1935.

Hammar, J.: Ueber Wachstum und Rückgang, über Standardisierung, Individualisierung und bäuliche Individualtypen im Laufe des normalen Postfötallebens. Leipzig, Akad. Leipzig Verlagsges., 1932.

Murray, R. G.: Pure Cultures of Rabbit Thymus Epithelium. Am. J. Anat., 81:369, 1947.

Murray, R. G.: The Thymus: in Histopathology of Irradiation from External and Internal Sources. National Nuclear Energy Series, 1948, Vol. 22, Chap. 9.

Smith, C., and Ireland, L. M.: Studies on the Thymus of the Mammal. I. The Distribution of Argyrophil Fibers from Birth through Old Age in the Thymus of the Mouse. Anat. Rec., 79:133, 1941.

Van Dyke, J. H.: On the Origin of Accessory Thymus Tissue, Thymus IV: The Occurrence in Man. Anat. Rec., 79:179, 1941.

XIV. GLANDS

We have seen that the cells forming the connective tissues and the nervous, muscular, and vascular systems have completely lost the arrangement of the cells of the primitive epithelial sheets from which they were derived.

It was pointed out in the chapter on epithelium that the most important and general function of the epithelium is its participation in the metabolism of the body through the absorption of substances from the outside medium, their modification in the body, and the elimination of other materials to the outside. Practically all substances which are normally received and given off by the body must pass through an epithelium.

In the organs to be described in the following chapters the epithelium persists as such or as special structures called *glands.* When glands secrete, they usually produce an aqueous fluid which differs from blood plasma or tissue fluid. This product of cellular activity is called the *secretion.* This difference in the composition of the secretion and the tissue fluid may manifest itself in the production of new substances present only in traces in the tissue fluid (insulin and other hormones, trypsin and other enzymes, mucin, milk).

By contrast, when no new substances are present in the secretion, their concentrations may be significantly different (sweat, cerebrospinal fluid, hydrochloric acid in the stomach). All glands perform work in producing such secretions, in addition to that which is expended in maintaining cellular integrity. The glomerular filtrate in the kidney is the only fluid produced from plasma which does not involve the expenditure of energy by the structure involved. For this reason, some authors call it an *excretion.*

Classification of Glands. Glands have been classified in many ways to emphasize differences (1) in the mode of secretion (*exocrine,* or to an external surface; *endocrine,* or to the blood or lymph vessels; or *mixed*); (2) in the nature of the secretion product (*cytogenous,* i.e., containing cells; or *noncellular,* i.e., free of cells); (3) in gland cell behavior during secretion (*merocrine,* which does not involve cell destruction; *holocrine,* which is accompanied by cell death; and *apocrine,* which takes place with a loss of some cytoplasm only); and (4) in the organization of the epithelial component of glands (*unicellular, simple* or *compound multicellular*).

Despite the great variety of schemes and elaborate interlocking classification of glands, it is not always possible adequately to characterize them all. This may be detected best in the difficulty of distinguishing clearly between exocrine and endocrine glands (see p. 269). It may be observed also in an attempt to categorize adequately the various kinds of noncellular producing glands. This difficulty appears also in the distinction between merocrine and apocrine glands. The inadequacy of the classification systems used for glands is common to many biological systems, and is due primarily to the lack of more fundamental data on (histo)physiology and (histo)chemistry of the organs.

Most of the glands elaborate an *external secretion* (*exocrine glands*). In these the glandular cavities open freely on the surface of the epithelium from which they have developed, and the secretion is poured out on this surface. Other glands have an *internal secretion* (*endocrine glands*). In the embryo the latter originate in the same way as the exocrine glands through the invagination of an epithelial sheet. Later, however, the connection with the sheet is severed, and the secretion passes into the blood or lymph vessels of the gland and is distributed in this way all over the body. In the majority of endocrine glands, the original simple epithelial arrangement of cells is completely lost.

The ovary and testis, and perhaps the hematopoietic organs, are *cytogenous* glands. The most characteristic parts of their secretion consist of living germ cells and blood cells. The presence of living cells in the secretion of all other glands is only incidental or a result of pathological processes, and is unrelated to their essential secretory products.

The type of secretion in which the glandular cell remains intact throughout a cyclic process of formation and discharge, and then formation again, followed by discharge, and so on, of secretory products is called *merocrine* secretion. In *holocrine* secretion the products accumulate within the cell body; the cell finally dies and is discharged as the secretion of the gland, new cells having arisen in the meantime to repeat the same cycle. The intermediate type of secretion is the so-called *apocrine* type. Here the secretion accumulates within the free end of the cell; after a time, this portion of the cytoplasm is pinched off, but the nucleus and most of the cytoplasm are undamaged, and, after a recovery period, the cell passes through the same process again. The details of these various types of secretion will be considered with the descriptions of specific organs: merocrine secretion with the salivary gland and pancreatic glands, holocrine secretion with the sebaceous glands, and apocrine secretion with the mammary gland.

Unicellular Glands. In mammals practically the only type of unicellular gland is the *mucous* or *goblet* cell, which secretes *mucin,* a polysaccharide protein which forms with water a lubricating solution called *mucus.* These cells are scattered on many mucous membranes, especially those covered with columnar or ciliated epithelium (Fig. 22). A fully developed mucous cell has an oval apical, and a slender basal, end; it resembles a goblet. The dilated part consists of a thin protoplasmic wall, the *theca,* and a

"cavity" which is filled with an almost homogeneous clear mass of cytoplasm containing a multitude of pale droplets of *mucigen.* These are best preserved by freezing and drying and are stained selectively by a method which visualizes the polysaccharide component of the mucigen. Less specific stains may also be used. The stalk of the goblet cell contains a more or less compressed and disfigured nucleus.

The droplets of mucigen leave the goblet cell from its free surface, and dissolve at once as mucin. The elimination of mucigen may proceed gradually, and the cell may keep its goblet form for a long time. In other cases the whole content is thrown out, and the emptied cell collapses and is compressed between the neighboring cells. After a while a new accumulation of mucigen may begin in the same cell. Small granules appear above the nucleus; they gradually enlarge, acquire the character of mucigen, and cause a new swelling of the apical part. A goblet cell seems to pass many times through the successive phases of secretory activity until it finally perishes and is shed.

Multicellular Glands. The simplest form of multicellular gland is an epithelial secretory sheet consisting only of secreting cells (Fig. 257). In mammals the epithelium of the choroid plexuses and the surface epithelium of the gastric mucosa are of this type. The epithelium of the mucous membrane of the uterus and oviducts, at certain stages, also belongs to this category. *Intraepithelial glands* are a special form of secretory epithelial sheet. They are small accumulations of glandular cells (usually mucous) which lie wholly within the epithelium and contain their own small lumen (Fig. 258). They are found in the human body in the pseudostratified columnar epithelium of the nasal mucosa and adjoining areas of the caruncula lacrimalis, of the ductuli efferentes and of the urethra.

All other multicellular glands arise as invaginations of the epithelial sheet into the underlying connective tissue (Fig. 259). The gland cells are gathered in the *secretory* or *terminal* portions. The secretion elaborated

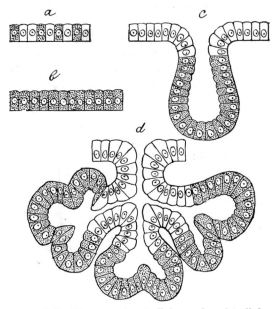

Fig. 257. Diagram of unicellular and multicellular glands. *a*, Granular, glandular cells are scattered singly among clear, common epithelial cells; *b*, glandular cells arranged in a continuous sheet—secretory epithelial surface; *c*, simplest type of multicellular gland: the area lined with glandular cells forms a saclike invagination into the subjacent tissue; *d*, multicellular gland of greater complexity: the glandular spaces are lined partly with glandular cells (terminal portions), partly with common epithelium (excretory ducts).

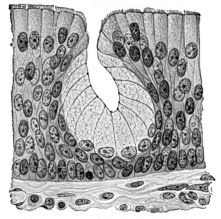

Fig. 258. Intra-epithelial gland from the pseudostratified ciliated epithelium of the laryngeal surface of the epiglottis, of a woman of seventy-two years. 534 ×. (After V. Patzelt, from Schaffer.)

by the gland cells reaches the surface directly, or through an *excretory duct* consisting of less specialized cells. In many glands the secreting surface is further increased by

many extremely fine canals, the *secretory capillaries*, which arise from the lumen of the terminal portion and penetrate between the glandular cells. They are *extracellular*, often branched, and end blindly before reaching the basement membrane. They have no wall of their own, but are formed by groovelike excavations in adjoining cells (Figs. 262, 263). Exceptionally, glandular cells may contain an *intracellular* system of fine canaliculi which seem to drain the secretion (parietal cells of the gastric glands, Fig. 356).

The free surface of the glandular cells is usually provided with *terminal bars*. They are stained black with iron hematoxylin, which shows them to extend along the secretory capillaries and gives them a characteristic aspect in sections (Fig. 28).

In the great majority of glands the epithelium lining the glandular cavities is separated by a basement membrane from the connective tissue with its blood vessels. In a few cases, however, the glandular epithelium is intimately associated with or penetrated by networks of blood vessels accompanied by connective tissue, as in the thyroid gland.

Simple exocrine glands consist of a secretory unit connected to the surface epithelium of origin directly or by an unbranched duct. The simple glands of man are classified as *tubular, coiled tubular, branched tubular,* and *acinous* or *alveolar* (Fig. 259).

1. **Simple Tubular Glands.** There is no excretory duct, and the terminal portion is a straight tubule which opens directly on the epithelial surface (Fig. 259, *a*). Such are the intestinal glands (crypts) of Lieberkühn.

2. **Simple Coiled Tubular Glands.** The terminal portion is a long coiled tubule which passes into a long excretory duct (Fig. 259, *b*). The sweat glands belong to this category. In the large axillary sweat glands of apocrine type, the terminal portions branch.

3. **Simple Branched Tubular Glands.** The tubules of the terminal portion are split forklike into two or more branches which sometimes are coiled near their ends (Fig. 259,

c,d). An excretory duct may be absent, as in the glands of the stomach and uterus, or there may be but a simple short excretory duct, as in some of the small glands of the oral cavity, the tongue and the esophagus, and in some of the glands of Brunner.

parts. The smallest which can be observed easily with the naked eye is called a (*macro*)-*lobule*. This in turn consists of smaller, frequently incompletely separated *microscopic lobules* which contain the glandular units. Glands of each order of complexity may be

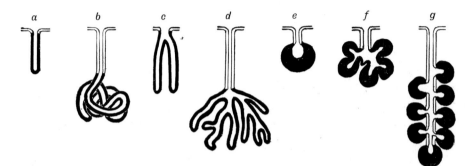

Fig. 259. Diagrams of simple exocrine glands. *a*, Simple tubular; *b*, simple coiled tubular; *c*, *d*, simple branched tubular; *e*, simple alveolus; *f*, *g*, simple branched acinous. The secretory portions are black.

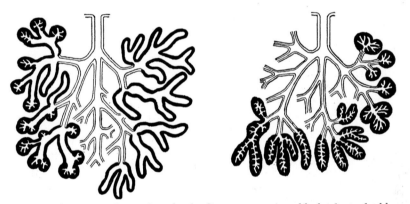

Fig. 260. Diagram of compound exocrine glands. Secretory portions black; ducts double contoured.

4. Simple Branched Acinous Gland. If the terminal portion has the form of a spherical or elongated sac, the gland is called *acinous* or *alveolar*. If only one acinus is present with one excretory duct, it is a simple acinous gland; this type does not occur in mammals. If the acinus is subdivided by partitions into several smaller bodies (Fig. 259, *f*), or if several acini are arranged along a duct (Fig. 259, *g*), it is a *simple branched acinous gland* (sebaceous glands of the skin, glands of Meibom in the eyelids).

Compound Exocrine Glands. A compound gland may consist of larger subdivisions called *lobes*, which are further subdivided by connective tissue into smaller

found in the body. A compound gland consists, then, of a varying number of simple glands whose small excretory ducts join to form ducts of a higher order, which in turn combine with other ducts of the same caliber to form larger ducts of a still higher order.

The compound exocrine glands are sometimes classified by the secretion they furnish. Thus *mucous*, *albuminous*, and *mixed* glands are distinguished. This classification can be applied with partial success chiefly to the glands of the oral cavity. Another classification is based on the form of the terminal portions.

1. In **compound tubular glands** the terminal portions of the smallest lobules are

more or less coiled, usually branching tubules (Fig. 260). To this category belong the pure mucous glands of the oral cavity, glands of the gastric cardia, some of the glands of Brunner, the bulbo-urethral glands, and the renal tubules.

In special cases, as, for instance, in the testis, the terminal coils anastomose with one another.

independently on a restricted area of a free epithelial surface (lacrimal, mammary and prostatic glands).

Organization of Glands. While glands are recognizably different, it is important to emphasize similarities in the general plan of organization which is shared by all. These may be discussed under four general headings: (1) connective tissue elements; (2)

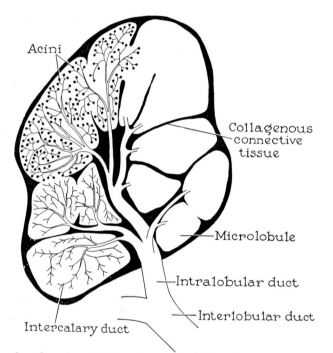

Fig. 261. Diagram to show branches of duct system and relations to secretory portion in a (macro)lobule. Collagenous stroma separates (often incompletely) the microscopic lobules. The main duct shown is a branch of the interlobular duct. The interlobular duct branches into intralobular ducts of several orders. These are continuous with the fine terminal intercalary ducts which end in the secretory portion. (Modified after Heidenhain.)

2. In the **compound acinous** or **alveolar** glands the terminal portions are supposed to have the form of oval or spherical sacs. However, as a rule, the form is that of irregularly branched tubules with numerous saccular outgrowths on the wall and on the blind ends (Fig. 260). These glands should be designated compound *tubulo-acinous*. To this group belong most of the larger exocrine glands—the albuminous and mixed glands of the oral cavity and respiratory passages, and the pancreas.

In some cases the excretory ducts do not all join into a single main duct, but open

blood vessels, lymphatics, and nerves, (3) ducts, (4) secretory cells.

Connective tissue constitutes 20 per cent or more of the total volume of glands. While the pattern of connective tissue cells and fibers varies in different glands, the kinds of cells and of fibers are the same in all. In compound exocrine glands and most endocrine glands, the connective tissue is disposed as a condensation of loose connective tissue, in which the gland has developed and which comes to be the largely collagenous capsule. This extends in the gland proper as strands or sheets which separate the lobes and, on further subdivision, the lobules. These separations are not complete, since ducts, blood vessels and lymphatics, and nerves in the connective tissue, connect the glandular portions of the lobes and lobules. The collagenous connective tissue usually penetrates the lobule only slightly, where it frequently continues as reticular connective tissue (Fig. 261). This is in intimate contact with the terminal secretory and duct elements, where it becomes continuous with the basement membrane, and also bears the capillaries, lymphatics and nerves. This important part of the connective tissue is common to all glands, unicellular or multicellular, exocrine or endocrine. It consists of the tissue fluid, which is important in the exchange of substances between cells and plasma, and the ground substance and fibrillar components of connective tissue; it contains blood and lymph capillaries and nerve fibers, as well as cells of the connective tissue.

Blood vessels, lymphatics and *nerves* of glands usually show a similar gross distribution. They penetrate the capsule and are subdivided in the collagenous connective tissue septa or strands between the lobules. Within the lobule they are ultimately enclosed by reticular connective tissue. The blood and lymph capillaries form networks about gland cells or terminal ducts, and are separated from them by ground substance and reticular fibers (which may form a basement membrane) and tissue fluid. The major vascular supply is supplemented in most glands by a collateral circulation mediated through capsular vessels of small caliber. The terminal nerve fibers branch, and their final divisions end in a multitude of small enlargements on the surface of capillaries and frequently of gland cells and ducts.

The *duct system* of complex exocrine glands effects an economy of space and organization, and conducts the product of gland cells to the secreting surface. It may also modify the secretion during its passage. The secretory duct divides in the collagenous connective tissue to form the lobar ducts, whose further branchings are named with reference to the lobular structure (Fig. 261).

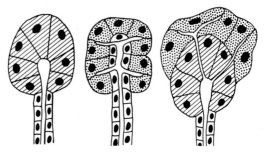

Fig. 262. Diagram to show relations of terminal portions of duct system (intercalary duct) and intercellular canaliculi to secreting cells. Cross-hatched portion generally mucous; stippled portion serous. (Modified after Zimmermann.)

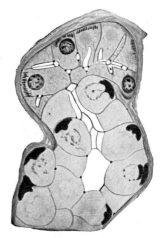

Fig. 263. Section of terminal portion of mandibular gland of man with clear mucous and darker albuminous cells. Between the latter are secretory capillaries and systems of terminal bars, stained black with iron hematoxylin. (Redrawn after Zimmermann.)

The main duct of the gross lobule is the *lobular* duct, while the ducts of the microscopic lobule are called *intralobular* ducts; both are connected by ducts of intermediate caliber. The intralobular ducts are continuous with the *intercalary* duct, whose branches are connected with the secretory acini or tubules by apposition, through the mediation of intercellular canaliculi, or by modifications or combination of both these methods. The epithelium of the largest ducts may be stratified squamous or columnar-cuboidal. As the duct becomes smaller, the epithelium may be simple columnar, cuboidal, and finally squamous.

Gland cells frequently have specific granules, vacuoles and chromophile substance in their cytoplasm, in addition to mitochondria and Golgi apparatus. Although not many gland cells have shown visible indications of secretory activity, reversible changes take

nuclear changes include an increase in volume with an apparent decrease in stainability and a displacement toward the lumen surface. The nucleolus is increased in size and deeply stained. Gland cells, like others, must be considered to be in a state of con-

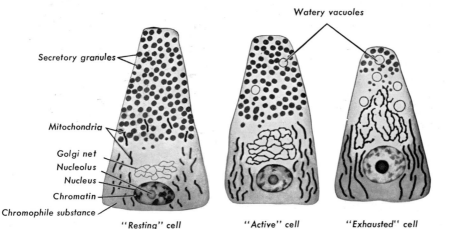

Fig. 264. Diagram of serous type of secretory cell in different stages of secretion to illustrate changes in cytoplasmic and nuclear structures which may take place during marked activity.

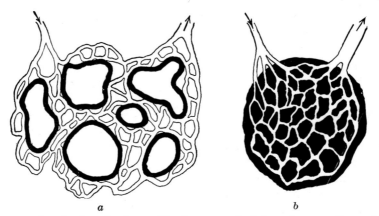

Fig. 265. Diagrams of endocrine glands. *a,* Gland composed of irregular sacs (heavy black lines) surrounded by connective tissue and blood vessels. This type includes the thyroid and ovary. *b,* In this type the epithelium (black) has no lumen and is penetrated by dense networks of blood vessels (white). To this group belong most of the endocrine glands: suprarenals, parathyroids, hypophysis, corpus luteum, and others.

place in others which are emphasized to an exaggerated, possibly pathological, degree by excessive stimulation (Fig. 264). The number of specific granules decreases, water vacuoles increase, the chromophile substance appears to be more prominent, the mitochondria become larger and more numerous, and the Golgi apparatus hypertrophies. The cytoplasmic volume is decreased. Coincident

tinual activity. Even "resting" cells are performing work in maintaining their integrity and internal organization, and in synthesizing and secreting their specific substances or secretions at minimal levels.

The cytological changes in secretion have called forth a massive literature on relations of mitochondria, Golgi apparatus, chromophile substance, and so on, to the secretion

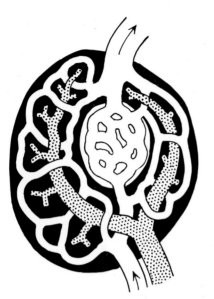

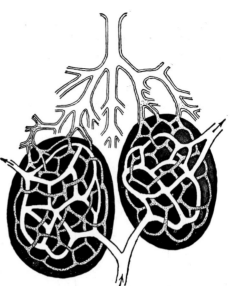

Fig. 266. Diagram of relations of secretory portions of a mixed endocrine and exocrine gland (pancreas) to blood vessels and duct system. Endocrine portion white, exocrine portion black, blood vessels white, duct stippled.

Fig. 267. Diagram of mixed exocrine and endocrine gland (liver), showing secretory portion in black, blood vessels in white, secretory capillaries stippled, and excretory ducts with double contours.

precursor. The current view is that none of these structures is transformed directly into secretory products and that their morphological changes reflect states of activity.

Endocrine Glands. As the endocrine glands develop in the embryo, their connection with the surface epithelium is lost. In some cases the gland consists of sacs lined with epithelium and surrounded by connective tissue (Fig. 265, *a*). In most cases the invagination of the epithelium loses its lumen or is solid from the very beginning. It is also effectively separated from the epithelial surface, and its cells form a compact mass thoroughly penetrated by a dense network of blood vessels and connective tissue (Fig. 265, *b*). As there are no excretory ducts, all secretions find their way into the general circulation.

Other endocrine glands which are not entirely dissociated from the excretory duct system are called *mixed glands*. In the liver, for example, the hepatic cells which secrete bile into the duct system also eliminate internal secretions directly into the blood vessels (Fig. 267). On the other hand, in the testis and pancreas, one group of cells secretes into the external duct system, while another group passes its internal secretion into the blood (Fig. 266).

The endocrine glands secrete their specific products, called *hormones*, directly into the blood stream. The endocrine glands are all circumscribed, with minor exceptions. They are thus set aside from numerous other structures believed to produce internal secretions and also important in coordination and integration within the organism. The circumscribed endocrine glands of man are the *adrenal, hypophysis, thyroid, parathyroid, islets of Langerhans,* and *portions of the testis and ovary*. Other glands which resemble these morphologically in some respects, but do not produce any known secretion, are the thymus, pineal body and the paraganglia.

General Properties of Endocrine Glands. There are three main integrative mechanisms which appear phylogenetically as well as ontogenetically. The earliest to appear is a group of substances which diffuses in the intercellular spaces and influences cells in a limited region. This is supplemented in coelenterates and in embryos of higher forms by a nervous system, including in the latter the autonomic and central nervous systems.

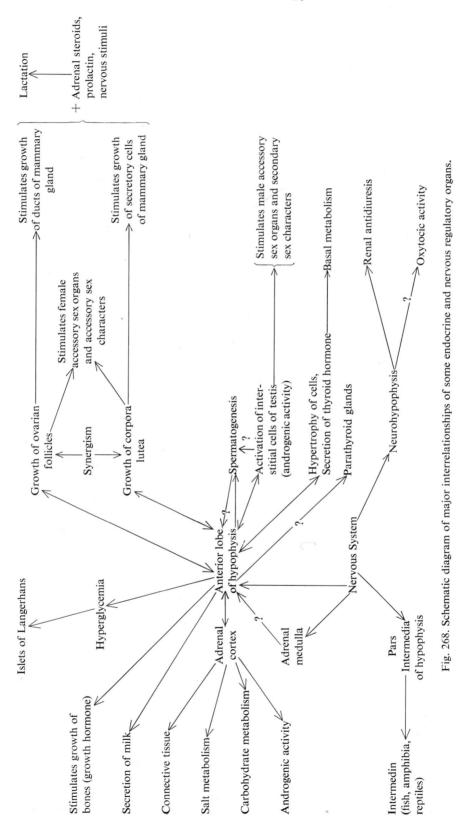

Fig. 268. Schematic diagram of major interrelationships of some endocrine and nervous regulatory organs.

Table 2. Some Properties of Major Hormones of Some Endocrine Glands

GLAND	HORMONE	CHEMICAL CLASSIFICATION	APPROXIMATE MOLECULAR WEIGHT	KNOWN ACTIVE PRINCIPLE OF HORMONE
Anterior lobe of hypophysis	Growth	Protein	39,300–44,250	
	Follicle-stimulating	Glycoprotein		
	Luteinizing	Glycoprotein	40,000–100,000	
	Lactogenic	Protein	22,000–32,000	
	Thyrotrophic	Protein	10,000	
	Adrenocorticotrophic	Protein or polypeptide	20,000 or 1200	
Neurohypophysis	Oxytocic + antidiuretic	Protein	30,000	
	Oxytocic and anti-diuretic	Polypeptide	500–1000	
Thyroid	Thyroglobulin	Glycoprotein	700,000	Thyroxine, di-iodo-tyrosine
Parathyroid	Parathyroid hormone	Protein	500,000–1,000,000	
Adrenal cortex	Cortical hormones	Steroids	346	Corticosterone
			331	Desoxycorticosteroid?
			360	Cortisone
Adrenal medulla	Epinephrine	Modified amino acid	183	Epinephrine
Islets of Langerhans (pancreas)	Insulin	Protein	46,000	
Testis	Androgen	Steroid	288	Testosterone
Ovary	Estrogen	Steroid	272	Estradiol
			270	Estrone
			314	Progesterone
	Relaxin	Polypeptide		

Demarcated endocrine glands appear at a later time (in arthropods, and in older embryos of higher forms) and are found in all vertebrates. The first system of integration through diffusion is poorly defined and slow, and has a limited extent in animals. The nervous system effects a coordination of slow effectors also, but reaches its highest development in dealing with highly complicated integrated patterns and in delicate, precise and rapid motor patterns. These systems are supplemented by the endocrine glands, which secrete substances which have a longer latent period (since they are distributed by the circulating blood) and produce sustained, persistent results.

The endocrine glands are specialized, generally circumscribed glands or tissues which secrete specific substances called hormones into the circulation. Their primary morphological orientation is not toward the ducts, but toward the vascular system, and it is not surprising that they are all characteristically highly vascular (see Figs. 275, 283). Endocrine glands are subject to control by the central nervous system, by other endocrine glands, by certain metabolites, or by a combination of these factors. There is, then, a complicated series of *endocrine interrelation-ships* which are highly important. Some of them are indicated in Figure 268.

Hormones as Integrators. Hormones have been defined as products of specialized tissues which are carried by the blood system to influence other cells, tissues or organs, or the organism as a whole. The integrative action of hormones consists in the depression, activation or maintenance of cells other than, as well as, themselves, as, for example, thyrotrophic hormone of the anterior lobe of the hypophysis and thyroglobulin. Some hormones affect certain organs and tissues almost specifically, under certain conditions, and these are called *target organs;* other hormones have a more general effect which probably influence some basic cell reactions about which little is known. The hormones may be secreted almost as rapidly as they are formed (adrenal cortex), or they may be stored intracellularly or extracellularly in the gland while the blood level is maintained (insulin in the pancreatic islets, thyroglobulin in the thyroid gland colloid). Hormones differ greatly in chemical composition, and include proteins, possibly polypeptides, modified amino acids, and steroids. The range of some of the properties of hormones may be summarized in a most general way in Table 2. The active principle may be a small portion of the hormone (thyroxine), or the whole molecule characterized by certain steric arrangement of the components (cortisone). Hormones, like certain drugs, vitamins and trace elements, may be effective in minute concentrations.

Other Kinds of Integrators. The definition of hormone as given here arbitrarily excludes a wide range of other chemical integrators which may be transmitted by diffusion, which may be intracellular, or which may arise either outside the body or as metabolites from all cells. The first class of integrators, which are transmitted by diffusion, includes *embryonic inductors* (such as are involved in differentiation of the central nervous system, and of the optic lens) and *epinephrine-like* and *acetylcholine-like* substances which may be involved in transmission of the nerve impulse across the synapse and at nerve endings. The second class of integrators, which remain intracellular, includes *genes* and certain enzymes. The third class of integrators, which arise outside the organism, includes certain *vitamins*, as well as *secretagogues* important in the control of the secretion of certain parts of the gastrointestinal tract. Related to these are the integrators which arise from or during metabolic activity. These include carbon dioxide, which aids in the regulation of respiration, and glycogen of the liver, which plays an important part in maintaining the constancy of the blood sugar level. Except for its general origin, the former so nearly resembles a hormone as to have been classified as a *parahormone*. Further, the release of glycogen from the liver was, in fact, the first instance characterized as *internal secretion*.

REFERENCES

Allen, E. (ed.): Sex and Internal Secretions. Baltimore, 1938.

Bernard, C.: Leçons de physiologie expérimentale au Collège de France. Paris, 1855.

Biedl, A.: Innere Sekretion. Ihre physiologischen Grundlagen und ihre Bedeutung für die Pathologie. Berlin, 1922.

Dawson, A. B.: Some Morphological Aspects of the Secretory Process. Federation Proc., 1:233, 1942.

Heidenhain, M.: Plasma und Zelle. Jena, 1907-11; Ueber die teilungsfähigen Drüseneinheiten oder Adenomeren sowie über die Grundbegriffe der morphologischen Systemlehre. Berlin, 1921.

Laguesse, E.: Trois leçons sur les glandes à sécrétion interne en général, et en particulier sur la gland endocrine du pancréas. L'Echo Médical du Nord, 1925.

Möbius, P. J.: Ueber das Wesen der Basedowschen Krankheit. Zentralbl. f. Nervenheilk., 8, 1887.

Schaffer, J.: Das Epithelgewebe. Handb. d. mikr. Anat. v. Möllendorff), (2), 1927.

Turner, C. D.: General Endocrinology. Philadelphia, W. B. Saunders Company, 1948.

Zimmermann, K.: Beiträge zur Kenntniss einiger Drüsen und Epithelium. Arch. f. mikr., Anat., (52), 1898.

XV. HYPOPHYSIS

The hypophysis is one of the most important organs for the normal functioning of the body. It is a prime example of an endocrine organ with a multiplicity of reciprocal interrelations with other structures and functions essential for the regulation of the normal metabolic patterns. The hypophysis exhibits a number of unique and complex interrelations and is markedly variable in several respects, as the following examples show: (1) The gland originates from two diverse structures, the buccal lining and the floor of the diencephalon. (2) The hypophysis is at least the major endocrine gland intimately related to its innervation; this is derived in large part from a portion of the brain, the hypothalamus. (3) The glandular capsule and blood vessels are profoundly influenced by the proximity of the gland to the dural membranes and periosteum. (4) The dimensions of the major subdivisions and the cell population of the gland are extremely variable throughout life. (5) The number of major varieties of cells in the gland is apparently smaller than the number of purified hormones.

Subdivisions. The extent and relations of the parts of the hypophysis have been revised on the basis of recent studies. These are tabulated below, shown diagrammatically in Figure 270, and illustrated in Figure 269.

Anatomical Relations. The human gland measures 10 to 16 mm. (transverse) by 8 to 11 mm. (sagittal) by 5 to 6 mm. (vertical). Stripped of its capsule (whose weight is 7.8 per cent [1.5 to 21.4 per cent] of the gland), the weight of the gland is 0.53 gm. (0.36 to 0.79) in males and 0.62 gm. (0.45 to 0.97) in females. The mean relative proportions of the weights of various subdivisions of the gland, together with the coefficient of variation, are: anterior lobe, 75 per cent (21); pars intermedia, 20 per cent (89); neural lobe, 23 per cent (29). In another study the pars tuberalis was found to be about as large as the pars intermedia. In the monkey the median eminence constitutes about 15 per cent of the total neurohypophysis. The gland is somewhat heavier in tall adults. The increased weight during pregnancy is due entirely to the gain in weight of the anterior lobe.

The hypophysis is lodged in a deep depression of the sphenoid bone, the sella turcica, and is covered by a tough diaphragm in which there is commonly one opening large enough to accommodate the hypophyseal stalk and, with few exceptions, some pia-arachnoid membrane. The latter occupies the space between the diaphragm and the capsule of the gland. Elsewhere the dense collagenous capsule is separated from the

Divisions		Subdivisions
Adenohypophysis....Lobus glandularis	{ Pars distalis (anterior lobe) { Pars tuberalis { Pars intermedia	
Neurohypophysis {	{ Lobus nervosus equivalent to infundibular process (neural lobe)	} Posterior lobe
	{ Infundibulum (neural stalk)	{ Infundibular stem { Median eminence of tuber { cinereum } With pars tuberalis to form hypophyseal stalk

Page 273

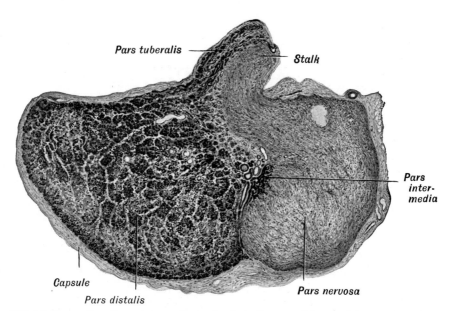

Fig. 269. Median section through hypophysis of a forty-five-year old man. 16 ×. (After Schaffer.)

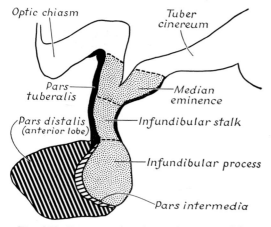

Fig. 270. Diagram of midsagittal section of hypothalamus and hypophysis of man to show relations of major divisions and subdivisions of the gland to the hypothalamus. (Modified after Tilney.)

equally tough periosteum of the sphenoid bone by a looser layer of connective tissue containing numerous veins. This layer appears to be separate from the pia-arachnoidal tissue. In mammals other than man, the diaphragm is commonly incomplete.

The *nerve supply* of the hypophysis is derived from the cervical sympathetic carotid plexus, sphenopalatine ganglion or petrosal nerves (parasympathetic), and the hypothalamo-hypophyseal tract. The last ori-

ginates chiefly from the supraoptic nucleus, situated close to the optic chiasma, and possibly to a certain extent from the paraventricular nucleus, situated in the wall of the third ventricle. Other hypothalamic and tuberal nuclei may also contribute to the tract. Its fibers, which are rarely myelinated, course down the infundibular stalk and reach the infundibular process. The ultimate distribution of the nerve fibers will be discussed with each subdivision of the gland.

The *blood supply* of the hypophysis consists of two inferior hypophyseal arteries and a series of twenty or more superior hypophyseal arteries. The former arise from the internal carotid arteries and arborize in the vascular layer of the capsule. The branches supply chiefly the posterior lobe, but also extend to the anterior lobe and anastomose with branches of the superior arteries. The latter arise from the internal carotid artery and the posterior communicating arteries of the circle of Willis and anastomose freely in the region of the stalk. Many continue, chiefly in the pars tuberalis, as vessels of a diameter of about 100 microns, and pass directly into the anterior lobe. Some break up into a characteristic, wide, anastomotic, capillary plexus in the pars tuberalis and neural stalk. The capillaries join to form venules which course together with the arteries into the substance of the anterior lobe, where they empty into its sinusoids. The venules thus constitute a *portal system* similar to the hepatic portal system. The capillaries of the hypophysis will be described with each subdivision of the gland. The venous drainage of the hypophysis is chiefly through veins which run in the vascular layer of the capsule toward the diaphragm into adjacent dural sinuses. Some of the venous blood enters sinuses in the sphenoid bone.

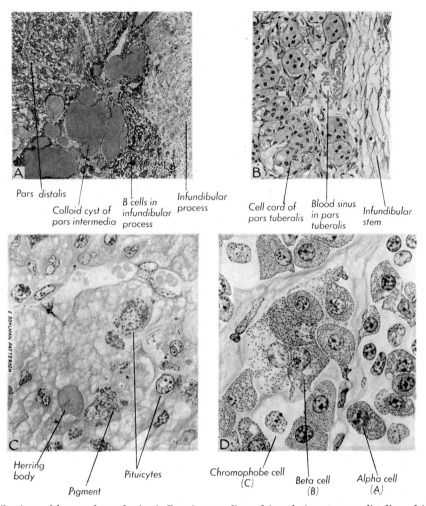

Fig. 271. Sections of human hypophysis. A, Pars intermedia and its relations to pars distalis and infundibular process. 60 ×. B, Cell cords of pars tuberalis, with numerous small blood vessels, and adjacent infundibular stem. 275 ×. C, Cells and intercellular substance of infundibular process. 690 ×. D, Cells of pars distalis. 690 ×. Zenker-formol, H + E.

Pars Distalis. The anterior lobe, or pars distalis, is the largest subdivision of the hypophysis. It is largely enclosed by the dense collagenous capsule. Collagenous bundles which surround branches of the superior hypophyseal arteries and the portal venules penetrate the lobe at the superior posterior pole adjacent to the pars tuberalis and stream bilaterally to a depth of about one third the thickness of the gland. Here, as elsewhere, the collagenous fibers are continuous with reticular fibers which constitute the major part of the supporting connective tissue of the lobe. The reticular fibers enclose

the smaller arterial vessels and the *sinusoids* with which they are continuous. The sinusoids are lined by phagocytes like those of the sinusoids of the adrenal cortex, liver, spleen and bone marrow. The sinusoids are similarly widely anastomotic (Fig. 275). Those near the capsule are gathered together to form collecting venules which become progressively larger in the vascular layer of the capsule. The reticular fibers are separated by a homogeneous basement membrane from the gland cells.

The gland cells are arranged as irregular cords and masses which vary from 20 to 180

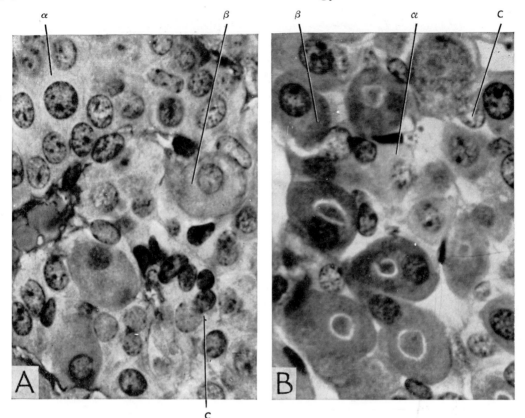

Fig. 272. Photomicrographs of anterior lobe of hypophysis of adult rats. A, Normal female rat; B, castrate female rat of same age. Enlarged beta cells with characteristic "signet ring" appearance and reduction in alpha and chromophobe cells follow castration. Zenker-formol, Mallory-azan. 1300 ×.

microns in thickness in man and are intimately related to the sinusoids. There may also be small acinus-like structures with lumina.

There are two major varieties of gland cells, the *chromophile cells* and the *chromophobe cells* (Fig. 271). The former are further classified as *alpha* and *beta cells*, according to the staining properties of their specific granules. The chromophobe cells are called *reserve cells, chief cells* or simply *C cells*. In some mammals the alpha or beta cells predominate in the outer or inner portion of the lobe, but in man their distribution is irregular and highly variable. The relative proportion of the gland cells varies markedly in man, and is different from that in other mammals. In some of the latter, cyclic variations occur during the female sexual cycle. Some representative percentages of cells are:

	C Cells	Alpha Cells	Beta Cells
Man	52(34–66)	37(23–59)	11(5–27)
Nonpregnant women	50(33–74)	43(19–57)	7(3–15)
Dog anestrus	29.5	59.8	10.6
estrus	31.0	49.4	19.6
late lutein phase	52.8	44.7	4.5
Pig estrus	20.6	50.5	28.8
late lutein phase	34.5	42.1	23.2
Guinea pig proestrus	46.2	52.0	1.8
estrus	45.4	53.2	1.4
metestrus	52.7	46.7	0.6

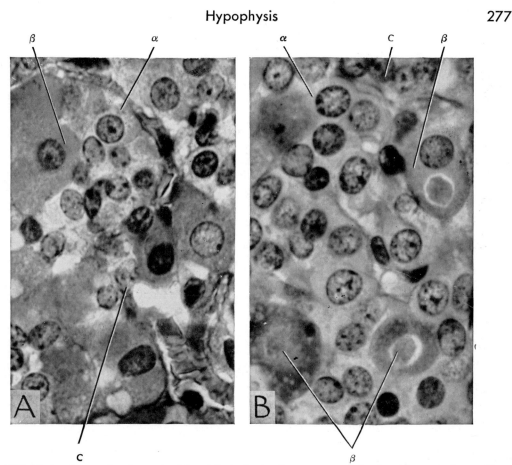

Fig. 273. Photomicrographs of anterior lobe of hypophysis of two young adult, thyroidectomized rats. Compare with anterior lobe of normal young adult rat (Fig. 272, A). In A, the beta cells are enlarged, the number of alpha cells is reduced, and they are smaller than normal. In B, the hypertrophied beta cells have cytoplasmic signet ring figures resembling those induced by castration. Zenker-formol. Mallory-azan. 1300 ×.

In succeeding paragraphs it will be shown that the relative proportions of cells may be markedly influenced by castration, thyroidectomy, and the like. In the absence of an appreciable number of mitoses, the conclusion that cells are transformed from one variety to another has led to the development of numerous, often contradictory proposals for a cell lineage based always on morphological 'transition" stages.

Alpha Cells. Before fixation these appear ovoid or spherical, with the cytoplasm crowded with small spherical granules. In sections they vary in size from 7 to 8 microns to 14 by 19 microns. The spherical or slightly ovoid nucleus is 7 to 8 microns in diameter and is excentrically placed. It has one or two nucleoli, a variable amount of chromatin dispersed on a coarse linin net.

The weakly stained cytoplasm contains a centriole with a diplosome, a Golgi net near the nucleus, and mitochondria distributed throughout the cytoplasm as minute spheres or rodlets. The specific alpha granules vary in size even in the same cell. They are stained by numerous dyes such as eosin, acid fuchsin, Congo red and azocarmine. In some mammals (man, dog, cat, horse) they are coarse; in others (guinea pig, mouse) they are fine. Also present in the cytoplasm are several small lipoid droplets. The reaction for ascorbic acid is strong. The cells vary not only in size, but in form, chromatin content and number of granules. Some cells are degranulated and hyperchromatic; others are stained pale.

Beta Cells. These are round, oval or angular in shape, and vary from 8 by 9 microns

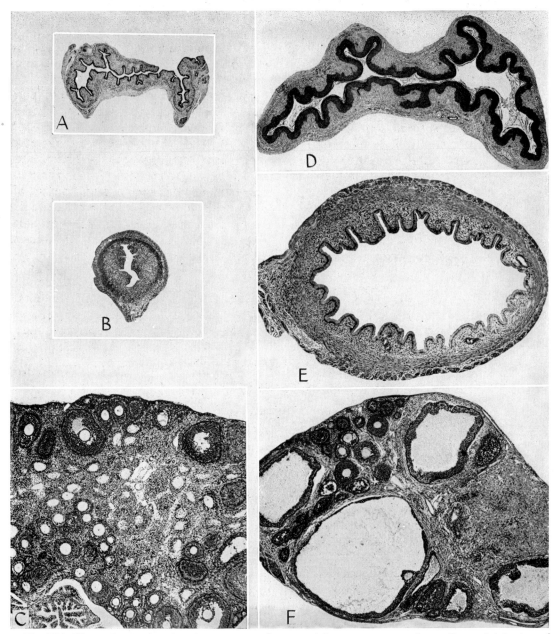

Fig. 274. Photomicrographs of vagina, uterus and ovary of immature rats to show effects of injection of follicle-stimulating hormone. A, B, C, From normal rat; D, E, F, from rat of same age injected with follicle-stimulating hormone for three days. A and D, Vagina; B and E, uterus; C and F, ovary. As a result of treatment with the hormone, all layers of the vagina have hypertrophied and the epithelium has become cornified. Marked hypertrophy of the uterus has taken place because of the hormone. In the ovary the hormone also caused growth of the follicles and the appearance of corpus luteum. Zenker-formol, H + E. A and D, 15 ×; B, C, E, F, 38 ×.

to 20 by 25 microns. The nucleus resembles that of alpha cells, but the chromatin masses are larger and more numerous. The cytoplasm contains a centriole with a rodlike diplosome, a loosely arranged Golgi net somewhat removed from the nucleus, and small granular or rodlike mitochondria. The specific beta granules are less numerous than are alpha granules in comparable cells. They vary somewhat in size in different mammals; for example, they are larger in the dog than in rabbits or cats. It has been reported that staining of the granules with basic dyes is prevented by previous treatment with ribonuclease, suggesting that the granules contain ribonucleic acid. They are stainable with aniline blue, resorcin fuchsin, hematoxylin and mucicarmine. The lipoid droplets are larger than in alpha cells, though fewer and more variable, and the reaction for ascorbic acid is weaker. Just as for alpha cells, the variants include nongranular or granular hyperchromatic cells as well as pale-stained ones.

C Cells. The reserve, chief or C cells are spherical, angular or elongated and may reach the dimensions of large alpha and beta cells. The nucleus is chromatin-poor. The cytoplasm is devoid of alpha or beta granules, but may contain pale-staining granules. The cytoplasm contains a loosely arranged Golgi net, and numerous mitochondria in the form of granules, rods and filaments. The C cells are rich in lipoid droplets, though this is variable, and the cytoplasmic reaction for ascorbic acid is weaker than in the beta cells. Variants include irregular-shaped cells with pyknotic nuclei and sometimes highly vacuolated cytoplasm.

Hormones of the Anterior Lobe. The anterior lobe of the hypophysis secretes a series of protein hormones which have been separated from one another in a nearly pure form (see p. 271 for some chemical properties of the hormones).

1. *Growth hormone* plays an important part in the normal growth of the body. Although hypophysectomy does not impair growth or regeneration in amphibian larvae or in chick embryos, it retards growth of young mammals until eventually they cease growing altogether. In somewhat older animals, growth ceases directly. Growth is restored by the administration of the hormone, and gigantism may be produced experimentally by excessive doses. Dwarfism in certain strains of mice has been traced to a congenital defect in the development of the hypophysis. The hormone has a nearly specific growth effect on epiphyseal cartilage. Simultaneous administration of thyroid extracts augments the action of the growth hormone, while simultaneous administration of adrenocorticotrophic hormone inhibits its action. Certain tumors of the anterior lobe cause *gigantism* in children; this occurs through continued growth in length of the bones if the adenomata become active before closure of the epiphyseal regions. If this occurs after closure of the epiphyseal plate, it causes *acromegaly*. The bones become thicker, the hands and feet become broader, the mandible heavier, and the calvaria thicker, together with splanchnomegaly and coarsening of the skin.

2. *Follicle-stimulating hormone* (FSH) promotes growth of ovarian follicles in the female and stimulates spermatogenesis in the male. Hypophysectomy causes atrophy of the sex organs, which may be restored nearly to normal by administration of the hormone. The secretion by the follicles of adequate amounts of estrogen and the complete restoration of spermatogenesis are augmented by subminimal doses of luteinizing hormone.

3. *Luteinizing hormone* (LH) alone has no direct action on the ovary of the hypophysectomized animal; it causes luteinization of follicles only after ripening by prior treatment with follicle-stimulating hormone. It activates the interstitial cells of the testis, the effect being augmented by the administration of follicle-stimulating hormone.

4. *Prolactin* causes secretion of milk after the ducts and secretory portions of the mammary gland have been developed in response to ovarian hormones. Hypophysectomy abolishes lactation promptly. Prolactin also exerts a luteotrophic action; i.e., it maintains existing corpora lutea in an active secretory

state. Follicle-stimulating hormone, luteinizing hormone and prolactin together form a gonadotrophic hormone complex.

5. *Adrenocorticotrophic hormone* (ACTH) causes growth of the adrenal cortex, particularly the glomerular and fascicular zones, and secretion of its hormones. The atrophic adrenal cortex of hypophysectomized animals is restored to normal by the hormone. Removal of one adrenal is followed by compensatory hypertrophy of the remaining gland, but this does not take place after hypophysectomy. The range of curative and ameliorative effects it has been found to exert in a great variety of diseases is extensive, and still remains to be probed.

6. *Thyrotrophic hormone* has not been as highly purified as the others. It stimulates hypertrophy of the thyroid gland cells and secretion. Hypophysectomy results in atrophy of the thyroid, which may be restored to normal by the administration of hormone extracts.

7. *Other Functions.* The hypophysis is involved also in some less defined activities reflected in protein, fat and carbohydrate metabolism. Whether some of these are primary activities of the gland, or are mediated by effects on other endocrine glands, is not always clear. Extracts of the anterior lobe have a *diabetogenic action*, which may be ascribed, at least in part, to actions of adrenocorticotropic hormone (and the adrenal cortex) and growth hormone. Repeated injections of a gland extract in a partially depancreatized dog results in a *diabetes mellitus* which becomes permanent if the treatment is prolonged. However, it may be that the hyperglycemia produced by the extract or by other means constitutes such a heavy strain on the islet cells that they become exhausted and atrophy. Hypophysectomy results in a low blood sugar and increased sensitivity to insulin. In the depancreatized dog, hypophysectomy diminishes the severity of the diabetes mellitus.

There is some evidence that the anterior lobe exercises some influence over the parathyroid glands. For example, in tadpoles, hypophysectomy is followed by atrophy of the parathyroid glands and a reduced blood calcium level. Again, parathyroid lesions were present in two thirds of hypophysectomized dogs. On the other hand, parathyroid changes following hypophysectomy in the monkey and rat appeared to be negligible.

Cells of Origin of Hormones. As the number of hormones in the anterior lobe exceeds the number of principal cell types, it is necessary to assign more than one function (hormone) to each cell type, or to make the assumption that a macromolecule gives rise to one or another hormone according to the stimulus. There is no evidence in support of the second possibility. The first possibility is not specific to the hypophysis; it has been proposed also for the acinus cells in the pancreas and the gland cells of the intestinal and fundic glands, where several enzymes are secreted by what is an apparently single cell type. The hormones of the neurohypophysis may serve as an example of the second possibility. The evidence associating a cell type in the anterior lobe with the secretion of a hormone is based almost entirely on biological considerations which are not altogether consistent or definite. Some examples of the types of evidence utilized will be cited in the following paragraphs.

Growth hormone is generally believed to arise from alpha cells. In a series of acromegalic patients with pituitary adenomata, alpha cells were prominent, while in a series of nonacromegalics with pituitary adenomata, alpha cells were scarce. The outer part of the ox pituitary is richer in alpha cells and has an effect on the growth of tadpoles, while the central part is richer in beta cells and has no effect on their growth. In dwarf mice the alpha cells are lacking, but a good analysis of the beta cells has yet to be made. Contrary to these findings, in the early pig embryo hypophysis there is a stage when the only chromophilic cell present is the beta cell; yet growth hormone is present in such glands despite the absence of alpha cells.

Gonadotrophic hormones are generally believed to arise from beta cells. After castration the rat hypophysis contains more gonadotrophic hormone, and at the same time the beta cells increase in number, some of them becoming markedly enlarged and vacuolated in a characteristic way. This reaction is reversed by the administration of estrogens injected into normal rats, which also cause an apparent decrease in beta cells and degranulation of those remaining. The central part of the anterior lobe of the ox hypophysis is rich in beta cells and also in gonadotrophic activity. In pigeons, beta cells first appear as the growth curve is about to reach a plateau, just preceding the appearance of sexual activity. In the posterior lobe of the human hypophysis, beta cells occur commonly and the lobe has gonadotrophic activity. In the rat and pig, beta granules are most numerous during proestrus, at a time when gonadotrophic activity should be greatest, and decrease rapidly in estrus, when gonadotrophic activity is at its lowest in the cycle. A histochemical test utilizing the high sugar content of gonadotrophic hormones for their identification has made it possible to localize them or their precursors in the beta cells. Larger amounts were found in the "castration cells" than in beta cells of rats in estrus. The amount observed varied during the estrus cycle, being greatest at proestrus and least during estrus. On the other hand, some workers have been led by their observations to associate gonadotrophic hormones with the alpha cells.

Although most of the evidence indicates that thyrotrophic hormone arises from beta cells, some equally good evidence points to the alpha cell or the undifferentiated cell as the source of the hormone. Evidence on the cells of origin of adrenocorticotrophic hormone is spotty. The administration of the rat hormone is said to cause no changes in the gland cells, or to cause degranulation of alpha and beta cells. Adrenalectomy results in a marked reduction in the beta cells in the dog, less marked changes in the rat. In chronic adrenal insufficiency in man, both alpha and beta cells are reduced in number. Cushing's syndrome is associated with hyalinization of the beta cells. An effort has been made to identify cytochemically cells which give origin to adrenocorticotrophic hormone. An antigen was prepared to purified hormones, and was tagged with a fluorescent dye. Frozen-dried sections of anterior lobe were treated with the fluorescent antibody to enable it to react with its specific antigen. When the excess was washed off, only the cytoplasm of beta cells was brilliantly fluorescent.

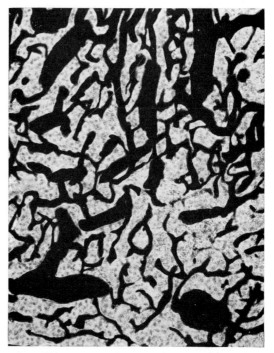

Fig. 275. Photomicrograph of anterior lobe of hypophysis of monkey injected with India ink to show the irregular, richly anastomotic sinusoids. 165 ×. Compare with Figure 277 of the infundibular process.

Mechanism of Release of Hormones from the Anterior Lobe. Three mechanisms have been proposed to explain how the cells of the anterior lobe are induced to release their hormones into the blood: neural, neurovascular, and humoral.

The anterior lobe contains a number of nerve fibers derived chiefly from the sympathetic chain and from the tract located in the stalk. The former are believed to be confined to the blood vessels along which they enter. The latter are believed to terminate in the reticular connective tissue or in even more intimate contact with the gland cells as simple end bulbs or pericellular baskets. The cells of origin lie chiefly in the supraoptic and paraventricular nuclei. Stimulation of the hypothalamus along the course of the supraopticohypophyseal tract in the unanesthetized rabbit caused secretion by the gland cells of the hypophysis of sufficient follicle-stimulating hormone to cause ovulation and of sufficient adrenocorticotrophic hormone to stimulate the adrenal gland. The same stimulus was ineffective in influencing the secretion of thyrotrophic hormone. Similarly, transection of the stalk commonly caused disturbances in sexual activities, but did not influence thyroidal activity. It is believed, then, that the secretion of thyrotrophic hormone is not under neural control normally, although under certain conditions of stress the nerve tract originating in the hypothalamus may influence secretion of the hormone. The neural influence may be direct, through the nerve terminations ending in proximity to the gland cells. It is also possible that the nerve fibers in the stalk, when stimulated, secrete a substance which passes into the profuse capillaries of the stalk, to the hypothalamo-hypophyseal portal veins, to the anterior lobe of the hypophysis, thence to be distributed to the sinusoids in intimate contact with the gland cells. Either method requires that the neurons giving rise to the hypothalamo-hypophyseal tract be sensitive to humoral stimuli. In conformity with this view is the extraordinarily rich capillary bed of the supraoptic and paraventricular nuclei. Somewhat more difficult to interpret are the colloid granules and droplets in the cytoplasm of neurons of these nuclei and their supposed resemblance to secretory granules. It is possible that epinephrine released from the adrenal medulla may stimulate the secretion of adrenocorticotrophic hormone.

Pars Intermedia. In most human hypophyses, as well as in those of certain anthropoids, the pars intermedia is poorly delimited (Figs. 269 and 271, A). But in a small proportion of adults and in many young children, the pars intermedia appears as in most mammals as a *cleft* enclosed by an an-terior and posterior wall. In man, the pars intermedia is small (about 2 per cent of the hypophysis); in other animals it is larger, as in the rat (about 8 per cent), rabbit (about 12 per cent) and mouse (about 19 per cent). It is variable in birds and absent in some. It is also absent in the whale, porpoise, manatee and armadillo. The pars intermedia of most men differs from that of most mammals in several respects: the cleft is rarely complete, cysts occur commonly, and beta cells extend into the neural lobe, sometimes to a surprising extent.

A relatively unmodified hypophyseal cleft persists in a small proportion of adults. The anterior wall comprises an irregular layer, one to two cells thick of undifferentiated alpha, beta and C cells, which blend into the cell cords of the anterior lobe. The posterior wall is thicker, with several layers of small undifferentiated cells among which may be ciliated cells and cells with a cuticular border.

In most men, remnants of the cleft persist as *cysts* 1 to 3 mm. long, chiefly in that portion of the pars intermedia farthest removed from the stalk. At the opposite pole of the pars intermedia, cysts arise as evaginations of the original pouch. The cells enclosing the cyst are largely undifferentiated, small cells without granules and C cells with pale-staining granules. They continue into a zone of chromophobe cells with some beta cells which lie between the anterior lobe and neural lobe and extend to the pars tuberalis. In addition, branched tubules of pale-staining columnar cells and strands of cells which may form cysts extend into the infundibular process. Finally, numerous beta cells somewhat smaller than those in the anterior lobe extend for a variable distance into the same lobe. This beta cell invasion of the neural lobe has been observed in embryos and children. The cystic colloid may vary in consistency from fluid to fairly solid, may be colorless to yellow, and may have free cells suspended in it. It is extremely inert, and in sections stains metachromatically.

Nerve fibers presumably arising from hypothalamic nuclei are rather numerous in the pars intermedia. The rich capillary bed is continuous with that of the neural lobe and with the sinusoids of the anterior lobe. Numerous anastomoses take place between the superior and inferior hypophyseal arterioles in the substance of the pars intermedia. Both nerve fibers and blood vessels are supported by a reticular fiber net which also contains some collagenous bundles.

The pars intermedia secretes *intermedin*, a hormone which causes melanophores to expand and thus darken the skin. The control of melanophore expansion in some animals is neural, in others (frog) humoral, in still others both. The secretion of the hormone is controlled by the nerve fibers derived from those which pass down the stalk to the neural lobe. Hypophysectomy in the frog is followed by a blanching of the skin, which may be caused to darken again by the administration of the hormone. Injury to the hypothalamus results in melanophore expansion, as do successful transplants. The hormone is effective also in fishes and reptiles. Though present in birds and mammals, the active substance exerts no known influence.

Pars Tuberalis. Like the pars intermedia, the pars tuberalis constitutes a small part of the hypophysis. Both are continuous with and adjacent to the anterior lobe. The pars tuberalis is about 25 to 60 microns thick, the thickest portion being on the anterior surface of the stalk (Fig. 270), and is frequently incomplete, especially on the posterior surface of the stalk. The outstanding morphological character is the longitudinal arrangement of cords and balls of epithelial cells, which interdigitate with the longitudinally oriented blood vessels (Fig. 271, B). The pars tuberalis is the most highly vascularized subdivision of the hypophysis, because it accommodates the major arterial supply for the anterior lobe and the hypothalamo-hypophyseal venous portal system. Some nerve fibers terminating on the epithelial cells have been observed. The pars tuberalis is separated from the infundibular stalk by a thin layer of connective tissue continuous with the pia. On the opposite surface, the connective tis-

sue is typical arachnoidal membrane. Between these, the blood vessels and groups of epithelial cells are supported by reticular fibers with some collagenous bundles.

The epithelial cells of the pars tuberalis include undifferentiated cells and some small alpha and beta cells. The main component is a cuboidal-columnar cell, which may reach 12 to 18 microns in size, and contains numerous small granules or sometimes fine colloid droplets. The mitochondria are spheres or short rods, and numerous small lipoid droplets may be present. They are the only cells in the adult hypophysis containing large amounts of glycogen. The cells may be arranged to form a follicle-like structure. Islands 50 to 70 microns in extent of squamous epithelial cells may also be present.

Despite the occurrence of a pars tuberalis in all vertebrates studied, the epithelial cells are not known to have any hormonal function.

Neurohypophysis. The median eminence of the tuber cinereum is included with the infundibular stem and process as a single unit, the neurohypophysis (Fig. 270). The vascular pattern of the median eminence and infundibular stem is identical, but differs markedly from that in the rest of the hypothalamus; the connections between the two vascular beds are through capillaries which appear functionally insignificant. All vessels of the neurohypophysis have the property in common of being particularly permeable to certain intravascularly injected dyes such as trypan blue and Evans blue. The cells characteristic of the infundibular process and stem are found in the median eminence, but not elsewhere in the tuber cinereum. After certain hypothalamic lesions, atrophy of the infundibular process and stem is shared also by the median eminence. Finally, the same active substances extracted from the infundibular process are obtained also from the median eminence.

The collagenous connective tissue of the capsule of the hypophysis extends somewhat along the blood vessels which penetrate it, and is then replaced by reticular fibers. These form a netlike support for the rich capillary bed and also enclose nests of neuroglial cells. Also enclosed are feltlike whorls of chiefly unmyelinated nerve fibers derived from the hypothalamo-hypophyseal tract. In the stalk

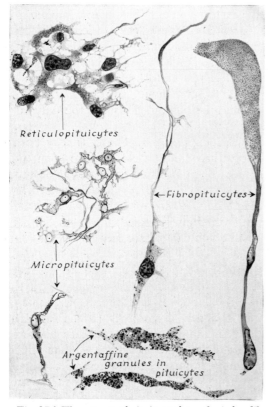

Fig. 276. Three types of pituicytes from the infundibular process of man. Granules may contain pigment, or they may be argentaphilic, or both. All cells 460 ✕, except the group of micropituicytes, which are 260 ✕. (Redrawn after Romeis.)

and median eminence, these are closely packed and parallel. Some of these fibers extend to the pars intermedia and anterior lobe, but the greater number by far terminate in the neurohypophysis, chiefly the infundibular process.

The cells peculiar to the human neurohypophysis, the *pituicytes*, have been studied most extensively by Romeis, who describes four types: *reticulopituicytes, micropituicytes, fibropituicytes,* and *adenopituicytes* (Fig. 276). The reticulopituicytes are cytoplasm-rich, glial syncytia with granules which

may be stained faintly or black with silver. The micropituicytes are separate cells whose slender, branching processes form an interlacing net. The cytoplasm contains vacuoles and granules. The fibropituicytes are elongated cells with unipolar, bipolar or multipolar processes which form an interwoven network. The processes are called fibers and may reach to 900 microns or more, though only 2 to 3 microns thick. Swellings may occur along the course of the fiber. The adenopituicytes are plump, cytoplasmic-rich cells which exist singly or in small or large groups. In addition, glia cells with fibers typical of the central nervous system are found. All these cell types are also found in the infundibular stem and the median eminence, where their shape and dimensions differ in accordance with the prevailing pattern of nerve fibers and blood vessels, and proximity to the third ventricle. In addition, small beta cells originating in the pars intermedia frequently extend for variable distances into the infundibular process.

In other mammals the specific cells of the neurohypophysis may contain numerous lipoid droplets or visible granules. In the rat these cells are reported to hypertrophy during water deprivation, to arise from undifferentiated precursors, and to respond also when the hypophyseal stalk is sectioned. These changes were correlated with pharmacological studies of the neural process; but these findings have been denied by other workers. A characteristic feature of the pituicytes of man and some other mammals is the occurrence of pigment granules (Fig. 271, C), which may reduce silver directly or blacken with the methods of Bielschowsky and Hortega. Some of these pigment granules may also contain iron, as shown by direct Prussian blue test.

Characteristic of the neurohypophysis is the large amount of intercellular substance. During fixation this homogeneous material is precipitated as granules of varying size and tinctorial capacities. These form the larger part of what has been called the Herring bodies (Fig. 271, C). Also included in this category, probably, are the swellings of fibro-pituicytes and nerve fibers, and some enlarged nerve endings.

Two major substances can be extracted from the neurohypophysis: (1) an *antidiuretic* substance, which counteracts a water diuresis when administered, by promoting reabsorption of water chiefly in the thin limb of the loop of Henle; and (2) an *oxytocic* substance, which causes smooth muscle of the uterus to contract. The two activities may be separated from each other nearly completely, and appear in such preparations to be of relatively small molecular weight. On the other hand, the two activities have been found to occur in a larger protein molecule which behaves as if it were a single substance. The evidence indicates that the antidiuretic substance is a hormone which plays an effective part in the organism; the evidence bearing on the hormonal nature of the oxytocic factor is not as convincing. It is clear now that both substances arise in the neurohypophysis, and are not carried there from anterior lobe or pars intermedia, for they are present in the neurohypophysis of animals in which there is a complete separation of pars nervosa and anterior lobe and in which a pars intermedia is lacking.

When lesions are made in the supraoptic tracts above the median eminence, secretion of the antidiuretic hormone ceases, as indicated by the pronounced polyuria and polydypsia which follow. This condition simulates diabetes insipidus as it occurs sometimes in patients. Urinary elimination of water in patients is restored to normal levels by the administration of antidiuretic extracts. In animals the neurohypophysis atrophies after the lesion, and its content of antidiuretic hormone and oxytocic activity decreases markedly. The same water disturbance follows when the supraoptic tracts are interrupted in the median eminence. But if the tracts are sectioned lower in the stalk, the disturbance may be temporary. Presumably, in the latter instance, hypertrophy or increased activity of remaining portions of the neurohypophysis is adequate for normal con-trol of renal function. It is necessary that the anterior lobe of the hypophysis should be functional for the polyuria to be permanent. Electric stimulation of the supraoptic tract or its immediate vicinity in the unanesthetized rabbit causes an antidiuresis.

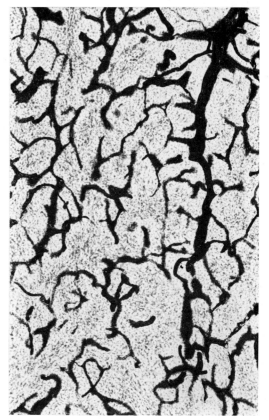

Fig. 277. Photomicrograph of infundibular process of monkey injected with Indian ink to show the pattern of small blood vessels. The arterioles break up into a number of arching, interconnected capillaries. 165 ×. Compare with Figure 275 of the anterior lobe.

The mechanism of the release of the antidiuretic hormone thus involves the hypothalamo-hypophyseal tract, chiefly the supraoptico-hypophyseal tract. Presumably, then, the neurons of the supraoptic nuclei are in an exquisite equilibrium with some component or property of the plasma which would enable a suitable degree of regulation of the neurohypophyseal gland cells to secrete antidiuretic hormone. For some peculiar properties of these neurons and their rich vascularity, see the reference by Scharrer. The suggestion has also been made that the substance which stimulates the gland cells to secrete travels within the nerve fibers of the supraoptic tract, where it may be stored. There is no good evidence to indicate that the secretory path of the antidiuretic hormone is other than by way of the blood capillaries.

The principal role of the oxytocic substance has been sought in the mechanism of parturition. It has been shown that the uterine threshold to oxytocin in mice and rabbits is higher at midterm than at term. Destruction of the major part of the supraoptic tract also leads to disturbances in parturition. But attempts at crucial experiments in removing the posterior lobe have led to highly contradictory results both as concerns the mechanism of parturition itself and the significance of the oxytocic substance.

Histogenetic Remarks. The hypophysis arises from two widely separated sources; one of these is an evagination of the ectoderm of the primitive buccal cavity and extends as the *pouch of Rathke* toward the embryonic brain; this constitutes the *pars buccalis*. Kingsbury *et al.* maintain that this is not an active outgrowth and that the hypophyseal part of the ectoderm and infundibular part of the brain are originally close together and that this relation is retained. The most advanced part of this outgrowth comes in contact with a ventral evagination of the diencephalon, the former becoming the pars intermedia; the latter, the *pars nervosa*. The remnants of the pars buccalis divide into two lateral lobes (in embryos of 10.5 mm.) and a large anterior portion. The latter is transformed into the anterior or distal lobe of the definitive gland. In 45-mm. embryos, the two lateral lobes of the pars buccalis fuse at the midline to form the pars tuberalis and begin to grow forward; this portion later grows backward, surrounds the infundibulum, and spreads for a short distance under the tuber cinereum. The pars buccalis in man normally becomes completely separated from the buccal ectoderm. The pars nervosa develops as a downward outpouching of the floor of the diencephalon. Although in some animals it is more or less completely surrounded by the par buccalis, this is not the case in man. The pars nervosa remains connected, by a stalk of the infundibulum, with the floor of the third ventricle; its cavity disappears in man, but is retained in the cat.

In early embryos and possibly also throughout life, undifferentiated cells are present in the anterior lobe. These may occur as discrete cells which have a non-granular cytoplasm and pale nuclei. In the human embryo, only undifferentiated cells are present at 24 mm. At 30 mm., beta cells are present, and occasionally an alpha cell. At 44 mm., the beta cells have increased in number, alpha cells are common, and some C cells are present. The time of appearance of the specific cells in the anterior lobe has been studied in a number of mammals and also in pigeons and some amphibians.

REFERENCES

Adams, A. E.: Variations in the Potency of Thyrotrophic Hormone of the Pituitary in Animals. Quart. Rev. Biol., 21:1, 1946.

Allen, F. (ed.): Sex and Internal Secretions. Baltimore, 1939.

Bailey, P.: The Structure of the Hypophysis Cerebri of Man and of the Common Laboratory Mammals, in Cowdry's Special Cytology. 2d ed. New York, (2), 771, 1932; The Pineal Body, ibid, 787.

Biedl, A.: Innere Sekretion. Ihre physiologischen Grundlagen und ihre Bedeutung für die Pathologie. Berlin, 1922.

Burrows, H.: Biological Actions of Sex Hormones. 2d ed. Cambridge University Press, London, 1949.

Catchpole, H. R.: Distribution of Glycoprotein Hormones in the Anterior Pituitary Gland of the Rat. J. Endocrinol., 6:218, 1949.

Dempsey, E. W., and Wislocki, G. B.: Histochemical Reactions Associated with Basophilia and Acidophilia in the Placenta and Pituitary Gland. Am. J. Anat., 76:277, 1945.

Dougherty, T. F., and White, A.: An Evaluation of Alterations Produced in Lymphoid Tissue by Pituitary-Adrenal Cortical Secretion. J. Lab. & Clin. Med., 32:584, 1947.

Erdheim, J.: Zur normalen und pathologischen Histologie der Glandula thyroidea, parathyroidea, und Hypophysis. Beitr. z. path. Anat. u. z. allg. Path., 33:158, 1903.

Friedgood, H. B., and Dawson, A. B.: Physiological Significance and Morphology of the Carmine Cell in the Cat's Anterior Pituitary. Endocrinology, 26: 1022, 1940.

Fulton, J. F.: The Hypothalamus. Ass. Res. in Nerv. Res. in Nerv. & Ment. Dis., (20), Baltimore, 1940; see especially Part I.

Geiling, E. M. K.: The Hypophysis Cerebri of the Finback (*Balaenoptera physalus*) and Sperm (*Physeter megalocephalus*) Whale. Bull. Johns Hopkins Hosp., 57:123, 1935.

Gilbert, M. S.: Some Factors Influencing the Early Development of the Mammalian Hypophysis. Anat. Rec., 62:337, 1935.

Giroud, A., and Leblond, C. P.: Localisations electives de l'acide ascorbique ou vitamine C. Arch. d'Anat. micr., 31:111, 1935.

Grollman, A.: Essentials of Endocrinology. 2d ed. Philadelphia, 1947.

Harris, G. W.: Neural Control of the Pituitary Gland. Physiol. Rev., 28:139, 1948.

Houssay, B. A.: Certain Relations between Parathyroids, Hypophysis, and Pancreas. Harvey Lectures, 31:116, 1936.

Hunt, T. E.: Mitotic Activity in the Anterior Hypophysis of Female Rats. Anat. Rec., 82:263, 1942.

Moore, C. R.: The Role of the Fetal Endocrine Glands in Development. J. Clin. Endocrinol., 10: 912, 1950.

Pomerat, G. R.: Mitotic Activity in the Pituitary of the White Rat following Castration. Am. J. Anat., 69:89, 1941.

Rasmussen, A. T.: The Morphology of the Pars Intermedia of the Human Hypophysis. Endocrinology, 2:129, 1928; Ciliated Epithelium and Mucus-Secreting Cells in the Human Hypophysis. Anat. Rec., 41:273, 1929.

Romeis, B.: Hypophyse. Handb. d. mikr. Anat. d. Menschen. (v. Moellendorff), 1940, Vol. 6, Pt. 3.

Scharrer, E.: see reference to Timme et al.

Selye, H.: Textbook of Endocrinology. Montreal, 1947.

Simpson, M. E., Asling, C. W., and Evans, H. M.: Some Endocrine Influences on Skeletal Growth and Differentiation. Yale J. Biol. & Med., 23:1, 1950.

Simpson, M. E., Evans, H. M., and Li, C. H.: Bioassay of Adrenocorticotrophic Hormone. Endocrinology, 33:261, 1943.

Simpson, M. E., Evans, H. M., and Li, C. H.: The Growth of Hypophysectomized Female Rats following Chronic Treatment with Pure Pituitary Growth Hormone. Growth, 13:151, 1949.

Smith, P. E.: Hypophysectomy and Replacement Therapy in the Rat. Am. J. Anat., 45:205, 1930.

Timme, W., Frantz, A. M., and Hare, C. C.: The Pituitary Gland. Assoc. Res. in Nerv. & Ment. Dis., (17), Baltimore, 1938; see especially Sec. I, and Chap. 22.

Turner, C. D.: General Endocrinology. Philadelphia, W. B. Saunders Company, 1948.

Van Dyke, H. B.: The Physiology and Pharmacology of the Pituitary Body. Chicago, 1939.

The references cited were selected primarily for orientation in this rapidly developing subject. Students are referred for the most recent developments to Annual Reviews of Physiology and to Vitamins and Hormones.

XVI. THYROID GLAND

The thyroid gland differs from all other endocrine glands in that hormone storage is developed to the highest degree and reflected morphologically most markedly. It is situated in the anterior middle portion of the neck close to the trachea, and consists of two lateral portions or *lobes* united by a thinner strip, the *isthmus*. Sometimes there is an irregular pyramidal lobe extending toward the thyroid cartilage.

The external connective tissue capsule of the gland continues into the surrounding cervical fascia; it is connected by loose connective tissue with another layer of dense connective tissue which adheres intimately to the organ. This separation of the capsule into two layers permits the organ to be removed easily.

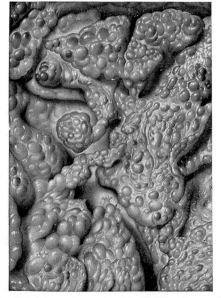

Fig. 278. Normal human thyroid. The shape of the parenchymatous regions varies from a triangular or quadrangular area to that of a cube or almost perfect sphere. About 5 ×. (After Rienhoff.)

Follicles. Each lobe is incompletely divided by connective tissue into plates, bars, stalks, and bands of gland tissue (Fig. 278). These irregular *lobules* consist of spherical follicles 0.02 to 0.9 mm. in diameter lined with an epithelium and containing a stiff jelly called *colloid*. The external surface of the follicles is commonly smooth, and nearly all contain a lumen (Fig. 279). Normally in man there is a preponderance of smaller over larger follicles. But in certain conditions they may increase in size, and the external surface may be markedly irregular. In man the size of the follicles varies considerably from region to region, with corresponding differences in the follicular cells and colloid. This has been attributed to cyclic states of activity which take place regionally rather than uniformly. In the thyroid of animals other than man, the follicles are more uniform. In the rat and guinea pig the follicles on the periphery of the gland are larger than the more central ones, and the colloid of the former is more basophile. Marked irregularity of the follicles may be produced in the rat by prolonged exposure to certain drugs (*allylthiourea, thiourea, and 2-acetyl-amino-fluorene*), a process which may terminate in the formation of benign or malignant tumors.

The follicles are enclosed by a network of reticular fibrils embedded in ground substance. In younger animals the fibers are finer, and the network they form is less dense than in older animals. A basement membrane appears at the base of the follicular cells only in older animals. The connective tissue supports a close net of anastomotic capillaries which surround the follicles like a basket (Fig. 283). Outside the capillary layer and between the capillary beds of adjacent

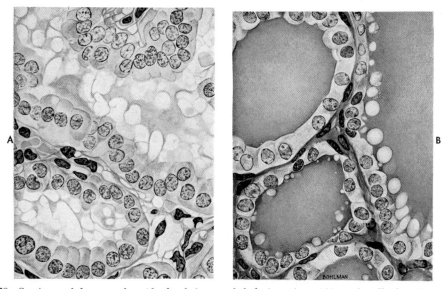

Fig. 279. Sections of human thyroid gland in exophthalmic goiter (A) and colloid goiter (B), from preparations of R. R. Bensley. Note the differences in the height of the epithelium and the amount and depth of staining of the colloid in the two conditions. Hematoxylin and eosin. 570 ×.

follicles are the terminations of the larger-meshed lymphatic vessels. Running along the arteries and their branches in the connective tissue are numerous nerve fibers; these terminate as simple thickenings, chiefly along the blood vessels, and also in direct contact with the base of some thyroid cells.

Gland Cells. Normally, each follicle of the human thyroid consists of an outer shell of gland cells which encloses the colloid. These cells are commonly low cuboidal, and are in close relation with the connective tissue and its network of blood and lymph capillaries. The epithelium of the gland varies in size and arrangement, depending on age, sex, season of the year, diet and certain pathological processes. In general, it is believed that the epithelium is squamous when the gland is underactive, and columnar and folded when it is overactive (Fig. 279). There are, however, so many exceptions that it is impossible to determine the functional state of the gland in all cases through histological examination alone.

The gland cells of any one follicle are more or less uniform, though occasionally some columnar cells may be present when most cells are cuboidal. Rarely, there may be *"colloid cells"* of Langendorff with a dark

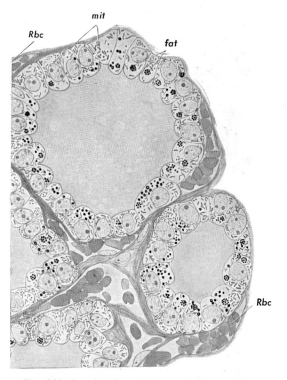

Fig. 280. Section through several follicles of human thyroid. *mit*, Mitochondria; *fat*, small fat droplets; *Rbc*, red blood corpuscles. Aniline-acid-fuchsin. (Courtesy of R. R. Bensley.)

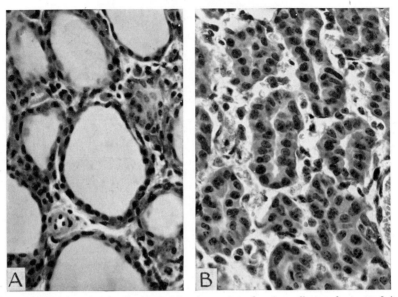

Fig. 281. Photomicrographs of thyroid glands of guinea pigs, showing effects of repeated injections of extracts of anterior lobe containing thyrotrophic hormone. A, Normal acini with low cuboidal epithelium and rich in colloid; B, treated, with acini consisting of columnar cells containing small amount of dilute colloid. Fixed by freezing and drying. H + E. 350 ×.

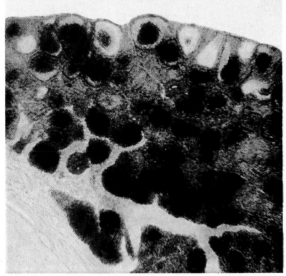

Fig. 282. Low power photomicrograph of autoradiograph of thyroid gland of rat previously injected with I[131]. The blackened areas represent sites of deposition of the radioactive material. There is great variability in the content of the isotope in the several follicles. In a few places the epithelium is blackened. (Courtesy of C. P. Leblond, D. Findlay and S. Gross.)

pyknotic nucleus and dense-staining, osmiophilic cytoplasm. They are probably dead or dying cells.

The nucleus of the gland cell is situated centrally or toward the base of the cell. It is commonly spheroidal and poor in chromatin, and contains one or more nucleoli. After stimulation of the gland cells, the nucleus enlarges and stains more lightly.

The cytoplasm is basophile with certain stains; it contains ribonucleic acid as identified by its ultraviolet spectrum. Mitochondria, which are usually short, thin and rodlike in the human gland, are more numerous in the apical portion of the cytoplasm. The Golgi apparatus is supranuclear, with a few strands extending sometimes over the sides of the nucleus. Rarely, this apparatus may be situated between the nucleus and the base of the cell. A centrosome is located in the apical cytoplasm—although mitoses are exceeding rare—and there are fine terminal bars. Lipoid droplets, *cytochrome-cytochrome oxidase, peroxidase,* and *acid and alkaline phosphatase* have also been described in the cytoplasm. Under certain conditions, organic iodine compounds tagged by I[131] have been demonstrated in the cytoplasm (Fig. 282). A variety of *inclusions* have been described in the cytoplasm: (1) round droplets of colloid (Langendorff); (2) clear vacuoles possibly related to the colloid vacuoles of Anderson;

(3) basal colloid vacuoles (Bensley); (4) minute granules stained supravitally with neutral red (Uhlenhuth); (5) colloid droplets varying in number from cell to cell and preserved only by freezing and drying (De Robertis). The relations of these to one another and to the secretion of colloid are still under discussion. The colloid droplets of De Robertis resemble the follicular colloid in that they stain with aniline blue, contain polysaccharide, and possibly in their ultraviolet absorption curve.

Colloid. The lumen of the follicles is normally filled with a characteristic material called colloid. This is a clear, viscous fluid whose consistency varies when the gland is in different states of activity. It is optically and probably chemically homogeneous, except for some desquamated cells and, under certain conditions, some macrophages. Irregularities in the colloid are rarely seen in follicles of living animals or after freezing and drying. However, the irregularities in the colloid which are seen after fixation and staining are useful indications of the state of the colloid and probably reflect variations in its protein concentration (Fig. 278). In ultraviolet absorption studies, *nucleic* acid was not found in the colloid. However, on the basis of its basophilia and the removal of the basophilic reaction with ribonuclease, it is claimed that ribonucleic acid is probably present in it. After fixatives the colloid in some follicles is more basophile than in others; the former are believed to have a more rapid iodine turnover than the latter.

The colloid has been shown to contain noniodinated and iodinated protein, the proportions of which vary from follicle to follicle. These proteins are presumably identical except for their content of *tyrosine, thyroxine* and *diiodotyrosine*, which have been demonstrated by microchemical analysis, by ultraviolet absorption and by the use of radioactive I^{131}. A second group of proteins present in the colloid is related to the *mucoproteins*. In addition, several enzymes have been identified in colloid—a proteolytic enzyme (probably a *cathepsin*), *peroxidase* and a *mucinase*. All these substances vary from follicle to fol-

licle at any moment, and probably in the same follicle at different times. The colloid is thus an active reservoir, which is in a continual state of flux rather than an inert storage center.

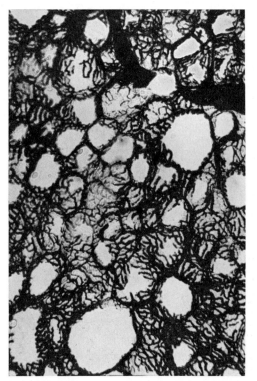

Fig. 283. Photomicrograph of thyroid gland of monkey injected with India ink to show pattern of small blood vessels. The richly anastomotic baskets of capillaries intimately enclose the follicles. Some of these are sectioned through the midportion; others are observed from above or below this level. 67 ×.

Funtional Mechanisms. The functions of the thyroid gland are related primarily to the action of *iodothyroglobulin*. About one fifth to one tenth of all the iodine of the body is located in the thyroid, nearly all of it in organic form. It is present chiefly as *diiodotyrosine* and *thyroxine*; most of the pharmacological properties of iodothyroglobulin are referable to the latter. The mechanism of synthesis, storage and release of the active principle is not well understood. Some of the processes involved may be summarized by stages:

1. *The fixation and concentration of circulating iodide* must be achieved against an

apparent concentration gradient. The mechanism is extremely rapid—ten minutes after an injection of inorganic iodide, 40 per cent of the circulating ion is concentrated in the gland. This reaction is partially inhibited by thiocyanates.

2. *Conversion of Iodide to Organic Iodine.* The first prerequisite for the conversion of the inorganic ion to an organic form is an oxidation to iodine or a hypo-iodate, possibly effected through a peroxidase. This enzymic activity is believed to be the point affected by certain thyroid inhibitors such as *thiourea* and *amino-benzene* compounds. The second prerequisite is an oxidative coupling of two diiodotyrosine moieties to form thyroxine. In a short time after the administration of iodide the normal ratio of diiodotyrosine to thyroxine is restored. This conversion of iodide ions to a bound organic form may be important in the first process mentioned, since it maintains a more favorable concentration gradient. As shown by autoradiographs, this process may take place first in the cytoplasm.

3. *Synthesis of Iodothyroglobulin.* The iodination of tyrosine to form diiodotyrosine, and by subsequent reaction thyroxine, was thought to take place at the amino acid level, the iodized amino acids being incorporated later into the protein. But it has become clear that tyrosine may be iodinated while it is part of the protein.

4. *Secretion into Colloid.* The iodinated protein seems to be segregated in the cytoplasm as visible droplets, which probably correspond with those described by De Robertis. The droplets are extruded into the colloid, where they are mixed with that already present.

5. *Release of the active component* may be achieved through the breakdown of the large protein molecule by the action of a proteolytic enzyme, probably cathepsin. The smaller molecules can more readily be absorbed through the gland cell toward the blood stream. The process of hydrolysis and absorption of the smaller moieties is accelerated by the reduction in the viscosity of the colloid through the action of a mucolytic enzyme on its substrate.

The mechanism thus proposed has been worked out by the use of numerous techniques involving microchemical analysis, and various cytochemical methods including autoradiographs, ultraviolet absorption, microdissection, and various chemical reactions yielding visible end reactions for enzymes and other proteins. Such methods have largely superseded the use of clinical material and methods which were the prime stimulus of earlier studies of thyroid function and gave tremendous impetus to them. However, for more controllable analysis of the processes of inhibition and acceleration of secretion, it became necessary to concentrate on animal studies. The marked hypertrophy and hyperplasia which may accompany these processes are not at all understood.

Control of Release of Secretion. Control of the rate of release of the active principle of the thyroid is thought to be mediated largely through other endocrine glands, particularly the anterior lobe of the hypophysis. An excess of thyroid hormone in the blood inhibits the secretion of *thyrotrophic* hormone, which results in reduced thyroid activity. A reduction of thyroid hormone in the blood stimulates the secretion of thyrotrophic hormone, resulting in increased thyroid activity. The accumulation of iodine from the blood, its conversion to the active principle, and its release into the circulation are all affected by thyrotrophic hormone.

Despite the rich innervation of the gland, little or no neural control of thyroid activity is believed to take place. Neural effects may, however, be expressed through the action of nervous impulses directly or indirectly on the pituitary gland, and may occur under unusual stresses.

Functions of the Thyroid Gland. Perhaps the most striking effect of the thyroid secretion is its control over the *metabolic rate* of the body above a minimal value. When a deficiency of thyroid hormone occurs, the metabolic rate is below normal; when there is an excess, the metabolic rate is above normal. When *hypothyroidism* begins in infancy and persists, it leads to *cretinism*; when hypofunction begins in adulthood and persists, it leads to *myxedema*. In both forms the basal metabolic rate is reduced, and in both the symptoms may be removed through timely oral administration of dried thyroid gland. Thyroidectomy may duplicate many of the symptoms of thyroid deficiency in man, but in adults of certain species (monkey), the effects of thyroidectomy are detectable with difficulty.

Hyperthyroidism occurs in persons suffering with *exophthalmic goiter* or with *toxic adenoma*. In both states, follicles become enlarged, with epithelial infoldings, the cells become columnar, the Golgi apparatus hypertrophies, mitochondria increase in number, and the follicular colloid decreases or may be absent (Fig. 279, A). The increased basal metabolic rate and associated symptoms return temporarily toward normal after the administration of iodine or of certain "antithyroid" drugs which are derivatives of thiourea.

Many of the symptoms of hyperthyroidism can be produced in other animals by the administration of an extract of the anterior lobe of the hypophysis containing thyrotrophic hormone. The thyroid of animals treated adequately with this extract shows the same changes as those in human hyperthyroidism. The marked morphological changes are not, however, diagnostic of hyperthyroidism, for they may be duplicated exactly by the administration of certain antithyroid drugs which result in hypothyroidism.

In two other conditions in man, the thyroid enlarges, but the basal metabolic rate is normal: *simple goiter* (Fig. 279, B), due possibly to iodine deficiency, and *nontoxic adenoma*.

As the primary effect of thyroid hormone is on the basal metabolic rate, it is not surprising that it influences carbohydrate metabolism (particularly glycogen storage) and probably also fat and protein metabolism. It is important also in growth of the animal as a whole, especially through its effects on os-sification centers, and on the development of certain organs, particularly the genital organs and the thymus. It also influences the functioning of the nervous system. There are certain interrelations with the anterior pituitary gland; thyroidectomy results in hypertrophy of the anterior lobe of the hypophysis, with degranulation of the alpha cells and the appearance of characteristically altered beta cells called thyroidectomy cells (see p. 281). The thyroid hypertrophies during menstruation and pregnancy. Finally, it becomes markedly hypoplastic in vitamin E deficient rats.

Phylogeny. Iodine is found in all marine invertebrates as well as some algae. Diiodotyrosine has been identified in some and may reach high concentrations in certain *sponges*. While there is no agreement on whether the *hypobranchial groove* in the floor of the pharynx of the protochordate *Amphioxus* is homologous with the thyroid gland, there seems to be more reason for homologizing the *endostyle* of the *lamprey* (a cyclostome) with the vertebrate thyroid. Although the endostyle of this animal can concentrate iodine and contains the active thyroid principle, there is nevertheless no evidence that the organ plays any endocrine role in the animal. The thyroid gland appears indisputably as an endocrine gland in certain fishes and remains remarkably constant in all higher animals.

Histogenesis. In man, the primordium of the thyroid gland arises early (embryos of 1.37 mm.) as a medial ventral outgrowth of the entoderm, cranial to that of the trachea. The *foramen cecum* at the base of the tongue of the adult is a vestige of the point from which the diverticulum arose in the embryo. In man there does not seem to be a contribution to the thyroid gland from the fourth branchial pouch.

At first the primordium is a hollow tube which grows caudally and thickens at its end. The connection between the tongue and the thyroid gland usually disappears (embryos of 4 to 7 mm.), but sometimes it persists either as the *thyroglossal duct* or as an irregular mass of thyroid tissue, usually eccentrically located, called the *pyramidal lobe*. The primodium then becomes a solid mass of epithelium, which later splits into ramifying plates and cords of epithelium. Hollows arise within these cords which are then known as *primary follicles*. They later fuse with one another and are invaded by mesenchyme. The walls of these hollows are two cells thick. Then the follicles of the mature organ arise by the repeated constriction of these plates into roughly spherical structures, in which a cavity lined by a single layer of epithelial cells develops; these *definitive follicles* are surrounded by mesenchyme (embryos of 24 mm.). Colloid may be present before birth, but does not become an important constituent of the follicles until after birth. In the pig, calf and rat, thyroid activity appears about the same time as the follicles begin to have stainable colloid. However, in amphibians the thyroid gland has some activity long before the cells appear "glandular" and before colloid formation.

Regeneration. The thyroid gland regenerates rapidly after surgical reduction if iodine is withheld from the diet, but will not regenerate if desiccated thyroid is administered. Autotransplantation is commonly successful, particularly if the animal is thyroid-deficient. Pure cultures of embryonic chick thyroid epithelium have been kept alive for some months.

REFERENCES

Astwood, E. B.: Chemotherapy of Hyperthyroidism. Harvey Lectures, Series 40, 195, 1944-45.

Bargmann, W.: Schilddrüse, in von Möllendorff's Handb. d. mikroskop. Anat. d. Menschen. 1939, Vol. 6, Pt. 2, p. 1.

Bensley, R. R.: Normal Mode of Secretion in Thyroid Gland. Am. J. Anat., 19:37, 1916.

Biedl, A.: Innere Sekretion. Ihre physiologischen Grundlagen und ihre Bedeutung für die Pathologie. Berlin, 1922.

Dempsey, E. W., and Singer, M.: Observations on the Chemical Cytology of the Thyroid Gland at Different Functional Stages. Endocrinology, 38:270, 1946.

Erdheim, J.: Zur normalen und pathologischen Histologie der Glandula thyroidea, parathyroidea, und Hypophysis. Beitr. z. path. Anat. u. allg. Path., 33: 158, 1903.

Gersh, I., and Baker, R. F.: Total Protein and Organic Iodine in the Colloid of Individual Follicles of the Thyroid Gland of the Rat. J. Cell. & Comp. Physiol., 21:213, 1943.

Giroud, A., and Lebond, C. P.: Localisations électives de l'acide ascorbique ou vitamine C. Arch. d'-Anat. micr., 31:111, 1935.

Goldsmith, DeRobertis, Dempsey, Astwood, Leblond,

Chaikoff and Taurog: Thyroid Function as Disclosed by Newer Methods of Study. Ann. New York Acad. Sc., 50:279, 1949.

Gorbman, A., and Evans, H. M.: Beginning of Function in the Thyroid of the Fetal Rat. Endocrinology, 32:113, 1943.

Grollman, A.: Essentials of Endocrinology. Philadelphia, 1947.

Leblond, C. P., Puppel, I. D., Riley, E., Radike, M., and Curtis, G. M.: Radioiodine and Iodine Fractionation Studies of Human Goitrous Thyroids. J. Biol. Chem., 162:275, 1946.

Leblond, C. P., and Gross, J.: Thyroglobulin Formation in the Thyroid Follicle Visualized by the "Coated Autograph" Technique. Endocrinology, 43:306, 1948.

Mackenzie, C. G., and Mackenzie, J. B.: Effect of Sulfonamides and Thioureas on the Thyroid Gland and Basal Metabolism. Endocrinology, 32:185, 1943.

Marine, D.: The Thyroid, Parathyroids, and Thymus, in Cowdry's Special Cytology. 2d ed. New York, (2), 797, 1932; The Pathogenesis and Prevention of Simple or Endemic Goiter, Glandular Physiology and Therapy. Chicago, 1935.

Nonidez, J. F.: Innervation of the Thyroid Gland. III. Distribution and Termination of the Nerve Fibers in the Dog. Am. J. Anat., 57:135, 1935.

Purves, H. D., and Griesbach, W. E.: Studies in Experimental Goitre. VII. Thyroid Carcinomata in Rats Treated with Thiourea. Brit. J. Exper. Biol., 27:294, 1946.

Rankin, R. M.: Changes in the Content of Iodine Compounds and in the Histological Structure of the Thyroid Gland of the Pig during Fetal Life. Anat. Rec., 80:123, 1941.

Salter, W. T.: The Endocrine Function of Iodine. Cambridge, Mass., 1940.

Selye, H.: Textbook of Endocrinology. Montreal, 1947.

Turner, C. D.: General Endocrinology. Philadelphia, W. B. Saunders Company, 1948.

The references cited were selected primarily for orientation in this rapidly developing subject. Students are referred for the most recent developments to Annual Reviews of Physiology and to Vitamins and Hormones.

XVII. PARATHYROID GLANDS

The parathyroid glands are small, yellow-brown, oval bodies usually intimately connected with the posterior surface of the thyroid gland. In man there are usually four or five glands, but as many as twelve have been reported. Their total weight varies from 0.05 to 0.3 gm. They may range from 3 to 8 mm. in length, 2 to 5 mm. in width, and 0.5 to 2 mm. in thickness. Most of the glands are in contact with the middle third of the thyroid, some with the anterior third, and the smallest number with the posterior third. About 5 to 10 per cent of the glands are associated with the thymus gland and may be deep in the anterior mediastinum. This association of parathyroid gland and thyroid and thymus stems from their close origin in the embryo.

Most parathyroid glands lie in the capsule of the thyroid, but they may be embedded in it. In either case, the parathyroid glands are separated from the thyroid by a connective tissue capsule. The capsular connective tissue extends into the parathyroid gland, and

these trabeculae bear the larger branches of blood vessels, nerves and lymphatics. Between the gland cells is a framework of loose-meshed reticular fibers. These support the rich capillary network (Fig. 286) and the nerve fibers which are distributed chiefly along the capillaries, though some may end blindly in the connective tissue, or on or between the gland cells. No basement membrane has been described.

Gland Cells. The parathyroid glands consist of densely packed groups of cells which may form a continuous mass of cells or may be arranged as anastomosing cords, or less commonly as follicles with a colloidal material in their lumen. Two main types of epithelial cells have been described: *principal cells* and *oxyphile cells* (Fig. 285). The *principal cell* is the more numerous and probably the more important. It has a larger, vesicular, centrally placed nucleus embedded in a faintly staining homogeneous cytoplasm which tends to shrink during fixation. The

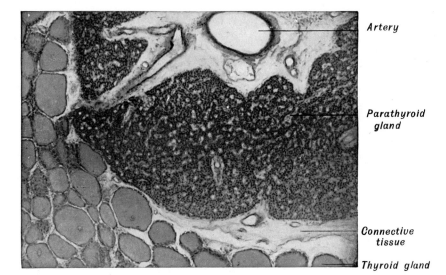

Fig. 284. Photomicrograph of section of thyroid and parathyroid glands of *Macacus rhesus*. 80 ×.

mitochondria are filamentous to granular and sometimes are close to the nucleus. The Golgi apparatus is short and situated close to the nucleus, with no evidence of vascular polarity. The cytoplasm is rich in glycogen and contains numerous fat droplets.

The *oxyphile cell* is larger than the principal cell. The nucleus is smaller and darker-staining, embedded in a deeply staining cytoplasm crowded with granular mitochondria. There is little or no demonstrable glycogen or fat in most oxyphile cells.

Another type of cell, intermediate between the two types, has been described. It has a fine granular cytoplasm which stains faintly with acid dyes, and a nucleus which is smaller and stains darker than that of the principal cells. Also, "water-clear" cells and dark oxyphile cells have been described.

A variety of cytoplasmic droplets, vacuoles and colloid materials have been described as secretion precursors on morphological grounds alone. More detailed cytological studies on experimental material are needed.

The parathyroid glands show certain changes with increasing age: (1) increase in amount of connective tissue, including increased numbers of fat cells as well as mast cells; (2) the oxyphile cells are said to appear at four and one half to seven years, and to increase in number especially after puberty; (3) in the closely packed masses of gland cells, some cords and follicles appear in the year-old infant and increase thereafter; colloid accumulation in the lumen of the follicles shows the same tendency.

When rats are given injections of a large dose of parathyroid extract, the cells of the parathyroid glands become smaller; the Golgi apparatus also becomes smaller and more compact. Both changes are suggestive of hypofunction. After two weeks the cells return to normal both in size and morphology of the Golgi apparatus; these changes are indicative of the resumption of normal secretory activity. During the hypertrophy of the parathyroid glands in rickets, the Golgi apparatus is described as undergoing changes which indicate great secretory activity as compared with normal cells. It is not possible to extend these conclusions to the human gland, for it has to be shown which cells in man are equivalent to those in laboratory animals. Of all mammalian parathyroid glands examined cytologically thus far, those of the horse seem most nearly to resemble those of man.

Function. The function of the parathyroid glands is closely linked with the states of *calcium* in the organism. The maintenance

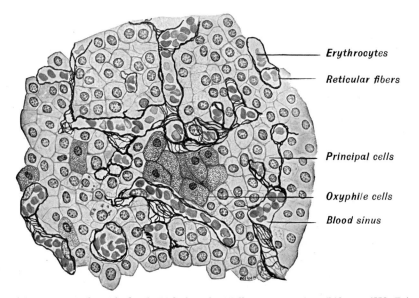

Fig. 285. Section of human parathyroid gland. Bielschowsky-Mallory-azan stains. 540 ×. (W. B.)

of a physiologically constant concentration of *calcium ions* in the blood plasma appears to be accomplished largely by regulation, by the parathyroid hormone, of the movement of calcium from bone to blood. (See p. 271 for some properties of the hormone.) The mechanism of the influence of the parathyroids upon movement of calcium from bone is but poorly understood. As a result of study of grafts of parathyroid gland to bone, it seems clear that a hormone from the gland acts directly on the bone and causes its absorption (Barnicot).

Evidence has also appeared that the action of parathyroid extract may not be on bone salt primarily, but rather on the ground substance of bone and perhaps on that of other connective tissues. The extract appears to act as a spreading factor; it causes a breakdown of the highly organized ground substance of subcutaneous connective tissue. In bone, in large doses, it causes a similar breakdown of the organic components prior to their absorption. The mobilization of calcium, and its solution and removal, occur coincidentally with this process. This seems to occur around all osteocytes in affected zones, and is not limited to the outer surface of bone spicules (see p. 115).

The parathyroid glands become large in rickets through increase in size and especially in number of their cells. The hypertrophy is greater in low calcium than in low phosphate rickets. Hypertrophy is also observed in nephritis with uremia, and has resulted from the experimental production of renal insufficiency and is associated with extensive bone changes (*renal rickets, renal osteitis fibrosa*) similar to those of primary hyperparathyroidism. It is probably a response to a lowered calcium ion concentration in the plasma resulting from phosphate retention. In birds deprived of sunlight, the parathyroid glands hypertrophy.

Tumor or hyperplasia of the parathyroids may lead to *hyperparathyroidism* associated with high plasma calcium, extensive bone resorption (*osteitis fibrosa*, see p. 138) and pathological calcification in soft tissues. Similar effects may be produced in susceptible

animals by the administration of toxic doses of *parathyroid extract.*

Extirpation of the parathyroid glands or atrophy due to some pathological process is followed by *hypoparathyroidism*, characterized primarily by a decrease in the concentration of calcium in the plasma, and *tetany*.

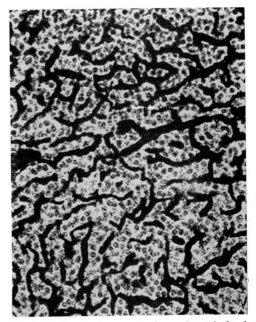

Fig. 286. Photomicrograph of parathyroid gland of monkey injected with India ink to show the extensively anastomotic capillary network in intimate contact with the gland cells. 165 ×.

The symptoms may be alleviated by the administration of calcium, an extract of parathyroid glands, or dehydrotachysterol, or by dietary control. A condition of *latent tetany* which occurs in man, with low plasma calcium but without symptoms, may be produced experimentally in dogs.

There is some evidence that a hormone of the pars distalis of the hypophysis affects parathyroid secretion (see p. 280).

Regeneration. The parathyroids have but insignificant powers of regeneration. The glands "take" readily in autotransplants, and may be maintained successfully in tissue culture.

Histogenesis. The parathyroid glands develop from thickenings of the third and fourth branchial pouches on each side. The primordium on the third arch is close to the bud of the thymus. This proximity of origin of the two organs is a probable explanation of the frequent occurrence of aberrant parathyroid bodies in or near the thymus.

Phylogenesis. Parathyroid glands are absent from invertebrates and fishes and are found in all higher orders of vertebrates.

REFERENCES

Bargmann, W.: Epithelkörperchen, Inseln, in von Möllendorff's Handb. d. mikroskop. Anat. d. Menschen. 1939, Vol. 6, Pt. 2, p. 1.

Bensley, S. H.: The Normal Mode of Secretion in the Parathyroid Gland of the Dog. Anat. Rec., 98:361, 1947.

Biedl, A.: Innere Sekretion. Ihre physiologischen Grundlagen und ihre Bedeutung für die Pathologie. Berlin, 1922.

Bobeau, G.: Recherches cytologiques sur les glandules parathyroïdes du cheval. J. de l'Anat., 47:371, 1911.

Collip, J. B.: The Parathyroid Glands. Harvey lectures, 21:113, 1925-6.

DeRobertis, E.: The Cytology of the Parathyroid Gland of Rats Injected with Parathyroid Extract. Anat. Rec., 78:473, 1940.

Erdheim, J.: Zur normalen und pathologischen Histologie der Glandula thyroidea, parathyroidea, und Hypophysis. Beitr. z. path. Anat. u. z. allg. Path., 33:158, 1903.

Marine, D.: The Thyroid, Parathyroids, and Thymus, in Cowdry's Special Cytology. 2d ed. New York, (2), 797, 1932.

Morgan, J. R. E.: The Parathyroid Glands. Arch. Path., 21:10, 1936.

Norris, E. H.: The Parathyroid Glands and the Lateral Thyroid in Man: Their Morphogenesis, Histogenesis, Topographic Anatomy and Prenatal Growth. Contrib. Embryol., Carnegie Inst., 26:249, 1937.

Sandström: On a New Gland in Man and Several Mammals, (trans. by C. M. Seipel.) Bull. Inst. Hist. Med., 6, No. 3, 1938.

Selye, H.: Textbook of Endocrinology. Montreal, 1947.

Shelling, D. H.: The Parathyroids in Health and in Disease. St. Louis, 1935.

Thompson, D. L., and Collip, J. B.: The Parathyroid Glands. Physiol. Rev., 12:309, 1932.

Turner, C. D.: General Endocrinology. Philadelphia. W. B. Saunders Company, 1948.

XVIII. ADRENAL GLANDS AND PARAGANGLIA

The paired adrenal or suprarenal glands of man are roughly triangular, flattened bodies, one at the cranial pole of each kidney. The glands together average about 10 to 12 gm. in the healthy adult, and measure approximately 5 by 3 by less than 1 cm. An indentation on the anterior surface, the hilus, admits an artery and emits the suprarenal vein. The surface made by cutting through the gland presents a bright yellow cortex in its outer part and a reddish-brown zone adjacent to the thin gray medulla.

Cortex. The cortex, which occupies the greater part of the gland, is disposed in three vaguely defined layers: a thin, outer *zona glomerulosa*, contiguous with the capsule; a middle, thick *zona fasciculata*; and an inner, moderately thick *zona reticularis*, which abuts on the medulla (Fig. 287). The transition from one zone to another is gradual, but may appear sharper in preparations injected to show the vascular pattern.

The zona glomerulosa consists of short columnar cells closely packed in ovoid groups or in columns which may form arcs. The nuclei stain deeply, and the rather scanty cytoplasm contains basophilic material which may be diffuse or, as in man, disposed in clumps. Lipid droplets, when present, are scarce and small in most animals, and may be numerous in others. Mitochondria may be filamentous (in man), rodlike (in the guinea pig and cat), or spherical (in the rat). The compact Golgi apparatus is juxtanuclear and may be polarized toward the capillary surface in some animals.

The zona fasciculata consists of polyhedral cells considerably larger than those of the zona glomerulosa. They are arranged as anastomosing "cords" of cells with a marked radial orientation, extending between the zona glomerulosa and the reticularis. The nuclei are centrally placed in the cells, and often there are two in one cell. The cytoplasm is basophile or contains basophile masses, more so in the peripheral portion than in the inner portion of the zone. Lipid droplets are numerous. In the outer portion, where they are commonly most numerous, the cytoplasm is reduced to thin films between them; consequently in stained sections from which the lipids have been removed, the cytoplasm appears vacuolated. The lipid droplets are small in some cells, larger in others, but of about equal size in any given cell. There may be a thin transitional region between the zona glomerulosa and zona fasciculata which is relatively free of lipid droplets. This is the region which may contain mitotic figures. The mitochondria appear generally to be less numerous than in the outer cortical zone. The Golgi apparatus is juxtanuclear, and in some animals appears to be somewhat less compact than in the zona glomerulosa.

In the zona reticularis the cells are arranged as clearly anastomosing cords. The transition between this zone and the zona fasciculata is gradual, the cells differing little. The cytoplasm contains fewer lipid droplets. Toward the medulla there is a variable number of "light" cells and "dark" cells which differ in their staining affinities. The nuclei of the light cells are pale-staining, while those of the dark cells are shrunken and hyperchromatic. Mitochondria are few in the former and numerous in the latter. The Golgi apparatus is compact or fragmented. The dark cells contain clumps of yellow or brownish pigment. Both the light and dark cells are regarded by some as degenerating cells. There may also be some dead cells.

Medulla. The boundary between zona reticularis and medulla in man is usually irregular in the adult, since columns of cortical cells project into the medulla. In other animals (e.g., mouse) the boundary may be are seen throughout these cells (Fig. 291). This is the *chromaffin reaction,* probably caused in large part by the presence of epinephrine. The medulla appears green with ferric chloride for the same reason. In addi-

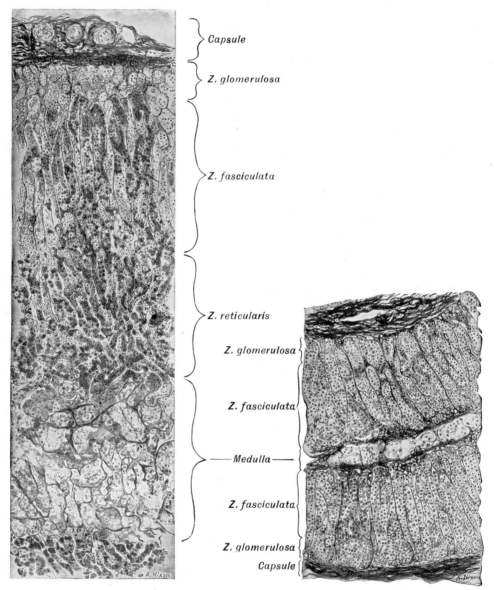

Fig. 287. Section of adrenal gland of a man. Mallory-azan stain. About 105 ×.

Fig. 288. Section of adrenal gland of a six months' infant. Mallory-azan stain. About 105 ×.

sharp. The irregular cells of the medulla are arranged in rounded groups or short cords surrounded by venules and blood capillaries. When the tissue is fixed in a fluid containing potassium bichromate, fine brown granules tion to the chromaffin cells, there are frequent, single or grouped, sympathetic ganglion cells whose axons end around the chromaffin cells (Fig. 291). The medulla also contains collections of small round cells with deeply staining nuclei and little cytoplasm. These are probably lymphocytes. In the fetal adrenal, similar small round cells occur which are the *sympathochromaffin* cells, the forerunners of the sympathetic and medullary cells.

Connective Tissue and Vascular System of Adrenal Gland. The connective tissue of the adrenal gland consists of a thick collagenous capsule which extends through the

work of the cortex consists of reticular fibers which lie between the capillaries and the gland cells and to some extent between the latter. The reticular fibers also enclose the medullary cell cords and support capillaries, veins and nerves. Collagenous fibers appear around the larger tributaries of the veins and merge with the capsular connective tissue.

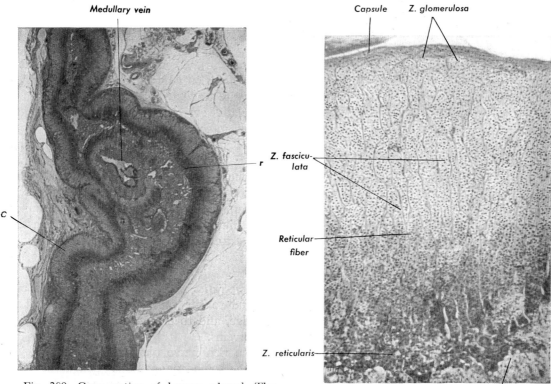

Fig. 289. Cross section of human adrenal. The cortico-medullary junction is indicated at *r* and the capsule at *c*. Both medulla and medullary vein are unusually thick. Photomicrograph H+E. 4×. (After von Herrath and Abramow.)

Fig. 290. Photomicrograph of cortex of human adrenal stained with Mallory-azan. 25×. (After von Herrath and Abramow.)

capsule to varying depths as trabeculae, and a prominent reticulum. The capsule contains a dense network of branches of the main arteries of the gland, some capillaries and venules, a nerve plexus and lymphatics. Major branches of arteries, nerves and lymphatics penetrate the cortex, often in the trabeculae. The arteries and nerves continue almost exclusively into the medulla, while the lymphatics are confined to the trabeculae in the cortex. Most of the supporting frame-

The vascular pattern is nearly uniform in man, dog, cat and rat. The cortical vessels arise from terminal branches of the network of capsular arteries. These penetrate the zona glomerulosa as sinusoids, where they form arcuate anastomoses, and then traverse the cortex radially from the capsule, to form the relatively straight, anastomosing network of the zona fasciculata, passing between the similarly arranged gland cell cords. Those from a given region converge in the zona

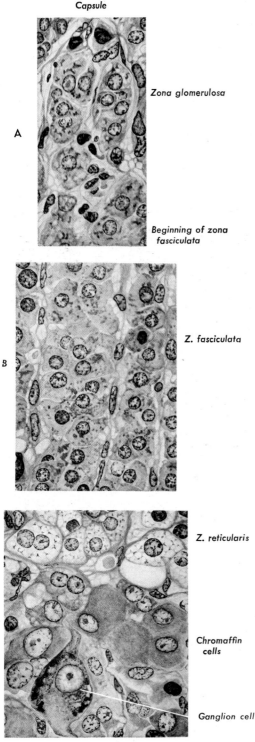

Fig. 291. Sections of adrenal gland of a man. A, From the zona glomerulosa; B, zona fasciculata, showing columns of cells separated by collapsed sinusoids; C, cortico-medullary junction. The medullary portion contains a sympathetic ganglion cell with Nissl sub-

reticularis toward a collecting vein at the medullary boundary (Fig. 293). There are some small venules in the capsule. There is no venous system in the cortex.

From the capsule, some major arterial branches penetrate the cortex in trabeculae with few or no branches until they reach the medulla. In the medulla, they branch repeatedly to form its rich capillary net around the cords and clumps of cells. An arterial vessel which penetrates at the hilus, branches to form capillaries in a similar way. The capillaries empty into the same venous system which drains the cortex, uniting to form the central veins, which emerge as the suprarenal vein. The central vein and its larger tributaries are lined by endothelium. They have abundant smooth muscle fibers arranged mainly in longitudinal bundles.

The cells lining the capillaries of the smaller vessels in the medulla are endothelial. On the other hand, the lining cells of the sinuses in the cortex are littoral cells of the macrophage system, much like those lining the sinusoids of the liver and hypophysis. They store lithium carmine, and in heavily stained animals their number is greatly increased.

Lymphatics and Nerves. Lymphatics are limited to the capsule and its cortical trabeculae, and to the connective tissue of the large veins.

The rich nerve plexus in the capsule includes some sympathetic ganglion cells. Branches penetrate the cortex in the trabeculae and are distributed with few exceptions to the medulla. They end mainly in clawlike terminations around individual cells of the medulla. The fibers are preganglionic.

Functions of Cortex. Hormones and Other Substances in Cortex. The cortex is essential for life. Its removal or destruction (in man, leading to *Addison's disease*) is fatal. The cortex is necessary for an extensive series of functions: (1) maintenance of *electrolyte*

stance and several greenish-brown-stained chromaffin cells. The cells of the zona reticularis are vacuolated. Hematoxylin-eosin-azure II. 730 ×. (Drawn by Miss Esther Bohlman.)

and water balance in the body. After ablation of the cortex there is excessive excretion of sodium in the urine, resulting in decreased plasma sodium concentration, with corresponding decline of the plasma chloride and bicarbonate levels. The tissues are dehydrated, and eventually hemoconcentration appears. Potassium, magnesium, urea, uric acid and creatinine in the plasma are all lowered. Water changes seem to be accompanied

cated by the diversity of miraculous effects of cortisone (a steroid from the adrenal cortex) on human beings suffering from a wide variety of diseases. Other effects are also indicated. Cortisone has been found effective in such diverse conditions as rheumatoid arthritis, rheumatic fever, periarteritis nodosa, exfoliative dermatitis, disseminated lupus, numerous allergic conditions, and ulcerative colitis. A common feature of all

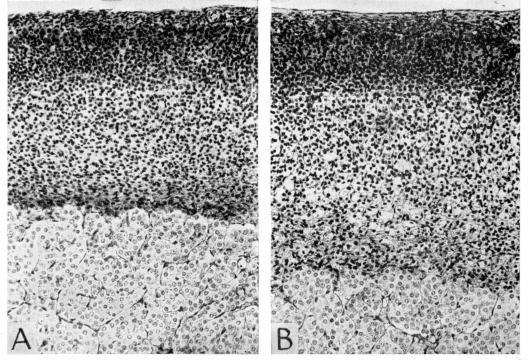

Fig. 292. Photomicrographs of adrenal gland of rats, showing effects of injection of adrenocorticotrophic hormone. A, Atrophic cortex of young hypophysectomized rat; B, hypophysectomized rat which had an injection for four days of purified adrenocorticotrophic hormone. The hypertrophy of the zona fascicula is most marked. Zenker-formol, H + E. 165 ×.

by a shift from extracellular spaces to tissue cells and by abnormal renal function (2) Maintenance of *carbohydrate balance*. Adrenalectomy results in a *hypoglycemia* with reduced glycogen stores in liver and muscle. Adrenalectomy in the diabetic animal tends to reduce the high blood sugar to normal levels, comparable with the well-known effect of hypophysectomy. There appears to be a concommitant disturbance of protein and fat metabolism. (3) *Maintenance of connective tissue* of the body. This has been indi-

these effects seems to be related to some property or properties of the connective tissues. The mechanism(s) involved are unexplained. This great advance in medicine offers a magnificent opportunity for exploring further the integrative mechanisms of the body. It also opens the door to a more fundamental study of connective tissues and their relations to other tissues. (4) Release of *immune bodies*. It has been claimed that the adrenocorticotrophic hormone of the anterior pituitary causes the liberation of hormonal

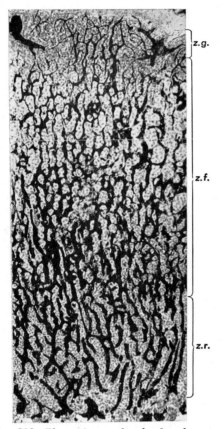

z.g.

z.f.

z.r.

Fig. 293. Photomicrograph of adrenal cortex of monkey injected with India ink to show the vascular pattern. The arcuate sinusoids of the zona glomerulosa (*z.g.*) empty into the more longitudinally oriented sinusoids of the zona fasciculata (*z.f.*). These are joined in the zona reticularis (*z.r.*), where they flow into veins in the medulla. 85 ×.

substances from the cortex, which produces a disintegration of lymphocytes with a resulting lymphopenia and atrophy of lymphatic tissue and an increase of beta and gamma globulin (immune body fraction) of the serum. However, a similar effect of the adrenal cortex has not been found on lymphocytes in cats. The extensive atrophy of lymphatic tissue which results from the action of a variety of noxious agents (part of the "*alarm reaction*" of Selye) is believed by some to be due to the liberation of adrenal cortical hormone; it does not occur if the adrenal cortex is removed. (5) Maintenance of a variety of functions such as those of the gastrointestinal tract, muscular system, ner-

vous system, sex, and so on. Cortical deficiency results in *hypotension* (low blood pressure) anorexia, diarrhea, vomiting, asthenia, lassitude, interference with normal sexual libido, and altered vascular "permeability."

All disturbed functions of cortical deficiency are restored by appropriate treatment with suitable extracts or synthetic products. The most notable of these are *dexoxycorticosterone* (electrolytes and water particularly), *corticosterone* (carbohydrate metabolism particularly) and *cortisone* (electrolyte, carbohydrate and protein metabolism, connective tissue and vascular permeability).

A number of compounds have been separated from the cortex. Twenty-eight adrenal steroids have separated; six of these have marked corticoid activity, and several others have sex hormone activity. While these are intimately concerned with the functions of the cortex, no one of them exhibits all the physiological effects of a crude extract; it is therefore not correct to designate any one, to the exclusion of others, as the adrenal cortical hormone. In addition, the cortex yields cholesterol, cholesterol esters, neutral fats and phospholipids, ascorbic acid, carotene, choline and glutathione.

Histochemistry of Adrenal Cortex. Numerous studies, particularly in recent years, have centered around the distribution of the first four compounds in this series and the 17-*ketosteroids*. Some workers claim that substances are present in the cortex which show all the following properties: (1) a positive test with phenylhydrazine, Schiff reagent and semicarbazide; (2) reduction of silver ions; (3) a positive Liebermann-Burchardt reaction; (4) birefringence; (5) yellow or greenish-white fluorescence; (6) solubility in acetone. A uniformly positive result is taken to be a specific identification for 17-ketosteroids. This view has been challenged, and it seems doubtful that the battery of tests is as specific as claimed. Nevertheless, with all the tests described as a "collective stain," some useful information has been obtained. The lipids have been studied by the use of Sudan stains and osmic acid. Tests used for cholesterol, cholesterol esters and ascorbic acid have certain limitations.

It is not known whether the variegated functions of the adrenal cortex are mediated equally by all parts of the cortex, or whether different layers have separate functions. Evidence has been presented which indicates that the zona glomerulosa is more involved in the secretion of a desoxycorticosterone-like compound than other zones, and that the zona fasciculata participates in the secretion of corticosterone more than other zones. The evidence is the following: (1) Hypophysectomy, which affects glucose metabolism more markedly than electrolyte metabolism, is said to be accompanied by atrophy of the zona fasciculata, with no marked effect on the zona glomerulosa. (2) The administration of desoxycorticosterone (which is involved in electrolyte metabolism) in small doses is claimed to result in atrophy of the zona glomerulosa, with no marked effect on the zona fasciculata. The administration of 11-oxysteroids (which affect glucose metabolism) has no marked effect on the zona glomerulosa, but leads to atrophy of the zona fasciculata. The atrophic changes are accompanied in each zone by reduction in lipid content of the cells and in the "ketosteroid" reactions.

Stress. With the exceptions just noted, the cortex appears to respond in a nonspecific manner to a wide variety of stresses which induce adrenal hyperfunction. The cortex enlarges with hypertrophy and hyperplasia, coincidentally with an extensive increase in the capillary bed. There may be an increase in the number of lipid droplets, which in late stages may revert to less than normal. It has been claimed that the cortical cholesterol and ascorbic acid also decline during stress. The "ketosteroid" reactions in the zona fasciculata increase. In general, the same morphological changes can be induced by the administration of adrenocorticotrophic hormone in certain dosages.

Effects of Hyperfunction of Cortex. The metabolic functions of the adrenal cortex are made manifest chiefly as effects of deficiency of cortical activity. Effects of hyperfunction (as in thyroid gland, for example) are lacking except for permeability and *spreading action* under certain experimental conditions. Adrenogenital (androgenic) tumors are characterized by masculinization (in women) or by premature development of male sex characters in children.

Age Change and Growth in Cortex. Marked age changes take place in the human adrenal cortex. Soon after birth, the inner or *boundary zone* of the cortex begins to involute and is largely gone after the first few weeks. The remaining smaller *subcapsular* portion of the cortex contracts upon the medulla (Fig. 288). Accordingly, for some time the infant's adrenal is smaller than at birth. Too rapid involution of the boundary zone may lead to fatal hemorrhage into the adrenals. The zona fasciculata appears early, and by the end of the third year the zona reticularis has developed.

The pigment in the zona reticularis is present after puberty and increases in amount with age. It is similar to the "lipochrome" pigment found in cardiac muscle and nerve cells in old age.

It is commonly believed that new cells are produced by mitosis in the capsule or the transitional zone between the zona glomerulosa and zona fasciculata, and that these are gradually moved into the zona fasciculata and eventually the zona reticularis, where they become "dark" cells or "light" cells and degenerate. The appearance of mitotic figures in certain circumstances in all zones has thrown doubt on this concept.

Relations with Other Endocrine Glands. It is doubtful if the nerve fibers in the adrenal cortex have any important role in the regulation of its activity. Control seems to be mediated almost entirely by the anterior lobe of the hypophysis through secretion of the adrenocorticotrophic hormone. During stress, as part of the "alarm reaction," the rate of secretion of the pituitary hormone appears to be proportional to the intensity of stress. Whether this reaction is mediated by fluctuations in the level of cortical hormones in the blood, or by an intermediate influence by the tissues of the body, is not known. Pituitary ablation leads to cortical atrophy. After unilateral adrenalectomy, compensatory hypertrophy of the remaining adrenal does not occur after hypophysectomy. In Addison's disease, or after adrenalectomy, there appears to be a decrease in the number of basophile cells in the anterior lobe of the pituitary.

There appears to be some relation between the adrenal cortex and the sex glands. Adrenalectomy is followed by loss of libido in male rats, and abnormal estrous cycles or diestrus in females. Orchidectomy in the male mouse delays the normal atrophy of the X-zone (reticularis) of the adrenal cortex. Certain natural and synthetic estrogens exert adrenal steroid effects on metabolism. Removal of the adrenal interrupts lactation. To what exent these effects are mediated through the anterior lobe of the hypophysis, or are direct, is not known.

Certain interrelations of adrenal and thyroid gland are also indicated by several contradictory reports: In rabbits the adrenal glands hypertrophy, sometimes to two or three times the normal size, after removal of the thyroid. Sublethal adrenal injury results in hyperthermia and increased basal metabolic rate. The administration of thyroid powder may be followed by adrenal cortical hypertrophy.

Functions of Medulla. The medulla is not essential for life; it is not certain that it plays any important part in the normal organism. The medulla elaborates *epinephrine*. Unlike the cortex, the medulla stores high concentrations of its specific product. The compound is readily oxidized, because of its phenolic and alcoholic groupings. For this reason, the medulla can be recognized by the chromaffin reaction and the color reactions with ferric salts and other compounds. It is auto-oxidizable, and may itself give a brown color through the subsequent polymerization of the reaction products. The same reactions are given by paraganglia (see p. 307). An epinephrine-like material is increased in the blood of the adrenal vein after stimulation of the splanchnic nerves and decreased after they are sectioned. Epinephrine appears to be re-formed rapidly in the gland after partial depletion following stimulation. A great variety of conditions (generally the same which cause adrenal cortical hyperactivity) cause an increased rate of secretion by the medulla. This may be due to the suggested stimulation of the cortex by adrenocorticotrophic hormone through release of epinephrine from the adrenal medulla. Epinephrine is rapidly destroyed in the blood and is measurable only in that of the adrenal vein.

Epinephrine has a powerful *sympathomimetic* action; its effect on clotting time of the blood, blood pressure, carbohydrate metabolism, and gastrointestinal tract is essentially the same as that produced by stimulation of sympathetic nerves alone.

The adrenal medulla is unessential for normal activity, even in sympathectomized animals, since no physiological disturbances are produced. There is no deficiency disease of the adrenal medulla. Some believe it to be important in sensitizing the nerve endings of sympathetic nerve fibers, and others to be important in emergencies. Hyperfunction of the adrenal medulla in man occurs rarely, with certain tumors of the medulla or of extramedullary chromaffin tissues containing epinephrine. In such cases there may be attacks of sweating, mydriasis, hypertension and hyperglycemia terminating suddenly in death. The paroxysmal hypertension of adrenal medullary tumors is decreased or abolished by intravenous administration of a series of compounds which have an epinephrine-inhibiting action.

Histogenesis of Adrenal Gland. The cortex develops from the celomic mesoderm on the median side of the wolffian ridge, and the medulla from the ectodermal tissue, which also gives rise to sympathetic ganglion cells. In a six weeks' embryo the cortical primordium consists of a rounded bud of cells cranial to the kidney. Strands of sympathochromaffin cells grow ventrally and penetrate the cortical bud in its medial side. At this stage they begin to exhibit the chromaffin reaction characteristic of adrenal medulla, and the cortical cells may already contain fine lipid droplets. At three months, the fetal cortex consists of a narrow outer zone of small cells with deeply staining nuclei, and an inner zone consisting almost entirely of large granular cells lying between capillaries. The outer zone develops into the definitive cortex, while the inner zone forms the zone which is destined to atrophy.

Phylogenesis of Adrenal Gland. Chromaffin tissue which yields adrenalin-like activity is present in the central nervous system of leeches; it is present also in the mantles of certain molluscs. In cyclostomes and teleosts the *interrenal bodies* (which are homologous with the cortex) are separate from the discrete chromaffin bodies. In amphibians the two components are in juxtaposition, or they may be intermingled; in reptiles and birds they are commonly intermingled. The well-known cortex and medulla relationship appears in mammals, in which this is the predominant form of organization.

Regeneration of Adrenal Gland. Cortical cells are particularly susceptible to injury. They are replaced by mitosis probably throughout the cortex, with a greater tendency for this to take place in the transition zone between zona glomerulosa and zona fasciculata. Successful transplantation seems to require the presence of a capsule. It is more successful also in totally adrenalectomized animals. The medulla does not survive transplantation readily.

THE PARAGANGLIA (CHROMAFFIN SYSTEM)

Under this term are grouped several widely scattered accumulations of cells which seem to have much in common with the medullary cells of the adrenal glands. These paraganglia include widespread, small accumulations of cells in the retroperitoneum—the organs of Zuckerkandl, and collections of similar cells in the kidney, ovary, liver, testis and heart. Most, but not all, authors believe that they arise from sympathogonia. The paraganglia all contain chromaffin cells. The chromaffin cells are clear in the fresh condition or after most fixatives, but stain positively with chromic and osmic acids and contain iron. These cells are usually arranged more or less as cords and have a rich blood supply.

It has not been proved that these paraganglia have an endocrine function. The assumption that they elaborate epinephrine, just like the chromaffin cells of the medulla of the adrenal, has not been established. Some authors include the medullary cells of

the adrenal in this group and speak of them all as the chromaffin system. The advisability of this must be questioned until it has been shown that all the chromaffin organs have the same internal secretion.

Carotid, Aortic and Coccygeal Bodies. These structures are often erroneously included with the endocrine glands. The carotid and aortic bodies are described on page 224, and the coccygeal body on page 219.

REFERENCES

Bennett, H. S.: Cytological Manifestations of Secretion in the Adrenal Medulla of the Cat. Am. J. Anat., 69:333, 1941.

Biedl, A.: Innere Sekretion. Ihre physiologischen Grundlagen und ihre Bedeutung für die Pathologie. Berlin, 1922.

Deane, H. W., and Greep, R. O.: A Morphological and Histological Study of the Rat's Adrenal Cortex after Hypophysectomy, with Comments on the Liver. Am. J. Anat., 79:117, 1946.

Dempsey, Gaunt and Eversole, Greep and Deane, Sayers and Sayers: The Adrenal Cortex. Ann. New York Acad. Sc., 50:1949.

Flexner, L. B., and Grollman, A.: The Reduction of Osmic Acid as an Indicator of Adrenal Cortical Activity in the Rat. Anat. Rec., 75:207, 1939.

Flint, J. M.: The Blood Vessels, Angrogenesis, Organogenesis, Reticulum, and Histology, of the Adrenal. Johns Hopkins Hosp. Rep., 9:153, 1900.

Hoerr, N.: The Cells of the Suprarenal Cortex in the Guinea-Pig. Their Reaction to Injury and Their Replacement. Am. J. Anat., 48:139, 1931.

Iwanow, G.: Das chromaffin and interrenale System des Menschen. Ergeb. d. Anat., 29:87, 1932.

Parkes, A. S.: The Adrenal-Gonad Relationship. Physiol. Rev., 25:203, 1945.

Rogoff, J. M.: The Suprarenal Bodies, in Cowdry's Special Cytology. 2d ed. New York, (2), 869, 1932.

Selye, H.: Thymus and Adrenals in the Response of the Organism to Injuries and Intoxications. Brit. J. Exper. Path., 17:234, 1936.

Selye, H.: Textbook of Endocrinology. Montreal, 1947.

Turner, C. D.: General Endocrinology. Philadelphia, W. B. Saunders Company, 1948.

The references cited were selected primarily for orientation in this rapidly developing subject. Students are referred for the most recent developments to Annual Reviews of Physiology and to Vitamins and Hormones.

XIX. THE PINEAL BODY

The pineal body (conarium, epiphysis cerebri) is a somewhat flattened, conical, gray body measuring 5 to 8 mm. in length, and 3 to 5 mm. in its greatest width. It lies above the roof of the posterior extremity of the third ventricle, to which it is attached by the pineal stalk. The cavity of the third ventricle extends for a short distance into the stalk as the pineal recess; this is lined with ependyma.

Except where it is attached to the habenular and posterior commissures of the midbrain, the pineal body is invested by pia mater. Connective tissue septa, containing many blood vessels, arise from this layer, penetrate the pineal body and separate its specific elements into cords of cells. In hematoxylin-and-eosin-stained sections the pineal body is seen to consist of cords of epithelioid cells with dark nuclei and little cytoplasm, embedded in a reticular framework. With advancing age, some of the small dark cells gradually develop into larger cells with much cytoplasm and paler nuclei.

Besides the presence of neuroglial cells—on which all authors are agreed—five types of cells have been described: (1) chief cells, which are large and have small processes and no vacuoles in their homogeneous protoplasm; (2) smaller cells with fine acidophile granules; (3) cells with large basophile gran-

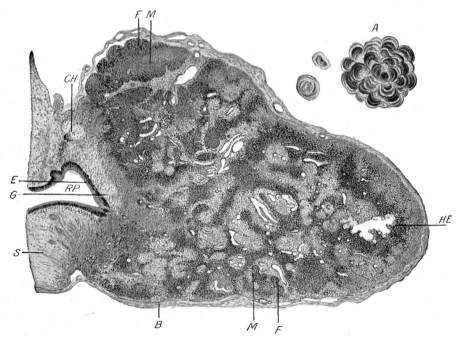

Fig. 294. Median section through pineal body of a newborn child. B, Connective tissue sheath (pia mater); CH, superior habenular commissure; E, ependyma; F, group of cells with little protoplasm; G, neuroglia; HE, posterior end of the pineal body; M, cells with much protoplasm; RP, pineal recess; S, connection with posterior commissure. Blood vessels empty. 32 ×. A, Acervulus from the pineal body of a woman sixty-nine years old. 160 ×. (After Schaffer.)

ules; (4) cells with lipoid granules; and (5) nerve cells. Some authors claim that the various granules are evidences of a secretory process.

According to the recent studies of del Río-Hortega on the pineal body, the parenchymatous cells of the organ are specific cells with a characteristic structure. They have long processes which extend for considerable distances and end in bulblike swellings in the interlobular connective tissue. In the center of the lobules, these processes radiate in all directions from the cells, while toward the periphery of the lobules the cells tend to become polarized in one or two processes. Occasionally, there are as many club-shaped ends of fibers in the center of the lobules as in the periphery; these may be considered evidences of atrophy. The specific elements hypertrophy greatly about the *sand granules* (Fig. 294, A) which develop in the pineal body. These parenchymatous cells arise from the same source as the neuroglia and nerve cells, but seem to be an intermediate cellular form.

It is generally believed that the pineal

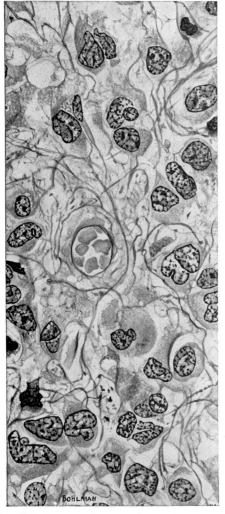

Fig. 295. Section of pineal body of man stained with hematoxylin and eosin, showing irregularly shaped cells and their processes. Note blood vessel in the center. Compare with Figure 296.

Fig. 296. Specifically impregnated section of pineal body of a young boy, showing, *C*, interlobular tissue, and, *D*, vessel with club-shaped processes of specific cells in its adventitia. Note parenchymatous cells and their claviform processes bordering on *C*. (After del Río-Hortega.)

body increases in size until about seven years of age. At this time involution is said to begin and to continue to fourteen years of age. It is manifested by an increase in the amount of neuroglia and by the development of hyaline changes in both the septa and the lobules. The so-called "brain-sand granules" (corpora arenacea) also begin to appear. These are laminated structures consisting mainly of phosphates and carbonates of calcium and magnesium.

The pineal body first appears at the beginning of the second month of gestation as a fold arising from the roof of the diencephalon before which is a collection of rounded cells. By the end of the sixth month, these have differentiated into neuroglia cells and pineal cells.

The function of the pineal body is unknown. Some authors regard the pineal body as a vestigial organ homologous to the pineal sense organ of the lower vertebrates. This is denied by others, who believe that the body is a gland of internal secretion and that its absence causes a marked increase in the rapidity of sexual development. Unfortunately, extirpation and injection of extracts of the organ have given inconstant and highly contradictory results. Typical secretory granules are not found in specific pineal cells.

REFERENCES

Bargmann, W.: Die Epiphysis cerebri. Handb. mikr. Anat. Menschen. von Möllendorff, 1943.

Gladstone, R. J., and Wakeley, C. P. G.: The Pineal Organ. London, 1940.

XX. THE SKIN

The skin covers the surface of the body and consists of two main layers, the surface epithelium or *epidermis* and the subjacent, connective tissue layer—the *corium* or *derma*. Beneath the latter is a looser connective tissue layer, the superficial fascia or *hypodermis*, which in many places is transformed into subcutaneous fatty tissue. The hypodermis is connected with underlying deep fasciae, aponeuroses or periosteum.

The skin is continuous with several mucous membranes through *mucocutaneous junctions*, the most important of which are the vermilion border of the lip, the vulva and the anus.

The skin protects the organism from injurious external influences, receives sensory impulses from the outside, excretes various substances and, in warm-blooded animals, helps to regulate the temperature of the body. The skin is provided with hairs, nails, and glands of various kinds.

On the free surface of the skin, in man, numerous ridges can be seen with the naked eye, which pass in various directions, cross one another in the form of a network, and frequently unite. On the soles, palms, and undersurfaces of the fingers and toes, in man and the primates, there is a regular pattern of parallel ridges which form complicated figures. This pattern undergoes marked individual variations, so that it is different in every person.

There is a sharp boundary between the epithelial and the connective tissue portions of the skin, but not between the derma and the hypodermis; here the fibers of one layer pass directly over into the other.

The surface of contact between the epidermis and the derma is uneven in most places. It appears as a straight line only on the forehead, the midline of the perineum and scrotum, and the external ear. In most of the skin of the body the outer portion of the derma is provided with a series of irregular ridges called *papillae*; into the spaces between them the lower layers of the epidermis intrude.

EPIDERMIS

The epidermis is a stratified squamous epithelium, the external layer of which hornifies. It is moistened by water only with difficulty and prevents the underlying tissues from drying; it thus serves as a protective layer.

The epidermis varies from 0.07 to 0.12 mm. in thickness on most parts of the body, although on the palms and the palmar surface of the fingers it may reach a thickness of 0.8 mm. and on the sole and toes of 1.4 mm. Continuous rubbing and pressure through heavy physical work cause a great thickening of the epidermis, especially of its horny layer. External mechanical causes are not the only factors, since it is well developed in the fetus, in the palms and soles.

Epidermis of the Palms and Soles. The structure of the epidermis is most typical in those places where it is thickest. Here, in sections perpendicular to the surface, four main layers can be distinguished: (1) the deep layer of Malpighi (*stratum germinativum* or *spinosum*) touching the derma; (2) the granular layer (*stratum granulosum*); (3) the clear layer (*stratum lucidum*); and (4) the horny layer (*stratum corneum*).

The *malpighian layer* (Fig. 298) is thicker between the dermal papillae than above them. The deepest or basal layer of cells, adjacent to the derma, are cylindrical and placed perpendicular to the surface of the skin; mitotic figures occur rather frequently.

The cells above these become polyhedral, and under the granular layer they are flattened. The surface of these cells is covered with thin spines which connect with similar spines of adjacent cells to form intercellular bridges (Fig. 299, y). The spines at the lower surface of the cylindrical layer of cells are finger-like processes which project into the connective tissue of the derma. The cytoplasm has a few mitochondria near the nucleus and numerous parallel bundles of fibrils. The fibrils pass through the intercellular bridges and penetrate rows of cells without interruption. Within each intercellu-

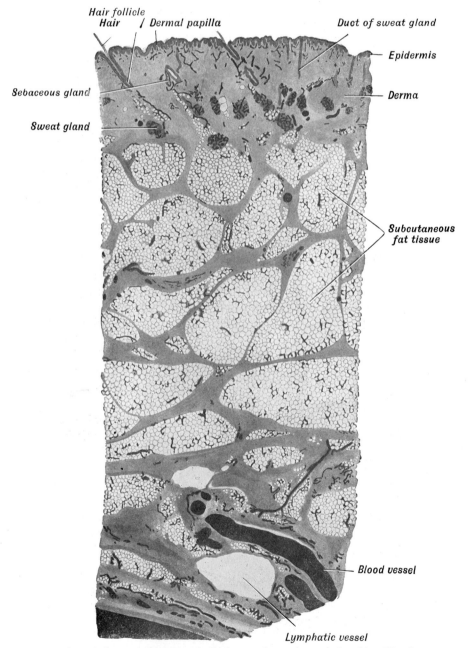

Fig. 297. Section through human thigh perpendicular to the surface of the skin. Blood vessels are injected and appear black. Low magnification. (A.A.M.)

lar bridge the fibril is thickened into a round or spindle-shaped granule.

The granular layer (Fig. 298) consists of three to five layers of flattened cells. Their cytoplasm, particularly in the vicinity of the nucleus, contains irregularly shaped granules of *keratohyalin*. Their origin has not been established. With the gradual increase in size and number of the granules, the nucleus disintegrates and becomes pale. At the same time the intercellular spaces become narrow and the bridges shorter and rather indistinct.

The *stratum lucidum* (Fig. 298) is formed by several layers of flattened, closely packed cells; in a section it appears as a pale, wavy stripe, in which the granules of keratohyalin have dissolved and become *eleidin*. Usually nothing remains of the nucleus in such cells.

The thick *stratum corneum* (Fig. 298) on the palms and soles consists of many layers

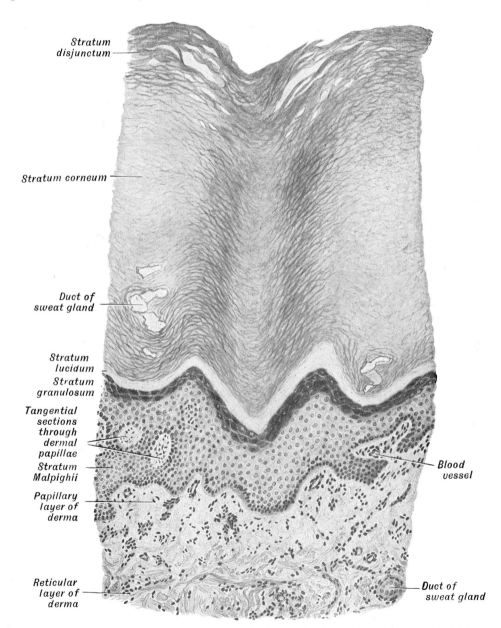

Fig. 298. Section of human sole; perpendicular to the free surface. 100 ×. (A.A.M.)

of cornified cells. Intercellular bridges are absent, and the spinous margins of the densely packed cells are in close contact. The mass which fills the cells of the horny layer is *keratin*, a product of the transformation of eleidin.

plantar skin of the cat he found mitoses slightly more numerous in the lower third of the spinous layer than in the basal layer. Both layers respond rapidly with an increased number of mitoses to mechanical stimulation of the skin in these areas.

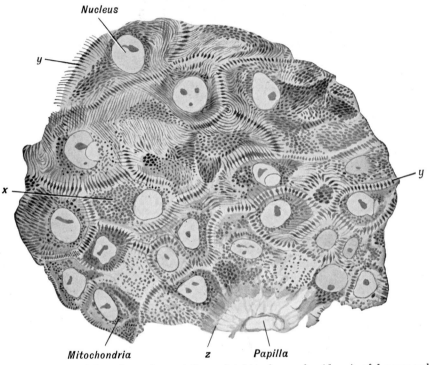

Fig. 299. Section, tangential to the surface, of the malpighian layer of epidermis of human palm, showing fibrils and intercellular bridges; z, scalloped, lower surface of epithelial cells connected with the derma. Intercellular bridges with swellings, in longitudinal section (y) and in cross section (x). Fixation Champy; Kull's stain (oil immersion). (A.A.M.)

The most peripheral layers of the stratum corneum are dried, horny plates which are constantly being desquamated (*stratum disjunctum*). The cells lost in this way are replaced by new ones from the lower layers. The number of mitotic figures in the malpighian layer corresponds with the intensity of desquamation in a given region.

Against the general view that mitosis in the skin occurs mainly in the basal layer of cells, Thuringer found that in the skin of the scalp and prepuce only 12 per cent of the mitoses were in the basal layer, with 30 per cent in the lower third, 46 per cent in the middle third and 12 per cent in the outer third of the spinous layer. In the palmar and

Epidermis of the Body. On the rest of the body the epidermis is thin and has a simpler structure. Two layers are always present—the stratum Malpighii and the stratum corneum. The granular layer usually consists of but one layer of cells (Fig. 300). Its frequent absence depends on the fact that the transformation of cells of the malpighian layer into those of the corneum does not proceed continuously, but occurs from time to time at different places. In contrast to what happens in the palms and soles, the epidermal cells in the other portions of the surface of the body become thin plates of keratin welded so closely together that they are hard to isolate.

The epidermis, entirely devoid of blood

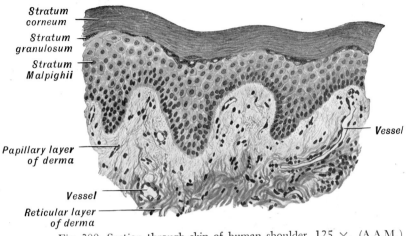

Fig. 300. Section through skin of human shoulder. 125 ×. (A.A.M.)

vessels, is nourished by the tissue fluid which penetrates the intercellular spaces of the malpighian layer from capillaries in the underlying connective tissue. Human skin, unlike that of practically all other vertebrates, blisters after exposure to thermal and certain chemical stimuli, such as the "blister" gases. This reaction is apparently made possible by the many layers of cells in human epidermis.

The color of the skin depends on three factors: its inherent color is predominantly yellow; the vascular bed gives a reddish hue; *melanin* is responsible for varying shades of brown. This pigment accumulates in varying amounts as fine granules within the cells of the stratum germinativum, particularly in its basal, cylindrical layer (Fig. 301, *Pb*). As these cells move toward the surface, the granular pigment gradually disappears, so that only a diffuse coloring is observed in the stratum corneum. The pigmentation of the skin of the Negro is due to the great amount of pigment in all the layers of the epidermis.

At the junction of the layer of pigmented basal epithelial cells with the derma, and projecting slightly into the latter, are branched pigment cells called "melanoblasts" (Fig. 301, *Mel*). The long axis of their nucleus is usually perpendicular to that of the basal cells, and their pigment-containing processes extend for great distances between the epidermal cells. These *melanoblasts* react positively and specifically with the "dopa" reagent—3, 4 dioxyphenylalanin—while the pigment cells of the malpighian layer and the *dermal*

chromatophores do not. Exposure to x-rays and ultraviolet light increases the "dopa" reaction in the melanoblasts. It has been suggested that the melanoblasts are specific cells that normally elaborate melanin for the epidermal cells.

Throughout the epidermis, but more frequently in its upper layers, peculiar black, star-shaped figures can be seen in gold chloride preparations. They are provided with long, irregular processes which penetrate the intercellular spaces and follow the intercellular outlines. They are the so-called *cells of Langerhans*. They have been considered, probably erroneously, as melanoblasts, nerve cells or lymphoid wandering cells by different investigators. It is not at all clear, however, that they are cells. No structural details can be seen in them in gold-impregnated sections, and no traces of them can be found in the usual histologic preparations.

Basement Membrane. Most authors now deny the presence of a basement membrane between epidermis and derma. The opinion that the tonofibrils of the epidermis are directly connected with the collagenous fibers of the derma has not been proved.

Mucocutaneous Junctions. These junctions differ in several respects from the skin and the mucous membranes to which they are joined. Their epithelium is thicker than that of the adjacent skin and more nearly resembles that of the mucosa. Normally, they contain no sweat or mucous glands, but often have superficially placed sebaceous glands. They are moistened by mucous glands within the orifices. As the lip has a thin stratum corneum and normally lacks a stratum granulosum, the underlying blood shines through and gives it a red color.

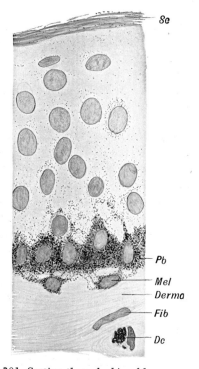

Fig. 301. Section through skin of human mammary papilla. *Sc*, Stratum corneum; *Pb*, pigmented basal cells of epidermis; *Mel*, melanoblast; *Fib*, fibroblast; *Dc*, dermal chromatophore. Silver nitrate, faintly counterstained with pyronin methyl green. 650 ×. (W. B.)

THE DERMA

The thickness of the derma cannot be measured exactly, because it passes over directly into the subcutaneous layer. The average thickness is approximately 1 to 2 mm.; it is less on the eyelids and the prepuce (up to 0.6 mm.), but reaches a thickness of 3 mm. or more on the soles and palms. On the ventral surface of the body and on the underside of the appendages it is generally thinner than on the dorsal and upper sides; it is thinner in women than in men.

The surface of the derma fused with the epidermis is usually uneven and covered with projecting ridges and papillae. This surface of the derma is soft and is called the *papillary layer*. The main dense portion of the derma is called the *reticular layer*. The two layers cannot be clearly separated (Fig. 298).

The reticular layer consists of bundles of collagenous fibers which form a dense felt-work; the bundles run in various directions (Fig. 59), but mainly more or less parallel to the surface; less frequently, approximately perpendicular bundles are found. In the papillary layer and its papillae the collagenous bundles are much thinner and more loosely arranged.

The elastic fibers of the derma form abundant, thick networks between the collagenous bundles and are condensed about the hair follicles and the sweat and sebaceous glands. In the papillary layer they are much thinner and form a continuous fine network under the epithelium in the papillae. In the cheeks, however, the elastic network immediately under the epithelium is particularly dense. The cells of the derma are the same as those of the subcutaneous layer (p. 54) and are more abundant in the papillary than in the reticular layer.

Under the epithelium, a few connective tissue pigment cells, *dermal chromatophores*, are scattered (Fig. 301, *Dc*). Their pigment granules are much larger and more irregular than those in the melanoblasts and epidermal cells. The dermal chromatophores are normally rare and are numerous only in definite places, as around the anus. Whether these pigmented cells of the derma are related to the pigment in the epidermis is not established. These chromatophores probably do not elaborate the pigment which they contain. In the skin of the ape, in the so-called "Mongolian spots" and in certain tumors, called "blue nevi," *dermal melanoblasts* appear. These cells give a positive "dopa" reaction, in contrast to the "dopa" negative dermal chromatophores.

Within the deep parts of the reticular layer in the mammary papillae, the penis, perineum and scrotum, numerous smooth muscle fibers are collected into a netlike layer. Such portions of the skin become wrinkled during contraction of these muscles. Smooth muscles are also connected with the hairs (p. 319). In many places in the skin of the face, cross-striated muscle fibers terminate in the derma. At various levels of the derma are the hair follicles, sweat and sebaceous glands, as well as blood vessels, nerves and many nerve endings.

Hypodermis. The subcutaneous layer consists of loose connective tissue and is a continuation of the derma. Its collagenous and a few elastic fibers pass directly into those of the derma and run in all directions, mainly parallel to the surface of the skin. Where the skin is flexible, the fibers are few; where it is closely attached to the underlying parts, as on the soles and palms, they are thick and numerous.

Depending on the portion of the body and the nutrition of the organism, varying numbers of fat cells develop in the subcutaneous layer (Fig. 297). These are also found in groups in the deep layers of the derma. The fatty tissue of the subcutaneous layer on the abdomen may reach a thickness of 3 cm. or more, while in the eyelids and penis the subcutaneous layer never contains fat cells.

The subcutaneous layer is penetrated everywhere by large blood vessels and nerve trunks and contains many nerve endings.

HAIRS

The hairs are horny threads which develop from the epidermis. They vary in length from several millimeters to 1.5 meters and from 0.005 to 0.6 mm. in thickness. They are distributed in varying density on the surface of the skin, except on the palms and soles, the lower and lateral surfaces of the fingers and toes, the upper surface of the third phalanx of all the fingers, the lips, the glans penis, the prepuce, and the internal surface of the labia majora.

Each hair arises in a tubular invagination of the skin, the *hair follicle*, the walls of which are composed of epidermis and derma. Into the bottom of the follicle projects the connective tissue papilla. The *root* of the hair develops into the hair *shaft*, the free end of which protrudes beyond the surface of the skin (Fig. 302).

One or more sebaceous glands are connected with each hair. They are usually located in the obtuse angle between the hair follicle and the surface of the skin, and open into the *neck* of the follicle. Here one end of a smooth muscle is attached to the middle of the connective tissue sheath of the follicle, while the other end disappears in the papillary layer of the derma.

The shaft of the hair is roughly cylindrical and appears as a circle or oval or sometimes angular in cross section. The shape of the

hair is not a reliable indication of the race of the person. The natural, free end of the shaft of each hair gradually thins down into a point.

The epidermis, which extends inside the hair follicle as far as the opening of the sebaceous gland, i.e., the neck of the follicle, directly adjoins the shaft of the hair and consists of the usual malpighian, granular and corneum layers. Below the neck, the corneum layer disappears, and so does the granular layer shortly afterward. As a result, in the deepest portion of the hair follicle, only the malpighian layer remains, where it forms the *external root sheath*. The *internal root sheath* grows upward with the hair from the base of the follicle to its neck, where it terminates with a free edge. The root and the two sheaths blend at the surface of the papilla into a mass of undifferentiated epithelial cells, the *matrix* of the hair.

Structure of the Hair. The hair is covered with the *cuticle*, which consists of thin, cornified epithelial cells with wavy outlines. These are arranged like shingles, their free margins directed toward the end of the hair.

The main mass of the hair is a dense, horny substance, containing varying amounts of pigment; air vacuoles occupy rows in the former intercellular spaces.

The horny tissue and the cuticle form the hairs on the head. In many of the thick hairs (in beards and eyebrows) there is, in addition a *medulla*, composed of shrunken, cornified cells separated by large amounts of air and connected by bridges.

The color of the hair depends on its content of pigment and air. The larger the amount of pigment, the darker is the hair. Light hairs appear still lighter, owing to the presence of a medulla filled with air. The loss of pigment makes the hair look gray. If this happens in hairs rich in medullary substance, the hair acquires a bright, silvery appearance.

Hair Follicle. The connective tissue portion of the wall of the hair follicle is a condensation of the derma and is made up of three layers. The external, poorly outlined layer consists of longitudinal collagenous and elastic fibers and a few fibroblasts. The thick, middle layer is formed by circular fibers and fibroblasts. The internal layer is a basement membrane between the epithelial and connective tissues (glassy membrane).

The *papilla* at the bottom of the follicle is an outgrowth of the connective tissue sheath. It is usually egg-shaped, with a thin

in which mitoses are frequent. These cells grow upward and form the internal root sheath and the hair. In the developing hair they become long, thin, pigmented spindles, and bundles of fibrils appear within them

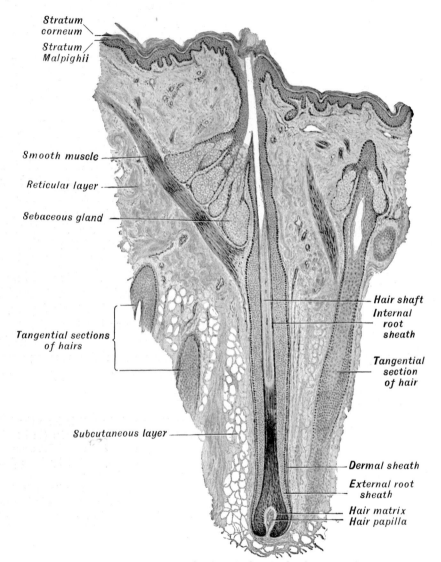

Fig. 302. Scalp of a man. Root of a hair in longitudinal section. 32 ×. (After Schaffer.)

pedicle. Its cellular connective tissue contains capillaries and is usually devoid of elastic fibers. Sometimes it contains pigment cells, particularly in dark-haired people. The glassy membrane becomes much thinner on its surface.

The surface of the papilla is covered with a continuous epithelial mass, the *hair matrix*,

and pass from cell to cell. At the boundary between the lower and middle thirds of the root, they become cornified elements without the participation of a granular substance like keratohyalin or trichohyalin.

In hairs with a medulla, the cells at the tip of the papilla move forward as a column of polyhedral cells interconnected by bridges.

Then, granules of trichohyalin appear in them. Higher up, these granules disappear and the cells become cornified, shrunken bodies between which air accumulates.

The cuticle of the hair develops from cells slightly below the middle of the side of the papilla. They gradually widen and overlap one another with their free margins to the outside. The nuclei disappear, and the cells become homogeneous, horny scales, closely welded to the cortical substance of the hair.

Internal Root Sheath. The next layers of cells down the slope of the papilla move upward and form the three layers of the internal root sheath. This, too, grows upward, but disintegrates below the opening of the sebaceous gland into the follicle.

The innermost layer, the *cuticle of the internal root sheath*, like the cuticle of the hair, consists of thin, horny scales which overlap, so that their free margins are toward the bottom of the hair sac. They thus abut the margins of the scales of the hair cuticle which are directed toward the outside.

The cells which form the second layer, or *layer of Huxley*, move from the lower part of the surface of the papilla, and are connected with one another by bridges. At the level of the summit of the papilla they develop trichohyalin granules which remain for a distance of forty to fifty cells, but disappear as the cells cornify. At the middle third of the follicle, the layer of Huxley consists of one to three layers of cornified cells.

The outermost layer (*of Henle*) consists of a single layer of elongated, horny bodies connected by intercellular bridges. Their flat, outer surface is closely welded to the external sheath. In this layer trichohyalin appears about the middle of the papilla, but disappears at the level of its summit.

External Root Sheath. The external root sheath at the neck of the papilla is one layer of flat cells. Moving upward, it becomes two-layered at the level of the middle of the papilla, and further on stratified. Since intercellular bridges were discovered between the two sheaths, it is possible that the elements of the external sheath gradually move toward the exterior from the bottom of the hair sac.

Muscle of the Hair. The hair muscle, the *arrector pili*, is a band of smooth muscle cells connected with its attachment by networks of elastic fibers. When this

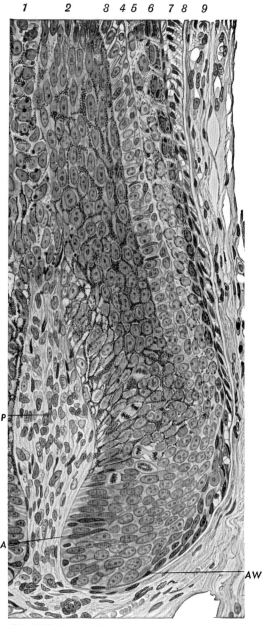

Fig. 303. Longitudinal section through a hair from head of a man twenty-two years old. *1*, Medulla; *2*, cortex; *3*, hair cuticle; *4*, inner sheath cuticle; *5*, Huxley's layer; *6*, Henle's layer; *7*, external root sheath; *8*, glassy membrane; *9*, connective tissue of the hair follicle; *AW*, external root sheath at the bulb; *A*, matrix; *P*, papilla. 350 ×. (After Hoepke.)

muscle contracts (from cold, and the like) it moves the hair into a more vertical position and depresses the skin, while the region around the hair is lifted. This is responsible for the so-called "goose flesh." By pressing on the base of the sebaceous gland, its contraction

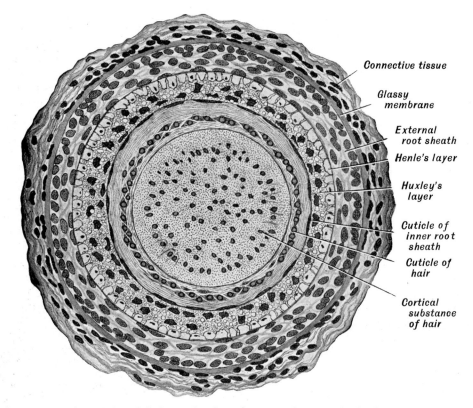

Connective tissue

Glassy
membrane

External
root sheath

Henle's layer

Huxley's
layer

Cuticle of
inner root
sheath

Cuticle of
hair

Cortical
substance
of hair

Fig. 304. Cross section through hair follicle, in the skin of a pig embryo, at the level where Henle's layer is completely cornified and Huxley's layer contains granules of trichohyalin. 375 ×.

liberates a fatty material which lubricates the shaft of the hair.

Replacement of Hairs. Throughout life, even in the embryo, hairs undergo replacement. The hair of every part of the body has a definite period of growth—the hairs of the head two to four years, the eyelashes three to five months. In man this change goes on continuously and passes unnoticed; in those mammals which renew their hair twice a year the process of replacement is rapid.

When the period of growth of the hair approaches its end, multiplication of the undifferentiated cells at the bottom of the hair sac in the matrix slows down and finally stops. The base of the shaft and the root gradually become thinner. The growth from below of the layers of the internal sheath stops. The elements which cover the summit of the papilla all become cornified spindles, and the hair becomes club-shaped. The root separates from the papilla, moves toward the neck of the follicle, and either falls out or is pulled out. The papilla becomes smaller and, according to some, atrophies and disappears.

Usually, even before the old hair drops out, the primordium of a new one is formed in the same hair sac. The epithelium of the matrix begins to multiply; the lower portion of the follicle becomes thicker and longer. The papilla enlarges, or, as some believe, a new

one is formed, and invaginates the epithelium at the bottom of the follicle. The cavity of the follicle is soon filled with a mass of young epithelial elements. Inside this mass a layer of hornified cells, filled with trichohyalin, becomes visible; this has the shape of a hollow cone opened in the direction of the papilla. This layer represents the internal root sheath of the new hair. The cells beneath this then form the substance of the hair proper.

Rats fed a diet deficient in zinc are reported to show hyperkeratinization of the skin with loss of hair follicles, although the sebaceous glands persist.

NAILS

The nails are horny plates on the dorsal surface of the terminal phalanges of the fingers and toes. The surface of the skin covered by them is the *nail bed*. It is surrounded laterally and proximally by a fold of skin, the *nail wall*. The slit between the wall and the bed is the *nail groove*. The proximal edge of the nail plate is the *root* of the nail. The visible part of the nail plate is surrounded by the nail wall and is called the *body of the nail*; the distal portion comes forward freely and is gradually worn off or cut off. The nail is semitransparent and shows the underlying tissue rich in blood vessels. Near the root the nail has a whitish color; this portion, the *lunula*, is usually covered by the proximal portion of the nail fold; it frequently appears only on the thumb.

The nail plate consists of closely welded, horny scales: cornified epithelial cells so arranged that in section the nail appears striated.

The *nail fold* has the structure of skin with all its layers. Turning inward into the nail groove, it loses its papillae, and the epidermis loses its horny, clear and granular layers. Under the proximal fold, the horny layer spreads onto the free surface of the nail body as the eponychium (Fig. 305). The stratum lucidum and the stratum granulosum also reach far inside the groove, but do not continue along the lower surface of the nail plate. On the surface of the nail bed only the malpighian layer of the epidermis is present.

In the nail bed the derma is directly fused with the periosteum of the phalanx. The surface of the derma under the proximal edge of the nail is provided with rather low papillae, but under the distal half of the lunula this surface is quite smooth. At the distal margin of the lunula, longitudinal, parallel ridges project

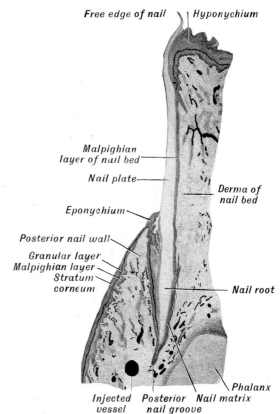

Fig. 305. Longitudinal section of nail of a newborn infant. Very low power. (A.A.M.)

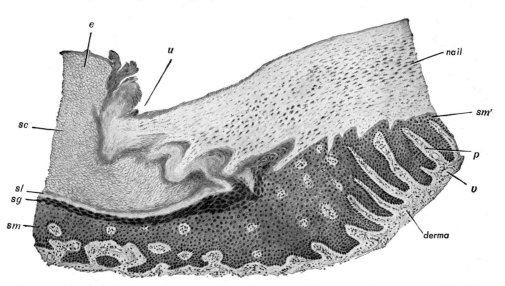

Fig. 306. Cross section of lateral edge of a nail and its surrounding parts: *d*, derma of nail bed; *e*, lateral nail wall; *n*, nail plate; *p*, dermal papilla; *sc*, stratum corneum of epidermis; *sg*, stratum granulosum; *sl*, stratum lucidum; *sm*, malpighian layer of epidermis; *sm'*, malpighian layer of nail bed; *u*, lateral nail groove; *v*, vessel. Higher power than in Figure 305. (A.A.M.)

instead of papillae. The boundary between the epithelium and the derma of the nail bed in a perpendicular section is, therefore, scalloped (Fig. 306), while it is smooth in longitudinal sections. Beyond the free edge of the nail the dermal ridges are replaced by cylindrical papillae.

The epithelium of the nail bed distal to the lunula retains the typical structure of the malpighian layer. The epithelium is thicker between the ridges of the derma than over them. The upper layer of cells which touches the substance of the nail is separated from it in places by an even line, while in others it is jagged. Under the free edge of the nail the usual horny layer again begins; it is thickened at this place and is called *hyponychium* (Fig. 305).

The epithelium which lines the proximal portion of the nail bed and corresponds roughly with the lunula is particularly thick; distally and upward it gradually passes over into the substance of the nail plate. Here the new formation of the nail substance proceeds; accordingly, this region of the epithelium is called the *nail matrix* (Fig. 305). The cells of the deepest layer are cylindrical, and mitoses can be observed frequently in them. Above these are six to ten layers of

Hair shaft

Sebaceous Connec- Indifferent
cells   tive   cells
           tissue

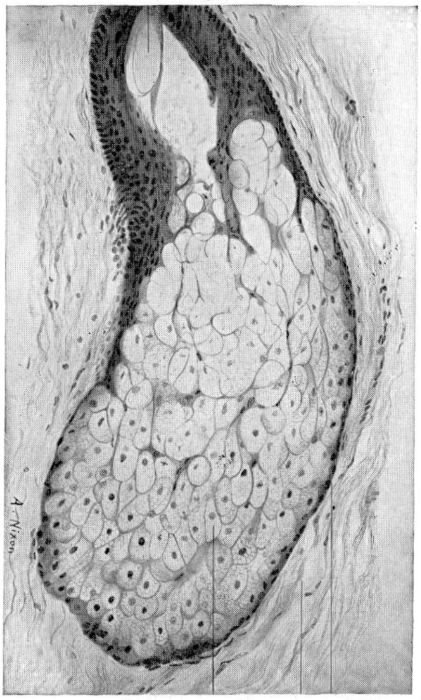

Fig. 307. Section of human sebaceous gland. 120 ×.

polyhedral cells joined by five to twelve layers of flatter cells; this entire mass is penetrated by parallel fibrils of a special "onychogenic" substance. On passing into the proximal edge of the nail plate, these cells cornify and become homogeneous.

As the new formation of the nail takes place in the matrix, the nail moves forward. Most authors deny the participation of the epithelium of the other portions of the nail bed in the formation of the nail substance, and believe that the nail simply glides forward over this region.

GLANDS OF THE SKIN

In man the glands of the skin include the sebaceous, sweat and mammary glands. The last are described in a separate chapter.

Sebaceous Glands. The sebaceous glands are scattered over the surface of the skin (except in the palms and soles). They lie in the derma, and their excretory duct opens into the neck of a hair sac. When several glands are connected with one hair, they lie at the same level. On the lips, about the corners of the mouth, on the glans penis and the internal fold of the prepuce, on the labia minora, and on the mammary papilla the sebaceous glands are independent of hairs and open directly on the surface of the skin; to this category also belong the meibomian glands of the eyelids. The sebaceous glands in mucocutaneous junctions are more superficial than those associated with hairs.

The sebaceous glands vary from 0.2 to 2 mm. in diameter; the largest, such as those on the nose, are not accessories of the hairs; on the contrary, each is provided with a small hair.

The secretory portions of the sebaceous glands are rounded sacs (alveoli). As a rule, several adjacent alveoli form a mass like a bunch of grapes, and all of them open into a short duct; in this way a simple branched gland results. Much less frequently, only one alveolus is present. In the meibomian glands of the eyelids there is one long, straight duct, from which a row of alveoli projects.

The ducts of sebaceous glands are lined by stratified squamous epithelium continuous with the external root sheath of the hair or the malpighian layer of the epidermis.

The wall of the alveoli is formed by a basement membrane supported by a thin layer of fibrillar connective tissue. Along the internal surface is a single layer of thin cells with round nuclei. Toward the center of the alveoli a few cells cornify, but most of them become larger, polyhedral, and gradually filled with fat droplets. The central portion of the alveoli is filled with large cells distended with fat droplets. The nuclei gradually shrink and then disappear, and the cells break down into fatty detritus mixed with horny scales. This is the oily secretion of the gland, and it is excreted onto the hair or upon the surface of the epidermis.

In sebaceous glands, the secretion results from the destruction of the epithelial cells and is, therefore, of the *holocrine* type; it is followed by a regenerative multiplication of epithelial elements. In the body of the gland, mitoses are rare in the cells lying on the basement membrane; they are numerous, however, in the cells close to the walls of the excretory ducts, whence the new cells move into the secretory regions.

Sweat Glands. The sweat glands are distributed along the surface of the skin, with the exception of the margins of the lips, the glans penis and the nail bed. They are simple, coiled, tubular glands; i.e., the secretory portion is a simple tube folded by several unequal twists into a ball, and the excretory duct is a narrow, unbranched tube (Fig. 308).

The mass of the secretory portion is located in the derma and measures 03. to 0.4 mm. in diameter. In the armpit and about the anus the bodies of some of the sweat glands may reach 3 to 5 mm. in diameter. In these regions they are red and are located deep in the subcutaneous layer.

At the transition of the secretory portion into the duct the tube suddenly becomes thin. Toward the surface, through the derma, the duct is slightly twisted and curved. In passing through the malpighian layer and in particular through the horny layer of the epidermis, it is spirally twisted. On the palms

and soles and on the ventral surface of the fingers, the rows of ducts open on the ridges with funnel-shaped openings which can be seen easily with a magnifying glass.

The walls of the secretory portion rest on a thick basement membrane. Directly inside

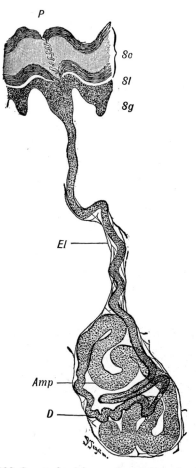

Fig. 308. Sweat gland from volar surface of an index finger. The drawing was combined from sections and a teased preparation; *P*, Sweat pore; *Sc*, stratum corneum; *Sl*, stratum lucidum; *Sg*, stratum germinativum; *El*, elastic tissue surrounding the duct; *Amp*, ampulla; *D*, sudoriferous duct. 45 ×. (Slightly modified after von Brunn.)

it are spindle-shaped cells 30 to 90 microns in length, with their long axis tangential to that of the glandular tube. They have an elongate nucleus, and fibrils. It is supposed that these "myo-epithelial" cells, by contracting, help to discharge the secretion. They are particularly numerous and are highly developed in the large sweat glands of the axillary and perianal regions.

The truncated pyramidal cells which excrete sweat form a single layer upon the myoepithelial cells At the base is a rather large round nucleus; the cytoplasm contains mito-

tory duct is devoid of a wall of its own and is simply an intercellular channel surrounded by concentrically arranged epidermal cells. The latter, in the malpighian layer, have fine, keratohyalin granules in their cytoplasm (Fig. 310).

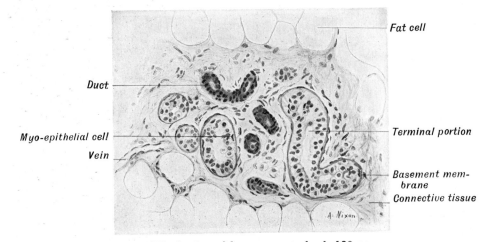

Fig. 309. Section of human sweat gland. 120 ×.

chondria and, near the lumen, a number of secretory vacuoles, varying with the functional state of the cell. Sometimes there are also fat droplets, glycogen and pigment granules. The pigment appears in the secretion of certain sweat glands, as in the axilla. The free surface of the cells often shows protrusions of protoplasm, which are believed to separate and become a part of the secretion (apocrine glands).

Between these glandular cells are typical secretory capillaries. The caliber and the shape of the free lumen of the secretory portion fluctuate greatly with the functional state of the gland.

The glandular tube, in passing over into the excretory duct, suddenly becomes much narrower, the lumen acquires a simple, slit-like or starlike shape, while the myo-epithelial and glandular cells on the basement membrane are replaced by a double-layered, thin epithelium. The cells of the external layer have comparatively large nuclei and rather abundant mitochondria; the free surface of the cytoplasm of the cells of the internal layer is condensed and refractile.

In the epidermis the lumen of the excre-

In certain parts of the skin the sweat glands have a peculiar arrangement and function. Such are the *glands which produce cerumen* in the external auditory meatus. They reach a considerable size and extend up to the perichondrium; their secretory portions branch, and the excretory ducts, which sometimes also branch, may open together with the ducts of the adjacent sebaceous glands into the hair sacs of the fine hairs. In the terminal portions are highly developed smooth muscle cells; the glandular cells located upon them are particularly rich in lipid-containing pigment granules.

Moll's glands of the margin of the eyelid are also a special kind of sweat gland with terminal portions which do not form a ball, but are only irregularly twisted and provided with a wide lumen. The excretory ducts open freely or into the hair sacs of the eyelashes.

The secretion of the sweat glands is not the same everywhere. The true sweat, a transparent, watery liquid, is excreted mainly by the small sweat glands, while a thicker secretion of complex, unknown composition is produced by those of the axilla and about the anus. In women the apocrine sweat glands of the axilla show periodic changes with the menstrual cycle. These changes consist mainly in enlargement of the epithelial cells and of the lumens of the glands in the premenstrual period, followed by regressive changes during the period of menstruation (Fig. 311).

Blood and Lymphatic Vessels of the Skin. The arteries which supply the skin are located in the subcutaneous layer. Their branches, reaching upward, form a network (rete cutaneum) (Fig. 312) on the boundary line between the derma and the hypodermis; this is parallel to the surface. From one side of this network, branches are given off which nourish the subcutaneous stratum with its fat cells, sweat glands, and the deeper portions of the hair sacs. From the other side of this network, vessels enter the derma; at the boundary between the papillary and reticular layers they form the denser, subpapillary network or the rete subpapillare. (Fig. 312). This gives off thin branches which enter the papillae and form networks inside them.

The veins which collect the blood from the capillaries in the papillae form the first network of thin veins immediately beneath the papillae. Then follow three flat networks of gradually enlarging veins on the boundary line between the papillary and reticular layers. In the middle section of the derma and also at the boundary between the derma and the subcutaneous tissue, the venous network is on the same level as the arterial rete cutaneum. Into this network the veins of the sebaceous and the sweat glands enter. From the deeper network the large, independent, subcutaneous veins pass, as well as the deep veins accompanying the arteries.

Each hair sac has its own blood vessels. It is supplied with blood from three sources: from a special small artery which gives off a capillary network into the papilla, from the rete subpapillare toward the sides of the hair sac, and from several other small arteries which form a dense capillary network in the connective tissue layer of the follicle.

There is a dense network of capillaries outside the basement membrane of the sebaceous and, in particular, of the sweat glands.

The skin is rich in lymphatic vessels. In the papillary layer they form a dense, flat meshwork of lymphatic capillaries. They begin in the papillae as networks or blind outgrowths which are always deeper than the blood vessels. From this peripheral network, branches pass to the deeper network, which lies on the boundary between the derma and the hypodermis, under the rete cutaneum; it has much wider meshes, and its vessels are provided with valves. From the deeper network large, subcutaneous lymphatic vessels originate and follow the blood vessels. Lymphatic vessels are not connected with the hairs or glands of the skin.

Nerves of the Skin. The skin, with its accessories, serves as an organ for receiving impulses from the external environment; it is accordingly abundantly supplied with sensory nerves. In addition, it contains nerves which supply the blood vessels, muscles, and the like.

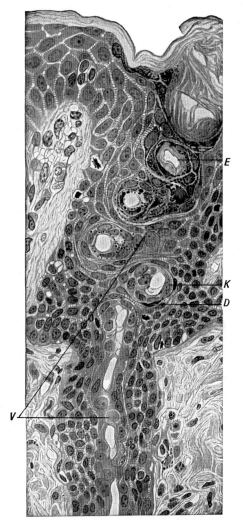

Fig. 310. Section through skin from the head of a man twenty-two years old. The end of the excretory duct of a sweat gland: E, eleidin; K, keratohyalin; D, degenerating cells; V, hypertrophic cells. 600 ×. (Drawing by Vierling, after Hoepke.)

In the subcutaneous stratum are rather thick nerve bundles which form networks composed mainly of myelinated and some nonmyelinated fibers. The branches given off by this reticulum form, in the derma, several new thin plexuses. Among them the network on the boundary between the reticular and papillary layers stands out clearly, as does also the subepithelial one.

In all the layers of the hypodermis, derma, and epidermis are many different kinds of nerve endings. These are discussed in the section on the Nerve Endings. Among them, the sensory endings probably are all connected with the craniospinal myelinated fibers; the nonmyelinated fibers lead to the blood vessels, smooth muscles and glands. The abundant nerves of

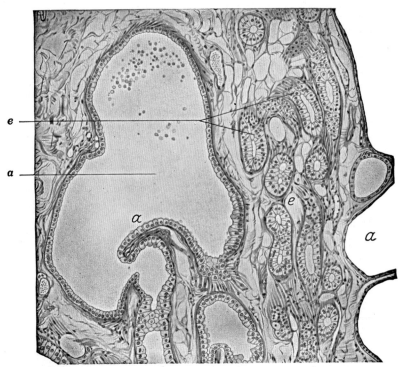

Fig. 311. Axillary glands, from a woman thirty-seven years old, during the premenstruum. *a*, Greatly enlarged glands which change with the menstrual cycle and, *e*, glands which do not change. Resorcin-fuchsin stain for elastic fibers. (Preparation of Loescke.) 110 ×. (After Hoepke.)

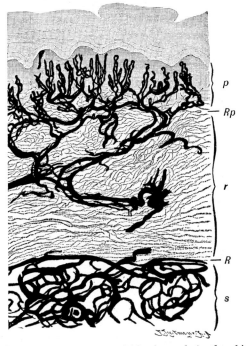

Fig. 312. Distribution of blood vessels in the skin. *s*, Subcutaneous tissue; *r*, reticular layer of derma; *p*, papillary layer of derma; *R*, rete cutaneum; *Rp*, rete subpapillare. (Modified slightly after von Brunn.)

the hair undoubtedly play an important part in the reception of tactile stimuli.

Histogenesis of the Skin and of Its Accessories. The epidermis develops from the ectoderm, while the derma arises from the mesenchyme.

Epidermis. The epidermis in the human embryo, during the first two months, is a double-layered epithelium. The basal layer, which lies on the mesenchyme, consists of cuboidal or cylindrical cells which multiply energetically. The peripheral layer consists of flat cells which are constantly formed anew from the elements of the deeper layer.

Beginning with the third month, the epidermis becomes three-layered. The new intermediate layer above the basal cells consists of polygonal cells which increase in number and become interconnected by intercellular bridges. At the end of the third month, in the peripheral portions of the intermediate layer, cornification begins and leads to the formation of the layers found in the adult. The horny scales are desquamated and form part of the vernix caseosa. Pigment granules, even in heavily pigmented races, usually appear in the deep cells of the malpighian layer only after birth.

The irregularities on the lower surface of the epidermis arise at the end of the third month on the inner surfaces of the fingers, palms and soles as parallel ridges protruding into the derma; from the beginning they show a characteristic pattern. From them sweat glands develop. Protruding, longitudinal cushions corresponding to the ridges are formed on the external free surface of the epidermis.

Derma. The derma and hypodermis consist during the first month and a half of mesenchyme with wandering cells. From the second month on, the fibrillar interstitial substance appears. Elastic fibers appear later. In still later stages, the mesenchyme divides into a peripheral dense layer with a compact arrangement of its elements—the derma—and the deep loose layer, the future subcutaneous layer. In the derma, in turn, the peripheral papillary layer differentiates.

Hair. In man, hair first appears in the eyebrows and on the chin and upper lip, at the end of the second month. At first, in the deep layer of the epidermis, a group of cylindrical, dividing cells appear. These grow into the underlying connective tissue and produce a gradually elongating epithelial cylinder. This is the primordium of a hair follicle, the so-called "hair germ;" it is rounded and slightly flattened on its end. Under the latter an accumulation of condensed connective tissue appears early. From it the hair papilla forms and protrudes into the epithelial mass of the bulb (or germ). The epithelial cells at the surface of the connective tissue papilla represent the matrix of the future hair. The connective tissue which surrounds the bulb later forms the connective tissue portions of the hair sac. On the surface of the epithelial hair bulb, two projections arise. The upper represents the primordium of the sebaceous gland; its central cells early undergo a fatty transformation. The lower protuberance is located at the place of attachment to the hair sac of the arrector pili muscle.

In the mass of the epithelium which forms the hair primordium, there differentiates a layer of rapidly cornifying cells. This layer has the shape of a hollow cone open toward the papilla; it is the primordium of the internal root sheath, in which Henle's layer is the first to appear. The mass of the cells on top of the papilla represents the primordium of the shaft itself and becomes cornified a little later. The layer of epithelium which remains on the outside of the sheath of Henle becomes the external root sheath. The shaft of the new hair elongates, owing to the multiplication of cells of the matrix on the summit of the papilla, and perforates the top of the hollow cone of Henle's sheath. The tip of the hair moves upward, pierces the epidermis, and protrudes above the surface of the skin.

Nails. The development of the nails begins in the third month by the formation, on the back of the terminal phalanx of each finger, of a flat area, the *primary nail field.* This is surrounded by a fold of the skin. In the region of the nail the epithelium has three or four layers. The true nail substance is laid down during the fifth month, and without the participation of keratohyalin, in the portion of the nail bed near the proximal nail groove. Here the deep layer of the epidermis is transformed into the nail matrix, and its cells are penetrated by the fibrils of onychogenic substance; they become flat, adjoin one another closely,

and give rise to the true nail plate. In the beginning it is still thin and is entirely buried in the epidermis of the nail field or bed. It gradually moves in the distal direction. The layers of epidermis which cover the plate eventually desquamate.

Sweat Glands. The development of the sweat glands in man proceeds independently of the hairs in most places of the skin. The first primordia appear during the fifth month on the palms and soles and the lower surface of the fingers. At first they are similar to the primordia of the hairs. An epithelial shaft with a terminal thickening grows into the underlying connective tissue. But, unlike that about the hairs, the connective tissue here does not condense about the epithelium. The shaft gradually elongates and becomes cylindrical, and its lower portion curls in the form of a ball. Beginning with the seventh month, an irregular lumen forms in this lower portion which constitutes the secretory part; along the course of the future excretory duct another lumen develops and later unites with the former. In the secretory portion the epithelium around the lumen forms two layers, which differentiate into an external layer of myo-epithelial elements and into an internal layer of glandular cells.

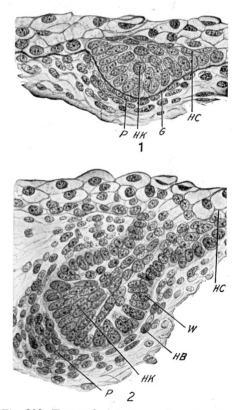

Fig. 313. Two early hair primordia of the frontal skin of a three months' embryo. *1,* First primordium; *G,* border of the derma; *HC,* hair canal cells; *HK,* hair germ; *P,* primordium of the papilla. *2,* slightly later stage; *HB,* primordium of the dermal hair sheath; *W,* external root sheath. 740 ×. (After Schaffer.)

REFERENCES

Becker, W. S.: Melanin Pigmentation. Arch. Dermat. & Syph., 16:259, 1927.

Cowdry, E. V., and Thompson, H. C., Jr.: The Localization of Maximum Cell Division in Epidermis. Anat. Rec., 88:403, 1944.

Danforth, C. H.: Physiology of Human Hair. Physiol. Rev., 19:94, 1939.

Felsher, Z.: Studies on the Adherence of the Epidermis to the Corium. Proc. Soc. Exper. Biol. & Med., 62:213, 1946.

Hoepke, H.: Die Haut. Handb. d. mikr. Anat. (v. Möllendorff). Berlin, 1927, Vol. 3, Pt. 1.

Kneberg, M.: Improved Technique for Hair Examination. Am. J. Phys. Anthropol., 20:51, 1935.

Masson, P.: Les glomus cutanés de l'homme. Bull. Soc. française de Dermatol. et de Syphil., 42:1174, 1935.

Pinkus, F.: Die normale Anatomie der Haut. Handb. d. Haut- u. Geschlechtskrankheiten, (1), 77, 1927.

Thuringer, J. M.: The Mitotic Index of fthe Palmar and Plantar Epidermis in Response to Stimulation. J. Invest. Dermatol., 2:313, 1939.

Trotter, Mildred: The Hair, in Cowdry's Special Cytology. 2d ed. New York, (1), 41, 1932.

Zimmermann, A. A., and Cornbleet, T.: The Development of Epidermal Pigmentation in the Negro Fetus. J. Invest. Dermatol., 11:383, 1948.

XXI. THE ORAL CAVITY AND ASSOCIATED STRUCTURES

GENERAL REMARKS ON THE DIGESTIVE SYSTEM

The digestive system is a long, winding tube which begins with the lips and ends with the anus. On its way through this tract the food undergoes complex mechanical and chemical changes. It is minced and ground by the teeth, is forwarded through the tube by the contraction of its muscular walls, and is digested by the secretions of the various parts of the alimentary system and its auxiliary glands. A part of the digested food is absorbed by the walls of the intestine and passes into the circulation, which carries it into the tissues of the organism; the residue is eliminated as feces.

The digestive tract consists of the following successive parts: mouth, pharynx, esophagus, stomach, small intestine, large intestine, and rectum. The functional condition of one segment causes certain functional changes in the following; thus the regular sequence of the processes necessary for the digestion of food is assured.

In the embryo the entoderm is transformed into the epithelial structures of the alimentary canal; the visceral mesoderm gives rise to its connective and muscular tissues. In the adult the inner surface of the wall of the digestive tube is lined by a *mucous membrane*. It consists of a superficial layer of epithelium and of a layer of connective tissue, the *lamina propria*. The wall of the tube contains smooth muscles which form the *muscularis externa* (see Fig. 314).

In most parts of the digestive tube the outer limit of the mucous membrane is marked by a thin, muscular layer, the *muscularis mucosae*. Between it and the muscularis externa is a layer of loose connective tissue, the *tela submucosa*. Where the muscularis mucosae is absent, the lamina propria gradually passes into the submucosa.

In the adult the mucous membrane forms numerous outgrowths which increase the surface of the epithelium. The mucous membrane of the mouth forms the teeth. The mucous membrane is provided with many invaginations, the *glands* or *crypts*. They are lined by epithelium which continues into them from the surface. Some of them elaborate liquids which split the food into its simple chemical constituents—digestion—while others produce mucus which lubricates the surface of the mucous membrane. Some of the glands remain confined to the thickness of the mucous membrane. Others grow to such an extent that they become separate organs, connected with the epithelial surface from which they originated by long excretory ducts. In the oral cavity, esophagus and rectum, the wall of the digestive tube is surrounded by a layer of dense connective tissue which attaches it to the neighboring organs. The outer surface of the stomach and intestines, which are suspended in the peritoneal cavity by the mesenteries, is covered with a serous membrane which permits these viscera to move freely in the cavity. The wall of the digestive tube is richly provided with blood vessels which bring nutritive materials and oxygen, as well as the raw materials necessary for the secretory activity. These vessels carry a large part of the absorbed products of digestion from the mucous membrane of the small intestine to the rest of the body. The remainder of the absorbed products enter the lymphatics of the intestines. The wall

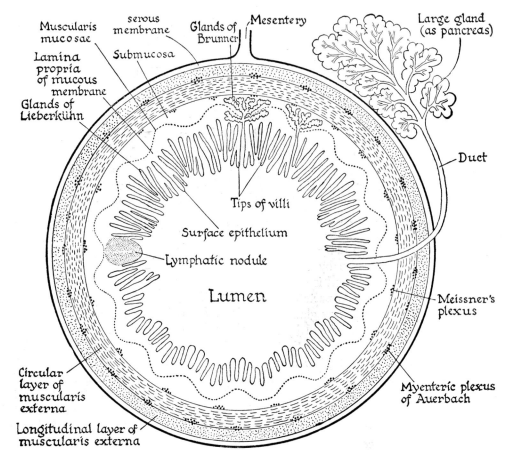

Fig. 314. Diagram of cross section of intestinal tract. In the upper half of the drawing the mucous membrane is provided with glands and villi; in the lower half it contains only glands.

of the digestive tract contains an intricate system of sympathetic nervous ganglia and plexuses which regulate the movements of the tube.

THE ORAL CAVITY

The mucous membrane in the mouth is similar to the skin. The epithelium is stratified squamous, and in its deeper layers is more or less distinctly fibrillated. In man, under physiological conditions, it does not undergo cornification. The nucleus of the cells of the superficial layers shrinks and degenerates, but does not disappear, and the cell body does not reach the same degree of flatness as in the epidermis. These superficial cells are always shed in large quantities and are found in the saliva. In some places they contain granules of keratohyalin. In the cells of the middle and superficial layers there is usually some glycogen. In many animals the epithelium of the oral cavity undergoes extensive cornification.

The *lamina propria* is provided, in most places, with papillae similar to those of the skin. The structure is, however, more delicate, and the collagenous and elastic fibers thinner than in the derma. In the posterior section of the oral cavity, it contains many lymphocytes which are often found migrating into and through the epithelium. The arrangement of the blood vessels is similar to that of the skin. There is a deep submucous plexus of large vessels, from which branches arise and form a second plexus in the lamina propria, which in turn sends small branches into the papillae. The lymphatics also show an arrangement similar to that in the skin, and begin with blind capillary outgrowths in the papillae.

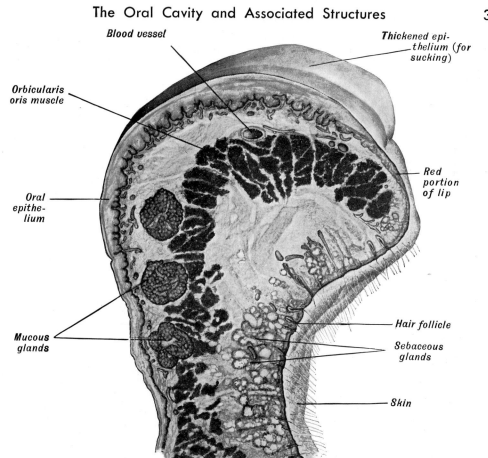

Fig. 315. Camera lucida drawing of sagittal section through lip of newborn infant. Stained with hematoxylin. 10 ×. (Drawn by Miss E. Bohlman.)

The *oral mucous membrane* is very sensitive and is provided with many nerves belonging to the sensory branches of the trigeminal nerve (lingual nerve). It also contains the specific end organs of the sense of taste (p. 335).

In most places under the lamina propria, especially in the cheeks, and on the soft palate, there is a fat-containing, loose *submucosa* into which the dense connective tissue of the mucosa gradually merges. In such places the mucous membrane can be easily lifted into folds. In those places against which the food is crushed and rubbed, as on the hard palate, there is no submucosa, and the mucous membrane is firmly connected with the underlying periosteum or muscles.

The inner zone of the lip margin in the newborn is considerably thickened and covered with hairless sebaceous glands and contains many high papillae. This seems to facilitate the process of sucking.

The *soft palate* consists of layers of striated muscle and fibrous tissue on both surfaces and on the posterior margin. It is covered with a mucous membrane. On the oral surface the latter has the structure typical of the oral cavity—a stratified squamous epithelium, high interepithelial papillae, and glands of the pure mucous type. These are surrounded by adipose tissue and are scattered in a loose submucous layer separated from the lamina propria by dense elastic networks. This oral type of mucous membrane also covers the posterior margin of the soft palate and continues upon the nasal surface. On this surface, at varying distances from the margin, the stratified epithelium is substituted by pseudostratified, ciliated columnar epithelium which rests on a thickened basement

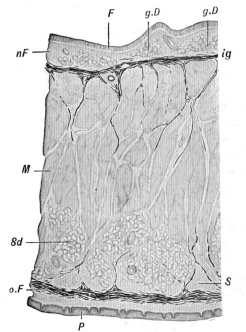

Fig. 316. Portion of sagittal section through the soft palate of a girl nine years old. *nF,* Nasal surface; *F,* ciliated epithelium with goblet cells; *g.D.,* mixed glands; *ig,* infraglandular layer of elastic fibers; *M,* musculature; *o.F,* oral surface; *P,* stratified squamous epithelium with papillae; *Sd,* mucous glands; *S,* submucosa. Resorcinfuchsin stain. 12 ×. (After Schumacher.)

membrane. The lamina propria contains small glands of the mixed type, but no adipose tissue, and is infiltrated with lymphocytes. A dense layer of elastic fibers is found between the glands and the muscles. A submucosa is not present (Fig. 316).

THE TONGUE

The tongue consists of interlacing bundles of striated muscle which run in three planes and cross one another at right angles; the muscular mass is covered by a tightly adherent, mucous membrane. The dense lamina propria is fused with the interstitial connective tissue of the muscle, and a submucous layer is present only on the under surface. The lower surface of the tongue is smooth. The uneven dorsal surface in its anterior part is covered by a multitude of small excrescences—the *papillae*—while in its posterior part it presents only irregular bulgings. The boundary line between the two regions is **V**-shaped, with the opening of the angle directed forward. This is the gustatory region of the tongue. At the head of the angle is a small invagination, the *foramen caecum.* It is the rudiment of the thyroglossal duct, which in early embryonic stages connects the thyroid gland primordium with the epithelium of the oral cavity.

Papillae. Three types of papillae are present on the body of the tongue: (1) the filiform, (2) the fungiform and (3) the circumvallate. The first are arranged in more or less distinct rows diverging to the right and left from the middle line and parallel to the **V**-shaped gustatory region. The fungiform papillae are scattered singly between the filiform and are especially numerous near the end of the tongue. The circumvallate papillae, numbering ten to twelve in man, are arranged along the gustatory lines.

The *filiform papillae* are 2 to 3 mm. long. Their core is a connective tissue ridge beset with secondary papillae with pointed ends. The epithelium covering these connective tissue outgrowths also forms short papillae which taper into pointed processes (Fig. 318). In man the superficial squamous cells are transformed into hard scales containing shrunken nuclei, but no true keratin. The axial parts of the scales at the point of the papilla are connected with its solid axial strand, and their lower edges project from the surface of the papilla like the branches of a fir tree. When digestion is disturbed, the normal shedding of these scales is delayed. They then accumulate, in layers mixed with bacteria, on the surface of the tongue, which thus is covered with a gray film—the "coated" tongue.

The *fungiform papillae* have a short, slightly constricted stalk and a spherical, slightly flattened upper part. The connective tissue core forms secondary papillae; the epithelium covering them has a smooth free surface (Fig. 319). On many of the fungiform papillae the epithelium contains taste buds in the secondary papillae. As the core is rich in blood vessels, the fungiform papillae have a marked red color.

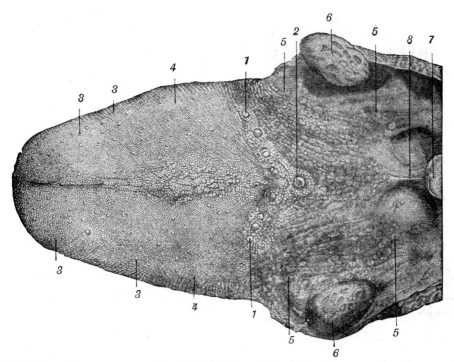

Fig. 317. Surface of human tongue. *1* and *2*, Vallate papillae; *3*, fungiform papillae; *4*, rows of filiform papillae; *5*, lingual tonsils; *6*, palatine tonsils; *7*, epiglottis; *8*, median glosso-epiglottic fold. (After Sappey, from Schumacher.)

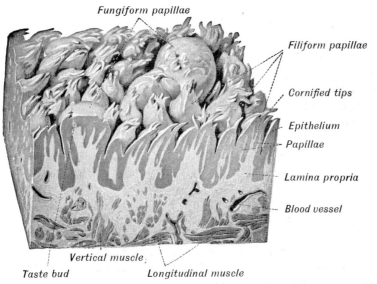

Fig. 318. Surface of dorsum of tongue, drawn through a combined study with the binocular microscope and of sections. The anterior cut surface corresponds with the long axis of the tongue—the tip of the tongue being to the reader's left. 16 ×. (After Braus.)

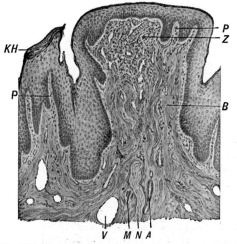

Fig. 319. Perpendicular section through a fungiform papilla from the tongue of a man. A, Artery; B, connective tissue stroma of the fungiform papilla; KH, keratohyalin granules in the superficial cells of a filiform papilla; M, cross-striated muscle fibers; N, nerve; P, secondary papillae; V, vein; Z, cellular stroma with lymphatic and blood vessels. 46 ×. (After Schaffer, from Schumacher.)

The *circumvallate papillae* are sunk into the surface of the mucous membrane, and each is surrounded by a deep, circular furrow. The connective tissue core forms secondary papillae only on the upper surface. The covering epithelium is smooth, while that of the lateral surfaces of the papillae contains many taste buds (Figs. 320, 322).

In a vertical section, ten to twelve of them

can be seen on the lateral surface of the papilla. In the outer wall of the groove surrounding the papilla a few taste buds may be present. The number of taste buds in a single papilla is subject to great variations. On the average it has been estimated at 250.

Connected with the circumvallate papillae are glands of albuminous type (*glands of von Ebner*) whose bodies are embedded deep in the underlying muscular tissue and whose excretory ducts open into the bottom of the furrow (p. 337).

On the lateral surface of the posterior part of the tongue the paired *foliate papillae* may be found. In man they are rudimentary, although in many animals they represent the main peripheral organ of taste. The fully developed foliate papillae (in the rabbit) are oval bulgings on the mucous membrane, consisting of parallel ridges with grooves between them. The epithelium of the sides of the ridges contains many taste buds. Small albuminous glands open into the bottom of the furrows.

Taste buds are also found on the glossopalatine arch, on the soft palate, on the posterior surface of the epiglottis, and on the posterior wall of the pharynx as far down as the inferior edge of the cricoid cartilage.

The bulgings on the root of the tongue are caused by lymphatic nodules, the *lingual tonsils* and *follicles* (Fig. 321). On the free sur-

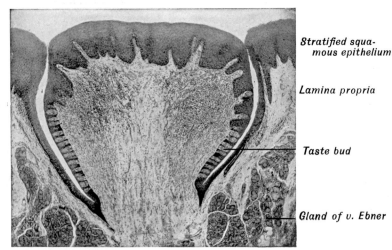

Stratified squamous epithelium

Lamina propria

Taste bud

Gland of v. Ebner

Fig. 320. Section through circumvallate papilla of *Macacus rhesus*. Photomicrograph. 42 ×.

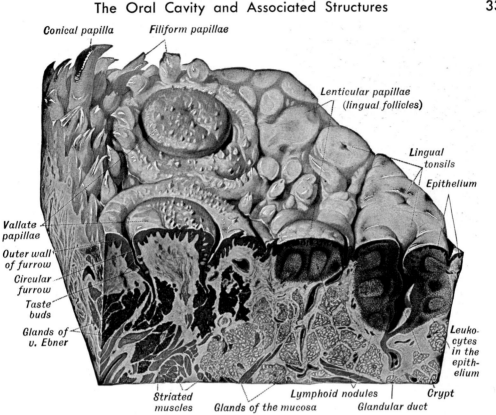

Fig. 321. Surface of tongue at the border between the root and the dorsum; prepared as Figure 318. 16 ×. (After Braus.)

face of each lingual tonsil a small opening leads into a deep invagination lined with stratified squamous epithelium—the *crypt*. The epithelium of the crypt is surrounded by lymphatic tissue; innumerable lymphocytes infiltrate the epithelium and assemble in the lumen of the crypt, where they degenerate and form masses of detritus with the desquamated epithelial cells and bacteria. The lingual tonsils are often connected with mucous glands embedded in the underlying muscle tissue; their ducts open into the crypt or on the free surface.

Taste Buds. The taste buds under low power are seen in sections as pale, oval bodies in the darker stained epithelium. Their long axis averages 72 microns. They extend from the basement membrane almost to the surface. The epithelium over each taste bud is pierced by a small opening—the *outer taste pore* (Fig. 322).

Two cell types are usually distinguished among the constituents of a taste bud: the *supporting cells*, and the *neuro-epithelial taste cells*. The first are spindle-shaped, and their ends surround a small opening, the *inner taste pore*, which leads into a pitlike excavation. The taste cells distributed between the supporting cells vary from four to twenty per taste bud. They have a slender, rod-shaped form with a nucleus in the middle and on the free surface a short *taste hair*, which projects freely into the lumen of the pit.

There are only four fundamental taste sensations: sweet, bitter, acid, and salty. It has been shown by the application of substances to individual fungiform papillae that they differ widely in their receptive properties. Some do not give any taste sensations, while others give sensations of one or more taste qualities. No structural differences in the various taste buds have been found, in spite of the differences in sensation mediated.

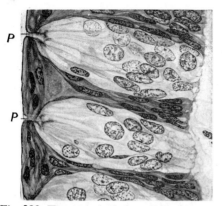

Fig. 322. Two taste buds from side of circumvallate papilla of *Macacus rhesus*, showing taste pores at *P*. (Drawn by Miss E. Bohlman.)

There is, moreover, a general chemical sensitivity in regions of the mouth where there are no taste buds.

Nerves. The anterior two thirds of the tongue is innervated by the lingual nerve, which contains trigeminal fibers of general sensibility and facialis fibers of gustatory sensibility. The latter enter the lingual nerve from the chorda tympani. The posterior third of the tongue is innervated by the glossopharyngeal nerve for both general and gustatory sensibility. Taste buds of the epiglottis and lower pharynx are innervated by the vagus. These nerve fibers are lightly myelinated. They branch profusely under the basement membrane, lose their myelin, and form a subepithelial plexus, from which fibers penetrate the epithelium. Some terminate as intergemmal fibers by free arborization between the taste buds; others, the perigemmal fibers, closely envelop the taste buds; and still others, the intragemmal fibers, penetrate the taste buds and end with small terminal enlargements in intimate contact with the taste cells. The functional significance of these different nerve endings is unknown.

GLANDS OF THE ORAL CAVITY

General Description. Numerous *salivary glands* open into the oral cavity. Many of them are small glands in the mucosa or submucosa and are named according to their location. They seem to secrete continuously and furnish a liquid, the *saliva*, which moistens the oral mucous membrane. In addition, there are three pairs of large glands which constitute the salivary glands proper. They are the *parotid*, the *mandibular* (*submaxillary*), and the *sublingual* glands. They secrete

only when mechanical, thermal or chemical stimuli act upon the nerve endings in the oral mucous membrane, and as the result of certain psychic or olfactory stimuli. The saliva secreted by the large glands may be abundant and helps prepare the food for digestion in the stomach and intestine.

The *saliva* collected from the oral cavity is a mixture of the secretions of the various salivary glands. It is a viscous, colorless, opalescent liquid which contains water, mucin, some proteins, mineral salts, and an enzyme (*ptyalin*) which splits starch into water-soluble, less complex carbohydrates. Saliva always contains a number of desquamated squamous epithelial cells and *salivary corpuscles*; most of the latter originate in the follicles of the tongue and in the tonsils, and are degenerated lymphocytes or granulocytes.

The quality of the saliva collected from the oral cavity varies with the predominant participation of one or the other of the glands in its formation. But even the secretion of one gland may change considerably with variations in the stimuli acting upon the oral mucous membrane, as, for instance, with different kinds of food.

These glands may be classified in three categories according to the type of their secretory cells. The glands containing only *mucous* cells elaborate a viscid secretion which consists almost exclusively of mucin. In glands with only *albuminous* cells the secretion is a "serous" or "albuminous," watery liquid which lacks mucus, but contains salts, proteins and ptyalin. In the *mixed glands*—containing serous and mucous cells—the secretion is a viscid liquid containing mucin, salts and ptyalin.

All glands of the oral cavity have a system of branching excretory ducts. The secretory portions in the pure mucous glands are usually long, branching tubules. In the pure albuminous and mixed glands the secretory portions vary from oval to tubulo-acinar forms provided with irregular outpocketings.

The initial intralobular ducts are thin, branched tubules called the *necks* or *intercalated ducts*. The next larger order of branches, also located in the interior of the smallest lobules, has a striated epithelium; these ducts are called "striated" tubules. Then follow the larger branches; among them (in the large glands) lobular, sublobular, interlobular, and primary ducts may be distinguished.

Mucous Cells. In the pure mucous glands the cells are arranged in a layer against the basement membrane and have an irregularly cuboidal form. In fresh condition their cytoplasm contains many pale droplets of *mucigen*, the antecedent of mucin, while the nucleus is invisible. In fixed and stained sections the droplets of mucigen are usually destroyed, so that the cell body appears clear and contains an artificial network of cytoplasm and precipitated mucigen. This network stains like mucin, that is, red with mucicarmine, or metachromatically purple with thionine. The nucleus is at the base of the cell and usually appears angular and compressed by the accumulation of mucigen. Between the droplets of mucigen a few mitochondria and fragments of a Golgi net can be found. The free surface of the mucous cells is usually provided with a network of terminal bars. Secretory canaliculi are absent. Usually the lumen of the terminal portions is large and filled with masses of mucin.

When the secretion leaves the cell, it collapses, its cytoplasm increases relatively in amount, and only a few granules of mucigen may remain confined to its free surface. The nucleus rises from the base of the cell and becomes round. In this condition the mucous cells may be mistaken for albuminous cells. The absence of secretory capillaries always distinguishes them from albuminous cells. The demonstration of these capillaries requires special staining methods. Under physiological conditions, the mucous cells rarely discharge all their granules.

The most reliable criterion for separating mucous and serous cells is the positive staining of mucus in the former. The staining reactions of the mucin elaborated by different mucous cells is not the same even in the same gland. Sometimes the mucous cell contains fat droplets. The mucous cells, as a rule, do not show any signs of degeneration; mitoses have occasionally been observed in them.

Albuminous Cells. These elements, when filled with secretion in a resting gland, in fresh condition, contain a multitude of small, highly refractile *secretion granules* in a homogeneous cytoplasm. The cell boundaries are not distinct. The roughly cuboidal cells surround a small tubular lumen.

The secretory granules of the albuminous cells accumulate between the nucleus and the free surface. After the gland has secreted for a certain time, the albuminous cells diminish in size; their granules become less numerous and are confined to the free surface of the cells. In extreme, nonphysiological cases, all the granules may disappear. As the albuminous cells are probably the source of ptyalin, the granules are to be looked upon as zymogen granules, the antecedents of the enzyme. Before leaving the cell they are transformed into secretory vacuoles.

In cells crowded with secretion the nucleus is spherical, small and darkly staining; it occupies a position at the base of the cell and may show irregular indentations. Besides the secretory granules, the cytoplasm contains rod-shaped mitochondria and a Golgi net above the nucleus. A cytocentrum near the free surface is distinct only in empty cells.

At the base of the cell around the nucleus, and sometimes above it, is an accumulation of chromophile substance, apparently ribose nucleoprotein, which stains darkly with basic dyes and, owing to its arrangement in parallel lamellae, causes a vertical striation. By appropriate technique, mitochondria can be demonstrated between the lamellae. The albuminous cells often contain fat or glycogen. On their free surfaces the albuminous cells are provided with a system of terminal bars; between their lateral surfaces there are always secretory capillaries. Mitoses occur occasionally.

The albuminous cells of the different glands of the mouth are not identical func-

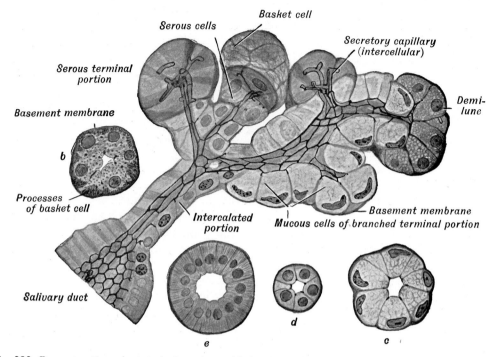

Fig. 323. Reconstruction of a terminal portion, with its duct, of a submaxillary gland. *b*, Cross section of a purely serous terminal portion, showing basal lamellae; *c*, cross section through a purely mucous terminal portion; *d*, cross section through an intercalated portion; *e*, cross section through a salivary duct. (Redrawn and modified after a reconstruction by Vierling, from Braus.)

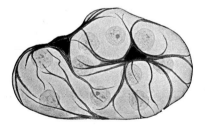

Fig. 324. Branching basal (basket or myo-epithelial) cells with dark fibrils; from an albuminous terminal portion of human submaxillary gland. Iron-hematoxylin stain. Oil immersion. (After Zimmermann.)

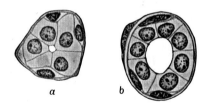

Fig. 325. Cross sections of two isthmuses from human submaxillary gland, each showing three basal cells. *a*, Thin and, *b*, thicker canal belonging to purely albuminous terminal portions. In *b* a fixed connective tissue cell is adhering to the basement membrane. (After Zimmermann.)

tionally, although they may seem to have the same structure. They are combined into one group and given a general name, because histological methods are not sensitive enough to make the differences visible microscopically. In many cases their secretory granules give a more or less distinct staining reaction for mucus with mucicarmine; such cells are called "muco-albuminous" or "mucoserous."

Cells in the Mixed Glands. The relative number of the two kinds of glandular cells in the mixed glands varies within wide limits. In some cases the albuminous cells are far more numerous than the mucous cells, while in other cases the reverse is true; in still other instances both cell types are present in about equal numbers. The mucous and albuminous cells line different parts of the terminal portion. In those mixed glands in which the albuminous cells predominate, some of the terminal portions may be exclusively albuminous. In others a part of the secretory portion is lined with mucous, and a part with serous cells. In sections the mucous portions can often be recognized by their clear aspect, but more certainly by their color after specific staining of the mucus.

As a rule, the mucous cells are near the excretory ducts, while the serous cells are confined to the blind end of the secretory portion. It is quite probable that the mucous cells in mixed glands arise through the mucous transformation of the cells in the smallest excretory ducts, the *necks* or intercalated ducts. Sometimes single mucous cells are scattered between the unchanged cells of the neck. In other cases the part of the neck directly adjoining the terminal portion is lined exclusively with mucous cells. If the mucous transformation affects all the cells in the neck, this part of the ducts ceases to exist as such. If the mucous cells are not numerous, the secretory portion of the gland will show an irregular mixture of pale mucous, and dark albuminous cells.

If the mucous cells are much more numerous, the albuminous cells are pushed to the blind ends of the terminal portion or into saccular outpocketings. Here they form small groups which in sections appear as darkly staining crescents surrounding the mucous tubules (*demilunes* of Gianuzzi). In them the albuminous cells are small and of irregular shape, and often seem to be entirely separated from the lumen by the large mucous cells. However, there are always secretory capillaries which lead the secretion through the clefts between the mucous cells into the lumen (Fig. 323).

Basal (Basket) Cells. In all the glands of the oral cavity the epithelium in the terminal portion, as well as in the excretory ducts, is provided with basal cells. They lie between the glandular cells and the basement membrane, and appear as slender spindles; usually only their nuclei can be discerned. When seen from the surface, they exhibit a stellate cell body with an angular nucleus and processes containing darkly staining fibrils.

The basal cells are supposed to act as smooth muscle cells and to facilitate the movement of the secretion into the excretory ducts; they are sometimes called "myo-epithelial cells." They are like the myo-epithelial cells of the sweat glands.

Excretory Ducts. The necks, of variable length and branching, have a low cuboidal epithelium. Between its cells and the basement membrane are scattered basal cells. The epithelium of the necks often shows a mucoid transformation.

In the columnar epithelium of the striated tubules the lower parts of the cell bodies show a parallel striation, caused by parallel rows of mitochondria (Fig. 323, *e*).

The epithelium of the striated tubules is believed by some to contribute water and calcium salts to the secretion. These tubules (as well as the larger ducts) sometimes present a succession of constricted and dilated sections. In the larger ducts the epithelium is columnar and pseudostratified, and occasionally contains goblet cells. Nearing the opening on the mucous membrane, it becomes stratified for a short stretch and is then succeeded by stratified squamous epithelium.

CLASSIFICATION OF ORAL GLANDS BY LOCATION

A. Glands which open into the vestibule of the mouth:
    1. Parotid gland, with a duct opening into the vestibule
    2. Labial glands, scattered in the mucous membrane of the upper and lower lips
    3. Buccal glands, a continuation of the labial glands in the mucous membrane of the cheek
B. Glands which open on the bottom of the oral cavity, between the tongue and the mandible:
    1. Mandibular (submaxillary) gland—a large gland with a duct opening at the side of the frenulum of the tongue
    2. Sublingual glands, situated beneath the mucous membrane at the side of the frenulum of the tongue. Among them:
        (a) The large sublingual gland with a duct opening into the duct of the mandibular gland
        (b) Several small glands varying in number and size. Their ducts open in many places along a fold of the mucous membrane, the plica sublingualis. At the posterior end of this group are the small glossopalatine glands.
C. Glands of the tongue:
    1. Anterior lingual gland (gland of Blandin or Nuhn), situated at the side of the median line under the apex of the tongue
    2. Posterior lingual glands:
        (a) Albuminous or gustatory glands (of von Ebner) connected with the circumvallate papillae and opening into the circumvallate groove
        (b) Mucous glands of the root of the tongue
D. Glands of the palate.

In the various mammals the glands of the oral cavity show great structural differences.

The following descriptions hold only for man:

The *parotid* is a pure albuminous gland. The necks are long and may branch several times. Their cells never undergo a mucous transformation. The striated tubules are fairly numerous. In the parotid gland of the newborn, however, the glandular cells often give a distinct staining reaction for mucus with mucicarmin.

In the *mandibular gland* the majority of the secretory portions are purely albuminous, while some are mucous with albuminous cells in the blind ends. Typical demilunes are rare. In some persons many of the albuminous cells show a slight mucoid reaction. The mucous cells are smaller than in the sublingual or the pure mucous glands. Some of the necks are short; others are long and branching. The striated tubules are numerous and long, and have many branches.

The *sublingual glands* are mixed glands with a markedly varying structure in their different parts. The mucous cells are far more numerous than in the mandibular gland, while the albuminous cells are in the minority and have a pronounced muco-albuminous character. For the most part they are arranged in thick demilunes, and the isthmuses are extremely variable in length; many undergo a complete mucous transformation, so that the terminal portions abut directly on the striated tubules. The latter are scarce and short and are sometimes represented by small groups of irregular, striated cells in the epithelium of the interlobular ducts.

In the *posterior lingual glands* the secretory portions are long-branching, sometimes anastomosing tubules. They contain only albuminous cells, which sometimes show a slight reaction for mucus. These glands are rarely of mixed character. The system of the excretory ducts is poorly developed; isthmuses and short tubes are absent. These glands form a thin, serous secretion, which is found only on the furrows of the circumvallate papilla and evidently serves to wash out the taste buds.

The *glossopalatine glands* are pure mucous glands.

The *anterior lingual gland*, in its posterior part, consists of mixed branched tubules, which contain mucous cells and, on their blind ends, thin demilunes of muco-albuminous cells. The anterior part contains secretory portions with muco-albuminous cells only.

The *labial* and *buccal glands* are of the mixed type. The secretory portion sometimes contains only muco-albuminous cells, but in most cases the latter are confined to the blind end, while the rest of the cavity is lined with mucous cells. Some of the secretory parts may contain only mucous cells. As the

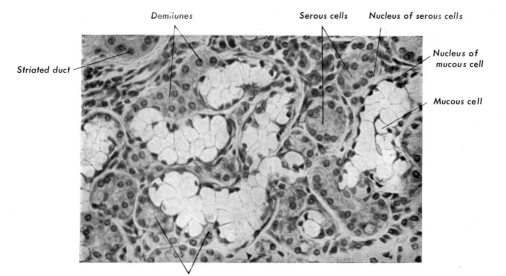

Fig. 326. Section of human mandibular gland with mucous, serous and mixed terminal portions, and demilunes. Photomicrograph. H + E. 240 ×. (After von Herrath and Abramow.)

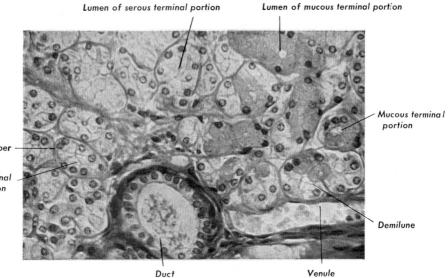

Fig. 327. Section of human mandibular gland stained with Mallory-azan. Mucous cells are blue stained. Photomicrograph. 240 ×. (After von Herrath and Abramow.)

necks are short and branch but little, the mucous secretory portions often pass directly into striated tubules.

The *glands of the root of the tongue* and the *palatine glands* are of the pure mucous variety. Short isthmuses have been found in the latter group.

Interstitial Connective Tissue; Blood and Lymphatic Vessels. In the interstitial reticular connective tissue of

the salivary glands are fibroblasts and macrophages, with fat cells scattered singly or in small groups; plasma cells are of common occurrence. Occasionally, small lymphocytes are also found. The larger blood vessels follow the excretory ducts; the loose capillary networks surround the ducts and the terminal portions. The lymph vessels are said to be scarce.

Nerves. Each salivary gland is provided with sensory nerve endings and two kinds of efferent secretory nerves, parasympathetic (cerebral) and sympathetic fibers. The cerebral preganglionic fibers for the man-

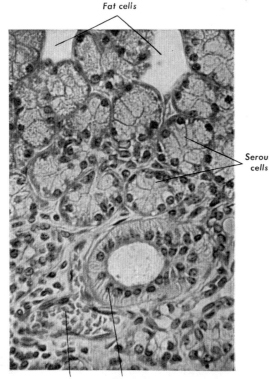

Fat cells

Serous cells

Venule   *Striated duct*

Fig. 328. Section of human parotid gland, showing serous terminal portions and a striated duct. Photomicrograph. H+E. 300 ×. (After von Herrath and Abramow.)

dibular and sublingual glands run in the chorda tympani nerve to the submaxillary ganglion; the sympathetic preganglionic fibers reach the superior cervical ganglion. From here the postganglionic fibers follow along the carotid artery. The vasodilators are believed to be included in the chorda tympani, the vasoconstrictors in the sympathetic nerves.

The parotid gland receives its secretory fibers from the glossopharyngeal nerve. In the interstitial tissue along the course of its blood vessels, plexuses of myelinated (preganglionic and sensory) and nonmyelinated fibers, and, close to the larger excretory ducts, groups of sympathetic multipolar nerve cells are found. On the outer surface of the terminal portions, nonmyelinated fibres form a network which sends small branches through the basement membranes. These branches form a second network on the inner surface of the membrane, and from this plexus small, final branches penetrate between the glandular cells, branch, and end on their surfaces with small, budlike thickenings.

Stimulation of the cerebral nerves of the mandibular gland causes the secretion of an abundant, thin saliva rich in water and salts, but poor in organic substances. Stimulation of the sympathetic nerve, on the contrary, yields a small quantity of thick saliva, with a high content of organic substances. The mechanism of the action of the nerves upon the glandular cells and the role of the vasodilators in the secretion are not known, and the presence of different kinds of nerve endings has not been proved. It is even doubtful whether the secretory fibers in the chorda tympani and in the sympathetic are of different nature.

After sectioning of the chorda tympani nerve in the dog, the so-called "paralytic" secretion in the corresponding submaxillary and retrolingual glands occurs. This secretion is accompanied by intense degeneration and atrophy of the gland cells, especially the mucous elements in the retrolingual gland.

Histogenesis of the Glands of the Oral Cavity. Each gland arises at a certain time of fetal life, at a particular place in the wall of the embryonic oral cavity, through the growth of a solid epithelial bud into the subjacent mesenchyme. The large glands, such as the submaxillary and the parotid, appear in embryos of six and eight weeks respectively; the smaller ones later. The epithelial bud grows and ramifies into a branched, treelike structure with club-shaped ends. It consists of undifferentiated polyhedral or cuboidal epithelial cells with many mitoses. Gradually a lumen appears in the older parts of the primordium, and this canalization proceeds distally, but does not reach the terminal branches as long as these continue to grow and to form additional buds. When the lumen reaches the terminal bud, the latter ceases to grow, and only specific differentiation and enlargement of its cells occur. Mucigen appears in the mucous cells and zymogen granules in the serous ones. The histogenetic development of the glands continues after birth.

TONSILS

The aperture by which the oral cavity communicates with the next section of the digestive tract, the pharynx, is called the *fauces*. In this region the mucous membrane of the digestive tract contains accumulations of lymphatic tissue. Besides small infiltrations with lymphocytes, which may occur anywhere in this part of the mucous membrane, well-outlined organs are formed by the lymphatic tissue. The surface epithelium invaginates them, and they are called "tonsils." The lingual tonsils have been described (p. 334).

Between the glossopalatine and pharyngopalatine arches are the *palatine tonsils*. These are two oval, prominent accumulations of lymphatic tissue in the connective tissue of the mucous membrane, with ten to twenty deep *crypts*. The stratified squamous epithelium of the free surface overlies a thin layer of fibrous connective tissue with papillae. The *crypts* almost reach the connective tissue *capsule* and are of simple or branching form.

The nodules with their prominent centers are embedded in a diffuse mass of dense lymphatic tissue 1 to 2 mm. thick, and are usually arranged in a single layer under the epithelium. The crypts with their surrounding sheaths of lymphatic tissue are partially separated from one another by thin partitions of loose connective tissue which invaginate from the capsule. In this connective tissue there are always lymphocytes of various sizes, and mast and plasma cells. The presence of large numbers of heterophile leukocytes indicates inflammation, which is common in mild degree. Frequently there are islands of cartilage or bone, which probably indicate a pathological process. In the deeper portions of the crypts, the limit between the

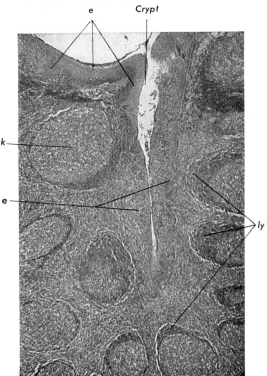

Fig. 330. Section of human tonsil. *e*, Stratified squamous epithelium of surface; *k*, germinal center; *ly*, concentration of lymphocytes toward the epithelium. H+E. 12 ×. (After von Herrath and Abramow.)

epithelium and the lymphatic tissue is effaced in most places by an intense infiltration of the epithelium with lymphocytes. The epithelial cells are pushed aside and disfigured, so that sometimes only a few remain on the surface. Heterophile leukocytes are always present in small numbers. Plasma cells are common here.

The lymphocytes which pass through the epithelium are found in the saliva as the *salivary corpuscles*. They appear here usually as degenerating vesicular elements with a more or less constricted nucleus and granules which show brownian movement. The salivary corpuscles which originate from heterophile leukocytes are recognized by the remnants of the granules and the polymorphous nucleus.

The lumen of the crypts may contain large accumulations of living and degenerated lymphocytes mixed with desquamated squamous epithelial cells, granular detritus and

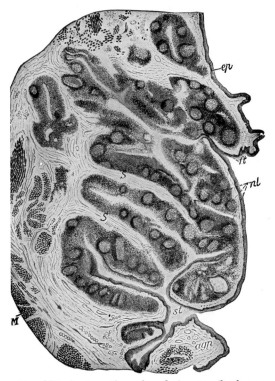

Fig. 329. Section through palatine tonsil of man. *agp*, Glossopalatine arch; *ep*, stratified squamous epithelium; *ft*, crypt; *M*, striated muscle; *nl*, lymphoid nodules; *S*, connective tissue septa; *st*, remains of tonsillar sinus. 6½ ×. (After Sobotta.)

micro-organisms. These masses may increase in size and form cheesy plugs which are gradually eliminated. If they remain for a long time, they may calcify. The micro-organisms are sometimes the cause of inflammation and suppuration; they may be responsible for some general infections.

Many small glands are connected with the palatine tonsils; their bodies are outside the capsule, and their ducts open for the most part on the free surface. Openings into the crypts seem rare.

In the roof (fornix) and somewhat to the posterior wall of the nasal part of the pharynx is the unpaired *pharyngeal tonsil*. In this region the mucous membrane shows numerous folds, but no crypts. The epithelium on its surface is the same as in the rest of the respiratory passages—pseudostratified, ciliated columnar epithelium with many goblet cells. Small patches of stratified squamous epithelium are common, however. The epithelium is abundantly infiltrated with lymphocytes, especially on the crests of the folds. A 2-mm. thick layer of diffuse and nodular lymphatic tissue is found under the epithelium and participates in the formation of its folds; it is separated from the surrounding parts by a thin capsule which contains many elastic networks and sends thin partitions into the core of the folds. Outside the capsule are small glands of mixed character.

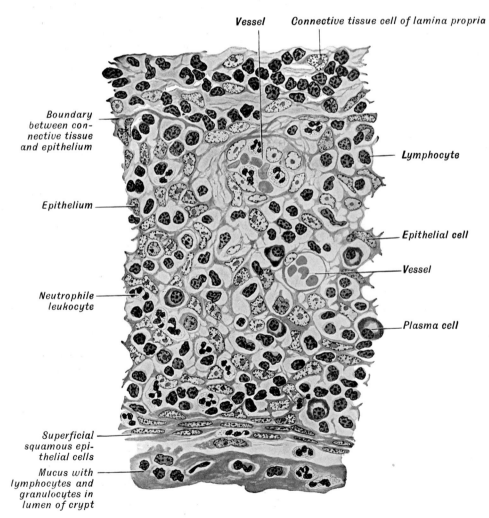

Fig. 331. Human tonsil; infiltration of the epithelium of the crypt with lymphocytes, neutrophile (heterophile) granular leukocytes and plasma cells. Hematoxylin-eosin-azure stain. 520 ×. (A.A.M.)

Their ducts—often markedly dilated—traverse the lymphatic tissue and empty into the furrows or on the free surface of the folds.

Other small accumulations of lymphatic tissue occur in the mucous membrane of the pharynx, around the orifices of the eustachian tube behind the pharyngopalatine arches, and in the posterior wall.

Unlike the lymph nodes, the tonsils do not have lymphatic sinuses, and lymph is not filtered through them. However, netlike plexuses of blindly ending lymph capillaries surround their outer surface.

The tonsils generally reach their maximal development in childhood. The involution of the palatine tonsils seems to begin about the age of fifteen, while the follicles of the root of the tongue persist longer. The pharyngeal tonsil in the adult is usually found in an atrophic condition, with its ciliated epithelium in great part replaced by stratified squamous epithelium.

The participation of the tonsils in the new formation of lymphocytes is the only established function that can be ascribed to them. It is generally believed, but not proved, that the infiltration of its epithelium with lymphocytes has something to do with the protection of the organism against the penetration of noxious agents and especially of micro-organisms into the body. Pathogenic bacteria have been found in the lymphatic tissue of the tonsils (and the nodules of the intestine) as an apparently normal phenomenon. It has been suggested that the bacteria penetrating the lymphatic tissue are made less virulent, and that they then act as antigens and instigate the production of antibodies. On the other hand, the tonsils (and the nodules of the intestine) have been shown to be the portals of entry for pathogenic micro-organisms, and general infections have been traced from them.

The palatine tonsils develop from the rudiments of the dorsal part of the second gill pouch. During the fourth month of fetal life the epithelium pushes solid outgrowths into the subjacent connective tissue; these later become hollow. Around these epithelial growths, lymphatic tissue gradually develops through isolation

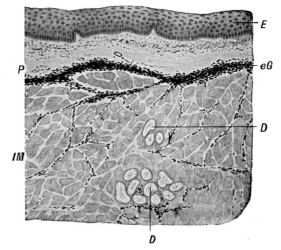

Fig. 332. Cross section through posterior pharyngeal wall of human adult. E, Stratified squamous epithelium; P, lamina propria mucosae; eG, elastic boundary layer separating the lamina propria from the longitudinal muscular layer, IM; D, mucous glands deep in the muscle. Resorcinfuchsin and hematoxylin stains. 50 ×. (After Schumacher.)

and mobilization of mesenchyme cells which are transformed into lymphocytes, while the cells which remain fixed furnish the reticular framework.

THE PHARYNX

The posterior continuation of the oral cavity is the pharynx. In this section of the digestive tract the respiratory passages and the pathway for the food cross and fuse with each other. The upper part of the pharynx is the nasal, the middle of the oral, and the lower the laryngeal portion. In the upper part it approaches the structure of the respiratory system, while in the lower its corresponds more to the general plan of the digestive tube.

Instead of a muscularis mucosae, the mucous membrane is provided with a thick, dense, netlike elastic layer. A loose submucous layer is well developed only in the lateral sides of the nasal part of the pharynx and where the pharynx continues into the esophagus; here the elastic layer becomes thinner. In all other places the mucous membrane is directly adjacent to the muscular wall, which consists of an inner longitudinal and an outer oblique or circular layer of striated muscle. The elastic layer fuses with

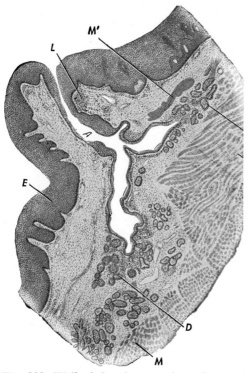

Fig. 333. Wall of the pharynx, of an eleven-year-old girl, in longitudinal section. A, Opening of a mucous gland, D, at the apex of a fold of the mucosa; E, stratified squamous epithelium; L, accumulation of leukocytes around the orifice of the gland; M, muscular layer; M', muscle fibers pushed aside by the body of the gland. 27 ×. (After Schaffer.)

the interstitial tissue of the muscle and sends strands of elastic fibers between the muscular bundles. In the fornix it is fused with the periosteum of the base of the skull.

The lamina propria mucosae consists of dense connective tissue containing fine elastic network; those places covered with stratified squamous epithelium are provided with small papillae. In the area covered with pseudostratified ciliated columnar epithelium there are no papillae.

The two lower sections of the pharynx and a part of the nasal region have stratified squamous epithelium; toward the roof (fornix) of the pharynx its epithelium first becomes stratified columnar and then pseudostratified columnar ciliated, with many goblet cells. On the lateral sides of the nasal part this ciliated epithelium continues downward beyond the aperture of the eustachian tube. With age the ciliated epithelium may be replaced by stratified squamous epithelium over large areas.

Glands of a pure mucous type are found in those places lined with stratified squamous epithelium. They are always located under the elastic layer, sometimes deep in the muscle. Glands of mixed type, similar to those of the dorsal surface of the soft palate, are confined to the regions covered with ciliated epithelium.

REFERENCES

Arey, L. B.: On the Development, Morphology and Interpretation of a System of Crypt Analogues in the Pharyngeal Tonsil. Am. J. Anat., 80:203, 1947.

Becks, H., and Wainwright, W. W.: Rate of Flow of Resting Saliva of Healthy Individuals. J. Dent. Research, 22:391, 1943.

Bensley, R. R.: Observations on the Salivary Glands of Mammals. Anat. Rec., 2:105, 1908.

Kolmer, W.: Geschmacksorgan, in von Möllendorff's Handbuch der mikr. Anat. des Menschen. Berlin, 1927, Vol. 3, Pt. 1, p. 154.

Langley, O.: On the Changes in Serous Glands during Secretion. J. Physiol., 2:1880.

Maximow, A. A.: Beiträge zur Histologie und Physiologie der Speicheldrüsen. Arch. f. mikr. Anat., 58:1, 1901.

Rawlinson, H. E.: The Changes in the Cells of the Striated Ducts of the Cat's Submaxillary Gland after Autonomic Stimulation and Nerve Section. Anat. Rec., 63:295, 1935.

Schumacher, S.: Die Mundhöhle, in von Möllendorff's Handbuch der mikr. Anat. des Menschen. Berlin, 1927, Vol. 5, Pt. 1, p. 1; Die Zunge, ibid., 35, 1927; Der Schlundkopf. ibid., 290, 1927.

Stormont, D. L.: The Salivary Glands, in Cowdry's Special Cytology. 2d ed. New York, (1), 151, 1932.

Zimmermann, K. W.: Die Speicheldrüsen, Handb. d. mikr. Anat. (von Möllendorff), (5), 1927.

XXII. THE TEETH

The teeth are derivatives of the oral mucous membrane. They may be considered modified papillae whose surface is covered by a thick layer of calcified substance originating in part from epithelium, and in part from connective tissue. The most primitive type of teeth, in which the character of cutaneous papillae is quite evident, is found in the placoid scales scattered all over the surface of the body of the selachians. Similar structures develop in many parallel rows in the mucous membrane of the oral cavity of the fishes, where they are subject to continuous renewal during life.

Two sets of teeth have to be distinguished in man and most mammals. The first set forms the *deciduous teeth* of childhood; their eruption starts about the seventh month after birth, and they are shed between the sixth and thirteenth years. They are gradually replaced by the *permanent teeth*. The microscopic structure of both kinds of teeth is similar in principle, but the permanent tooth reaches a higher development. Each of the various types of teeth in each set has a different form adapted to its specific functions, i.e., the incisors for biting and the molars for grinding and pounding the food.

All teeth consist of the same two portions, the *crown*, projecting above the gingiva (gum), and the tapering *root*, which fits into an excavation, the *alveolus*, of the maxillary or mandibular bone. Where the crown and the root meet is sometimes called the *neck*. The lower molars have two, the upper molars three, roots. The tooth contains a small cavity which corresponds roughly with the outer form of the tooth. It is called the *pulp cavity* and continues into each root as a narrow canal that communicates through one or more openings at the apex of the root with the *periodontal membrane.*

The *hard portions of a tooth* consist of three different tissues: dentin, enamel, and cementum. The bulk of the tooth is formed by the *dentin*, or ivory, which surrounds the pulp cavity. It is thickest in the crown and tapers down to the points of the roots. Its outer surface is covered, in the region of the crown, by a layer of *enamel*, which reaches its greatest thickness on the exposed part of the crown and thins down toward the neck. In the region of the root the dentin is covered by a thin layer of *cementum* which leaves the opening of the canal free. The edge of the enamel meets the cementum at the neck.

The *soft parts* associated with the tooth are (1) the pulp, which fills the pulp cavity; (2) the periodontal membrane, which connects the cementum-covered surface of the root with the bone of the alveolus; (3) the gingiva, that portion of the oral mucous membrane surrounding the tooth. In young persons the gingiva is attached to the enamel; with increasing age it gradually recedes from the enamel, so that in old people it is attached to the cementum.

Dentin. The dentin is yellowish and semi-transparent in fresh condition; when dried, it acquires a silky appearance because air has entered its tubules. It is harder than compact bone, although it resembles bone in its structure, chemical nature, and development.

As in bone, the substance of macerated dentin consists of an organic (28 per cent) and an inorganic (72 per cent) part. They can be separated by decalcification in acids, when the organic part remains and the substance becomes soft, or by incineration when only the inorganic material remains. The latter is much the same as in bone except that it is denser and less soluble. The organic part contains a glycoprotein, dissolves in boiling water, and yields a solution of gelatin.

In a ground section passing through the axis of a macerated tooth, the dentin has a radially striated appearance. This is caused by the presence of innumerable, minute canals, the *dentinal tubules*, which diverge from the pulp cavity toward the periphery and penetrate every part of the dentin. Near the pulp in the innermost part of the dentin, their diameter is 1.3 to 2.2 microns; in the

outer portions they become narrower. On their way from the pulp cavity most of the tubules describe an **S**-shaped curve. The tubules branch and, especially in the outer layers of dentin, frequently form loop-shaped anastomoses.

The layer of dentin which is immediately adjacent to the tubules and surrounds them as a sheath of Neumann differs from the rest of the dentin by its high refringence and distinct staining in decalcified specimens.

Between the dentinal tubules are systems of collagenous fibrils arranged in bundles 2 to 4 microns thick and kept together by a

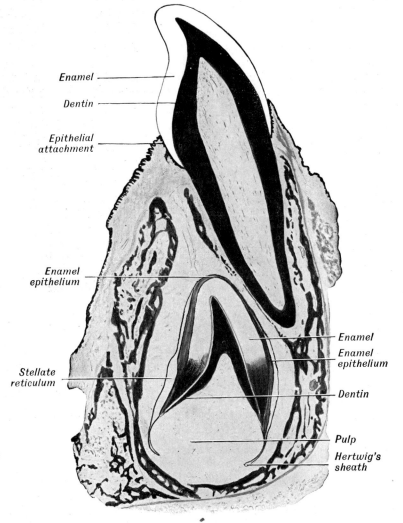

Fig. 334. Diagram of deciduous tooth and its corresponding permanent tooth germ (below). Note the surrounding alveolar bone. Retouched photomicrograph. 8 ×. (Courtesy of B. Orban.)

cementing substance, containing glycoprotein; they correspond to the ossein fibrils of bone.

The course of the fibrillar bundles is, in general, parallel to the long axis of the tooth and perpendicular to the dentinal tubules. They also run obliquely and around the tubules; in the crown they are tangential to the free surface. The fibrils in the adjacent layers form angles of varying degrees—smaller in the outermost portions of the dentin and larger in the proximity of the pulp cavity.

Some investigators distinguish a peripheral layer of *cover dentin*, with coarser fibers, from the *circumpulpar dentin*, which forms the inner mass and consists of thinner fibrils.

The calcification of the developing dentin is not always complete and uniform. The deposits of calcium salts which appear during development in the organic ground substance have the form of spheres which gradually gain in size and finally fuse. In incompletely calcified regions, between the calcified spheres, there remain angular "interglobular" spaces which contain only the organic matrix of the dentin. The dentinal tubules continue without interruption through the spheres and interglobular spaces. In a macerated tooth, from which all organic parts have disappeared, the tubules as well as the interglobular spaces are filled with air and appear dark in transmitted light. In many otherwise normal teeth there are layers of large, interglobular spaces in the deeper parts of the enamel-covered dentin of the crown—the *lines of Owen*. Immediately under the dentino-cemental junction, in the root there is always a layer of small interglobular spaces, the *granular layer of Tomes* (Fig. 335, *e*).

In sections through a decalcified tooth fixed with its soft parts, each dentinal tubule contains a protoplasmic fiber (of Tomes) which in life probably completely fills the lumen of the tubule, but which in fixed preparations appears shrunken. When the tubules are seen in cross section, each small oval contains a dark dot. These fibers of Tomes are processes of the *odontoblasts*, which are arranged on the wall of the pulp cavity and send their protoplasmic processes into the dentinal tubules.

The dentin is sensitive to touch, to cold, to acid-containing foods, and the like. Only occasional nerve fibers penetrate the dentin

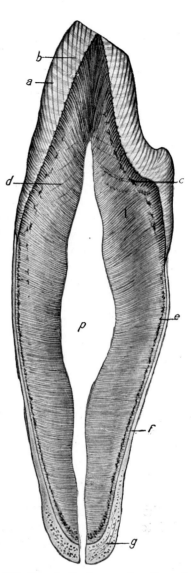

Fig. 335. Longitudinal ground section of human cuspid. The top of the crown has been abraded. *a*, Parallel stripes of Retzius; *b*, Schreger's lines of the enamel; *c*, large interglobular space (of Owen); *d*, dentin; *e*, Tomes' granular layer of the dentin; *f*, cell-free and, *g*, cellular cementum of root; *p*, pulp cavity. 7 ×. (After von Ebner, from Schaffer.)

and extend for short distances. It is believed that the fibers of Tomes transmit the sensory stimulation to the pulp, which contains many nerves.

With the aid of radioactive phosphorus it has been shown that there is an active interchange of calcium and phosphorus between dentin and enamel on one hand and the

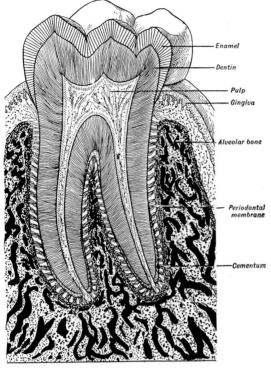

Fig. 336. Diagram of sagittal section of adult human lower first permanent molar. (Courtesy of I. Schour.)

blood on the other. The interchange persists on a diminished scale via the dentino-cemental junction in teeth in which the pulp cavity has been filled.

In bone the cells are evenly distributed in the hard intercellular substance and send their processes out in all directions, while the cells of dentin remain on the surface of the intercellular substance and only send their processes into it. Although the odontoblasts undoubtedly play a role in the nutrition of the dentin, the latter does not become necrotic after the destruction of the pulp and the "filling" of a tooth.

In old age the dentinal tubules are often obliterated through calcification; the dentin then becomes transparent. When the dentin is denuded because of extensive abrasion of the crown, or when the outside of the tooth is irritated, a production of new or "secondary" dentin of irregular structure may often be observed on the wall of the pulp cavity. This may be so extensive as to fill the cavity completely.

Enamel. This cuticular formation of epithelial origin is the hardest substance found in the body; it gives sparks with steel. It is bluish-white and transparent in thin-ground sections. When fully developed, enamel consists almost entirely of calcium salts in the form of large apatite crystals, while only 3 per cent of it is organic substance which contains a glycoprotein. Consequently, after decalcification of a fully developed tooth, the enamel is completely dissolved as a rule.

The enamel consists of thin prisms or rods which stand upright on the surface of the dentin, usually with a pronounced inclination toward the crown. They are kept together by a small amount of cement substance. Every rod runs through the whole thickness of the enamel layer. This, however, cannot be seen in sections of the enamel, because the rods are twisted.

The substance of a rod in its longitudinal section seems homogeneous in a ground preparation. But after acid acts upon such a section, a distinct cross striation appears in the rods; this indicates that the calcification probably proceeds by layers.

In the human tooth most of the rods in cross section have the form of fluted semicircles. The convex surfaces of all rods face the dentin, and their cross sections show a scalelike formation (Fig. 339).

This form and arrangement are explained by calcification beginning earlier on the side of the rods which lies nearest the dentin. This inner, harder side is supposed to press

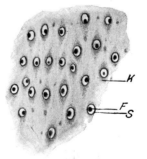

Fig. 337. Tangential section through the root of a molar of an ape. F, Shrunken dentinal fiber; S, margin of the tubules (Neumann's sheath); K, matrix. 740 ×. (After Schaffer.)

into the softer side of the adjacent rod, compressing it and leaving one or two groovelike impressions.

The exact course of the enamel rods is extremely complicated and seems to be perfectly adapted to the mechanical requirements connected with the grinding and pounding of food. Starting from the dentin, the rods run perpendicularly to the surface; in the middle zone of the enamel they bend spirally and in the outer zone again assume a direction perpendicular to the surface. In addition, the rods show numerous, small, wavy curves. On the lateral surfaces of the crown the rods are arranged in zones which encircle the tooth in horizontal planes. The bends of the rods in two neighboring zones cross one another. In axial, longitudinal, ground sections, the crossing of groups of rods appears in reflected light as light and dark lines, more or less perpendicular to the surface—the lines of Schreger (Fig. 335).

In a cross section of the crown the enamel shows concentric lines which are brown in transmitted light and colorless in reflected light. In longitudinal, axial sections they are seen to run obliquely inward from the surface and toward the root. They are called the *lines of Retzius* and are connected with the circular striation on the surface of the crown.

The free surface of the enamel is covered by two *membranes*. The inner is about 1 micron thick and is the last product of the activity of the ganoblasts before they disappear. It is somewhat more resistant to acid than is the rest of the enamel. A second membrane, external to the first, is formed of a carbohydrate-containing protein. It is 2 to 10 microns thick and resistant to acids as well as to alkalies. In the adult both membranes are gradually worn off.

In an axial section of the tooth the line of junction between the dentin and the enamel (*dentino-enamel junction*) is uneven and scalloped. Pointed processes of dentin penetrate the enamel and are separated from one another by excavations. Some dentinal tubules penetrate the enamel and end blindly. The spindle-shaped processes of the dentinal matrix penetrating a short distance into the enamel are called *enamel spindles*.

Local disturbances of the enamel during development cause the so-called *enamel lamellae* and *tufts*. These lamellae are organic material extending from the surface of the enamel toward and sometimes into the dentin. The tufts extend from the dentino-enamel junction into the enamel for one third of its thickness. The tuftlike shape, however, is an optical illusion due to the projection of fibers lying in different planes into one plane. They are groups of poorly calcified, twisted rods with abundant cementing substance between them.

Cementum. The cementum covering most of the root is coarsely fibrillated, interstitial bone substance. Near the apex bone cells (also called cementocytes) are embedded in it. Canaliculi, haversian systems and blood vessels are normally absent. The layer of cementum increases in thickness with age, especially near the end of the root, and then haversian systems with blood vessels may appear. Coarse collagenous bundles from the periodontal membrane penetrate the cementum. These fibers of Sharpey remain uncalcified, and in ground sections of the macerated tooth appear as empty canals.

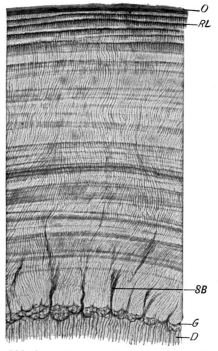

Fig. 338. Ground cross section of crown of a human cuspid. *D*, dentin; *G*, wavy boundary between enamel and dentin; *O*, surface of the tooth; *RL*, parallel stripes of Retzius; *SB*, enamel tuft. 80 ×. (After Schaffer.)

Unlike the high resistance of the dentin, which may remain unchanged even after the destruction of the pulp and odontoblasts and after the "filling" of the pulp cavity, the cementum readily undergoes necrosis when the periodontal membrane is destroyed and may be resorbed by the surrounding connective tissue. On the other hand, new layers of cementum may be deposited on the surface

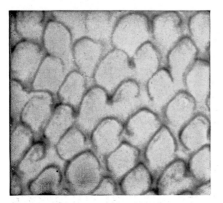

Fig. 339. Cross section of human enamel rods. The dark lines are the cementing substance between the pale rods. Photomicrograph. High magnification. (Courtesy of B. Orban.)

of the root. If this deposition becomes extensive, it may be called *cementum hyperplasia* and is a favorable reaction to irritation.

Pulp. The pulp of the tooth fills the pulp cavity and is the connective tissue which formed the dental papillae during embryonic development. In the adult tooth it has an abundant, gelatinous, basophile ground substance similar to that of mucoid tissue. It contains a multitude of thin collagenous fibrils running in all directions and not combined into bundles. The spindle- or star-shaped cells suggest embryonic mesenchymal elements; macrophages and lymphoid cells are also present. The cells of the pulp adjacent to the dentin are large, elongated, and radially arranged in the fashion of an epithelium; they are called *odontoblasts* and contain mitochondria and a Golgi net in their central part. The odontoblasts send one or more processes into the dentinal tubules; these are the fibers of Tomes.

The pulp continues into the narrow canal

of the root, where it surrounds the blood vessels and nerves, and continues through the openings in the apex into the periodontal membrane. The pulp contains many blood vessels. Several small arteries enter each root and are accompanied by veins. The arteries give rise to a dense network of wide capillaries whose loops reach the layer of the odontoblasts and then continue into the veins which occupy a more central position. True lymphatic capillaries have been found by some investigators. Numerous bundles of myelinated nerve fibers, which arise from small cells in the gasserian ganglion, enter the pulp cavity through the canals of the root. They form a plexus in the pulp from which a finer plexus of nonmyelinated fibers in the peripheral layers arises; nerve endings have been described between the odontoblasts.

Periodontal Membrane. The periodontal membrane, which also serves as periosteum to the alveolar bone, furnishes a firm connection between the root and the bone. It differs from the usual periosteum by the absence of elastic fibers. It consists of thick collagenous bundles, which generally run obliquely from the alveolar wall to the cementum. At the bottom of the alveolar cavity they are thinner, and the softer tissue continues into the pulp. At the neck of the tooth the fibers are especially prominent, are firmly attached to the cementum, and are called the "horizontal groups of fibers" of the tooth. Nearer the surface they run from the bone upward to the edge of the cementum. The fiber bundles of the periodontal membrane have a slightly wavy course; when the tooth is not functioning, they are relaxed and permit it to move slightly on the application of stress.

In many places in the periodontal membrane, blood and lymph vessels and nerves embedded in a small amount of loose connective tissue, and small islands of epithelium are scattered, especially near the surface of the cementum. These islands are vestiges of the epithelial sheath of Hertwig. The epithelial rests frequently degenerate and undergo calcification, giving rise to the *cementicles.*

The Gingiva (Gum). The gingiva is that part of the mucous membrane which is firmly connected with the periosteum at the crest of the alveolar bone. It is also linked to the surface of the tooth by the *epithelial attachment of Gottlieb*, which gradually approaches the apex of the tooth with advancing age. The gingiva has high papillae. The epithelial attachment is devoid of papillae except when chronically inflamed. Between the epithelium and the enamel there is a small furrow surrounding the crown, the *gingival crevice*. No glands are found in the gums.

Histogenesis of the Teeth. The enamel is a product of the ectodermal epithelium; all the other parts are derivatives of the connective tissue.

In human embryos of the fifth week the ectodermal epithelium lining the oral cavity presents a thickening along the edge of the future upper and lower jaws. The thickening consists of two solid epithelial ridges which extend into the subjacent mesenchyme. Of these, the labial ridge later splits and forms the space between lip and alveolar process of the jaw. The lingual ridge, nearer the tongue, produces teeth and is called the *dental lamina*. According to most investigators, both ridges are independent from the beginning.

The edge of the dental lamina extends into the connective tissue of the jaw and shows at several points budlike thickenings—the primordia of the teeth, the *tooth germs*. There are ten tooth germs in each jaw, one for each deciduous tooth. In each germ a dense group of epithelial cells becomes conspicuous as the *enamel knot*; it is a temporary structure that later disappears. The cells of the mesenchyme under the enamel knot form a dense group, the primordium of the papilla.

The dental lamina then extends beyond the last deciduous tooth germ and slowly forms germs of the permanent molars, which are not preceded by corresponding deciduous teeth.

Beginning with the tenth to twelfth week, the remainder of the dental lamina again produces solid epithelial buds—the *germs for the permanent teeth*—one on the lingual side of each deciduous germ. After the formation of the permanent tooth germs the dental lamina disappears. The transformations of the permanent tooth germ are the same as in the deciduous germ.

The papilla enlarges and invaginates the base of the epithelial tooth germ (Fig. 343). The latter, while still connected by an epithelial strand with the dental lamina, becomes bell-shaped and caps the convex surface of the papilla. From now on it is called the *enamel organ*, because it produces the enamel in its further development. Both the papilla and the enamel organ gradually gain in height, and the latter soon acquires approximately the shape of the future organ.

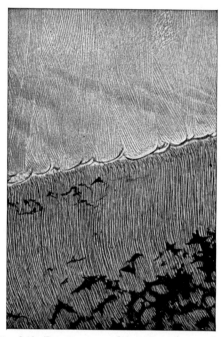

Fig. 340. Dentino-enamel junction of a tooth of a man; ground section. The enamel prisms appear as a fine, wavy striation. The interglobular spaces in the dentin are black (air filled). Between these lacunae are the dentinal tubules. 80 ×. (After Braus.)

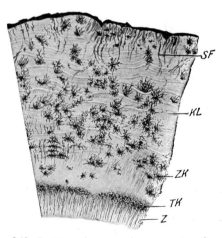

Fig. 341. Portion of a ground cross section through the lower part of a root of a macerated human tooth. Air has filled the lacunae. *KL*, Refractile boundary between the apparently lamellated layers; *SF*, uncalcified Sharpey's fibers; *TK*, Tomes' granular layer; *Z*, dentin; *ZK*, cementum corpuscles. 80 ×. (After Schaffer.)

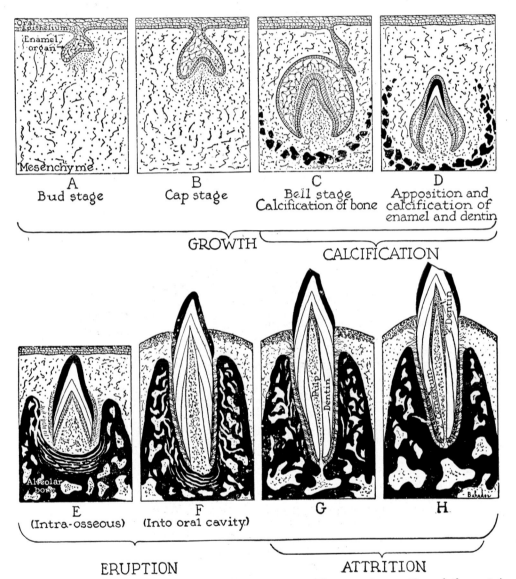

Fig. 342. Diagram of life cycle of a human deciduous incisor. The normal resorption of the root is not indicated. Enamel and bone are drawn in black. (Slightly modified after Schour and Massler.)

A concentric layer of connective tissue, the dental sac, develops around the tooth primordium and interrupts its epithelial connection with the oral cavity. Around the sac and at a certain distance from it the bone of the jaw develops.

The peripheral cells of the enamel organ are arranged in a regular, radial fashion. On the convex surface the outer enamel epithelium remains small and cuboidal. On the invaginated base the cells of the inner enamel epithelium become tall and regular. They help in the elaboration of the enamel and are called *ameloblasts* or *ganoblasts*. Their attachments are provided with a system of terminal bars. In the inner mass of epithelial cells a clear liquid accumulates between the cell bodies, which remain connected with one another by long processes. The epithelium thus acquires a reticular connective tissue-like appearance—the *stellate reticulum* (enamel pulp).

When the formation of the hard tooth substances begins (embryos of about twenty weeks), the mesenchyme of the papilla contains numerous blood vessels and a few reticular fibrils between its cells. The cells adjacent to the layer of ganoblasts become transformed into odontoblasts (Fig. 344, O).

The dentin first appears as a thick limiting line between ganoblasts and odontoblasts, sometimes called the *membrana preformata*. Some believe that the odontoblasts do not form the dentin, but are probably concerned in its nourishment and possibly with the deposition of calcium in it. In any event, just before the dentin is formed, the odontoblasts develop large amounts of glycoprotein, which may be related to the ground substance.

The layer of dentin extends down the slopes of the papillae. It gradually grows thicker and is transformed into a solid cap of dentin through the apposition of new layers on its concave surface. As the odontoblasts recede from the dentin, thin processes of their cytoplasm remain in the mass of deposited dentin as the **dentinal fibers**.

When the dentin first appears, it is a soft fibrillar substance—the *predentin*. The fibrils are continuations of the fibrils of the papilla. They are of the argyrophile type and are generally called *Korff's fibers*. They enter the dentin, spread out fanlike, and change into the collagenous, fibrillated matrix of the dentin (Fig. 345).

In dentin formation, calcification follows closely

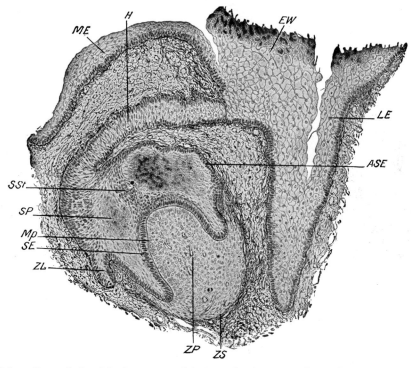

Fig. 343. Primordium of the right lower central incisor of a human embryo of ninety-one days, in sagittal section. Collagenous fibers black. *ASE*, External enamel epithelium; *EW*, epithelium of the dental lamina; *H*, neck of the enamel organ; *LE*, labial epithelium; *ME*, epithelium on the floor of the mouth; *Mp*, preformed membrane; *SE*, internal enamel epithelium; *SP*, enamel pulp; *SSt*, enamel cord; *ZL*, internal end of the dental lamina; *ZP*, dental papilla; *ZS*, dental follicle. Mallory's connective tissue stain. 80 ×. (After Schaffer.)

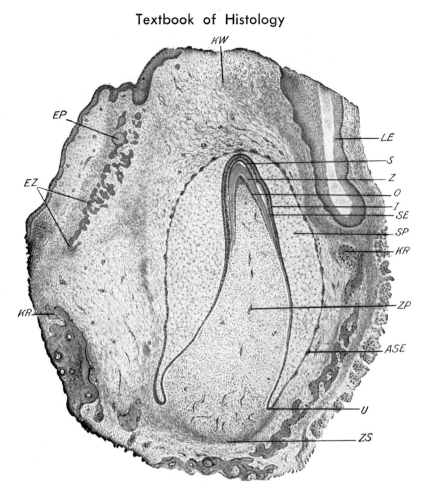

Fig. 344. Primordium of lower central incisor of a five months' embryo; sagittal section. *ASE*, External enamel epithelium; *EP*, epithelial pearls in the rests of the permanent dental lamina, *EZ*; *I*, stratum intermedium; *KR*, alveolar bone; *KW*, gum wall; *LE*, stratified squamous epithelium of the lip; *O*, primordium of the odontoblasts; *S*, enamel cap; *SE*, internal enamel epithelium; *SP*, enamel pulp; *U*, transition of the external into the internal enamel epithelium: *Z*, dentin; *ZP*, dental pulp; *ZS*, dental follicle. 30 ×. (After Schaffer.)

the deposition of the fibrillar soft substance. But during the whole process there is always a thin layer of uncalcified dentin near the odontoblasts.

The process of dentin formation is much the same in nature as the formation of bone. Almost immediately after the appearance of the first calcified dentin on the convexity of the papilla, the ganoblasts begin the elaboration of enamel. It is deposited layer by layer on the surface of the calcifying dentin.

The ganoblasts grow into tall and regular, columnar cells; in the earlier stages each cell contains a cytocentrum and a Golgi net above the elongated, oval nucleus. The attached part of the cell contains granular material which stains brown with osmic acid. In vitally stained animals this part stores the dyes in granular form. On the slopes of the papilla the ganoblasts become lower, and at the base of the papilla they continue into the outer enamel epithelium.

As the mass of enamel increases, the ganoblasts recede, and their basal surfaces remain covered by thin, cuticular plates and connected with one another by terminal bars. The most recent investigations demonstrate the development of the enamel rods from their beginning as individual rods and not from a homogeneous mass. Thus the *Tomes' processes* are the primordia of the enamel rods; each corresponds to a separate ganoblast and remains connected with it until the enamel is complete. It is probable that the processes of Tomes are a cuticular secretion of the basal ends of the ganoblasts.

Calcification starts at the periphery of each row and proceeds toward its interior. When the cementing substance finally calcifies, so little organic material remains in the enamel that it is completely dissolved in decalcification. Complete calcification is not reached until late, and for a long time dyes and other substances may penetrate the partly calcified enamel. That the calcification is seldom absolutely uniform has been mentioned. One of the most striking causes of hypocalcification is parathyroidectomy.

Schour (1936) studied the rate of deposition of enamel with sodium fluoride and of dentin with vital injections of alizarine. He found that the daily thickening of dentin is about 4 microns and that unusual increments (*neonatal lines*) appear in the enamel and dentin formed in the deciduous teeth at the time of birth.

The disturbances in the development of the teeth due to vitamin deficiencies are described by Mellanby.

When the definitive thickness and extension of the enamel capsule are reached in the neck region, the ganoblasts become small cuboidal cells and then atrophy. Before they disappear, they elaborate the inner cuticle of the enamel which covers the ends of the rods.

At the end of the enamel organ, the outer and inner enamel epithelium form a fold, the *epithelial sheath of Hertwig*. The *development of the root* begins shortly before the eruption of the tooth, continues after the crown has emerged from within the mucous membrane, and is not completed until much later; the epithelial sheath disappears when the root development is finished.

When the germ of the permanent tooth begins to develop, its growth pressure causes resorption, first of the bony partition between the two teeth, then of the

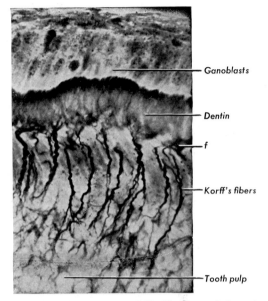

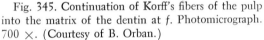

Fig. 345. Continuation of Korff's fibers of the pulp into the matrix of the dentin at *f*. Photomicrograph. 700 ×. (Courtesy of B. Orban.)

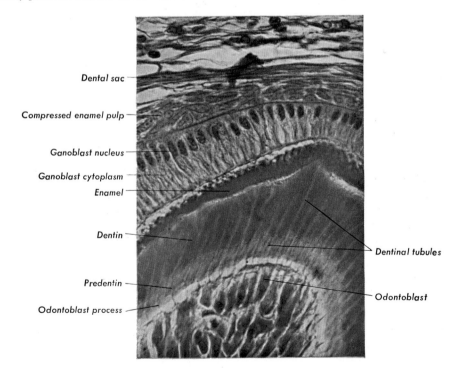

Fig. 346. Section of incisor of human fetus of five months, showing formation of enamel and dentin. Photomicrograph. Mallory-azan stain. 500 ×. (After von Herrath and Abramow.)

root, and eventually even of a part of the enamel of the deciduous tooth. Osteoclasts are prominent in this process of destruction just as in the resorption of bone. The crown of the permanent tooth moving upward gradually takes the place of the former deciduous crown.

REFERENCES

Becks, H., Collins, D. A., Simpson, M. E., and Evans, H. M.: Changes in the Central Incisors of Hypophysectomized Female Rats after Different Postoperative Periods. Arch. Path., 41:457, 1946.

Engel, M. B.: Glycogen and Carbohydrate-Protein Complex in Developing Teeth of the Rat. J. Dent. Res., 27:681, 1948.

Hampp, E. G.: Mineral Distribution in the Developing Tooth. Anat. Rec., 77:273, 1940.

Hoffman, M. M., and Schour, I.: Quantitative Studies in the Development of the Rat Molar. II. Alveolar Bone, Cementum, and Eruption (from Birth to 500 Days). Am. J. Orthodontics, 26:854, 1940.

Kitchin, P. C.: Some Observations on Enamel Development as Shown in the Mandibular Incisors of the White Rat. J. Dent. Res., 13:25, 1933.

Lehner, J., and Plenk, H.: Die Zähne. Handb. d. mikr. Anat. d. Menschen (v. Möllendorff), (5)³, 449, 1937.

Mellanby, M.: Influence of Diet on Structure of Teeth. Physiol. Rev., 8:345, 1928.

Noyes, F. B., Schour, I., and Noyes, H. J.: Oral Histology and Embryology. 6th ed. Philadelphia, 1948.

Orban, B.: Oral Histology and Embryology. 2d ed. St. Louis, 1949.

Saunders J. B. de C. M., Nuckolls, J., and Frisbie, H. E.: Amelogenesis. A Histologic Study of the Development, Formation and Calcification of the Enamel in the Molar Tooth of the Rat. J. Am. Coll. Dentists, 1, 1942.

Schour, I.: The Teeth, in Cowdry's Special Cytology. 2d ed. New York, (1), 69, 1932; The Neonatal Line in the Enamel and Dentin of the Human Deciduous Teeth and First Permanent Molar. J. Am. Dent. A., 23:1946, 1936.

Schour, I., and Massler, M.: The Effects of Dietary Deficiencies upon the Oral Structures. Physiol. Rev., 25:442, 1945.

Stahl, S. S., Weinmann, J. P., Schour, I., and Budy, A. M.: The Effect of Estrogen on the Alveolar Bone and Teeth of Mice and Rats. Anat. Rec., 107:21, 1950.

Weidenreich, F.: Ueber den Bau und die Entwicklung des Zahnbeines in der Reihe der Wirbeltiere. Zeit. f. Anat. u. Entwicklungsgesch., 76:218, 1925.

Wislocki, G. B., and Sognnaes, R. F.: Histochemical Reactions of Normal Teeth. Am. J. Anat., 87:239, 1950.

Wolbach, S. B., and Howe, P. R.: The Incisor Teeth of Albino Rats and Guinea-pigs in Vitamin A Deficiency and Repair. Am. J. Path., 9:275, 1933.

XXIII. ESOPHAGUS AND STOMACH

THE ESOPHAGUS

The esophagus is a muscular tube which conveys the food rapidly from the pharynx to the stomach. Its wall presents all the layers characteristic of the digestive tube in general.

The mucous membrane is 500 to 800 microns thick. The stratified squamous epithelium continues into the esophagus from the pharynx. At the transition of the esophagus into the stomach in the cardia, it is abruptly succeeded by the simple columnar epithelium of the stomach. On macroscopical examination the boundary line between the smooth white mucous membrane of the esophagus and the pink surface of the gastric mucosa appears as a jagged line.

In man the flattened cells of the superficial layers of the epithelium contain a small number of keratohyalin granules, but do not undergo true cornification. The lamina propria is bent by numerous longitudinal ridges

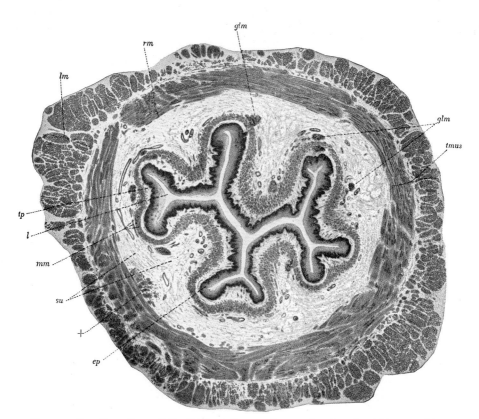

Fig. 347. Cross section from the middle third of the esophagus of a twenty-eight year old man. *ep*, Epithelium; *glm*, mucous glands; *l*, lumen; *lm*, longitudinal muscle; *mm*, lamina muscularis mucosae; *rm*, circular muscle; *su*, submucosa; *tmus*, tunica muscularis; *tp*, lamina propria mucosae; +, inner longitudinal muscle. 8 ×. (After Sobotta.)

which fuse with one another in many places and carry high conical papillae. These ridges and the papillae penetrate the epithelium, but do not cause any prominences on its free surface.

The lamina propria consists of loose connective tissue with relatively thin collagenous fibers and a few fine elastic networks the latter do not penetrate the papillae. Besides the usual connective tissue cells, numerous lymphocytes are scattered throughout the tissue. Around the excretory ducts of the mucous glands, small lymphatic nodules are found.

At the level of the cricoid cartilage the elastic boundary layer of the pharynx is succeeded by the *muscularis mucosae*. It consists of longitudinal smooth muscle fibers and thin elastic networks. Toward the stomach the muscularis mucosae attains a thickness of 200 to 400 microns.

The dense connective tissue of the *sub-*

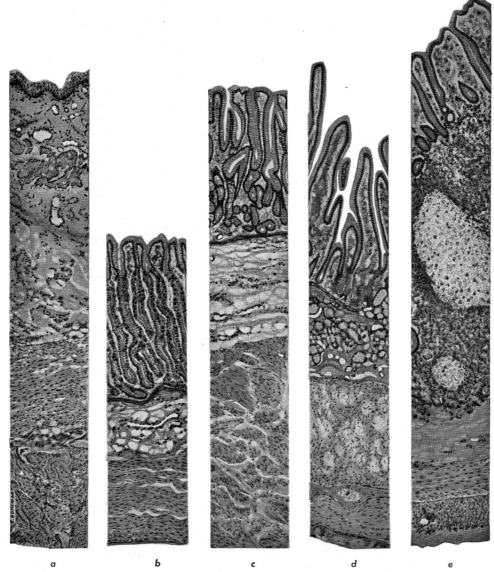

Fig. 348. Sections through five segments of human alimentary canal. *a,* Esophagus; *b,* fundus of stomach; *c,* pylorus of stomach; *d,* duodenum; *e,* appendix. H + E. 35 ×.

mucous layer consists of thick collagenous and elastic networks, and small infiltrations of lymphocytes about the glands. Together with the muscularis mucosae, it forms numerous longitudinal folds which cause the irregular form of the lumen in cross section. During the swallowing of food these folds are smoothed out. This is made possible by the elasticity of the connective tissue which forms the submucous layer.

The *muscularis externa* of the human esophagus is 0.5 to 2.2 mm. thick. In the cranial quarter of the esophagus both its layers consist of striated muscle; in the second quarter the striated muscle is gradually substituted by bundles of smooth muscles; in the caudal third only the latter are found. The relations between the two types of muscular tissue are subject to individual variations. The two layers of the muscularis externa are not regularly circular and longitudinal, respectively: in the inner layer there are many spiral, elliptical or oblique bundles; the longitudinal muscular bundles of the outer layer in many places are irregularly arranged.

The outer surface of the esophagus is connected with the surrounding parts by a layer of loose connective tissue called the *tunica adventitia*.

Glands of the Esophagus. Two kinds of small glands occur in the esophagus: *esophageal glands proper* and *esophageal cardiac glands*. The esophageal glands proper are unevenly distributed, small, compound glands with richly branched tubulo-alveolar secretory portions containing only mucous cells. They are located in the submucous layer and can just be recognized with the naked eye as elongated white granules. The branches of the smallest ducts are short and fuse into a cystically dilated main duct which pierces the muscularis mucosae and opens through a small orifice. The epithelium in the smallest ducts is low columnar; in the enlarged main duct stratified squamous epithelium is found. The mucous glands often give rise to cysts of the mucous membrane.

The *esophageal cardiac glands* closely resemble the cardiac glands of the stomach.

Two groups of them can be distinguished: one is in the upper part of the esophagus at the level between the cricoid cartilage and the fifth tracheal cartilage; the other is in the lower part of the esophagus near the cardia. They show great individual variations and sometimes are entirely absent.

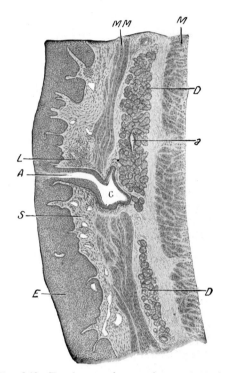

Fig. 349. Esophagus of man; lower third; longitudinal section. A, Excretory duct of a mucous gland, D; a, smaller excretory duct which passes over into the secretory portion; C, ampulla-like dilatation; E, stratified squamous epithelium; L, collection of leukocytes in the lamina propria mucosae, S; MM, muscularis mucosae; M, circular muscle layer of the muscle coat. 27 ×. (After Schaffer.)

Unlike the esophageal glands proper, they are always confined to the lamina propria mucosae. Their terminal portions are branched and curled tubules that contain columnar or cuboidal cells with a pale granular cytoplasm, which sometimes seems to give the mucin reaction; secretory canaliculi are present. The smallest ducts fuse into a large duct, which is sometimes cystically dilated and always opens on the summit of a papilla. Its columnar epithelium often gives a distinct reaction for mucin and more or less resembles

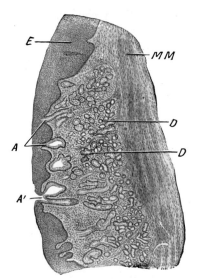

Fig. 350. Longitudinal cross section through upper end of esophagus with glands of the cardiac type, *D*, in the mucosa. *A*, *A'*, Openings of the glands at the apex of papillae; *E*, stratified squamous epithelium; *MM*, muscularis mucosae. From an eleven year old girl. 27 ×. (After Schaffer.)

the mucous epithelium of the gastric foveolae.

In the regions of the mucous membrane which contain the upper and lower cardiac glands, the stratified squamous epithelium may be substituted in places by a simple columnar epithelium of the same aspect as in the gastric pits. Such patches suggest erosions, that is, places denuded of epithelium. Sometimes the patches lined with mucous gastric epithelium are of considerable size and are provided with pitlike invaginations and even with tubular glands like those of the fundus; they may even contain typical zymogenic and parietal cells.

The number and development of the cardiac glands as well as of the islands of gastric mucosa in the esophagus are subject to great individual variations. According to some investigators, the presence of this ectopic gastric epithelium may be of some importance for the origin of diverticula, cysts, ulcers and carcinomas of the esophagus.

In many mammals, especially those which consume coarse vegetable food (rodents, ruminants and the horse), the stratified squamous epithelium of the esophagus undergoes cornification. The esophageal glands are present in most of the mammals, but instead of being purely mucous, as in man, they have a mixed character. In some species no glands are found (rodents, horse, cat).

Histogenetic Remarks. The histogenesis of the epithelium of the esophagus in man presents certain peculiarities, which are especially important in connection with the question of metaplasia, *i.e.*, of the transformation of one epithelial type into another. At first the entodermal layer is a simple, low columnar epithelium. It then becomes two-layered, and in the ninth week the superficial cells become ciliated. In the eleventh week, vesicle-like, glycogen-containing elements appear between the ciliated cells, soon outnumber them, and later are transformed into squamous cells. Finally, all the ciliated cells disappear, and the epithelium becomes stratified squamous. In embryos of the other mammals the epithelium does not seem to contain any ciliated cells.

THE STOMACH

In the stomach the food is thoroughly moistened, softened and partly dissolved by the gastric juice, ground by the contractions of the muscular wall, and transformed into a pulplike mass—the *chyme*. When the chyme has attained the necessary softness, it is transferred to the intestine in small portions. Thus the function of the stomach is in part mechanical and in part chemical. The first is taken care of by the external muscular coat, whose different parts work in perfectly regulated coordination, the second by the glands of the mucous membrane.

The cavity of the empty stomach in its living condition is not much larger than that of the intestine. The trumpet-shaped opening which leads from the esophagus into the stomach is called the *cardia*. To the left of the cardia the wall of the stomach forms a bulging which is directed upward—the *fundus* (or *fornix*); it continues down the right concave and the left convex margins, which are called the *lesser* and the *greater curvatures*. The transition of the stomach into the duodenum, the first part of the small intestine, is called the *pylorus*. Some investigators believe that the wall of the stomach is constricted in its middle part into the *isthmus*. The wall of the stomach consists of the usual layers of the digestive tube.

The mucous membrane of the stomach in the living condition is grayish-pink, except for narrow, pale, ring-shaped areas at the pylorus and cardia. The surface of the filled stomach is stretched evenly. In the empty, contracted stomach it forms numerous high, mostly longitudinal folds. This is made possible by the loose consistency of the submucous layer and the action of the muscularis mucosae. Another much finer and more constant relief is brought about by a system of furrows which subdivide the suface of the mucous membrane into small, slightly bulging, gastric areas 1 to 6 mm. in diameter. With a magnifying lens the surface of each area is seen to be further subdivided by tiny grooves into irregularly convoluted ridges. In a perpendicular section through the mucous membrane the furrows, which are cut across, appear as invaginations, the so-called *gastric pits* or *foveolae gastricae*.

The thickness of the mucous membrane in all parts of the stomach is occupied by a multitude of glands which open into the bottom of the gastric pits. The epithelium which lines the gastric pits and covers the free surface of the mucosa between them has everywhere the same structure. On the basis of differences in the glands, three portions are distinguished in the stomach.

The first zone, which forms a narrow (5 to 30 mm.) ring-shaped area around the cardia, is called the *cardiac area* and contains glands of the same name. The second zone comprises the *fundus and proximal two thirds* of the stomach and contains the gastric glands proper or the *glands of the fundus*. The third part, the *pyloric region*, occupies the distal ninth of the stomach and extends for a greater distance on the lesser curvature than on the greater; it is characterized by the presence of *pyloric glands*. These zones are not separated by sharply drawn limits; along the borderline the glands of one mix to a certain extent with those of the other. According to some, between the second and third zones is a narrow strip, some millimeters in width, occupied by a fourth type of glands, the *intermediate glands*. In the dog, the animal especially used for physiological experimentation, this intermediate zone reaches a high development and a width of 1 to 1.8 cm.

In various other mammals the subdivisions of the stomach are much more sharply pronounced and are marked by deep constrictions which separate the organ into chambers. The esophageal, stratified squamous, sometimes cornified epithelium may invade a smaller

or larger part of the stomach; this first esophageal part, as a rule, has few or no glands. In the ruminants the three first chambers—the rumen, the reticulum, and the omasus (or psalterium)—are all of esophageal nature; only in the fourth portion, the abomasus, are gastric glands found, and here only does digestion occur. In the monotremes and marsupials the whole stomach is occupied by the esophageal region, and the stratified squamous epithelium reaches as far as the glands of Brunner. In the pig the second, or cardiac, region, with mucus-secreting gastric epithelium and cardiac glands, is highly developed; the third, physiologically most important portion is the region of the corpus or fundus, while the fourth portion is the pyloric region.

Surface Epithelium. The ridges between the gastric pits and their walls are lined by a tall (20 to 40 microns), regular columnar epithelium. At the cardia it begins abruptly under the overhanging edge of the stratified squamous epithelium of the esophagus. In the pylorus it is replaced by the intestinal

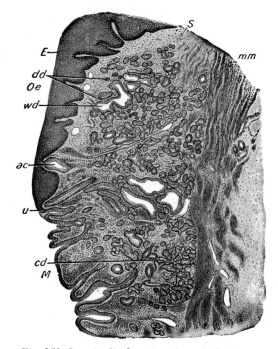

Fig. 351. Longitudinal section through the junction of esophagus and stomach of man. *E*, Stratified squamous epithelium of the esophagus; *M*, stomach; *Oe*, esophagus; *S*, lamina propria mucosae; *ac*, esophageal cardiac glands; *cd*, cardiac glands; *dd*, glandular tubes; *mm*, muscularis mucosae; *u*, transition of stratified squamous epithelium into cylindrical epithelium of the stomach; *wd*, dilated glandular duct. 120 ×. (After Schaffer.)

epithelium. In the cells on the free surface round granules fill the supranuclear part of the cells. Downward into the foveolae they become more and more confined to the free surface. In the bottom of the pits only a thin layer of granules lines the surface; these elements continue down into the neck of the glands. The granules consist of mucigen or of mucin of a peculiar type. After proper

bars. In the midst of the clear substance a diplosome is located. A Golgi net is also present above and sometimes around the nucleus. The cytoplasm in the basal part of the cell contains threadlike mitochondria. Fat droplets and glycogen granules have been found in these cells. The introduction of glucose into the stomach does not influence the amount of glycogen in its epithelium.

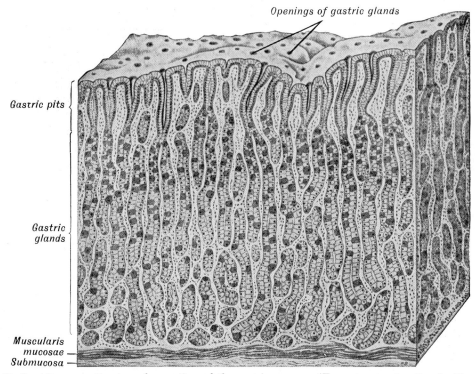

Fig. 352. Semidiagrammatic view of a portion of the gastric mucosa. (From a reconstruction by Kaunhoven and Stein. After Stöhr-von Möllendorff.)

fixation it can be stained with some of the dyes which are elective for typical mucus, as mucicarmine. With other mucin dyes the result is negative. Having left the cells, the granules furnish the layer of alkaline mucus which lubricates the surface of the mucosa. Unlike the mucus secreted by the mucous glands of the oral cavity, it is not precipitated by acetic acid.

In sections in which the granules of mucigen have not been preserved, the supranuclear parts of the cells appear clear and transparent and only faintly granular; the free surfaces are covered with thin terminal

Even under physiological conditions many of the surface cells are desquamated and perish. Signs of regeneration are seen only in the deeper part of the foveole, where mitoses are frequent in the less differentiated cells which contain but a small quantity of mucigen granules under their free surface. The newly formed cells are slowly pushed upward through growth pressure and replace the lost ones.

Gastric Glands. These glands, which are the most important contributors to the secretion of the gastric juice, are simple, branched tubules. They are densely arranged, perpendicularly to the surface of the mucosa, and penetrate its whole thickness, which measures from 0.3 to 1.5 mm. They open in small groups through a slight constriction into the bottom of the foveolae. The diameter of the glandular tubule is 30 to 50 microns, but the lumen is narrow. The blind ends are slightly thickened and coiled and sometimes divide into two or three branches; they almost reach the muscularis mucosae. The number of these glands is estimated at 35,-000,000.

There are four types of cells in these glands. Many different names have been proposed for them, so that the nomenclature is rarely alike in any two descriptions. The four types are: (1) body chief, or zymogenic cells, (2) parietal cells, (3) mucous neck cells, and (4) argentaffine cells (of Heidenhain).

Zymogenic Cells. The zymogenic cells are arranged in a simple layer on the inner surface of the basement membrane and line the lumen in the lower half or third of the glandular tubule. After death they begin to disintegrate almost immediately unless there was no acid in the stomach, when they may remain for some time. In fresh condition, especially after a period of fasting, the cells are full of coarse, brilliant granules. After intense secretory activity the cells are smaller and contain but few granules near their surface. The granules are believed to contain pepsinogen, the antecedent of the enzyme pepsin. Only some osmic-sublimate and formalin mixtures preserve the granules; in most cases they dissolve, and the fixed cytoplasm shows an alveolar structure. The spherical nucleus does not show any peculiarities. Under the nucleus in the basal part of the cell the cytoplasm contains radially striated accumulations of chromophile substance; the zymogenic cells contain mitochondria and a Golgi net.

The free surfaces of the cells are provided with terminal bars. True secretory capillaries are not present. It is not clear whether the zymogenic cells under physiological conditions are subject to degeneration and renewal, or not. Mitoses are never found in

them. It is possible that they may arise from the mucous neck cells, although in the adult, transitions between them—zymogenic cells with a slight mucin content near the free surface—are rare.

Parietal Cells. Between the zymogenic cells, but more numerous toward the neck, parietal cells are scattered singly. They are of spherical, sometimes slightly triangular form

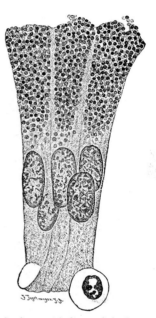

Fig. 353. Surface epithelium of the human stomach; fixed with sublimate-osmic acid and stained with gentian to show the mucous droplets. (After Heidenhain.)

and occupy a peripheral position between the zymogenic cells and the basement membrane. Sometimes they even cause bulgings on the outer surface of the glands, especially after prolonged activity when the zymogenic cells are small.

The parietal cell contains a large round nucleus; sometimes two or even more nuclei are present in one cell. The cytoplasm stains readily with acid aniline dyes. The cell contains a diplosome and numerous short rod-shaped mitochondria, but no distinct secretory granules. The most typical features of the parietal cells are secretory canaliculi which occupy an intracellular position and form a loose network between the surface and nucleus. They communicate, through a small cleft between the adjacent zymogenic cells, with a branch of the main lumen. Through this canal the secretion of the parietal cells enters the lumen. The parietal cells do not seem to undergo any morphological changes with the various stages of functional activity.

Mucous Neck Cells. These are found in the neck of the glands, where they are arranged in one layer and fill the spaces between the parietal cells. In passing toward

hematein, the cytoplasm is filled with brightly stained granules, while the zymogenic cells remain colorless. This indicates that the mucous neck cells are mucus-secreting elements. Their mucus, however, gives staining reactions different from that of the mucus of the gastric surface epithelium and from that of the glands of the oral cavity.

Where the necks of the glands open into the narrow bottoms of the foveolae, the mucous neck cells are connected with the

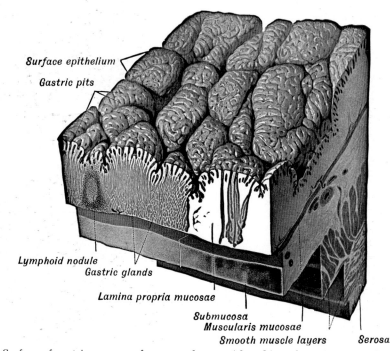

Fig. 354. Surface of gastric mucosa of a man; drawn with a binocular microscope. The cut surfaces are slightly diagrammatic. At the left, the normal distribution of the gastric glands; to the right, only a few are indicated. Glands, gray; gastric pits, black. 17 ×. (After Braus.)

the bottom of the gland they are abruptly succeeded by the zymogenic cells. In fresh condition they are filled with pale, transparent granules.

In sections in which the secretory granules are not preserved and which are stained only with nuclear dyes, they are similar to the zymogenic cells and were overlooked by many investigators. Their nuclei, however, are different from those of the zymogenic cells because they are usually flat, sometimes concave, and occupy the base of the cell. In sections stained with mucicarmine or muci-

surface epithelium by a series of gradual transitional forms. As mitoses are not found in the mucous neck cells of the adult, it is probable that new ones arise through a gradual transformation of the undifferentiated epithelium in the bottom of the foveolae.

In many gastric glands the mucous neck cells advance far toward the bottom and are sometimes scattered singly between the zymogenic cells. This is especially prominent in the glands near the pyloric region. According to some, the glands of the narrow intermediate zone may contain only mucous neck and parietal cells and be devoid of zymogenic cells.

Argentaffine Cells. Argentaffine cells, like those in the intestine, are moderately abundant in the fundic glands and are less frequent in the pyloric glands. These cells are

brane (to one half of its thickness) and have more branches than in the body of the stomach. The glands here are also of the simple, branched tubular type, but the lumen is larger, and the tubules are coiled, so that in perpendicular sections they are seldom seen

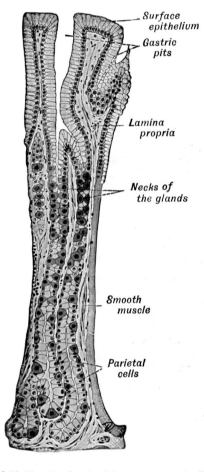

Fig. 355. Fundic glands of human stomach. Zymogenic cells gray; parietal cells dark gray. 130 ×. (After Braus.)

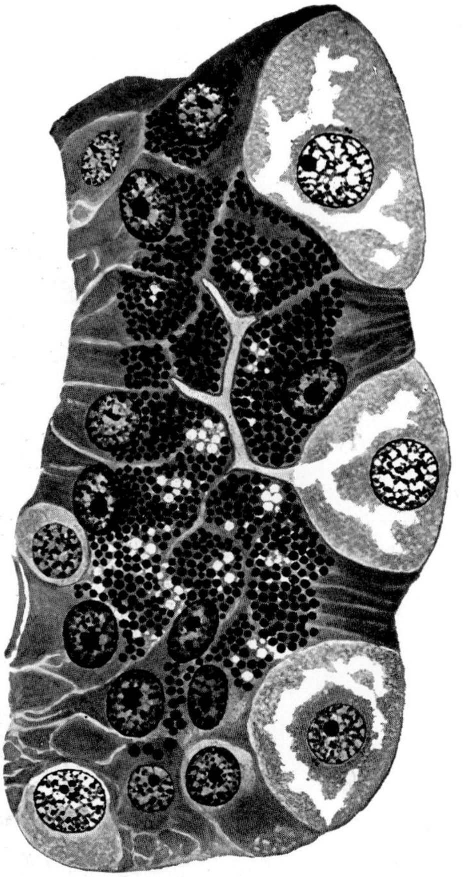

Fig. 356. Blind end of gastric gland of monkey. Zymogenic cells with black secretory granules; between them, secretory capillaries; three parietal cells with intracellular canaliculi. Iron-hematoxylin stain. 1000 ×. (A.A.M.)

scattered singly, between the basement membrane and the zymogenic cells, and have a somewhat flattened form. Their cytoplasm is filled with small granules which can be stained with silver or chromium salts. They are more numerous in the duodenum. It has been suggested that they may be related to a hematopoietic substance.

Pyloric Glands. In the pyloric region the foveolae reach deeper into the mucous mem-

as longitudinal structures. The pyloric glands contain only one type of cell; its cytoplasm is pale and contains an indistinct granulation (Fig. 358). Secretory capillaries have been described between them. The nucleus is often flattened against the base of the cell. In sections stained with hematoxylin and eosin, they sometimes resemble the mucous neck cells or even the zymogenic cells, or the cells of the glands of Brunner of the duodenum. Some investigators believe that the pyloric glandular cells are identical with the mucous neck cells, since both give similar staining reactions for mucus. Certain dyes (cresyl violet, Giemsa mixture), however, seem to stain them in a specific way; they may be compared, perhaps, only with the cells of the cardiac glands. In the human stomach, the pyloric glands in the region of the sphincter may contain parietal cells. Argentaffine cells have also been described in the pyloric glands.

Fig. 357. Two cells from the boundary between neck and body of a gastric gland of *Macacus rhesus*. A zymogenic cell with black-stained secretory granules, and a mucous neck cell with pale vacuoles, previously occupied by mucous droplets. On the free surface, a net of terminal bars. Iron-hematoxylin stain. 1000 ×. (A.A.M.)

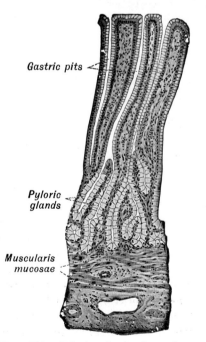

Gastric pits

Pyloric glands

Muscularis mucosae

Fig. 358. Pyloric glands from human stomach. Slightly diagrammatic. 75 ×. (After Braus.)

Cardiac Glands. These are compound tubular glands much like the cardiac glands of the esophagus. The terminal portions open directly into the gastric pits and show enlargements in many places. The clear glandular cells are found either alone or alternating with numerous parietal cells.

Ectopic Intestinal Epithelium and Glands in the Stomach. In the cardiac as well as in the pyloric region of the gastric mucosa, patches of intestinal epithelium and glands may be found among the gastric foveolae. Some believe them to be signs of chronic inflammation. The intestinal epithelium may be identified at once by its striated border and by the scattered goblet cells. The cardiac glands may open into these glands of Lieberkühn (see Chap. XXIV).

Lamina Propria. The scanty connective tissue of the lamina propria fills the narrow spaces between the glands and the muscularis mucosae and forms larger accumulations only between the necks of the glands and between the foveolae. It consists of a delicate network of collagenous and argyrophile fibrils and is almost devoid of elastic elements. Its cells have not been investigated satisfactorily. Besides oval pale nuclei which seem to belong to fibroblasts or reticular cells, the meshes of the fibers contain numerous small lymphocytes, and some plasma cells, eosinophile leukocytes, and mast cells. Sometimes, cells with coarsely granular acidophile inclusions are found between the epithelial cells of the glands; these are *Russell's bodies*, which may develop under physiological conditions, but are common in pathological cases. In the lamina propria, especially in the pyloric region, small, spherical accumulations of lymphatic tissue occur normally. Strands of smooth muscle also occur.

Other Layers of the Wall. The *muscularis mucosae* consists of an inner circular and an outer longitudinal layer of smooth muscle; in some places there is a third, outer circular layer. From the inner layer strands of smooth muscle cells run between the glands toward the surface. The contraction of these strands compresses the mucous membrane and probably facilitates the emptying of the glands.

The *submucous layer* consists of dense connective tissue which contains fat cells and is rich in mast cells, lymphoid wandering cells and eosinophile leukocytes. This layer contains the large blood and lymph vessels and venous plexuses.

The *muscularis externa* consists of three layers—an outer, mainly longitudinal, a middle circular, and an inner oblique. The outermost layer is formed by the continuation of the longitudinal fibers of the esophagus. They keep their longitudinal course only along the two curvatures, while on the anterior and posterior surfaces they gradually bend toward the larger curvature. In the pyloric region the longitudinal fibers are assembled in a layer which continues into the same layer of the intestinal wall.

The middle layer is the most regular and continuous of the three. In the pylorus it forms a thick, circular sphincter which helps control the evacuation of the stomach. The emptying of the stomach depends primarily on the contraction of the gastric musculature.

The work of all the parts of the muscular coat just described is regulated with marked precision. The wall of the stomach adapts itself to the volume of its contents without raising the pressure in its cavity.

The *serous membrane* is a thin layer of loose connective tissue attached to the muscularis externa and covered with mesothelium. It continues into the large and small omentum.

Histophysiological Remarks. The quantity of *gastric juice* secreted during twenty-four hours by the human stomach is estimated at 1000 to 1500 cc. It is a clear, colorless liquid which contains, besides water and salts, 0.4 to 0.5 per cent hydrochloric acid and enzymes. *Pepsin*, which digests protein in acid medium and clots milk, is the most important of these; it is a protein and has been crystallized by Northrop. He finds it probable "that the various pepsins vary from species to species, as do the hemoglobins." The other ferments are *rennin*, which has a stronger clotting action on milk than pepsin and is present mainly in infancy, and small amounts of a *lipase* (which splits fat). In the dog it is possible to obtain the

secretion of the two main parts of the stomach separately. Whereas the body of the stomach secretes only when certain stimuli act upon the mucous membrane (for instance, the ingestion of food or psychic impressions), the pyloric region secretes continuously. The secretion of the body contains

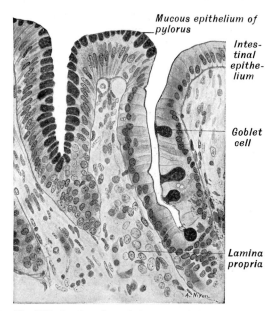

Fig. 359. Section through junction of the pyloric and duodenal epitheliums of an eight year old child. Stained with hematoxylin and for mucus with mucicarmine. 220 ×.

both pepsin and hydrochloric acid. It is also possible to distinguish two kinds of secretion furnished by the gastric glands—the secretion of the ordinary acid gastric juice, rich in pepsin, and of a juice which is also rich in pepsin, but contains a mucin-like substance and has only a weakly acid or even an alkaline reaction.

It is generally believed that pepsin is secreted by the zymogenic cells and that their granules are transformed into active pepsin only when acted upon by the hydrochloric acid. Analyses show that the pepsin content is higher, the more zymogenic cells in a given location (Linderstrøm-Lang and Holter). Injection of histamine causes the secretion of large amounts of acid gastric juice low in pepsin, while stimulation of the vagus nerve results in a great increase in the pepsin content of the juice. Bowie has shown that this is accompanied by an extensive discharge of zymogen granules. It has been observed that, if a small fragment of the fresh mucous membrane with gastric glands is treated with hydrochloric acid, the zymogenic cells disintegrate rapidly, while the parietal cells remain unchanged for a while. According to

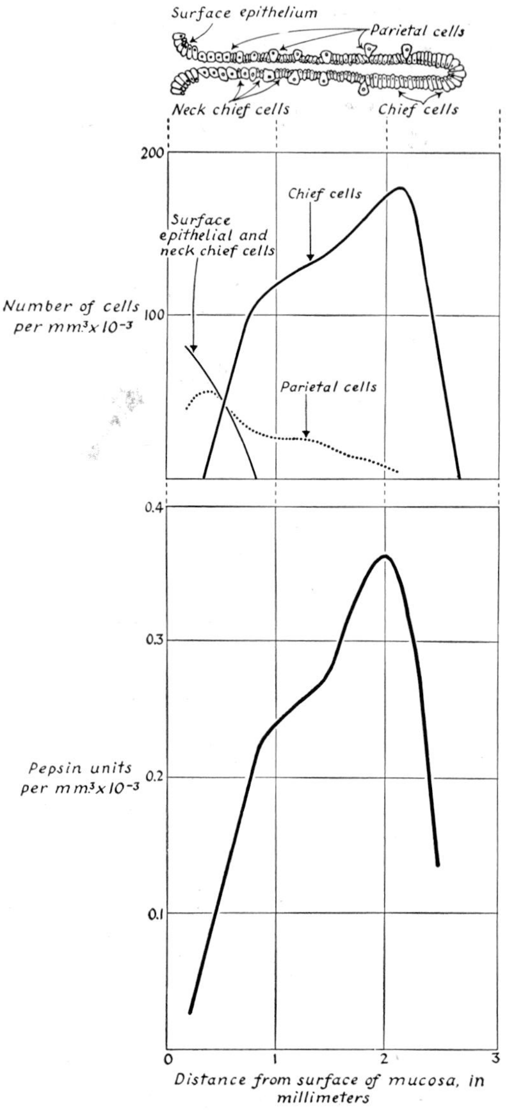

Fig. 360. In the upper part of the figure is a schematic disposition of cells in a single fundic gland. Upper graph shows the numbers of each cell type in sections at different levels, and the lower graph shows the pepsin activity in sections adjacent to those from which the cell counts were made. (After Linderstrøm-Lang.)

Ivy, the pyloric fluid does not contain enzymes in significant amounts.

Physiological and histological evidence supports the idea that the parietal cells are the source of the hydrochloric acid of the gastric juice, although the mechanism of formation of the acid is unknown. Earlier histologists tried to locate hydrochloric acid itself within or at the surface of the parietal cells. The problem is particularly difficult, since the acid is highly diffusible. It was realized in the course of time that no cell could tolerate the free acid in its cytoplasm, and attempts were then made to locate the chloride. The bulk of evidence favors the view that the process is similar to that of acidification of the urine which occurs in the distal convolution of the nephron. According to current theory, it is probable that neutral salt is excreted by the parietal cells and then follows reabsorption of the base in combination with bicarbonate, the process involving carbonic anhydrase and possibly urease. The over-all mechanism is an *ion exchange procedure*. In the actively secreting stomach, chloride is concentrated in the connective tissue of the submucous and, to a lesser extent, of the subepithelial layers. Chlorides have not been demonstrated in any of the epithelial cells except the zymogenic ones, and in them in only small amounts.

The mucous neck cells and the surface epithelium secrete *mucus*. The gastric mucus forms a layer on the surface of the mucous membrane which is supposed by some to protect it against autodigestion by delaying the diffusion of pepsin and hydrochloric acid, by inhibiting the action of pepsin, and by combining with the acid, for the mucosa is neutral during periods of inactivity. According to another opinion, autodigestion in life is prevented by an antiferment elaborated by the mucous membrane. Immediately after death autodigestion begins.

The gastric mucosa also contains a substance necessary for the production of erythrocytes.

Blood Vessels and Lymphatics of the Stomach. See page 383.

Nerves. The nerves of the stomach are of the same types and distribution as those of the intestine (see p. 383).

Histogenetic Remarks. In the young embryo the stomach is lined by an even layer of pseudostratified columnar epithelium. In embryos of 22.8 mm., groups of tall and low cells alternate, so that small pits arise, although the basement membrane remains even. In later stages (42 mm.) the pits begin to project into the underlying mesenchyme, while the tall cells between them begin to elaborate mucus. In embryos of 90 mm., at the bottom of the crypts, solid buds of granular cells appear—the primordia of the glands. In the 120-mm. stage the glandular primordia establish two kinds of cells. Some of them stain intensely with eosin and are accumulated at the blind ends and later assume a peripheral position—they are the future parietal cells; others remain pale—the future zymogenic cells.

At birth the length of the glands equals one half of the thickness of the mucosa. Their number gradually increases, partly through division of the blind ends of the tubes, partly through the formation of new buds of undifferentiated cells. The pyloric and cardiac glands seem to arise from the very beginning as structures different from the gastric glands.

REFERENCES

Bensley, R. R.: The Gastric Glands, in Cowdry's Special Cytology. 2d ed. New York, (1), 197, 1932.

Bowie, D. J., and Vineberg, A. M.: The Selective Action of Histamine and the Effect of Prolonged Vagal Stimulation on the Cells of Gastric Glands in the Dog. Quart. J. Exper. Physiol., 25:247, 1935.

Dawson, A. B.: Argentophile and Argentaffin Cells in the Gastric Mucosa of the Rat. Anat. Rec., 100: 319, 1948.

Hoerr, N. L., with an Introduction by R. R. Bensley: Cytological Studies by the Altmann-Gersh Freezing-drying Method. II. The Mechanism of Secretion of Hydochloric Acid in the Gastric Mucosa. Anat. Rec., 65:417, 1936.

Holter, H., and Linderstrøm-Lang, K.: Beiträge zur enzymatischen Histochemie; die Verteilung des Pepsins in der Schleimhaut des Schweinemagens. Ztschr. physiol. Chem., 226:149, 1934.

Landboe-Christensen, E.: Extent of the Pylorus Zone in the Human Stomach. Acta path. Microbiol. Scand., Suppl. 54, 671, 1944.

Langley, J. N.: On the Histology of the Mammalian Gastric Glands and the Relation of Pepsin to the Granules of the Chief Cells. J. Physiol., 3:269, 1880–82.

Lison, L.: Recherches histochimiques sur la sécrétion chlorhydrique de l'estomac. Ztschr. f. Zellforsch., 25:143, 1936.

Müller, E.: Drüsenstudien. II. Ueber die Fundusdrüsen des Magens. Ztschr. f. wiss. Zool., 64:624, 1898.

Oppel, A.: Schlund und Darm. Lehrbuch der vergl. mikr. Anat. der Wirbeltiere. Jena, 1897.

Plenk, H.: Der Magen. Handb. d. mikr. Anat. (v. Möllendorff), 1932, Vol. 5, Pt. 2, p. 1.

XXIV. THE INTESTINES

THE SMALL INTESTINE

The small intestine is a tube about 7 meters long and divisible into three portions, the *duodenum,* the *jejunum,* and the *ileum,* which gradually pass into one another. Their structure, although showing some differences, is everywhere the same in principle, so that one description applies to all. The main functions of the small intestine are (1) the forwarding of the chyme along its course, (2) continued digestion of the chyme by means of special juices secreted by its walls and by the accessory glands, and (3) absorption of the liquefied nutritive material into the blood and lymph vessels.

Surface of the Mucous Membrane. In the small intestine, from which the organism receives all its food material, the surface is enormously increased through the formation of circular folds, or *valves of Kerkring,* and the villi.

The folds are constant structures and do not disappear even when the intestinal wall is distended. They begin 2 to 5 cm. from the pylorus and reach their maximal development in the distal half of the duodenum and the proximal part of the jejunum; in the ileum they become smaller and less numerous and disappear in its middle. In the lower duodenum they reach a height of 8 mm. and usually extend over two thirds of the circumference. Often the folds branch; folds which run uninterruptedly around the whole intestinal tube are rare. The folds are formed by all the layers of the mucosa, including the muscularis mucosae; their core is submucosa.

The *villi* are outgrowths of the mucous membrane and have a length of 0.5 to 1.5 mm. They cover the entire surface of the mucosa and give it a typical velvety appearance; they vary from ten to forty to the square millimeter. In the duodenum they are

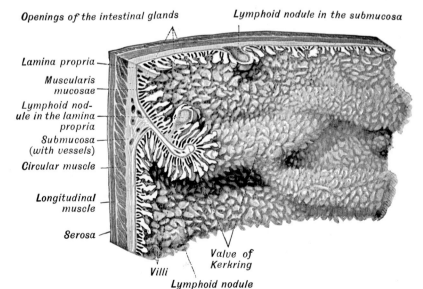

Openings of the intestinal glands — Lymphoid nodule in the submucosa

Lamina propria

Muscularis mucosae

Lymphoid nodule in the lamina propria

Submucosa (with vessels)

Circular muscle

Longitudinal muscle

Serosa

Villi

Valve of Kerkring

Lymphoid nodule

Fig. 361. Portion of small intestine; drawn with binocular microscope and from sections. 17 ×. (After Braus.)

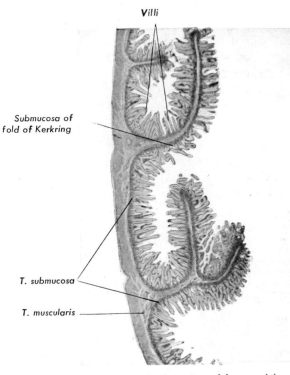

Fig. 362. Longitudinal section of human jejunum, showing three folds of Kerkring. Photomicrograph. H+E. 3 ×. (After von Herrath and Abramow.)

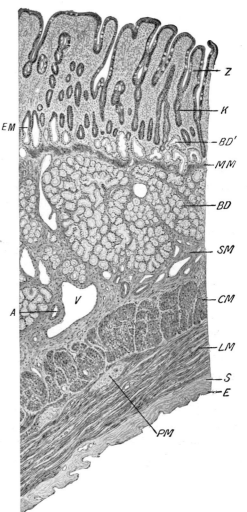

Fig. 363. From longitudinal section of human duodenum. A, Artery; BD, Brunner's glands in the submucosa; BD', Brunner's glands in the mucosa; CM, circular muscle cut across; E, mesothelium of serosa; EM, emptying of a Brunner gland into a crypt; K, crypt of Lieberkühn; LM, longitudinal muscle layer; MM, muscularis mucosae; PM, plexus myentericus with a ganglion cell in cross section; S, serosa; SM, submucosa; Z, villus. 30 ×. (After Schaffer.)

broad, leaflike structures arranged with their long diameter in the transverse direction and in alternating, longitudinal rows; in the ileum they gradually become more fingerlike.

Many villi, especially in the infant, are divided on their summits into two or more lobes by slits which extend for varying distances into the villi. In this way the villi are supposed to increase in number during the growth of the intestine. The innumerable openings of the glands, or *crypts of Lieberkühn*, may be seen between the bases of the villi with a magnifying lens. They are simple tubes 320 to 450 microns long, which penetrate the thickness of the mucous membrane and almost reach the muscularis mucosae. The spaces between them are wider than those between the glands in the stomach.

Epithelium. The epithelium, which covers the free surface of the mucous membrane, is simple columnar. Three types of cells can be distinguished in it: (1) columnar cells with a striated border, (2) goblet cells, (3) argentaffine cells.

The columnar cells have a prismatic form and a height of 22 to 26 microns; their outlines change considerably with the movement of the villi. The free surface is covered with a striated border rich in phosphatase, and the lower part of the cell contains the oval nucleus. Under the striated border there

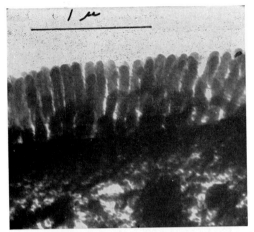

Fig. 364. Electron micrograph showing the minute processes which constitute the striated border of epithelium of ileum of rat. Osmic acid fixation. 32,500 ×. (After Granger and Baker.)

is always a thin layer of homogeneous cytoplasm. Under this layer longitudinally arranged, wavy mitochondria are accumulated. The Golgi net occupies the space between these mitochondria and the nucleus. Beneath the nucleus the cytoplasm contains a group of granular mitochondria.

The bases of the cells are connected with the surface of the lamina propria. This close connection of the epithelium with the connective tissue condition withstands successfully the strain arising from the movements of the villi and the mechanical action of the passing food material. After fixation the epithelium often appears detached from the stroma on the summit of the villi, and a cavity is seen between the two tissues. This free space is an artefact, caused especially by the agonal contraction of the smooth muscles in the core of the villi.

Goblet cells are scattered between the cylindrical epithelial cells. The *argentaffine cells* are more common in the glands of Lieberkühn. Everywhere in the small intestine, irregularly distributed lymphocytes can be seen penetrating from the lamina propria into the epithelium of the villi.

The epithelium of the villi, under physiological conditions, is shed in considerable quantities and, together with the mucus, forms a part of the feces. In experimental animals a short section of the small intestine may be separated from the rest of the gut and its ends connected to form a loop, while its attachment to the mesentery remains unaltered and the remaining ends of the intestine are sewed together. After a time the isolated loop is found greatly distended with

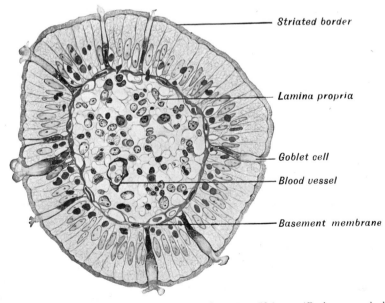

Striated border

Lamina propria

Goblet cell

Blood vessel

Basement membrane

Fig. 365. Cross section of villus of human jejunum. Iron-hematoxylin-azan. 514 ×. (Redrawn and slightly modified after V. Patzelt.)

digestive juices, masses of mucus and desquamated epithelium. This explains why a certain amount of feces is formed even in a starving organism. It is clear that such extensive losses require a corresponding regeneration.

Crypts of Lieberkühn. The epithelium covering the villi continues into the glands of Lieberkühn. Above the bottom of the crypt, their walls are lined with a low columnar epithelium which contains numerous mitoses. Here regeneration takes place, and the new cells moving upward differentiate into goblet cells and into the columnar cells with striated borders. All the stages in this process are to be seen in the upper half of the crypt.

In the bottom of the glands of Lieberkühn in the small intestine, the large *cells of Paneth* occur regularly. The base of these cells is occupied by chromophile substance. Around the large, spherical nucleus are a few mitochondria. Above the nucleus the cytoplasm is filled with large, round, acidophile, secretory granules. Sometimes each granule is surrounded by a clear vacuole; a discharge into the lumen is rarely seen except under the influence of pilocarpine. The granules dissolve in acids and in mineral salts, but are resistant to alkalies. Their nature is not clear.

Argentaffine Cells. Between the cells lining the glands of Lieberkühn (rarely in the epithelium of the villi) are found the argentaffine cells, which differ from the rest of the epithelium by their form and by the presence of specific granules in their cytoplasm. They are scattered singly, and their number varies greatly. Moderate numbers are found in the stomach. In the jejunum and ileum they are relatively rare; they are more common in the duodenum and particularly in the appendix. Their body, as a rule, adheres closely to the basement membrane and even bulges into its outer surface. The cytoplasm of the base of the cells is filled with small granules which stain easily with eosin. They are electively stained black by solutions of silver ammonium oxide, and acquire a brownish-yellow color after the action of chromates. They vary from species to species;

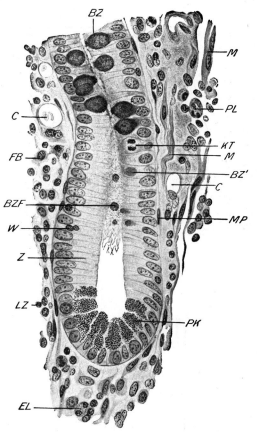

Fig. 366. A crypt of Lieberkühn with surrounding lamina propria. *BZ*, Goblet cells; *BZ'*, goblet cells at end or beginning of secretion; *BZF*, goblet cells cut tangentially; *C*, capillary; *EL*, eosinophile leukocyte; *FB*, reticular cells; *KT*, mitosis in an epithelial cell; *LZ*, lymphocyte; *M*, smooth muscle cells; *MP*, reticular cells beneath basement membrane; *PK*, Paneth cells; *PL*, polymorphonuclear leukocytes; *W*, wandering cells in the epithelium; *Z*, epithelial cells of the gland. 380 ×. (After Schaffer.)

they give positive tests for polysaccharides in some. Their nature and function are obscure.

Lamina Propria. The lamina propria of the mucous membrane fills the spaces between the glands of Lieberkühn and forms the core of the villi. It is a peculiar type of connective tissue and contains a stroma of argyrophile fibers similar to that of the lymphatic tissue. Close to the fibers are fixed cells with oval, pale nuclei; these are perhaps comparable with the primitive reticular elements of the lymphatic tissue stroma. Some of them become macrophages which may contain pigment inclusions; sometimes they

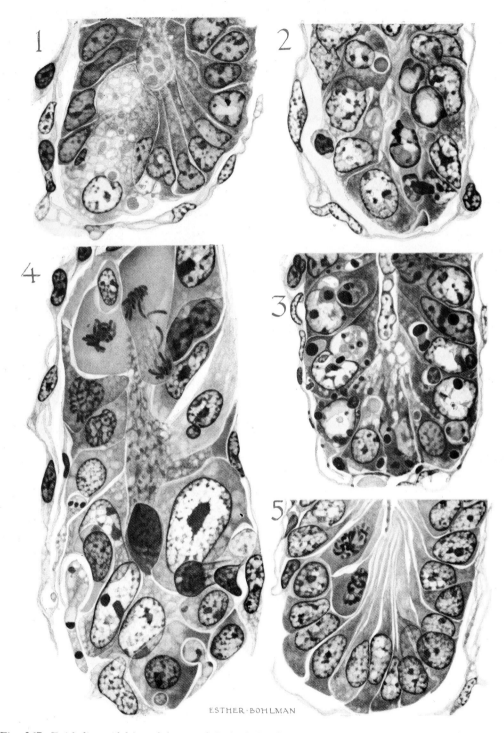

ESTHER·BOHLMAN

Fig. 367. Epithelium of base of crypts of Lieberkühn from duodenum of rat, showing degenerative and regenerative changes after total body exposure to 600 roentgens of x-rays. *1*, normal; *2*, one-half hour; *3*, three hours; *4*, twenty-eight hours, and *5*, five days after irradiation. (After M. Pierce, in Histopathology of Irradiation from External and Internal Sources. Courtesy of Atomic Energy Commission.)

react positively to tests for iron. In vitally stained animals, however, they contain, as a rule, only few dye granules. The dye storing is more pronounced in the macrophages of the lower ileum and cecum.

The argyrophile framework of the lamina propria at the epithelium-covered surface is condensed to a reticular basement membrane. Fine elastic networks extend from the muscularis mucosae along the blood vessels; they also surround the glands of Lieberkühn and take part in the formation of their basement membrane. The argyrophile framework in many places contains strands of smooth muscle which arise from the inner surface of the muscularis mucosae, run toward the surface, and are especially prominent in the core of the villi. Here they are arranged parallel to the axis of the villus, around the central lacteal.

The meshes of the argyrophile framework contain large numbers of free cells. The most numerous are small lymphocytes; medium-sized forms also occur; large lymphocytes are rare. Plasma cells are numerous in all stages of development. They are said to increase greatly in number during digestion. Many of them degenerate and produce Russell's bodies. The lamina propria always contains granular leukocytes, mainly eosinophils, most of which migrated from the blood vessels. Sometimes, especially in the guinea pig, a few eosinophile myelocytes of local origin, with occasional mitoses, can be found. Mast cells are infrequent in the human intestine. Among them are small, young cells with but a few granules.

Many lymphocytes and a few granular leukocytes penetrate the epithelium on the villi or the glands of Lieberkühn, and occasionally even pass into the lumen. This phenomenon increases in intensity in the caudal direction and reaches its highest development in the large intestine.

Another peculiar type of wandering cell found in the epithelium of the crypts in many animals is a cell with a small, round, dark nucleus and a large, swollen body containing a number of large, round granules or droplets which stain bright red with eosin—

the *globular leukocyte*. Sometimes they divide mitotically; they are also found in a degenerating condition with a pyknotic nucleus.

Lymphatic Tissue. The lamina propria of the small intestine contains great numbers of isolated lymphatic nodules ("solitary follicles") varying from 0.6 to 3 mm. in diameter. They are scattered all over the intestine, but are more numerous and larger in the distal part (Fig. 370); in the ileum they may be found on the surface of the *valvulae conniventes* or between them. If they are

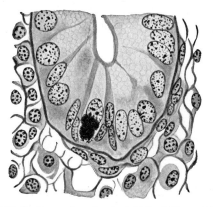

Fig. 368. Bottom of a gland of Lieberkühn, with an argentaffine cell. (Redrawn from Masson.)

small, they occupy only the deeper layer of the mucous membrane above the muscularis mucosae. The larger ones occupy the whole thickness of the mucosa, bulge on its surface, and may even extend through the muscularis mucosae into the submucous layer. They are visible to the naked eye, and their surface is free from villi and usually also from crypts.

Groups of many solitary nodules massed together are called *patches of Peyer* or *aggregated nodules*. They occur, as a rule, only in the ileum, but occasionally may be found even in the duodenum; their number is estimated at thirty to forty. They always occur on the side of the intestinal wall opposite to the line of attachment of the mesentery; they are elongated, oval, slightly prominent areas. Their long diameter varies from 12 to 20 mm., the short from 8 to 12 mm. They consist of dense lymphatic tissue with large lymphocytopoietic or reaction centers in

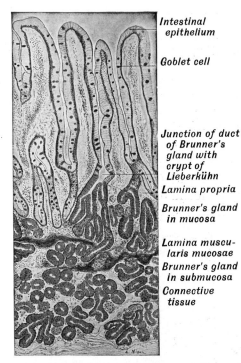

Intestinal
epithelium

Goblet cell

Junction of duct
of Brunner's
gland with
crypt of
Lieberkühn
Lamina propria

Brunner's gland
in mucosa

Lamina muscu-
laris mucosae
Brunner's gland
in submucosa
Connective
tissue

Fig. 369. Section of duodenum of a child of eight years. Mucicarmine and hematoxylin stains. 65 ×.

their interior. Their periphery is marked by a thin layer of condensed reticular fibers.

The lamina propria and the submucosa in the vicinity of the nodules are always infiltrated with lymphocytes. Large numbers of them penetrate the epithelium and finally reach the cavity of the intestine. In old age the follicles and the patches of Peyer undergo involution.

Muscularis Mucosae. This layer averages 38 microns in thickness and consists of an inner circular and an outer longitudinal layer of smooth muscle and of elastic networks.

Other Coats of the Wall. The submucous layer consists of dense connective tissue with numerous elastic networks and occasional lobules of adipose tissue. In the duodenum it is occupied by a thick layer of duodenal glands.

The external and internal layers of the muscular coat are well developed and regular in the small intestine. Carey (1921) showed that these are not arranged, as in the conventional descriptions, in an inner circular and

an outer longitudinal layer, but that the outer layer is wound as an open spiral (one turn in 200 to 500 mm.), and the inner as a close spiral (one turn in 0.5 to 1 mm.). Between them is the sympathetic myenteric nerve plexus (Fig. 376). Some strands of muscular cells pass from one layer into the other. The external coat consists of a layer of mesothelial cells resting on loose connective tissue. At the attachment of the mesentery, the serous layer of the intestines continues onto the surface of the mesentery.

Duodenal Glands (of Brunner). The glands of Brunner appear in the region of the sphincter of the pylorus with the first glands of Lieberkühn. Sometimes they extend into the pyloric region for several centimeters. They are arranged in lobules 0.5 to 1 mm. in diameter. Their terminal portions are richly branched and coiled tubules. These fuse into branching ducts which open into the bottom or side of a crypt of Lieberkühn. The gland is located for the most part in the submucosa, while the ducts pierce the muscularis mucosae. The cuboidal glandular cells contain fine granules, which stain with mucihematein after fixation in alcohol. After fixation and staining in aqueous solutions they present the usual aspect of a mucous cell—a pale, irregular cytoplasmic network with large, empty meshes and a flattened dark nucleus at the base. The cells of the terminal portions gradually pass into the cells of the ducts. They become smaller and contain less of the mucous secretion. The transition into the crypts of Lieberkühn is abrupt.

In the distal two thirds of the duodenum the glands of Brunner gradually diminish in size and finally disappear. They show a tendency to occupy the core of the circular folds and are separated by increasing, free intervals. In some cases they extend into the upper part of the jejunum.

THE APPENDIX

The appendix is a blindly ending evagination of the cecum in man and many animals. Its wall is thickened by an extensive development of lymphatic tissue which forms an

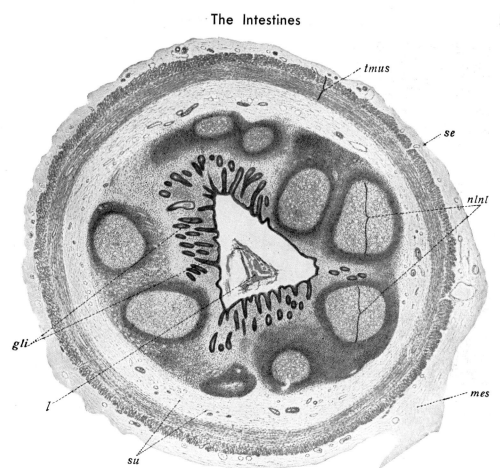

Fig. 370. Appendix from a twenty-three year old man. *l*, Lumen with feces; *gli*, crypts of Lieberkühn; *nlnl*, centers of lymphatic nodules; *su*, submucosa; *tmus*, muscularis externa; *se*, serosa; *mes*, mesentery. 22 ×. (After Sobotta.)

almost continuous layer, with many large and small lymphatic nodules. The small lumen in cross section has an angular form. Sometimes it contains masses of dead cells and detritus; in other cases it is obliterated. It is difficult to draw a distinct line between the normal and certain pathological conditions in this organ. The glands of Lieberkühn radiate from the lumen; they have an irregular shape and variable length and are embedded in the lymphatic tissue. The epithelium of the surface of the glands contains only a few goblet cells and consists mostly of columnar cells with a striated border. The zone of undifferentiated cells with mitoses is shorter than in the small intestine. In the bottom of the glands, besides occasional cells of Paneth, argentaffine cells are regularly

present. They are more numerous than in the small intestine and average five to ten to a gland; they also occur in the upper part of the glands. Villi are absent.

The lymphatic tissue of the appendix is similar to that of the tonsils. Often it presents chronic inflammatory changes. The muscularis mucosae of the appendix is poorly developed. The submucosa forms a thick layer with blood vessels and nerves, and occasional fat lobules. The muscularis externa is reduced in thickness, but always shows the two usual layers. The serous coat is similar to that covering the rest of the intestines.

THE LARGE INTESTINE

The mucous membrane of the large intestine does not form folds except in its last

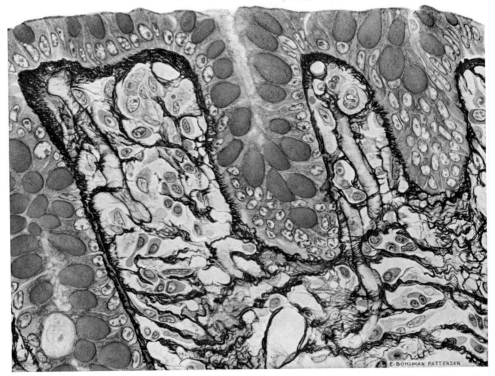

Fig. 371. Slightly tangential section through mucous membrane of human colon. The reticular fibers are condensed beneath the epithelium and about the blood vessels. The mucigen of the goblet cells stains blue. Bielschowsky-Foot and Mallory-azan stains. 600 ×.

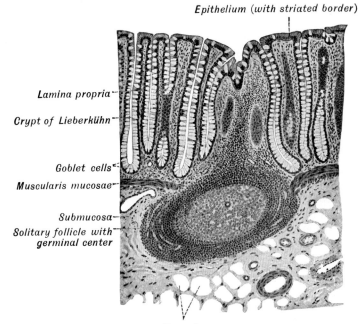

Epithelium (with striated border)

Lamina propria

Crypt of Lieberkühn

Goblet cells

Muscularis mucosae

Submucosa

Solitary follicle with germinal center

Fat cells

Fig. 372. Mucosa of human transverse colon, showing a solitary follicle. 70 ×. (After Braus.)

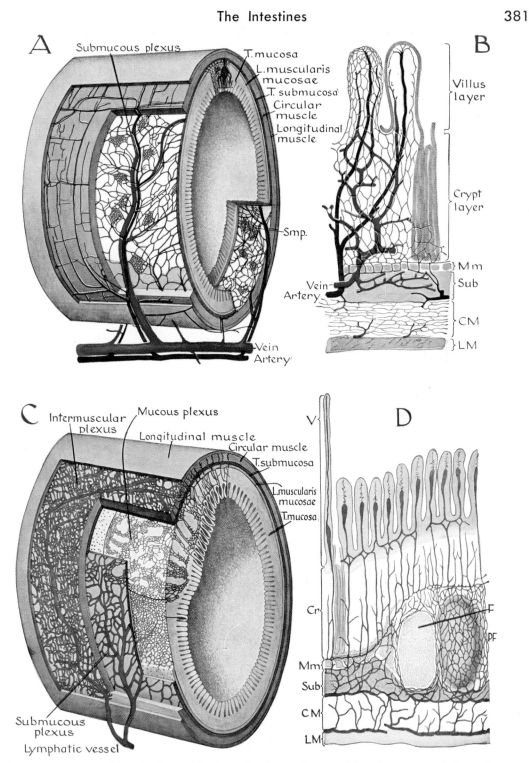

Fig. 373. Diagrams of distribution of blood vessels, A and B, and of lymphatics, C and D, in the small intestine of the dog. B and D are drawn on a larger scale to show details. CM, Circular muscle; Cr, crypt; LM, longitudinal muscle; Mm, lamina muscularis mucosae; Sub, tunica submucosa; V, villus; F, follicle; PF, perifollicular plexus. (Redrawn and slightly modified after Mall.)

portion, the rectum. Being devoid of villi, it has a smooth surface. The villi cease, as a rule, above the ileocecal valve.

The *glands of Lieberkühn* are straight tubules and attain a greater length than in the small intestine—up to 0.5 mm., and in the rectum to 0.7 mm. Their structure differs from that in the small intestine by the richness in goblet cells. The free surface, between

The *muscularis mucosae* is well developed and consists of longitudinal and circular strands. It may send slender bundles of muscle cells toward the surface of the mucosa. The submucous layer does not present any peculiarities. The muscularis externa differs from the same coat in the small intestine by the arrangement of its outer longitudinal layer, which is massed into three thick, longi-

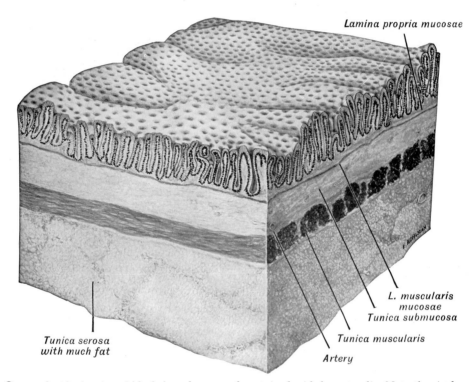

Fig. 374. Camera lucida drawing of block from human colon stained with hematoxylin. Note the single muscle layer. The openings of the glands of Lieberkühn are clearly shown. 24 ×. (Drawn by Miss E. Bohlman.)

the openings of the glands, is lined with simple columnar epithelium with a thin striated border. At the bottom of the crypts are the usual proliferating, undifferentiated epithelial cells and occasionally argentaffine cells; as a rule there are no cells of Paneth.

The structure of the *lamina propria* is essentially the same as in the small intestine; eosinophile leukocytes are abundant, often penetrating the epithelium of the crypts. Scattered lymphatic nodules are always present in varying numbers and are also found in the rectum. They reach far into the submucous layer.

tudinal strands—the *taenia coli*. In the rectum it again becomes continuous all around the periphery of the wall. The serous coat of the colon in its free portion forms the *appendices epiploicae*; these protuberances consist of adipose tissue and accumulations of cells similar to those in the omentum.

In the anal region the mucous membrane is thrown into longitudinal folds, the *rectal columns of Morgagni*. The crypts of Lieberkühn suddenly become short and disappear, while on the surface, along a jagged line about 2 cm. above the anal opening, stratified squamous epithelium appears with superficial, flattened cells. This is a transition zone between the mucous membrane and skin. At the level of the external sphincter the surface layer assumes the structure of the skin, and here sebaceous and large apocrine, circumanal glands appear. The lamina propria here contains convolutes of large veins, which, when abnormally dilated, appear as hemorrhoidal nodes.

Blood Vessels. The arrangement of the blood and lymph vessels in the wall of the stomach and intestine is similar in principle. As the important differences depend mainly on the presence of villi, the small intestine shows significant peculiarities.

In the stomach the arteries arise from the two arterial arches along the lesser and greater curvatures and are distributed to the ventral and dorsal surfaces. The arteries reach one side of the intestine with the mesentery. They run in the serous coat and break up into large branches which penetrate the muscularis externa and enter the submucous layer, where they form a large submucous plexus.

In the stomach and colon the submucous plexus gives off branches directed toward the surface. Some break up into capillaries supplying the muscularis mucosae; others form capillary networks throughout the mucosa and surround the glands with dense meshes. The capillary net is especially prominent around the foveolae.

From the superficial, periglandular capillary networks, veins of considerable caliber arise. They form a venous plexus between the bottom of the glands and the muscularis mucosae. From this plexus, branches run into the submucosa and from a venous plexus. From this submucous plexus, the large veins follow the arteries and pass through the muscularis externa into the serous membrane. The veins of the submucous plexus (in the stomach) are provided with valves and a relatively thick, muscular coat.

In the small intestine the submucous arterial plexus gives off two kinds of branches which run toward the mucosa. Some of these arteries ramify on the inner surface of the muscularis mucosae, and break up into capillary networks which surround the crypts of Lieberkühn in the same way as about the glands of the stomach. Other arteries are especially destined for the villi, each villus receiving one or sometimes several such small arteries. These vessels enter the base of the villus and form a dense capillary network immediately under its epithelium. Near the tip of the villus one or two small veins arise from the superficial capillary network and run downward, anastomose with the glandular venous plexus, and pass into the submucosa, where they join the veins of the submucous plexus. These veins in the intestine have no valves. Their continuations which pass through the muscularis externa with the arteries are provided, however, with valves. Valves disappear in the collecting veins of the mesentery.

Lymph Vessels. In the stomach the lymphatics begin as an extensive system of large lymphatic capillaries in the superficial layer of the mucous membrane between the glands. They are always deeper than the blood capillaries. They anastomose everywhere throughout the mucous membrane, surround the glandular tubules, and take a downward course to the inner surface of the mucous membrane, where they form a plexus of fine lymphatic vessels. Branches of the plexus pierce the muscularis mucosae and form a plexus of lymphatics provided with valves in the submucosa. From this submucous plexus larger lymphatics run through the muscularis externa; here they receive numerous tributaries from the lymphatic plexus in the muscular coat and then follow the blood vessels into the retroperitoneal tissues. In the wall of the colon the lymphatics show a similar arrangement.

The lymphatic vessels of the intestine are important in the absorption of fat from the small intestine. During digestion, all their ramifications are filled with milky white lymph—a fine emulsion of neutral fats. This white lymph, drained from the intestine, is called *chyle*, and the lymphatics which carry it, *lacteals*.

In the small intestine the most conspicuous parts of the lymphatic system are the *central lacteals* in the core of the villi. Each conical villus has one lacteal which occupies an axial position and ends blindly near the tip. The broader villi of the duodenum may contain two or perhaps more lacteals which intercommunicate. The lumen of these lacteals, when distended, is considerably larger than that of the blood capillaries. The wall consists of thin endothelial cells and is everywhere connected with the argyrophile reticulum and surrounded by thin, longitudinal strands of smooth muscle.

The central lacteals at the base of the villi anastomose with the lymphatic capillaries between the glands, which have a similar arrangement as in the stomach and also form a plexus on the inner surface of the muscularis mucosae. Branches of this plexus, provided with valves, pierce the muscularis mucosae and form on its outer surface, in the submucosa, a loose plexus of larger lymphatics. The latter also receives tributaries from the dense network of large, thin-walled lymphatic capillaries which closely surround the surface of the solitary and aggregated follicles. The large lymphatics which run from the submucous plexus through the muscularis externa into the mesentery receive additional branches from a dense, tangential plexus located between the circular and longitudinal layers of the muscularis externa.

Nerves. The nerve supply seems to be similar in principle in all parts of the gastro-intestinal tube and consists of an intrinsic and an extrinsic part. The first of these is comprised of nerve cells and their fibers located and originating in the wall of the intestine. The extrinsic nerves are represented by the pregangli-

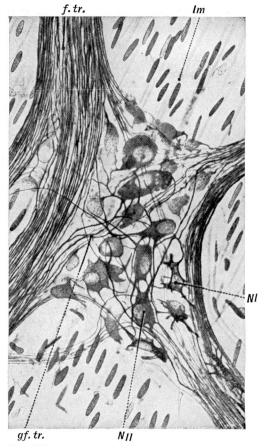

f. tr.   *lm*

gf. tr.   *N II*

Fig. 375. Ganglion of myenteric plexus from small intestine of guinea pig. N_I, Neuron of Type I; N_{II}, neuron of Type II; *f.tr.*, interganglionic fiber tract; *lm*, longitudinal muscle coat; *gf.tr.*, intraganglionic fibers. Silver nitrate. 335 ×. (After C. J. Hill.)

onic fibers of the vagus and the post-ganglionic fibers of the sympathetic. The latter run to the intestine from the celiac plexus. They enter the intestinal wall through the mesentery along the branches of the large vessels.

Numerous groups of nerve cells and bundles of nerve fibers are seen in the narrow space between the circular and the longitudinal layers of the muscularis externa. This is the *myenteric plexus of Auerbach.* In the submucosa similar elements form the *submucous plexus of Meissner.* These plexuses form the intrinsic nervous mechanism of the intestinal wall.

The nerve cells of the enteric ganglia are connected with one another by strands of nonmyelinated nerve fibers of both extrinsic and intrinsic origin. These nerve cells appear in two principal forms, which may present differences in their secondary characters (Fig. 375). The first type occurs exclusively in the myenteric plexus. It is a multipolar cell with short dendrites which terminate in brushlike arborizations on the

bodies of cells of the second type in the same ganglion. The axon can be traced for a considerable distance through neighboring ganglia and is supposed to form connections with cells of the second type in other ganglia. These neurons are associative.

The cells of the second type are far more numerous and show great variations in their forms. Their dendrites vary in number and are often missing. They begin as diffuse receptive endings in relation with nerve cells of the first and second types in the ganglia of origin or in other ganglia. The axon enters a fiber bundle and divides; its branches terminate in the circular or longitudinal layer of the muscularis externa in connection with individual smooth muscle cells. Thus the neurons of the second type are motor. Those in the myenteric plexus supply the muscularis externa; those of the submucous plexus supply the muscularis mucosae and the muscles of the villi.

A third cell type occurs in the enteric plexuses and also scattered in the submucosa and in the interior of the villi. This is the "interstitial cell," with a finely vacuolated protoplasm and short, branching processes which interlace with other processes to form an irregular feltwork. It does not contain neurofibrils, and may possibly be of microglial nature.

Most of the nonmyelinated fibers of the bundles which connect the ganglia and the fibers in the ganglia are processes of the enteric neurons. The rest is formed by extrinsic fibers, mainly of vagal, and to some extent of sympathetic origin.

The vagal fibers terminate as pericellular arborizations on cells of the second type in the enteric ganglia. The sympathetic fibers cannot be distinguished from the axons of the motor cells in the fiber bundles. They do not seem to enter into synaptic relationship with the nerve cells of the ganglia but take part, together with the motor axons, in the formation of the intramuscular plexuses and terminate in connection with the muscular cells. The sympathetic fibers supply the blood vessels, too. Some of them have also been described as forming a plexus in the subserous coat and ending freely in the connective tissue.

If the intestine is detached from the mesentery and placed in warm Tyrode solution, it will show normal peristaltic movements if the mucous membrane is stimulated by objects introduced into the lumen. This shows that the intestine is an automatic organ whose movements are determined by the local neuromuscular mechanism and that they are only regulated through the extrinsic nerves. Numerous nerve endings of sensory nature have been found under and in the epithelial layers of the villi.

Some investigators believe that the enteric plexuses mediate complete reflex arcs, the sensory component being enteric, a cell of the plexus, with dendritic endings in contact with the epithelium of the villi or the glands of Lieberkühn, while the axons transmit the impulse to another enteric neuron whose axon ends in the smooth muscles. Most authors hold, however, that all neurons of the enteric plexuses are of efferent nature and that therefore the sensory nerve endings in the mucous membrane must be of extrinsic nature. The local reflexes in the intestine are explained as "axon reflexes." The axons of the enteric neurons are supposed to divide into two branches, one of which receives stimuli transmitted to the other branch without passing through the cell body.

Histophysiological Remarks. An important role in the digestion of the chyme in the small intestine is played by the two large glands attached to the duodenum: the *liver,* which secretes the bile, and the *pancreas,* which secretes the pancreatic juice. The wall of the intestine itself adds an important secretion, the *intestinal juice.*

The glands of Brunner, like the pyloric glands, secrete continuously. Their secretion is a viscid, mucous, alkaline liquid. It contains a proteolytic enzyme activated by hydrochloric acid and closely resembles pepsin. It is supposed to be especially active in the digestion of the collagen of adipose tissue, and thus makes the fat of the latter easily accessible to the action of fat-splitting enzymes.

The intestinal juice proper is secreted by the portions of the small intestine which do not contain glands of Brunner. It is a yellow, alkaline liquid which always contains small flakes of mucin mixed with desquamated epithelial cells and many micro-organisms. There are several important enzymes in the juice: *erepsin,* which breaks down the proteins to amino acids, a *lipase,* a *nuclease,* several *enzymes for splitting carbohydrates,* and *enterokinase,* which activates trypsinogen. The mucin of the intestinal juice is important in the formation of feces. *Secretin,* a hormone formed in the duodenal mucosa, is absorbed by the blood and stimulates the pancreas.

The surface of the villi serves primarily for

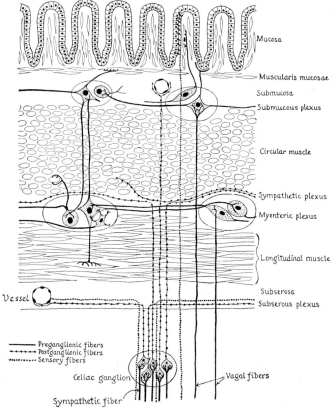

Fig. 376. Diagrammatic representation of the relations of the elements of the gut plexuses as seen in longitudinal section of the gut wall. (Redrawn and modified from C. J. Hill.)

absorption, while the intestinal juice is secreted by the glands of Lieberkühn. What cells of the latter are instrumental in the secretion of the enzymes is not known. The mucus obviously originates from the goblet cells in the crypts and on the villi.

The *secretion of the large intestine* contains small quantities of enzymes. Its main

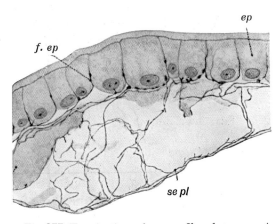

Fig. 377. Terminations of sensory fibers between epithelial cells of villus of newborn rabbit; Silver method of de Castro. *ep,* Epithelium of villus; *se pl,* subepithelial plexus; *f. ep,* fibrils between the epithelial cells. 560 ×. (After C. J. Hill.)

constituent, the mucus, plays a mechanical role in providing the necessary consistency to the feces and lubricating the mucous membrane.

The nutritive components of the chyme are converted into soluble, easily diffusible substances so that they can be absorbed. The partially digested proteins coming from the stomach are broken down into their constituent amino acids by the action of trypsin and erepsin. The neutral fat is split into glycerol and fatty acids. The carbohydrates are transformed into simple sugars, mainly glucose. These substances are absorbed by the surface epithelium of the intestine, especially by that of the villi. The total surface is estimated at 4 to 5 square meters.

The absorptive process cannot as yet be explained on known laws of diffusion and osmosis. After passing through the outermost layer of the epithelium, the different substances undergo complex transformations whose nature is for the most part obscure.

The description of the intestinal epithelium, as given earlier, applies to the resting epithelial cells. During absorption, especially of proteins, changes in the mitochondria have been described by some authors. Some believe the Golgi net to be the first part of the cell to show changes in connection with absorption; the lacunae are said to enlarge and to contribute to the formation of vacuoles.

Proteins can rarely be seen on their way through the epithelium, since they are absorbed in the form of soluble amino acids and probably carried at once by the blood of the portal vein to the liver. However, in young, especially in suckling animals, the striated border of the epithelium seems to be much more permeable to foreign substances than in the adult. It is possible that even unchanged protein, including some antibodies, may enter by the intestinal epithelium of the young. In suckling mice the epithelium of the small intestine, especially in its lower part, contains many large granules apparently of protein nature. They may be compared with the meconium corpuscles found in human fetuses (Fig. 379). Even microscopically visible particulate matter, as granules of India ink, when fed to suckling mice penetrate the epithelium, a phenomenon never observed in adults.

Of all the nutritive substances, the transformation of fat is the easiest to follow, because it appears as sharply outlined droplets which give characteristic staining reactions. During absorption of fat, the striated border and the subjacent homogeneous protoplasmic layer always remain free of fat droplets. The claim that fat droplets occur within the striated border during absorption has not been confirmed, except, perhaps, for suckling animals. An increasing accumulation of fat droplets, at first small, and then larger, develops during absorption above the Golgi net and the nucleus. Thus at least some glycerol and fatty acids are absorbed through the striated border and are at once synthesized into neutral fat. In what way the synthesized fat finds its way into the lacteals of the villi is not known.

The *amino acids* and *glucose* enter the blood of the subepithelial capillaries and with it are brought through the portal vein into the liver, where they undergo further transformations. The largest part of the absorbed fat is carried away from the intestine with the chyle.

An important mechanism for the transmission of substances absorbed by the epithelium into the blood and lymph are the movements of the villi. They can be observed in a living animal if a loop of the intestine is split open and the surface of the mucous membrane is watched with a binocular microscope. There seems to be no relation between the movements of the individual villi. Every villus contracts independently, approximately six times a minute. Here and there a villus suddenly becomes shorter by about one half its length, while its thickness remains unchanged; then it expands again. Thus, during the contraction, the volume of the villus is greatly reduced and the contents of its capillaries and especially of the central lacteal are forwarded into the submucous plexus. When the villus expands, the liquid which penetrates the epithelium is believed to reach the central lacteal and the blood capillaries. The expansion

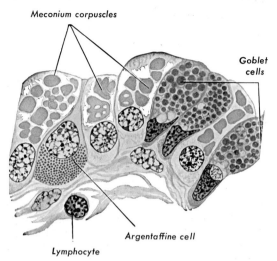

Fig. 379. Epithelium from tip of villus in small intestine of 4½ month human fetus: Hematoxylin-eosin-azure II. 1040 ×. (A.A.M.)

calls forth another contraction, and so on. The contraction is obviously due to the shortening of the longitudinal muscular strands of the core of the villus. The movement is believed to be regulated by the submucous plexus of Meissner. Direct mechanical stimulation of the base of a villus with a bristle also calls forth a contraction; the stimulus radiates from the affected villus to the surrounding ones.

Histogenetic Remarks. The histogenesis of the mucous membrane of the intestine resembles that of the stomach. At first the boundary between the epithelium and the connective tissue is even. The development of villi begins in embryos of 20 mm. in the duodenum and gradually extends downward. In the duodenum, jejunum and the upper part of the ileum they arise as isolated epithelial outgrowths. In the remaining parts of the intestine, longitudinal ridges develop which later are subdivided by the transverse furrows into single villi. The number of the villi in a given stretch increases through the appearance of new outgrowths in the hollows between the older villi. In a fetus of 100 mm. villi are found all along the intestine, including the colon, although they disappear from the latter in the later stages. This is due either to a fusion of the villi from their base upward or to their shortening through the stretching of the growing wall. In an embryo of 55 mm. the supranuclear protoplasm of the epithelial cells on the tips of the villi acquires a transparent aspect, while on the free surface a condensed cytoplasmic layer develops. Between these elements, scattered goblet cells appear.

In a fetus of four months, the epithelium of the

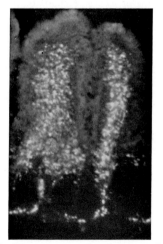

Fig. 378. Fluorescence photomicrograph of small intestine of rat during absorption of vitamin A concentrates. The vitamin A fluorescence is imparted by the epithelium, by the lamina propria of the villi, and by the contents of the lacteals. (After Popper and Greenberg.)

villi has a manifold appearance. In the lower parts of the small intestine the common epithelial cells with the clear supranuclear parts contain a multitude of coarse, yellow granules. They are called *meconium corpuscles* and are similar to those seen in the lumen of the intestine. Their yellowish color is due to adsorption of bile pigment.

Between the common epithelial cells are many typical goblet cells. Beginning with the fourth month, argentaffine cells make their appearance. During the seventh month the cells of Paneth appear. In the human fetus they seem to occur not only in the crypts, but also on the villi.

The development of the glands of Lieberkühn also starts in the duodenum and proceeds downward. In a fetus of the fourth month the excavations between the villi are lined with small crowded cells with a cytoplasm darker than that of the epithelium of the villi. From these cells, evaginations arise which penetrate the subjacent connective tissue. In the seventh month, besides the formation of glands from new invaginations, a dichotomous division of the blind ends of the glands contributes largely to the continuing increase of the number of glands. Bifurcation of the crypts proceeds in the newborn.

The glands of Brunner make their appearance during the sixth month as massive, epithelial ingrowths in the depth of the duodenal crypts. In a fetus of 290 mm. they are numerous in the upper part of the duodenum and consist of branching tubules. Farther downward they are smaller, and the intervals between them larger.

REFERENCES

Bensley, R. R.: The Structure of the Glands of Brunner. The Decennial Publ., University of Chicago, 10:279, 1903.

Dempsey, E. W., and Deane, H. W.: The Cytological Localization, Substrate Specificity, and *p*H Optima of Phosphatases in the Duodenum of the Mouse. J. Cell. & Comp. Physiol., 27:159, 1946.

Emmel, V. M.: Alkaline Phosphatase in the Golgi Zone of Absorbing Cells of the Small Intestine. Anat. Rec., 91:39, 1945.

Florey, H. W., Wright, R. D., and Jennings, M. A.: The Secretions of the Intestine. Physiol. Rev., 21: 36, 1941.

Gage, S. H., and Fish, P. A.: Fat Digestion, Absorption, and Assimilation in Man and Animals as Determined by the Dark Field Microscope and a Fat Soluble Dye. Am. J. Anat., 34:1, 1924.

Granger, B., and Baker, R. F.: Electron Microscope Investigation of the Striated Border of Intestinal Epithelium. Anat. Rec., 107:423, 1950.

Hill, C. J.: A Contribution to Our Knowledge of the Enteric Plexuses. Phil. Tr. Roy. Soc., London, S. B., 215:355, 1927.

Landboe-Christensen, E.: The Duodenal Glands of Brunner in Man, Their Distribution and Quantity, an Anatomical Study. Ejnar Munksgaard, Copenhagen; London, Oxford University Press, 1944.

Macklin, C. C., and Macklin, M. T.: The Intestinal Epithelium. Special Cytology (Cowdry). 2d ed. New York, (1), 231, 1932.

Mall, F. P.: Die Blut- und Lymphwege im Dünndarm des Hundes. Abh. sächs. Ges. Wiss., math.-physikal. Kl., 14:153, 1888.

Möllendorff, W. von: Ueber die Anteilnahme des Darmepithels an der Verarbeitung enteral und parenteral zugeführter saurer Farbstoffe, Münch. med. Wochenschr., 18:569, 1924.

Patzelt, V.: Der Darm. Handb. d. mikr. Anat. d. Menschen (v. Möllendorff), (5)[3], 1, 1937.

XXV. LIVER, BILE DUCTS AND GALLBLADDER

THE LIVER

The liver plays an indispensable part in the metabolism of the body, and elaborates bile. It is the largest gland of the organism, weighing about 1.5 kilograms in men and slightly less in women. It occupies the upper right quadrant of the abdominal cavity, a part of its surface being attached to the diaphragm. It arises in the embryo as an evagination of the intestine, and develops into a compound gland whose secretory portions are branching and anastomosing tubules. In the lower vertebrates this condition remains throughout life, but in the mammals the original architecture undergoes a complete remodeling.

Lobule of the Mammalian Liver. The mammalian liver is made up of polygonal prisms, each representing an architectural unit or lobule, 0.7 to 2 mm. in diameter. The periphery of each lobule is translucent and gray, while its center is brown. In man the outlines of the lobules are usually indistinct, because the connective tissue partitions between them are poorly developed. In the pig, on the contrary, each lobule is completely surrounded by a layer of connective tissue, and the lobulation is obvious. When a freshly sectioned surface of such a liver is scraped with a knife, the soft tissue is squeezed out of the lobules and the remaining partitions give the impression of a honeycombed structure. In cirrhosis of the liver in man, the connective tissue is greatly increased and the lobulation completely distorted.

In the salivary and pancreatic glands each lobule represents a mass of glandular tissue drained by a duct of a certain order and size. The liver lobule, however, is best conceived as depending not on the duct system, but as centering on the hepatic vein. This is clearly seen in microscopic sections of a liver whose blood vessels have been injected with colored masses.

The liver lobule has also been described as the amount of liver tissue which surrounds and is drained by the smallest interlobular bile ducts. According to this idea, the center of the liver lobule would be the structures in the periportal areas, and the lobule would extend into the parenchyma of the several surrounding anatomical lobules. This theory considers only the bile excretory function of the liver and overlooks entirely the fact that the liver is predominantly an endocrine gland. It also disregards the structure of this organ as seen in such species as the pig, in which the liver lobule is demarcated by a continuous connective tissue layer. (See Pfuhl, Arey, Opie for discussions of this point.)

The lobule of the liver in cross section has five, six or seven sides. The diameter of the cross section is decidedly smaller than the height of the lobule. Running through the center of the lobule, in its long axis, is the central vein, while at the periphery are the branches of the portal vein (introlobular vein), the interlobular bile ducts, branches of the hepatic artery, and the lymphatics which form a network about the portal vein and its branches.

Blood Vessels. The principal afferent blood vessel of the liver is the portal vein. It collects the blood from the viscera of the digestive tract and from the spleen and enters the liver at the porta together with the hepatic artery. The liver of mammals receives a smaller part of its blood supply from the hepatic artery. This relatively small vessel supplies the interlobular connective tissue and

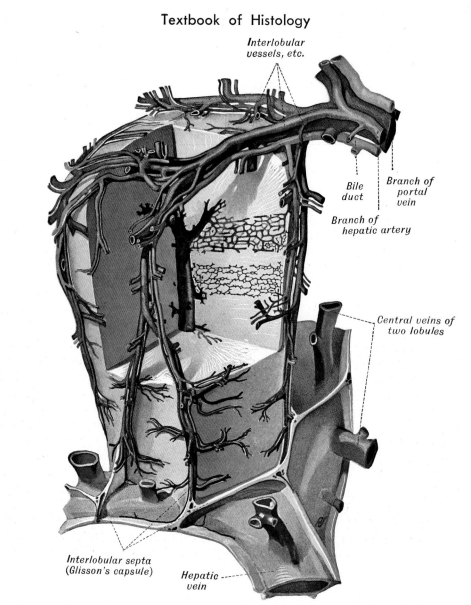

Fig. 380. Lobule of liver of a pig. Wax reconstruction by Vierling. A portion of the lobule is cut away to show the bile capillaries and sinusoids. 400 ×. (After Braus.)

its contained structures and helps to nourish the parenchyma of the gland. In the living frog liver, numerous anastomoses have been seen between the terminals of the hepatic artery and those of the portal vein. The blood is drained from the liver by the two or more *hepatic veins*; these enter the inferior vena cava as it passes through the fossa for this vessel.

Throughout the liver the terminal branches of the portal vein and the radicles of the

hepatic vein are about equal distances apart. Each radicle of the hepatic vein is surrounded by a layer of liver tissue of uniform thickness, and this mass constitutes the *hepatic lobule* (Fig. 383). Because of their central position in the long axis of the lobules, the intralobular branches of the hepatic vein are called *central veins*. Several central veins join to form an *intercalated vein*—the sublobular vein of the older literature. Several of these veins unite to form a *collecting vein*;

these in turn join to form the hepatic veins, which pursue a course through the liver independent of the portal venous system.

Hepatic Sinusoids. The plates of liver cells (p. 394) are separated from one another by the sinusoids of the liver. These are irregular tortuous blood spaces which pursue a radial course in the lobule and connect the ends of the interlobular portal veins with the intra-

vessels determines the amount of arterial blood reaching a sinusoid at any given time.

The sinusoids must be distinguished from capillaries (see p. 208). As seen in living animals, the lining of the hepatic sinusoids appears as a continuous refractile line. As seen in sections, the lining is composed of an irregular alternation of two kinds of cells connected by many intermediate forms. One of

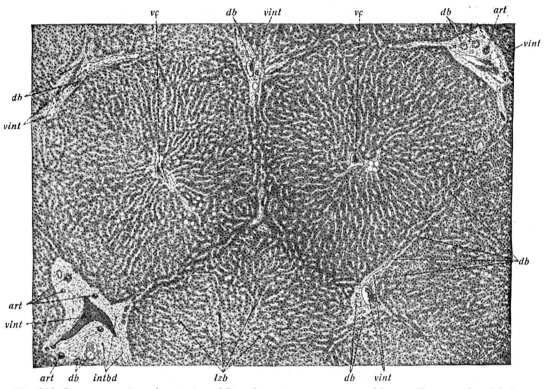

Fig. 381. Low power view of a portion of liver from a twenty-two year old man. Two complete lobules are surrounded by portions of other lobules. *db*, Bile duct; *vint*, interlobular vein; *art*, branch of hepatic artery; *vc*, central vein; *intbd*, interlobular connective tissue; *lzb*, liver cell cords. 70 ×. (After Sobotta.)

lobular central veins. They also receive blood from the branches of the hepatic artery. Although the direct connections of the sinusoids with both interlobular and intralobular (central) veins can be traced in sections, the connection between the hepatic artery and the sinusoids can be seen only in injection preparations and in the living animal. The finest branches of the hepatic artery empty into the sinusoids at the periphery of the lobule. The contraction or dilatation of these

these, the *undifferentiated lining cell*, has a small dark nucleus so compact that practically no structural details can be made out within it (Fig. 385, *a*). Its cytoplasm extends as a thin film along the sinusoid. The other lining cells are fixed macrophages—the phagocytic stellate cells of von Kupffer. They are distinctly larger than the cell type just described. In sections their cytoplasm often extends into well-defined processes, and one often gets the impression that these cells

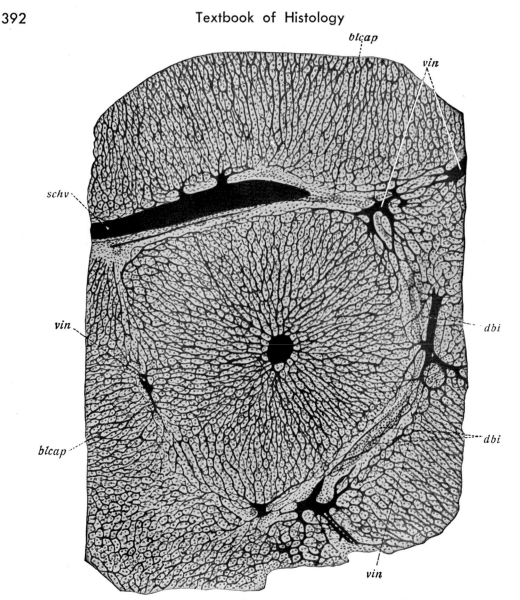

Fig. 382. Portion of liver of a rabbit injected through the portal vein with Berlin blue and gelatin. A complete lobule surrounds the central vein. *blcap,* Hepatic sinusoids; *vin,* interlobular veins; *dbi,* interlobular bile ducts; *schv,* large interlobular vein. 54 ×. (After Sobotta.)

project into the lumen. They have large oval nuclei with a small, prominent nucleolus. Frequently these cells contain granules of green waste pigment, or engulfed erythrocytes in various stages of disintegration, and iron-containing granules. In animals vitally stained with lithium carmine or trypan blue they store large amounts of these dyes in granular form. The undifferentiated lining cells of the first type do not store vital dyes. When, however, finely divided particulate matter such as Higgins' India ink is injected intravenously, the relatively large carbon particles are deposited in the Kupffer cells and in the indifferent lining cells of the liver sinusoids. The Kupffer cells take up more of the ink. Numerous transitional forms connect the two cell types (Fig. 385, *a, b, c, d*). The more vital dye introduced, the more numerous and larger are the phagocytes. The increase is thought to be due to mobilization of the undifferentiated lining cells.

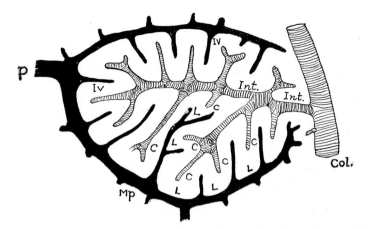

Fig. 383. Diagram showing that the branches of the portal vein (black) are separated from the radicles of the hepatic veins (cross hatched) by a uniform layer of hepatic tissue (white). P, Large branch of portal vein; Mp, medium-sized branch of portal vein; Iv, interlobular veins; C, central veins; Int, intercalated vein; Col, collecting vein; L, hepatic lobules. (Redrawn and slightly modified after Pfuhl.)

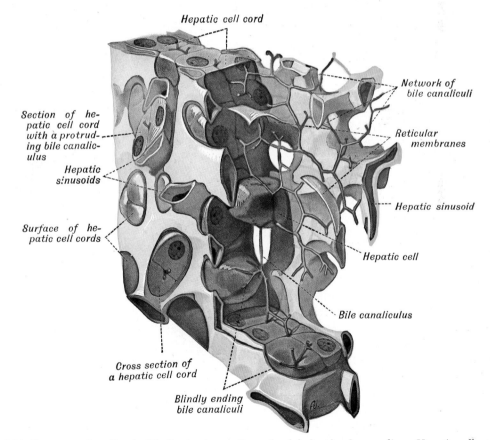

Fig. 384. Reconstruction (by A. Vierling) of a portion of a lobule of a human liver. Hepatic cell cords in yellow, with red nuclei; sinusoids, blue; bile capillaries, green. 1000 ×. (After Braus.)

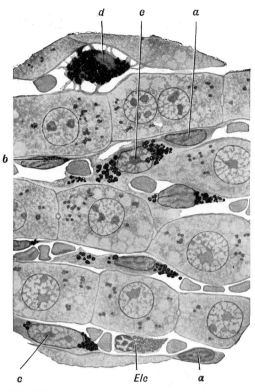

Fig. 385. Liver of rabbit, injected intravenously with India ink. *Elc*, Eosinophile leukocyte; *a*, cells of wall of sinusoid in resting condition; *d*, stellate cell of Kupffer; *b* and *c*, transitions from *a* to *d*. Note absence of carbon in liver cells. Hematoxylin-eosin-azure II stain. (A.A.M.)

Smooth muscle cells have been described at the junction of the sinusoids with the central veins. Marked changes occur continuously in the caliber of the sinusoids and in the rate of flow of blood through them. For the frog these changes have been explained as resulting from the activity of sphincters controlling the inflow and outflow of the blood of the sinusoids. This mechanism permits the storage and release of blood from the liver.

Hepatic Cells. As seen in sections, the liver cells are arranged more or less regularly in columns or plates extending radially from the central vein to the periphery of the lobule. It is claimed that this appearance in sections is due to the fact that the liver is made of a mass of hepatic cells penetrated at close intervals by the sinusoids and that only one hepatic cell separates adjacent sinusoids (Elias).

This disagrees with the conventional description of the epithelium arranged in cords which in section are two cells thick. The plates may branch slightly and anastomose with nearby ones, but in spite of this their general direction is perpendicular to that of the central vein. Between them are broad, irregular, thin-walled sinusoids. The liver cells are polygonal in shape and have six or more surfaces. Most liver cells have one large round nucleus, although binucleated cells are not uncommon. The nucleus is quite vesicular; it has a smooth membrane and one or more prominent nucleoli and a few small chromatin dots.

The cytoplasm of the liver cell presents an extremely variable appearance which reflects to some extent the functional state of the cell. Both glycogen and fat are dissolved in the preparation of the usual sections, but by appropriate methods both types of inclusion are readily demonstrable (Figs. 9, 3, 1; 6). Their actual content of these constituents shows great variations under normal conditions. Sometimes the liver cells may be almost completely filled with glycogen, while

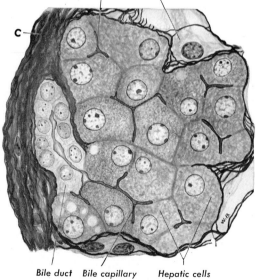

Fig. 386. Section through margin of lobule from human liver, showing the connection between liver cells and an interlobular bile duct. The latter is surrounded by collagenous tissue, C. Bielschowsky silver impregnation and Mallory-azan stain. 480 ×.

at other times they may contain a large number of fat droplets. There are great variations in the protein inclusions in the liver cell. They are often intensely basophile and presumably contain ribonucleic acid. The relative amounts of these substances demonstrable in the liver cells depend primarily on the amounts of carbohydrate, fat and protein in the diet and on the stage of digestion.

The liver cells contain a cytocentrum which may be obscured in the large cytoplasm, mitochondria of extremely variable appearance, and a Golgi net sometimes close to the nucleus, but usually near the bile capillary. There are also vacuoles in the liver cells which stain supravitally with neutral red. Many attempts have been made to correlate the Golgi net and the mitochondria with the various functional states of the liver.

The liver lobule in the white mouse may be divided, on differences in the mitochondria, into three zones: (1) zone of permanent repose, (2) zone of permanent function, (3) an intermediate zone. The zone of permanent repose surrounds the central vein. Here the mitochondria are fine, long, irregularly curving threads of uniform thickness with a few granular ones between them (Fig. 387, A). The mitochondria of this zone do not change during normal alimentation or in starvation. This zone probably constitutes a region of reserve, which becomes active only when feeding is excessive or when the adjoining parenchyma is injured. The zone of permanent function lies at the periphery of the lobule (Fig. 387, C). Here the mitochondria always are more granular or rounded bodies, and filaments are rare. When the mice were not fed for eighteen to twenty-four hours, the mitochondria were filamentous in practically all the cells of a given lobule except in this zone of permanent activity. The intermediate zone lies between the other two; in it the mitochondrial morphology changes with the activity of the liver (Fig. 387, B). This zone is at rest during starvation; its mitochondria begin to change with digestion. Accordingly, it is believed that differences in appearance in the mitochondria reflect differences in function of the cells and

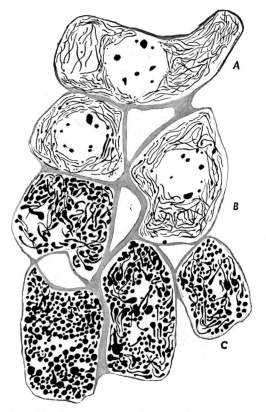

Fig. 387. Cells from the liver of white mouse fed proteins two hours previously, showing differences in mitochondria. A, Cell from the zone of permanent repose; B, cells of the variable zone; C, cells from the zone of permanent function. 1200 ×. (After Noel.)

that activity proceeds from the periphery to the center of the lobule during the course of digestion.

On feeding fat, the liver cells become somewhat larger and full of fat droplets. The mitochondria decrease as the fat increases. On feeding carbohydrates the cells become pale, and between the glycogen granules, small, iron-containing particles and some fat droplets appear. On feeding proteins the cells become large and full of protein inclusions.

In spite of the manifold functions which the liver cells perform, there is a marked similarity in appearance in all of them. This is at variance with what is seen in other organs, in which highly specialized functions are carried on by cells which morphologically are highly differentiated. It would appear that all the liver cells are equally endowed with the same functional capacities, but that

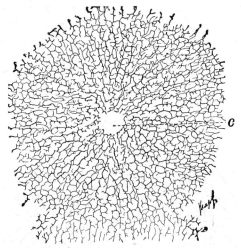

Fig. 388. Human bile capillaries. The capillaries of one lobule anastomose with those of the adjoining lobule (below in the figure). C, Central vein. Chrome silver method. 110 ×. (After Böhm, Davidoff and Huber.)

their active participation in these processes under normal conditions depends on the location of the cell in the lobule.

Bile Canalicules. In adult man the thin bile canalicules run between the hepatic cells. They are a condensation of the membrane of the hepatic cells and require special methods for their demonstration. The bile canalicules run through the liver cell plates and receive short lateral branches which extend between the sides of adjoining liver cells. In planes running parallel to several adjacent plates the bile canalicules of adjoining masses of liver cells anastomose with one another. The canalicules are always intercellular; this has been verified by studies on the liver of living frogs. In some species the canalicules are stained by the methods for demonstrating phosphatase.

Connective Tissue of the Liver. The lobules of the liver are partially separated by the thin strands of dense connective tissue called periportal connective tissue. This is a part of *Glisson's capsule*, the dense connective tissue sheathing the intrahepatic portions of the portal vein, bile duct and hepatic artery, and is also continuous with the thin layer of connective tissue of the peritoneum covering the liver. In the human liver it is normally small in amount and

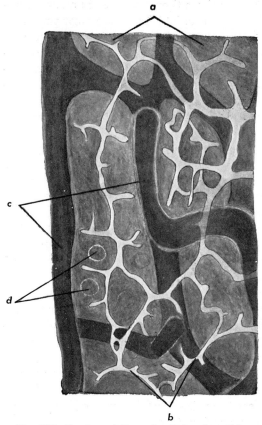

Fig. 389. Portion of liver of a living frog. Natural injection with fluorescein, as seen by ultra-violet light. *a*, Liver cells; *b*, bile capillaries; *c*, sinusoids; *d*, indications of nuclei of hepatic cells. 600 ×. (Redrawn and slightly modified after Ellinger and Hirt.)

barely suffices to form a framework for the interlobular artery, portal vein, bile ducts and lymphatics (see Fig. 231). In chronic inflammatory conditions the connective tissue may be increased in amount and may show an accumulation of lymphoid cells and macrophages. In sections stained for collagenous and reticular fibers by Mallory's aniline blue mixture or with one of the silver impregnation methods, the intralobular reticular fibers become visible. The periportal collagenous connective tissue continues directly into the dense network of reticular fibers which surrounds the sinusoids. Of the latter fibers, the larger ones, as a rule, run parallel to the long axis of the sinusoid, while the smaller ones form a dense interlacing network of cross fibers. This network of fibers supports the liver parenchyma.

It is quite likely that the reticular fibers with their ground membrane, together with the lining and Kupffer cells, form a complete wall for the sinusoids (Fig. 390). This lining completely separates the blood from direct contact with the liver cells, and the space between this membrane and the hepatic cells is available in the interior of the lobule for the transfer of lymph.

Lymph Spaces. In the liver the site of origin of the lymph and its mode of entry into the periportal lymphatics are unknown. As seen in ordinary sections, the liver cells are in intimate contact with the thin lining of the sinusoids on one side and the bile capillaries on the opposite side. According to some estimates, one third to one half of all the lymph of the body originates in the liver, and yet the lymphatic vessels begin in the periportal connective tissue about the terminal ramifications of the portal vein. Lymphatic capillaries have not been demonstrated within the liver lobule. Accordingly, it has been assumed that there is a *potential lymphatic space* between the sinusoidal lining and the liver cells. This space cannot be demonstrated by injection methods.

Regeneration. If portions of the liver are removed from a rat or dog so that only a small part of its substance remains, most of the tissue lost will be re-formed in a few days. The increase in the number of hepatic cells takes place by mitosis of liver cells, and the new tissue will soon look like that from a normal liver. Partial hepatectomy with the ensuing regeneration has become an important method for studying a great variety of biological problems.

Histophysiological Remarks. No structural characteristics of the liver cells have been correlated constantly with the excretion of any of the biliary constituents. All the hepatic epithelial cells seem to have the same abilities.

The liver plays an important part in the intermediate metabolism and storage of carbohydrates, in the metabolism of fats and of amino acids, and in the synthesis of proteins. It serves as a depository for numerous vitamins, enzymes and hormones. The number of chemical syntheses carried out by the liver is large. It secretes bile into the bile passages, synthesizing the bile salts and excreting the bile pigments elaborated elsewhere from the hemoglobin of destroyed red blood cells. It is rich in fixed macrophages—

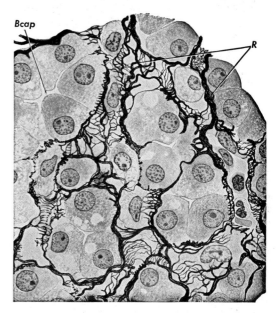

Fig. 390. Section of human liver. *Hc*, Hepatic cells; *Bcap*, bile capillaries; *R*, reticular fibers forming a continuous membrane on the surface of the hepatic cells facing the sinuses. Bielschowsky-Foot stain. 840 ×. (A.A.M.)

the Kupffer cells—which have functions similar to those of macrophages elsewhere in the body. Changes in the caliber of its vessels make the liver an important storehouse and regulator of the circulating blood.

When the liver is removed by ordinary surgical methods, the animals die in a few minutes. However, when a collateral circulation has developed as a result of preliminary operations, dogs may survive hepatectomy for thirty-six to forty hours if they are given frequent injections of sugar solutions.

In contrast to the other glands of internal secretion which elaborate potent hormones, the endocrine functions of the liver are concerned with the storage of various foodstuffs and of the antianemic factor necessary for red blood cell formation. Heparin is stored and perhaps made in the liver. Fibrinogen is made in the liver and given off to the passing blood.

One of the most important functions of the liver is the *formation of glycogen*. It increases in the liver after meals and decreases

in mice the first site of deposition and removal of glycogen is about the central vein.

Another important function of the liver is the *formation of urea* by deamination of arginine.

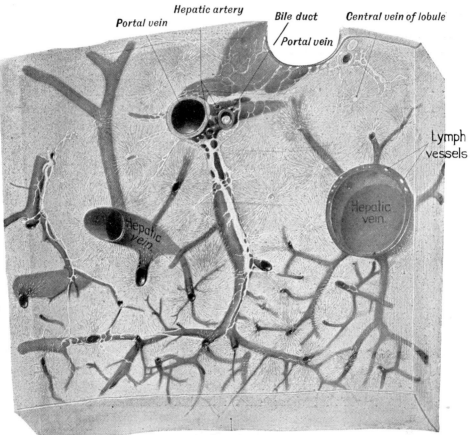

Fig. 391. Thick section of liver of adult cat; cleared in oil of wintergreen. The lymphatic network appears pale and the blood vessels dark. The lymphatic vessels are confined to the interlobular connective tissue, where they surround the branches of the larger blood vessels and bile ducts. 16 ×. (After F. C. Lee.)

during fasting, and may even disappear completely. It is present in submicroscopic particles; the granular appearance in sections is due to the fixation. When stored in increasing amounts in the liver cells, it is seen at first in those around the central vein; when sufficient carbohydrate food is eaten, all the liver cells may take up glycogen. The liver gives up its glycogen in the reverse order; that is, the cells at the periphery of the lobule are the first to lose it. It is claimed that

The liver cells contain much fat, but an estimate of the amount present cannot be determined by staining methods, for a good deal of it may be present in a masked form in the liver. Under some pathological conditions the liver cells may take up so much fat that most of the other constituents of their protoplasm are obscured.

Bile, the external secretion, is apparently elaborated continuously. It contains water, bile pigments, bile acids, cholesterol, lecithin, neutral fats and soaps, inorganic salts and traces of urea. The bile receives, from the epithelium of the bile ducts and possibly from the neck of the gallbladder, a mucinous nucleo-albumin. Bile pigment (from broken-down erythrocytes) is formed outside the liver cells. The *bile acids* are formed in the liver cells, for, if the liver is extirpated, no trace of bile acids can be found in the blood or urine. It is probable that cholesterol is not formed in the liver. When the excretion of bile is interrupted by mechanical obstruction of the bile ducts, bile continues to be formed and is absorbed from the liver at first through the lymphatics and later also by the blood vessels of the liver. When bile pigment reaches a concentration in the blood and tissues sufficient to stain the entire body yellow, the condition is known as *jaundice*. It may also be produced through the action of certain blood-destroying agents. Occlusion of the common bile duct causes a great disturbance in the digestion and absorption of fats, owing to the absence of bile acids from the intestine.

After certain dyes are introduced into the organism, they may be found in the bile. If a bit of liver be teased at an appropriate time after the injection of sodium sulfindigotate, the bile capillaries will be beautifully demonstrated.

BILE DUCTS

The constituents of the bile are emptied into the bile canalicules, which communicate with the interlobular bile ducts by the canals of Hering. The finest radicles of the bile ducts are 15 to 20 microns in diameter and have a small lumen surrounded by cuboidal epithelial cells. They do not have a cuticular border, and their cytoplasm rarely contains fat droplets. The cells show an occasional mitosis. These small ducts lie on a basement membrane immediately surrounded by dense collagenous bundles.

The interlobular bile ducts form a richly anastomosing network which closely surrounds the branches of the portal vein. In progressing toward the porta, the lumen of

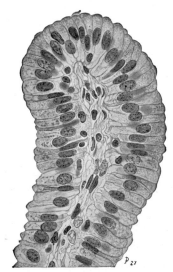

Fig. 392. Tip of fold of mucosa of human gallbladder, with migrating lymphocytes in the epithelium. Blood vessels in lamina propria are collapsed. 500 ×. (Courtesy of B. Halpert.)

the ducts becomes gradually larger, while the epithelium becomes taller (the ducts of the second order) and has a layer of mitochondria at the base of the cell and another near the free border. These cells contain large numbers of fat droplets and, when these are numerous, cholesterol crystals. Although a faint thickening of the periphery of these cells may be seen in some animals, it is not found in man. Lymphocytes are frequently seen migrating through the epithelium into the lumen. As the ducts become larger, the surrounding layers of collagenous connective tissue become thicker and contain many elastic fibers. At the transverse fossa of the liver, the main ducts from the different lobes of the liver fuse to form the common hepatic duct, which, after receiving the cystic duct, continues to the duodenum as the common bile duct.

The epithelium of the extrahepatic ducts is tall columnar. The mucosa is thrown into many folds and is said to yield an atypical variety of mucus. The scanty, subepithelial connective tissue contains large numbers of elastic fibers, some lymphoid cells and occasional leukocytes; many of these penetrate the epithelium and pass into the lumen.

Scattered bundles of smooth muscles first appear in the common bile duct; they run in the longitudinal and oblique directions, and form an incomplete layer around the wall of the duct. As it nears the duodenum, the smooth muscle layer of the ductus chole-dochus becomes more prominent, and its intramural portions function as a sort of sphincter in regulating the flow of bile.

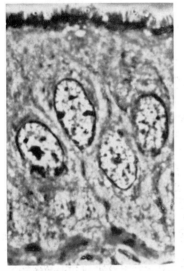

Fig. 393. Epithelium of human gallbladder, showing striations like cilia on free border. Phase contrast photomicrograph of a section. 2000 ×. (Courtesy of P. H. Ralph.)

THE GALLBLADDER

The gallbladder is a pear-shaped, hollow viscus closely attached to the posterior surface of the liver. It consists of a blindly ending fundus, a body, and a neck which continues into the cystic duct. Normally it measures approximately 10 by 4 cm. in adult man and has a capacity in most animals of 1 to 2 cc. per kilogram of body weight. It shows marked variations in shape and size, and is frequently the seat of pathological processes which change its size and the thickness of its wall. The mucosa is easily destroyed, so that in most specimens removed even a short time after death, large areas of epithelium are found to be desquamated or disintegrating.

The wall consists of the following layers: (1) a mucous layer consisting of a surface epithelium and a lamina propria, (2) a layer of smooth muscles, (3) a perimuscular connective tissue layer, (4) a serous layer, covering a part of the organ. The *mucous layer* is thrown into frequent *folds*. The major folds are subdivided by many smaller folds; they are easily seen in the contracted or even partially distended organ. But when the viscus is greatly distended, its wall becomes much thinner and most of the folds disappear, although some of them can always be seen.

The epithelium consists of tall columnar cells with oval nuclei, containing a few scattered chromatin granules, toward the base of the cell. The cytoplasm stains faintly with eosin. A typical striated border is lacking here, although fine cilia-like processes have been seen with phase contrast microscopy (Fig. 393). Occasionally, neutral fat and other lipids may be demonstrated in the cell bodies. Mitochondria occur in two zones of these cells as in the epithelium of the bile ducts. Goblet cells do not occur. Except in the neck of the viscus, there are no glands in its mucosa.

In the lamina propria and in the perimuscular layer near the neck of the gallbladder are simple tubulo-alveolar glands. Their epithelium is cuboidal and clear, and the dark nuclei are compressed at the base of the cell. They thus stand out sharply against the darker, tall columnar epithelium of the gallbladder. These glands are said to secrete mucus.

Outpouchings of the mucosa have sometimes been confused with glands. These outpouchings are lined with and are continuous with the surface epithelium and extend through the lamina propria and the muscular layer. These are the *Rokitansky-Aschoff sinuses* and probably are indicators of a pathological change in the wall of the organ which thus permits an evagination of the mucosa through the enlarged meshes of the muscular network. They are not found in embryonic gallbladders and should not be confused with the "true" ducts of Luschka described later, for the latter never communicate with the lumen of the gallbladder.

The next layer of the wall is composed of an irregular network of longitudinal, transverse, and oblique smooth muscle fibers, accompanied by a network of elastic fibers. The spaces between the bundles of muscles are occupied by collagenous, reticular and some elastic fibers, with a sprinkling of fibroblasts. The blood vessels and lymphatics contained in the perimuscular layer send branches into and through the muscular layer to the mucosa.

Under the muscular layer is a fairly dense *connective tissue layer* which completely surrounds the gallbladder and is in places continuous with the interlobular connective tissue of the liver (Fig. 395). It contains many collagenous and a few elastic fibers and scattered fibroblasts with a few macrophages and lymphoid wandering cells, small lobules of fat cells, and the blood vessels, nerves and lymphatics supplying the organ.

Not infrequently, particularly in the hepatic surface and near the neck, are peculiar, ductlike structures. They may be traced for considerable distances in this connective tissue layer, and some of them connect with the bile ducts. They are never connected with the lumen of the gallbladder, and are

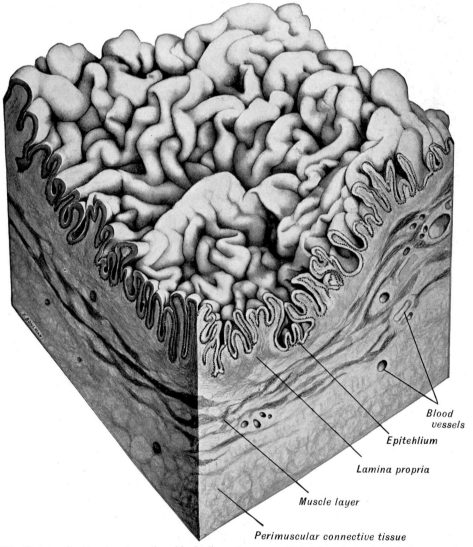

Blood vessels

Epitehlium

Lamina propria

Muscle layer

Perimuscular connective tissue

Fig. 394. Camera lucida drawing of a block from human gallbladder. Stained with hematoxylin. 32 ×. (Drawn by Miss E. Bohlman.)

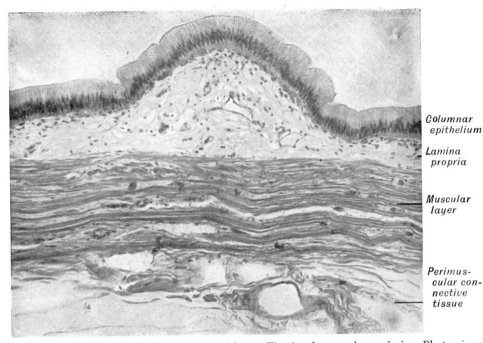

Fig. 395. Section of wall of gallbladder of *Macacus rhesus*. Fixation by vascular perfusion. Photomicrograph. 142 ×.

Columnar epithelium

Lamina propria

Muscular layer

Perimuscular connective tissue

probably aberrant bile ducts laid down during the embryonic development of the biliary system. They have been called "true" *Luschka ducts* to distinguish them from epithelial outpouchings of the mucosa.

The portion of the gallbladder not attached to the liver is covered with the peritoneum. Through it the ramifying arteries, veins and lymphatics can be seen with the unaided eye. This *serosal layer* is continuous with that covering the liver.

The gallbladder at its neck continues into the cystic duct. The wall of the latter is thrown into prominent folds which constitute the *spiral valve of Heister*. These are said to contain smooth muscle bundles, and are thought to prevent distention or collapse of the cystic duct when the latter is subjected to sudden pressure.

Blood Vessels. The gallbladder is supplied with blood by the cystic artery. The venous blood is collected by veins which empty primarily into capillaries of the liver and only secondarily into the cystic branch of the portal vein. A prominent feature of the gallbladder is its rich supply of lymphatic vessels, of which there are two main plexuses: one in the lamina propria (but not within the rugae) and the other in the connective tissue layer. The latter plexus receives tributaries from the liver, thus affording an explanation for hepatogenous cholecystitis. These plexuses are collected into larger lymphatics which pass through the lymph node or nodes at the neck and then accompany the cystic and common bile ducts. They pass through several lymph nodes near the duodenum and finally communicate with the cisterna chyli.

Nerves. The nerves are branches of the splanchnic sympathetic and the vagus nerves. The effects of stimulation of these nerves have given rise to contradictory results in the hands of different investigators. It is probable that both excitatory and inhibitory fibers are contained in each of them. Of greater clinical importance are the sensory nerve endings, since overdistention or spasms of the extrahepatic biliary tract inhibit respiration and set up reflex disturbances in the gut tract.

Histophysiological Remarks. The gallbladder serves as a reservoir for bile, which is probably excreted by the liver continuously, if at different rates. Ingestion of fat or meat automatically discharges this reservoir. After a standard meal of egg-yolks, three fourths of its contents are expelled within forty minutes.

The prevalent view that bile is expelled by

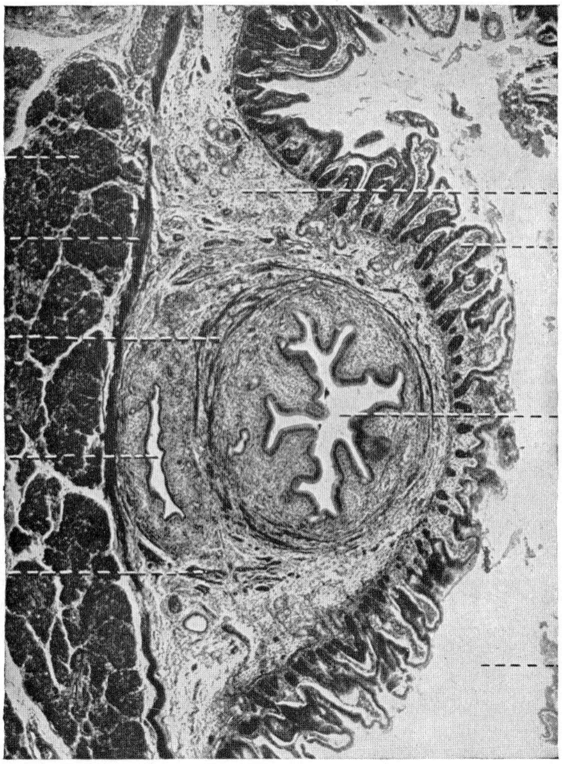

Fig. 396. Transverse section of plica longitudinalis of a 43-cm. human fetus. 34 ×. (After Boyden: Surgery, 1937.)

the gallbladder musculature is supported by much physiological evidence, including the fact that it responds to intravenous injection of *cholecystokinin*—a secretin-like substance extracted from the mucosa of the small intestine.

Of special clinical importance is the inspissating function of the gallbladder. Its mucous membrane withdraws water and inorganic ions from the bile and it concentrates the x-ray opaque halogen salts of phenolphthalein (Graham-Cole test). Failure to visualize the gallbladder after this test indicates that the organ is diseased or occluded. Whether, under normal conditions, it will absorb more than negligible amounts of other constituents of the bile has never been demonstrated. But if the mucosa be damaged, it may lose its concentrating power or become semipermeable. Undoubtedly, absorption of bile salts under such conditions is an important factor in the precipitation of gallstones. After obstruction of the cystic duct the bile may be resorbed *in toto* or replaced by "white bile," a colorless fluid consisting largely of exudate and mucus.

There is a little evidence in favor of a secretory function of the gallbladder. A variety of mucus is added to the bile as it passes down the larger bile ducts, and mucus-secreting glands are fairly numerous in the neck. In a few animals a gallbladder is never present. Its surgical removal in man is often followed by a marked dilatation of the biliary passages.

THE CHOLEDOCHO-DUODENAL JUNCTION*

In man this zone comprises the portion of the duodenal wall that is traversed by the ductus choledochus and pancreaticus and by the short ampulla into which they usually empty. For most of its length it consists of

* This section was contributed by E. A. Boyden.

an oblique passage through the submucosa of the plica longitudinalis, but proximally it is guarded by a contractile "window" in the muscle of the duodenum and distally by the valvules of the ampulla of Vater. From "window" to ostium, associated bile and pancreatic passages are invested by a common musculus proprius, the sphincter of Oddi.

Sphincter of Oddi. In man this may consist of four parts: (1) *the sphincter choledochus* (Fig. 396), a strong annular sheath a centimeter or less in length, which invests the common bile duct from just outside the fenestra to its junction with the pancreatic duct; (2) *the fasciculi longitudinales*, anterior and posterior longitudinal bundles

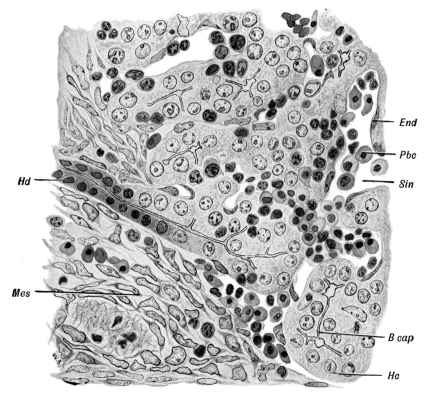

Fig. 397. Head of hepatic duct of 16-mm. human embryo. *B cap*, Bile capillaries; *End*, lining cells of sinusoids; *Hc*, hepatic cells; *Hd*, hepatic duct; *Mes*, mesenchyme; *Pbc*, primitive blood cells; *Sin*, sinusoids. Note continuity of hepatic duct and its lumen with hepatic cell cords and bile capillaries respectively. Eppinger stain for bile capillaries. 700 ×. (W. B.)

Fenestra Choledocha. Upon removing the ducts the aperture in the intestinal musculature is seen to resemble a "gridiron incision"—a lengthwise hiatus in the longitudinal layer superimposed upon an obliquely transverse window in the circular layer, the two being somewhat camouflaged by "reinforcing fibers" and by "connecting fibers" that pass to the ducts from the margins of the aperture. The shape and size of the latter determine the gauge of calculi that can enter the wall. As soon as the ducts enter this "window" they begin to taper.

which cover the interval between the two ducts and extend from the margins of the fenestra (or from the extraduodenal portion of the ducts) to the ampulla; (3) *the sphincter ampullae*, a delicate meshwork of fibers about the ampulla of Vater (if present) and strongly developed in only one sixth of adults; and (4) *the sphincter pancreaticus*, present in one third of adults as a band encircling the pancreatic duct just before it joins the ampulla. The first is so placed as to stop the flow of bile (thus causing the gallbladder to fill during fasting), the second to shorten the intramural portion of the ducts (thus facilitating the flow into the duodenum), and the third, when strongly developed, to create abnormally a continuous channel between bile and pancreatic ducts (thus permitting reflux of pancreatic juice into the biliary tract, and vice versa).

Histophysiological Remarks. The most important part of the musculus proprius is the sphincter choledochus. During fasting this muscle retains the bile against the secretory pressure of the liver, causing it to back up into the gallbladder, the mucosa of which then concentrates it. Upon ingestion of food, the sphincter relaxes and the gallbladder contracts, with the result that concentrated bile usually reaches the duodenum within seven to fifteen minutes.

After cholecystectomy or chronic obstruction of the cystic duct, the sphincter of Oddi usually hypertrophies. Under other conditions it may become spastic for longer or shorter periods, often causing pain in the right hypochondrium similar to that of gallbladder disease—a condition known as *biliary dyskinesia*. Reflux of pancreatic juice into the biliary passages, after spasm of the sphincter ampullae, is thought to be one cause of cholecystitis. In pregnancy, increase in tone of the sphincter delays the discharge of bile after meals; and in the presence of certain foods to which the patient has become sensitized, it may prevent the flow of bile entirely. In the presence of peptic ulcer, however, gallbladder bile is discharged more rapidly than under normal conditions. Only three substances relax a spastic sphincter of Oddi—egg-yolk, nitroglycerine, and amyl nitrite.

The sphincter of Oddi differentiates *in situ* from mesenchyme and is not an emanation from intestinal muscle, although it may connect with it subsequently. It first appears about the 45-mm. stage, as an iris-shaped ring within the eye-shaped fenestra of the circular muscle of the duodenum; then it differentiates in the direction of the papilla, much as the musculus proprius of the ureter grows from the bladder toward the kidney. Upon this gradient is superimposed a preampullary zone of growth which carries the developing sphincter choledochus away from the intestinal muscle and sets it up as an independent mechanism.

Histogenesis of the Liver and Its Ducts. The liver arises early in the embryo as a diverticulum of the midgut. It appears as a ventral outgrowth which soon becomes hollow and lined by columnar epithelium; its cavity is continuous with that of the intestine. The hepatic diverticulum then extends into the mesenchyme of the septum transversum. In a 4-mm. embryo the liver consists of a thin stalk capped by a proliferating mass of liver cell cords. In a 10-mm. embryo the stalk has divided into two main branches which go to the right and left lobes of the liver. There is also a caudal diverticulum of the stalk which is the primordium of the future gallbladder and cystic duct. The liver cell cords continue to proliferate and even in embryos of 10 mm. contain bile capillaries. At these stages, the liver cords are distinctly tubular and may have five or six liver cells radiating around each lumen. In embryos of about 20 mm., with the ingrowth of connective tissue about the portal vein into the liver, interlobular bile ducts appear in this connective tissue and accompany the portal vein throughout its future ramifications.

As the connective tissue continues to extend into the liver substance along with the branches of the portal vein, the liver becomes divided into lobules. The exact mechanism by which the small liver of the newborn grows into the large organ of the adult is not known.

Blood formation begins early in the liver and becomes so developed here that for a time it is the main blood-forming organ of the embryo. Blood formation stops in the liver about the seventh month of fetal life, although this potency remains here for the life of the individual and not infrequently is brought into play in the course of certain diseases in extra-uterine life.

Bile capillaries form a continuous system in the youngest human embryos. At first these canalicules are continuous with the main hepatic ducts and, during the progressive embryonic development of the liver, with the finer branches of the interlobular ducts. There are two main theories as to the mode of origin of the ducts. The more probable of these is that the liver cells develop by branching from the head of the embryonic duct primordium and that, with the ingrowth of connective tissue into the liver substance, those liver cords nearest the connective tissue are transformed into ducts.

REFERENCES

Arey, L. B.: On the Presence of So-called Portal Lobules in the Seal's Liver. Anat. Rec., 51:315, 1932.

Beams, H. W., and King, R. L.: Effect of Ultracentrifuging on the Mitochondria of the Hepatic Cells of the Rat. Anat. Rec., 59:395, 1934.

Boyden, E. A.: An Analysis of the Reaction of the Human Gallbladder to Food. Anat. Rec., 40:147, 1928; see also Gerdes and Boyden: Surg., Gyn., Obst., 66:145, 1938.

Buchanan, J. M., and Hastings, A. B.: The Use of Isotopically Marked Carbon in the Study of Intermediary Metabolism. Physiol. Rev., 26:120, 1946.

Claude, A.: Fractionation of Mammalian Liver Cells by Differential Centrifugation. I. Problems, Methods, and Preparation of Extract. II. Experimental Procedures and Results. J. Exper. Med., 84:51, 1946.

Deane, H. W.: The Basophilic Bodies in Hepatic Cells. Am. J. Anat., 78:227, 1946.

Elias, H.: A Re-examination of the Structure of the Mammalian Liver. I. Parenchymal Architecture Am. J. Anat., 84:311, 1949. II. The Hepatic Lobule and Its Relation to the Vascular and Biliary Systems. Am. J. Anat., 85:379, 1949.

Ellinger, P., and Hirt, A.: Mikroskopische Untersuchungen an lebenden Organen. I. Methodik. Zeit. f. Anat. u. Entwicklungs., 90:791, 1929.

Fiessinger, N.: La cellule hépatique. Revue générale d'histologie, Fasc. 13, 1911.

Hall, E. M., and MacKay, E. M.: The Relation between the Mitochondria and Glucose-glycogen Equilibrium in the Liver. Am. J. Path., 9:205, 1933.

Halpert, B.: Morphological Studies on the Gallbladder. II. The "True Luschka Ducts" and "Rokitansky-Aschoff Sinuses" of the Human Gallbladder. Bull. Johns Hopkins Hosp., 41:77, 1927.

Ivy, A. C.: The Physiology of the Gallbladder. Physiol. Rev., 14:1, 1934.

Johnson, F. P.: The Isolation, Shape, Size, and Number of the Lobules of the Pig's Liver. Am. J. Anat., 23:273, 1918.

Kater, J. McA.: Variations in the Mitochondria of the Hepatic Cells in Relation to Alterations of the Glycogen-glucose Equilibrium. Anat. Rec., 49:277, 1931.

Knisely, M. H.: The Structure and Mechanical Func-

tioning of the Living Liver Lobules of Frogs and Rhesus Monkeys. Proc. Inst. Med. Chicago, 16:286, 1947.

Kupffer, C. von: Ueber die sog. Sternzellen der Säugetier Leber. Arch. f. mikr. Anat., 54:254, 1899.

Lazarow, A.: Particulate Glycogen. A Submicroscopic Component of the Guinea Pig Liver Cell; Its Significance in Glycogen Storage and the Regulation of Blood Sugar. Anat. Rec., 84:31, 1942.

Lee, F. C.: On the Lymph Vessels of the Liver. Carnegie Inst., Contrib. to Embryol., No. 74, 65, 1925.

Noel, R.: Histophysiologie du lobule hépatique chez la souris blanche. C. R. de l'assoc. des Anat. 17, Gand., 1922; Recherches histo-physiologiques sur la cellule hépatique des mammifères. Arch. d. anat. micro., 19:1, 1923.

Opie, E. L.: Mobilization of Basophile Substance (Ribonucleic Acid) in the Cytoplasm of Liver Cells with the Production of Tumors by Butter Yellow. J. Exper. Med., 84:91, 1946.

Petrén, T.: Die Venen der Gallenblase und der extrahepatischen Gallenwege beim Menschen und bei den Wirbeltieren. Stockholm, 1933.

Pfuhl, W.: Die Leber. Die Gallenblase und die extrahepatischen Gallengänge. Handb. d. mikr. Anat. (v. Möllendorff), 1932, Vol. 5, pp. 235, 426.

Schmidt, C. R., and Ivy, A. C.: The General Function of the Gall Bladder. Do Species Lacking a Gall Bladder Possess Its Functional Equivalent? The Bile and Pigment Output of Various Species of Animals. J. Cell & Comp. Physiol., 10:365, 1937.

Schwegler, R. A., Jr., and Boyden, E. A.: The Development of the Pars Intestinalis of the Common Bile Duct in the Human Fetus, etc. Anat. Rec., 67:441; 68:17, 193, 1937.

Wakim, K. G., and Mann, F. C.: The Intrahepatic Circulation of Blood. Anat. Rec., 82:233, 1942.

Wilson, J. W.: Liver. Ann. Rev. Physiol., 13:133, 1951.

Wilson, J. W., and Leduc, E. H.: Abnormal Mitosis in Mouse Liver. Am. J. Anat., 86:51, 1950.

XXVI. PANCREAS

Next to the liver, the pancreas is the largest gland connected with the alimentary tract. It consists of an *exocrine portion*, which elaborates certain digestive juices, and an *endocrine portion*, whose secretion plays an important part in the control of the intermediate carbohydrate metabolism of the body. Unlike the liver, in which both exocrine and endocrine functions are carried on by the same cells, the exocrine and endocrine functions of the pancreas are carried on by distinctly different groups of cells.

The pancreas is a pink-white organ which lies in the retroperitoneum about the level of the second and third lumbar vertebrae; on the right it is intimately adherent to the middle portion of the duodenum and extends transversely across the body to the spleen. In the adult it measures from 20 to 25 cm. in length and varies in weight from 65 to 160 gm. It is covered by a thin layer of connective tissue which does not, however, form a definite, fibrous capsule. It is finely lobulated, and the outlines of the larger lobules can be seen with the naked eye. It is usually described as having a head, a body and a tail. The head is slightly thicker than the rest and fills the loop formed by the middle portion of the duodenum, to which it is intimately adherent. It partially encircles this viscus and in rare cases may surround it completely. The lower part of the head contains a groove through which the mesenteric vessels pass.

Exocrine Portion. The pancreas is a compound *acinous* gland whose lobules are bound together by loose connective tissue through which run blood vessels, nerves, lymphatics and excretory ducts (Fig. 398). The

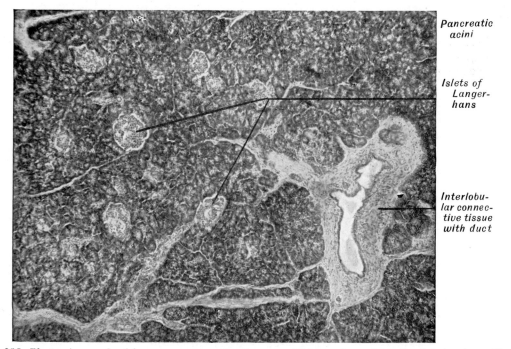

Pancreatic acini

Islets of Langer-hans

Interlobu-lar connec-tive tissue with duct

Fig. 398. Photomicrograph of human pancreas, showing several islets and one large interlobular duct. 65 ×.

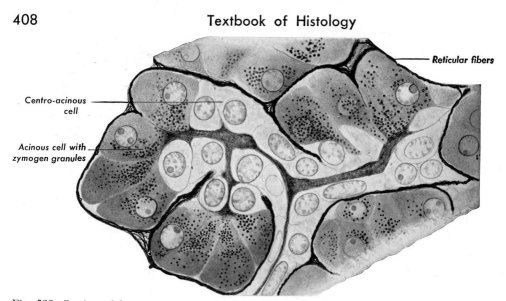

Fig. 399. Section of human pancreas, showing relation of acinar to centro-acinar cells. Bielschowsky-Foot and Mallory-azan stain. 1260 ×. (Drawn by Miss Agnes Nixon.)

acini which form the external secretion vary from rounded structures to short tubules. They consist of a single row of pyramidal epithelial cells resting on a delicate reticular membrane and converging toward a central lumen. The size of the lumen varies with the functional condition of the organ; thus it is small when at rest, but during active secretion becomes distended with secreted material. Between the acinar cells are fine secretory capillaries connected with the central lumen.

The acinar cells show rather striking differences in the various stages of secretion. In general, the basal part of the cell, when seen in the living condition, is homogeneous or may show a faint longitudinal striation, owing to the presence of filamentous mitochondria in it. The supranuclear portion—the part between the nucleus and the lumen—is filled with a number of highly refractile granules. These are the secretion granules, which vary greatly in number, depending on the stage of secretion. Occasionally, even in the living cell, fine clefts can be observed between these granules. This is probably the canalicular apparatus; if the secretion granules are stained supravitally, these canals become still more prominent. In sections stained with hematoxylin and eosin after Zenker-formol fixation, the basal parts of the

acinar cells stain a dark purple, while the secretory granules are a bright orange-red.

The relationships between the basophile homogeneous zone at the base (Figs. 399, 400), apparently rich in ribose nucleoprotein, and the amount of secretory granules depend on the state of digestion; these relationships are clearly shown in Figure 401, in which the Golgi apparatus is stained black and the secretory vacuoles appear as paler dots. In B, which is an acinus from a resting gland, the proximal portion of the cells is homogeneous, while the distal portion contains a moderate number of secretion granules, more or less separated from the remainder of the cell by the network of the Golgi apparatus. In A, which is from a starving animal, the number of secretion granules has increased greatly; in several places these have extended into the basal or proximal zone of the cell, and the Golgi apparatus is much more diffuse than in B. In C, which is an acinus from a mouse into which pilocarpine had been injected three hours previously, the amount of homogeneous protoplasm is greatly increased, and all the secretory granules have been discharged into the lumen, about which the Golgi apparatus forms a limiting network.

The nucleus is spherical and it contains much chromatin, and one or two prominent oxyphile nucleoli. In some animals the cells frequently contain two nuclei, but this is relatively infrequent in man. Mitotic figures are rarely found in the acinar cells of a normal, active gland in the adult.

Between periods of active secretion the resting cells accumulate secretory granules, apparently at the expense of the homogeneous basal cytoplasm, but, as with secretion granules in general, the chemical precursors of the granules are unknown (see Chap. XIV).

Islets of Langerhans. In addition to these external secreting portions of the gland, the pancreas also contains islands of Langerhans. These are irregular structures, more or less completely delimited from the acini by a thin reticular membrane and provided with an extensive blood supply. Indeed, their great vascularity early suggested the possibility of their being endocrine organs. In some places the cells of the islands seem to be in direct continuity with either acinar cells or undifferentiated ductule epithelium.

By staining the entire gland through the arterial injection of neutral red or Janus green, which stains the islands differentially, it has been found that the number of islands

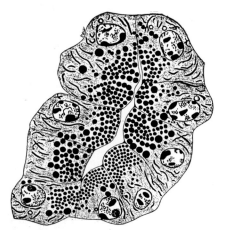

Fig. 400. Section of pancreatic acinus of a guinea pig, showing mitochondrial filaments embedded in the homogeneous basal substance. Secretion granules are rounded and in distal parts of the cytoplasm. Acid fuchsin methyl green stain. 1000 ×. (After Bensley.)

of Langerhans in adult man may vary from about 200,000 to 1,800,000. The number in the tail is slightly higher than in the body or head.

As seen in the usual preparations stained by hematoxylin and eosin, the islands of Langerhans seem to be composed of almost syncytium-like cords of irregularly prismatic

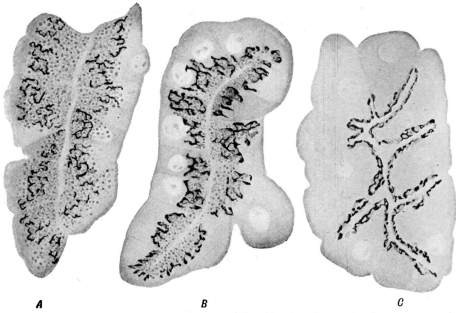

Fig. 401. Sections through three pancreatic acini of mice, showing changes in the zymogen granules and Golgi apparatus. A, During starvation; B, normal pancreas; C, three hours after the injection of pilocarpine. Method of Kolatschew. 950 ×. (Redrawn after Nassonow.)

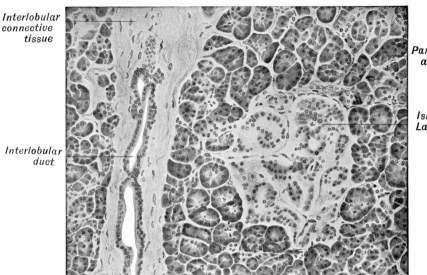

Interlobular
connective
tissue

Pancreatic
acinus

Islet of
Langerhans

Interlobular
duct

Fig. 402. Section of human pancreas, showing contrast between the islet of Langerhans and the surrounding acinous tissue. 470 ×. (Drawn by Miss A. Nixon.)

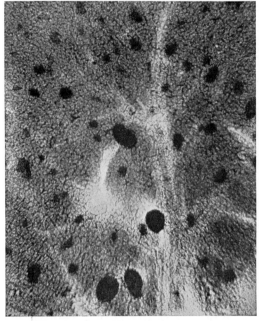

Fig. 403. Photomicrograph of portion of guinea pig pancreas, in which the islands of Langerhans have been stained differentially by injection of neutral red into the vessels. Note the variations in size of the islands. 38 ×. (After Bensley.)

cells distinctly paler than the surrounding acinar cells. With such a technique, no secretion granules are to be seen in the cells of the islets. By special methods, however, it can be shown that several types of granular cells are present which stain quite differently from those of the acini and accordingly must have a different constitution. One of these is found in a small number of cells, called *alpha* or *A cells*; these granules are insoluble in alcohol. Other cells, the *beta* or *B cells*, constitute the bulk of the island. The granules in these cells are soluble in alcohol. In the guinea pig some of the cells in the islands do not contain granules; these are called *C cells*.

In sections of the mammalian pancreas freshly fixed in Zenker-formol and stained with the Mallory-azan or Masson method, three types of granular cells are found in the islands. The A cells have granules which are large and stain a brilliant red; the B cells have smaller, brown-orange granules; while a third type of cell, called *D*, is filled with small, blue-stained granules. Whether the D cells are a separate type of cell or are a stage in the development of the B or A cells remains to be determined. In the dog, Hunt found the A, B and D cells to constitute 20, 75 and 5 per cent of the cells, respectively.

Several cases of a rare disease in man have been associated with small tumors of the pancreas. Most of the cells composing some of these tumors are considered to be atypical B cells because of the staining reactions of their granules. Curiously, these tumor cells often contain chromophile substance like that in the acinar cells.

The mitochondria of the islands resemble those of the duct cells; that is, they are usually small rods or delicate filaments, and thus contrast sharply with the heavier, granular or filamentous mitochondria of the acinar cells. The acini contain chromophile substance and zymogen granules; the islets do not contain either of these, but do have their several kinds of specific granules. The Golgi net in the islets is much smaller than in the acini.

The islands may be distributed in the following positions: (1) They may occur in the interstitial tissue, particularly along the main duct and its primary branches, with which they are connected either directly by short ducts or by the system of undifferentiated tubules described later. (2) Most of the islets are located intralobularly and in direct continuity with the acini or the ducts, or both. (3) A few islets may be present in either the interstitial tissue or intralobularly, but are not connected with either the acini or the ducts.

Ducts. The pancreas usually communicates with the duodenum by a large and a small duct. The large, or main, duct (of Wirsung) begins in the tail and runs through the substance of the gland, receiving throughout its course numerous accessory branches, so that it gradually increases in size as it nears the duodenum. In the head of the organ, it runs parallel with the ductus choledochus, with which it may have a common opening, or it may open independently in the ampulla of Vater. The opening and closing of these ducts are controlled by the sphincter of Oddi (p. 404). The accessory duct (of Santorini) is about 6 cm. long. It is practically always present and lies cranial to the duct of Wirsung.

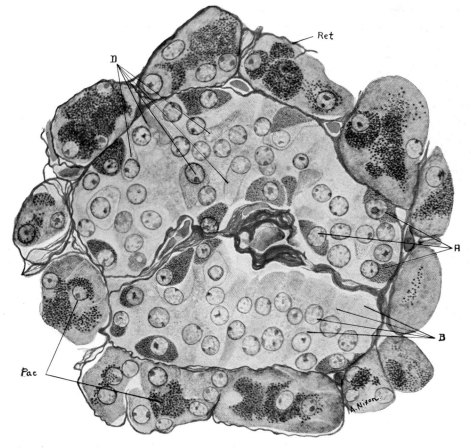

Fig. 404. Section of human pancreas. The central part of the figure is an islet of Langerhans with granular cells of types A, B and D; Pac, pancreatic acini; Ret, reticular fibers. Mallory-azan stain 960 ×. (After Bloom, 1931.)

The ducts represent two separate primordia. They are lined by a columnar epithelium in which goblet cells and occasional argentaffine cells are interspersed. At times small mucous glands bulge slightly from the ductal epithelium. The primary ducts are surrounded by a layer of dense, collagenous connective tissue which contains a few scattered elastic fibers. The intralobular ducts are of low columnar epithelium and rest on a reticular basement membrane. The terminals of the intralobular ducts continue into the acini as the *centro-acinous cells*. In sections stained with the Mallory-azan technique, the pale orange stained centro-acinous cells are in sharp contrast to the purple stained acinar cells with their bright red zymogen granules.

In addition to these ducts, the pancreas contains a system of anastomosing small *tubules* which arise from the large ducts and run in the connective tissue surrounding them. These tubes have a diameter of 12 to 27 microns; they are connected with both the islets of Langerhans and the small mucous glands and only occasionally with the acini. These structures, although studied most extensively in the guinea pig, are also said to be present in man. The epithelium of these tubules is of a low, irregularly cuboidal type. They contain occasional mitoses. The cytoplasm is homogeneous in most cases. Occasional goblet cells and a few cells with true mucous granules may be found within them.

Some of the projections in these tubules consist of island cells, singly or in groups, but the most striking feature of these tubules is their connection by one or more short stalks, with large islands of Langerhans. These ductules are composed of undifferentiated epithelium, and from them new islands, and probably also new acini, arise from time to time, particularly after injury to the pancreas. They do not carry any secretion.

Blood Vessels, Lymphatics and Nerves. The arterial supply of the pancreas is from branches of the celiac and superior mesenteric arteries. From the celiac it receives branches through the pancreaticoduodenal and the splenic arteries; it also receives small branches from the hepatic artery. The inferior pancreaticoduodenal artery is a branch of the superior mesenteric. The vessels run in the interlobular connective tissue and give off fine branches which enter the lobules. Veins accompany the arteries throughout and lead the blood either directly into the portal vein or indirectly through the splenic vein.

The exact lymphatic supply of the gland has not been worked out in detail. The lymphatic drainage is mainly into the celiac nodes about the celiac artery.

The nerve supply is mainly of unmyelinated fibers arising from the celiac plexus. These fibers accompany the arteries into the gland and end about the acini with fine terminals. There are many sympathetic ganglion cells in the interlobular connective tissue. The organ also receives myelinated fibers from the vagus nerves; it has been suggested that these are of secretory nature.

Histogenesis. The pancreas arises from two diverticula of the duodenum close to the hepatic diverticulum. The two primordia of the pancreas are known as the *ventral* and *dorsal pancreases*; these fuse, and the duct of the ventral pancreas becomes part of the main pancreatic duct. The great mass of the organ is formed by the dorsal pancreas, which gives rise to the body and tail and part of the head. The duct of this primor-

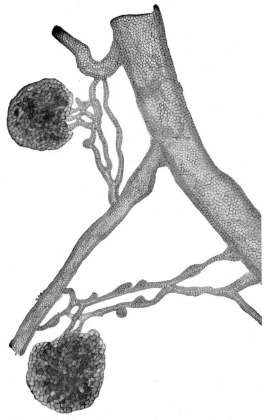

Fig. 405. Duct of pancreas of a guinea pig, showing multiple connections with two islands. 70 ×. (Redrawn after Bensley.)

dium becomes the future accessory duct. Most of the main pancreatic duct of the adult is formed from the remainder of the duct of the dorsal primordium which fuses with the duct of the ventral primordium.

At first the primordium consists of a network of anastomosing tubules lined by a single layer of cells. These differentiate into acini, in which the characteristic secretion granules appear, and also into islands. It is said that specific granules are to be found in human embryos 31 cm. long. Although the question has not been finally settled, it is probable that the acini do not develop into islands, but that the latter come directly from the embryonic tubules of the duct.

Regeneration. If the great mass of the pancreas is removed experimentally, the organ regenerates but slightly. If a portion of the tissue be injured by a wound, mitotic figures appear in the ductal epithelium, and many new islands are formed, but few, if any, new acini develop as a result of the injury. If the main pancreatic ducts be ligated, there is at first a rapid disintegration of the pancreatic acini followed by a much slower disintegration of the original islands, but at the same time ducts begin to proliferate and give rise to many new islands and to some new acini. This process extends over a period of months and even years. One week after the ligation, in the guinea pig and rabbit, most of the acini have regenerated; after one month, there is considerable regeneration of new islands and some acini from the ducts; then, most of the acini degenerate (year and a half). After nearly three years, it is said that only the main duct is present as a blindly ending structure, that there are no acini left, and that a few new islands have arisen by sprouting from the ducts. It seems fairly well assured that the pancreas, even in the adult, is provided with undifferentiated cells which can give rise to new acini and, to a great extent, to new islands.

Histophysiological Remarks. *Internal Secretion.* Extirpation of the pancreas in animals results in severe *diabetes*, a disturbance in carbohydrate metabolism in which the concentration of glucose in the blood rises and the excess is excreted in the urine. Such a condition results shortly in the death of the animal, but is prevented, at least in part, if the pituitary gland is also removed.

If the pancreatic ducts are ligated, the animals do not suffer diabetes, although the acinar tissue degenerates, and the islands persist and may even increase in number. One of the great achievements in modern therapeutics, the *insulin* treatment of diabetes, rests upon the demonstration that extracts of pancreas tissue, in which degeneration of the acinar tissue had been induced by ligation of

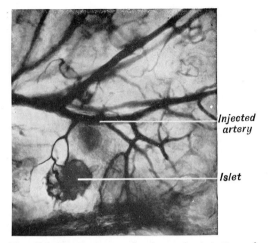

Fig. 406. Photomicrograph of vascular injection of pancreas of guinea pig, showing blood supply to an islet of Langerhans. From a preparation of R. R. Bensley. 95 ×.

the ducts, relieved the symptoms of diabetes. Insulin was subsequently obtained from the whole or intact pancreas by preventing the destructive effect of the acinar secretion upon the internal secretion of the islets of Langerhans. Crystalline insulin is a simple protein with a high labile sulfur content and a molecular weight of about 35,000. All crystalline insulin so far obtained has contained zinc, and this metal is sometimes added to preparations of insulin to enhance their activity. A combination of insulin with protamines is used to extend the activity of the preparation over longer periods of time. There are many indications that the B cells are concerned with the production of insulin, although the proof of this is not certain.

When glucose is administered continuously intravenously in guinea pigs, the B cells at first lose their granules and later become more numerous, through mitosis and through transformation of acinar cells, and loaded with granules. If the injection of glucose is continued for several days, many of the B cells lose their granules and become vacuolated (exhaustion). Cells like these also occur after removal of large parts of the pancreas.

The exact mode of action of insulin is not known, but it is an important factor in the endocrine balance which determines the level of the blood sugar. It is possible, since pathological changes in the pancreas are not found regularly in diabetes, that this syndrome may include cases of pituitary diabetes and even of thyroid or adrenal cortical diabetes, since all these endocrine glands are also concerned with the regulation of carbohydrate metabolism, transport or storage. Diabetes results when there is either an absolute or a relative lack of insulin; consequently this condition may be associated with the finding of normal amounts of insulin in the organism.

Animals injected with alloxan suffer a severe hyperglycemia and die, owing to degeneration of the *B* cells. The diabetogenic action of alloxan can be prevented by a prophylactic injection of 1, 2 dimercapto-propanol.

Accompanying the tumors of the pancreas composed of atypical *B* cells, there is a great decrease in the concentration of sugar in the blood. The symptoms of hypoglycemia in these cases may be relieved temporarily by administration of glucose, and some patients have been cured by removal of the tumors.

External Secretion. The external secretion of the pancreas follows a rhythmical cycle seemingly dependent on the fact that, in certain stages of digestion, the acid content of the stomach, on reaching the duodenum, produces there a substance called *secretin*. This substance, carried to the pancreatic cells by the blood, induces them to secrete. Then the alkaline secretion in the duodenum neutralizes the acid material from the stomach and inhibits the formation of secretin until new acid is brought from the stomach. The nature of secretin and how its acts upon the pancreatic cells are not known.

The *zymogen granules* in the pancreatic acini decrease in number after the injection of pilocarpine or stimulation of the vagus nerve, and during digestion. It is claimed, however, that in normal secretion there is not an extensive diminution of zymogen granules; accordingly, the formation of pancreatic juice, rich in ferment, does not remove all granules. The pancreatic juice contains several types of pro-enzymes. One of

these when activated becomes trypsin, a proteolytic enzyme; another, an amylase or sugar-splitting enzyme; a third, lipase, a fat-splitting enzyme; and, finally, an enzyme like the rennet of gastric juice.

As these enzymes are present as inactive precursors, they cannot injure the pancreas. In certain pathological conditions, however, these pro-enzymes may be converted into the active enzymes which destroy the pancreatic tissue itself.

REFERENCES

Andrew, W.: Senile Changes in the Pancreas of Wistar Institute Rats and of Man with Special Regard to the Similarity of Locule and Cavity Formation. Am. J. Anat., 74:97, 1944.

Babkin, B. P., Rubaschkin, W. J., and Ssawitch, W. W.: Ueber die morphologischen Veränderungen der Pankreaszellen unter der Einwirkung verschiedener Reize. Arch. f. mikr. Anat., 74:68, 1909.

Banting, F. G., and Best, C. H.: The Internal Secretion of the Pancreas. J. Lab. & Clin. Med., 7:251, 1922.

Bast, T. H., Schmidt, E. R., and Sevringhaus, E. L.: Pancreatic Tumor with Hypoglycemic Status Epilepticus. Acta Chirurgica Scandinavica, 71:82, 1932.

Beams, H. W.: Golgi Apparatus, Canalicular Apparatus, Vacuome, and Mitochondria in the Islets of Langerhans of the Albino Rat. Anat. Rec., 46:305, 1930.

Bensley, R. R.: Studies on the Pancreas of the Guinea Pig. Am. J. Anat., 12:297, 1911.

Bensley, S. H., and Woerner, C. A.: The Effects of Continuous Intravenous Injection of an Extract of the Alpha Cells of the Guinea Pig Pancreas on the Intact Guinea Pig. Anat. Rec., 72:413, 1938.

Best, C. H.: The Significance of Choline as a Dietary Factor. Science, 94:523, 1941.

Diamare, V.: Studii comparativi sulle isole di Langerhans del pancreas. Internat. Monatschr. f. Anat. u. Physiol., 16:155, 1899.

Dunn, S. J., Sheehan, H. L., and McLetchie, N. G. B.: Necrosis of Islets of Langerhans Produced Experimentally. Lancet, 1:484, 1943.

Gomori, G.: Pathology of the Pancreatic Islets. Arch. Path., 36:217, 1943.

Ham, A. W., and Haist, R. E.: Histological Study of Trophic Effects of Diabetogenic Anterior Pituitary Extracts and Their Relation to the Pathogenesis of Diabetes. Am. J. Path., 17:787, 1941.

Laguesse, E. L.: Le pancréas. La glande exocrine. La glande endocrine. Revue générale d'histologie, 1 and 2, 1906.

Lane, M. A.: The Cytological Characters of the Areas of Langerhans. Am. J. Anat., 7:409, 1907.

Latta, J. S., and Harvey, H. T.: Changes in the Islets

of Langerhans of the Albino Rat Induced by Insulin Administration. Anat. Rec., 82:281, 1942.

Lazarow, A.: Protection against Alloxan Diabetes. Anat. Rec., 97:37, 1947.

McHenry, E. W., and Patterson, J. M.: Lipotropic Factors. Physiol. Rev., 24:128, 1944.

O'Leary, J. L.: An Experimental Study on the Islet Cells of the Pancreas in Vivo. Anat. Rec., 45:27, 1930.

Opie, E. L.: The Relation of Diabetes Mellitus to Lesions of the Pancreas. Hyaline Degeneration of the Islands of Langerhans. J. Exper. Med., 5:527, 1902; Cytology of the Pancreas, in Special Cytology (Cowdry). 2d ed. New York, (1), 373, 1932.

Soskin, S.: The Blood Sugar: Its Origin, Regulation and Utilization. Physiol. Rev., 21:140, 1941.

Zimmermann, K. W.: Die Speicheldrüsen der Mundhöhle und die Bauchspeicheldrüse, in von Möllendorff's Hand. d. mikr. Anat. des Menschen. Berlin, 1927, Vol. 5, Pt. 1, p. 61.

XXVII. THE RESPIRATORY SYSTEM

The respiratory system serves mainly for the intake of oxygen by the body and the elimination of carbon dioxide. It may be divided into *conducting* and *respiratory portions*. The former are air-conducting tubes connecting the external air with that portion of the lungs where the exchange of gases between blood and the air takes place. These tubes are the hollow passages of the nose, the pharynx, the larynx, the trachea, and bronchi of various sizes. The ends of the smallest branches of the air-conducting passages are capped by the respiratory portion of the lungs, formed by many small air vesicles, called *alveolar sacs* and *alveoli*. The pharynx also connects the mouth with the esophagus; the larynx contains the vocal organ.

THE NOSE

The nose is a hollow organ composed of bone, cartilage, muscles and connective tissue. Its skin is provided with unusually large sebaceous glands and a few small hairs. The integument continues into the vestibule through the anterior nares. The epithelium here is stratified squamous, and there are some hairs which are believed to help in removing particles of dust from the inspired air. The remainder of the nasal cavity is lined with ciliated epithelium, with a specialized, nonciliated epithelium in the olfactory area.

The nose, like the larynx and trachea, is lined with pseudostratified, ciliated, columnar epithelium in which goblet cells are richly interspersed. A basement membrane separates the epithelium from the underlying connective tissue layer with its mixed mucous glands. The mucus from these glands keeps the walls of the nasal cavity moist. In the lower nasal conchae are rich venous plexuses which warm the air passing through the nose. These plexuses differ from erectile tis-

sue by the absence of septa containing smooth muscle.

Leukocytes and lymphocytes migrating through the epithelium, and collections of lymphatic tissue beneath it, are characteristic of the respiratory epithelium of the nose, especially near the nasopharynx.

After leaving the nasal cavity, the inspired air passes by way of the nasopharynx and pharynx to the larynx. The nasal part of the pharynx is lined by ciliated columnar epithelium. In its oral part, it is lined by stratified squamous epithelium which is continuous with that of the mouth above and the esophagus below. The structure of the pharynx is described on page 345.

The Organ of Smell. The receptors for the sense of smell are located in the *olfactory epithelium*. In fresh condition it is yellowish-brown in contrast to the surrounding pink mucous membrane. The olfactory area extends from the middle of the roof of the nasal cavity some 8 to 10 mm. downward on both sides of the septum and on the surface of the upper nasal conchae. The surface of these areas of both sides is about 500 sq. mm. The outlines of the olfactory area are irregular.

The olfactory epithelium is pseudostratified columnar and about 60 microns thick. Unlike the ciliated epithelium, it lacks a distinct basement membrane. It consists of three kinds of cells: (1) supporting cells, (2) basal cells, and (3) olfactory cells.

The *supporting cells* are tall, slender elements with an axial bundle of tonofibrils. At the free surface they form small cuticular plates kept together by a system of thin terminal bars. Small, round openings for the sensory cells remain between the borders of the cuticles. Under the cuticle each cell contains a diplosome, from which a tiny flagellum emerges. The upper part of the cell contains a small Golgi net and pigment granules which cause the brown color of the olfactory area.

Between the bases of the supporting cells,

olfactory vesicle, which contains at its surface six to eight tiny granules similar to the basal bodies of the ciliated cells; each granule sends out a fine olfactory cilium 2 microns long.

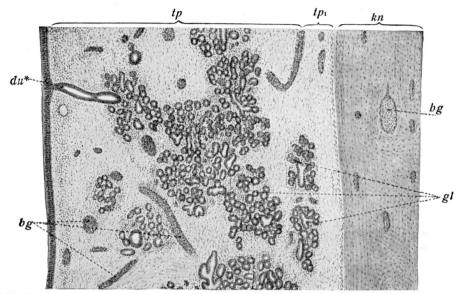

Fig. 407. Respiratory mucosa of osseous portion of nose of a twenty-two year old man. *du**, Opening of duct; *tp*, lamina propria, with glands (*gl*) and blood vessels (*bg*), which acts as a periosteum (*tp₁*) for the bone (*kn*). 45 ×. (After Sobotta.)

the *basal cells* form a single layer of small conical elements with dark nuclei and branching processes.

The *olfactory cells*, evenly distributed between the supporting cells, are bipolar nerve cells. Their round nuclei occupy a zone between the nuclei of the supporting cells and the connective tissue. The periphery of the cell, a modified dendrite, extends as a cylindrical process from the nucleus to the surface. The proximal end tapers into a thin, smooth filament about 1 micron thick. It is an axon—a fiber of the olfactory nerve. It passes into the connective tissue and, with similar fibers, forms small nerve bundles. These are collected into about twenty macroscopically visible *fila olfactoria*.

The cytoplasm of the olfactory cell contains a network of neurofibrils which are especially distinct around the nucleus. The head of the olfactory cell protrudes freely through the opening of the cuticular membrane. It enlarges slightly to the so-called

The unmyelinated fibers of the olfactory nerve are kept together by a delicate connective tissue rich in macrophages. The fila olfactoria pass through openings of the cribriform plate of the ethmoid bone and enter the olfactory bulb of the brain, where the primary olfactory center is located. The olfactory mucous membrane is also provided with myelinated nerve fibers originating from the trigeminal nerve. After losing their myelin they enter the epithelium and end with fine arborizations under its free surface between the supporting cells. These endings are receptors for stimuli other than odors.

The *lamina propria* of the olfactory mucous membrane is fused with the periosteum. Among its cells are numerous pigment cells, and some lymphoid cells which migrate into the epithelium.

Beneath the epithelium the lamina propria contains a rich plexus of blood capillaries. In its deeper layers it contains a plexus of large veins and dense networks of lymph capillaries. The latter continue into large lymphatics which course toward the lymph nodes on the sides of the head. A colored mass injected into the subarachnoid spaces of the brain can penetrate into the lymph capillaries of the olfactory region as well as into the sheaths of the fila olfactoria. This indicates a possible pathway for infections to spread from the nasal mucous membrane to the meninges.

The lamina propria in the olfactory area contains the *olfactory glands* of Bowman of branched, tubulo-alveolar type. The secretory portions are mainly parallel to the surface, while the narrow duct assumes a perpendicular course and opens on the surface.

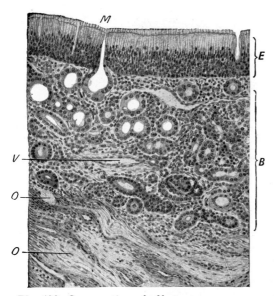

Fig. 408. Cross section of olfactory mucous membrane on the medial surface of the middle concha, from a man. *B*, glands of Bowman; *E*, olfactory epithelium; *M*, opening of a gland on the surface; *O*, bundle of olfactory fibers; *V*, vein. 70 ×. (After Schaffer.)

Immediately under the epithelium the duct is often considerably enlarged. The low pyramidal cells of the secretory portions are serous, containing secretory granules.

Histophysiological Remarks. The olfactory stimuli are probably of chemical nature. The secretion of the glands of Bowman keeps the surface of the olfactory epithelium moist and furnishes the necessary solvent. As most odoriferous substances are much more soluble in lipids than in water, and as the olfactory cells and their cilia contain a considerable amount of lipids, odoriferous substances, even if present in extreme dilution, may become concentrated in these structures. The continuous stream of the secretion of the olfactory glands, by removing the remains of the stimulating substances, keeps the receptors ready for new stimuli. In this respect the olfactory glands doubtless have a function similar to that of the glands connected with the taste buds.

The olfactory epithelium in man is easily affected by inflammation of the mucous membrane of the nose and is often more or less altered and replaced by atypical epithelium.

Histogenetic Remarks. The olfactory region appears in the embryo a little later than the primordia of the

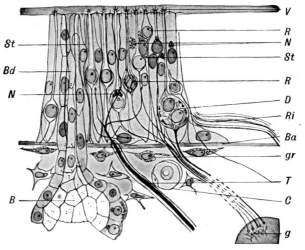

Fig. 409. Diagram of human olfactory mucous membrane. *B*, Gland of Bowman, with diplosomes in its cells, and with its excretory duct, *B*; *Ba*, layer of basal cells; *C*, capillary; *D*, large binucleated olfactory cell; *g*, olfactory glomerulus; *gr*, connective tissue cells; *N*, Golgi net in the suporting and in the olfactory cells; *R*, olfactory cells with neurofibrils and the olfactory vesicles, *V*; *Ri*, olfactory fibers; *St*, supporting cells with tonofibrils; *T*, myelinated fibers of the N. Trigeminus. (After Kolmer.)

eye and ear. In embryos of 4.9 mm. it is a paired, thickened, ectodermal area at the anterior edge of the medullary plate. The plate is later gradually invaginated and recedes from the surface. Some of the epithelial cells are transformed into olfactory elements, which send out axons growing toward the anterior part of the brain vesicle.

Nasal Sinuses. Connected with the nasal cavity, and forming cavities in the respective bones, are the frontal, ethmoidal, sphenoidal, and maxillary sinuses—the *accessory sinuses of the nose.* They are lined with an epithelium similar to that of the nasal cavity, but containing fewer and smaller glands. The mucosa of all the sinuses is delicate and cannot be differentiated as a separate layer from the periosteum of the bones, to which it is usually tightly adherent.

THE LARYNX

The larynx is an elongated, irregularly tubelike structure, whose walls contain hyaline and elastic cartilages, connective tissue, striated muscles, and a mucous membrane with glands. It serves to connect the pharynx with the trachea. As a result of changes in its shape resulting from the contraction of its muscles, it produces variations in the opening between the vocal cords. The size of this opening conditions the pitch of the sounds made by the passage of air through the larynx.

The main framework of the larynx is made of several cartilages. Of these the thyroid and cricoid cartilages and the epiglottis are unpaired, while the arytenoid, corniculate, and cuneiform are paired. The thyroid and cricoid and the lower parts of the arytenoids are hyaline cartilages. The *extrinsic* muscles of the larynx connect it with surrounding muscles and ligaments and facilitate deglutition. The *intrinsic* muscles connect the cartilages of the larynx; by their contraction they give different shapes to the laryngeal cavity and thus are active in phonation.

The anterior surface of the *epiglottis* and the upper half of its posterior surface, the *aryepiglottic folds,* and the *vocal cords* are covered with stratified squamous epithelium. In the adult, ciliated epithelium usually be-

gins at the base of the epiglottis and extends down the larynx, trachea and bronchi.

The cilia are 3.5 to 5 microns long and beat toward the mouth; thus they move foreign particles, bacteria and mucus from the lungs toward the exterior of the body. After

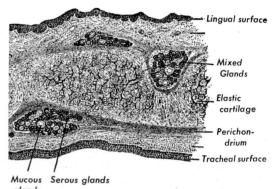

Fig. 410. Cross section through middle of epiglottis of a twenty-two year old man. 27 ×. (After von Ebner.)

death, the cilia have been seen to beat for fifty to seventy hours; in tissue cultures of rabbit lung they may beat for twelve days or more.

A centriole has not been demonstrated in the ciliated epithelium of the respiratory tract. Evidences of regeneration of the tracheal epithelium are rare; this may be associated with the absence of a centriole. Goblet cells in varying numbers are scattered between the cylindrical cells. The glands of the larynx are of the tubulo-acinous, mixed mucous variety. Some of the ducts secrete mucus; the alveoli secrete mucus and may have crescents. A few taste buds are scattered on the under surface of the epiglottis.

The *true vocal cords* enclose the vocal or inferior thyro-arytenoid ligaments. Each of these (one on each side) consists of a band of elastic tissue bordered on its lateral side by the thyro-arytenoid muscle and covered medially by a thin mucous membrane with a stratified squamous epithelium. The space between the vocal cords is usually given as 23 mm. long in men, and 18 mm. in women. Its shape undergoes great variations in the phases of respiration and in the production of different sounds in talking and singing. Contraction of the thyro-arytenoid muscle approximates the arytenoid and thyroid cartilages, and this relaxes the vocal cords.

The larynx is supplied by the upper, middle and lower laryngeal arteries, which, in turn, arise from the superior and inferior thyroid arteries. The veins from the larynx empty into the thyroid veins. The larynx contains several rich plexuses of lymphatics which lead into the upper cervical lymph nodes and to those about the trachea. The superior laryngeal nerve sends sensory nerves, and the inferior laryngeal, motor nerves to the larynx.

TRACHEA

The trachea is a thin-walled, fairly rigid tube about 11 cm. long and 2 to 2.5 cm. in diameter. It is continuous with the larynx above and ends by dividing into the two main bronchi below.

The epithelium of the trachea is ciliated

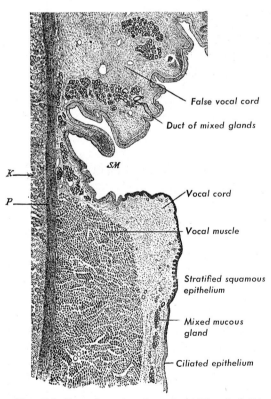

Fig. 411. Frontal section through middle of glottis of a boy of nine years. K, Thyroid cartilage with its perichondrium, P; SM, laryngeal ventricle. 15 ×. (After von Ebner.)

pseudostratified columnar and rests on a distinct basement membrane. Numerous goblet cells are scattered throughout the epithelium. The lamina propria contains many elastic fibers and numerous small glands like those of the larynx. These glands, most of which are external to the elastic fibers, open by short ducts on the free surface of the epithelium. In the posterior portion of the trachea, the glands extend through the muscular layer. Stimulation of the recurrent laryngeal nerve activates secretion in these glands. The lamina propria also contains accumulations of lymphatic tissue.

The most characteristic part of the trachea is its framework of sixteen to twenty hyaline cartilages. These are **C** or **Y**-shaped and encircle the tube except in its posterior part. Because of the spaces between them they give the tube much more pliability and extensibility than if they formed a continuous sheet. The cartilages pass obliquely down the trachea. With advancing age they become fibrous, but do not ossify as the thyroid cartilage does. They are surrounded by dense connective tissue which contains many elastic and reticular fibers.

The posterior wall of the trachea, close to

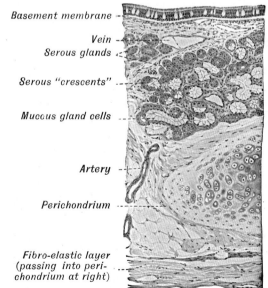

Fig. 412. Cross section through part of a human trachea. 60 ×. (After Braus.)

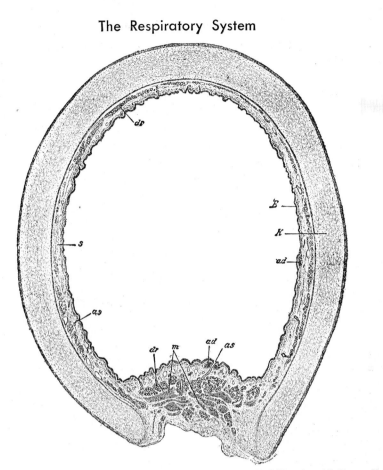

Fig. 413. Cross section through trachea of a boy of nine years. *E,* Ciliated epithelium; *K,* cartilage; *ad,* lymphoid tissue; *dr,* glands with a duct, *as; m,* smooth muscle of the membranous portion of the wall; *s,* mucosa. 8 ×. (After Kölliker-von Ebner.)

the esophagus, is devoid of cartilages. Their place is taken by a thick layer of smooth muscle bundles which run mainly transversely. They are inserted into the dense, elastic fiber bundles surrounding the trachea and especially its cartilages, and are joined to the mucous membrane by a layer of loose connective tissue, some adipose tissue, and mucous glands.

A delicate network of lymphatics is found in the mucosa, and a much coarser plexus occurs in the submucosa. These lead into the lymphatic nodes which accompany the trachea along its entire length. The arteries for the trachea are mainly from the inferior thyroid. The nerves supplying the trachea arise from the recurrent branch of the vagus nerve and from the sympathetic. The sympathetic nerves of the trachea contain small ganglia, from which fibers lead to the muscle of the organ. Myelinated sensory nerves are also found.

THE LUNGS*

The lungs constitute a paired organ occupying a great part of the thoracic cavity and constantly changing in form with the different phases of respiration. The right lung consists of three lobes and the left lung of two, and each lobe receives a branch of the primary bronchi. The outer surface of the lungs is closely invested by a serous membrane, the *visceral pleura.*

In children the lungs, because of their great blood supply, are a pale pink. With advancing age they become gray, owing to the inhalation of carbon particles, particularly in city dwellers.

Each of the five lobes of the lungs is divided by thin connective tissue septa into great numbers of roughly pyramidal portions

* This section has been revised by C. G. Loosli.

of pulmonary tissue, the *lobules*. These are so arranged that the apex of each points toward the hilus and the base toward the pleura. In the adult lung, these gross lobules are not so easily seen, except under the pleura, as in the embryonic lung. Under the lobes has become important. According to Boyden, the right lung is made up of ten principal bronchopulmonary segments, while the left lung can be divided into eight segments. The basic pattern of the secondary bronchi appears, however, to be subject to

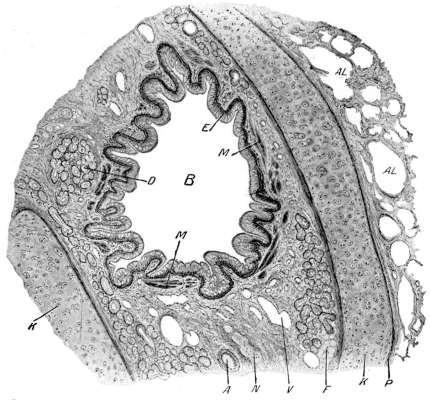

Fig. 414. Cross section through small bronchus of a man. A, Artery; AL, alveoli; B, bronchus; D, mixed glands; E, ciliated epithelium with goblet cells; F, fat tissue; K, cartilage; M, circular muscle; N, nerve; P, perichondrium; V, vein. Mallory's connective tissue stain. 30 ×. (After Schaffer.)

pleura, however, the progressive deposition of carbon from the inspired air marks the outlines of these lobules distinctly. Each lobule is supplied by a small bronchiole.

Bronchial Tubes. The trachea divides into two main branches called *bronchi*. These tubes enter the substance of the lungs at the hilus, one on each side, and, maintaining a downward and outward direction, divide into two smaller bronchi on the left side and three on the right. These give rise to smaller bronchi, from which *bronchioles* of several orders originate. With the development of lung surgery, knowledge of the segmental distribution of the secondary bronchi in the considerable variation. It has been estimated that there are from fifty to eighty terminal bronchioles in each lobule. This number is probably somewhat high. Each *terminal bronchiole* continues into one, two or more respiratory bronchioles. These break up into two to eleven *alveolar ducts*, from which arise the *alveolar sac* and *alveoli*. Thus the main successive divisions of the bronchial tree are primary bronchi, secondary bronchi, bronchioles, terminal bronchioles, respiratory bronchioles, alveolar ducts, alveolar sacs, and alveoli. An *atrium* has been described as connecting the alveolar sacs and the alveolar ducts (see p. 427).

Before the bronchi enter the lung their structure is practically identical with that of the trachea. But as soon as they enter the lung, the *cartilage rings* disappear and are replaced by irregularly shaped *cartilage plates* which completely surround the bronchus. As a result, the intrapulmonary bronchi and their branches are cylindrical and not flattened on one side like the trachea and the extrapulmonary portions of the bronchi. At the same time as the cartilage plates become irregularly distributed around the tube, the muscular layer completely surrounds the bronchus. The cartilages disappear when the diameter of the bronchiole reaches 1 mm.

The innermost layer of the bronchi is a mucous membrane continuous with that of the trachea and lined by the same type of epithelium. The lamina propria consists of a small amount of reticular and collagenous connective tissue and many elastic fibers; it contains a few lymphoid cells and is delimited from the epithelium by a basement membrane. The mucosa of the bronchi, in histologic sections, shows a marked longitudinal folding due to the contraction of the muscle. It is claimed that these folds disappear when the lung is distended.

Next to the mucosa is a layer of smooth muscles which run in all directions around the tube, but never form a closed ring as in the blood vessels and intestines. The muscles form an interlacing feltwork whose meshes become larger in the smaller bronchioles. Numerous elastic fibers are intimately associated with the smooth muscle cells. As will be discussed later, the elastic fibers and smooth muscles throughout the lung play an important part in the changes in its structure which occur during respiration. A dense network of blood vessels accompanies and penetrates this myo-elastic layer.

The outermost layer of the bronchial wall consists of dense connective tissue which contains many elastic fibers. It surrounds the plates of cartilage and continues into the connective tissue of the surrounding pulmonary tissue and into that accompanying the large vessels.

Mucous and mucoserous glands are found, as in the trachea, as far out in the bronchial tree as the cartilage extends. The glands are usually under the muscular layer, through which their ducts penetrate to open on the free surface.

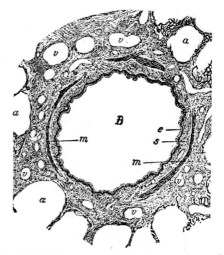

Fig. 415. Cross section through a bronchiole (B) 0.7 mm. thick. *a*, Alveoli; *e*, epithelium; *s*, lamina propria with cross sections of elastic fibers; *m*, circular muscle; *v*, veins. Lung fixed by filling it with alcohol. 55 × (After von Ebner.)

Lymphatic tissue, diffuse and often with nodules, occurs regularly in the mucosa and in the fibrous tissue around the cartilage, especially where the bronchi branch.

With the progressive decrease in the size of the bronchi and bronchioles as they proceed from the trachea, the layers of their walls become thinner, and some of them fuse into one layer. The smooth muscle, however, is distinct up to the end of the respiratory bronchioles and even continues in the walls of the alveolar ducts.

RESPIRATORY STRUCTURES OF THE LUNGS

The *unit* of the lung is composed of all the structures, beginning with a respiratory bronchiole and extending to and including the alveoli with all the blood vessels, lymphatics, nerves and connective tissue. In the newborn, the pulmonary lobule (unit) is small. The respiratory bronchiole has not yet developed, and the alveoli are represented as shallow pouches on the walls of the alveolar

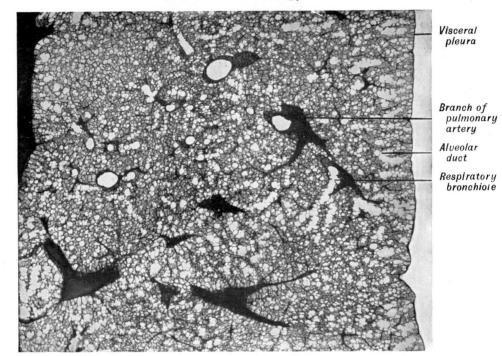

Fig. 416. Photomicrograph of a thick (120 microns) section of lung of *Macacus rhesus*. 10 ×.

ducts. (Compare Figures 419, *left*, and 428, *right*, with Figures 419, *right*, and 417.)

In a thin section of a lung the respiratory portion of the organ appears as a lacework of large spaces separated from one another by thin-walled septa (Fig. 417). Here and there this lacework is traversed by the thick-walled bronchi and various-sized arteries and veins. But a different picture is seen in a thick section with the binocular microscope. Here the lung appears as an irregular honeycomb in which the polyhedral alveoli and alveolar sacs form the "cells" (Figs. 416, 418). These form a honeycomb traversed by the system of bronchioles and the alveolar ducts into which the atria, alveoli and alveolar sacs open (Figs. 424, 425).

The contradictory views on the detailed structure of the lung are due in part to several factors: The lungs must be fixed, for histological purposes, either by way of the trachea or by injection through the pulmonary artery, with the lungs still in the body to prevent over-distention. The usual method of dropping a bit of lung into fixing fluid gives highly distorted pictures, for the lung shrinks greatly when the reduced pressure of the pleural cavity is raised and the air in the organ prevents the penetration of the fixative. As the pul-

monary parenchyma is normally distended with air, thick sections should be used; indeed, the structure of this organ is often seen best in sections of 60 to 120 microns. Hematoxylin and eosin staining gives but a poor idea of the constitution of the lung; special staining and injection methods are necessary. Further, the lung changes its form continuously with every inspiration and expiration (Fig. 430).

Respiratory Bronchioles. In the adult the respiratory bronchioles begin with a diameter of about 0.5 mm. They are short tubes, lined in their first part with a ciliated columnar epithelium devoid of goblet cells. A short distance down the bronchiole, the ciliated columnar epithelium loses its cilia and becomes low cuboidal. These bronchioles have walls composed of collagenous connective tissue in which bundles of interlacing smooth muscles and elastic fibers course. They lack cartilage. A few alveoli bud off from the side of the respiratory bronchiole opposite that along which the branch of the pulmonary artery runs. These alveoli are the first of the respiratory structures of the lung and are responsible for the term "respiratory bronchiole." These bronchioles soon branch and

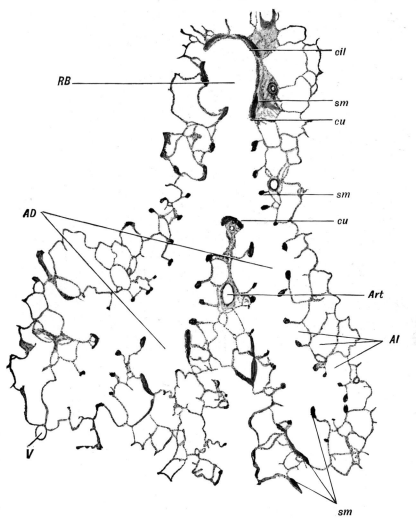

Fig. 417. Section through respiratory bronchiole (*RB*) and two alveolar ducts (*AD*) of human lung, showing the smooth muscle, *sm* (in black), in the walls of the alveolar ducts; *cil*, ciliated epithelium; *cu*, cuboidal epithelium; *Art*, arteriole; *Al*, alveolar sacs; *V*, vein. (Slightly modified from Baltisberger.)

radiate conelike into two to eleven alveolar ducts which extend for relatively long distances. They are surrounded by alveoli which have arisen from adjacent ducts.

Alveolar Ducts. The structure of the alveolar ducts is hard to visualize in thin sections of the distended lung. In thick sections, particularly when studied with the binocular microscope, the alveolar ducts are seen as thin-walled tubes. They usually follow a long, tortuous course and give off several branches which in turn may branch again. They are closely beset with thin-walled outpouchings, the alveolar sacs (and single alveoli). These blind, polyhedral sacs open

only on that surface which faces the alveolar duct. As the alveolar sacs are closely packed against one another, their openings form the greatest part of the wall of the alveolar duct. The wall of the alveolar duct between the mouths of the alveolar sacs consists of strands of elastic and collagenous fibers and smooth muscle cells. In thin sections of the lung, only small portions of these fibers and muscles are seen; they appear as short knobs parallel to the long axis of the alveolar duct.

In thick sections it becomes evident that the short knobs seen in the thin sections are merely tangentially cut, small portions of the long connective tissue fibers and muscle bun-

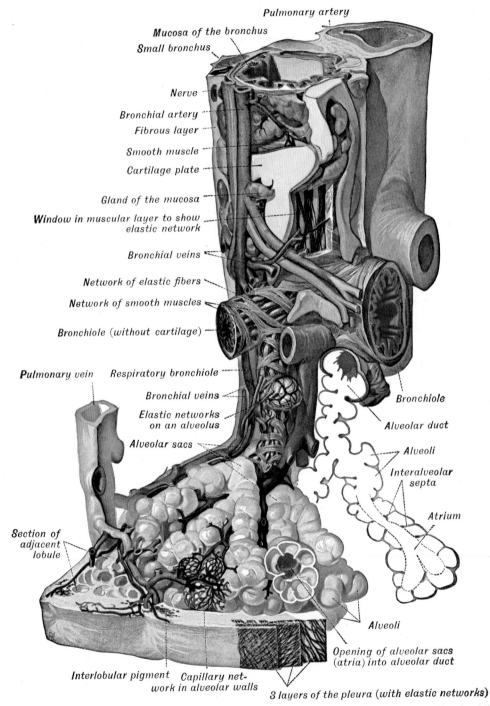

Fig. 418. Portion of a pulmonary lobule from the lung of a young man. Free reconstruction by Vierling, somewhat foreshortened. Mucosa and glands, green; cartilage, light blue; muscles and bronchial artery, orange; elastic fibers, blue-black; pulmonary artery, red; pulmonary and bronchial veins, dark blue. 32 ×. (After Braus.)

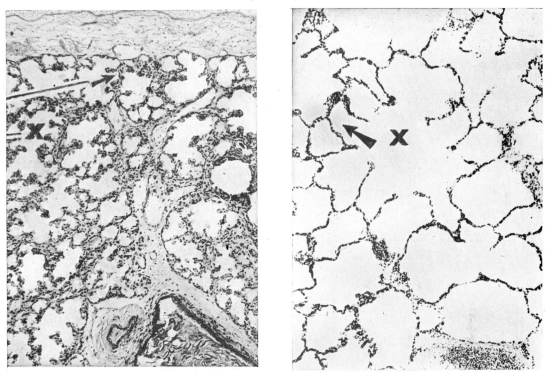

Fig. 419. Section of lung of human newborn (*left*) and of twelve year old girl (*right*). Both specimens fixed immediately after death by the intratracheal injection of Zenker-formol solution. Note increase in size of alveolar ducts (*x*) and alveoli (arrow head). Mallory-azan stain. Photomicrographs. 82 ×. Courtesy of C. G. Loosli.)

dles which interweave in three planes between the mouths of the alveolar sacs.

Alveolar Sacs and Alveoli. From the alveolar ducts arise single alveoli and alveolar sacs containing two to four or more alveoli.

It has been suggested that the space between the alveolar duct and the alveolar sacs be termed the *atrium*, especially at the ends of the alveolar ducts. The structures described under this term have not been generally accepted as forming a distinct entity, for some authors consider them parts of the alveolar ducts.

The alveoli are thin-walled polyhedral formations, one side of which is always lacking, so that air may diffuse freely from the alveolar ducts into the alveolar sacs and thus into the cavities of the alveoli. The most conspicuous feature of the alveolar walls after the age of viability is a dense, single network of capillaries. These capillaries anastomose so freely that many of the spaces between them are smaller than the diameter of the vessel lumina. The alveolar walls contain a close meshed network of branching reticular fibers. These, along with fewer elastic fibers, form the supporting framework for the thin-walled air vesicles and their numerous capillaries (compare Figs. 424 and 425). The capillaries are so situated that the greater portion of their surface is exposed to the alveolar air. The larger reticular and elastic fibers occupy a central position in the septa, with the anastomosing capillaries weaving back and forth in the meshes of the fibers to jut into the adjacent alveolar spaces. This relationship of supporting fibers to capillaries is best seen in the lung of the newborn, which has a thick, cellular central stroma, and becomes less conspicuous with advancing age, owing to the thinning and stretching of the alveolar walls.

The mouths of the alveolar sacs are completely surrounded by a wavy wreath of collagenous fibers. These continue from one sac to the next and help to give thickness to the wall of the alveolar duct. It is probable that these curled wreaths may straighten out with deep inspirations. Elastic fibers accompany the collagenous fibers. The dense networks of reticular fibers within the walls of the alveoli and alveolar sacs are continuations of these collagenous fibers, which, in turn, are connected with the collagenous fibers in the walls of the arteries, veins and bronchioles. The elastic fibers are likewise continuations of those of the bronchioles.

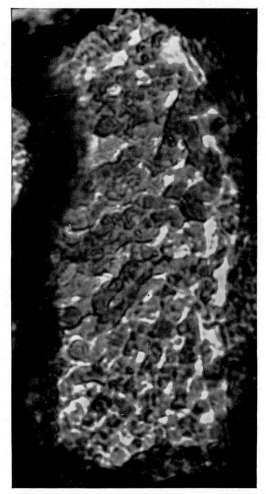

Fig. 420. Thick section of lung of eighteen year old man, showing surface view of alveolar septum. Specimen fixed immediately after death by intratracheal injection of Zenker-formol solution after pulmonary veins and artery had been ligated to keep blood in capillaries. Note close network of capillaries. Mallory-azan stain. Photomicrograph. 625 ×. (Courtesy of C. G. Loosli.)

Cells Lining the Alveoli. All authors accept the presence of nucleated cells located in some of the intercapillary spaces on the alveolar walls. Some histologists, using the intratracheal injection of silver nitrate as a method for marking the limits between cells, describe a continuous membrane composed of large, exceedingly thin plates devoid of nuclei and smaller nucleated cells. The non-nucleated plates have never been seen desquamated from the surface of the alveoli, and stages in their formation have not been described. Although the question is by no means settled, there is a growing tendency to deny the existence of these plates, as many of the older histologists did (see Macklin).

According to Loosli, the irregular wavy lines produced by silver nitrate introduced intratracheally or intravascularly in the alveolar walls of mammalian lungs are the outlines of the endothelial cells lining the capillary blood vessels. This is also true of the respiratory portion of the lungs of birds. In frogs and turtles, the injection of silver nitrate shows that, in addition to the endothelial cells, the alveoli are lined by a continuous layer of flattened epithelial cells.

It is obvious that the crude silver nitrate technique has classed several types of cells into one group, in which practically all cytological details are obscured. There can be little doubt that the so-called "nucleated alveolar epithelial cells" of the older authors are composed of certain pericapillary cells (to be discussed shortly), probably also the endothelial cells of the capillaries and even some of the blood corpuscles within these vessels.

Other workers, denying the existence of non-nucleated plaques, consider that the alveolar surfaces are covered by thin cytoplasmic expansions of the nucleated cells, although such a membrane has not been demonstrated in normal lungs. For support of this theory, histological findings in certain chronic lung diseases showing so-called alveoli lined by a layer of cuboidal cells are described (Miller and Bell). The walls of such spaces also show marked thickening of the connective tissue stroma and a decrease in the number of capillaries, thus resembling in no respect a normal septum. The pathogenesis of such lesions has not been worked out. Some pathologists consider these lining cells a downgrowth of epithelium from the terminal bronchioles, secondary to destruction of the normal architecture of the alveolar walls by the disease process. Evidence to support this view is found in studies of the pathogenesis of certain experimental virus infections in animals (Loosli-Dungal) and so-called "alveolar cell tumors" in man.

In certain strains of mice, nonmetastasizing pulmonary tumors undisputedly arising from the nucleated cells, "alveolar epithelial cells," on the alveolar walls have been produced by the subcutaneous injection of carcinogenic agents. On serial transplantation in the subcutaneous tissue, some of these tumors undergo change from an epithelial pattern to a fibrosarcoma.

In tissue cultures of the lungs and in certain *in vivo* experiments, these inconspicuous cells in the septa mobilize in a few hours and assume the appearance and function of typical macrophages. The name "septal cells" has been suggested for them. In acute pneumococcal infections of the lungs of dogs and monkeys, the principal reaction of the "septal cells" appeared to be one of enlargement without detachment from the alveolar walls. No phagocytic properties were observed in the attached cells. The chief source of the macrophages was from the hypertrophy of the hematogenous lymphocytes and monocytes after they entered the air spaces in the early stages of the disease.

In practically every section of lung, free macrophages (alveolar phagocytes) can be found in the alveoli. They are indistinguishable from the macrophages in other parts of the body. When they contain particles of dust, they are called "dust cells." In certain cardiac diseases they become filled with granules of hemosiderin and are then called "heart failure" cells. They are derived according to most authors from the "alveolar epithelium" or the "septal cells," as indicated earlier. The majority probably arise from the agranulocytes of the blood which have wan-

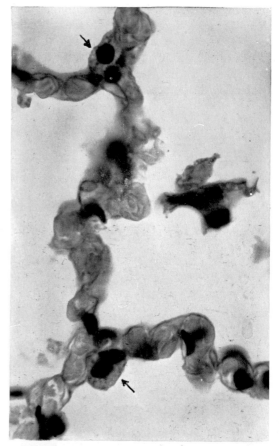

Fig. 421. Photomicrograph of alveolar wall of lung of eighteen year old man. From same specimen as that in Figure 420. Note the thin membrane between the lumina of the capillaries and the air spaces. Arrowheads point to "septal cells" in their characteristic location on the alveolar walls. Hematoxylin-eosin-azure II stain. 1000 ×. (Courtesy of C. G. Loosli.)

dered into the alveoli and hypertrophied into macrophages. Whatever the embryologic origin of the cell, it certainly acts in defense of the lung, including the removal of the dust particles, as a typical macrophage.

The nature of the nucleated cells, "septal cells," outside the capillaries in the alveolar walls is not clear. While some speak of them as epithelial, others regard them of connective tissue origin. In the normal lung, they are in intimate association with the connective tissue stroma at the interstices of the alveolar walls (Fig. 421). Some lie across the septa with their cytoplasm projecting into the adjacent alveolar spaces. When the lung of a rabbit is completely collapsed for several weeks by repeated injections of air into the pleural cavity after section of the phrenic nerve of the same side, the nucleated cells do not thicken to form a membrane over the capillaries. On the other hand, they appear to blend with the central stroma of the walls.

scattered, isolated perivascular cells. Their origin from entoderm or mesenchyme, or both, has not been settled. The capillaries and their perivascular cells are contained in an exceedingly thin-walled, ground membrane in which the supporting reticular and

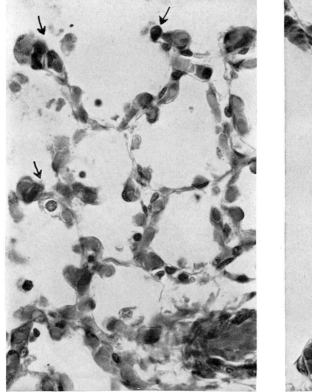

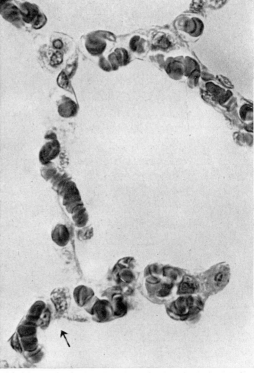

A   B

Fig. 422. Sections of lungs of newborn (A) and of a twelve year old girl (B), fixed as described in Fig. 419. The alveolar walls consist of a central stroma of connective tissue fibers and cells which support a close network of capillaries free of an epithelial covering. Arrowheads in A point to bundle fibers (cut in cross section) which surround the mouths of the alveoli. The arrow in B points to a septal cell. Mallory-azan stain. Photomicrographs. 600 ×. (Courtesy of C. G. Loosli.)

leaving the capillaries filled with blood cells free of an epithelial covering and abutting directly against the thin clefts representing the former air spaces. In the lungs of the newborn unexpanded by extra-uterine respirations, the alveolar capillaries are likewise bare (Fig. 429).

The walls of the alveoli in the adult lung seem to consist primarily of a dense network of anastomosing capillaries, accompanied by

elastic fibers run. See Macklin (1937) for an exposition of the contradictory views on this problem.

Openings or "pores" in the interalveolar septa connecting adjacent alveoli are much more numerous in some species of mammals than in others. There is no doubt of their normal occurrence. In certain pathological conditions, such as lobar pneumonia, threads of fibrin pass through the alveolar walls and connect the inflammatory exudate in adjacent alveoli. The pores permit the spread of bacteria from one alveolus to its neighbors in pneumonia. They also provide a collateral air circulation, which aids in preventing

laries of the pleura and from the capillaries of the alveolar septa and portions of the alveolar ducts and run in the intersegmental connective tissue, independently of the arteries, and fuse to form the pulmonary veins.

pleura

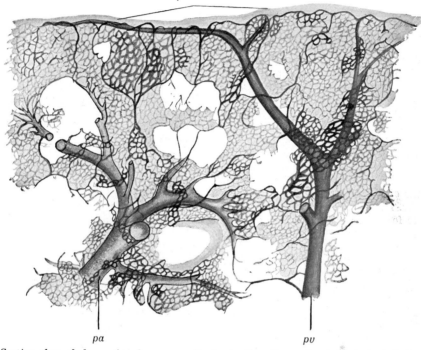

pa   *pv*

Fig. 423. Section through lung of a dog, perpendicular to the pleura, showing relation of the pulmonary artery (*pa*) and the pulmonary vein (*pv*) to the pleura. Artery gray, veins black. About 100 ×. (Redrawn and slightly modified after W. S. Miller.)

atelectasis when secondary bronchi become obstructed.

Blood Vessels. The lungs receive most of their blood from the pulmonary arteries. These are of large caliber and of elastic type. The branches of these arteries in general accompany the bronchi and their branches as far as the respiratory bronchioles. The arterial paths in the lung, however, are subject to considerable variation. It would appear that the rather easily resectable bronchopulmonary segment should not be considered a morphological bronchovascular unit (Boyden). From the respiratory bronchioles they divide, and a branch passes to each alveolar duct and is distributed in a capillary network over all the alveoli which communicate with this duct. The venules arise from the capil-

In passing through the lung, the pulmonary artery is usually above and behind its accompanying bronchial tube, while the vein is below and in front of it.

The bronchial arteries and veins are much smaller than the pulmonary vessels. These arteries arise from the aorta or the intercostal arteries and follow the bronchi. They are distributed to the walls of the bronchi, their glands, and the interlobular connective tissue beneath the pleura. Most of the blood carried by the bronchial arteries is brought back by the pulmonary veins. In the alveoli which arise from the respiratory bronchioles, there is a capillary anastomosis between the terminations of both the pulmonary and bronchial arteries.

Lymphatics. There are two main divisions of the lymphatics of the lungs. One set is in the pleura, and the other in the pulmonary tissue. They communicate infrequently; both of them drain into the lymph nodes at the hilum of the lung. The lymphatics of the pleura form a dense network with large and small polygonal meshes. The large meshes are surrounded by large vessels and demark the lobules; the small meshwork is formed of smaller vessels which mark out the anatomical unit. There are many valves in these lymphatics which control the flow of lymph, so that it passes to the hilum and not into the pulmonary tissue. These pleural lymphatics combine into several main trunks which drain into the lymph nodes at the hilum.

The pulmonary lymphatics may be divided into several groups which include those of the bronchi, of the pulmonary artery, and of the pulmonary vein. The lymphatics in the bronchi form an anastomosing network. They terminate in the alveolar ducts, and their end branches join the lymphatic radicles of the plexuses about the pulmonary artery and vein. There are no lymphatic vessels beyond the alveolar ducts. The pulmonary artery is accompanied and drained by two or three main lymphatic trunks. The lymphatics associated with the pulmonary vein begin with its radicles in the alveolar ducts and in the pleura. All the lymphatics of the pulmonary tissue drain toward the hilus nodes. Efferent trunks from the hilar nodes anastomose to form the right lymphatic duct, which

is the principal channel of lymph drainage from both the right and left lungs. There are no valves in the intrapulmonic lymphatics except in a few vessels, in the interlobular connective tissue near the pleura, which accompany the branches of the pulmonary veins. These lymphatic vessels connect the pulmonary and pleural lymphatic plexuses. As their valves point only toward the pleura, they provide a mechanism whereby lymph can flow from the pulmonary tissue into the pleural lymphatics if the normal flow of lymph in the former toward the hilum is interrupted.

As has been mentioned, the mucous membrane of the bronchi is infiltrated with lymphocytes and often contains lymphatic follicles. There are other accumulations of lymphatic tissue in the adventitia of the pulmonary arteries and veins, but these, as a rule, do not form nodules in the normal lung.

Nerves. The pulmonary plexuses at the root of the lung are formed by branches of the vagus and from the thoracic sympathetic ganglia. The bronchoconstrictor fibers are from the vagus nerve, while the bronchodilator fibers are from the sympathetic and arise mainly from the inferior cervical and first thoracic ganglia. The pulmonary vessels are supplied with both sympathetic and parasympathetic nerve fibers.

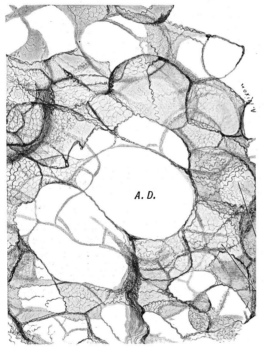

Fig. 424. Thick section from same block as in Figure 416, stained for reticular fibers by the Bielschowsky-Foot method. A. D., Alveolar duct. Note how much more numerous are the reticular fibers than the elastic fibers in Figure 425. Drawn by Miss Agnes Nixon.

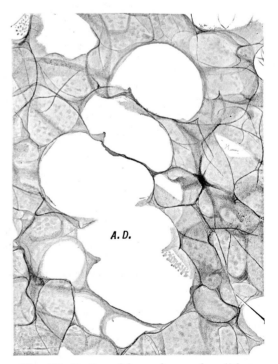

Fig. 425. Portion of lung of a monkey (*Macacus rhesus*), fixed *in situ* and stained with resorcin-fuchsin for elastic fibers and counterstained with light green. A. D., Alveolar duct. Thick section. Compare with Figure 424. Drawn by Miss Agnes Nixon.

Their effect on these vessels is not understood, as the experimental evidence is contradictory. The sympathetic fibers act as vasoconstrictors for the bronchial arteries.

The Pleura. The serous membrane lining the pleural cavities is reflected over the lungs as the *visceral pleura.* It consists of a thin layer of collagenous tissue containing some fibroblasts and macrophages, and several prominent layers of elastic fibers running at various angles to the outer surface. It is covered by a layer of mesothelial cells like those of the peritoneum. A similar serous layer lines the wall of the thoracic cavity and is called the *parietal pleura.* A prominent feature of the pleura is the great number of blood capillaries and lymphatic vessels distributed in it. The few nerves of the parietal pleura are connected with the phrenic and intercostal nerves. The nerves to the visceral pleura are believed to be branches of the vagus and sympathetic nerves supplying the bronchi.

Histogenetic Remarks. The lung arises in the embryo as a medial diverticulum of the foregut, caudal to the branchial clefts; it extends caudally and divides into two branches. The medial diverticulum is the primordium of the future larynx and trachea, and the first two lateral branches will form the two main bronchi of the adult lung. These two branches divide repeatedly; they become surrounded by a relatively dense mass of mesenchyme, so that throughout most of the embryonic period, up to six months, the lung has a suggestively glandlike structure (Fig. 428, A).

The primitive bronchi are lined with cuboidal epithelium. They branch dichotomously and are capped by end buds lined with cylindrical epithelium. The lumen of the end knobs is distinctly larger than that of the ducts. The knobs continue to branch perpendicularly to the axis of their ducts. In the three- to four-month stage the connective tissue cells and fibrils become prominent, and the connective tissue contains many blood vessels. The lymphatics at this time are large and divide the pulmonary tissue into fairly distinct lobules. The end knobs now begin to branch irregularly.

In the eighteen- to twenty-week stage the lobulation becomes decidedly less prominent as the connective tissue diminishes in amount and the lymphatics become much narrower. The end knobs become much smaller.

At six to seven months, in a 35-cm. fetus, the small bronchi are lined in part with ciliated epithelium, which flattens toward the peripheral ends of the bronchi. These branch and end in the terminal ducts capped with the end knobs. The latter finally become alveoli, according to most authors. This view is probably incorrect.

About the beginning of the sixth month of gestation, the lung undergoes rapid structural alterations. It loses its glandlike appearance (compare Figs. 419 and 429) and becomes a highly vascular organ. The cuboidal entodermal cells lining the end buds disappear and are replaced by a network of blood capillaries

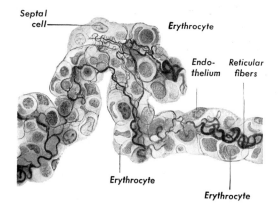

Fig. 426. Section of interalveolar septum of human lung. The erythrocytes seem to be separated from the air spaces only by the endothelium of the capillaries. Bielschowsky-Foot and Mallory-azan stains. 720 ×. (Drawn by Miss Agnes Nixon.)

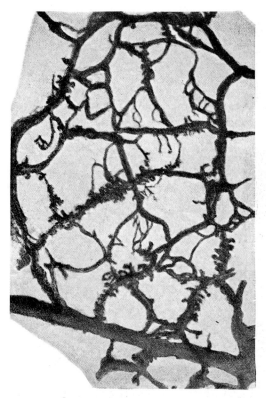

Fig. 427. Injected lymphatic plexus of pleura of a human lung. The area bounded by the large vessels is the base of a pulmonary lobule. It is composed of numerous, smaller, polygonal areas demarcated by the smaller lymphatics; these correspond to the pulmonary units. 8 ×. (After W. S. Miller.)

which lie on the surfaces of the relatively thick-walled, saccular air spaces.

The factors responsible for these morphological changes are not known. Although the human fetus begins a pattern of respiratory activity early in intra-uterine life (Davis and Potter), such activity is not necessary for the normal development of the lungs (Potter and Bohlender).

It seems clear that in human embryos (Palmer, Barnard and Day) and in pig embryos (Clements, Ham and Baldwin) the continuous epithelial membrane becomes interrupted and replaced by blood vessels on the walls of the future air spaces. The fate of the cuboidal entodermal cells lining the end buds as the lung continues to grow has not been determined completely. Whether some of them persist or are replaced by cells of mesenchymal origin can be settled only by a thorough embryological investigation of the lung in the later stages of intra-uterine life.

The manner in which the lung grows beyond the initial glandlike stage is not known. In all probability the few cells of epithelial origin which remain on the walls of the future air spaces have little if anything to do with the new formation of alveoli. More important in the postnatal growth of the respiratory por-

tion of the lung is the further development of the elastic, smooth muscle, and vascular systems (Loosli, 1938).

The majority of investigators consider the initial respiratory air spaces to be alveoli similar in size to those seen in the adult lung (Bremer, Willson). In man it would seem that these saccular spaces correspond more correctly to alveolar ducts and that definitive alveoli are absent. At term, the alveoli are shallow indentations on the respiratory channels. According to Dubreuil and co-workers, the adult type of respiratory unit does not become apparent until several years after birth. One has only to compare in Figure 419 the inflated lung of the newborn with the expanded lung of a twelve-year-old, to note the marked increase in size of the alveolar ducts and the alveoli. Whether growth of the lung takes place only by an increase in size and distention of existing ducts and alveoli or by some other process needs further study.

Repair of the Lung. The lung is frequently the seat of inflammatory conditions which leave it unimpaired or healing. There are certain infections, however, notably tuberculosis, in which large masses of pulmonary tissues are destroyed. In this case healing is always attended by connective tissue scar formation; there is

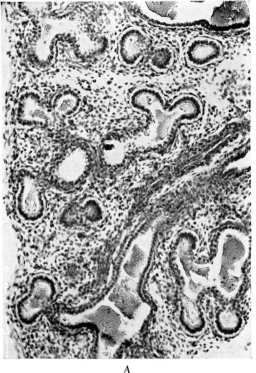
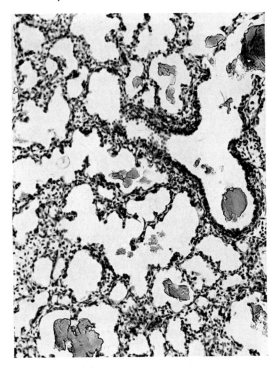

A   B

Fig. 428. A, Photomicrographs of section of lung of 147-gm. (4 months') fetus, and, B, of a 440-gm. (6½ months') fetus. Both specimens show thorotrast aspirated by intra-uterine respirations. The lung of the 6½ months' fetus was expanded by extra-uterine respiration. Note change in character of lung structure from glandular type (previable) to respiratory type (viable). Respiratory portion of lung of older fetus consists essentially of alveolar ducts; alveoli are absent or are represented only by shallow indentations on duct walls. Hematoxylin and eosin stain. 45 ×. (After Davis and Potter.)

no evidence to show that the pulmonary tissue can regenerate after destruction.

Histophysiological Remarks. The primary function of the lungs is to serve as a means for the assimilation of oxygen from the air and for the removal of carbon dioxide from the body. The network of blood capillaries in the wall of the air vesicles is separated from the air by a thin, moist membrane which permits the ready diffusion of oxygen into the blood and carbon dioxide out of it. The question whether the passage of the gases is to be looked upon as a secretion or as a simple process of diffusion must be decided in favor of the latter view for the present, except that liberation of carbon dioxide from carbonic acid by dehydration is now known to be greatly accelerated by *carbonic anhydrase*. The capillaries in the respiratory portions of the human lung are estimated to have a surface area of 140 square meters. The lung also eliminates approximately 800 cc. of water a day in the expired air; under abnormal conditions it may also remove certain other substances from the blood, such as alcohol.

The lung has a large margin of reserve; that is, the body at rest uses but a small portion—about one twentieth—of the pulmonary aerating surface.

The alveoli probably change but little during inspiration, and the flow of blood is actually faster then. It is becoming more and more probable that the great increase in the volume of the lungs in inspiration takes place mainly through a great distention of the alveolar ducts. The smaller bronchi and bronchioles also distend with inspiration.

The pressure within the lung is that of the atmosphere. The lungs are maintained in a partially distended position by the reduced pressure of the potential space between the two layers of the pleura. An increase in the size of the thorax, such as occurs with every inspiration, still further decreases pressure in the pleural cavity; consequently the lung sucks in more air and becomes larger, and its elastic and reticular fibers are put under still greater tension. This is a purely passive activity on the part of the lung. In expiration, as

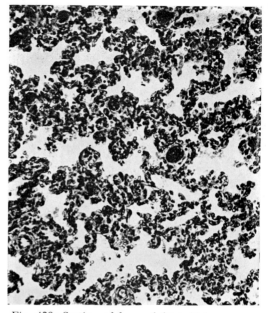

Fig. 429. Section of lung of fetus at term, unexpanded by extra-uterine respiration. Note absence of glandular character. (After Adair and Potter.)

the thoracic cavity becomes smaller, the pressure in the pleural cavity rises slightly (although it is still below atmospheric pressure). This decreases the tension on the elastic and reticular fibers, and they pull the lung into a more contracted state, thus forcing some of the air out of it. It is probable that the smooth muscles of the alveolar ducts and the bronchioles also help force the air out of the lung by their contraction.

When the pleural cavity is connected with the outside air, either by accident or by surgical intervention, the pressure in the lungs and the pleural cavity becomes equalized at that of the atmosphere. The lung in this side of the chest collapses immediately, because the force which normally opposes the contraction of its elastic elements has been removed. This condition is known as *pneumothorax*. Such a lung remains collapsed until pressure in the pleural cavity is reduced by absorption of the air contained in it.

With each inspiration the descent of the diaphragm enables the bronchi in the lower lobes of the lungs to extend. Since the main bronchi are not fixed in the thorax, but descend on inspiration, a mechanism is pro-

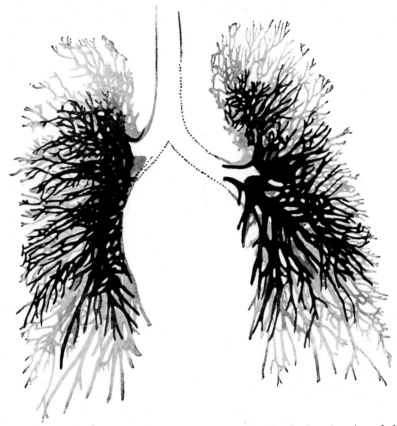

Fig. 430. Tracings from x-ray shadows of human lungs in deep inspiration (gray) and forced expiration (black). (Redrawn and slightly modified after Macklin.)

vided whereby the bronchi of the upper lobes of the lungs extend at the same time.

The lung of a normal adult who has lived in the vicinity of a large city is usually greatly blackened by a pigment which, on chemical analysis, has been found to be carbon. This material has been inhaled with the air. Part of it is returned to the exterior by the action of the cilia in the bronchi; part of it is expelled in the so-called "dust cell"; and part of it is accumulated in the interstitial lymphoid tissue of the lung or in the peribronchial and peritracheal lymph nodes. The particles of dust in the alveoli are taken up by the ameboid "dust cells." It is probable that these cells, by their own motion, reach the ciliated epithelium in the terminal bronchioles or enter the finer lymphatic radicles. Carbon-containing macrophages may be seen frequently in the lymphatics, but the manner in which they enter these vessels has not been described.

REFERENCES

Bargmann, W.: Die Lungenalveole. Handb. d. mikr. Anat. d. Menschen (v. Möllendørff), (5)[3], 799, 1936.

Barnard, W. G., and Day, T. D.: The Development of the Terminal Air Passages of the Human Lung. J. Path. & Bact., 45:67, 1937.

Bell, E. T.: Hyperplasia of the Pulmonary Alveolar Epithelium in Disease. Am. J. Path., 19:901, 1943.

Boyden, E. A.: The Intrahilar and Related Segmental Anatomy of the Lung. Surgery, 18:706, 1945.

Bremer, J. L.: Postnatal Development of Alveoli in the Mammalian Lung in Relation to the Problem of the Alveolar Phagocyte. Contrib. Embryol., Carnegie Inst., 25:85, 1935.

Clements, L. P.: Embryonic Development of the Respiratory Portion of the Pig's Lung. Anat. Rec., 70:575, 1938.

Davis, M. E., and Potter, E. L.: Intrauterine Respiration of the Human Fetus. J.A.M.A., 131:1194, 1946.

Dubreuil, G., Lacoste, A., and Raymond, R.: Observations sur le développement du poumon humain. Bull. d'Histologie Appliquee à la Physiol. et à Path., 13: 235, 1936.

Dungal, N.: Experiments with Jaagsiekte. Am. J. Path., 22:737, 1946.

Florey, H., Carleton, H. M., and Wells, A. Q.: Mucus Secretion in the Trachea. Brit. J. Exper. Path., 13:269, 1932.

Fried, B. M.: The Lungs and the Macrophage System. Arch. Path. 17:76, 1934.

Grady, H. G., and Stewart, H. L.: Histogenesis of Induced Pulmonary Tumors in Strain A Mice. Am. Jour. Path., 16:417, 1940.

Ham, A. W., and Baldwin, K. W.: A Histological Study of the Development of the Lung, with Particular Reference to the Nature of the Alveoli. Anat. Rec., 81:363, 1941.

Hartroft, W. S., and Macklin, C. C.: The Size of Human Lung Alveoli Expressed as Diameters of Selected Alveolar Outlines as Seen in Specially Prepared 25 Micron Microsections. Tr. Roy. Soc. Canada, Sec. V.: 63, 1944.

Heiss, R.: Der Atmungsapparat. Handb. d. mikr. Anat. d. Menschen (v. Möllendorff), (5)[3], 709, 1936.

Herbut, P. A.: "Alveolar Cell Tumor" of the Lung. Further Evidence of Its Bronchiolar Origin. Arch. Path., 41:175, 1946.

Kolmer, W.: Geruchsorgan. Handb. d. mikr. Anat. (v. Möllendorff), 1927, Vol. 3, p. 192.

Lang, F. J.: Ueber die Alveolarphagozyten der Lunge. Virch. Arch., 275:104, 1930.

Larsell, O., and Dow, R. S.: The Innervation of the Human Lung. Am. J. Anat., 52:125, 1933.

Loosli, C.: The Rabbit's Lung after Phrenicotomy and Pneumothorax. Anat. Rec., 62:381, 1935; Interalveolar Communications in Normal and in Pathologic Mammalian Lungs. Arch. Path., 24:743, 1937; The Pathogenesis and Pathology of Experimental Type I Pneumococci Pneumonia in the Monkey. J. Exper. Med., 76:79, 1942. The Pathogenesis and Pathology of Experimental Air-Borne Influenza A Virus Infection in Mice. Proc. Federated Societies. (V), No. 3, 1946.

Macklin, C. C.: The Musculature of the Bronchi and Lungs. Physiol. Rev., 9:1, 1929; Pulmonic Alveolar Epithelium. A Round Table Conference. J. Thoracic Surg., 6:82, 1936; Residual Epithelial Cells on the Pulmonary Alveolar Walls of Mammals. Tr. Roy. Soc. Canada, Sec. V: 93, 1946.

Miller, W. S.: The Lung. 2d ed. Springfield, Ill., Charles C Thomas, 1947.

Ogawa, G.: The Finer Ramifications of the Human Lung. Am. J. Anat., 28:315, 1920.

Oppel, A.: Atmungsapparat. Lehrbuch der vergl. mikrosk. Anat. der Wirbeltiere, (6), 1905.

Palmer, D. W.: The Lung of a Human Foetus of 170 mm. C. R. Length. Am. J. Anat., 58:59, 1936.

Potter, E. H., and Bohlender, G. P.: Intrauterine Respiration in Relation to Development of the Fetal Lung. Am. J. Obst. & Gynec., 42:14, 1941.

Robertson, O. H.: Phagocytosis of Foreign Material in the Lung. Physiol. Rev., 21:112, 1941.

Ross, I. S.: Pulmonary Epithelium and Proliferative Reactions in the Lungs. Arch. Path., 27:478, 1939.

Schaeffer, J. P.: The Mucous Membrane of the Nasal Cavity and the Paranasal Sinuses, in Cowdry's Special Cytology. 2d ed. New York, (1), 105, 1932.

Schultze, F. E.: Die Lungen. Stricker's Handb. d. Gewebelehre, 1871, Vol. 1, p. 464.

Stewart, H. L., Grady, H. G., and Andervont, H. B.: Development of Sarcoma at Site of Serial Transplantation of Pulmonary Tumors in Inbred Mice. J. Nat. Cancer Inst., 7:207, 1947.

Stewart, F. W.: An Histogenetic Study of the Respiratory Epithelium. Anat. Rec., 25:181, 1923.

Wearn, J. T., and others: The Normal Behavior of the Pulmonary Blood Vessels, with Observations on the Intermittence of the Flow of Blood in the Arterioles and Capillaries. Am. J. Physiol., 109:236, 1934.

Willson, H. G.: The Terminals of the Human Bronchiole. Am. J. Anat., 30:1922.

XXVIII. URINARY SYSTEM

THE KIDNEY

The mammalian kidney is a compound tubular gland which elaborates the urine. Its glandular tubules are called uriniferous tubules and are provided with a peculiar filtration apparatus, a tuft of capillaries, the glomerulus.

The human kidney is a paired, bean-shaped body situated in the posterior part of the abdominal cavity, one on either side of the vertebral column. From the excavated edge, or *hilus*, a large excretory duct, the *ureter*, leads to the *urinary bladder*, the reservoir for the urine. The *urethra*, the last section of the excretory passages of the kidneys, conveys the urine outside the body. The male urethra also serves for the discharge of semen.

The kidney is loosely invested by a *capsule* of dense collagenous bundles and a few elastic fibers. The glandular part of the kidney surrounds a large cavity, the *sinus*, adjacent to the hilus. The sinus contains the *renal pelvis* and is filled with loose connective and fat tissue through which the vessels and nerves pass to the renal tissue.

The pelvis is an enlargement of the excretory passages of the kidney. Distally, it is continuous with the ureter; toward the renal tissue, it forms two or more outpocketings, the *major calices*. These again are subdivided into a varying number of smaller outpocketings, the *minor calices*.

The glandular substance consists of an outer mass—the cortex—which covers the medullary substance composed of eight to eighteen *renal pyramids* (*of Malpighi*). These are roughly conical bodies placed with the base outward and with the apex, or

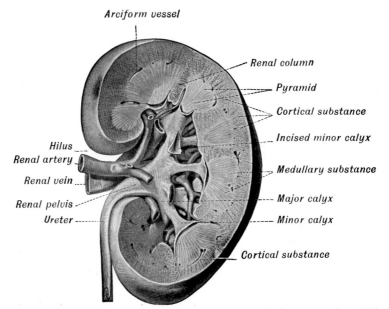

Fig. 431. Human kidney, seen from behind after removal of part of the organ; three-fifths natural size. (After Braus.)

papilla, projecting into the lumen of each minor calyx. The tip of the papilla is perforated by ten to twenty-five small openings —the *area cribrosa.*

The gray substance of each pyramid is radially striated by brownish lines which converge toward the apex of the papilla. This striation is caused by the straight parts of the uriniferous tubules and the blood vessels which parallel them.

Owing to the different character of the straight tubules in its various levels, each pyramid can be subdivided into an inner and an outer zone. In the latter, again, a darker and thicker inner, and a lighter and thinner outer layer can be distinguished on macroscopic examination of the fresh section.

Where the dark brown cortex separates the lateral surfaces of the pyramids it forms the *renal columns (of Bertin).* From the bases of the medullary pyramids, thin, radially directed processes arise which enter the cortical substance, but do not reach the surface of the organ. They show the same striation as the substance of the pyramid and are called *medullary rays (of Ferrein).*

The pyramids can be considered the lobes of the kidney. In the fetal period they are separated from each other by connective tissue, and fuse only in later stages, although in the ox, and sometimes in man, the lobated condition remains throughout life.

Each pyramid can be subdivided into smaller structural units, the *renal lobules,* on the basis of the branching of the excretory ducts. Adjoining lobules are not separated from one another by connective tissue partitions (see p. 447).

Uriniferous Tubules. As in most other glands, the kidney contains two kinds of tubules: the first are the secretory portions which help form the urine; the second are excretory ducts which convey the urine to the ureter. In contrast to other glands, which arise from a single primordium, the secretory portions of the kidney tubules develop from the metanephrogenic blastema and unite secondarily with the excretory ducts which arise from the wolffian duct. The secretory portions are long, tortuous simple tubes, each of

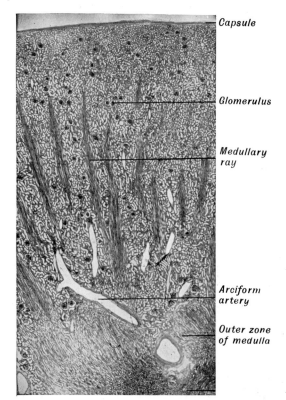

Fig. 432. Low power view of section of kidney of *Macacus rhesus.* Fixation by vascular perfusion—hence the empty blood vessels. Photomicrograph (slightly retouched). 13×.

which ends in a saclike enlargement, the *capsule of Bowman.* As the uriniferous tubules follow a tortuous course, the form and relation of the tubules can be elucidated only by teasing the tissue after maceration or by reconstructing the tissue in wax from serial sections.

Secretory Portion, the Nephron. Each tubular secretory portion, beginning with the capsule of Bowman and ending at the junction with the excretory ducts, is the structural and functional unit of the kidney—the *nephron* (Fig. 433). Each part of the nephron has a peculiar configuration, occupies a definite position in the cortex or medulla, and is lined with a specific type of epithelium. The successive parts of the nephron are renal corpuscle with its capsule of Bowman, the proximal convolution, descending and ascending limbs of Henle's loop, and distal convolution. A short connecting tube joins

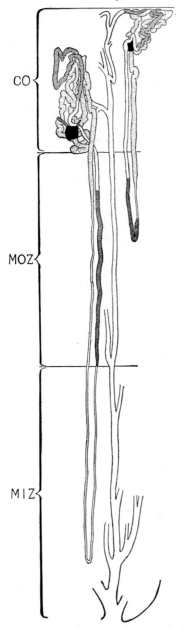

CO

MOZ

MIZ

Fig. 433. Diagram of two nephrons and their connection with collecting tubules. CO, Cortex; MOZ, outer zone of medulla; MIZ, inner zone of medulla; Malpighian corpuscles, black; proximal convolution, stippled; thin limb of Henle, white; limb of Henle, crosshatched and then white (to indicate the opacity and clearness seen in macerated preparations, but not in sections); distal convolution, obliquely striated; collecting tubules white. (Redrawn and slightly modified after Peter.)

the collecting tubule or excretory duct with the nephron.

Renal Corpuscle. The capsule of Bowman arises in the embryo as a spherical epithelial vesicle which is later invaginated by a tuft of blood capillaries, the glomerulus, and thus is transformed into a double-walled cup. The capsule and the glomerulus together form the roughly spherical renal corpuscle (of Malpighi). The original cavity of the capsule of Bowman is transformed into a cleftlike space. At one pole of the corpuscle the outer or "parietal" layer of the wall continues into the next section of the nephron. On the oposite side the glomerulus is connected with its afferent and efferent arterioles. Here the parietal wall is reflected onto the surface of the glomerulus as the "visceral" layer of the capsule. The glomeruli are scattered throughout the cortical tissue between the medullary rays.

Estimates of the number of glomeruli vary from 1,000,000 or less to about 4,500,000 in one human kidney. Since the glomerulus is essentially a filtration apparatus, the size of its free surface is important. The values given by various investigators (e.g., 0.78 square meter for all the glomeruli of one kidney) cannot be considered reliable.

The "visceral" epithelial cells covering the surface of the glomerulus adhere closely in a continuous layer to the capillary loops. They contain a few mitochondria and a Golgi net. The claim that the visceral epithelium consists of isolated perivascular mesenchymal cells or pericytes has not been generally accepted. The "parietal" epithelium is usually of the simple squamous type, and the limits of its polygonal cells can be demonstrated fairly well.

The glomerulus is a convolute of tortuous capillaries interposed in the course of an artery. The afferent arteriole lacks a distinct adventitial coat; its media consists of circularly arranged smooth muscle cells. Near the entrance of the vessel into the glomerulus, the smooth muscle cells of the vas afferens become large and pale-staining, an appearance which gave them the name "epi-

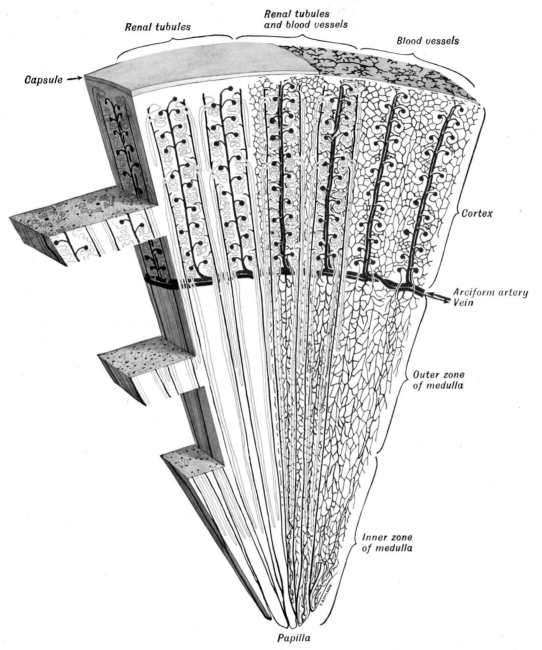

Fig. 434. Diagram of relations of blood vessels, nephrons and collecting ducts in kidney. The actual structures are much more complicated than those indicated here. *Arteries*, red; *veins*, blue; *glomeruli*, red dots; *nephrons*, greeen; *collecting ducts*, black. Six interlobular arteries and attached glomeruli are shown. The right-hand pair shows their relation to the veins, the left-hand pair their relation to nephrons, and the central pair shows their relations to both nephrons and veins. (Extensively modified from the diagrams of Peter, Braus, and von Möllendorff.)

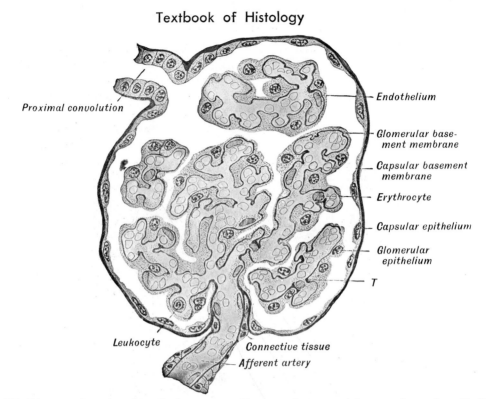

Fig. 435. Diagram of section through the greatest diameter of a normal human glomerulus: *T*, thickening of glomerular basement membrane—often seen at orifice into another loop. (Slightly modified after McGregor.)

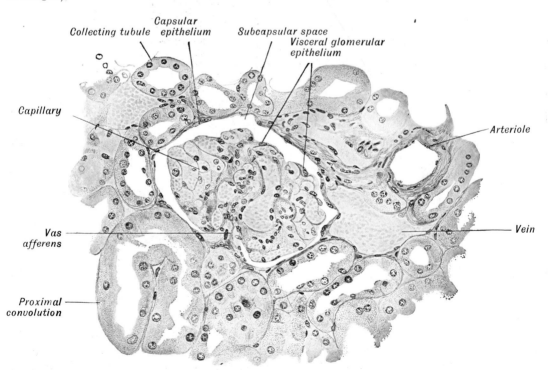

Fig. 436. Section of cortex of kidney of a young human adult, showing a renal corpuscle. Hematoxylin-eosin-azure II stain. (Drawn by Miss A. Nixon.)

thelioid." They suggest the cells in the carotid body. They form a cuff extending for 25 to 85 microns along the arteriole and, because of their position, have been called the *juxtaglomerular cells*. They are absent from children below the age of two years. Unlike by a basement membrane on which rest the visceral epithelial cells. The epithelial nuclei are believed to be ten times as numerous as the endothelial nuclei. A few reticular fibers have been found in the glomerulus, and, according to some, a few fibroblasts.

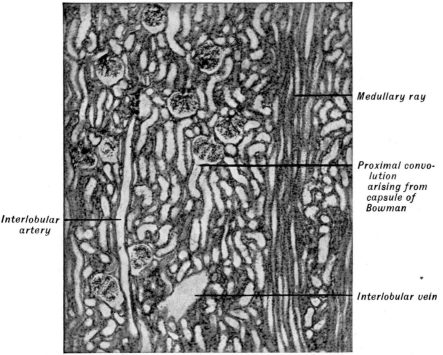

Fig. 437. Section in long axis of a renal lobule of *Macacus rhesus*. Photomicrograph. 58 ×.

the cells in the carotid and aortic bodies, which have a rich supply of nerves, the innervation of the juxtaglomerular cells is not different from that of the unchanged smooth muscle cells of the vas afferens. The internal elastic lamella is well developed, but ceases with the branching of the vessel.

The vas afferens, entering the renal corpuscle, divides into two to four, rarely up to ten, primary branches, which in turn divide into secondary branches. From these arise about fifty tortuous capillary loops which only exceptionally anastomose before they fuse to form the vas efferens.

Silver nitrate fails to bring out all the cellular outlines in the endothelium of the glomerular capillaries, so that this endothelium is supposed to have a partly syncytial character. Each capillary loop is covered

The efferent arteriole has a layer of circular smooth muscle fibers, but is devoid of an elastic membrane. Its diameter is distinctly smaller than that of the afferent vessel. It is probable that the contractility of the vas efferens helps regulate the pressure in the glomerulus.

Proximal Convolution. The short transition from the capsule to the following part of the tubule is sometimes referred to as the "neck," although a marked constriction is by no means typical. The next part of the tubule, the *proximal convolution*, averages 14 mm. long and 60 microns in diameter, has a tortuous course, and constitutes most of the cortical substance. In it begins the transformation of the glomerular filtrate into urine by reabsorption of some constituents and addition of others by secretory processes.

In addition to many small loops, it always forms a large loop directed toward the periphery, then returns to the vicinity of its renal corpuscle, approaches the nearest medullary ray, and runs toward the medulla. In the outer zone of the pyramid, the proximal convolution tapers down into its terminal portion, which continues into the **U**-shaped *loop of Henle*.

degenerative process in pathological conditions. The superficial part of the cell body contains granular mitochondria and often small vacuoles which stain supravitally with neutral red.

The free surface of the cells lining the lumen is covered by a *brush border* (Fig. 438). The limit between the latter and the cytoplasm is marked by a layer of granules

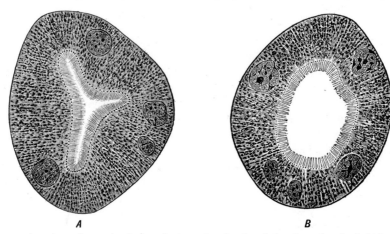

Fig. 438. Cross section through proximal convolution, showing brush border, of a dog's kidney: A, in anuria; B, at maximal secretion. (After Sauer, from Metzner.)

The epithelium of the proximal convolution consists of one layer of truncated pyramidal cells. Their cytoplasm is abundant and stains deeply with eosin; each cell contains a large, pale, spherical nucleus. Only three or four nuclei are usually seen in a transection of the tubule. The limits between the cells are rarely seen, because the sides of the cells are provided with grooves and ridges perpendicular to the basement membrane and interdigitating with the same structures of the adjacent cells.

In fresh condition the cells appear opaque and granular. They undergo postmortem changes rapidly, and it is not easy to preserve them satisfactorily in fixed material. After suitable fixation and staining, the basal parts of the cells are occupied by parallel rods, perpendicular to the basement membrane and reaching the level of the nucleus. They stain like mitochondria. In poorly fixed slides this typical striation of the epithelium is invisible, because the rods disintegrate into granules. This also occurs during life as a

which in section appear as a darkly staining line. Under this line, above the nucleus, are a pair of centrioles and a Golgi net; in compensatory hypertrophy of the kidney this organoid recedes to the infranuclear region. The edges of the free surfaces of the cells, under the brush border, are provided with a system of terminal bars.

In the normal human kidney the epithelium of the proximal convolution does not contain lipoid inclusions. In pathological conditions, as well as in postmortem autolysis, droplets of neutral fat and of phosphatids readily appear. In some animals (cat) they are of normal occurrence.

During diuresis the lumen of the proximal convolution is large, the cells are low and flattened, and the brush border high. In the resting condition the cells are high and provided with a bulging surface which transforms the lumen into an irregular, star-shaped cleft. Other structural changes, such as vacuolization of the apical parts, bulging of drops of the superficial cytoplasm through

have a clear cytoplasm. The latter contains a few fine mitochondria and, at the surface, a pair of centrioles with a central flagellum.

As the collecting tubules grow larger, the cells also grow higher, and finally acquire in the ducts of Bellini a tall columnar form. They are always arranged in a regular, single layer, with all the nuclei at one level and with the free surfaces bulging slightly into the lumen. The cytoplasm keeps its pale appearance. The centrioles remain at the free bulging surface. In the area cribrosa the simple columnar epithelium of the ducts of Bellini continues onto the surface of the papilla.

The length of the collecting tubules is estimated at 20 to 22 mm.; the length of the nephron at 30 to 38 mm.

Renal Lobule. Each renal lobule is composed of the glandular tissue surrounding a medullary ray. The slender, pyramidal form of the renal lobule and the presence of a medullary ray forming its core are the results of the straight, radial course of the collecting tubules, of the gradual increase of their branchings toward the capsule and of the accumulation of nephrons in the cortex. Each medullary ray contains several straight collecting tubules, the loops of Henle, and the terminal portions of the proximal convolution. It is surrounded by the convoluted portions of the tubules and by the renal corpuscles. At the apex of the lobule, which reaches far into the papilla of the pyramid, the collecting tubules begin to fuse with one another and finally open, as the ducts of Bellini, on the area cribrosa. A large number of lobules form the malpighian pyramid.

A few authors prefer to consider that the renal lobules center about the radial branches of the arciform artery extending toward the capsule of the organ. According to this view, the interlobular arteries are really *intralobular* arteries. In view of the embryonic development of the organ from a series of branching ducts, it seems best to consider the lobule as centering about these ducts rather than about the arterial tree. A similar problem is found in the determination of the hepatic lobule.

Interstitial Connective Tissue. The interstitial connective tissue in the normal kidney is small in amount and is of the reticular type. Its branching fibers, accompanied by a few fibroblasts and fixed macrophages, form networks in the narrow spaces between the convoluted and straight tubules. The fibers are especially numerous and thick in the apex of the pyramids, where most of them are arranged concentrically around the ducts of Bellini and are embedded in an abundant, amorphous ground substance.

Thick, collagenous fibers are found only in the ad-

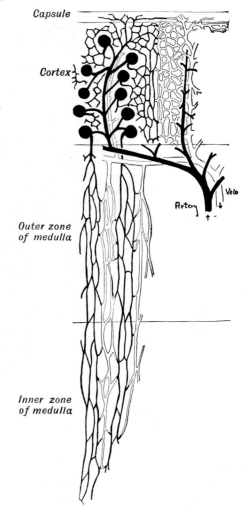

Fig. 441. Diagram of blood supply to kidney. Arteries and arterial capillaries, black; veins and venules, double-contoured.

ventitia of the larger blood vessels. A few collagenous fibers surround the capsules of Bowman and the larger papillary ducts. Elastic fibers are absent except in the walls of the blood vessels. In old age the amount of collagenous tissue in the kidney may increase considerably through a transformation of the reticular fibers.

Basement Membrane. The epithelium of the nephron and of the excretory ducts rests upon a well-developed basement membrane which is hyaline in its central part. It is found in the renal corpuscle, where it separates the endothelium of the capillary loops from the "visceral" epithelial layer, and also lies beneath the parietal epithelium. In the proximal convolution the hyaline membrane is particularly thick. Its inner surface, to which the bases of the epithelial cells are attached, is provided with numerous, small circular ridges. The interstitial reticular fibers fuse with the outer surface of the membrane.

Blood Vessels of the Kidney. Roughly, one quarter of the cardiac output enters the kidney and passes through the glomeruli before being distributed to the rest of the organ (see Figs. 434, 441). The renal artery enters the hilus of the kidney and divides into two sets of principal branches, a ventral and a dorsal. The first set has a wider distribution

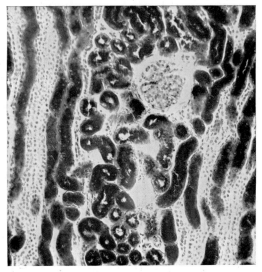

Fig. 442. Section of rabbit kidney stained to show alkaline phosphatase as black material, apparently limited to the proximal convolutions. 100 ×. (Courtesy of G. Gomori.)

in the organ than the second. These principal branches of the renal artery are "end arteries" and are not connected by large anastomoses. In the fat tissue surrounding the pelvis they branch into *interlobar arteries;* these are in the columns of Bertin between the malpighian pyramids or lobes of the kidney.

The interlobar arteries break up into branches which run approximately parallel to the surface of the kidney at the limit between the bases of the pyramids and the cortex. They have a more or less arched course (arterial arcades) with the convexity directed toward the periphery of the organ. They are called *arciform* or *arcuate arteries.* At more or less regular intervals they give off smaller branches which run radially to the surface of the kidney. Since these radial branches are located in the cortical substance

between the medullary rays, they are called *interlobular arteries.*

The interlobular arteries give off numerous smaller branches, each of which is the afferent vessel of a glomerulus. From the glomerulus the blood is carried away by the efferent vessel. The vas efferens breaks up into a network of arterioles which supply the convoluted uriniferous tubules of the cortex with blood. It is probable that the efferent artery of a glomerulus supplies much of the nephron belonging to the same renal corpuscle.

The tissues of the medulla and the medullary rays also receive their blood supply from the efferent glomerular arterioles. The medullary rays are supplied by the efferent vessels of the nearest glomeruli. The pyramids of Malpighi are supplied by the *arteriolae rectae spuriae,* which arise as efferent vessels from the glomeruli near the medulla. The arteriolae rectae spuriae assume a straight course toward the pelvis. This arrangement causes a radial striation of the outer zone of the malpighian pyramid. Having entered the medullary substance, they branch profusely at acute angles and form a capillary network with radially elongated meshes about the straight tubules.

The existence of the so-called "arteriolae rectae verae," which are supposed to arise directly from the arcuate or the interlobular arteries and to enter the medulla, is denied by most investigators. It has been claimed that apparently direct communications between arterioles and venules may arise through partial obliteration of glomeruli.

The veins of the cortex arise from the capillary networks in the outermost layers of the cortex through the confluence of radially arranged branches, which form the so-called *stellate veins.* These continue into interlobular veins, which follow the corresponding arteries and everywhere receive additional capillaries from the labyrinth. The interlobular veins fuse to form the large arcuate or arciform veins which run beside the arteries of the same name. In the medulla straight, radially arranged veins arise (*venulae rectae*) which join the arciform veins directly. The latter fuse and form interlobar veins which accompany the large arteries and finally give rise to the renal vein.

Lymphatics. Networks of lymphatic capillaries are found in both the capsule of the kidney and in the glandular tissue. Both groups are connected by occasional anastomoses. The lymphatics of the capsule join the lymph vessels of the neighboring organs. The lymph capillaries in the glandular tissue form dense networks between the uriniferous tubules, especially in the cortex. They pass into lymphatics which accompany the larger blood vessels, and leave the kidney at the hilus. They are not present in the glomeruli or medullary rays.

Nerves. Macroscopic dissection shows that the sympathetic celiac plexus sends many nerve fibers into the kidney. Their distribution in this organ has not been worked out satisfactorily. It is relatively easy to follow nonmyelinated and myelinated fibers along the course of the larger blood vessels. They provide the adventitia with sensory nerve endings and the muscular coat with motor endings. Along with the afferent arterioles, nerve fibers may reach the renal corpuscles, and some of them seem to form end branches on their surface. The nerve supply of the uriniferous tubules, however, has not been clearly demonstrated. Some investigators describe plexuses of fine nerve fibers which surround and seem to penetrate the basement membrane. On its inner surface they are supposed to form another plexus from which terminal branches arise to end with minute end knobs between the epithelial cells.

Histophysiological Remarks.

The kidneys, in elaborating the urine, eliminate water and some of the substances dissolved in the blood. With minor exceptions they do not produce new material. In addition to their *excretory functions*, by which they dispose of waste products and substances foreign to the organism, the kidneys have equally important *conservative* functions, by which they retain the necessary amounts of water, electrolytes and other chemical substances in the body, while permitting any excess of these substances to be eliminated. They thus play a large part in the maintenance of the constancy of composition of the internal environment of the organism. It may be inferred from the structure of the kidney that the malpighian corpuscle acts as a filtration apparatus with pressure supplied in the capillaries and that differences in structure of the several parts of the tubule reflect secretory and conducting functions.

Before considering the complex processes in the kidney, it is necessary to recall that the transport of substances across cell membranes may occur by simple diffusion or may take place in the opposite direction, in which case work is done. The concentration of substances despite an opposing osmotic force is an example of secretion. In other circumstances the substance which is accumulated arises as a result of specific synthesis. Secretion proceeds only when the diffusion is offset by hydrostatic or electrical pressures. The translation of energy is often indirect, with the energy initially derived from chemical transformations appearing as muscular work, membrane potentials and ionic exchange mechanisms.

Dixon gives an example of the machinery for osmotic work as follows: The chemical machinery for the transport of carbohydrate may consist of adenosine triphosphate (ATP), phosphokinase and phosphatase. A membrane is assumed permeable to carbohydrate, but not (or less) permeable to its phosphorylated form. If, inside the cell, there is a system of phosphokinase plus adenosine triphosphate which phosphorylates any entering carbohydrate, it then will be trapped in the cell at the expense of the phosphate bond energy in adenosine triphosphate, which is in turn regenerated by oxidative processes. At the opposite side of the cell one may postulate a phosphatase which breaks down the phosphorylated carbohydrate, leaving it free to diffuse out on the opposite side. So far, phosphatase has been found on the wrong side of the cell for this theory as applied to kidney.

Glomerulus. Fluid aspirated from the glomerular space (with the rest of the nephron blocked) in the living frog is similar in composition to the plasma, except for the absence of fats, plasma proteins and substances combined with these large molecules. This fluid contains water, phosphates, reducing substances, creatinine, uric acid, urea and chloride; certain dyes are also found in it after being introduced into the animal.

That the glomerulus functions as an ultrafilter in mammals, including man, is supported by less direct but no less convincing evidence. The passage of fluorescein and esculin from the blood stream into the capsular space has been observed with the aid of ultraviolet light. Intravenously injected potassium ferrocyanide and uric acid are found in the capsular space, but, when injected into rabbits whose blood pressure had been low-cred beneath the osmotic pressure of the blood, neither of these substances is found within the nephron. The trend in study of renal secretion has been toward a more quantitative evaluation of the process. Urine formation is energetically costly and is rendered extremely inefficient by the presence of the glomerulus in the nephron. It has been calculated that in man about 1300 ml. of blood pass through the kidneys per minute, and that, with normal blood pressures, all the glomeruli form about 125 ml. of filtrate of plasma per minute, and that the cells of all the renal tubules reabsorb 124 ml. of this and return it to the blood, leaving a volume of 1 ml. to be excreted. This fraction (remainder) is not simply derived by absorption of water, but its contents have been modified by (1) passive diffusion back into the blood (urea), (2) absorption by osmotic work, and (3) excretion into the lumen of other substances. The origin of this state of affairs has been explained by some on the premise that fishes evolved, not in the sea, but in fresh water. With their tissues hypertonic to the milieu, there was a copious urine to be excreted, and a glomerulus was of real value. Those fishes which returned to the sea (elasmobranchs) became adapted to a hypertonic milieu, retaining large amounts of urea in the blood and tissues by reducing the number and size of glomeruli or by losing their glomeruli. Unfortunately, man has retained the glomerulus, although it would be far more efficient to excrete all the water and wastes by secretory activity.

The transport of certain substances into and out of the nephron is capable of rather precise measurement in healthy people and is the basis of a variety of measures of their kidney function. Inulin is a nonmetabolized carbohydrate which, when injected intravenously, does not appear in the urine of aglomerular fish; it has been found in glomerular filtrate, and is not secreted or absorbed by the tubules. It has been used as a measure of the amount of plasma filtered by the combined glomeruli. This is calculated from the concentrations of inulin in the urine and in the plasma during the experiment. The volume of plasma containing the same amount of inulin as that found in the urine is the amount of plasma which has been "cleared" of this substance by filtration. The inulin clearance furnishes a standard from which it may be estimated what proportions of other substances are reabsorbed or excreted by cells in various parts of the tubule.

Proximal Convolution. It is also well established for a wide variety of animal forms that the renal tubules have both excretory and absorptive functions. Various segments of the tubules have been studied by direct methods in the frog and salamander. Tubules were punctured at various levels and fluid removed for analysis, and fluid of known composition was perfused through a part of the tubule between two micropipettes. It was found that sodium and chloride are absorbed in the distal portions of the tubule, where acidification of the urine also takes place. Absorption of glucose takes place in the proximal portion in Necturus. As a result of this system of filtration and absorption, nearly ½ pound of glucose and more than 3 pounds of sodium chloride per day must be recovered from the glomerular filtrate in man. When the level of glucose in the blood is raised experimentally above a definite level, it is not completely absorbed from the glomerular filtrate, and it appears in the urine. The *tubular maximum for reabsorption of glucose (glucose Tm)* is thus an index of reabsorptive capacity of the kidney tubules.

In current research it is considered that in the proximal convolution, in addition to glucose, amino acids, vitamin C and other constituents are absorbed by osmotic work.

As certain poisons more or less selectively affect particular portions of the proximal convolution, and as certain dyes and iron salts are eliminated in greater amounts in some parts of this segment of the nephron than in others, it is probable that different parts of the proximal convolution have different functions.

Substances such as phenol red, diodrast (an organic iodine compound), para-amino-hippuric acid (P.A.H.) and creatinine are added to the glomerular filtrate by secretory work. Phenol red has been seen to be eliminated by the proximal convolution in living frogs; the same part of the nephron in cultures from a human fetus of three and a half months secretes this indicator if it is added to the medium, while the epithelium of the rest of the tubules does not.

There is now adequate evidence that tubular excretion plays an important part in the excretion of phenol red, diodrast and creatinine in man.

Certain substances, when introduced into the blood in moderate concentrations, are entirely removed during a single passage of blood through the kidneys. Among these are diodrast and para-aminohippuric acid. Since it is impossible to remove all the substances dissolved in the plasma by filtration and have any fluid plasma left, the complete removal of a substance in one passage of blood through the kidney must occur in part by filtration and in part by excretory work. Knowing the concentration of such substances in the blood and the amount found in the urine produced in a given period of time, one can calculate the blood flow through the kidney. The blood flow is equal to the plasma flow plus the cell volume found by hematocrit. From the values for diodrast (or P.A.H.) clearance, and for inulin clearance one can determine the fraction of renal plasma flow which is filtered by the glomeruli. Thus

$$\text{Filtration fraction} = \frac{\text{Inulin clearance}}{\text{P.A.H. clearance}}$$

If now one raises the concentration of diodrast or para-aminohippuric acid in the blood, a point is reached at which the kidney fails to remove all the material from the blood. The maximum concentration which is completely cleared of the substance is taken as a measure of the *excretory capacity of the tubule* (*Tm—tubular maximum*). If the values are known for renal plasma flow and inulin clearance, the measurement of other substances—e.g., urea, uric acid, phosphate and bicarbonate buffers—in the blood and urine may be related to the activities of

the total number of nephrons with regard to these substances. In this fashion it has been calculated which substances are secreted, which are reabsorbed, and which diffuse passively from the glomerular filtrate. The localizations of these specific events in various portions of the tubule are less well known.

Loop of Henle and Distal Convolution. The loop of Henle seems to be primarily concerned with the reabsorption of water and sodium. Perhaps for this reason the antidiuretic hormone of the posterior pituitary appears to be effective only in animals having a loop of Henle. With respect to water regulation, the kidney is working hardest when there is minimal urine flow.

A different sort of mechanism is postulated to account for excretion of acid of the urine. Although the evidence is physiological and biochemical without a close correlation with histology, the process has been ascribed to the distal region of the nephron. It must be borne in mind that, in the elimination of acid in the urine, there is a maximum gradient of acidity (hydrogen ion concentration) possible in the kidney, so that the urine is limited in acidity to pH 4.5, the blood being pH 7.4. The elimination of additional acid therefore requires the simultaneous elimination of additional base. According to current theory, it is probable that neutral salt is excreted by the cells, followed by reabsorption of the base in combination with bicarbonate, this process involving the enzyme carbonic anhydrase. The over-all mechanism is an ion exchange procedure resulting in free hydrogen ions in the urine; it is analogous to those operating in the excretion of hydrochloric acid by gastric glands. If the acidity achieved makes too drastic demands upon the alkaline reserve of the body, it is neutralized by ammonia derived from glutamine and by oxidative deamination of some amino acids.

Relations to Disease. It would appear that knowledge of the absorptive and excretory capacities of the kidneys for various substances should be particularly informative in renal disease in which nephrons may be altered or obliterated both morphologically and functionally. Such is indeed the case, but the diseased kidney is much more complex than the normal. The calculations given earlier are based on the knowledge or assumption of a definite blood flow moving diffusely through the kidney with certain hydrostatic pressures operating at the glomeruli. The hemodynamics of the kidney are complicated, and its vascular system is particularly responsive to systemic changes. Thus, with lowered blood pressure, as in shock, the kidney may shut down, becoming *ischemic*. In other circumstances some of the nephrons may degenerate structurally or functionally throughout their length or in part.

The substance *renin* has been extracted from mammalian kidneys and found to have the property of raising the general arterial blood pressure. The relation of this material, and of substances which inactivate it, to hypertension is the subject of active study. Goldblatt summarizes the situation as of 1947 as follows: "Renin, an enzyme from the kidney, enters the blood stream through the renal vein, and acts upon hypertensinogen, a globulin in the blood plasma, to form hypertensin, a polypeptide, which is the active vasoconstrictor substance, and which can be inactivated by hypertensinase, an enzyme in the blood and in extracts of some organs." It is claimed that the juxtaglomerular cells of the vas afferens undergo a rapid hyperplasia and elaboration of granules after partial clamping of the renal artery in rabbits and dogs, a procedure which results in an increased blood pressure. It has been suggested that these cells secrete a substance concerned with the maintenance of the increased arterial tension. But Selye and Stone believe that the hypertensive materials are secreted by the tubular epithelium, since the juxtaglomerular apparatus often disappeared completely in the kidney of rats after partial clamping of the renal artery.

EXCRETORY PASSAGES OF THE KIDNEY

The excretory passages convey the urine from the parenchyma of the kidney to the outside. No appreciable changes in the composition of the urine occur in these passages except a slight admixture of mucus. The walls of the excretory passages are provided with a well-developed coat of smooth muscle; its contractions move the urine forward.

The calices, the pelvis, the ureter and the bladder all have a similar structure, although the thickness of the wall gradually increases in the sequence indicated. The inner surface is lined with a mucous membrane. There is no distinct submucosa in man, and the lamina propria of the mucosa is attached to the smooth muscle coat, which is covered by an adventitial layer of connective tissue. The upper part of the bladder is covered by the serous membrane of the peritoneum.

Although of mesodermal origin in the ureter and of entodermal in the bladder, the lining of the mucous membrane in all the parts just mentioned is the same "transitional" epithelium. In the calices it is two to three cells thick, in the ureter four to five; in the empty bladder six to eight cell layers are seen. In the contracted condition of the wall of the viscus, the epithelium is thick and its cells are round, or even columnar or club-shaped. In the distended condition the epithelium is thin, and the cells are greatly flattened and stretched parallel to the surface. Scattered lymphoid cells migrate between the epithelial cells. Owing to the similarity of the epithelial structure in these parts of the excretory tract, no conclusions can be drawn on the exact origin of epithelial cells found in the urine.

The epithelium lining the excretory passages seems to be impermeable to the normal, soluble substances of the urine. If the viscus is damaged, this property may, of course, be greatly altered. *Intra-epithelial cysts*—round or oval cavities filled with a peculiar colloidal substance—often develop in the epithelium of the ureter and bladder. No true glands are present in the calices, the pelvis and the ureter; glands may be simulated here by small, solid nests of epithelial cells located in the thickness of the epithelial sheet. In the urinary bladder, however, and in the vicinity of the internal urethral orifice, small, sometimes branched invaginations of the epithelium into the subjacent connective tissue can be found. They contain numerous clear mucus-secreting cells and are similar to the glands of Littré in the urethra.

No distinct basement membrane between the epithelium and the lamina propria can cause a festooned appearance of the edge of the lumen in cross sections. In the bladder the deep, looser layer of connective tissue is especially abundant, so that in the contracted condition of the organ the mucous membrane forms numerous, thick folds. In some

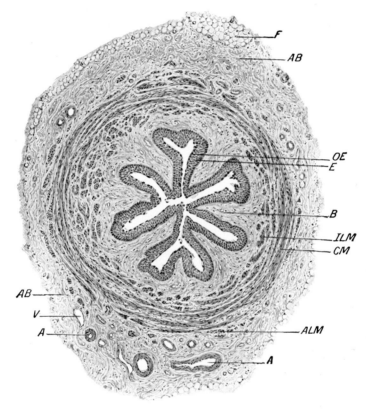

Fig. 443. Cross section of markedly contracted human ureter. A, Arteries; AB, adventitial connective tissue; ALM, external longitudinal muscle bundles; B, lamina propria; CM, circular muscle bundles; E, deep layer of the epithelium; F, fat tissue; ILM, internal longitudinal muscle bundles; OE, superficial epithelial cells; V, veins. 30 ×. (After Schaffer.)

be discerned. The connective tissue of the latter, especially in the ureter, forms thin folds which may penetrate deep into the epithelium. The blood capillaries which they contain sometimes lie deep in the epithelial sheet.

The dense connective tissue of the mucous membrane generally does not form any papillae. It contains elastic networks and sometimes small lymphatic nodules. Its deeper layers have a looser arrangement; therefore the mucous membrane in the empty ureter is thrown into several longitudinal folds, which places a thin layer of smooth muscle fibers seems to divide the connective tissue into a superficial lamina propria and a deeper submucous layer.

The muscular coat of the urinary passages generally consists of an *inner* longitudinal and an *outer* circular layer. Beginning with the lower third of the ureter, a third external longitudinal layer is added, which is especially prominent in the bladder. In contrast to the intestine, the smooth muscles in the urinary passages do not form regular layers, but appear as loose, anastomosing strands, separated from one another by abundant connective tissue and elastic networks, which continue into the lamina propria mucosae.

In the small calices, which are hollow cones capping the papillae of the pyramids, the strands of the inner longitudinal muscle layer end at the attachment of the calyx to the papilla. The outer circular strands reach higher up and form a muscular ring around the base of the papilla.

The calices show periodic contractions moving from their base to their apex. This muscular activity helps to move the urine out of the papillary ducts into the calices. The muscular coat of the ureter also performs slow peristaltic movements. The waves of contraction proceed from the pelvis toward the bladder.

As the *ureters* pierce the wall of the bladder obliquely, their openings are usually closed by the pressure of the contents of the bladder and are open only when the urine is forced through them. A fold of the mucous membrane of the bladder acts as a valve and usually prevents the backflow of the urine. In the "intramural" part of the ureters, the circular muscular strands of their wall disappear, and the connective tissue of the mucous membrane is occupied by longitudinal muscular strands whose contraction opens the lumen of the ureter.

The muscular coat of the *bladder* is very strong. Its thick strands of smooth muscle cells form three layers which, however, cannot be distinctly separated from each other. The outer longitudinal layer is developed best on the dorsal and ventral surfaces of the viscus, while in other places its strands may be wide apart. The middle, circular or spiral layer is the thickest of all. The innermost layer consists in the body of the bladder of relatively rare, separate longitudinal or oblique strands. In the region of the trigone, thin, dense bundles of smooth muscle form a circular mass around the internal opening of the urethra—the internal sphincter of the bladder.

Blood Vessels and Nerves. The blood vessels of the excretory passages penetrate first through the muscular coat and provide it with capillaries; then they form a plexus in the deeper layers of the mucous membrane. From here small arteries mount to the surface and form a rich capillary plexus immediately under the epithelium.

The deeper layers of the mucosa and the muscularis in the pelvis and the ureters contain a well-developed network of lymph capillaries. In the bladder they are said to be present only in the muscularis.

In the adventitial and muscular coats of the ureter, nerve plexuses, small ganglia and scattered nerve cells can be found. Most of the fibers supply the muscles; some fibers of apparently efferent nature have been traced into the mucosa and the epithelium.

A sympathetic nerve plexus, the plexus vesicalis, in the adventitial coat of the bladder is formed in part by the pelvic nerves which originate from the sacral nerves, and in part by the branches of the plexus hypo-

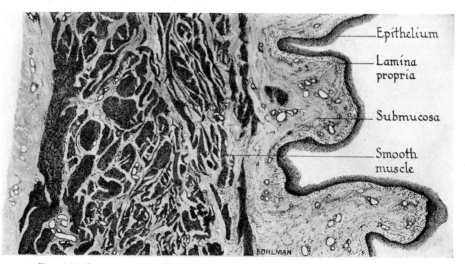

Fig. 444. Low power view of contracted urinary bladder of *Macacus rhesus*.

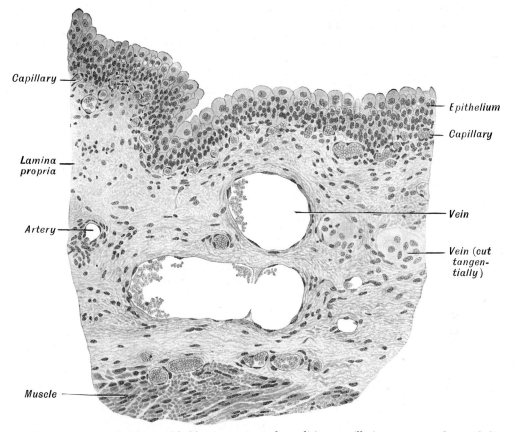

Fig. 445. Wall of human urinary bladder in contracted condition; capillaries penetrate the epithelium. 150 ×. (A.A.M.)

gastricus. The vesical plexus sends numerous nerves into the muscular coat. A continuation of the nerve plexus, seemingly without nerve cells, however, is found in the connective tissue of the mucous membrane. Here the sensory nerve endings are located. Many fibers penetrate into the epithelium, between the cells of which they form free end branchings provided with varicosities.

URETHRA

Male Urethra. The male urethra has a length of 18 to 20 cm. Three parts can be distinguished in it. The proximal, short part, surrounded by the prostate, is the *pars prostatica*. Here the posterior wall of the urethra forms an elevation, the colliculus seminalis. On its surface in the middle line the *vesicula prostatica* opens; to the right and to the left of this the two slitlike openings of the ejaculatory ducts and the numerous openings of the prostatic gland are located. The second, also very short part (18 mm. long), the *pars*

membranacea urethrae, stretches from the apex of the prostate to the bulb of the corpus cavernosum penis. The third stretch, the *pars cavernosa*, about 15 cm. long, passes lengthwise through the corpus cavernosum of the urethra.

The prostatic part is lined by the same "transitional" type of epithelium as the bladder. The pars membranacea and the pars cavernosa are lined by a stratified or pseudostratified columnar epithelium. Patches of stratified squamous epithelium are common in the cavernous parts; in the terminal enlarged part of the canal, the fossa navicularis, stratified squamous epithelium occurs as a rule. In the surface epithelium occasional mucous goblet cells may be found. Intraepithelial cysts containing a colloid-like substance are common. Lymphocytes migrating through the epithelium are rare.

The lamina propria mucosae is a loose con-

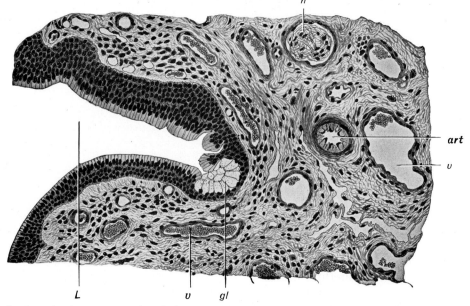

Fig. 446. Section of cavernous part of male human urethra. *L*, Lacuna; *gl*, intra-epithelial group of glandular cells; *v*, veins; *art*, artery; *n*, encapsulated sensory nerve ending. 165 ×. (A.A.M.)

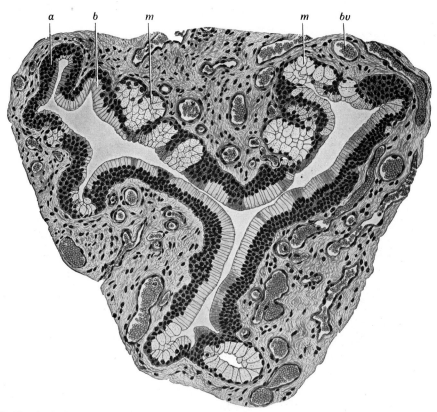

Fig. 447. Urethral gland (gland of Littré) from human pars cavernosa urethrae. *a*, Darkly staining, stratified columnar epithelium; *b*, epithelium with clear cells; *m*, outpocketings with clear mucous cells; *bv*, blood vessels. 165 ×. (A.A.M.)

nective tissue with abundant elastic networks; no separate submucous layer can be distinguished. This connective tissue contains numerous scattered bundles of smooth muscle, mainly longitudinally directed. In the outer layers, however, circular bundles are also present. The lamina propria has no distinct papillae; the latter appear only in the fossa navicularis. The membranous portion of the urethra is surrounded by a mass of striated muscle, a part of the urogenital diaphragm.

The surface of the mucous membrane of the urethra shows many recesses, the *lacunae of Morgagni*. These outpocketings continue into deeper, branching tubules, the *glands of Littré*; the larger ones among them are found especially on the dorsal surface of the cavernous portion of the urethra. They run obliquely in the lamina propria and are directed with their blind end toward the root of the penis; they sometimes penetrate far into the spongy body. The glands of Littré are lined with the same epithelium as the surface of the mucous membrane, but in many places this epithelium is transformed into compact intra-epithelial nests of clear cells, which give the reaction of mucus. In old age some of the recesses of the urethral mucosa may contain concretions similar to those of the prostate.

The deeper venous plexuses of the urethral mucosa in the pars cavernosa gradually merge into the cavernous spaces of the spongy body (p. 485). Numerous sensory nerve endings are present in the urethral mucous membrane.

Female Urethra. The female urethra is 25 to 30 mm. long. The mucous membrane forms longitudinal folds and is lined with stratified squamous epithelium; in many cases, however, pseudostratified columnar epithelium can be found. Numerous invaginations are formed by the epithelium; the outpocketings in their wall are lined in many places with clear mucous cells, as in the glands of Littré of the male urethra. The

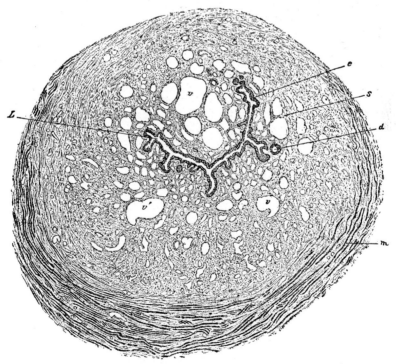

Fig. 448. Cross section through urethra of a woman. *L*, Lumen; *d*, glandlike lacuna; *e*, epithelium; *m*, cross-striated muscle bundles of the urethral muscle; *s*, lamina propria with small and large veins, *v* (corpus spongiosum). The darker portions of the lamina propria are smooth muscle bundles. 10 ×. (After von Ebner.)

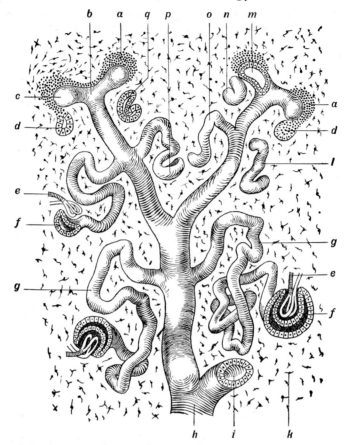

Fig. 449. Diagram of development of metanephros. *a*, Metanephrogenic tissue capping ampulla of collecting tubule; *b*, T-shaped branching of growing end of collecting tubule; *c*, enlarged blind end of same (ampulla); *d*, primordium of uriniferous tubule just formed from metanephrogenic tissue; *e*, vessel which forms the glomerulus; *f*, capsule of Bowman cut open; *g*, uriniferous tubule in later stage of development; *h*, collecting tubule; *i*, cross section of same; *k*, connective tissue; *l*, uriniferous tubule before establishment of a connection with the collecting tubule; *m*, ampulla of collecting tubule cut open; *n*, primordium of uriniferous tubule just separated from metanephrogenic tissue; *o*, newly formed uriniferous tubule which has just become connected with collecting tubule (stage immediately following *l*); *p*, spoon-shaped enlargement of blind end of uriniferous tubule—capsule of Bowman; *q*, primordium of uriniferous tubule just separated from metanephrogenic tissue (same as *n*), cut open. (Modified after Corning.)

glands may accumulate colloid material in their cavities or may even contain concretions.

The lamina propria, devoid of papillae, is a loose connective tissue with abundant elastic networks. It is provided with a highly developed system of venous plexuses and has, therefore, a cavernous character (corpus spongiosum).

The mucous membrane with its veins is surrounded by a thick mass of smooth muscles; the inner layers of the latter have a longitudinal, the outer layers a circular, ar-

rangement. Distally, the smooth muscles are strengthened by a striated muscle sphincter.

Histogenesis of the Kidney. The independent origin of the nephrons and the collecting tubules in the embryo has been mentioned. The nephrons develop through differentiation of a compact, mesenchyme-like tissue, the *metanephric blastema*, which arises from the mesoderm. The system of excretory ducts arises as a hollow outgrowth of the wolffian duct, in much the same manner as other epithelial glands develop. This outgrowth grows forward in the mesenchyme as the primordium of the ureter and of the renal pelvis. It forms four branches—the primordia of the calices, which end blindly in club-shaped dilatations, each of which forms secondary, tertiary, and so on, branches—the collecting tubules of various orders.

In human embryos of 7 mm. the metanephric blastema adheres to the wall of the dilated pelvis primordium and appears in sections as a semilunar *cap*. As the branches of the pelvis form, the metanephric cap separates into a piece for each branch (human embryos of 9.5 mm.), so that the ampullar dilatation of each branch carries its own metanephric cap.

In human embryos 13 to 19 mm. in length, the edges of the cap covering each blind end of the collecting tubules swell and glide down its sides. As the ampulla divides dichotomously, the metanephrogenic cap is divided equally between the two new ampullae.

The roundish, compact metanephric body soon acquires an eccentric lumen around which its cells become radially arranged; it is now called the metanephric vesicle. Next it stretches and is transformed into an **S**-shaped tubule which grows rapidly in length and becomes tortuous. It is the future nephron. One end of it coalesces with, and opens into, the neighboring collecting tubule. The other end enlarges, flattens slightly, and is invaginated by a tuft of capillaries from a branch of the renal artery. In this way the malpighian or renal corpuscle is formed with its capsule and glomerulus. In the meantime the collecting tubules continue to grow toward the periphery and to branch dichotomously, still keeping their metanephrogenic caps.

Succeeding generations of nephrons with their renal corpuscles are added to the branching tree of the collecting tubules, until the whole metanephric blastema is exhausted. This continues in the human fetus throughout the latter period of intra-uterine life and comes to its end six or eight days after birth.

When the glomerulus invaginates the wall of the capsule of Bowman, the visceral epithelium is much thicker than the parietal. Later, both layers become simple squamous epithelia. Soon after the **S**-shaped tubule of the nephron becomes connected with the collecting tubule, the histological differentiation of the different parts of the nephron begins. The proximal part, adjacent to the capsule, becomes tortuous, and its epithelium develops a glandular character, increases in height, and its cytoplasm stains with acid dyes. The following stretch of the tubule forms a loop, which slips out of the coils formed by the convoluted tubule and extends toward the renal pelvis. It is forced out of the tubular convolute surrounding the renal corpuscle, because the initial part of the future distal convolution early becomes attached to the glomerulus and consequently cannot be removed from this place as the nephron grows in length. The epithelium of the collecting tubules soon acquires its typical clear appearance; this differentiation begins in the deeper parts, which are nearer to the pelvis, and gradually extends peripherally. The evidences of beginning function in the developing embryonic mammalian kidney have been studied experimentally by Gersh and Flexner (1937), Cameron and Chambers (1938) and Flexner (1938).

The terminal branches of the collecting tubules and the nephrons may sometimes miss each other and remain disconnected. In such cases the convoluted tubules with their renal corpuscles continue for some time to elaborate urine and, having no outlet, are gradually transformed into cysts. The cystic kidney is a not uncommon abnormality of development.

REFERENCES

Abell, R. G., and Page, I. H.: The Effects of Renal Hypertension on the Vessels of the Ears of Rabbits. J. Exper. Med., 75:673, 1942.

Bensley, R. R., and Bensley, R. D.: The Structure of the Renal Corpuscle. Anat. Rec., 47:147, 1930.

Chambers, R., and Kempton, R. T.: Indications of Function of the Chick Mesonephros in Tissue Culture with Phenol Red. J. Cell. & Comp. Physiol., 3:131, 1933.

Christensen, K.: Renal Changes in the Albino Rat on Low Choline and Choline-deficient Diets. Arch, Path., 34:633, 1942.

Edwards, J. G.: Studies on Aglomerular and Glomerular Kidneys. Am. J. Anat., 42:75, 1928; The Vascular Pole of the Glomerulus in the Kidney of Vertebrates. Anat. Rec., 76:381, 1940.

Ellinger, R., and Hirt, A.: Mikroskopischen Untersuchungen an lebenden Organen. II. Zur Funktion der Froschniere. Arch. f. exp. Path., 145:193, 1929.

Flexner, L. B.: Biochemical Changes Associated with Onset of Secretory Activity in the Metanephros of the Fetal Pig. The Cytochrome Oxidase-cytochrome System and Oxidation-Reduction Potentials. J. Biol. Chem., 131:703, 1939.

Gersh, I.: Histochemical Studies on the Mammalian Kidney. II. The Glomerular Elimination of Uric Acid in the Rabbit. Anat. Rec., 58:369, 1934; The Correlation of Structure and Function in the Developing Mesonephros and Metanephros. Contrib. Embryol., Carnegie Inst., 26:35, 1937.

Goldblatt, H.: The Renal Origin of Hypertension. Physiol. Rev., 27:120, 1947.

Goormaghtigh, N.: Existence of an Endocrine Gland in the Media of the Renal Arterioles. Proc. Soc. Soc. Exper. Biol. & Med., 42:688, 1939.

Heidenhain, R.: Physiologie der Absonderungsvorgänge. Hermann's Hand. der Physiologie, Leipzig, 1883.

Höber, R., and Briscoe-Woolley, P. M.: Conditions Determining the Selective Secretion of Dyestuffs by the Isolated Frog Kidney. J. Cell. & Comp. Physiol., 15:35, 1940.

Holton, Sylvia G., and Bensley, R. R.: The Functions of the Differentiated Parts of the Uriniferous Tubule in the Mammal. Am. J. Anat., 47:241, 1931.

Huber, G. C.: Renal Tubules, in Cowdry's Special Cytology. 2d ed. New York, 2: 933, 1932.

Kirkman, H., and Stowell, R. E.: Renal Filtration Surface in the Albino Rat. Anat. Rec., 82:373, 1942.

Ludwig, C.: Von der Niere. Stricker's Handbuch der Gewebelehre, 1871, Vol. 1, p. 489.

MacCallum, D. B.: The Bearing of Degenerating Glomeruli on the Problem of the Vascular Supply of the Mammalian Kidney. Am. J. Anat., 65:69, 1939.

Marshall, E. K., Jr.: The Comparative Physiology of the Kidney in Relation to Theories of Renal Secretion. Physiol. Rev., 14:133, 1934.

Möllendorff, W. v.: Der Exkretionsapparat. Handb. d. mikr. Anat. (v. Möllendorff), (7)¹, 1, 1930.

Noll, A.: Die Exkretion (Wirbeltiere). Handb. d. vergl. Physiol. (Winterstein), (2)², 760, 1924.

Oliver, J.: New Directions in Renal Morphology: A Method, Its Results and Its Future. Harvey Lectures, Series 40, 102, 1944–45.

Peirce, E. C.: Renal Lymphatics. Anat. Rec., 90:315, 1944.

Peter, K.: Untersuchungen über Bau und Entwickelung der Niere. Jena, 1909, 1927.

Pitts, R. F.: Renal Excretion of Acid. Federation Proc., 7:418, 1948.

Policard, A.: Le tube urinaire des mammifères. Rev. gén. d'histologie, Lyons, 1908.

Richards, A. N., and Walker, A. M.: Methods of Collecting Fluid from Known Regions of the Renal Tubules of Amphibia and of Perfusing the Lumen of a Single Tubule. Am. J. Physiol., 118:111, 1937, and following papers; Processes of Urine Formation. Proc. Roy. Soc., London, S. B., No. 844, 126:398, 1938.

Schloss, G.: The Juxtaglomerular E-Cells of Rat Kidneys in Diuresis and Antidiuresis, after Adrenalectomy and Hypophysectomy, and in Avitaminosis A, D and E. Acta Anatomica, 6:80, 1948.

Selye, H., and Stone, H.: Pathogenesis of the Cardiovascular and Renal Changes Which Usually Accompany Malignant Hypertension. J. Urol., 56:399, 1946.

Shannon, J. A.: Renal Tubular Excretion. Physiol. Rev., 19:63, 1939.

Singer, E.: Observations on the Frog's Kidney with the Fluorescence Microscope. Am. J. Anat., 53:469, 1933.

Smith, H. W.: The Kidney. New York, Oxford University Press, 1951.

Walker, A. M., Bott, P. A., Oliver, J., and MacDowell, M. C.: The Collection and Analysis of Fluid from Single Nephrons of the Mammalian Kidney. Am. J. Physiol., 134:580, 1941.

Zimmermann, K. W.: Ueber den Bau des Glomerulus der Säugetiere, Weitere Mitteilungen. Zeit. f. mikr.-anat. Forsch., 32:176, 1933.

XXIX. MALE GENITAL SYSTEM

The male reproductive system consists of the testes, a complex system of excretory ducts with their auxiliary glands, and the penis.

THE TESTIS

The testis is a compound tubular gland surrounded by a firm, thick white capsule, the albuginea testis—a typical fibrous membrane. At the posterior edge of the organ, the thickening of the capsule projects into the gland as the *mediastinum testis*. From the mediastinum thin partitions, the *septula testis*, extend radially to the capsule and divide the organ into about 250 conical compartments, the *lobuli testis*, which converge with their apices toward the mediastinum. As the septula are interrupted in many places, the lobules intercommunicate, especially in their peripheral portions.

The cavity of each lobule contains the terminal portions of the seminiferous tubules. These are 30 to 70 cm. long and 150 to 250 microns in diameter. Their combined length in man is estimated at 250 meters. One to three of them occupy a lobule. They have an extremely tortuous course, rarely branch, and are called the *convoluted seminiferous tubules* (Fig. 467). The tubules in adjacent lobules may be connected by loops. The spermia are formed in the convoluted tubules. The testes are suspended in the scrotum by the spermatic cords. Each of these contains the excretory duct (*ductus deferens*), blood vessels and nerves supplying the

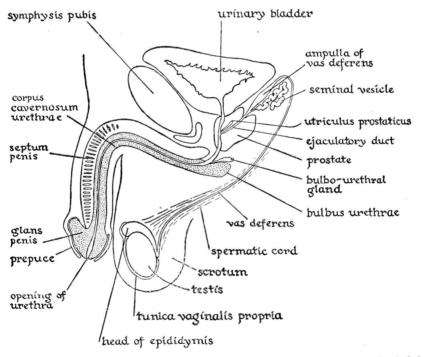

Fig. 450. Diagrammatic median section of male sexual apparatus. (Redrawn from Eberth, slightly modified.)

Page 461

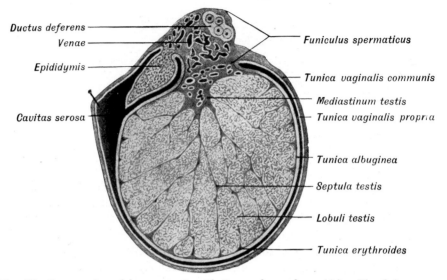

Ductus deferens
Venae
Epididymis
Cavitas serosa

Funiculus spermaticus
Tunica vaginalis communis
Mediastinum testis
Tunica vaginalis propria
Tunica albuginea
Septula testis
Lobuli testis
Tunica erythroides

Fig. 451. Cross section of human testis with its envelopes. 2 ×. (After Eberth.)

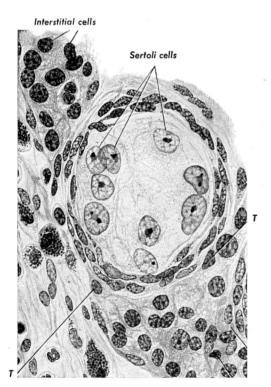

Interstitial cells

Sertoli cells

T

T

Fig. 452. Portion of seven months' cryptorchid testis of an adult guinea pig stained vitally with lithium carmine several days before death. The spermatogenic cells have disappeared, and the tubules are filled with a syncytium of Sertoli cells; the interstitial cells do not store carmine, in contrast to the dye-storing macrophages; T, transition from mesenchymal cells to interstitial cells. Hematoxylin stain. 490 ×. (After Esaki.)

testis on that side of the body. The *epididymis*, an elongated body attached to the posterior surface of the testis, contains the proximal parts of the excretory duct system of this organ.

The anterior and lateral surfaces of each testis and epididymis are surrounded by a cleftlike serous cavity, a detached part of the peritoneal cavity, in the dorsal wall of which the testes develop in the embryo before descending into the scrotum. The wall of this cavity, the *tunica vaginalis propria testis*, comprises an outer parietal, and an inner visceral, layer. At the posterior edge of the testis, where the epididymis is attached and the blood vessels and nerves enter the organ, the parietal layer is reflected into the visceral layer. After removal of the parietal layer, the *visceral coat* covering the testis appears as a free, smooth surface, lined with mesothelium. This is the remnant of the germinal epithelium which covers the primordium of the gonad in the embryo and gives rise to the glandular tissue of the testis. The *tunica vaginalis propria* enables the testis, which is sensitive to pressure, to glide freely in its envelopes. Obliteration of the serous cavity of the tunica vaginalis may cause atrophy of the testis.

SEMINIFEROUS EPITHELIUM

In the adult the convoluted seminiferous tubule is lined by the complex seminiferous epithelium with its two kinds of cells. The first are nutrient and supporting elements—the *sustentacular cells* (*of Sertoli*). The others, forming the vast majority, are the *sex* (*germ* or *spermatogenic*) cells, which,

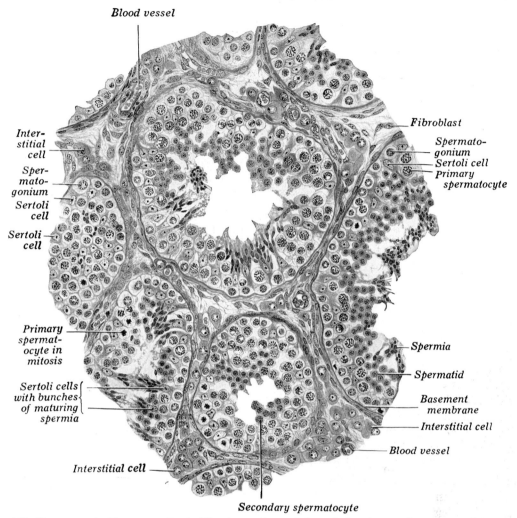

Fig. 453. Human testis (from operation). The transections of the tubules show various stages of spermatogenesis. 170 ×. (A.A.M.)

through proliferation and complex transformations, furnish the mature spermia.

Cells of Sertoli. In a tubule with active spermatogenesis the Sertoli cells are slender, pillar-like elements perpendicular to the basement membrane, to which they are attached. They are separated from one another at fairly regular intervals by the densely crowded spermatogenic cells.

The outlines of the sustentacular cells cannot be seen distinctly, and there is a widespread opinion that the spermatogenic cells are embedded in a continuous "Sertolian syncytium." However, in sections parallel to the basement membrane, the bases of the Sertoli cells are sometimes seen as distinctly outlined, polygonal areas. In pathological conditions, when the spermatogenic cells degenerate and disappear to a large extent, the lumen of the depleted seminiferous tubules appears surrounded by a loose protoplasmic network with scattered Sertoli nuclei and the few spermatogenic cells which escaped destruction. Occasionally a Sertoli cell may round off and float in the lumen, where it may phagocytose degenerating spermatogenic cells or spermia.

The characteristic nucleus of the Sertoli cell has an oval shape and an average size of 9 by 12 microns. In the human testis it is

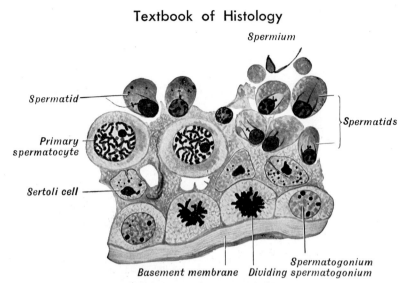

Fig. 454. Human testis, from young adult; seminiferous epithelium with mitoses of spermatogonia. The spermatids show a caudal sheath. Iron-hematoxylin stain. 750 ×. (A.A.M.)

usually at some distance from the basement membrane with its long axis directed radially. The membrane of the Sertoli nucleus is usually wrinkled, and the folds often extend deep into the interior of the nucleus (Fig. 454). This is probably not a sign of amitotic division. The vesicular nucleus is in striking contrast to the nuclei of the spermatogenic cells. The nucleus contains a large, compound nucleolus which consists of an oval, central acidophile part and of one to three small, round basophile granules.

The cytoplasm of the Sertoli cells in fixed preparations has a loose reticular structure. It contains small mitochondria, wavy fibrils, granules staining with iron hematoxylin, and

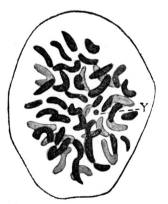

Fig. 455. Human spermatogonial plate, showing forty-eight chromosomes. Iron-hematoxylin stain. 3600 ×. (After Evans and Swezy.)

lipoid droplets which cause the brown color of the sectioned surface of the fresh testis and are supposed to be an evidence of the nutrient activity of these cells. In the human testis each Sertoli cell contains one spindle-shaped crystalloid near the nucleus.

At certain periods during spermatogenesis, the Sertoli cells enter temporarily into an intimate connection with the developing spermatogenic cells.

Under normal conditions the Sertoli cells are never seen to divide either mitotically or amitotically. They are highly resistant to various noxious factors which easily destroy the spermatogenic cells.

Spermatogenesis. *General Remarks.* The testis produces by mitosis large numbers of spermatogonia from which the mature germ cells are derived by two successive processes, the first nuclear and the second primarily cytoplasmic. The first (meiosis) results in cells with half the somatic number of chromosomes in their (haploid) nuclei. In the second process the spermatids formed by meiosis undergo transformation into highly differentiated spermatozoa.

As a rule the earliest generations of spermatogenic cells are near the basement membrane of the seminiferous tubule, while the more mature forms line the lumen. The cells from which spermatogenesis starts are called *spermatogonia.* They divide mitotically in

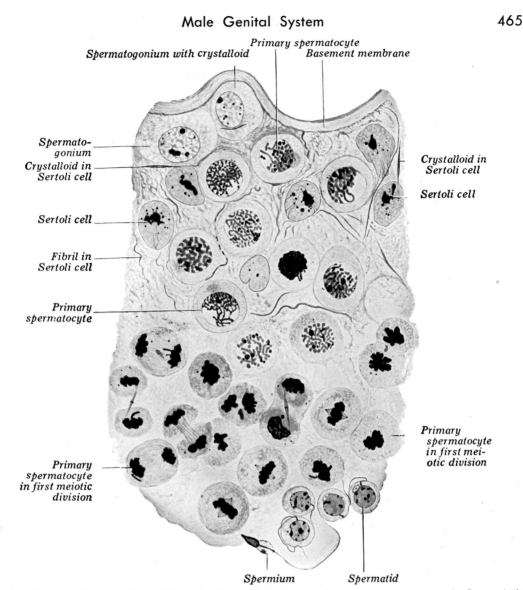

Spermatogonium with crystalloid

Primary spermatocyte
Basement membrane

Spermato-
gonium

Crystalloid in
Sertoli cell

Sertoli cell

Fibril in
Sertoli cell

Primary
spermatocyte

Primary
spermatocyte
in first meiotic
division

Crystalloid in
Sertoli cell

Sertoli cell

Primary
spermatocyte
in first mei-
otic division

Spermium   Spermatid

Fig. 456. Same testis as in Figure 453: seminiferous epithelium with primary spermatocytes in first meiotic division. Iron-hematoxylin stain. 750 ×. (A.A.M.)

the *period of proliferation*. Some of the spermatogonia persist as such along the inner surface of the basement membrane and by their continued multiplication are the source of the countless spermia produced during the life of the individual.

In the *period of growth* each spermatogonium gradually increases in size, and its nucleus changes markedly. This growth causes a shifting of the cells toward the lumen of the tubule. The growing cell is known as a *primary spermatocyte*. When it has reached its full development, the *period*

of maturation begins, and the primary spermatocyte divides into two new cells—the *secondary spermatocytes*. Each secondary spermatocyte soon divides, giving rise to two *spermatids*. By individual transformations they become *spermia*.

The two divisions leading from one primary spermatocyte to four spermatids differ from the common somatic mitoses and are called maturation divisions or "meiotic divisions." Through them the nucleus of each spermatid receives only one half of the somatic number of chromosomes typical for

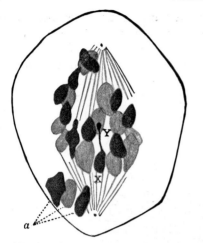

Fig. 457. Spindle of human primary spermatocyte, showing twenty-four chromosomes. The chromosomes at *a* were behind the others and were drawn outside the spindle for clearness. Iron-hematoxylin stain. 3600 ×. (After Evans and Swezy.)

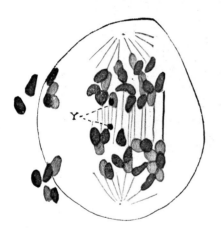

Fig. 458. Anaphase of human secondary spermatocyte, showing the two small Y chromosomes—the last to divide. There are twenty-four chromosomes in each group. Iron-hematoxylin stain. 3600 ×. (After Evans and Swezy.)

the respective animal species (forty-eight in man).

Spermatocytogenesis. The nucleus in the earlier generations of mammalian spermatogonia contains dustlike particles of chromatin and a round body that stains like chromatin. Near the nucleus is a thin *crystalloid body* smaller than that of the Sertoli cells. The later generations of spermatogonia are smaller and are found either at or near the basement membrane. The crystalloid seems

to be absent. In the nucleus the chromatin is arranged in darkly staining flakes on the inner surface of the membrane. These differences between the earlier and the later generations of spermatogonia are not distinct in man.

In the human spermatogonium there are twenty-three pairs of chromosomes of varying sizes and shapes and one pair of heterochromosomes (X-Y). The X and Y chromosomes in man were first accurately figured by Painter (1923).

The changes undergone by a spermatogonium developing into a primary spermatocyte (period of growth) represent a gradual preparation for the meiotic divisions and the reduction of chromatin.

The primary spermatocytes occupy the middle zone of the seminiferous epithelium and are large, spherical or oval cells. The nucleus undergoes a series of transformations which lead to the first meiotic division. The chromatin forms long, thin threads which conjugate two by two, probably side by side, and form a haploid number of bivalent chromosomes (*parasynapsis*), each consisting of two synaptic mates. Thus in the human primary spermatocyte there are twenty-four bivalent chromosomes, one of which is X-Y (Fig. 457). In mammals the history of their development is not as clear as in many invertebrates.

In the first meiotic division of the human spermatocytes each bivalent chromosome, including the X-Y chromosome, separates into its two constituent chromosomes along the line of their previous conjugation. As a result, of the two secondary spermatocytes originating from a dividing primary spermatocyte, one will contain twenty-three ordinary chromosomes and an X chromosome, while the other will have twenty-three chromosomes and the Y. The secondary spermatocytes are smaller than the primary.

The difference between mitosis and the first meiotic division is essentially this: In a somatic mitosis the individual chromosome splits and the half chromosomes separate, while in the first meiotic division whole chromosomes, the *synaptic mates* (the halves of the bivalent chromosomes), move away from each other toward the poles.

In mammals the interval between the two meiotic divisions is unknown. In the second meiotic division the spindle is more slender than in the first mitosis and extends nearly to the surface of the cell. Each of the twenty-four chromosomes, which are now small and

later divides into a distal centriole touching the cell surface and a proximal one deeper in the cytoplasm.

The details of spermatid formation and the phenomena of spermiogenesis are not completely known for human material. For a more general and complete idea of the process and its genetic importance, a com-

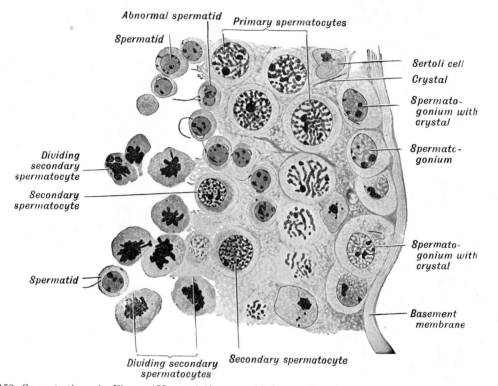

Fig. 459. Same testis as in Figure 453; seminiferous epithelium with mitoses of secondary spermatocytes—second meiotic division. 750 ×. (A.A.M.)

dumbbell-shaped, divides into halves by longitudinal splitting. Thus the second meiotic division corresponds in principle to an ordinary but haploid somatic mitosis. Each of the relatively small daughter cells of the secondary spermatocytes, the spermatids, has a nucleus about 5 to 6 microns in diameter containing several chromatin granules. Half of the spermatids have the X chromosome and half the Y.

The large attraction sphere (idiozome) is surrounded by the Golgi apparatus. The idiozome separates from the centriole as a darkly staining spherical body with a central clear area—the *acroblast*. The centriole

parative study of the testis of various animal species, including invertebrates, is necessary. (See also Gatenby and Beams.)

Spermiogenesis. The spermatids are the last generation of spermatogenic cells. They do not divide, and each undergoes a long series of peculiar transformations, to form the mature spermium (Fig. 461).

The most striking changes at the beginning of spermiogenesis concern the centrioles and the acroblast. From the distal centriole, a thin filament grows out (Fig. 461), the primordium of the axial thread of the tail of the spermium. It grows longer and thicker and straightens out. In the interior of the

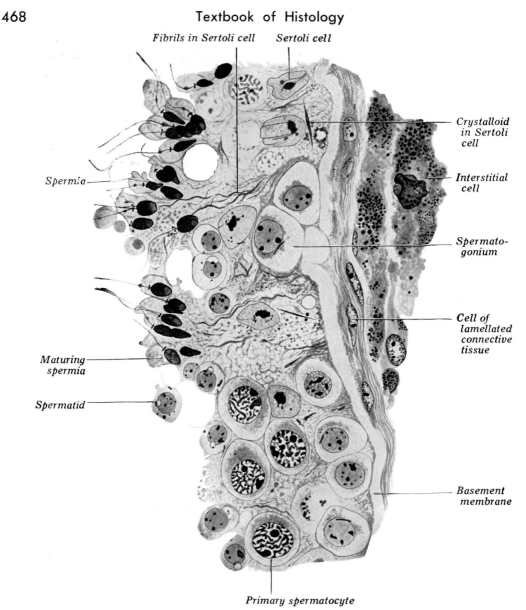

Fibrils in Sertoli cell   *Sertoli cell*

— *Crystalloid in Sertoli cell*

— *Interstitial cell*

Spermia—

— *Spermato-gonium*

— *Cell of lamellated connective tissue*

Maturing spermia

Spermatid

— *Basement membrane*

Primary spermatocyte

Fig. 460. Same testis as in Figure 453; seminiferous epithelium with bunches of maturing spermia, connected with Sertoli cells. Iron-hematoxylin stain. 750 ×. (A.A.M.)

clear central area of the acroblast a small, darkly staining, round body—the *acrosome*—appears. Then the acroblast, flattening against the nucleus, becomes hemispherical, and the acrosome touches the nuclear membrane. The darker peripheral layer of the acroblast (Golgi material) recedes into the protoplasm as the *acroblast remnant* and later disintegrates. The clear layer, covering the acrosome, extends beyond the equator of the nucleus.

In the human spermium it forms a delicate membrane, the *head cap*, which covers the anterior pole of the nucleus, the head of the future spermium.

The nucleus moves to the periphery of the cell body (Fig. 461). Then it assumes a slightly flattened, oval form, while the chromatin condenses into a darkly staining homogeneous mass. In this way the *head of the spermium* is formed.

During these transformations of the nucleus a temporary structure—the caudal sheath—appears (Fig. 461). It is a thin membrane which has the form of a wide tube or funnel. It begins at the equator of the nucleus and extends a short distance backward, where it ends with a free edge in the cytoplasm. Its significance is obscure, and it soon disappears.

The centrioles undergo important transformations. The proximal centriole becomes attached to the posterior pole of the nucleus and is transformed into the anterior knob of the neck of the spermium. The distal centriole divides into two parts. Its anterior part constitutes the posterior knob of the neck. The axial thread remains connected with this body. The posterior part of the distal centriole becomes a ring surrounding the axial thread (Fig. 461). It moves along the axial filament away from the posterior knob until it reaches the surface of the cell body, where it marks the posterior limit of the *middle piece* of the spermium.

During the migration of the centrioles toward the nucleus the extracellular part of the axial filament grows in length and finally reaches the size of the tail of the spermium. On its surface an extremely thin sheath is formed; it is missing on the end section of the tail. Around that part of the axial thread extending between the posterior knob and the ring some of the mitochondria fuse into a heavily staining filament surrounding the axial thread in a spiral coil—the *spiral sheath* of the middle piece of the spermium.

The cytoplasm of the spermatid gradually recedes from the nucleus and acquires an elongated, pearlike shape. It contains, besides some mitochondria, the disintegrating acroblast remnant, fat and lipoid droplets and heavily staining granules of undefinable nature. For some time the cytoplasm remains attached to the middle piece of the young spermium; it probably furnishes an external sheath for this part. Finally, it is sloughed off as an irregular round mass and disintegrates in the lumen of the seminiferous tubule. A part of this is carried into the semen

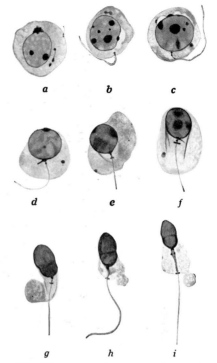

Fig. 461. Nine successive stages of spermiogenesis from human testis; explanation in the text (p. 467). Iron-hematoxylin stain. 1500 ×. (A.A.M.)

as granular detritus. The major part, however, seems to be absorbed and utilized by the Sertoli cells. A small drop of cytoplasm remains attached to the middle piece of the spermium for a long time.

Mature Spermium. The mature human spermium consists of a head, a connecting or middle piece, and a tail. In ordinary sections the spermia do not show any particular inner structure. For seeing the details, special histological methods such as iron hematoxylin and highest magnifications are necessary.

The *head* is a flattened, almond-shaped body measuring 4 to 5 microns in length and 2.5 to 3.5 microns in width. It is a condensed nucleus. The middle piece is of cylindrical or spindle shape and connects the posterior pole of the head with the tail. It has a length of 5 microns and a thickness of 1 micron. The tail has a length of 52 microns. At its anterior end it has the same thickness as the middle piece, but gradually tapers toward the free end. It can be subdivided into

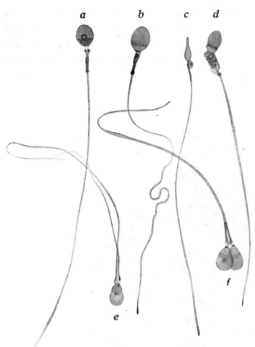

Fig. 462. Human spermia (spermatozoa). *a* and *b*, Head seen from flat surface; *c*, head seen in profile; in *c* and *d*, a bit of protoplasm remained attached to the middle piece; *e*, abnormal spermium with one head and two tails; *f*, abnormal spermium with two heads and one tail. Iron-hematoxylin stain. 1500 ×. (A.A.M.)

the principal part and a short terminal part of extreme thinness.

In fresh preparations from the testis the spermia either are motionless or display only a slight motility.

In man, two kinds of spermia are produced in equal numbers—spermia containing in their head the chromatin of twenty-three chromosomes and an X chromosome, and spermia with twenty-three chromosomes and a Y chromosome. All mature egg cells, however, are alike, having twenty-three chromosomes and an X chromosome. The fertilization of an ovum, carrying twenty-four chromosomes—one of which is X—by a spermium with twenty-four chromosomes—one of which is X—results in the formation of a new individual with forty-eight chromosomes (including X-X) in its cells, and is a female. In the case of a spermium with the Y chromosome and an ovum with its twenty-three

and X chromosomes, a male individual with forty-six plus X-Y chromosomes in the body cells is produced. Two types of mature, human spermia containing either the X or the Y chromosome have not been described morphologically. In the process of fertilization, the centrioles of the spermium, and especially the anterior knob, are supposed to furnish the egg with the active cytocentrum needed for its cleavage divisions.

Spermatogenetic Wave. The successive phases of spermatogenesis are arranged in the seminiferous tubules according to certain definite rules. The least developed elements are always located nearer the basement membrane, the most developed nearer the lumen. This movement is due to growth pressure. The spermatogonia remain adjacent to the basement membrane. The primary spermatocytes, in the early stages of the growth period, may keep this position for a while. The larger cells move toward the lumen and form a second, third and even fourth layer of cells. The spermatids form the inner layer of the epithelium and are usually found in large groups, all the cells of which, originating from a single spermatogonium, show the same stage of development. The same typical arrangement in groups is characteristic of the first and second meiotic divisions. The transformations of all cells of one generation occur more or less synchronously.

During spermiogenesis the spermatids become closely connected with the Sertoli cells. When the spermia have reached a certain degree of maturity and their cytoplasm has been sloughed off, the whole group leaves the Sertoli cell. After a period of inactivity the same Sertoli cell receives a fresh crop of spermatids.

In the human testis, spermatogenesis, having started at puberty, continues without interruption during the whole period of sexual activity. This also holds true for domesticated mammals, whose sexual activity is not distinctly regulated by the seasons of the year.

There are, as a rule, four generations in a given cross section—spermatogonia, spermatocytes (one or both types), spermatids, and spermia. But the degree of maturity of each generation varies in the different combinations. As a rule, a cross section of a tubule shows the same combination of generations along its periphery. In following a *longitudinal section* of an isolated and straightened

spermatogenesis. In other mammals and especially in man the succession of the generations and the combinations of the different cell types are much less regular. Shorter or longer stretches in the tubules may be in

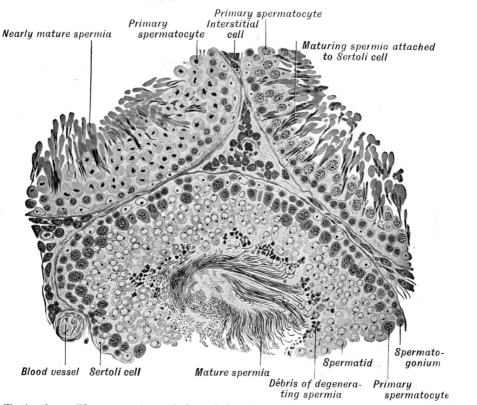

Fig. 463. Testis of rat. The transections of the tubules show various stages of spermatogenesis. 190 ×. (A.A.M.)

tubule, one can see the epithelium changing continuously. This depends on the fact that spermatogenesis is a wavelike activity proceeding along the tubule in the direction from the excretory ducts (the tubuli recti) to the periphery of the testis. In the rat the length of the spermatogenetic wave has been found to be 32 mm. The time necessary for the development of a spermium from a spermatogonium is estimated at twenty days for the rat.

The regular succession of generations of spermatogenic cells and the definite phases of the spermatogenetic wave have been worked out mainly for the testis of the rat, which is a classical object for studies on

resting condition and not show any spermatogenesis. They alternate with relatively small patches of active epithelium.

In seasonal breeding mammals active spermatogenesis, having begun at puberty, is repeated and discontinued periodically for the rest of their lives. Each time it continues only during the period of rut, at the end of which the spermatogenic cells degenerate and are cast off. Concomitantly, the seminiferous tubules shrink, and contain only Sertoli cells and some few spermatogonia. In this condition they resemble in structure the tubules of a prepubertal testis. At the beginning of a new period of sexual activity, spermatogonia multiply and rapidly produce the various generations of spermatogenic cells, while the Sertoli cells are compressed and become inconspicuous.

In the lower vertebrates, these cyclic changes of the testis in connection with the seasons are still more prominent.

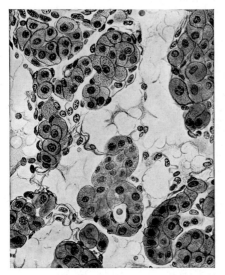

Fig. 464. Testis of an eighteen months cryptorchid guinea pig. Note the groups of interstitial cells, absence of seminiferous tubules. The interstitial connective tissue is slightly edematous. (Drawn by Miss A. Nixon from a preparation of C. R. Moore.)

Degenerative and Regenerative Phenomena. In an active human testis the tubules often contain in their lumen masses of degenerating spermatogenic cells which finally disintegrate into granular and fatty detritus. This is not pathologic unless it exceeds certain limits. The degenerating cells are usually seen close to stretches of active seminal epithelium with normal spermatogenesis in full progress.

Often, abnormal spermatogenic cells can be found. In the spermatogonia this manifests itself usally by an excessive hypertrophy. Among the spermatocytes giant forms are also common, as well as cells with two or more nuclei, sometimes of unequal size. They arise through fusion or abnormal mitosis. The spermatids often fuse to form multinucleated giant cells. Spermatids with two or even more nuclei may continue their development; thus monster spermia with two

or many tails and sometimes with one tail and two heads may arise.

The degenerating and monster spermatogenic cells are carried, with the mature spermia, into the epididymis, where their substance is perhaps reabsorbed by the epithelium of the excretory ducts.

The sex cells of the seminiferous epithelium are sensitive to noxious factors of various kinds. In pathological conditions of general (infectious diseases, alcoholism, dietary deficiencies) or local (injury, inflammation) character, and under the influence of mental depression, the degenerative changes, especially the formation of multinucleated giant cells by the coalescing spermatids, may become prominent. Exposure of the testis to a sufficient dose of x-rays causes an extensive degeneration of spermatogenic cells and even temporary sterilization. They are also sensitive to high temperature. Even the normal temperature of the body of a mammal is incompatible with their normal development. In the majority of the mammals the testes, in the adult, are lodged in the scrotum, which has a lower temperature than the body. Cryptorchid testes, which remain in the abdomen, never produce mature spermia, and show atrophic tubules containing Sertoli cells with a few scattered spermatogonia. In experimental cryptorchidism the testis soon shrinks and contains only Sertoli cells and remnants of sex cells; after a long time the tubules may disappear. The seminiferous tubules atrophy in rats fed on a diet lacking vitamin E; they degenerate to a lesser extent in vitamin A deficiency.

In all such cases the Sertoli cells are more resistant than spermatogenic cells. Some of the spermatogonia, however, seem in many cases to remain intact at the basement membrane between the Sertoli elements. Under favorable conditions, when the noxious factor is removed (for instance, on replacing the artificially ectopic testis in the scrotum), a more or less complete regeneration of the seminiferous epithelium from these residual cells may take place. In the seminiferous epithelium regenerating after x-ray sterilization, neoformation of spermatogonia from mitotically dividing Sertoli cells has been described.

In mammals with a short life, spermatogenesis continues until death without change. In man, although spermatogenesis continues far into the senile period, the seminiferous tubules undergo gradual involution with advancing age. A testis of a man older than thirty-five will always show an increasing quantity of scattered atrophic tubules; in the remaining parts of the gland, spermatogenesis may continue without visible alterations. Sometimes in very old persons all the tubules are depleted of spermatogenic cells and contain only atrophic Sertoli cells.

Capsule and the Interstitial Tissue of the Testis. The tunica albuginea, the mediastinum and the septula of the testis consist of dense connective tissue. The mediastinum contains a few smooth muscle fibers. On the inner surface of the albuginea the dense tissue passes into a looser layer containing many blood vessels—the "tunica vasculosa testis." This layer continues into the interstitial tissue which fills the angular spaces between the convoluted tubules.

The seminiferous epithelium rests on the inner surface of a basement membrane which has a faintly fibrillar structure. Externally the basement membrane is strengthened by a layer of lamellated connective tissue. The interstitial tissue contains thin collagenous fibers, blood and lymph vessels, nerves and several types of cells: fibroblasts, macrophages, mast cells and embryonic perivascular elements. The specific interstitial cells (of Leydig) are also present.

Interstitial Cells. These are scattered in the angular spaces between the tubules in compact groups without a definite relation to the blood vessels. Their body, measuring 14 to 21 microns in diameter, is irregularly polyhedral and is often provided with processes. Transitional forms to much smaller, round or elongated cells are common. The large, spherical or wrinkled nucleus contains coarse chromatin granules, and one or two large nucleoli. Cells with two nuclei are common. Adjacent to the nucleus is a large, clear attraction sphere. It contains centrioles

which appear as a group of small round granules or as two rod-shaped bodies. The sphere is surrounded by a Golgi apparatus. The peripheral cytoplasm contains numerous mitochondria. In fresh condition the cytoplasm is filled with refractile granules, many

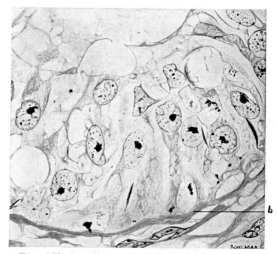

Fig. 465. Atrophic seminiferous tubule from otherwise normal testis of thirty-five year old man. b, Basement membrane. The tubule is lined with Sertoli cells containing crystalloids. Note absence of spermatogenic cells. Formalin. Iron-hematoxylin stain. 615 ×. (From a preparation of H. Okkels.)

of which react positively to tests for neutral fat and lipids (sometimes cholesterol esters). Some brownish granules are waste pigment (lipofuscin). The most interesting inclusions are rod-shaped crystalloids with rounded or pointed ends (Fig. 466). These are characteristic of the human testis, although they are not of constant occurrence and show great variations in size. They are monorefringent, swell in a 10 per cent solution of potassium hydroxide, and are dissolved by hydrochloric acid with pepsin. They are insoluble in 10 per cent hydrochloric, nitric or acetic acid, and in fat solvents.

It seems that the interstitial cells are modified connective tissue cells. In inflammatory lesions of the testis and in tissue cultures they divide mitotically and become fibroblasts. They may increase in number through transformation of spindle-shaped connective tissue elements, probably of embryonic na-

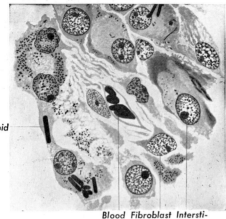

Crystalloid

Blood Fibroblast Intersti-
vessel   tial cell

Fig. 466. Human testis from young adult. Groups of interstitial cells with centrioles, darkly stained granular inclusions, and crystalloids. Iron-hematoxylin stain. 650 ×. (A.A.M.)

ture, scattered between the tubules and around the blood vessels.

Some authors claim that the interstitial cells of the testis arise from the same source as the elements of the seminiferous epithelium in the tubules; others believe them to be remnants of the epithelium of the tubules of the mesonephros. Groups of interstitial cells may be found in the connective tissue of the epididymis.

The "epithelioid" character of the interstitial cells suggests the possibility of an endocrine glandular function.

Endocrine Function of the Testis. The testis, besides producing spermia, causes the development and maintenance of the "secondary sexual characters" and of the sex impulse. In the developing organism it helps to regulate the growth of the skeleton and of other parts. Castration before puberty delays the cessation of growth of the long bones, and the secondary sexual characters do not develop. With castration after puberty, the libido gradually disappears, the secondary sexual characters and the auxiliary sex glands (Figs. 476 and 480) undergo partial involution, and disorders of metabolism eventually appear. The implantation of a testis into such a person may restore normal conditions to a certain extent. In experimental animals the injection of testicular hormone prevents

many of these changes, and implantation of a testis may cause the appearance of secondary male characters in a spayed female. This is due to a hormone (testosterone), secreted by the testis. Cancer of the prostate often undergoes marked regression after castration (or treatment with female sex hormones).

Some authors ascribe the production of this hormone to the interstitial cells; others, to the seminiferous epithelium (spermatogenic and Sertoli cells). A third possibility is, of course, the participation of both elements. Most of the data favor the first hypothesis. Persons with cryptorchid testes display, in most cases, a normal sexual behavior and normal secondary characters; they usually retain their virility, although sterility is the rule. The seminiferous tubules of such males are always atrophic, as a result of the higher temperature in the abdomen. In experimental animals with cryptorchid testes of long duration, the seminiferous tubules seem to disappear completely, leaving large masses of interstitial cells. Such individuals, as a rule, keep their libido, the potentia coeundi, and the secondary sexual characters. Similar results were obtained after ligation of the vas deferens or the ductuli efferentes and after large doses of x-rays. Grafts of testicular tissue into castrated animals are supposed to act through their interstitial cells, which proliferate, while the seminiferous tubules become atrophic. These and many other facts indicate that the male sexual hormone is probably secreted by the interstitial cells rather than by the seminiferous epithelium.

The reciprocal effects of hormones of the hypophysis and testis are discussed in Chapter XV. Here it need be recalled only that the follicle-stimulating hormone (FSH) stimulates spermatogenesis in animals, although not always in man. In the rat, follicle-stimulating hormone has no effect on androgen production. The interstitial cell-stimulating hormone (ICSH or LH) activates the interstitial cells, and this effect is increased if follicle-stimulating hormone is administered at the same time. Hypophysectomy leads to testicular atrophy, which can be restored by the injection of gonado-trophins. Administration of androgen de-creases the gonadotrophin level; after castration, gonadotrophin accumulates in the pars distalis of the hypophysis, where the beta cells show characteristic changes, the so-called "castration cells." The influence of the adrenal cortex on the gonads is discussed in Chapter XVIII.

Blood Vessels, Lymphatics and Nerves of the Testis. The blood supply of the testis is derived mainly from the internal spermatic artery. Some branches penetrate the interior of the gland in the region of the mediasti-num, while others run to the anterior side, in or under the albuginea, in the tunica vasculosa. From the mediastinum and from the septula testis, the smaller branches penetrate into the interior of the lobules and break up into capillaries, forming loose networks around the seminiferous tubules. The course of the veins corresponds to that of the arteries. Everywhere in the interstitial tissue between the seminiferous tubules, networks of lymph capillaries can be demon-strated. The nerves, from the plexus spermaticus in-ternus, surround the blood vessels with fine plexuses. The existence of end branches penetrating through the basement membrane into the epithelium of the seminiferous tubules seems doubtful.

EXCRETORY DUCTS

Tubuli Recti and Rete Testis. At the apex of each lobule, its seminiferous tubules join and pass abruptly into the first section of the system of excretory ducts—the *tubuli recti.* These are short and straight and have a diameter of but 20 to 25 microns. They enter the mediastinum testis and form in its dense connective tissue a system of irregular, anas-tomosing, epithelium-lined cavernous spaces —the *rete testis.*

At the transition of the seminiferous tu-bules into the tubuli recti the spermatogenic cells disappear and only the Sertoli cells re-main. Here they are tall columnar cells, with a cytoplasm containing numerous fat drop-lets. The cavernous spaces of the rete testis are lined with a cuboidal or squamous epi-thelium. Its cells are provided with a "central flagellum" and contain fat droplets.

Ductuli Efferentes. At the upper part of the posterior edge of the testis, twelve or more efferent ductules arise from the rete and emerge on the surface of the testis. They measure about 0.6 mm. in diameter and 4 to 6 cm. in length. Through numerous spiral windings and convolutions they form five to thirteen conical bodies about 10 mm. in length—the *vascular cones.* These have their bases toward the free surface of the head of the epididymis and their apices toward the mediastinum testis. They are kept together by connective tissue and constitute part of the head of the epididymis.

The ductuli efferentes have a typical epi-thelium. Their lumen has a festooned out-line, because it is lined by alternating groups of tall and low cells. The latter form "intra-epithelial glands," small, cuplike excavations in the thickness of the epithelium, not affect-ing the basement membrane. The clear cells of these excavations contain pale secretion and pigment granules. There is a brush bor-der and a central flagellum on the free sur-face. The formation of bleblike outgrowths as a sign of secretory activity has also been described. In animals intravitally stained they contain dye inclusions, presumably by absorption from the lumen. The tall cells usually have a conical form with the broad end toward the lumen. On their free surface are cilia which beat toward the epididymis and move the spermia in this direction. Their cytoplasm stains intensely and contains nu-merous fat droplets and pigment granules. Often both cell types are distributed irregu-larly.

Outside the thin basement membrane is a thin layer of circularly arranged smooth mus-cle cells. In the ducts forming the coni vas-culosi, the muscular layer becomes more prominent.

Ductus Epididymis. The winding tubules of the vascular cones gradually fuse into the single ductus epididymidis (Fig. 467). This highly tortuous, long canal (4 to 6 m.) forms, with the surrounding connective tissue, the body and the tail of the epididymis. The duct gradually straightens out and merges into the ductus deferens which has a length of 40 to 45 cm.

In the proximal, convoluted part (the body) the lumen is lined by a tall, pseudo-stratified columnar epithelium. The cross sec-

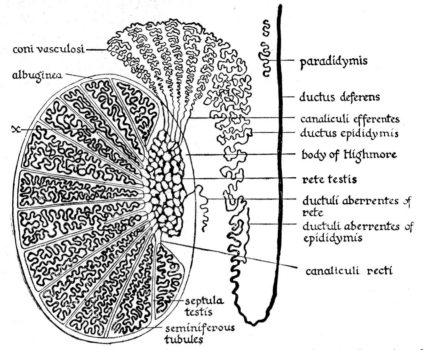

Fig. 467. Diagram of arrangement of seminiferous tubules and excretory ducts in the testis and epididymis.
x, Communication between seminiferous tubules of different lobules.

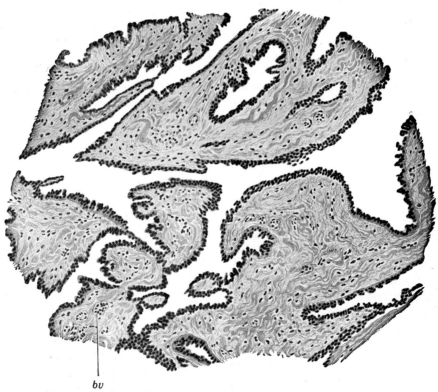

Fig. 468. Rete testis, human: *bv*, blood vessel. 140 ×. (A.A.M.)

tions of the duct have a regular, circular outline. On the inner surface of the basement membrane, small angular basal cells containing lipoid droplets form a discontinuous layer. On their free surface the columnar cells carry a tuft of long (30 microns), nonmotile *stereocilia*, kept together by cytoplasm. In the cytoplasm immediately above the nucleus a Golgi apparatus is present. Nearer to the free surface, secretion granules, vacuoles, fat droplets and pigment inclusions are found. They move toward the lumen, leave the cell through the stereocilia, and represent the secretion. In the distal part of the duct the epithelium gradually becomes lower.

The basement membrane is surrounded by a highly developed capillary network and by a circular layer of smooth muscular fibers which probably help to forward the spermia.

Nerves (mostly nonmedullated) form a plexus of fine fibers connected with the muscles of the vessels and of the wall of the duct. Small sympathetic ganglia have also been described.

A number of rudimentary structures are found attached to the testis and epididymis and to the further sections of the excretory duct.

The *appendix testis* (*hydatis Morgagni*) is the remainder of the abdominal end of the duct of Mueller. It is located at the upper pole of the testis, near the head of the epididymis, as a small nodule consisting of vascular connective tissue and lined with columnar, sometimes ciliated epithelium. The *appendix epididymidis* is believed to be the rudiment of the wolffian

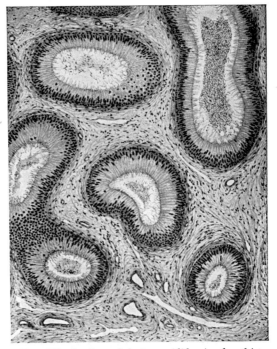

Fig. 470. Section of ductus epididymis of a thirty-two year old man. The stereocilia are prominent. The lumens contain spermia. Iron-hematoxylin-chromotrop 2 R. 72 ×. (After Stieve.)

body (mesonephros). It is a nodule, 3 by 2 mm., containing a cyst lined with columnar epithelium and connected with the head of the epididymis by a stalk of variable length. The *ductuli aberrantes* are blindly ending epithelial tubules, one in connection with the rete testis, another with the lower part of the ductus epididymis. They are rudiments of the tubules of the mesonephros. The *paradidymis*, also a rudiment of the wolffian body, is a group of coiled epithelial tubules in the connective tissue of the spermatic cord at the level of the head of the epididymis. In some cases, especially in newborn infants, small nodules with the structure of the cortex of the adrenal may be found in the connective tissue of the tail of the epididymis. In the neighborhood of the paradidymis small accumulations of chromaffin tissue have been described.

Ductus Deferens. On passing into the ductus deferens, the duct develops a larger lumen and a thicker wall. Under the basement membrane the lamina propria mucosae rises in longitudinal folds which cause the deeply festooned outlines seen in cross section. The pseudostratified columnar epithelium is lower than in the epididymis, and the cells usually have stereocilia. The connective tissue of the mucous membrane contains ex-

Ciliated cells   **Secreting cells**

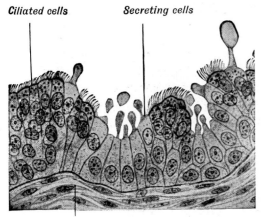

Circular muscle

Fig. 469. Part of cross section of human ductus efferens. Groups of ciliated cells alternate with groups of secreting cells. 450 ×. (After Eberth.)

tensive elastic networks. The 1 mm.-thick layer of smooth muscles reaches a high grade of development; it consists of inner and outer longitudinal layers with a powerful circular, intermediate layer. On the periphery there is an adventitial coat of connective tissue. The

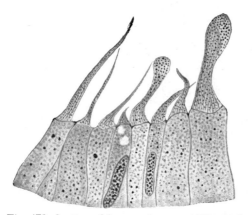

Fig. 471. Section of human ductus epididymis; free surface of epithelium, with stereocilia, discharging secretion. 1000 ×. (Redrawn after M. Heidenhain and F. Werner.)

duct is easily palpable through the thin skin of the scrotum.

The duct is accompanied by loose, longitudinal strands of smooth muscle—musculus cremaster internus—which form a part of the *spermatic cord*. It also contains arteries, the veins of the pampiniform plexus with muscular walls, and nerves of the plexus spermaticus.

The vas deferens, after crossing the ureter, dilates into a spindle-shaped enlargement, the *ampulla*. At the distal end of the latter it forms a large, blind, glandular evagination—the *seminal vesicle*. Then, as the short (19 mm.) and straight *ejaculatory* duct (0.3 mm. in diameter), it pierces the body of another gland, the *prostate*, attached to the bottom of the urinary bladder, and opens by a small slit into the prostatic part of the urethra, on a small thickening of its posterior wall—the *colliculus seminalis* or *verumontanum*. The openings of the ejaculatory ducts are located to the right and to the left of the

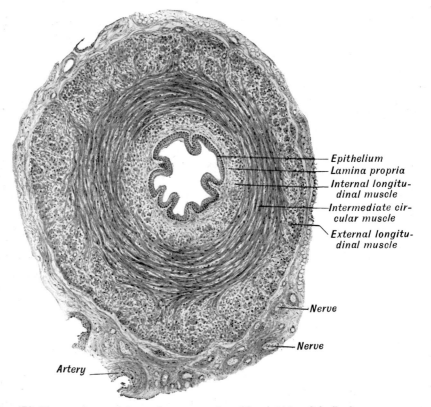

— Epithelium
— Lamina propria
— Internal longitudinal muscle
— Intermediate circular muscle
— External longitudinal muscle

— Nerve

— Nerve

Artery ____

Fig. 472. Human ductus deferens in cross section. 30 ×. (After Schaffer.)

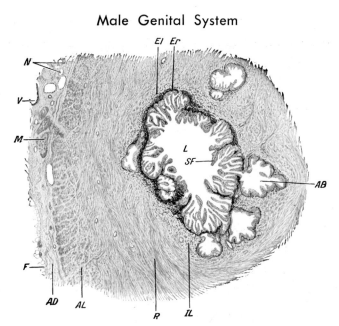

Fig. 473. Portion of cross section through ampulla of human ductus deferens. AB, Glandlike outpouchings of main lumen; L, Lumen; AD, adventitia; AL, external longitudinal muscle layer; El, longitudinal and, Er, ring-shaped elastic fibers; F, fat tissue; IL, internal longitudinal muscle layer; M, smooth muscle bundles in adventitia; N, nerves; R, circular muscle layer; SF, folds of mucosa; V, veins. Orcein stain. 26 ×. (After Schaffer.)

utriculus prostaticus, a blind invagination on the summit of the colliculus.

In the ampulla of the ductus deferens, the mucous membrane with its epithelium is thrown into numerous, thin, irregularly branching folds (Fig. 473) which in many places fuse with one another, producing in a section a netlike system of partitions with angular meshes. The epithelium may show signs of secretion. From the excavations between the folds, numerous tortuous, branched outpocketings reach far into the surrounding muscular layer (Fig. 473) and are lined with a single layer of columnar, clear cells of glandular nature containing secretion granules. The musculature is much less regularly arranged than in the other parts of the ductus deferens.

Ejaculatory Ducts. The epithelium lining the ejaculatory ducts is a simple or pseudo-stratified columnar epithelium, probably endowed with glandular functions. Its cells contain a large quantity of yellow pigment granules. Near the opening of the ducts the epithelium often assumes the structure of "transitional" epithelium. The mucous membrane of the ducts forms many thin folds

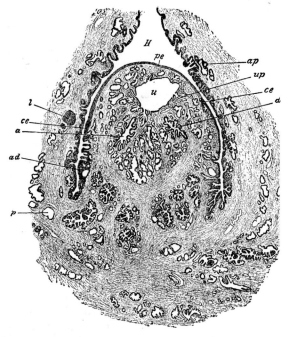

Fig. 474. Cross section through colliculus seminalis of a young man. Urethra, H, incised above; a, ejaculatory canal; ad, adenoid tissue; ap, accessory prostatic gland; ce, stratified cylindrical epithelium; l, lacuna in cross section; p, prostatic ducts; pe, stratified epithelium; up, prostatic ducts, which empty into utriculus of prostate, u. 10 ×. (After von Ebner, from Schaffer.)

reaching far into the lumen; its connective tissue is provided with abundant elastic networks. The dorsomedial wall of the ducts contains a series of outpocketings of glandular nature, which may be accessory seminal vesicles. The ducts proper are surrounded only by connective tissue.

AUXILIARY GLANDS

The glands associated with the excretory duct of the testis are the seminal vesicles, prostate and bulbo-urethral glands.

Seminal Vesicles. The seminal vesicles are tortuous, elongated, hollow bodies with an irregular, branched lumen and numerous outpocketings. They are evaginations of the

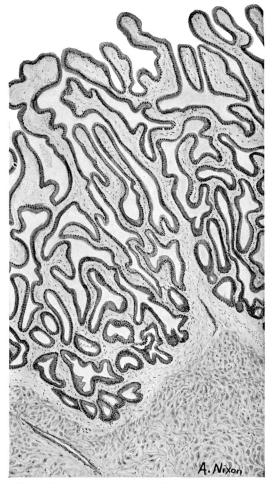

Fig. 475. Section through wall of human seminal vesicle, showing the folded tunica mucosa, the pale-staining lamina propria and the darker muscle coat. 85 ×.

ductus deferens and are similar to it in structure. Their wall consists of an external connective tissue sheet with elastic nets, of a middle layer of smooth muscle thinner than in the duct, and of a mucous membrane resting upon a thin submucous layer. The mucous membrane forms an intricate system of thin, primary folds, which branch into secondary and tertiary folds. These project far into the lumen and anastomose frequently with one another. In this way numerous cavities of different sizes arise, separated from one another by thin, branching partitions; all open into the larger central cavity. In sections, however, many of them seem to be isolated (Fig. 475). Some are provided with glandlike invaginations similar to those in the ampulla.

The epithelium shows great individual variations, which probably depend on age and on functional influences. As a rule, it is pseudostratified and consists of a layer of round basal cells and of a layer of larger, superficial, cuboidal or low columnar cells. All basal cells have a pair of centrioles above the nucleus, while in the superficial cells the centrioles are located at the surface and form a central flagellum. Terminal bars have also been described. The cells contain numerous granules or even large lumps of a yellow pigment; it has a fatty nature, reacts negatively to tests for iron, and makes its first appearance at the time of puberty. A similar pigment is also found in the smooth muscles and in the connective tissue of the seminal vesicles. In many places the epithelial cells, especially in the deeper crypts between the folds and in the glandlike structures, contain secretion granules; on the free surface drops or bleblike formations appear which are cast off into the lumen. The secretion of the seminal vesicles is a yellowish, viscid, sticky liquid containing globulin. In sections it forms coagulated, netlike, deeply staining masses in the lumen. After castration, the epithelium atrophies, but can be restored by injections of testis hormone (Fig. 476).

The muscular wall of the seminal vesicles is provided with a plexus of nerve fibers and with small sympathetic ganglia.

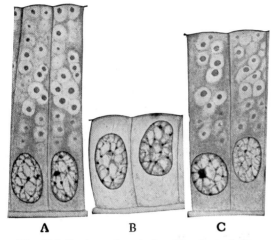

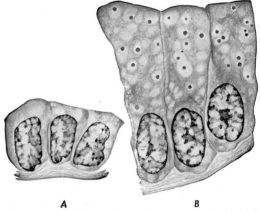

A   **B**   **C**

Fig. 476. Sections of seminal vesicle of rat. A, From normal animal; B, from twenty-day castrate; C, from twenty day castrate receiving twenty-nine injections of testis hormone in twenty days. Note absence of secretion granules in B. Bouin; hematoxylin. High magnification. (After Moore, Hughes and Gallagher.)

A   **B**

Fig. 477. A, Atrophic epithelium of seminal vesicle removed from a rat fed on a diet deficient in vitamin B for thirty-two days. B, epithelium of other seminal vesicle after injection for thirteen days with male hormone. Note the return to normal appearance and compare with Figure 476. Bouin, hematoxylin preparations of C. R. Moore. 2000 ×. (Drawn by Miss E. Bohlman.)

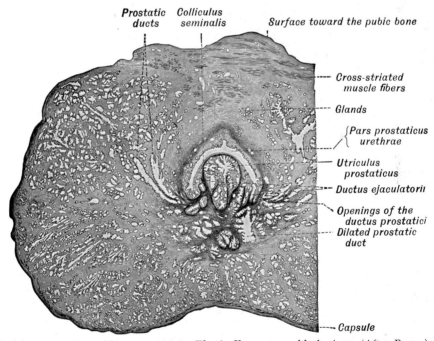

Fig. 478. Low power view of human prostate. Elastic fibers appear black. 4 ×. (After Braus.)

Prostate Gland. The prostate is the size of a horse chestnut and surrounds the urethra at its origin from the urinary bladder. It is a conglomerate of thirty to fifty small, compound tubulo-alveolar glands; they give origin to sixteen to thirty-two excretory ducts, which open independently into the urethra on the right and left sides of the colliculus seminalis. The form of the glands is irregular. Large cavities, sometimes cystic, alternate with narrow, branching tubules. The blind ends of the secreting portions are sometimes narrower than the excretory ducts. In many places branching papillae and folds with a

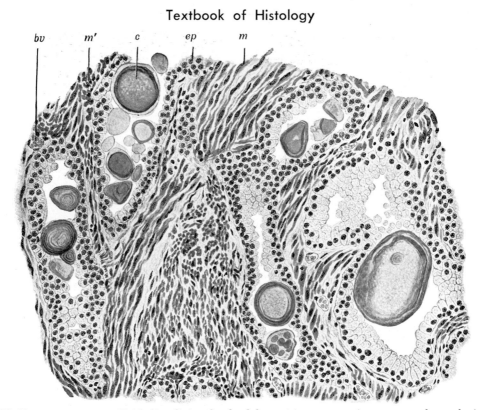

Fig. 479. Human prostate. *ep*, Epithelium lining the glandular cavities; *c*, concretions; m, smooth muscles in interstitial tissue in longitudinal section; *m'*, same in cross section; *bv*, blood vessels. 190 ×. (A.A.M.)

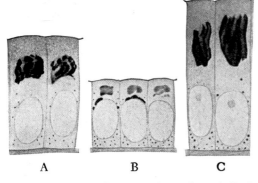

Fig. 480. Sections of prostate gland of rat. A, B, C, From posterior lobe cells; B, from a twenty day castrate; C, from twenty day castrate receiving twenty nine injections of testis hormone in twenty days. The changes in the Golgi net are quite striking. Mann-Kopsch technique. High magnification. (After Moore, Price and Gallagher.)

thin core of connective tissue project far into the lumen. In sections they may appear as free, epithelium-lined islands in the cavities. There is no distinct basement membrane, and the glandular epithelium rests upon a

layer of connective tissue with dense elastic networks and numerous blood capillaries. In the larger alveolar cavities it may be low cuboidal or even squamous, but in most places it is simple or pseudostratified columnar. The cytoplasm of the cells contains numerous secretory granules. Some of them stain black with iron hematoxylin, but the majority are of lipoid nature. Sometimes, on the free surface of the cells, drops of cytoplasm seem to become detached from the cell body. The epithelial cells become small and lose their secretion granules after castration. Injections of testicular hormone restore the cells quickly to their normal appearance and activity (Fig. 480).

The abundant interstitial tissue of the prostate consists of dense connective tissue with collagenous fibers, and elastic networks and many smooth muscles arranged in strands of varying thickness. The connective tissue forms a capsule at the periphery of the organ. Together with the smooth muscles it

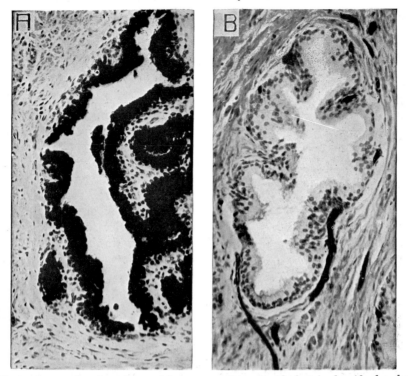

Fig. 481. Photomicrographs of sections of human prostate. A, Black-stained acid phosphatase obscures the epithelium. B, Black-stained alkaline phosphatase is limited to the blood vessels. 180 ×. (Courtesy of G. Gomori.)

is arranged in thick, broad septa, widely separating the glands from one another and radiating from the region of the colliculus seminalis to the periphery. Around the urethra the smooth muscles form a thick ring —the internal sphincter of the bladder.

The *secretion of the prostate* is a thin, opalescent liquid with a slightly alkaline reaction and the odor of semen. The liquid contains proteins, fine lipoid granules in suspension, but no mucus. In sections the secretion in the glandular cavities appears granular. It contains occasional desquamated cells and spherical or oval, often concentrically striated, bodies—the *prostatic concretions* (Fig. 479). These originate through condensation of the secretions, may become calcified, and exceed 1 mm. in diameter. The concretions are added to the semen and can be found in the ejaculate; the larger ones sometimes remain in the gland and are lodged in cysts. Their number increases with age.

The prostate is abundantly provided with plexuses of mostly nonmyelinated nerve fibers connected with small sympathetic ganglia. Sensory nerve endings of various kinds (end bulbs, genital corpuscles, and so on), belonging to myelinated fibers, are scattered in the interstitial connective tissue. Free nerve endings occur in the epithelium.

The *utriculus prostaticus*, lodged in the mass of the prostate gland and opening on the colliculus seminalis, according to some recent observations, is not a vestigial organ without any function, but is an accessory gland of the male sexual apparatus. It is a blind vesicle of considerable size lined by a mucous membrane with many folds and with glandlike invaginations. The epithelium is similar to that of the prostate. Sometimes patches of ciliated columnar epithelium can be found.

Bulbo-urethral Glands. The bulbo-urethral glands (of Cowper), each the size of a pea, are of compound tubulo-alveolar variety and in some respects resemble mucous glands; their ducts enter the posterior section of the cavernous part of the urethra. The ducts as well as the secreting portions are of irregular size and form, and in many places show

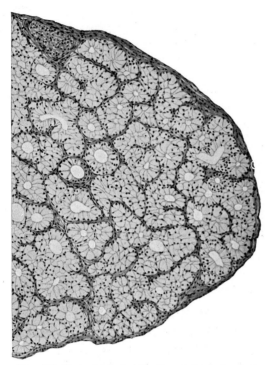

Fig. 482. Part of lobule of bulbo-urethral gland of a twenty-three year old man. Zenker. 120 ×. (Slightly modified after Stieve.)

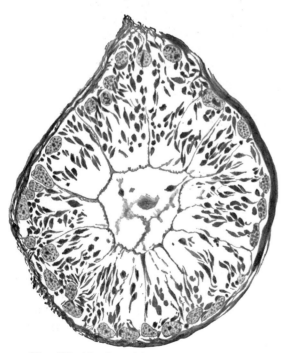

Fig. 483. Alveolus of human bulbo-urethral gland (Cowper's gland). Spindle-shaped, darkly stained inclusions in the cells and in the lumen. Mallory stain. 740 ×. (Redrawn after Schaffer.)

cystlike enlargements. The terminal portions end blindly or are connected with one another by anastomoses. The connective tissue partitions between the glandular lobules measure 1 to 3 mm. in diameter and contain elastic nets and thick strands of striated and smooth muscles. The latter may penetrate with the connective tissue into the interior of the lobules.

The structure of the epithelium in the secreting portions and in the ducts is subject to great functional variations. In the enlarged alveoli the cells are usually flattened; in the other glandular spaces they are cuboidal or columnar with the nuclei at the base. The cytoplasm contains small mucoid droplets and spindle-shaped inclusions staining with acid dyes (Fig. 483). They are supposed to leave the cell body as such and then to dissolve and mix with the mucin. The cells also contain various-sized colloidal spherules. The presence of secretory capillaries is doubtful. The excretory ducts are lined with a pseudostratified epithelium resembling that of the urethra and may contain large patches of secreting cells. They are also provided with small accessory glandular outpocketings having the structure of the glands of Littré of the urethra.

After fixation, the secretion appears in the lumen of the glandular spaces and ducts as angular precipitates which stain brightly with eosin. In life it is a clear, viscid and lubricant, mucus-like substance which can be drawn out easily into long thin threads. Unlike true mucus, it does not form a precipitate with acetic acid.

THE PENIS

The penis is formed by three cylindrical bodies of cavernous, erectile tissue—the *two corpora cavernosa penis and* the unpaired *corpus cavernosum urethrae.* The first two are separated from each other in their posterior, divergent parts, but join at the pubic angle and run side by side to their pointed ends. On the upper surface of the penis, along the line of their junction, is a shallow longitudinal groove where the dorsal artery and vein are located. On the lower surface the corpora cavernosa form a deep groove occupied by the corpus cavernosum urethrae (spongiosum). The latter, beginning with the bulbus urethrae between the crura of the corpora cavernosa penis, is pierced throughout its length by the *urethra* and ends with a

Each of the *cavernous bodies* is surrounded by a thick (1 mm.), resistant, fibrous membrane, the *tunica albuginea*. Its collagenous fibers are arranged in an outer, mainly longitudinal, and an inner circular, layer, and are accompanied by elastic nets. Between the

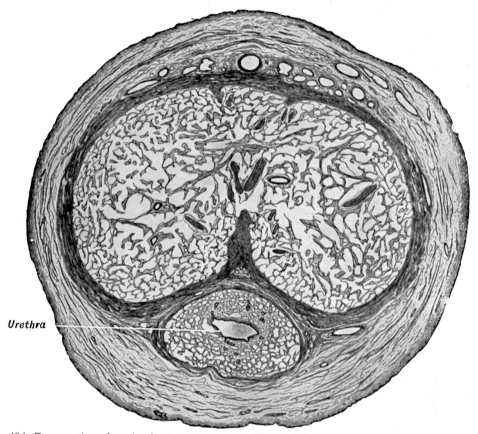

Urethra

Fig. 484. Cross section of penis of a twenty-one year old man. The septum in the corpus cavernosum penis is incomplete, since the section is from the distal part of the organ. The penis was fixed by injection of formalin into the corpus cavernosum. 3½ ×. (Slightly modified after Stieve.)

mushroom-shaped enlargement, the *glans penis,* which caps the conical ends of both corpora cavernosa penis.

The erectile tissue of the corpora cavernosa penis is a vast spongelike system of irregular vascular spaces, intercalated between the afferent arteries and the efferent veins. In the relaxed condition of the organ the cavernous spaces contain but little blood and appear as irregular clefts. In erection they are large cavities filled with blood under high pressure. This causes the enlargement and the rigidity of the penis.

two cavernous bodies the albuginea forms a fibrous partition, which, especially near the end of the penis, is pierced by numerous clefts through which the cavernous spaces of both sides communicate. On the inner surface of the albuginea, especially in the posterior part of the erectile bodies, there is a layer of dense connective tissue containing a multitude of small veins draining the cavernous spaces.

The cavernous spaces are largest in the central zone of the cavernous bodies. In the collapsed condition, they may have a diameter of 1 mm. Toward the periphery they gradually diminish in size. The partitions between them, the *trabeculae*, consist of dense fibrous tissue and contain thick collagenous bundles with fibroblasts, elastic networks, the axis of the corpus cavernosum gradually pass into the venous plexus of the urethral mucosa.

The *glans penis* consists of dense connective tissue containing nets of large anastomos-

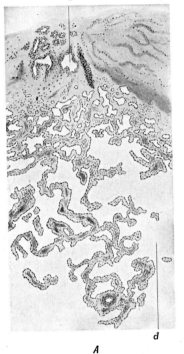

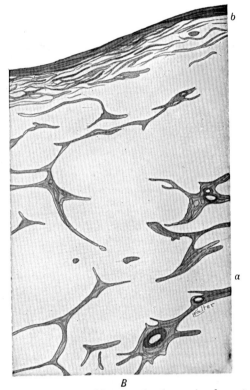

Fig. 485. A, Cross section of crus penis of a man of twenty-seven. *a*, Vena profunda penis; *d*, central cavernous spaces. B, Crus penis of man; fixed in artificial erection by injection of gelatin. *a*, Central zone; *b*, peripheral zone. (Modified and redrawn after Kiss.)

and strands of smooth muscle fibers. Their surface is lined with endothelium, which continues into that of the arteries and of the veins.

The albuginea of the corpus cavernosum urethrae is much thinner than in the corpora cavernosa penis and contains circularly arranged smooth muscle fibers in its inner layer. It also is provided with abundant elastic networks. Unlike those of the corpora cavernosa penis, the blood lacunae here are everywhere the same in size. The trabeculae between them contain more numerous elastic fibers, whereas smooth muscles are relatively scarce. The cavernous spaces occupying

ing veins, with circular and longitudinal smooth muscles in their thick walls. The longitudinal muscle strands often bulge into the lumen of the veins.

The skin covering the penis is thin and is provided with an abundant subcutaneous layer containing smooth muscles, but is devoid of fat tissue. The skin has no hairs on the distal part of the penis and only small sweat glands. The glans is covered by a circular fold of the skin, the *prepuce*. Its inner surface, adjacent to the glans, is moist and has the character of a mucous membrane. On the surface of the glans penis the derma of the skin is fused with the connective tissue between the veins just described. In this region peculiar sebaceous glands are described (*glands of Tyson*), which are not connected with hairs. They show great individual variations in number and distribution.

Blood Vessels. The erectile tissue of the penis is supplied with blood from the arteria penis. It breaks up into several large branches (arteria profunda penis, dorsalis penis, and so forth) which run to different parts of the organ, but all anastomose with one another. In all these branches, even before they enter the erectile tissue, the intima forms long ridgelike thickenings which project into the lumen. They consist of loosely arranged collagenous and elastic fibers, and contain strands of smooth muscle fibers, mostly arranged longitudinally.

Wherever the arterial branches enter into the corpora cavernosa through the albuginea, they assume a longitudinal, forward course, and give off many new branches. In the quiescent condition of the penis they have a convoluted or curled course—*helicine arteries*. They have a thick media. When they reach 65 to 80 microns in diameter (precavernous arteries), they run in the longitudinal trabeculae of the corpora cavernosa, and open directly into the cavernous spaces.

The intima of the helicine arteries is also provided with longitudinal ridges of connective tissue and smooth muscle, as in the branches of the arteria penis before they enter the erectile tissue. The ridges are located especially at the places of division of the vessel.

The arterial supply of the corpus spongiosum is similar to that of the corpora cavernosa penis.

The major part of the blood leaves the corpora cavernosa penis through the vena profunda penis. Its radicles have a thick muscular wall. They arise under the albuginea, especially in the posterior regions of the erectile bodies, through confluence of a multitude of branched "postcavernous" venules. The latter run parallel to the surface under the albuginea, have a length of 300 to 400 microns or more, and do not have any muscles in their thin walls. They originate from the peripheral cavernous spaces which are in direct or indirect communication with the largest axial blood spaces. The blood from the corpus spongiosum is drained mainly through the vena dorsalis penis. Unlike those of the corpora cavernosa penis, the first radicles of this vein start from the lacunae with large openings and leave the corpus by the shortest way, by piercing the albuginea.

The arrangement and structure of the afferent and efferent blood vessels in the corpora cavernosa penis explain the *mechanism of erection*. The arteries play the active, the veins the passive, role. The erection begins with the relaxation of the tonus of all smooth muscles in the arteries and in the erectile bodies. The

blood pressure overpowers the remaining elastic resistance of the tissue, and stretches the media in the arteries. The presence of longtiudinal ridges in their intima is believed to enable the lumen in such places to enlarge quickly. The lacunae of the cavernous bodies are filled with arterial blood. As the helicine arteries open especially into the axial, largest spaces, these spaces compress the peripheral, smaller spaces and the thin-walled veins under the albuginea which drain the latter. In this way the outflow of the blood is throttled down, the blood accumulates in the corpora cavernosa under increasing pressure, and the erectile tissue becomes rigid. The helicine arteries during erection are passively stretched, and their convolutions are evened out. Since in the corpus spongiosum there is no difference between axial and peripheral lacunae and the draining veins are not compressed, there is no noticeable retention of blood, and the circulation continues freely. Consequently the corpus spongiosum never attains a great rigidity during erection.

After ejaculation the arterial musculature regains its tonus. The afflux of the arterial blood is reduced to the usual degree. The excess of blood, which has accumulated in the corpora cavernosa penis, is slowly pressed out into the veins through the action of the smooth muscles of the trabeculae and through the retraction of the elastic networks. Owing to the compression of the peripheral small veins and to the valves, the return of the penis to the flaccid condition is accomplished only gradually.

Lymphatics. Dense, superficial networks of lymphatic capillaries are found in the skin of the penis, of the prepuce and of the shaft. They form a dorsal superficial lymph vessel, which runs toward the medial inguinal lymph nodes. Deep nets of lymphatic capillaries collect the lymph from the glans; they form a plexus on each side of the frenulum and continue into a dorsal subfascial lymph vessel.

Nerves. The nerves of the penis belong to the cerebrospinal (nervi pudendi) and to the sympathetic (plexus cavernosus) systems. They first supply the striated muscles of the penis (such as the bulbocavernosus) and also furnish the sensory nerve endings in the skin and the mucous membrane of the urethra. Among these sensory endings, free-branching nerve endings in the epithelium of the glans, the prepuce and the urethra can be distinguished. Besides, there are free nerve endings in the subepithelial connective tissue of the skin and the urethra. Thirdly, numerous encapsulated corpuscles of various types are present: corpuscles of Meissner in the papillae of the skin of the prepuce and the glans, genital corpuscles in the deeper layers of the stratum papillare of the derma of the glans and in the mucous membrane of the urethra, and corpuscles of Vater-Pacini along the dorsal vein in the subcutaneous fascia, in the deeper connective tissue of the glans and under the albuginea in the corpora cavernosa. The sympathetic nervous plexuses are connected with the smooth muscles of the vessels and form extensive, nonmyelinated networks in the smooth muscles of the trabeculae in the corpora cavernosa.

SEMEN

As the spermia pass along the excretory ducts, the secretions of the ducts and accessory glands are added to them; the final product is the semen. The spermia in the seminiferous tubules seem to be nonmotile. They are slowly forwarded into the tubuli recti and the rete testis, perhaps by passive pressure of liquid accumulating in the tubules, which cannot expand because they are surrounded by the firm albuginea. In the ductuli efferentes, the epithelium with cilia beating toward the epididymis takes care of the further transport of the spermia. The glandular cells devoid of cilia undoubtedly add their secretion to the moving mass.

The long, winding duct of the epididymis is slowly traversed by the spermia. They are kept here, especially in the tail, for a long time, sometimes for months. Here the majority of them lose the last remnant of cytoplasm attached to the middle piece.

What forces move them forward in the canal is not quite clear. Capillary forces may play a role, and a part of the way seems to be made through the movements of the spermia themselves. During ejaculation the contractions of the circular smooth muscles surrounding the tubules are of primary importance.

The viscid secretion of the epithelium of the ductus epididymidis adds nutritive material to the spermia. As a rule, spermia taken from the epididymis are more resistant to environmental changes than those from the testis.

The spermia do not accumulate in the ductus deferens. This part of the excretory system with its heavy muscular coat is adapted only to their speedy transportation.

The function of the seminal vesicles seems to be primarily glandular; their thick secretion is added, during ejaculation, to the mass of the spermia, which pass through the vas deferens and the ampulla into the ejaculatory ducts.

In the process of *ejaculation* the muscular tissue of the prostate also contracts and discharges its abundant liquid secretion; it dilutes the thick part of the semen and stimulates the movements of the spermia. The semen, entering the urethra and mixing with the secretion of the glands of Cowper and Littré, is thrown out through the contraction of the bulbocavernosus muscle compressing the bulbus urethrae.

The spermia are believed to number about 60,000 in a cubic millimeter of semen; each ejaculate on the average contains 200 to 300 million spermia. The tail performs whipping, undulatory movements; the spermium, therefore, advances with the head forward and simultaneously rotates around its long axis. Its speed is 14 to 23 microns in a second.

Under suitable conditions the spermia may remain alive outside the body for several days and also in the excretory ducts after death. In the uterus and the fallopian tube, living spermia have been found some days after coitus.

Besides the spermia, the semen contains degenerated cells, probably cast off from the epithelium of the excretory ducts and the urethra. Occasionally, columnar epithelial cells and wandering cells of connective tissue origin may also occur. There are, furthermore, round, hyaline bodies of unknown origin, lipoid granules, at times concretions from the prostate and a multitude of fat, protein and pigment granules. When the semen cools and begins to dry, peculiar crystals of various forms develop—the *spermia crystals of Böttcher*. They are believed to consist of phosphate of spermin.

It has been claimed that the different components of the semen are discharged from the urethra in a certain sequence. With the development of the erection the slimy secretion of the glands of Cowper and Littré lubricates the urethra. At the beginning of the ejaculation the prostatic secretion is discharged first. Being alkaline, it neutralizes the acid reaction of the urethra, where remnants of urine may be present, and the equally acid reaction of the vaginal mucus. Then the masses of spermia accumulated in the vas deferens and the ductus epididymidis are thrown out. The final portion of the ejaculate is probably represented by the thick, alkaline, globulin-containing secretion of the seminal vesicles. In some animals (mouse) the abundant secretion of the seminal vesicles is coagulated in the vagina by an enzyme contained in the prostatic juice, and thus a solid plug is formed in the vagina which temporarily occludes its lumen and prevents the backflow of the semen.

Histogenesis of the Testis. See page 529.

REFERENCES

Allen, E.: Sex and Internal Secretions. Baltimore, 1939.

Burrows, H.: Biological Actions of Sex Hormones. 2d ed. London, Cambridge University Press, 1949.

Elftman, H.: The Sertoli Cell Cycle in the Mouse. Anat. Rec., *106*:31, 1950.

Gatenby, J. B., and Beams, H. W.: The Cytoplasmic Inclusions in the Spermatogenesis of Man. Quart. J. Microsc. Sc., 78:1, 1935.

Huggins, C.: The Physiology of the Prostate Gland. Physiol. Rev., 25:281,1945.

Macklin, C. C., and Macklin, M. T.: The Seminal Vesicles, Prostate and Bulbo-urethral Glands, in Cowdry's Special Cytology. 2d ed. New York, 3: 1771, 1932.

Metz, C. W.: The Male Germ Cells, in Cowdry's Special Cytology. 2d ed. New York, 3:1727, 1932.

Moore, C. R.: The Physiology of the Testis and Application of Male Sex Hormone. Jour. Urol., 47: 31, 1942.

Moore, C. R.: Biology of the Testes, in Allen, E.: Sex and Internal Secretions. 2d ed. Baltimore, 1939, p. 353.

Moore, C. R., Price, D., and Gallagher, T. F.: Rat Prostate Cytology as a Testis-Hormone Indicator and the Prevention of Castration Changes by Testis Extract Injections. Am. J. Anat., 45:71, 1930.

Painter, T. S.: Studies in Mammalian Spermatogenesis. J. Exper. Zool., 37:3, 1923.

Price, D.: Normal Development of the Prostate and Seminal Vesicles of the Rat, with a Study of Experimental Post-natal Modifications, Am. J. Anat., 60:79, 1936.

Rasmussen, A. T.: Interstitial Cells of the Testis, in Cowdry's Special Cytology. 2d ed. New York, 3: 1673, 1932.

Riddle, O.: Factors in the Development of Sex and Secondary Sexual Characteristics. Physiol. Rev., 11: 63, 1931; Endocrine Aspects of the Physiology of Reproduction. Ann. Rev. Physiol., 3:573, 1941.

Romeis, B.: Hoden, samenableitende Organe und accessorische Geschlechtsdrüsen. Handb. der norm. und pathol. Physiol., etc. Berlin, 14:693, 1926.

Roosen-Runge, E. C., and Giesel, L. O., Jr.: Quantitative Studies on Spermatogenesis in the Albino Rat. Am. J. Anat., 87:1, 1950.

Scott, W. W.: The Lipids of the Prostatic Fluid, Seminal Plasma and Enlarged Prostate Gland of Man. J. Urol., 53:712, 1945.

Stieve, H.: Männliche Genitalorgane, in Möllendorff's Handb. der mikr. Anat. des Menschen. Berlin, 1930, Vol. 7, Pt. 2.

Waldeyer, W.: Die Geschlechtszellen. Hertwig's Handb. d. vergl. u. exp. Embryol. Jena, 1901, Vol. 1, Pt. 1.

Young, W. C.: Die Resorption in den Ductuli efferentes der Maus und ihre Bedeutung für das Problem der Unterbindung im Hoden-Nebenhoden System. Zeit. f. Zellforsch. u. mikr. Anat., 1933.

XXX. FEMALE GENITAL SYSTEM

The female genital organs consist of the ovaries, a system of excretory ducts (the oviducts, the uterus and vagina) and the external genitalia. In the sexually mature female, the ovary and its ducts undergo marked cyclic changes.

THE OVARY

The human ovary is a slightly flattened bean-shaped body measuring 2.5 to 5 cm. in length, 1.5 to 3 cm. in width and 0.6 to 1.5 cm. in thickness. One of its edges, the *hilus*, is attached by the mesovarium to the broad ligament, which extends laterally from the uterus. The free surface of the ovary bulges into the peritoneal cavity. Embedded in its connective tissue are the *follicles* in which the female sex cells, the *ova*, develop. When the follicles reach maturity, they rupture on the surface of the ovary, and the ova gain access to the open end of the oviduct.

The thick peripheral layer or cortex of the ovary contains the various-sized follicles and surrounds the medulla (zona vasculosa) except at the hilus. The medulla consists of loose connective tissue and a mass of contorted blood vessels which are large in proportion to the size of the ovary. At the hilus, strands of smooth muscle fibers extend in from the mesovarium.

Germinal Epithelium. The epithelium covering the free surface of the ovary is called the "germinal epithelium," because in the embryo ova appear to arise from it (p. 530). In the infant it is a simple cuboidal or columnar epithelium. In the adult its cells gradually become lower and may be flattened when under tension. A basement membrane is absent. In vitally stained animals the cells of the germinal epithelium store masses of dye granules in the infranuclear zone. Be-neath this germinal epithelium is a layer of dense connective tissue—the *tunica albuginea*.

Follicles. The younger the person, the more numerous are the follicles. In the newborn infant the follicles in both ovaries were believed to number 400,000. However, a study of serial sections of the ovaries from a normal mature woman of twenty-two years revealed a total of 420,000. Their number decreases progressively throughout life, and at the menopause they are hard to find. Most of this decrease is due to atresia (pp. 501–503). A few may persist even in old age.

Primary Follicles. The vast majority of the follicles are primary follicles. These are found mainly in the periphery of the cortex, and in young females they form a thick layer immediately beneath the tunica albuginea. They are probably the source of all the other follicles in primates.

They are spheroidal bodies about 45 microns in diameter. The center is occupied by the large, round ovum. Its eccentric nucleus contains a loose network of linin threads with small chromatin granules and a large chromatin nucleolus. The side of the nucleus with the larger amount of cytoplasm contains an accumulation of small mitochondria, the cytocentrum and the Golgi net. The ovum in the primary follicle lacks a membrane; it is separated from the adjacent interstitial tissue by a layer of flattened follicular cells, seven to ten of which appear in a section.

Growing Follicles. The progressive development of a primary follicle consists in growth and changes in the ovum, follicular cells, and the adjacent connective tissue. As the egg increases in size, its nucleus enlarges, and the mitochondria become more evenly distributed in the cytoplasm. Later, yolk granules of two kinds appear. When the

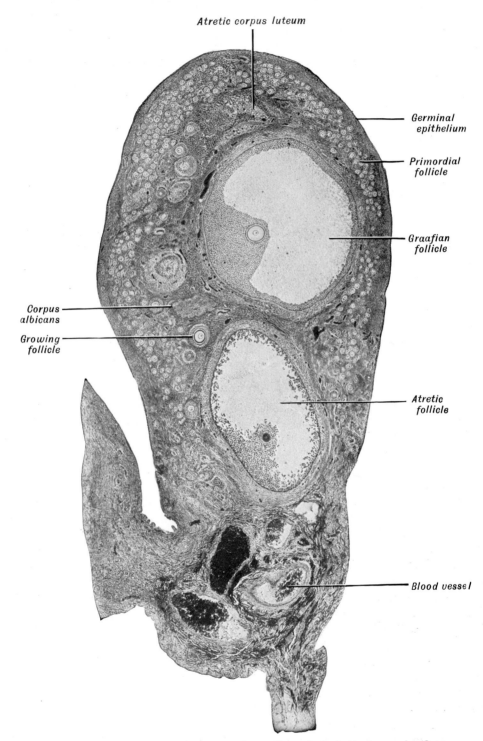

Atretic corpus luteum

Germinal
epithelium

Primordial
follicle

Graafian
follicle

Corpus
albicans

Growing
follicle

Atretic
follicle

Blood vessel

Fig. 486. Transection of ovary of *Macacus rhesus*. Retouched photomicrograph. 42 ×.

ovum reaches a diameter of 60 to 80 microns, a refractile, deeply staining cell membrane appears, the *zona pellucida*. It is probably elaborated by both the ovum and the surrounding follicular cells; it gradually becomes thicker.

side. This is the *cumulus oophorus*, which surrounds the ovum. The follicular cells have a columnar or polyhedral shape; where the liquor accumulates between them they are angular or stellate and are connected with one another by their processes.

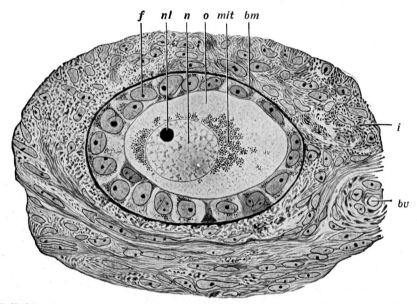

Fig. 487. Follicle in first stages of growth from ovary of adult woman. *f*, Follicular cells with mitochondria; *nl*, nucleolus of ovum; *n*, nucleus of ovum; *o*, protoplasm of ovum; *mit*, perinuclear accumulation of mitochondria (yolk nucleus); *bm*, basement membrane; *i*, interstitial connective tissue; *bv*, blood vessel. Aniline-acid fuchsin stain. 780 ×. (From a preparation of C. M. Bensley.) (A.A.M.)

The growing follicle enlarges mainly through mitotic proliferation of the follicular cells. The few squamous cells of the primary follicle turn first into a layer of columnar cells surrounding the ovum and then into a stratified epithelium which thickens more rapidly on one side of the ovum. The follicle becomes oval, and the ovum eccentric in position. Follicles in the deeper zones of the cortex are the first to develop.

When the follicle is about 0.2 mm. in diameter, several irregular spaces filled with the clear *liquor folliculi* appear between the follicular cells. The increase in amount of this liquid causes a further increase in the size of the follicle, which is now a graafian follicle. In the human ovary the separate cavities usually flow together, and the resulting vesicle has a stratified epithelial lining of follicular cells which is thickened on one

In growing follicles, round, darkly staining bodies (of Call-Exner) surrounded by follicular cells may be found. They probably represent new centers of secretion of follicular liquid. In tissue cultures the follicular epithelium shows both connective tissue and epithelial characteristics.

A follicle 0.4 mm. in diameter has a decided polar structure (Fig. 486). The ovum is nearly full grown and is embedded in a solid mass of follicular epithelial cells—the *cumulus oophorus* or *discus proligerus*—which protrudes into the large, liquid-filled cavity. On the other side the stratified epithelium forms a continuous, even layer. Meanwhile the connective tissue surrounding the growing follicle differentiates into a capsule, the *theca folliculi*, separated from the follicle by a basement membrane.

At first the spindle-shaped cells and reticular fibers are arranged in several concentric layers around the basement membrane. Later this capsule becomes subdivided into two layers. In the *theca interna*, the layer immediately surrounding the basement membrane, an increasing number of blood capillaries de-

The follicle continues to grow, owing to the rapid mitotic proliferation of the follicular epithelium and to the progressing accumulation of the follicular liquid. If a follicle is to reach maturity and rupture, it must gradually extend toward the free sur-

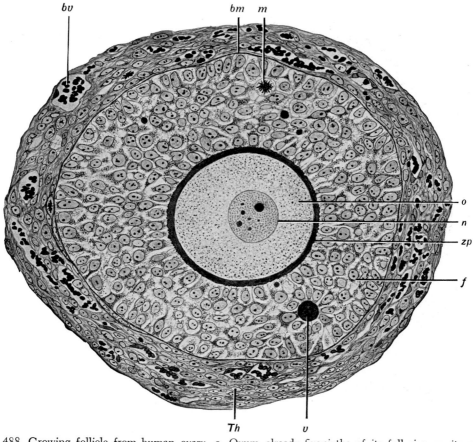

Fig. 488. Growing follicle from human ovary. *o*, Ovum already five-sixths of its full size; *n*, its nucleus; *zp*, zona pellucida; *f*, follicular epithelium with mitochondria; *v*, vacuoles of Call-Exner; *Th*, theca folliculi (outer and inner layer not yet differentiated); *bv*, blood vessels with erythrocytes; *bm*, basement membrane; *m*, mitosis of follicular cell. 375 ×. (From same section as Figure 487.) (A.A.M.)

velops. When the follicle has become a vesicle of 2 to 3 mm., the connective tissue cells increase in size and become loosely arranged. The *theca externa*, or outer layer, keeps its dense structure of concentrically arranged, fusiform cells and thick fibers. As the follicle continues to enlarge, these layers become more and more prominent. There is no sharp limit between the two layers of the theca or between the theca externa and the surrounding stroma.

face of the ovary. The cause of this is probably the eccentric development of the theca interna, which is thicker and looser on the outer side of the follicle.

Mature Graafian Follicles. The mature follicles are large vesicles which occupy the thickness of the ovarian cortex and bulge on the free surface of the organ. The liquid in the follicular cavity is under considerable pressure, and the outer part of the wall is thin.

It is believed that a follicle requires about ten to fourteen days to reach maturity. Even with careful study it is somewhat difficult to determine whether a follicle is still growing, has reached maturity, or is beginning to involute. In the human ovary a 10-mm. follicle has been found with a normal ovum developing the first polar body.

in later stages. The connection of the ovum with the membrana granulosa is further loosened by the development of new, liquid-filled, intercellular spaces in the cumulus.

A layer of columnar follicular cells remains attached to the ovum; near maturity these cells become tall and conspicuous, forming

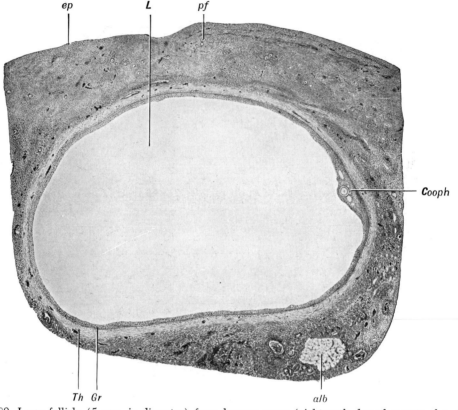

Fig. 489. Large follicle (5 mm. in diameter) from human ovary (eighteenth day of menstrual cycle). *ep,* Surface of ovary with germinal epithelium; *L,* follicular liquid; *pf,* primary follicle; *Cooph,* cumulus oophorus with ovum; *alb,* corpus albicans; *Gr,* membrana granulosa; *Th,* theca externa and interna. 20 ×. From same ovary as Figure 487. (A.A.M.)

The protein-containing follicular liquid appears finely granular in fixed sections. The follicular epithelium lining the cavity is often called the *membrana granulosa* and is intimately adherent to the *glassy membrane* which separates it from the connective tissue capsule (*theca*) of the follicle. Between the polyhedral cells of the inner layers of the membrana granulosa, intercellular vacuoles are common. Mitotic figures gradually decrease in number among the granulosa cells

the *corona radiata,* which probably has protective and nutritive functions similar to those of the Sertoli cells in the testis.

The ovum in the mature follicle reaches a diameter of 120 microns or more. Its surface is immediately surrounded by a thick membrane—the *oolemma,* or *zona pellucida.* A "perivitelline space" between the oolemma and the ovum has not been demonstrated in the mammalian egg prior to polar body formation. The cytoplasm of the human ovum contains some yolk granules, and in fixed material its peripheral layer is quite clear. The eccentric nucleus (vesicula germinativa) measures 25 microns in diameter, and has a thick membrane, a slightly granular linin network, and a large chromatin nucleolus—the *macula germinativa*. A cytocentrum has not been found in the mature ovum. In the living

laries in the theca interna, close to the basement membrane.

Upon reaching maturity the follicles either rupture or involute, but follicles may degenerate at any stage of development from primordial follicles.

Rupture of Graafian Follicles. Ovulation. The follicular fluid accumulates faster than

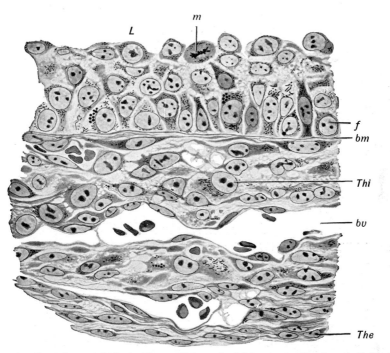

Fig. 490. Part of wall of large follicle in Figure 489, under higher magnification. *f*, Follicular epithelium; *bm*, basement membrane; *Thi*, cells of the theca interna; *bv*, blood vessel; *The*, cells of theca externa; *m*, mitosis of follicular epithelial cells; *L*, cavity of follicle; all cells contain mitochondria. 780 ✕, reduced to four-fifths. (A.A.M.)

state, yolk granules of various sizes and colors are uniformly distributed through the cytoplasm (Fig. 492).

In the mature follicle the connective tissue capsule reaches its highest development. Its theca externa consists of concentrically arranged fibers and fusiform cells and contains large blood vessels. The theca interna is composed of large polyhedral cells with oval nuclei and fine lipoid droplets in their cytoplasm. These are modified connective tissue cells. Between the large cells of the theca interna is a network of thin fibrils continuous with those of the theca externa and the rest of the ovarian stroma. There are many capil-

the follicle grows, and so the superficial part of the follicular wall, bulging on the surface of the ovary, becomes progressively thinner. The follicular fluid which forms just before ovulation is more watery than the rest and appears to be secreted at a rapid rate. The blood vessels are compressed, and the small spot at the apex of the bulging finally opens (Fig. 493).

Through the small opening in the wall of the follicle on the free surface of the ovary, the follicular liquid oozes out into the peritoneal cavity. The ovum, whose connections with the cells of the cumulus oophorus were loosened in the last stages of development, is

Mitosis of follicular cell

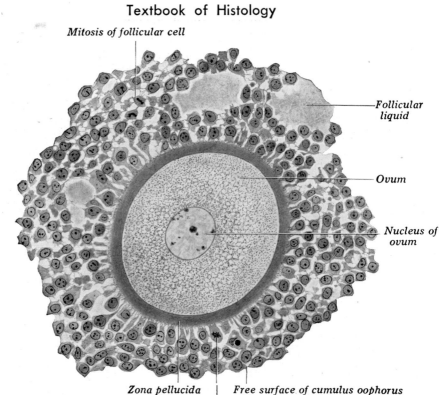

Follicular liquid

Ovum

Nucleus of ovum

Zona pellucida | *Free surface of cumulus oophorus*
Mitosis of follicular cell

Fig. 491. Ovum of follicle in Figure 489 with surrounding follicular cells under higher magnification. 375 ×. (A.A.M.)

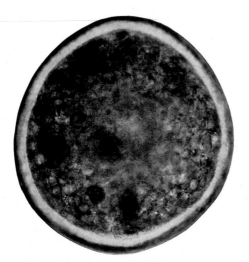

Fig. 492. Photomicrograph of living human ovum. Note yolk granules. The nucleus is not visible. The zona pellucida appears as a bright layer. 450 ×. (Courtesy of W. H. Lewis.)

torn away with the corona radiata from the cumulus and is discharged with the liquid. The immediate cause of the rupture of the follicular wall is not known. In women it usually occurs spontaneously in the inter-menstrual period.

This process which frees the ovum and enables it to meet the male sex cell for the purpose of fertilization is called "ovulation." Each time one ovum is set free; in some cases, two or, rarely, even more. Sometimes the maturation of a follicle with consequent ovulation occurs alternately in both ovaries, but the same ovary may develop a follicle several times in succession. In the human female a follicle ripens at intervals averaging twenty-eight days, although variations of a week or more are common. Cycles of typical duration not associated with ovulation may occur.

It is probable that the fimbriae of the tube closely invest the ovary at the time of ovulation.

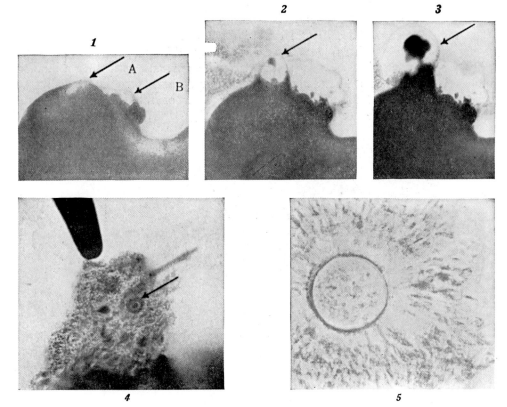

Fig. 493. Several frames of a moving picture film of ovulation in the rabbit. *1*, Follicular exudate with blood of a ruptured follicle at *B*, and a secondary cone starting to form at apex of large follicle in profile (*A*). *2*, Apical cone, large and clear, with blood lake showing at tip. *3*, Sudden rupture of large follicle (profile). Note clear gelatinous material with secondary flow of blood obscuring it. (Eight seconds between *2* and *3*.) *4*, Follicular exudate still attached to follicle below; the ovum is surrounded by follicle cells. *5*, Higher power view of ovum of *4*; the zona pellucida fits tightly about the vitellus; the corona radiata is clearly defined. (*1*, *2*, *3*, Taken with Tessar lens; *4*, with 16-mm. objective, and *5*, with 4-mm. objective. Slightly retouched.) (After Hill, Allen and Kramer, 1935.)

Maturation of the Ovum. The ova in the ovary of an adult mammal are in the period of growth and are called *primary ovocytes*; they are homologues of primary spermatocytes. The period of growth in ovogenesis is followed by a period of maturation in which the primary ovocyte undergoes two maturation divisions. The resulting four cells have a haploid number of chromosomes (twenty-four in the human species). Only one develops into the mature ovum; the other three are thrown off as rudimentary structures and degenerate (Fig. 494).

The first maturation division begins shortly before ovulation. The chromatin is equally divided between the daughter cells, but only one of them, the *secondary ovocyte*, receives practically all the cytoplasm of the mother cell; the other becomes the *first polar body* —an abortive secondary ovocyte which degenerates.

Immediately after the expulsion of the first polar body, the nucleus of the secondary ovocyte enters the second meiotic division. The spindle remains at the metaphase, and the division is not completed until fertilization. The chromatin mass is divided equally, but the bulk of the cytoplasm is again retained by one daughter cell—the mature *ovum* (corresponding to the spermatid). The other daughter cell is the small, abortive *second polar body*. In the human subject incomplete observations on the formation of the polar bodies have been published.

Transformation of the Graafian Follicle after Rupture. The Corpus Luteum. After the rupture of the follicle and the discharge of the liquor and the ovum with its corona radiata, the wall of the follicle collapses, and the epithelial membrane granulosa is thrown into folds and appears considerably thickened. The follicular epithelial cells and the cells of the theca interna change into large pale-staining cells, somewhat like those of the suprarenal cortex. The former follicle is now called the *corpus luteum*. The cavity now has an irregular, stellate shape. The

licle cells are called *granulosa lutein cells*, although the characteristic lipoid pigment, *lutein*, is at first found only in traces. Simultaneously the spindle-shaped cells of the theca interna, and with them a multitude of capillary sprouts, penetrate radially into the thick layer of follicular cells. When these connective tissue elements reach the inner

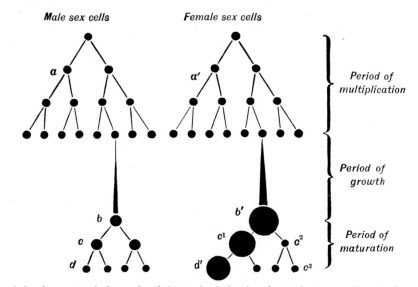

Fig. 494. Diagram of development of the male (left) and of the female (right) sex cells. (Redrawn after Boveri.)

theca externa keeps its regular, ovoid outlines (Fig. 497), while the theca interna, on the contrary, loses them. At the base of the folds of the granulosa, the cells of the theca interna accumulate in triangular masses, while between the folds they are scarce or absent.

The details of development of the corpus luteum depend on whether its ovum is fertilized or not. In the former case the corpus luteum becomes a *corpus luteum of pregnancy*, in the latter case a *corpus luteum of menstruation*.

The principal role in the formation of the corpus luteum is played by the epithelial follicular cells. They begin at once to hypertrophy and in a few days attain a considerable size. The cell body becomes polyhedral; the nucleus also swells and assumes a spherical form with a coarse chromatin network, and one or two nucleoli. Mitoses may be found, but are rare. Such hypertrophied fol-

surface of the folded granulosa layer, they rapidly form a loose, gelatinous connective tissue which covers the inner surface of the wall and leaves a space free in the center. This is filled with the remains of the liquor folliculi, transuded serum, and a varying, usually small number of extravasated erythrocytes. The large, lipid-containing, epithelioid cells of the theca interna remain scattered at the periphery of the folded layer of lutein cells and accumulate in the angle of the folds (Fig. 497). Their aspect and their inner structure are similar to those of the granulosa lutein cells. They have therefore been given the name of *theca lutein cells* (*paralutein cells*). There are no transitions between these two types of lutein cells.

The granulosa lutein cells have a clear, slightly vacuolated cytoplasm, and a distinct cycocentrum in the vicinity of the nucleus. The theca lutein cells are smaller and more

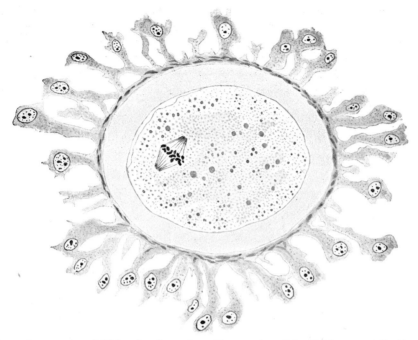

Fig. 495. Ovum from mature follicle of guinea pig, with corona radiata, thick zona pellucida and the first polar spindle. 530 ×. (Redrawn after Rubaschkin.)

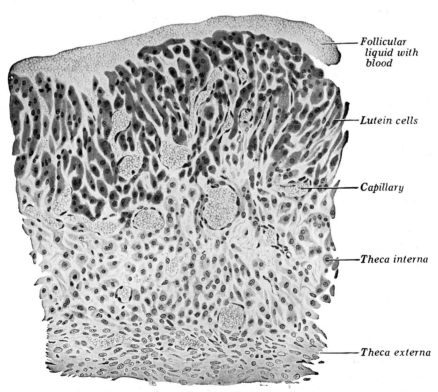

Fig. 496. Early stage of formation of human corpus luteum. Capillaries invade the granulosa, which is transformed into a layer of lutein cells. (Redrawn from R. Meyer.)

highly vacuolated in ordinary sections. The granulosa lutein cells contain phosphatides, cerebrosides and lutein pigment. In the peripheral layers, especially in the theca lutein cells, cholesterol esters occur. Active and regressing corpora lutea give a greenish phosphorescence in ultraviolet light, perhaps

size. The lutein and neutral fat content of the lutein cells is much less than in the corpus luteum of menstruation, and the color is not as yellow as in later stages. Involution of the true corpus luteum usually begins at the fifth or sixth month of gestation. After delivery it proceeds rapidly in

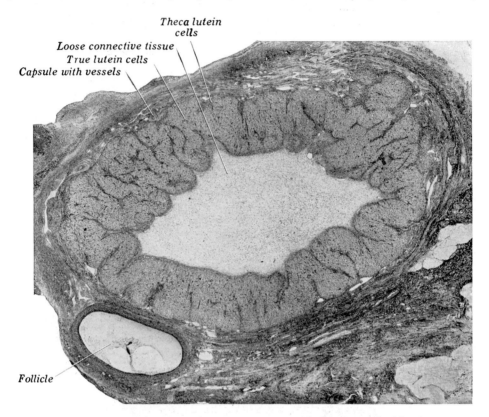

Fig. 497. Corpus luteum from human ovary. Photomicrograph. 11 ×.

owing to vitamin A. In vitally stained animals the lutein cells may contain granular dye inclusions in regressive stages of their development.

The polyhedral lutein cells are surrounded by a network of sinusoidal blood capillaries with a thin endothelium. They seem to be arranged in radial cords or strands. Between them networks of reticular fibers can be revealed by appropriate methods (Fig. 498).

If the ovum is fertilized, the corpus luteum passes through a period of growth and a period of regression. The corpus luteum of pregnancy grows larger than that of menstruation, and its lutein cells reach a larger

qualitatively the same way as in the corpus luteum of menstruation; but, as the corpus luteum of pregnancy is larger, it takes a longer time before the stage of the corpus albicans is reached. The final scar is also larger, persists longer, and, through its shrinking, usually causes a distinct retraction of the surface of the ovary.

A considerable effusion of blood into the follicle at the moment of ovulation does not occur in the human subject. In the early stages only an insignificant diapedesis of erythrocytes occurs in the wall of the collapsed follicle.

After regression has begun the granulosa lutein cells show an increasing infiltration with neutral fat in addition to other lipids. As the quantity of pigment increases in the human species, the lutein border assumes a brighter yellow color. If there has been a hemorrhage into the corpus luteum, the connective tissue on the inner surface of the lutein cell layer organizes the blood clot; hemosiderin accumulates in the connective tissue cells; sometimes, extracellular crystals of hematoidin can be found. Later, between the lutein cells, streaks of a hyaline substance appear. The theca lutein cells shrink and gradually disappear.

continues on a smaller scale throughout the period of sexual life, and is completed after the menopause. Every normal ovary, therefore, contains degenerating follicles. *Atresia may begin at any stage of development of the follicle*—even in apparently mature ones. It is not known why a few follicles reach maturity and rupture, while others degen-

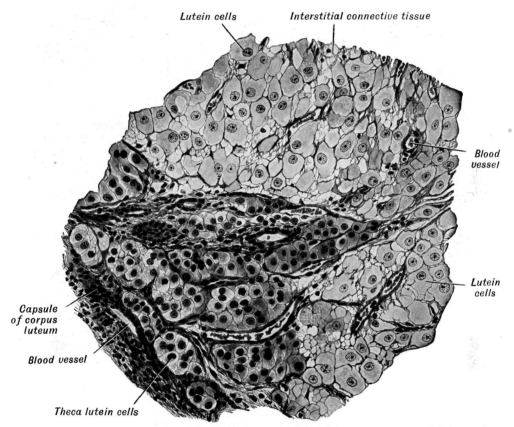

Fig. 498. Cross section of peripheral layer of human corpus luteum of pregnancy, stained for reticular fibers by the Bielschowsky method. 235 ×. (A.A.M.)

Involution (Atresia) of Follicles. As the period of sexual activity in the human female lasts about thirty years, and since one ovum is not discharged oftener than once a month in ovulation, the number of ova which reach maturity and are discharged from the ovary does not exceed 400. The remainder of the 400,000 or more original follicles gradually degenerate and disappear. This involution of a follicle is called "atresia." It begins in intra-uterine life, becomes prominent at birth and before puberty,

erate at various stages of development. The ovum always seems to be affected primarily.

If a primary follicle is doomed to destruction, the ovum shrinks and degenerates. The follicular cells may show a tendency to engulf its debris, but they also degenerate quickly, after which the small cavity in the connective tissue stroma is closed without leaving a trace. In the vesicular follicle the ovum and the follicular cells show various signs of degeneration. The connective tissue cells of the theca interna penetrate into the epithelium and absorb it.

With the increase in size of the follicle undergoing atresia, the histological pictures become more compli-

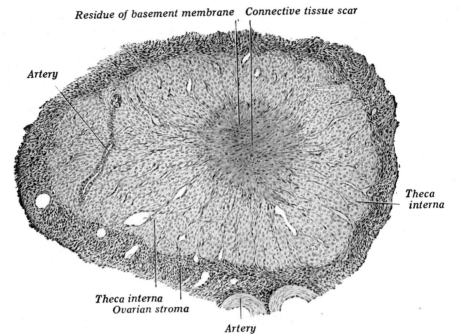

Fig. 499. Corpus atreticum with a well-developed theca interna, from the ovary of a thirty-nine year old woman. 85 ×. (After Schaffer.)

cated and variable. The first signs of retrogression are always noticed in the egg cell. Its cytoplasm is filled with fat droplets, and it becomes coarsely granular and disintegrates. The zona pellucida is highly resistant; it shrinks and collapses, but otherwise seems unchanged. In the substance of the degenerating ovum which has lost its corona radiata and floats freely in the follicular liquid, small cells have often been observed. They were thought to be cells of the follicular epithelium; it is more probable, however, that they are connective tissue wandering cells which actively penetrate the dead ovum and destroy it.

Before undergoing complete degeneration and disintegration, the ovum in an atretic follicle often shows signs of an atypical development. Maturation spindles may appear and lead to the formation of more or less characteristic polar bodies. Amitotic fragmentation of the nucleus and division of the protoplasm also occur. These changes result in the appearance in the interior of the zona pellucida of several cell bodies of varying size and with more or less distinct nuclei. These changes have been considered by some authors as possibly being an attempt at parthenogenetic development. They must, of course, be sharply distinguished from cases of ovarian pregnancy in which an ovum retained in a ruptured follicle is fertilized by a spermium finding its way into the ovary.

The follicular epithelium in an atretic follicle always degenerates. The cells first affected are those near the cavity of the follicle. The peripheral cell adjacent to the basement membrane, as well as the cells of the cumulus, may remain alive for a considerable time and

are even said to show mitoses. The retrogressive changes are manifested in chromatolysis of the nucleus and fatty or hyaline degeneration of the cytoplasm. The cells round off, shrink, and float in the liquor folliculi as small, round particles; they contain deeply staining granules of chromatin.

At an early stage of atresia, at a time when the follicular epithelium may still seem normal, but undoubtedly is already changed, the connective tissue elements of the theca and blood vessels penetrate the basement membrane in many places and invade the degenerating epithelium. The cavity of the follicle collapses, its outlines, marked by the basement membrane, become wavy, and the cavity is filled by a large number of fibroblasts, wandering cells and blood capillaries. Some of these elements in vitally stained animals accumulate granular dye inclusions. The remnants of the degenerated, follicular epithelium are rapidly resorbed. The folded and collapsed zona pellucida remains alone amid the connective tissue elements.

Simultaneously, the theca interna undergoes important changes (Fig. 500). The folded basement membrane which separates it from the epithelium often increases in thickness, and is transformed into a layer of hyaline substance. The large cells of the theca interna increase further in size and are usually arranged in radial groups or strands, separated from one another by partitions of smaller, fusiform cells, and fibers (Fig. 489). The cells acquire a typical epithelioid character and are filled with lipid and fat droplets. They are identical with the theca lutein cells, but reach a higher degree of development in the atretic follicle.

The cavity of the atretic follicle, containing the collapsed zona pellucida and connective tissue, is now surrounded by a broad, festooned layer of epithelioid, lipid-containing theca interna cells, arranged in radial cords and provided with a rich capillary network. The microscopic aspect of such an atretic follicle is similar to that of an old corpus luteum; therefore, such structures have been called *corpora lutea atretica*. The main differences are, of course, the presence of the degenerated ovum in the center of an atretic follicle, and the degenerate granulosa cells.

The ultimate fate of an atretic follicle is shrinkage. Strands of fibrous connective tissue penetrate, together with blood vessels, through the hyaline membrane into the interior, and compress and destroy the remains of the degenerated elements. The resulting scar with its hyaline streaks sometimes resembles a corpus albicans, but is usually much smaller and sooner or later disappears in the stroma of the ovary.

The layer of hypertrophic theca interna cells, which surrounds the cavity of the atretic follicle, is broken up into separate cell islands of various forms and sizes by the invading strands of fibrous tissue. These islands are irregularly scattered in the stroma and may persist for a time. They constitute the so-called "interstitial gland" of the ovary.

Stroma. The interstitial connective tissue or stroma of the human ovarian cortex consists of networks of reticular fibers and spindle-shaped cells which resemble smooth muscle cells, but do not have fibrils in their cytoplasm. True smooth muscle cells have been described in the theca externa of the follicles of the pig's ovary. The cells of the ovarian stroma are not common fibroblasts, for they may give rise to interstitial cells and, in ovarian pregnancy, to decidual cells. Elastic fibers occur in the cortex only in the walls of the blood vessels. Beneath the "germinal" epithelium the interstitial connective tissue is condensed into the tunica albuginea. The peculiar layer of stroma surrounding the follicles, the theca folliculi, has been described.

The medulla is made of loose connective tissue with many elastic fibers and, accompanying the blood vessels, strands of smooth muscle cells.

Interstitial Cells. Much has been written on the "interstitial cells" of the ovary. In the adult human ovary they are either absent or present in small numbers, as irregular

cords of large polyhedral "epithelioid" cells scattered in the stroma. In postembryonic life they arise from the theca interna of atretic follicles. The "interstitial gland" reaches its greatest development in the postembryonic human ovary the first year of life —at a time when atretic follicles are most numerous. It involutes at puberty with the beginning of menstruation and the formation of corpora lutea. During pregnancy, and especially at its end, it may increase slightly for a short time.

In the early stages of atresia, the interstitial cells form a layer around the cavity. When this layer is broken up later into separate cell clusters, the stress of growth changes in the stroma scatters the interstitial cells, and their original relations to the atretic follicles are obscured. In the human ovary they soon degenerate and disappear.

In animals with large litters (rodents) the development of the "interstitial gland," also connected with atresia of follicles, may be enormous. The cell foci originating from the breaking up of the hypertrophied theca interna of atretic follicles persist, enlarge and fuse. Through the continuous addition of new cells, most of the organ is transformed into a diffuse mass of

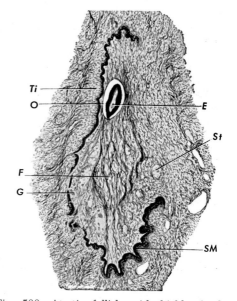

Fig. 500. Atretic follicle with highly developed glassy membrane, *SM*, which is partly broken through. *E*, Residue of the ovum; *F*, fibrin-like network which is the residue of the follicular cavity; *G*, scattered granulosa cells; *O*, zona pellucida; *St*, invading stroma with vessels; *Ti*, cells of the theca interna. Ovary of a young woman. Mallory's connective tissue stain. 85 ×. (After Schaffer.)

large, closely packed, lipid-containing, interstitial cells, almost identical with true granulosa lutein cells. The remaining follicles and the corpora lutea are embedded in this huge cell mass, and only a thin albuginea separates the latter from the germinal epithelium on the surface.

In the hilus of the ovary, groups of large, epithelioid cells can be found in connection with bundles of nonmyelinated nerve fibers—*sympathicotrophic cells.* Although they are usually considered chromaffin cells, their chromaffin nature is not certain, since they do not always stain with chromates and since their cytoplasm contains cholesterol esters not typical for these elements.

In the broad ligament and in the mesovarium, small accumulations of "interrenal" tissue (cortex of adrenal) have also been described.

Vestigial Organs. Certain vestigial organs are found in connection with the ovary. The most important of them is the *epoophoron.* It consists of several parallel or divergent tubules, located in the mesovarium, running from the hilus of the ovary toward the oviduct and fusing into a longitudinal canal, which is parallel to the oviduct. All these tubules end blindly; they are lined by a low cuboidal or columnar, sometimes ciliated, epithelium, and are surrounded by a condensed connective tissue layer containing smooth muscle. The lateral end of the longitudinal duct sometimes ends in a cystlike enlargement—the *hydatid of Morgagni*—while its inner end may extend far toward the uterus as the so-called *duct of Gärtner.* Between the epoophoron and the uterus in the tissue of the broad ligament, especially in the fetus, irregular fragments of epithelial tubules—the *paroophoron*—may be found. The epoophoron is the rudiment of the genital part of the mesonephros and corresponds to the epididymis of the male. The paroophoron is the remnant of the caudal part of the mesonephros and corresponds to the paradidymis in the male.

Vessels and Nerves. Relatively large vessels from the anastomosis of ovarian and uterine arteries enter the hilus and, branching profusely, run through the medulla. Because of their tortuous course, they were called arteriae helicinae. As in the corpora cavernosa penis, they may show longitudinal ridges on their intima. In the periphery of the medulla they form a plexus from which smaller twigs penetrate radially between the follicles into the cortex and break up into capillaries. These form dense networks in the theca of the larger follicles at the surface of the basement membrane. In comparison with such capillary nets, that of the cortex is coarse. The veins accompany the arteries; in the medulla they are large and tortuous and form a plexus in the hilus.

Networks of lymph capillaries arise in the cortex, especially in the theca externa of the large follicles. Lymph vessels with valves are found only outside the hilus.

The nerves of the ovary are derived from the ovarian plexus and from the uterine nerves. They enter the organ through the hilus, together with the blood vessels. They consist for the most part of nonmyelinated fibers; thin myelinated fibers are also present. The presence of sympathetic nerve cells in the ovary has not been confirmed. The majority of the nerves supply the muscular coat of blood vessels. Many fibers penetrate into the cortex and form plexuses around the follicles and under the germinal epithelium on the surface. It seems doubtful whether they penetrate through the basement membrane into the epithelium of the follicles. Sensory fibers ending in corpuscles of Pacini have been described in the stroma.

THE OVIDUCT OR FALLOPIAN TUBE

The oviduct, a muscular tube 1 cm. thick and about 12 cm. long, is attached by the mesosalpinx at the broad ligament to the base and side of the pelvis; it is the proximal part of the müllerian duct of the embryo. Since the uterus arises from the fusion of the two müllerian ducts, the tubal and uterine epithelium are continuous. The myometrial mesenchyme secondarily envelops the uterine end of the tube, and so in the

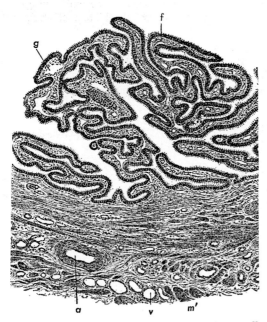

Fig. 501. Portion of cross section through ampulla of tube of a twenty-seven year old woman. S, Mucosa, passing over without a sharp border into the muscular layer; *a*, artery; *f*, folds of mucous membrane covered with ciliated epithelium and containing blood vessels, *g*; *m*, smooth muscle bundles cut longitudinally and in cross section at *m'*; *v*, veins. 50 ×. (After von Ebner, from Schaffer.)

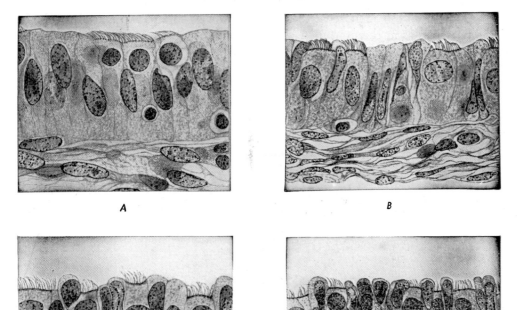

Fig. 502. Epithelium of human fallopian tube, showing physiological changes. A, Midinterval; B, late interval; C, premenstrual; D, pregnancy. 700 ×. (After Snyder.)

adult the tube pierces the fundus of the uterus. The abdominal part of the tube (ampulla) ends in a funnel-shaped opening, the infundibulum, whose edge is split into many fringes, the fimbriae, the largest of which extends toward the ovary. The ampulla continues into the narrower isthmus adjoining the uterus. The part of the tube traversing the wall of the uterus is the pars interstitialis.

The wall of the oviduct consists of a mucous membrane, a muscular layer and an external serous coat. The mucous membrane in the ampulla is thick and forms numerous, high, branched folds. In transection the lumen, therefore, looks like a labyrinth of narrow spaces between epithelium-lined partitions. In the pars isthmica the longitudinal folds are much smaller. In the interstitial part they are reduced to low ridges.

The epithelium is of the simple, sometimes pseudostratified, columnar variety. It is highest in the ampulla and diminishes in height toward the uterus. It consists of two kinds of cells. One of these, especially numerous on the fimbriae and ampulla, carries cilia which beat toward the uterus. The other is devoid of cilia, but is of glandular nature and contains granules. The secretion probably provides the ovum with nutritive material and, in some species, with an albuminous envelope. In the marsupials a shell as well as albumen is formed about the ova. The two types of epithelial cells are probably merely different functional conditions of one element. In women the epithelium of the oviduct undergoes slight cyclic changes with the uterine mucous membrane. True glands are absent in the oviduct.

The lamina propria of the mucous membrane of the oviduct consists of a network of thin fibers and of numerous fusiform or angular cells. Wandering cells and mast cells also occur. The fixed cells here seem to have the same potencies as in the uterus. In cases of tubal pregnancy, some of them may be transformed into decidual cells.

No true muscularis mucosae, and therefore no submucous layer, can be distinguished.

peritoneal coat of the fallopian tube has the usual serosal structure.

At the time of ovulation both ovary and oviduct exhibit active movements (Westman). The abdominal opening of the oviduct contains, in its mucosa, a ring of large

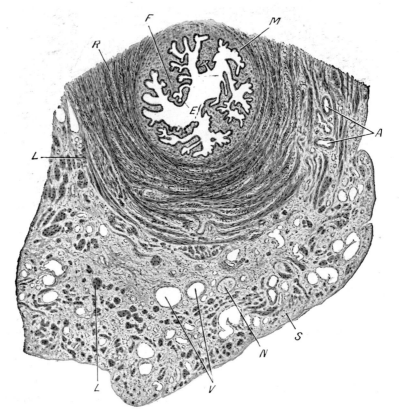

Fig. 503. Portion of cross section of fallopian tube of a thirty-nine year old woman. Uterine portion (isthmus): A, arteries; E, ciliated epithelium; F, longitudinal folds of mucosa in cross section; L, longitudinal muscle; M, lamina propria; N, nerve; R, circular muscle; S, serosal covering; V, veins. 32 ×. (After Schaffer.)

The mucous membrane is immediately surrounded by the muscular coat, which consists of two layers of smooth muscle bundles. The inner layer is circular or spiral; the outer is longitudinal. There is no distinct limit between the two, however, because of various spirally directed bundles. Toward the periphery the longitudinal bundles gradually appear in increasing quantities between the circular bundles. They are embedded in an abundant, loose connective tissue with elastic networks, and extend far into the serous layer and into the ligamentum latum. Toward the uterus the muscularis increases in thickness. The

blood vessels, especially veins, extending into the fimbriae. Between them muscle fibers form a network. It is a sort of erectile tissue. At the time of ovulation the vessels are filled with blood, and the enlargement and turgescence of the fimbriae, together with the contraction of the muscles, bring the opening of the funnel in close contact with the surface of the ovary.

The rhythmic contractions of the oviduct are probably of primary importance in the transport of the ovum. Contraction waves pass from infundibulum to uterus, and the cilia beat in the same direction.

The mucous membrane and its folds as well as the serous coat contain abundant blood and lymph vessels. Larger nerve bundles are found together with the vessels in the serous layer and in the peripheral parts of the longitudinal muscle. The circular mus-

layers: the outer—the serous membrane of the peritoneum which is found only on a part of the viscus; the middle—a thick (2 cm.) mass of smooth muscle, the *myometrium*; the inner—the mucous membrane, the *endometrium*.

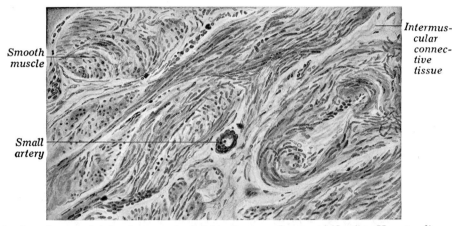

Smooth muscle

Intermuscular connective tissue

Small artery

Fig. 504. Section of myometrium of a woman of thirty-six years. Low magnification. Hematoxylin-eosin-azure II stain. (Drawn by Miss A. Nixon.)

cle layer contains a dense plexus of thin nerve bundles supplying the muscle fibers and penetrating the mucous membrane.

UTERUS

The uterus is that part of the reproductive passages in which the ovum develops until the time of delivery. In the human subject it is single and represents the parts of the embryonic müllerian ducts which have fused in the midline. Developmental abnormalities range from a deep notch in the fundus to two intact uteri, cervices and vaginae.

The human uterus is a pear-shaped organ flattened in the dorsoventral direction and provided with a correspondingly flattened cavity and a thick muscular wall. Four parts may be distinguished in it: (1) the body (corpus uteri) with its rounded upper end, the fundus; (2) the isthmus—the middle, slightly constricted part; (3) the cervix—the cylindrical lower part with the cervical canal; and (4) the portio vaginalis—the lower end, protruding into the vagina, and pierced by the cervical canal.

The wall of the uterus consists of three

The serous membrane has the usual structure of the peritoneum.

Myometrium. The smooth muscle fibers of the muscular layer are arranged in cylindrical or flat bundles separated from one another by interstitial connective tissue containing isolated smooth muscle cells. According to the direction and disposition of the bundles, several layers of muscles can be distinguished in the myometrium, but are not sharply outlined, because fibers frequently pass from one layer into another.

Immediately under the mucous membrane, a thin layer of mostly longitudinal, but some circular and oblique, bundles may be distinguished. This is called the *stratum submucosum*. It forms distinct muscular rings around the intramural parts of the oviducts. The next layer to the outside is the thickest; it is called the *stratum vasculare*, because it contains many large blood vessels, especially veins, which give it a spongy appearance; here circular and oblique muscle bundles predominate. Farther outside, a layer with circular and longitudinal fibers follows, the *stratum supravasculare*. Finally, immediately under the serous coat, there is a thin longitudinal muscle layer, the *stratum subserosum*. The two last-named layers send out their muscular bundles into the wall of the oviducts and into the broad and round ligaments.

The cervix is composed mainly of dense fibrous tissue in which, according to Danforth, a variable number of smooth muscle cells is distributed at random.

The smooth muscle cells of the myometrium have a length of about 50 microns.

cal reticulum continuous with the collagenous intermuscular tissue. Elastic networks are especially prominent in the peripheral layers of the uterine wall, at the limit between the serosa and the muscularis. From here they extend inward between the muscle

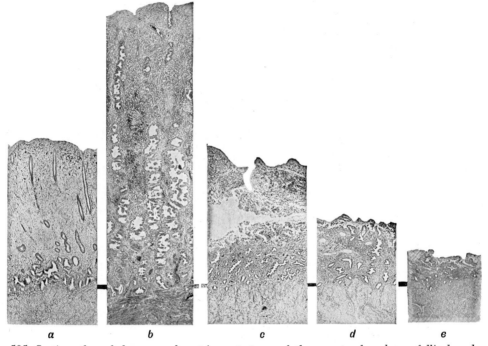

Fig. 505. Sections through human endometrium at stages of the menstrual cycle: *a*, follicular phase, on day eleven of cycle; *b*, lutein phase, on day twenty-three of cycle; *c*, first day of menstruation; *d*, second day of menstruation; *e*, fourth day of menstruation. 18 ×. (Courtesy of G. W. Bartelmez.)

In the pregnant uterus, when the mass of the organ increases about twenty-four times, they hypertrophy to a length of more than 500 microns. In this condition there seems also to occur an increase in the number of the muscle fibers through division (Fischer-Wasels) and through transformation of the embryonic connective tissue cells and lymphocytes into new muscular elements, especially in the innermost layers of the myometrium (Stieve). In the puerperium the muscle cells show fatty infiltration and rapidly diminish in size. It is possible that some of them degenerate.

The connective tissue between the muscular bundles consists of collagenous bundles, fibroblasts, embryonic connective tissue cells, macrophages and mast cells. There is a typi-

bundles. The innermost layers of the myometrium do not contain elastic fibers. The latter are, of course, found everywhere in the wall of the blood vessels. In the cervix the collagenous and elastic elements are especially numerous. This is the cause of the firmer consistency of this part of the uterus.

In pregnancy the connective tissue of the uterus becomes more abundant and succulent, which causes a considerable loosening of coherence between the muscle bundles.

Endometrium. In a sexually mature, nonpregnant woman, the uterine mucosa is subject to cyclic menstrual changes closely related to ovarian activity. Beginning with puberty (at the average age of fourteen) and ending with the menopause (usually at the age of forty-five to fifty), every twenty-one to thirty-five days the mucous membrane of the corpus undergoes marked changes. These culminate in its partial destruction, which is accompanied by a more or less abundant extravasation of blood and appears as a bloody vaginal discharge—the *menstrual*

the *stroma*, which resembles mesenchyme. Its irregularly stellate cells have a large, ovoid nucleus. The cell processes appear to anastomose throughout the tissue and adhere to the framework of reticular fibers, which are condensed as basement membranes under

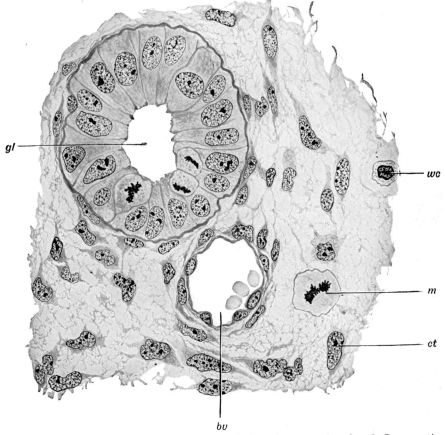

Fig. 506. Mucous membrane of human uterus, eleventh day of menstrual cycle. *gl*, Cross section of gland with mitotically proliferating epithelium; *bv*, blood vessel; *ct*, connective tissue cell of lamina propria; *m*, mitosis of same; *wc*, wandering cell. 415 ×. (From the same mucous membrane as in Figure 505, *a*.) (A.A.M.)

flow. The flow, which marks the beginning of the cycle, lasts for three to five days.

The uterus is lined by a simple columnar epithelium. From fundus to vagina small groups of ciliated cells are scattered among the secreting cells. As far as the beginning of the cervical canal, this surface epithelium is substantially like that of the *uterine glands* which grow out from it in infancy. These are simple tubules slightly branched in a zone adjacent to the myometrium. They are separated from one another by connective tissue,

the epithelium. Elastic fibers are absent except in the walls of the arterioles. There is a ground substance at times rich in tissue mucoid; in it are lymphoid wandering cells and granular leukocytes. Macrophages are not uncommon, but for some unknown reason they are not mobilized for phagocytosing extravasated blood. This may perhaps be due to conditions similar to those responsible for the failure of blood to clot after it has been in contact with the endometrial stroma.

The number of uterine glands varies from

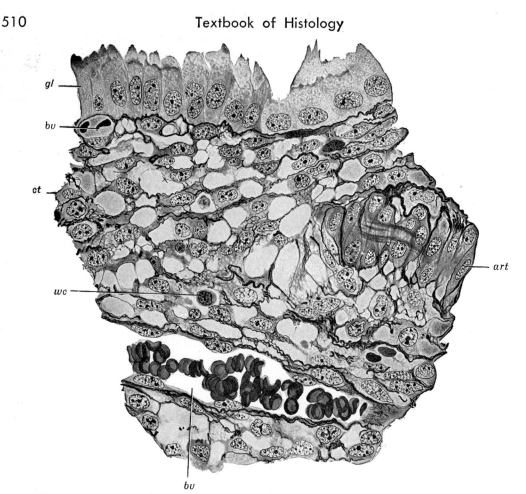

Fig. 507. Mucous membrane of human uterus, twenty-fifth day of menstrual cycle. *gl*, Glandular epithelium; *bv*, blood vessels; *ct*, connective tissue of lamina propria, with silver-impregnated fibrils; *wc*, wandering cell; *art*, artery. 625 ×. (A.A.M.)

one person to another and may be rapidly increased by budding and growth toward the surface from the basal zone (O'Leary). Such buds which do not reach the surface become dilated (cystic). The glands seem to vary in their proximity to one another during the cycle, owing largely to changes in the diameter of the glands and in the amount of stromal ground substance (Fig. 505).

The uterine mucous membrane is firmly bound to the underlying myometrium. Occasional strands of endometrium extend down among the muscle bundles. Under pathological conditions the myometrium may be extensively invaded in this manner (adenomyosis). In old age, the endometrium, together with the other parts of the genital system, atrophies and becomes thin; the glands may become partly obliterated and form small cysts.

Endometrial Blood Supply. Certain arteries pass through the myometrium and basal endometrium with but few branches, to spread out into a rich capillary bed superficially. These vessels are more or less contorted, and are termed "coiled arteries." During most of the cycle they constrict and dilate rhythmically, so that the surface is alternately blanched and suffused with blood (Markee). The basal half of the endometrium is supplied by arterioles with many branches which supply a dense capillary bed in the endometrium and the adjoining myometrium. The zone of endometrium between the superficial and basal circulations is supplied by vessels intermediate in form and has a coarser capillary mesh. The thin-walled veins form an irregular anastomosing net with sinusoidal enlargements at all levels.

Endometrial Cycle. Four phases of activity can be recognized in the endometrial cycle: (1) The follicular phase comprises the first half of the cycle and is typically associated with a rapidly growing graafian follicle. (2) Progravid (lutein phase) is usually associated with an active corpus luteum. (3) Ischemic phase, when little blood flows through the coiled arteries. (4) Menstrual phase, associated with endometrial damage and extravasation.

1. The *follicular phase* usually begins at the end of a menstrual flow and is characterized by numerous mitoses in all endometrial tissues. The glands in the superficial two thirds or more are straight with narrow lumina (Fig. 505, *a*). The secretion accumulates in the glands, and their lumina widen as they become wavy in form. Glycogen is present in the gland cells, but only a thin mucoid is secreted at this time. The abundant stroma is rich in tissue mucoid. Coiled arteries are not found in the superficial third, which has only capillaries and venules.

The phase of hyperplasia may continue for a day or two after ovulation, which is believed to occur usually between the tenth and sixteenth days after the onset of a menstrual period. There may be a brief halt in the thickening of the endometrium at this time, a diapedesis of erythrocytes may occur under the surface epithelium, and some blood may occasionally enter the uterine lumen and reach the vagina. This has been termed *intermenstrual bleeding*. According to some, it corresponds to the estrous bleeding of the dog.

2. During the *progravid phase* the thickening of the endometrium is due largely to the increase of secretion and edema fluid. The glands become tortuous and then irregularly sacculated, i.e., "progravid" in form, especially in the middle half of the endometrium (Fig. 505).

The secretion now contains glycogen, and the mucoid is thicker. The gland cells are lower and wider; in the superficial zone they may contain lipoid granules which, however, do not enter the gland lumen. During this phase the cells readily change their form when immersed in the fixing solution, owing to the presence of much intracellular secretion, and have tongues projecting beyond the terminal bars (Fig. 507) (Bartelmez). In poorly preserved material the cells may even appear continuous with the secretion in the lumen.

In pregnancy the "progravid" changes progress for six to eight weeks (p. 514).

3. *Ischemic Phase.* In the nonpregnant cycle extensive vascular changes occur thirteen to fourteen days after ovulation and constitute the ischemic phase. This phase was discovered by Markee in transplants of endometrium to the eyes of monkeys.

A day or more before menstruation the coiled arteries constrict so that the superficial zone is blanched for hours at a time. With this the endometrium shrinks, and in the course of two days or more a transplanted bit of endometrium may decrease as much as 76 per cent in area. This involution is due to a loss of secretion and water (edema fluid). The stroma becomes denser. The closely packed stroma cells, irregularly collapsed glands and coiled arteries are characteristic of this phase. Usually many leukocytes are found in the stroma and between the epithelial cells. Sooner or later the coiled arteries clamp down, so that the superficial zone becomes anemic, while the blood continues to flow in the more basal portion of the endometrium.

4. *Menstrual Phase.* After a variable number of hours, the constricted arteries open up for a short time, the walls of vessels near the surface burst, and blood pours into the stroma and soon discharges into the uterine lumen. Such blood does not clot. Subsequently, patches of blood-soaked tissue separate off, leaving the torn ends of glands and arteries and veins open to the surface. Blood may ooze from such veins, a reflux from the intact basal circulation. The menstrual discharge thus contains altered arterial and venous blood, with normal and hemolyzed, sometimes agglutinated, erythrocytes, disin-

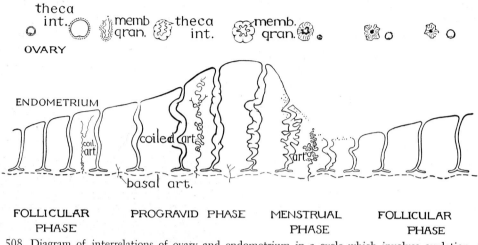

Fig. 508. Diagram of interrelations of ovary and endometrium in a cycle which involves ovulation. Cycles are said to begin with the onset of menstrual bleeding. One complete cycle and the beginning of another are indicated. The ovarian changes involve the growth of a graafian follicle, its rupture, corpus luteum formation and regression. The endometrial development is indicated by changes in thickness, in the form of the glands and the coiled arteries. These changes depend in part on the time between the onset of menstruation and ovulation as well as on the duration of the cycle. Ovulation may occur normally as early as the seventh day or as late as the twenty-second day after the beginning of a menstrual period, but in most instances it probably occurs between the ninth and sixteenth days. The normal variability in cycle length is from twenty-one to forty days. *art.*, Coiled arteries; *memb. gran.*, membrana granulosa of the graafian follicle and the granulosa lutein cells; *theca int.*, theca interna. (Courtesy of G. W. Bartelmez.)

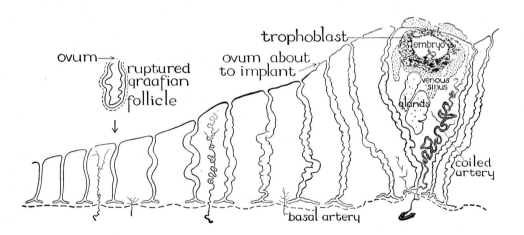

BEGINNING OF A PREGNANT CYCLE

Fig. 509. Diagram showing beginning of a pregnant cycle. It is identical with Figure 508 until after implantation, which probably occurs about a week after ovulation. The relation of a recently implanted ovum to the endometrium is from a reconstruction of the ovum described by Brewer and about fourteen days old. It is buried in the endometrium and surrounded by dilated veins which had been opened by the trophoblast. Areas about the ovum with extravasated maternal blood are stippled; two glands below the ovum are dilated with blood. (Courtesy of G. W. Bartelmez.)

tegrated or autolyzed epithelial and stroma cells as well as the secretions of the uterine, the cervical and the vulval glands. Sometimes there are tissue fragments, but blood clots are abnormal. The average loss of blood is 35 cc. By the third or fourth day of the flow the entire uterus may present a raw wound surface. The superficial gland and stroma cells are normal histologically.

Below the zone of extravasation the endometrium remains intact during menstruation, although it does shrink down. Typical progravid glands may be recognizable as such until the end of menstruation (Fig. 505). The surviving zone is accordingly wider than the "basalis" of many authors.

Before the vaginal discharge has ceased, epithelial cells glide out from the torn ends of the glands, and the surface epithelium is quickly restored. Then the superficial circulation is resumed, the stroma again becomes succulent, and the follicular phase of the new cycle may begin at once.

The "typical" conditions illustrated in Figures 505 and 508 are not always realized. In fact, the ovary may not produce a ripe follicle in the course of a cycle, and then the endometrial changes are minimal. Nevertheless, a clinically typical bleeding occurs at the expected time. This has been termed "anovulatory menstruation."

Such variability introduces difficulties in the evaluation of endometrial tissue removed at operation or biopsy. Errors are also introduced when only small fragments of endometrium are available, as in curettings. The various phases of the cycle in "typical" cases are identified by certain characters: (1) follicular phase: endometrium 1 to 5 mm. thick; straight, narrow glands becoming wavy, the epithelium tall, becoming vacuolated (glycogen), many mitoses in all tissues, no coiled arteries in the superficial third, and a subepithelial zone free of reticulum postmenstrually. (2) Progravid phase: endometrium 2 to 6 mm. thick, glands wavy or sacculated with wide lumen, epithelial cells broad with blebs, stroma edematous superficially, mitoses confined to coiled arteries which are present near the surface. (3)

Ischemic phase: endometrium 3 to 4 mm. thick, greatly contorted arteries and glands, dense stroma with leukocytosis. (4) Menstruation: endometrium 0.5 to 3 mm. thick, superficially extravasated blood, the glands and arteries appear collapsed, the stroma is dense, and the surface is denuded.

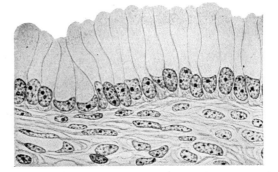

Fig. 510. Epithelium of endocervix of a woman of forty-six years, fourteen days after the beginning of the last menstrual period. 540 ×. (After Stieve.)

Isthmus and Cervix. The mucous membrane of the corpus passes sometimes gradually, more often abruptly, into that of the isthmus, which remains thin and shows few signs of cyclic change. It lacks coiled arteries and usually does not bleed during menstruation. It has a dense stroma. The glands are sparse and are oblique to the surface.

The mucosa of the cervix has a different structure. It has a firmer consistency, a thickness of 2 to 3 mm., and shows, on its surface, branching folds (plicae palmatae, arbor vitae). The surface is lined by a tall columnar epithelium; in fixed material the oval nuclei are at the base of the cells with mucus in their apical parts. In the mucosa numerous large glands are present which differ from those of the corpus in that they are extensively branched, and are lined with a mucus-secreting, tall, columnar epithelium. Some of its cells, especially on the surface, are ciliated. The canal of the cervix is usually filled with mucus. Often some of the cervical glands are transformed into cysts which may reach the size of a pea—the so-called *nabothian follicles*.

The mucosa of the cervix does not take part in the menstrual changes. An increase in vaginal mucus (which comes largely from the cervix) has been described about the middle of the cycle (Papanicolaou). In pregnancy the cervical glands enlarge, proliferate, and accumulate large quantities of mucus. The connective tissue between them is reduced to thin partitions.

is just inside the external opening of the cervix. In some cases patches of columnar epithelium may extend for short distances upon the outer surface of the portio vaginalis, forming so-called "physiologic erosions"; in others the vaginal end of the cervical canal has stratified epithelium.

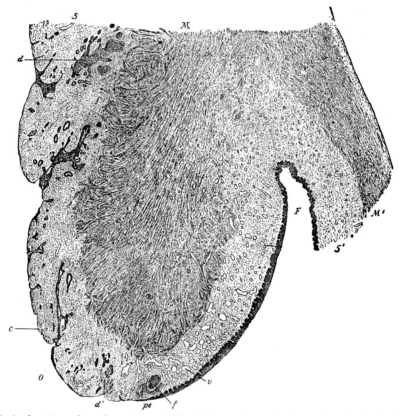

Fig. 511. Sagittal section through posterior half of the portio vaginalis uteri and the fornix vaginae of a young woman. F, Fornix; M, muscle coat of the cervix; M', muscle coat of the vagina; O, external orifice of the uterus; S, mucosa of the cervix; S', mucosa of the vagina; d, d', cervical glands; c, cylindrical epithelium; f, lymph follicle; pe, beginning of stratified squamous epithelium with papillae; v, veins. 10 ×. (After von Ebner.)

The outer surface of the portio vaginalis is smooth, covered with a mucous membrane similar to that of the vagina, and consists of a stratified squamous epithelium with glycogen in its cells and a lamina propria with small papillae well separated from one another.

The transition between the columnar mucous epithelium of the cervical canal and the stratified squamous epithelium of the portio vaginalis is abrupt; as a rule the borderline

Endometrium in Early Pregnancy. Great advances in our knowledge of early stages of placentation in man have been made by Hertig and Rock (1941, 1945) and in primates by Streeter and his colleagues, Wislocki, Hartman and Heuser, at the Carnegie Institution. Their papers as well as the extensive monograph on the human and monkey placenta by Wislocki and Bennett should be consulted for the details and peculiarities of human placentation.

The changes which occur in the first week after fertilization of the ovum have not been observed in man and can only be inferred from observations on monkey ova. After fertilization, segmentation occurs as the ovum moves down the tube and enters the uterus. Unlike the monkey ovum, however, the human ovum burrows into the endometrium, (nine days) found by these authors, the ovum has burrowed deeper into the endometrium and is almost covered with uterine surface epithelium. The syncytial trophoblast has increased in amount, and intercommunicating lacunae have developed in it. Some of these contain blood liberated by the penetration of the trophoblast into the maternal

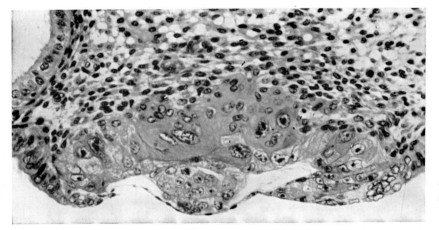

Fig. 512. Section of a seven and one-half day human ovum which is just embedding. Note broad layer of trophoblast penetrating endometrium. The faint cleft is probably the future amnion. 300 ×. Hertig-Rock. (Courtesy of Carnegie Institution of Washington.)

presumably through the activity of the outer layer of cells of the blastocyst. These cells will also help to form the *placenta*, the organ for the transfer of nutritive materials from the maternal circulation to the embryo and the removal of its waste products. These nourishing cells are therefore called *trophoblasts*.

At the time the ovum enters it, the endometrium may resemble that in Figure 505, *b*: the glands are distended with glycogen and a mucoid, there are lipoid granules in epithelium and stroma, and the latter is edematous.

The youngest human ovum studied is believed to be about seven and one-half days old (Fig. 512). It shows the blastocyst attached to the endometrium and invading its stroma. The advancing edge of the blastocyst consists of a multinucleated protoplasmic mass, the *syncytial trophoblast*. Closer to the primordium of the embryo proper the trophoblast is made up of distinct cells, the *cytotrophoblasts*. In the next older specimen

vessels. This is the beginning of the uteroplacental circulation, on which the continued growth of the embryo depends. In all probability the cytotrophoblast is giving rise to syncytial trophoblast externally and has begun to form mesoblastic cells on its inner surface. The embryo proper at this time consists of a well-defined epithelial disk; an amniotic cavity is beginning to develop.

In the eleven-day specimen of Hertig and Rock (Figs. 513, 514) the trophoblast has increased in amount and, with the primitive mesoblast, forms the *chorion*. There are more frequent communications between the lacunae in the syncytial trophoblast and the maternal vessels.

This invasion of the maternal blood vascular system by trophoblast becomes progressively extensive. The syncytium continues to enlarge the implantation cavity during the earliest weeks of pregnancy. Until term it is concerned with the absorption of nutriment and the excretion of wastes for the embryo and its membranes.

During the next few days the ovum enlarges by the growth of the trophoblast and the accumulation of fluid in the primitive chorionic mesoblast. By the end of the second week the conditions shown in Figure 509 are reached, in which a reconstruction of the ovum described by Brewer (1937) is

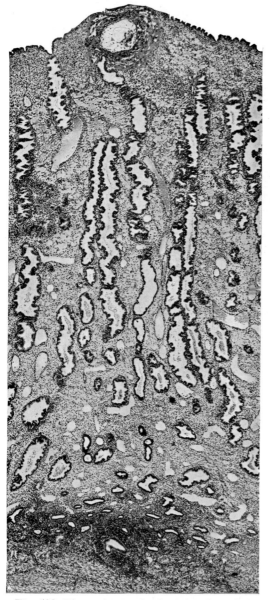

Fig. 513. Photomicrograph of section through implantation site of the eleven-day Hertig-Rock ovum. The entire thickness of the endometrium is shown. The glands are progravid, the stroma edematous, and the superficial veins are dilated. 22 ×. (After Hertig and Rock, 1941.)

shown. The wide lacunae in the plasmodial trophoblast are in open communication with dilated maternal veins, and there has been considerable extravasation of blood about the ovum. A cap of blood overlies the implantation site. Adjacent to the nutrient-laden maternal tissue, the trophoblast has grown more luxuriantly. The embryo is attached to the chorion on this side by a mass of mesenchymal cells, the future umbilical cord.

At several points on the chorionic wall, mesoblast is beginning to spread out into the trophoblast to produce the first *villi*; these outfoldings of the chorion serve to increase its absorbing surface. Fetal blood vessels develop in the connective tissue core, which is covered by cellular and syncytial trophoblast (Fig. 517). The deeply staining syncytium has granular mitochondria and usually droplets of lipid. In the cellular trophoblast, usually called Langhans cells in the villi, the mitochondria are elongate and sparse. The cytoplasm of these cells usually stains feebly and is rich in a labile form of glycogen.

During the third week the cellular trophoblast at the tips of the villi begins to grow rapidly and, mushrooming out, serves to anchor the villus to the decidua basalis. As this process continues, the cellular proliferations of adjacent villi merge, and thus an outer wall of trophoblast is formed through which the maternal vessels communicate with the space between the villi. This *intervillous space*, which has developed from the trophoblastic lacunae and the dilated maternal veins, is bounded throughout pregnancy by normal or degenerated trophoblast except where it communicates with maternal vessels. It contains more or less maternal blood; the villi absorb nutriment from it and excrete wastes into it. The development of a functional vascular system during the fourth week makes possible the nutrition of the rapidly growing embryo.

Figure 515 shows the relations of chorion and endometrium at the end of the fourth week. The implantation site occupies only a small part of the endometrium, all of which, except for a basal zone, is sloughed off after delivery. During pregnancy it has accordingly

Primitive   Embryonic Surface   Cellular   Syncytial
mesoblast   Entoderm   disk   epithelium Amnion   C   trophoblast   trophoblast

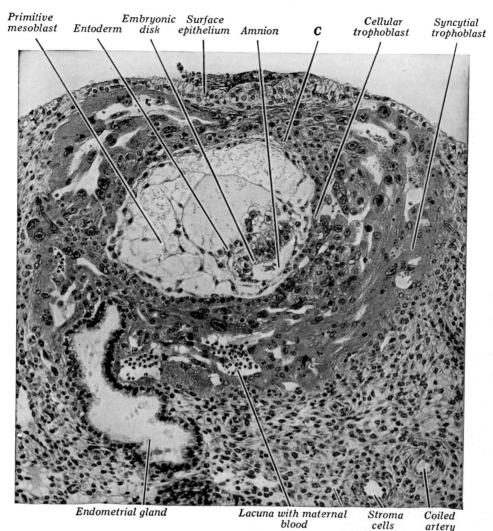

Endometrial gland   Lacuna with maternal   Stroma   Coiled
                                    blood   cells   artery

Fig. 514. Photomicrograph from the same section as Figure 513, magnified 160 diameters. The bulk of the ovum consists of masses of trophoblast (syncytium) invading the endometrium. Within the syncytial trophoblast is the cellular trophoblast with obvious cell boundaries. The cells are arranged as a simple epithelium except for the clump at C. The cellular trophoblast immediately surrounds the primitive chorionic mesoblast in which the embryo is suspended. (After Hertig and Rock, 1941).

been called the *decidua* and is divided into three regions: overlying the ovum is the *decidua capsularis*; underlying it is the *decidua basalis*, which comprises the maternal component of the placenta; the rest of the endometrium as far as the internal os uteri is the *decidua vera*.

The vera continues to thicken during the first eight or ten weeks of pregnancy as the glands become more dilated with secretion and edema fluid accumulates. The stroma cells in the superficial third round up and

enlarge, often becoming epithelioid. The superficial zone so formed has narrow glands and is called the *stratum compactum* in contrast to the underlying *stratum spongiosum*, which may extend to the myometrium; or, as in Figure 515, there may be an intervening *stratum basale* of narrow tortuous glands and dense stroma.

The villi of the inner wall grow and branch profusely; together with the *chorionic plate* from which they arise, they constitute the *chorion frondosum*. The superficial villi, on

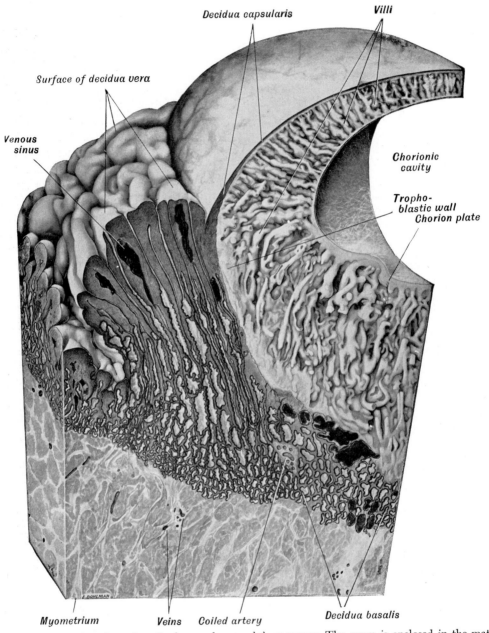

Fig. 515. Margin of implantation site from a four weeks' pregnancy. The ovum is enclosed in the maternal decidua. The villi adjacent to the decidua basalis are long, have many secondary and a few tertiary branches, and are anchored to the decidua by a wall of cytotrophoblast. The decidua vera exhibits three zones: (1) a superficial compact zone with decidual cells; (2) a spongy zone of dilated and sacculated glands; (3) a basal zone of narrow glands, which may be entirely absent. In the implantation site the compact zone has been obliterated by the developing ovum except for the attenuated decidua capsularis. The embryo and the amnion surrounding it are not shown. 17 ×. (Courtesy of G. W. Bartelmez. Drawn by Miss Esther Bohlman.)

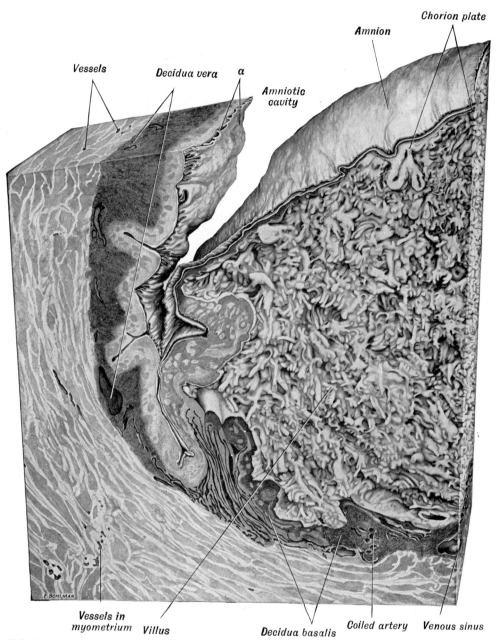

Fig. 516. Margin of placenta from a sixteen weeks' pregnancy. The growth of embryo and amnion as well as the enlargement of the uterus as a whole has changed the relations shown in Figure 515. The connective tissue of amnion and chorion has fused everywhere, obliterating the exocelom. Decidua capsularis and chorion laeve have fused with the stretched and regressing decidua vera, obliterating the uterine cavity as far as the internal os. The placental villi have grown and branched profusely, increasing the size of the placenta. The end of each villous trunk remains attached to the decidua basalis, and the small twigs float freely in the fluid of the intervillous space. The placenta now has a well-defined margin where the villi are shorter and there are wide communications between intervillous space and maternal veins. a, Fused amnion and chorion. 7.5 ×. (Courtesy of G. W. Bartelmez. Drawn by Miss Esther Bohlman.)

the other hand, soon appear stunted and during the third month they degenerate, leaving the chorionic plate smooth; this is the *chorion laeve*.

The amnion closely enswathes the embryo for the first two months, and there is a large cavity between amnion and chorion, the *exocelom*. Early in the third month the amniotic fluid increases rapidly, and the amnion is soon in contact with the chorion on all sides. As the membranes fuse, the exocelom is obliterated (Fig. 516). The uterus begins to enlarge, and chorion laeve as well as all three deciduae is stretched and becomes thinner. But the placental villi are growing, and

the margin of the placenta becomes well defined. A section of the placenta from this stage shows, beginning at the fetal surface, first the amniotic epithelium, then the fused connective tissue of amnion and chorionic plate, followed by the villi cut in various planes. Some villi are fused to the decidua basalis, and there are bands of necrotic trophoblast adjoining the decidua basalis. Here there are dilated and stretched glands and greatly modified coiled arteries which carry maternal blood to the intervillous space.

During the second half of pregnancy the terminal branches of the villi grow smaller and more numerous, but the rapid growth of

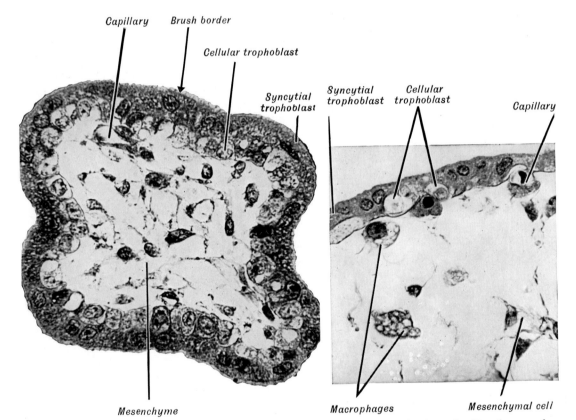

Fig. 517. Section of villus from a three and a half weeks' pregnancy. The syncytium with its fuzzy brush border forms the outermost layer; within it is a continuous layer of cellular trophoblast, which in turn surrounds the loose mesenchyme with its capillaries. Photomicrograph 590 ×. (Courtesy of G. W. Bartelmez.)

Fig. 518. Section of villus from a four months' placenta. The syncytium is practically the same as in Figure 517, but most cells of the cellular trophoblast have become syncytium. Free macrophages (Hofbauer cells) are common in the mesenchyme. Capillaries are closely applied to the syncytium. Photomicrograph 590 ×. (Courtesy of G. W. Bartelmez.)

the fetus involves an actual decrease in the thickness of the placenta with an increase in its circumference. By the fifth month most of the cellular trophoblast (Langhans cells) has differentiated into syncytium. The syncytium thins out, and in many spots overlying fetal capillaries it becomes a delicate membrane.

The detailed cytology and histochemistry of the trophoblast at various stages of pregnancy are given by Wislocki and Bennett, who suggest that the steroid hormones of the placenta are produced by the syncytial trophoblast and the gonadotrophic hormone by the cellular trophoblast. (See also Dempsey and Wislocki.)

Textbooks of embryology and obstetrics must be consulted for more details on the development of the placenta and its circulation.

Vessels and Nerves. The larger branches of the uterine artery run chiefly in the stratum vasculare of the myometrium. From here radial branches run directly to the mucosa and form "coiled arteries." During progravid stages these vessels grow and become progressively more tortuous, soon reaching the surface and forming a rich capillary net. The basal zone is supplied by arterioles from the adjacent muscle. In the myometrium the capillaries have a peculiarly thick endothelium and sometimes a small lumen. The veins form plexuses in the deeper layer of the lamina propria mucosae. Another plexus of large veins without valves is found in the stratum vasculare of the myometrium.

Pregnancy causes irreversible changes in the vessels. In a uterus which has been pregnant, the wall of the vessels at the placental site shows an irregular thickening of the intima with neoformation of smooth muscle, while in the media the muscle is largely substituted by coarse elastic networks.

The lymph vessels of the myometrium are readily demonstrated, but their presence in the endometrium has been questioned.

The nerves of the uterus are for the most part nonmyelinated, although many fine and some thick, myelinated fibers occur also. They form the plexus uterovaginalis and are connected with a sympathetic "cervical" ganglion, located in the lateral, upper wall of the vagina. The ganglion contains, besides nerve cells, a considerable quantity of chromaffine elements. Inside the myometrium no nerve cells are found. Branching bundles of nerve fibers accompany the blood vessels and supply the muscular elements of the latter and of the myometrium. Some branches run through the mucosa toward the epithelium. The endings of the uterine nerves are not known exactly, but there is good physiological evidence for afferent and efferent fibers to the myometrium. There is, however, no intrinsic coordinating mechanism like that of the gut. The rich innervation suggests an interplay of nervous and hormonal effects normally, even though in transplants the characteristic myometrial and vasomotor responses can be obtained under conditions that appear to rule out the nervous system completely.

VAGINA

The vagina arises from the distal ends of the müllerian ducts, fused in the midline; the outer part develops from the urogenital sinus. Its lower end is marked by a dorsal, transverse, semicircular fold of the wall, the hymen. The wall of the vagina consists of three layers: (1) the mucous membrane; (2) the muscular coat; and (3) the adventitial connective tissue.

The adventitial coat is a thin layer of dense, connective tissue which merges into the loose connective tissue joining the vagina to the surrounding parts. In this connective tissue there is a large venous plexus, nerve bundles, and small groups of nerve cells.

The interlacing smooth muscle bundles of the middle layer are arranged circularly and longitudinally; the longitudinal bundles are far more numerous, especially in the outer half of the layer. The interstitial connective tissue contains abundant, coarse, elastic networks. Striated muscle fibers form a ring-shaped sphincter around the introitus of the vagina.

The mucous membrane consists of a lamina propria and an epithelium on the free surface. The lamina propria is a dense connective tissue; toward the muscular layer it becomes looser, and this part may be considered a submucosa. While in the anterior wall of the vagina, papillae are scarce and small, in the posterior wall the lamina propria sends numerous high papillae deep into the covering epithelium. Immediately under the epithelium there is a dense network of fine elastic fibers; from here fine fibers run downward to the muscular layer and become condensed in the walls of the blood vessels. Accumulations of lymphocytes are numerous,

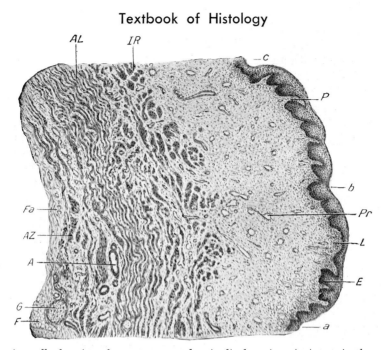

Fig. 519. Anterior wall of vagina of young woman; longitudinal section. A, Artery in the muscle; AL, external longitudinal layer and, AZ, external circular bundles of muscular layer; a, b, c, furrows between the rugae, of which two are shown in cross section; E, stratified squamous epithelium; F, fat lobules; Fa, fibrous layer; G, ganglion; IR, internal circular muscle layer; L, papillary layer of the lamina propria; Pr, infiltrated with leukocytes; P, papilla. 26 ×. (After Schaffer.)

and sometimes lymph nodules are found. Lymphocytes are always seen migrating into the epithelium. The deeper layers of the lamina propria contain dense plexuses of small veins.

The epithelium is of the stratified squamous variety and has a thickness of 150 to 200 microns. Under normal conditions the superficial cell layers in primates do not show cornification, although they contain granules of keratohyalin. The nuclei usually remain stainable, and the cells become loaded with glycogen and fat. In a prolapsed vagina, when the mucous membrane is exposed to air, the superficial cells are cornified as in the epidermis.

Glands are missing in the vagina; exceptionally, some few glands of the cervical type are found in the fornix. The mucus, lubricating the vagina, originates from the cervix and is made acid by the fermentative action of bacteria on the glycogen from the vaginal epithelium.

The *hymen* is a fold of the mucous membrane with a thin connective tissue core and stratified squamous epithelium on both surfaces.

In spayed animals the vaginal epithelium is low, whereas epithelial proliferation is clearly associated with a high level of the ovarian hormone, estrone. The estrone response of the vaginal epithelium in the spayed rat and mouse remains the best quantitative test for the hormone.

In primates, partly because of the normal presence of bacteria, the vaginal contents vary so greatly as to be of little value in diagnosing ovarian conditions. Sometimes a reduction in the number of leukocytes can be recognized about the middle of the menstrual cycle which corresponds to the preovulatory phase in rodents, and the like. A high estrone level is indicated by the thick epithelium and occasionally by erythrocytes of uterine origin. Usually three zones can be recognized: (a) a basal zone of columnar and polyhedral cells with many mitoses; (b) a narrow and variable zone with flattened cells sometimes containing granules that resemble keratohyalin; and (c) an outer zone of squamous cells loaded with glycogen and fat. The nuclei of these cells stain readily in most cases. During menstruation the microscopic picture of the vaginal lavage is dominated by erythrocytes, normal and hemolyzed, and leukocytes. Blood-soaked fragments of endometrium may occur in normal women, but blood clots are abnormal.

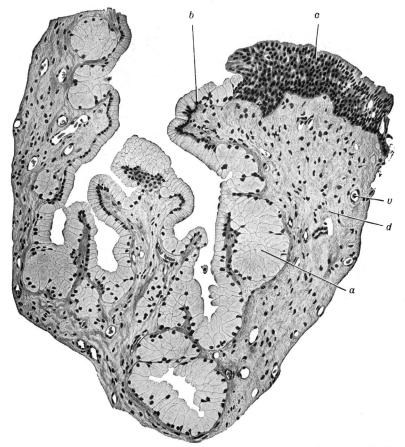

Fig. 520. Gland of Bartholin. A large duct with patches of stratified columnar epithelium (c) gives off smaller branches lined with columnar mucous cells (b) and continuing into tubulo-alveolar terminal portions; these are lined with large mucous cells (a); d, interstitial connective tissue; v, blood vessel. 281 ×, reduced to two-thirds. (A.A.M.)

In sexually inactive states such as childhood and old age, a vaginal proliferation is readily produced by the administration of estrone. This has proved to be a valuable method of clearing up vaginal infections.

In *gestation* the smooth muscle fibers enlarge and recede from one another. The connective tissue elements—the collagenous bundles and the cells—enlarge and are arranged more loosely. The blood vessels, especially the veins, also enlarge, and the capillary endothelium swells. The thickness of the epithelium increases considerably during the first half and then diminishes greatly.

In various mammals (rat, guinea pig, opossum, and others) the cyclic changes in the vaginal epithelium can be correlated with the ovarian and uterine changes, so that it is simply necessary to examine washings from the vagina to make a diagnosis of the stage in the ovarian cycle. The cyclic vaginal changes in the rat and guinea pig are as follows: During the rapid growth period of the graafian follicle the epithelium grows rapidly, so that ten to fifteen layers can be recognized,

and leukocytes which were previously abundant disappear from the mucous membrane. A thick layer of squamous cells forms, in which the nuclei can no longer be stained. About the time of ovulation the squamous cell layer is sloughed, and leukocytes swarm through the epithelium in vast numbers. The cheesy mass which fills the lumen is discharged. In the guinea pig the vaginal orifice is sealed by an epithelial proliferation. During the rest of the cycle the epithelium is of the low stratified squamous type, and leukocytes continue to pass through it.

Vaginal lavages can accordingly be assigned to definite stages of the estrus cycle.

I. Proestrus associated with rapidly growing follicles. Leukocytes disappear from the lavage, and only nucleated epithelial cells are present.

II. *Estrus* associated with ripe follicles. All nucleated epithelial cells are gradually replaced by squamous "plates" with no visible nuclei. The female will mate only during this stage, rarely during stage I.

III. *Metaestrus.* The vagina is filled with a mass of

sloughed epithelial plates; leukocytes begin to appear and rapidly become numerous. Ovulation occurs during this stage or between stages II and III.

IV. *Diestrus.* Until the beginning of the next cycle the lavage has nucleated epithelial cells, squamous plates and large numbers of leukocytes.

EXTERNAL GENITALIA

The outer sexual organs comprise the clitoris, the labia majora and minora, and certain glands which open into the vestibulum vaginae.

The *clitoris* corresponds embryologically to the dorsal part of the penis; it consists of two small, erectile, cavernous bodies, ending in a rudimentary glans clitoridis, which is covered by the mucous membrane of the vestibulum vaginae, the space flanked by the labia minora. Into this space the vagina and

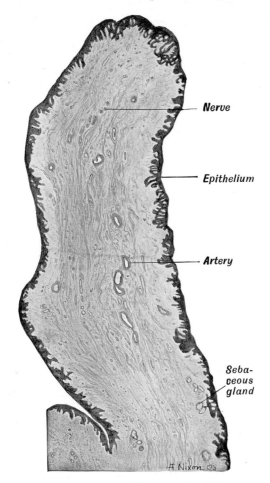

Fig. 521. Cross section of labium minus of a woman of thirty-four years. 10 ×.

the urethra open; it is lined with stratified squamous epithelium. Around the opening of the urethra and on the clitoris are several small glands—*glandulae vestibulares minores*; they resemble the glands of Littré in the male urethra, and contain mucous cells.

Two larger glands, the *glandulae vestibulares majores*, or *glands of Bartholin*, each the size of a bean, are located in the lateral walls of the vestibule. They open on the inner surface of the labia minora. They are of tubulo-alveolar character, closely correspond structurally to the bulbo-urethral glands of men, and secrete a similar lubricating mucus. After the thirtieth year they gradually begin to undergo involution.

The *labia minora* are covered with stratified squamous epithelium and have a core of spongy connective tissue with fine elastic networks and a large quantity of blood vessels, but without fat cells. It forms high papillae penetrating deep into the epithelium; the latter contains pigment in its deeper layer, while on the surface a thin, horny layer is present. Numerous, large sebaceous glands are found on both surfaces; they are devoid of hair.

The *labia majora* are folds of skin with a large amount of fat tissue and a thin layer of smooth muscle, as in the scrotum. The outer surface is covered with hair; the inner is smooth and hairless. On both surfaces sebaceous and sweat glands are numerous.

The outer genital organs are richly supplied with sensory nerve endings. The epithelium contains the usual free nerve endings. In the papillae, Meissner corpuscles, in the subpapillary layer, genital corpuscles are scattered. In the deeper parts of the connective tissue of the labia majora and in the cavernous bodies of the clitoris, pacinian corpuscles have been found.

CORRELATIONS IN THE FEMALE REPRODUCTIVE SYSTEM

Hormones are concerned in the embryonic development of the reproductive tract, but opinion is divided on whether these are exactly the same as the hormones of the adult (see reviews by Jost and by

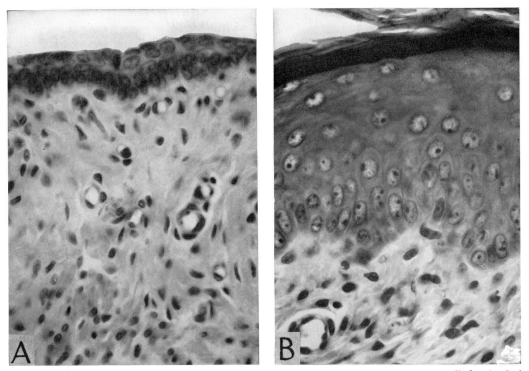

Fig. 522. Photomicrographs of vagina of immature rats to show effects of injection of follicle-stimulating hormone. A, Mature, B, immature rat injected with hormone. The hypertrophied epithelium is in process of shedding cornified epithelium on the free surface. For lower magnification, see Figure 272. Zenker-formol, H + E. 510 ×.

Moore). The changes of puberty are under hormonal control, and estrogens are probably the immediate agents concerned. Excision of both ovaries at an early stage arrests the development of the uterus and the secondary sex characters. During the period of sexual activity the ovarian hormones, *estrone* and *progesterone*, control the tubal, uterine and vaginal changes. Removal of the ovaries in a sexually mature female abolishes menstruation in women and estrus in animals. This is accompanied by involution of the uterus and is an artificial menopause. Injection of estrogens for a short time into ovariectomized females will produce uterine bleeding. But injection of estrogen over long periods will inhibit menstruation, even if the ovaries are intact.

The follicle-stimulating and luteinizing hormones of the hypophysis together cause the preovulatory growth and rupture of ovarian follicles; the increased secretion of these hormones is caused by the action of estrogen and possibly progesterone on the pituitary. Other endocrines are also involved in the control of pregnant and nonpregnant cycles. Psychic states may influence the menstrual rhythm in women, and direct relations between the central nervous system and the hypophysis have been demonstrated. The complex interrelationships which control the reproductive organs are reviewed in detail in *Sex and Internal Secretions*, edited by E. Allen, and more recently in books by Burrows and by Turner.

In the vast majority of mammals, mating occurs only when the female is in "in heat," or estrus. In primates there is no definite period of heat. In the human species the most obvious external indications of the reproductive cycle are hemorrhages. The menstrual cycle is, however, fundamentally similar to the estrus cycle, if it is divided into preovulation and postovulation phases. Under optimal conditions the correlated ovarian and uterine changes are more or less as in-

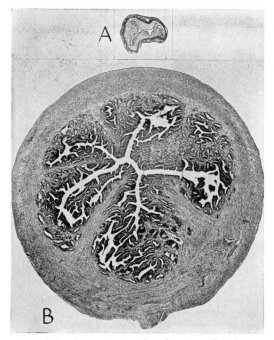

Fig. 523. Photomicrographs of uterus of immature rabbits to show effects of priming with small doses of estradiol (five days) followed by six daily injections of progesterone. A, Normal, B, injected with estradiol and progesterone. For estradiol effects with larger dose, see Figure 525. Progesterone caused a marked hypertrophy of all layers of the uterus. The uterine epithelium is strikingly affected. Zenker-formol, H+E. 14 ×.

dicated in Figure 508, which illustrates nonpregnant cycles. Thus ovulation may occur from seven to twenty-two days after the onset of a menstrual flow, and the endometrium will vary accordingly. One cycle may be twenty-four days in length, the next twenty-eight or thirty-two days.

It is believed that secretion of *estrone* by the growing follicle causes regeneration of the endometrium after menstruation, while *progesterone*, secreted by the corpus luteum, causes the progravid changes of the endometrium as a potential nidation site for a fertilized ovum.

Estrone is probably secreted by the follicular cells, although there is some evidence which suggests that it may be formed by the theca interna. The interval between the follicular phase and the lutein phase involves a superficial endometrial hyperemia and sometimes diapedesis of erythrocytes with the ap-

pearance of blood in the vagina. If the follicular phase has been produced with estrone in a spayed female, progravid changes will appear on the administration of progesterone. It would seem that the ischemic phase with the associated involution of the endometrium is due to a reduction in the available ovarian hormones, and there is evidence that the corpus luteum is regressing at this time. It has been suggested that the ovarian hormones, having been kept at a definite high threshold for a definite time, inhibit the gonadotrophic activity of the distal hypophysis, and this is the reason for the diminished production by the ovary (Corner). Whether the hemorrhagic changes involve other hormonal mechanisms or not remains to be seen.

If the ovum is not fertilized, the corpus luteum regresses, and the anterior pituitary makes follicle-stimulating hormones; this starts a new ovarian cycle. If the ovum is fertilized, the developing placenta secretes a luteinizing hormone (placental gonadotrophin), which keeps the corpus luteum active and probably inhibits the hypophysis from secreting follicle-stimulating hormone. After several months' pregnancy, the placenta produces large amounts of progesterone, and removal of the ovaries will not interrupt pregnancy.

The estrus state appears at intervals which vary according to the species (four to five days in the rat, fifteen to seventeen days in the guinea pig, about three weeks in the sow, twice yearly in the bitch and ewe). Wild species such as the opossum and ground squirrel, which have a definite breeding season, exhibit several cycles if pregnancy is prevented. In the absence of pregnancy, the cycles in domestic animals continue throughout the year when food and temperature conditions are kept optimal.

During estrus graafian follicles are approaching maturity, the content of estrone in the blood is high, and its action is manifested by the behavior of the animal and the anatomical and physiological reactions of the reproductive tract. In the rat (Long and Evans, 1922), as the follicles approach maturity, there is a rapid secretion of fluid by the uterine glands, so that the

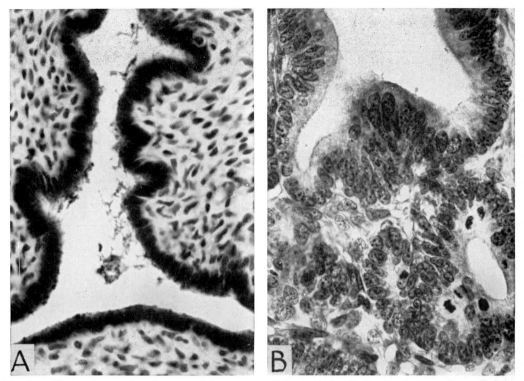

Fig. 524. Photomicrographs of uterus of immature rabbits to show effects of priming with small doses of estradiol (five days) followed by six daily injections of progesterone. A, Normal, B, injected with estradiol and progesterone. For estradiol effects alone, see Figure 526. For lower magnification, see Figure 523. Note mitotic figures in B accompanying the epithelial hypertrophy. Zenker-formol, H + E. 400 ×.

organ is greatly distended. The active proliferation of vaginal epithelium is interpreted by Papanicolaou as an adaptation for mating. The changes of these phases of the cycle (proestrus and estrus) have been produced experimentally by estrogens in spayed animals.

After ovulation the ova pass into the tube and reach the uterus on the fourth day. In the interim the uterus has collapsed and the vaginal epithelium has been sloughed. As the corpora lutea develop, the uterine muscle becomes less active, and then the ova, if fertilized, are regularly spaced along the uterine horns. If mating has not occurred, regressive changes appear in the corpora lutea, uterus and vagina, and a new cycle begins.

In the rabbit, ovulation is not spontaneous. An isolated female in heat has about ten large graafian follicles in the ovaries. After mating, these follicles grow rapidly, and in about ten hours ovulation occurs. The stimulus of coitus involves the portio vaginalis of the cervix and an erogenous area of skin on the flanks. The resulting nervous impulses pass to the spinal cord and brain. Through a center in the hypothalamus the pars distalis of the hypophysis is stimulated to secrete gonadotrophic hormones which activate the ovaries. If one and one quarter hours elapse between mating and hypophysectomy, enough gonadotrophic substance enters the blood stream to induce ovulation

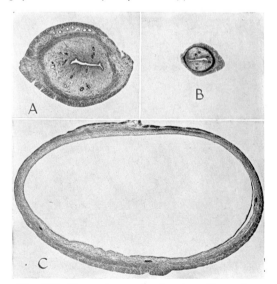

Fig. 525. Photomicrographs showing effects of castration and of injection of estradiol benzoate for ten days on uterus of adult rats. A, Normal, B, castrate of same age; C, castrate of same age injected with estrogen. The atrophic uterus of the castrate is markedly affected by the estrogen. All layers are hypertrophied, and lumen is distended. Zenker-formol, H + E, 15 ×.

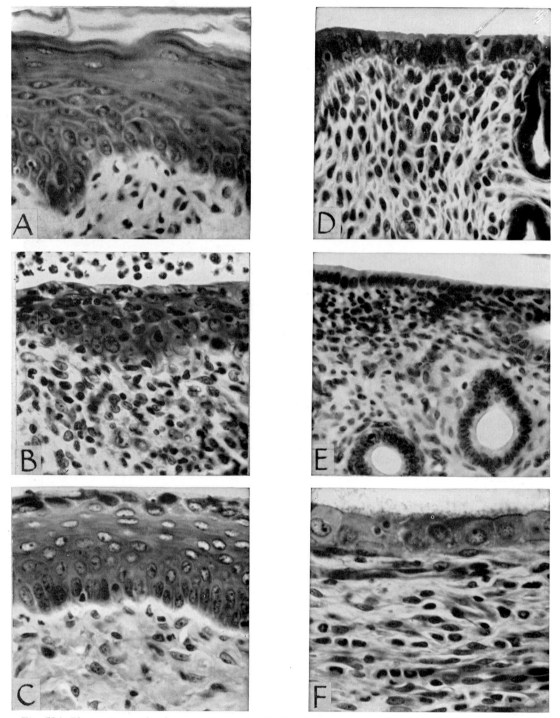

Fig. 526. Photomicrographs showing effects of castration and of injection of estradiol benzoate for ten days on vagina (A, B, C) and uterus, (D, E, F) of adult rats. A and D, Normal rat; B and E, castrate of same age; C and F, castrate of same age injected with estrogen. For lower magnification, see Figures 527 and 525. The atrophic epithelial and connective tissue components are restored toward normal by the estrogen. Zenker-formol, H + E. 510 ×.

(Fee and Parks). Under these conditions corpora lutea develop, but they promptly regress (Smith and White), and, in the consequent absence of progesterone, the fertilized eggs die. Such corpora can be maintained in a functional state either by gonadotrophins or by estrone (Westman, 1937).

Comparison of the Structure of Testis and Ovary. The sex cells in the testis and ovary of the embryo arise from the same germinal epithelium. In the testis of the adult it persists as a flattened mesothelium on the outer surface of the albuginea. On the surface of the adult ovary it remains more or less unchanged.

The spermatogenic cells and the ova undergo comparable developmental transformations; both pass through a period of intense mitotic activity of the ordinary somatic type —period of multiplication. After that they both grow without dividing and are transformed into primary spermatocytes and primary ovocytes respectively (Fig. 494, b, b') —period of growth. Finally, both spermatogenic cells and ova pass through the period of maturation, characterized by the two "meiotic" divisions. In both cases the result is a sex cell ready for fertilization, with a nucleus containing but one half of the somatic number of chromosomes.

Spermia are produced anew continuously, or at certain intervals, during the whole sexual life of the individual, while the ova in primates probably complete their period of multiplication shortly before birth or in the first weeks of extra-uterine life. Then, slowly, one by one, they undergo the maturation divisions. The vast majority of them degenerate before they reach this stage.

In various rodents, eggs develop from the germinal epithelium throughout infancy and even during sexual maturity.

The embryonic origin of the Sertoli cells in the testis and of the follicular epithelium in the ovary is the same. In the adult, both protect the developing sex cells and furnish them suitable nutritive material. The possibility of production of spermatogenic cells by Sertoli cells has been mentioned; a similar production of new ova by the follicular cells in the mammals has not been observed.

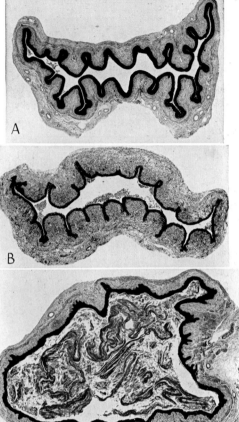

Fig. 527. Photomicrographs showing effects of castration and of injection of estradiol benzoate for ten days on vagina of adult rats. A, Normal, B, castrate of same age; C, castrate of same age injected with estrogen. Same animals as those used to show uterine effects (see Fig. 525). The squamous epithelium of the normal is converted in the castrate to an epithelium riddled with polymorphonuclear cells which pass into the lumen. This is transformed by estrogen to a heavily cornified epithelium which has shed many cornified cells into the lumen. Zenker-formol, H + E. 15 ×.

The interstitial cells are far less constant in the mammalian ovary than in the testis. They probably arise from the theca interna of atretic follicles; in the human ovary they may even be absent.

The morphological relations and similarities between the two sex glands are revealed best in their embryonic histogenesis.

Histogenesis of the Sex Glands. The primordia of the gonads arise as thickened strips of mesodermal epithelium on the surface of the urogenital folds—the

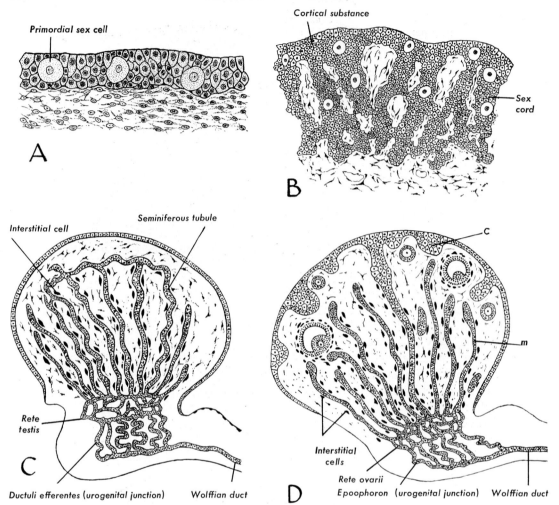

Fig. 528. Diagram of development of the sex glands. A, Primordium in early indifferent stage (*germinal plate*) with primordial sex cells. B, Later but still indifferent stage, showing formation of sex cords. C, Development of testis. D, Development of ovary: c, cortical substance with formation of follicles; the medullary cords (*m*) are homologues of seminiferous tubules (in C) and, like them, are derivatives of the sex cords (in B). (After Kohn.)

genital ridges. The *germinal epithelium* of the ridge has the same structure at first in both sexes. This is the "indifferent" stage of the gonad, although the sex of the embryo is probably determined at the time of fertilization.

The excretory ducts of the sexual apparatus develop in close connection with the embryonic urinary system, being laid down as two longitudinal ducts on both sides—the *ducts of Wolff* and of *Müller*. They arise from the mesoderm which lines the celom, and both open into the urogenital sinus. When the thickened germinal epithelium in the male embryo develops into the seminiferous tubules, the wolffian duct comes into connection with them and furnishes the excretory system of the male sexual gland, while the duct of Müller involutes, leaving only small rudiments.

In the female the same mesodermal primordium of the gonad is transformed into the ovary. Here the wolffian ducts regress, whereas the müllerian ducts furnish the oviducts, the uterus and the vagina.

The germinal epithelium of the "indifferent" gonad consists of two kinds of cells. The majority are small, cuboidal or columnar elements in a pseudostratified layer or in several layers. They contain threadlike mitochondria and show numerous mitoses. Between them, large spherical elements are scattered—the *primitive sex cells.* They are far less numerous, and their number can be counted in some species. They have a clear cytoplasm, a large vesicular nucleus and granular mitochondria. They show occasional mitotic divisions.

There is a massive penetration of the subjacent mesenchyme by epithelium in which the sex cords de-

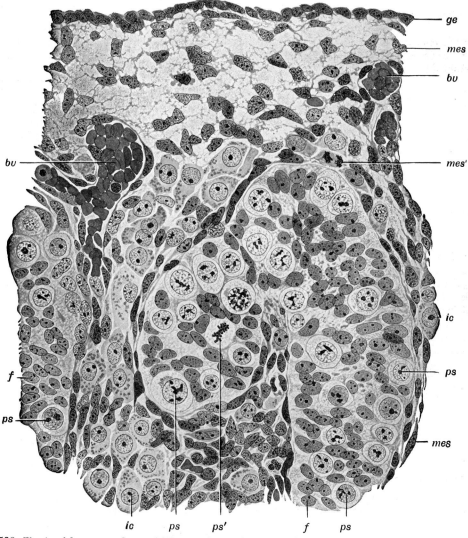

Fig. 529. Testis of human embryo of 70 mm. Seminiferous tubules without free lumen, with two kinds of cells. *ps* and *ps'*, Primordial sex (spermatogenic) cells and, *f*, follicular (future Sertoli) cells. Between the tubules abundant interstitial tissue, with mesenchymal cells (*mes, mes'*) and interstitial cells (*ic*); *bv*, blood vessels; *ge*, germinal epithelium. 585 ×. (A.A.M.)

velop. They consist of the same two cell types as the germinal epithelium. The deepest parts of the epithelial mass consist of smaller cells arranged in a network which later receives a lumen—the rete. It is present in both sexes.

In the male human embryo the testis becomes recognizable at about seven weeks. The sex cords are transformed into convoluted seminiferous tubules. Their peripheral ends anastomose and open through the rete testis into the tubules of the mesonephros (the future coni vasculosi) and beyond into the wolffian duct (the future vas deferens, Fig. 528).

Throughout the prepubertal period, the seminiferous tubules seem to contain the same two apparently independent cell types. The primary sex cells are scattered singly between the small epithelial cells (Figs. 529, 530).

At the onset of puberty, the sex cells begin to proliferate. They become spermatogonia, and the "follicular" epithelial cells gradually assume the structure of Sertoli cells. Once spermatogenesis starts, it continues without interruption throughout the sexual life.

The beginning of sexual differentiation may be determined in female embryos at eight weeks. Mesenchyme grows into the solid epithelial mass and separates it into thin *medullary cords* (Fig. 528), homologues of the seminiferous tubules, and become connected with the tubules of the mesonephros. They contain primitive sex cells (*primitive ova*) and may even show transient formation of rudimentary follicles which disappear.

In human embryos of four to five months a new cortical layer of epithelium is formed (Fig. 531). This second proliferation period produces the primitive cortex of the ovary. Mesenchymal strands with blood vessels penetrate the epithelial cortex, and subdivide it into cell clusters of irregular form. The ova are surrounded by the smaller epithelial cells—the primary follicles.

The sex cells in the cortex of the embryonic human ovary now show the same nuclear transformations as in the spermatogenic cells (Fig. 531). The resting nuclei of the ova have a few large chromatin particles and a nucleolus. Such cells, at the end of the period of multiplication, correspond to spermatogonia and are called *oogonia*.

The older oogonia enter the period of growth and become *primary ovocytes*—homologues of the primary spermatocytes. Their body enlarges, and the chromatin is arranged in thin threads interlacing in the nuclear space (leptotene stage, Fig. 531). Later, the threads, often joining one another side by side, are coiled up at one pole of the nucleus (synaptene stage, Fig. 531). The pachytene and diplotene stages develop later in the same way as in spermatogenesis.

After the diplotene stage is reached, further transformation of the ovocytes ceases for a long time. Such ovocytes in the follicles contain a large chromatin nucleolus and, near the nucleus, a crescentic accumulation of mitochondria. After birth the ovocytes in the primary follicles gradually undergo the transformations described early in this chapter.

In the ovary of a human embryo of about 180 mm., mesenchyme reaches the surface layer of germinal epithelium and forms the albuginea which separates the definitive cortex from the epithelial sheet on the surface. After this, according to the dominant opinion,

additional ova are not formed from the germinal epithelium. Thus the medullary cords of the ovary are homologous to the seminiferous tubules of the testis.

Interstitial Cells. The interstitial cells of the testis appear first in the human embryo of 19.5 mm. They arise from mesenchymal cells, although some claim that they may come from cells of the sex cords. In the second half of embryonic life, the interstitial cells in the testis are arranged in broad strands between the seminiferous tubules. Toward the end of gestation their number decreases relatively. At the beginning of puberty they again become more conspicuous.

The first interstitial cells are found in human embryos of 4 cm. Mesenchymal origin seems clear, but some investigators derive them from germinal epithelium. After a period of numerical increase, they involute or become connective tissue cells. In embryos of 7 cm. another period of development begins in the medulla of the ovary; hypertrophy of the mesenchymal cells is more pronounced. Involution occurs again shortly after birth. The third generation of interstitial cells appears in the cortex around the follicles before the second has disappeared. In post-embryonic life there are no cells resembling interstitial cells except the theca cells of atretic follicles.

Origin of Definitive Sex Cells. A disputed question is the origin of the definite sex cells.

In some lower invertebrates (Ascaris) the sex cells are separate from somatic cells in early stages of ontogenesis. This continuity of the sex or germ cells throughout innumerable generations is called the "germ track."

Many investigators have tried to establish the existence of a germ track in mammals. Cells have been found in early stages of development in the guinea pig which have the aspect of ova—the primitive sex cells. They were first found in the mass of undifferentiated cells at the posterior end of the primitive streak and in the entoderm of the posterior part of the in-

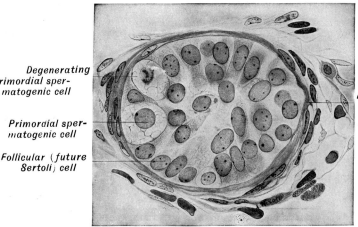

Degenerating primordial spermatogenic cell

Primordial spermatogenic cell

Follicular (*future Sertoli*) cell

Basement membrane

Fig. 530. Section of seminiferous tubule of testis of six months' infant. Iron-hematoxylin. 720 ✕.

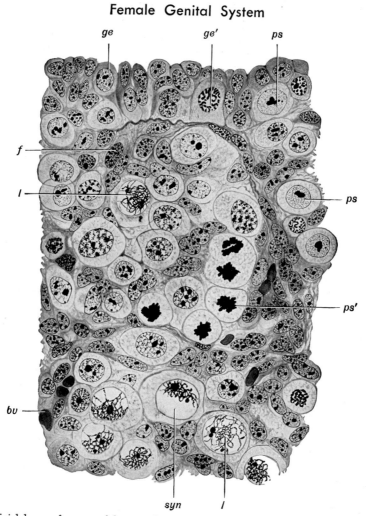

Fig. 531. Superficial layer of ovary of human fetus of 4.5 months. *ge*, Germinal epithelium with mitosis (*ge'*); *ps*, *ps'*, primordial sex cells (ova) with mitosis; *l*, leptotene nuclei in growing ovocytes; *syn*, synaptene nuclei; *f*, follicular cells, *bv*, blood vessels. 625 ×. (A.A.M.)

testine. These primitive sex cells were seen to migrate through the mesenchyme to the root of the mesentery and to enter the thickened celomic epithelium of the primordium of the gonad. In the description given they were mentioned as one of the two cell types present in the germinal epithelium.

In many of the lower vertebrates (chick, reptiles, amphibians, fishes) cells with a similar history have been found. If, in young amphibian and chick embryos, the parts containing the primitive sex cells are excised on one side, the corresponding gonad does not develop, or remains sterile. Although the primitive sex cells have not been traced back to the earliest stages of ontogenesis, the evidence seems to be in favor of the existence of a germ track in the other mammals and, perhaps, in man.

This conclusion is, however, far from being generally admitted. Numerous investigators point out that

the primitive sex cells sooner or later degenerate and disappear among the epithelial cells of the sex cords and follicles, especially in mammalian embryos. They claim that the definitive sex cells of the adult develop secondarily in the germinal epithelium or, later, in the sex cords, through transformation of the common celomic epithelial cells. If this is true, then there is no germ track in the vertebrates. This conception of the nature of the definitive sex cells would gain strong support if certain observations mentioned for the mature sexual glands could be confirmed—the neoformation of spermatogonia from Sertoli cells as described in the regeneration of the seminiferous epithelium after x-raying, the postpubertal neoformation of ova from the germinal epithelium and the regeneration of the ovarian cortex after injuries.

It may be, however, that the apparently undifferentiated cells which give rise to definitive sex cells are primordial sex cells which have de-differentiated during development and do not again differentiate until an adequate stimulus is given.

REFERENCES

Allen, E. (ed.): Sex and Internal Secretions. Baltimore, 1939.

Allen, E., Pratt, J. P., Newell, S. U., and Bland, L. J.: Human Ova from Large Follicles; Including a Search for Maturation Divisions and Observations on Atresia. Am. J. Anat., 46:1, 1930.

de Allende, I. L. C., Shorr, E., and Hartman, C. G.: A Comparative Study of the Vaginal Smear Cycle of the Rhesus Monkey and the Human. Contrib. to Embryol. Carnegie Inst. Wash., 31:1, 1945.

Bartelmez, G. W.: Some Effects of Fixation and Other Insults on Uterine Epithelial Cells in Primates. Anat. Rec., 77:509, 1940; Menstruation, Glandular Therapy, Symposium, Chap. 13, Chicago, 1942.

Bartelmez, G. W., and Bensley, C. M.: Human Uterine Gland Cells, in Cowdry's Special Cytology. 2d ed. New York, (3), 1523, 1932.

Burrows, H.: Biological Actions of Sex Hormones. London, 2d ed. Cambridge University Press, 1949.

Corner, G. W.: Cytology of the Ovum, Ovary, and Fallopian Tube, in Cowdry's Special Cytology. 2d ed. New York, (3), 1565, 1932; Influence of the Ovarian Hormones, Oestrin and Progestin upon the Menstrual Cycle of the Monkey. Am. J. Physiol., 113:238, 1935; Corner, G. W.: Ourselves Unborn. Yale University Press, 1945.

Danforth, D. N.: The Fibrous Nature of the Human Cervix, and Its Relations to the Isthmic Segment in Gravid and Non-Gravid Uteri. Am. J. Obst. & Gyn. 53:541, 1947.

Daron, G. H.: The Arterial Pattern of the Tunica Mucosa of the Uterus in *Macacus Rhesus*. Am. J. Anat., 58:349, 1936.

Dempsey, E. W., and Wislocki, G. B.: Histo-chemical Reactions Associated with Basophilia and Acidophilia in the Placenta and Pituitary Gland. Am. J. Anat., 76:277, 1945.

Duke, K. L.: The Germ Cells of the Rabbit Ovary from Sex Differentiation to Maturity. J. Morphol., 69:51, 1941.

Engle, E. T.: Proceedings of the Conference on Diagnosis in Sterility. Springfield, Ill., Charles C Thomas, 1946.

Engle, E. T., and Smith, P. E.: Some Uterine Effects Obtained in Female Monkeys during Continued Oestrin Administration, with Especial Reference to the Cervix Uteri. Anat. Rec., 61:471, 1935.

Everett, J. W.: Pituitary-Ovarian Relationships. Progress in Clin. Endocrin., Jan., 1950.

Everett, W. B.: The Origin of Ova in the Adult Opossum. Anat. Rec., 82:77, 1942.

Gellhorn, A., Flexner, L. B., and Hellman, L. M.:
The Transfer of Sodium across the Human Placenta. Am. J. Obst. & Gyn., 46:668, 1943.

Gruenwald, P.: The Development of the Sex Cords in the Gonads of Man and Mammals. Am. J. Anat., 70:359, 1942.

Hertig, A. T., and Rock, J.: Two Human Ova of the Pre-villous Stage, Having a Developmental Age of about Seven and Nine Days Respectively. Contrib. Embryol., Carnegie Inst. Wash. Publ. No. 557, 65, 1945.

Hisaw, F. L.: Development of the Graafian Follicle and Ovulation. Physiol. Rev., 27:95, 1947.

Jost, A.: Le controle hormonal de la differentiation du sexe. Biol. Rev., 23:201, 1948.

Kohn, A.: Der Bauplan der Keimdrüsen. Arch. f. Entwicklungsmech., 47:95, 1920.

Latta, J. S., and Pederson, E. S.: The Origin of Ova and Follicle Cells from the Germinal Epithelium of the Ovary of the Albino Rat as Demonstrated by Selective Intravital Staining with India Ink. Anat. Rec., 90:23, 1944.

Lewis, W. H.: A Human Tubal Egg, Unfertilized. Bull. Johns Hopkins Hosp., 48:368, 1931.

Long, J. A., and Evans, H. M.: The Oestrus Cycle in the Rat and Its Associated Phenomena. Mem. Univ. California, (6), 1922.

Markee, J. E.: Menstruation in Intraocular Endometrial Transplants in the Rhesus Monkey. Contrib. Embryol., Carnegie Inst. Wash. Publ. 518, 219, 1940.

Moore, C. R.: On the Role of Sex Hormones in Sex Differentiation in the Opossum. Physiol. Zool., 14:1, 1941; Moore, C. R.: The Role of the Fetal Endocrine Glands in Development. J. Clin. Endocrinology, 10:942, 1950.

Nielson, P. E.: A Study with Radioactive Phosphorus of the Permeability of the Rat Placenta to Phospholipid. Am. J. Physiol., 135:670, 1942.

Papanicolaou, G. N.: The Sexual Cycle in the Human Female as Revealed by Vaginal Smears. Am. J. Anat., 52:519, 1933.

Rock, J., and Hertig, A. T.: Information Regarding the Time of Human Ovulation Derived from a Study of Three Unfertilized and Eleven Fertilized Ova. Am. J. Obst. & Gyn., 47:343, 1944.

Rossman, I.: On the Lipin and Pigment in the Corpus Luteum of the Rhesus Monkey. Contrib. Embryol., Carnegie Inst. Wash. Publ. No. 541, 97, 1942.

Sawyer, C. H., Everett, J. W., and Markee, J. E.: A Neural Factor in the Mechanism by Which Estrogen Induces the Release of Luteinizing Hormone in the Rat. Endocrinology. 44:218, 1949.

Schmidt, I. G.: Proliferation in the Genital Tract of the Normal Mature Guinea Pig Treated with Colchicine. Am. J. Anat., 73:59, 1943.

Schroeder, R.: Die weiblichen Genitalorgane. Handb. d. mikr.-Anat. (v. Möllendorff), (70), 329, 1930.

Snyder, F. F.: Changes in the Human Oviduct during the Menstrual Cycle and Pregnancy. Bull. Johns Hopkins Hosp., 35:141, 1924.

Strassmann, E. O.: The Theca Cone and Its Tropism toward the Ovarian Surface, a Typical Feature of Growing Human and Mammalian Follicles. Am. J. Obst. & Gynec., 41:363, 1941.

Wislocki, G. B., and Bennett, H. S.: The Histology and Cytology of the Human and Monkey Placenta, with Special Reference to the Trophoblast. Am. J. Anat., 73:335, 1943.

Wislocki, G. B., and Dempsey, E. W.: Histo-chemical Reactions of the Endometrium in Pregnancy. Am. J. Anat., 77:365, 1945.

Witschi, E.: Migration of the Germ Cells of Human Embryos from the Yolk Sac to the Primitive Gonadal Folds. Carnegie Institute of Washington Publication, Contributions to Embryology, 32:67, 1948.

XXXI. THE MAMMARY GLAND

The mammary gland undergoes extensive structural changes which depend on the age and sex of the person and the functional condition of the sexual apparatus. In its structure and development, the mammary gland suggests somewhat a sweat gland. In man, only one pair develops normally and is laid down in the same manner in the embryos of both sexes. In males the gland involutes after birth. In females it continues to develop; it reaches its final development only at the end of pregnancy and remains in this condition until the end of the period of lactation, when it undergoes a partial involution; it becomes markedly atrophic after the menopause.

Resting Mammary Gland. Each mammary gland of a woman consists of fifteen to twenty-five closely adjoining, irregular lobes radiating from the mammary papilla, or nipple. These are separated from one another by layers of connective tissue and much adipose tsisue. Each lobe is provided with an excretory duct 2 to 4.5 mm. in diameter and lined by stratified squamous epithelium. This is the *lactiferous duct*, which runs toward and opens on the nipple and has an irregular, angular form in cross section. Each duct under the areola—the pigmented circular area of skin surrounding the nipple—has a local dilatation, the *sinus lactiferus*; it then becomes constricted again and, curving toward the surface of the skin, opens at the summit of the nipple as an independent opening, 0.4 to 0.7 mm. in diameter.

Each lobe is subdivided by layers of connective tissue, rich in lobular masses of adipose tissue, into lobules of various orders. The smallest consist of elongated tubes or sacs, the alveolar ducts, covered by round evaginations, the alveoli.

The interlobular connective tissue is of the dense type. The intralobular connective tissue is much more cellular than the interlobular tissue and contains fewer collagenous fibers and practically no fat (Fig. 534). This layer of loose connective tissue about the ducts undoubtedly has a functional significance in providing an easily distensible medium for the hypertrophy of the epithelial portions of the organ during pregnancy and lactation.

The wall of the secretory portions, the alveolar ducts and the alveoli, consists of a basement membrane, a layer of myo-epithelial cells and, on the internal surface, a row of low columnar glandular cells. The myo-epithelial cells are especially prominent near the excretory ducts. These cells serve to associate the mammary gland morphogenetically with the sweat glands.

There has been much discussion as to the presence of *alveoli* in the nonlactating breast. According to most descriptions, the epithelial structures consist, during the resting phase, only of ducts and their branches. Some authors, however, believe that the resting breast always has a few alveoli budded off from the ducts and that these are grouped into small lobules. These pass over without definite boundaries into the primary excretory ducts by a simple constriction. The latter, in turn, gradually unite with similar ducts into larger and larger ducts which finally form the lactiferous duct; along its course the latter receives, directly, small ducts from the alveoli close to the nipple.

Each lobe of the mammary gland is thus an independent, compound alveolar gland. The mammary gland is a conglomeration of a variable number of such independent glands—each with its own excretory or lac-

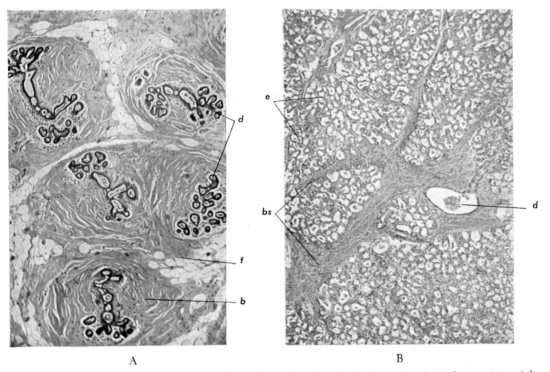

Fig. 532. Sections of human mammary gland. In the resting gland (A) the scattered lobules consist mainly of ducts (d) without terminal portions, and are embedded in dense connective tissue (b) and fat cells (f). In the lactating gland (B) the lobules with their secreting terminal portions (e) are separated by connective tissue septa (bs) which contain the ducts (d). Photomicrographs. H + E. 6 ×. (After von Herrath and Abramow.)

tiferous duct which has its separate opening on the surface of the nipple.

In a mature mammary gland periodical changes undoubtedly take place in connection with the sexual cycle of the ovaries and the uterus. The exact changes which take place have not been studied thoroughly in women. This is due to the difficulty in obtaining portions of the gland in healthy women and correlating their structure with the functional condition of the ovaries and uterus. To date the few studies made are based mainly on postmortem material. This obviously does not help much in elucidating the changes in normal women. It is probable that the changes in the breast which occur with menstruation consist in a hyperemia and perhaps edema of the interstitial connective tissue. The claim that the ductule and acinar epithelium undergoes a marked cyclic hyperplasia—on the order of the progravid changes in the endometrium—is probably unfounded. In laboratory animals, an extensive literature shows quite clearly that the cyclic changes in the breast of the female are intimately bound up with the functional state of the ovaries and uterus.

Nipple and Areola. The skin of the nipple and areola has tall, complex papillae. The epidermis is deeply pigmented, especially after the first pregnancy. Smooth muscles are located both circularly around the papilla mammae and along the length of the lactiferous ducts. In the papillary area are special accessory mammary glands; these are the *areolar glands of Montgomery*. They occupy an intermediate position between the true mammary gland and the sweat glands. Along the margin of the areola are large sweat and sebaceous glands which lack hairs or rudimentary hairs (Fig. 533). These glands often open to the exterior by a common opening with the sweat glands.

Mammary Gland during Gestation. From the time of implantation of the ovum in the uterus, progressive, deep-seated changes take place in the mammary gland. These develop during the period of gestation and can be separated into two phases. During the first half of pregnancy rapid multiplication of the epithelium is noticed at the ends of excretory ducts, and secretory portions are formed devoid of a lumen, but provided with pocket-like evaginations, the alveoli. The masses of interstitial fatty tissue disappear for the most part and make room for the hypertrophy of the epithelial structures. Parallel to this process, an infiltration with round lymphoid cells begins in the surrounding interstitial tissue. During the second part of the pregnancy the multiplication of epithelial cells gradually decreases in intensity, while the glandular cells gradually begin to produce a secretion; at the end of pregnancy the *colostrum* appears. During the first days after delivery the colostrum is replaced by milk, and the infiltration of the stroma of the gland by lymphoid elements becomes less intense.

Mammary Gland during Lactation. The different parts of the active mammary gland are usually not in the same functional state at the same time; therefore their histological appearance varies in different parts of the organ. In some places the secretory portions are filled with milk, their lumen is wide, and the walls are dilated and thin; in others, on the contrary, the lumen is narrow, and the epithelium forms a thick layer; in certain places the glandular elements may be greatly

distended with secretion, while in others they may appear more or less free of it.

The shape of the glandular cells fluctuates from cylindrical or conical to flat. The boundary between them is usually indistinct. If the cells are tall, then their distal ends, as in sweat glands, are often definitely separated from one another and project into the lumen of the alveoli as free, rounded, scalloped or star-shaped protrusions. The nucleus may be round or oval and is located at about the middle of the cell. If the cells are short, their free surface is usually more or less smooth; the nucleus here is frequently shrunken.

In the cytoplasm of the glandular cells are short or long rod-shaped or granular mitochondria. In the flattened cells they are few in number; in the tall conical ones they are more abundant. At the base of the cells is some chromophile substance.

The most characteristic expression of the secretory function is the drops of fat, sometimes of considerable size, which accumulate mainly on the free surface of the cell body projecting into the lumen. After the dissolution of the fat in preparing sections, clear

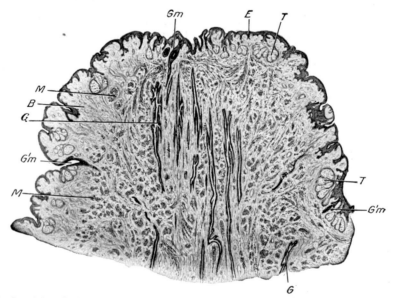

Fig. 533. Nipple of female breast in perpendicular section. B, Connective tissue stroma; E, epidermis; G, longitudinally cut mammary ducts, which open at the apex, Gm, and the sides of the nipple, G'm; M, cross section of circular smooth muscle bundles; T, sebaceous glands without hairs. 6 ×. (After Schaffer.)

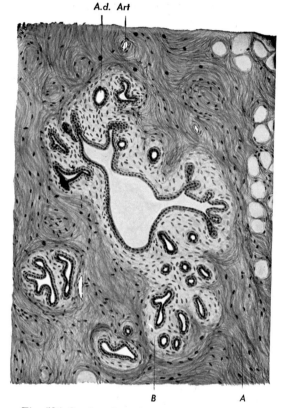

A.d. Art

B   A

Fig. 534. Section through mammary gland (resting state) of a thirty-seven year old woman. A, Interlobular and, B, intralobular connective tissue; Art, artery; A.d., alveolar duct. Hematoxylin-eosin-azure stain. 75 ×. (Drawn by R. L. McKinney.)

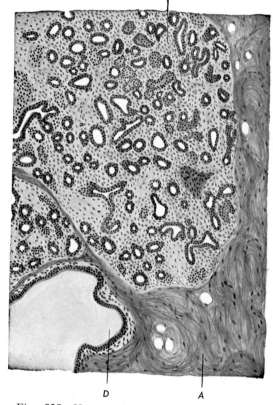

B

D   A

Fig. 535. Hypertrophy of lobule of mammary gland from a woman in the fourth month of pregnancy. D, Duct; A, interlobular connective tissue; B, intralobular connective tissue. Hematoxylin-eosin-azure stain. 75 ×. (Drawn by R. L. McKinney.)

vacuoles remain in place of the fat drops. Sometimes, granules of albuminous substance, with which fat had probably been mixed, also can be seen. Some authors have even described the presence of fat droplets in the nucleus, but this has not been confirmed sufficiently. It is unlikely that the mitochondria change into fat droplets. Cyclic changes in the Golgi net during the phases of secretion have been described.

Besides the fat drops in the peripheral portions of cells, round secretory granules and vacuoles of unknown, probably albuminous nature are sometimes seen. The fat drops, which accumulate in the end of the cell protruding into the lumen, pass out of the protoplasm; in preparations treated with osmic acid this can be observed directly, and the

free fat drops can also be noticed in the lumen of the alveoli (Fig. 537). In preparations from which the fat has been dissolved, the resulting vacuoles appear in many places to be open to the outside, and the distal end of the cell, therefore, appears torn and uneven. The secretory granules of albuminous character have probably been dissolved previously.

It is possible, however, that the process of secretion may, during strong sucking, be accompanied by a partial disintegration of the glandular cell. The portion of the cell, filled with fat drops, which protrudes into the lumen of the alveolus sometimes becomes constricted off from the remaining, larger portion of the cell body which remains in its place. The detached part flows into the

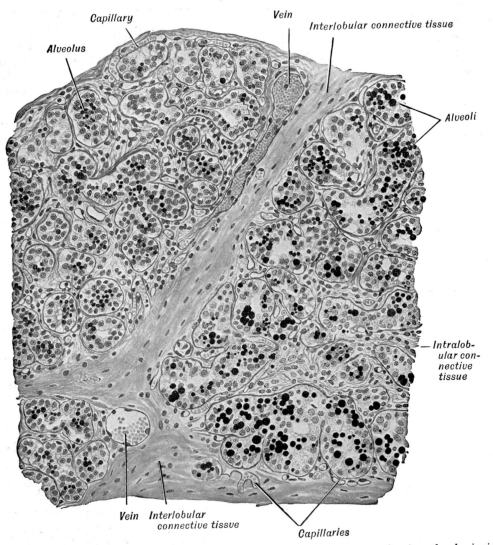

Fig. 536. Mammary gland of woman in the sixth month of pregnancy, showing the beginning of secretory activity with osmic acid-stained droplets of fat (black) in the hypertrophic epithelium. 187 ×. (A.A.M.)

lumen, where the remains of the protoplasm and albuminous granules dissolve and the drops become free. The glandular cell rapidly replaces the lost protoplasm and, after having again accumulated secretion, excretes it in the same way. This type of secretion is intermediate between the merocrine and the holocrine types and is called *apocrine*.

The epithelium of the excretory ducts is cubical or even low cylindrical in the small ones. Between it and the basement membrane, elongated, spindle-shaped myo-epithelial cells are ordinarily seen. In the larger ducts the epithelium becomes taller and cylindrical; in the main lactiferous ducts it is stratified and is replaced by a stratified squamous epithelium at some distance from the opening on the nipple.

The interstitial connective tissue of the lactating mammary gland, which separates the lobes and lobules of various orders, is a rather dense connective tissue distributed in stripes of varying widths. In the functioning gland the mass of the connective tissue is much less than that of the glandular elements. In addition to the collagenous fibers, the interstitial substance contains elastic fibers which form dense networks, particularly along the external surfaces of the excretory ducts. Normally, there are no elastic fibers within the lobules.

In certain places, particularly in the peripheral portions of the organ near the nipple, the interstitial tissue is penetrated by peculiar shafts of smooth muscles connected with tendons of elastic networks.

Those portions of the interstitial connective tissue which extend between the small alveoli and directly cover the secretory portions have different properties—here the tissue is rich in blood vessels, is much looser, and contains a much larger number of cells. In addition to fibroblasts and macrophages, lymphocytes of various types and plasma cells are present here in considerable numbers. In man granular leukocytes are rare, and the presence of a noticeable number of them is always an indication of abnormal, inflammatory changes which have induced the migration of these elements from the blood vessels. In abnormal function of the mammary gland, the penetration of a few wandering elements into the glandular epithelium and inside the alveoli can be observed.

Regression of the Mammary Gland. With the end of the nursing period, a regression takes place in the mammary gland. The glandular elements return to a resting state. The production of milk ceases, the secretion remaining in the glands is absorbed rapidly, an apparent increase in the stroma begins, and the alveoli, owing to a decrease in size and the degeneration of the glandular cells, diminish greatly and lose their lumen. The gland, however, does not return to its original state, because many of the alveoli which had formed during the period of pregnancy do not disappear entirely, and the remains of the secretion may sometimes be retained in the mammary ducts for a considerable time. In such a resting condition the gland remains until the following pregnancy, when the same cycle of changes is repeated.

Involution of the Mammary Gland. In old age the mammary gland gradually undergoes involution. The epithelium of the secretory portions, and partly also of the excretory ducts, atrophies, and the gland tends, in a general way, to return to the prepubertal condition in which there are only a few scattered ducts. On the other hand, the epithelium is not infrequently the seat of a pathological growth.

Equally striking changes occur in the interstitial connective tissue. This becomes decidedly less cellular; the number of collagenous fibrils decreases, and the whole mass becomes more homogeneous and stains much less intensely with eosin. One author has pictured the change as having occurred through a "melting down" of the fibrillar intercellular tissue into a homogeneous mass. When stained with aniline blue, the interstitial substance in such a breast appears finely granular and deep blue.

Blood and Lymphatic Vessels. The blood supply of a functioning mammary gland is much greater than that of a resting gland. The arteries arise from the internal mammary artery, the thoracic branches of the axillary artery and from the intercostal arteries. They pass mainly along the larger ducts and break up into dense

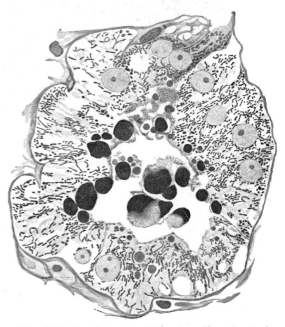

Fig. 537. Alveolus of lactating mammary gland of a rabbit. The cells contain mitochondria and droplets of fat (stained black with osmic acid). The latter, with the adjacent protoplasm, are extruded into the lumen. 1000 ×. (A.A.M.)

capillary networks on the external surface of the basement membrane of the secretory portions (Fig. 536). The veins empty into the axillary and internal mammary veins.

The lymphatic vessels begin with capillary networks located in the connective tissue layers surrounding separate alveoli. They collect along the course of the mammary ducts into a subpapillary lymphatic network. From here several large vessels lead the lymph mainly into the lymphatic nodes in the axilla, but also into connection with the lymphatics leading beneath the sternum, and even into those of the other breast.

Nerves. Besides the nerves which supply the smooth muscles of the blood vessels and of the papilla, the mammary gland has also secretory nerve endings closely connected with the glandular elements, as well as rather numerous sensory nerve endings of the nipple; some of the latter have a structure similar to that of the genital bodies.

Histogenesis of the Mammary Gland. The primordium of the mammary gland appears in a human embryo of 8 mm. as a paired thickening of the epidermis, the "milk line," which begins at the root of the upper extremity and proceeds to the inguinal fold. It continues to thicken and becomes the mammary fold; this is retained in man in only a limited region of its cranial portion as a pair of flat, lens-shaped thickenings. These become hemispherical or club-shaped, epithelial thick-

enings directed toward the underlying connective tissue. This, in turn, thickens and lifts the developing gland slightly above the rest of the surface of the organism (in human embryos 19 to 30 mm. long). In most mammals several pairs of such thickenings are formed.

The cells of this epithelial bud are cylindrical in shape and are arranged radially, while the deeper layers are polyhedral. By continuing to multiply they form, in human embryos of 50 to 60 mm., on the lower convex surface of the body, the primordia of sixteen to twenty-five projections, with swellings at their ends. These projections gradually elongate in the direction of the connective tissue layer and become the mammary ducts. Their number fluctuates with the age of the embryo, since they do not all originate at once; for this reason their lengths, at any given moment, are not equal. The peripheral cells at first maintain their cylindrical shape, while the others are multiangular and have round nuclei. Externally they are gradually covered by a condensing connective tissue. In the course of time each of these cylindrical, epithelial projections or shafts gives rise, by elongation and twisting, to larger and larger numbers of branches; these are also swollen at their ends and are the primordia of the future excretory ducts. A lumen appears in them, except in the terminal swellings, owing to the moving aside and to partial degeneration of the constituent cells. Some of the cells which touch the connective tissue develop into basket cells of so-called "myo-epithelial" nature.

In newborn of both sexes the glands have a diameter of 3.5 to 9 mm., and at this time contain a number of distinct alveolar portions, some of which, however, are rudimentary. At the same time, in the lumen of the developing and branching ducts, a substance is formed which suggests colostrum. This secretion is called witch's milk and contains little but degenerating, fatty epithelial cells; it can be squeezed out of the papilla in newborn infants; it soon disappears.

In males the mammary gland undergoes a regression, and only the nipple remains with the surrounding areola. In females, however, the development, although rather slow, continues, and the slow elongation and branching of the epithelial shaft goes on throughout childhood. With the onset of sexual maturity, the development does not change qualitatively, but increases in intensity and quantity; each original epithelial shaft forms numerous branches through the multiplication of its constituent cells. Having reached a certain degree of development, the organ undergoes but slight changes and remains in a state of functional rest. There is no secretion, and even the secretory portions are missing, according to most authors, who believe that only excretory ducts are present at this time.

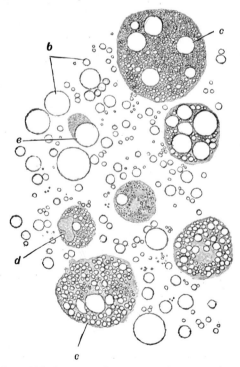

Fig. 538. Human colostrum, fresh preparation. *b*, Milk globules of various sizes; *c*, colostrum bodies with fat droplets of various sizes; *d*, colostrum bodies with nuclei; *e*, milk globules with "caps." 1000 ×.

Histophysiological Remarks. Milk is an aqueous solution of albumins (mainly casein), lactose and inorganic salts (including small amounts of iron) in which numerous fat drops, the *milk globules*, are suspended. Some of these are at the limit of visibility; most of them are 2 to 5 microns and seldom up to 10 to 12 microns in diameter. These are the same fat drops produced and given off by the glandular cells. Small numbers of milk globules with one-sided caps, free disintegrating nuclei, nucleated or non-nucleated fragments of glandular cells, and transformed leukocytes are also found.

All these constituents of the milk can be seen in histological preparations in the lumina of the dilated secretory portions and of the excretory ducts; this is particularly clear after fixation with osmic acid, when the milk globules are stained black. The number of the cellular fragments and leukocytes appears to be larger in the alveoli than in the excreted milk; this shows that these structures autolyze during the excretion of milk.

During the last days of pregnancy, the first two or three days after delivery, and at the end of the period of lactation, the secretion of the mammary gland is quite different from milk and is called *colostrum*. It differs from milk by being poor in fat. But it contains numerous globules with particles of cellular fragments, free nuclei and *colostrum bodies* (9 to 40 microns in diameter). These globular bodies are often capable of active ameboid movements. After fixation and staining they appear as free, large cells with usually one constricted nucleus; their cytoplasm is filled with many small and a few large fat drops. A considerable portion of these elements shows indications of degeneration.

Many authors recognize the colostrum bodies as transformed epithelial glandular cells which are filled with the products of secretion and have become detached. But it is more probable that they are wandering lymphoid cells of various kinds, which have escaped from the connective tissue into the epithelium and into the lumen of the glandular spaces, and which ingest fat droplets by phagocytosis. During the periods when colostrum appears, the interstitial connective tissue which surrounds the secretory portions is heavily infiltrated by hematogenous and histogenous lymphocytes. In fixed preparations these elements may often be seen on their way through the basement membrane into the epithelium and thence into the lumen of the alveolus.

The colostrum bodies always appear when the equilibrium between the secretion of the milk and its excretion is upset, that is, either when the feeding of the child has not yet begun, as in the last days of pregnancy, or when it has come to an end. The presence in the colostrum of hematogenous granular leukocytes, particularly of the neutrophile type, is usually an indication of an inflammatory process in the mammary gland.

The proliferative changes in the gland during gestation are due mainly to hormones arising in the ovary (estrone and progesterone) and apparently acting through the pars distalis of the hypophysis, for these hormones have no effect on the mammary gland in hypophysectomized animals. A mammogenic duct growth factor has been extracted from the pars distalis of the hypophysis. The initiation of lactation seems to be due to the lactogenic hormone of the pars distalis of the hypophysis. The factors involved in lactation are discussed by Petersen.

The production of the colostrum in newborn infants probably depends on the same hormones which bring about the production of milk in the mother. Some believe that there are indications of a dependence of this process on the hypophysis of the embryo.

REFERENCES

Corner, G. W.: The Hormonal Control of Lactation. Am. J. Physiol., 95:43, 1930.

Dempsey, E. W., Bunting, H., and Wislocki, G. B.: Observations on the Chemical Cytology of the Mammary Gland. Am. J. Anat., 81:309, 1947.

Eggeling, H. von: Die Milchdrüse, in Möllendorff's Handbuch der mikroskopischen Anatomie des Menschen. Berlin, 1927, Vol. 3, pp. 1, 117.

Jeffers, K. R.: Cytology of the Mammary Gland of Albino Rat. Am. J. Anat., 56:257, 279, 1935.

Lewis, A. A., and Turner, C. W.: The Mammogenic Hormones of the Anterior Pituitary. I. The Duct Growth Factor. Research Bulletin 310, University of Missouri, College of Agriculture, 1, 1939.

Loeb, L.: The Cytology of the Mammary Gland, in Cowdry's Special Cytology. 2d ed. New York, 3: 1631, 1932.

Lyons, W. R.: Lobulo-alveolar Mammary Growth Induced in Hypophysectomized Rats by Injections of Ovarian and Hypophysial Hormones. Essays in Biology, University of California Press, 1943.

Nelson, W. O.: Endocrine Control of the Mammary Gland. Physiol. Rev., 16:488, 1936.

Petersen, W. E.: Lactation. Physiol. Rev., 24:340, 1944.

Rawlinson, H. E.: The Use of an Iron Stain for the Study of Alveolar Development in the Mouse Mammary Gland. Canadian J. Res., E, 28:1, 1950.

Richardson, K. C.: Contractile Tissues in the Mammary Gland, with Special Reference to Myoepithelium in the Goat. Proc. Roy. Soc. London, s. 136: 30, 1949.

Weatherford, H. L.: A Cytological Study of the Mammary Gland. Golgi Apparatus, Trophospongium, and Other Cytoplasmic Canaliculi. Mitochondria. Am. J. Anat., 44:199, 1929.

Williams, W. L.: Normal and Experimental Mammary Involution in the Mouse as Related to the Inception and Cessation of Lactation. Am. J. Anat., 71:1, 1942.

XXXII. THE EYE

The ability to react to light is a widespread property of living matter, but in complex animals certain cells are specifically adapted to respond to light. Scattered photoreceptive cells in lower animals probably distinguish only varying intensities of light and only crudely perceive the direction of the light stimuli. In the vertebrates, more efficient organs evolved, the eyes, which react not only to various intensities and qualities of light, but are capable of distinguishing the form, size and minute changes in the position of external objects. The photoreceptor organ, the retina, developed from a bilateral outgrowth of the front end of the brain.

STRUCTURE OF THE EYE IN GENERAL

The anterior segment of the eye, the *cornea*, is transparent and permits the rays of light to enter. The rest of the wall of the eye is opaque. It has a darkly pigmented inner surface which absorbs light rays, and is to a great extent lined with photosensitive nervous tissue, the *retina*. The cavity of the eyeball is filled with transparent media arranged in separate bodies. Their surfaces, with those of the cornea, act as a system of convex lenses. These produce an inverted, reduced and real image of the objects of the outside world in the photoreceptive layer of the retina, the rods and cones.

The wall of the eyeball is composed of three coats. The thick and tough outer *fibrous tunic* gives the organ its form and protects its inner delicate structures. It is subdivided into a large, opaque, posterior portion, the *sclera*, and a smaller anterior, transparent segment, the *cornea*. The middle *vascular tunic* or *uvea* is concerned with the nutrition of the ocular tissues, and its smooth muscles provide the mechanism for accommodation. Part of the uvea extends anteriorly as far as the ora serrata and is called *choroidea*. Its anterior portion, the *ciliary body*, is the muscular instrument for the accommodation of the refraction of the eye; it forms a girdle 5 to 6 mm. wide between the ora serrata and the sclerocorneal junction. The *iris*, a thin membrane, is a continuation of the ciliary body and projects over the anterior surface of the lens. The diameter of the iris is approximately 12 mm. Its opening, the *pupil*, can be reduced or expanded through the contraction or relaxation of the *constrictor* and the *dilator muscles* of the pupil. In this way the iris functions as an adjustable *optic diaphragm* regulating the amount of light entering the eye.

The third or innermost tunic, the *retina*, contains in its functioning or optic part the receptors for light and the first links of the nervous pathways conveying impulses through the optic nerve to the brain. The spot where the nerve inserts into the eyeball, the *papilla of the optic nerve*, is a pink disk about 1.4 mm. in diameter. It is situated about 3 mm. nasal to the posterior pole of the eye. The portion of the retina lining the inner surface of the ciliary muscle (*ciliary portion of the retina*) and that lining the posterior surface of the iris (*iridial portion of the retina*) are not photosensitive.

The space enclosed by the tunics of the eye is filled with the transparent *dioptric media*, which must also include the *cornea*. Because of the considerable difference between the index of refraction of the cornea (1.376) and of the surrounding air (1.0), the cornea is the chief refractive apparatus of the eye. Of the enclosed transparent media

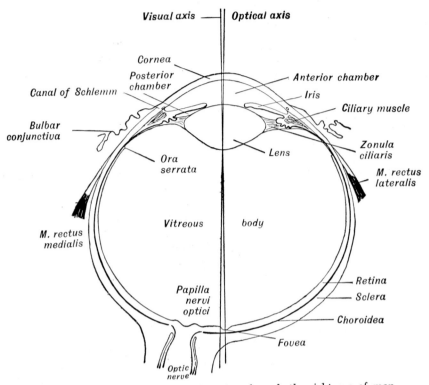

Fig. 539. Diagram of horizontal section through the right eye of man.

the most anterior is the *aqueous humor*. It is contained in the *anterior chamber*, a small cavity bordered in front by the cornea and behind by the ciliary body, the iris and the central portion of the anterior surface of the lens. The *posterior chamber*, also filled with aqueous humor, is a narrow, circular space enclosed by the iris, the lens, and the ciliary and vitreous bodies.

The next of the transparent media is the *crystalline lens*. This is an elastic biconvex body suspended from the inner surface of the ciliary body by a circular ligament, the *ciliary zonule*. It is placed directly behind the pupil, between the aqueous humor of the anterior chamber and the cornea anteriorly, and the vitreous body posteriorly. The lens is second in importance to the cornea as a refractive apparatus of the eye, and is the dioptric organ of accommodation.

The large posterior portion of the cavity of the eye, between the posterior surface of the lens, the ciliary body, and the posterior wall of the eyeball, called *vitreal cavity*, is filled with a viscous transparent substance,

the *vitreous humor* or *body*. It adjoins the retina and permits light to pass freely to the photoreceptors.

The retina is transparent during life. Only its outermost layer, the pigment epithelium, is opaque and forms the first barrier to the rays of light.

MEASUREMENTS AND LANDMARKS

The adult human eyeball is a roughly spherical body about 24 mm. in diameter and weighing 6 to 8 gm. The center of the cornea is the *anterior pole*; the *posterior pole* is located between the fovea and the optic papilla. The line connecting the two poles is the *anatomical axis*. The *visual axis* is the line drawn from the center of the fovea—the spot of most distinct vision—to the apparent center of the pupil. The equatorial plate is vertical to the axis and passes through the greatest expansion of the eyeball, the *equator*. Planes passing through the axis subtend the *meridians* of the eye. The two most important are the vertical and the horizontal meridians. The first passes through the fovea and divides the eyeball, including the retina, into nasal and temporal halves. The plane of the horizontal meridian divides the eyeball and retina into an upper and a lower half. These two planes divide the eyeball and the retina into four quadrants, an upper nasal and an upper temporal, a lower nasal and a lower temporal.

The *anteroposterior diameter* along the axis of the eye is 24 mm., or a little more. The *inner axis*, the distance between the inner surface of the cornea and the inner surface of the retina at the posterior pole, measures a little less than 22 mm. The *optical axis* passes through the optical centers of the refractive media, and is almost identical with the anatomical axis. The visual axis, where it touches the retina, is from 4 to 7 degrees lateral and 3.5 degrees below the optical axis.

The *radius of the curvature* of the large posterior segment around the fundus measures somewhat less than 13 mm., and gradually decreases toward the corneoscleral junction. The cornea has the smallest radius of curvature, approximately 7.8 mm. (outer corneal surface).

The eyeball is lodged in a soft cushion filling the bony orbit of the skull and made up of loose connective and fatty tissue, muscles, fasciae, blood and lymphatic vessels, glands and nerves. This permits the eye to move freely around its *center of rotation*. The eye is connected with the general integument by the conjunctiva. The lids are a mechanical protection against external noxious agents.

FIBROUS TUNIC

The Sclera. The sclera is 1 mm. thick at the posterior pole, 0.4 to 0.3 mm. at the equator, and 0.6 mm. toward the edge of the cornea. The sclera consists of flat collagenous bundles which run in various directions parallel to the surface (Figs. 540, 542, 544). The tendons of the eye muscles are attached to its outer surface. Between these bundles are fine elastic nets. The cells of the sclera are flat, elongated fibroblasts. Chromatophores can be found in the deeper layers, especially in the region of the entrance of the optic nerve.

The outer surface of the sclera is con-

nected with a dense layer of connective tissue—the *capsule of Tenon*—by an exceedingly loose system of thin collagenous membranes separated by clefts—the *space of Tenon*. This arrangement makes rotating movements of the eyeball possible in all directions.

Between the sclera and the choroid is a layer of loose connective tissue with numerous chromatophores, fibroblasts and elastic networks. When these tunics are separated, part of this loose tissue adheres to the choroid and part to the sclera as its *suprachoroid lamina* (Fig. 540).

Cornea. The cornea is slightly thicker than the sclera and measures 0.8 to 0.9 mm. in the center and 1.1 mm. at the periphery. In man the refractive power of the cornea, which is a function of the index of refraction of its tissue (1.376) and of the radius of curvature of its surface (7.8 mm.), is twice as high as that of the lens. The *transparency of the cornea* is high, though less than that of the aqueous humor and of glass. It is due partly to the great regularity of its structural composition, and partly to other factors of chemical nature still incompletely understood.

In a vertical section through the cornea, the following layers can be seen: (1) the epithelium, (2) the membrane of Bowman, (3) the stroma or substantia propria, (4) the membrane of Descemet, (5) the corneal mesenchymal epithelium.

Epithelium. The epithelium is stratified squamous with an average thickness of 50 microns and consists, as a rule, of five layers

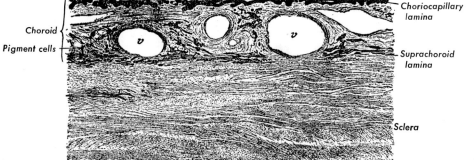

Fig. 540. Choroid and sclera of human eye in cross section. 135 ×. (After Schaffer.)

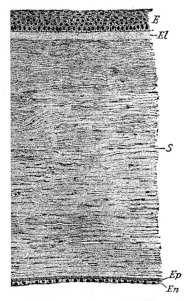

Fig. 541. Vertical transection of middle part of human cornea. *E*, Epithelium; *El*, Bowman's membrane; *S*, substantia propria; *Ep*, membrane of Descemet; *En*, corneal mesenchymal epithelium. 135 ×. (After Schaffer.)

of cells. The outer surface is quite smooth and is composed of large squamous cells. As in other types of stratified squamous epithelium, the cells are connected with one another by thin intercellular bridges. Often lymphoid cells penetrate between the cells and appear as irregular, branched cells of Langerhans; they come from the blood vessels at the periphery of the cornea.

The epithelium of the cornea is extremely sensitive and contains numerous free nerve endings (Fig. 179). It is endowed with a remarkable capacity for regeneration. Small defects of the epithelial layer, caused by injuries, heal rapidly by a flattening and gliding movement of the adjacent epithelial cells. Mitoses in the basal epithelial cells set in later and may be found at considerable distances from the wound. In normal conditions a few mitoses can be found in the basal cell layer.

Bowman's Membrane. The corneal epithelium rests upon the 6 to 9 microns thick, indistinctly fibrillated membrane of Bowman. This is a condensed outer layer of the subadjacent substantia propria, from which

it cannot be isolated. At the periphery of the cornea it ends abruptly. The membrane does not contain elastin.

Substantia Propria. This layer forms about 90 per cent of the cornea (Fig. 541). It is a transparent, regular connective tissue whose bundles form thin lamellae arranged in many layers. In each layer the direction of the bundles is parallel; in adjacent lamellae the bundles intercross at various angles. The lamellae everywhere interchange fibers and thus are kept tightly together. Between the fibrils, the bundles and the lamellae, there is a *mucoid cement* substance. The branching, flattened, corneal fibroblasts store a few dye granules in vitally stained newborn animals. The substantia propria always contains a number of lymphoid wandering cells which migrate from the blood vessels of the corneal limbus. In inflammation enormous numbers of heterophile leukocytes and lymphoid cells penetrate between the lamellae. The substantia propria contains fine elastic networks especially abundant in the innermost layers in front of the membrane of Descemet.

Membrane of Descemet. This is a homogeneous lamella 5 to 10 microns thick. It can be isolated from the posterior surface of the substantia propria. At the periphery of the cornea the membrane of Descemet continues as a thin layer on the surface of the trabeculae of the iridial angle. Although it stains with resorcinfuchsin, its reactions are different from those of elastin. It is a basement membrane probably secreted by the corneal mesenchymal epithelium.

Corneal Mesenchymal Epithelium. The inner surface of the membrane of Descemet is covered by a layer of large, squamous cells.

Sclerocorneal Junction. In a meridional section the boundary between the opaque sclera and the transparent cornea appears as an oblique line (Fig. 544). The outer edge of the sclera overlaps the border of the cornea. When the collagenous bundles of the sclera continue directly into those of the cornea, their striation loses its distinctiveness, and the tissue becomes homogeneous and transparent.

At the marginal zone or limbus of the cornea, the epithelium of the cornea gradually changes into that of the conjunctiva of the bulb. Where the membrane of Bowman ends, a subepithelial layer of loose connective tissue begins; it contains the loops of the vessels which furnish the nutritive materials to the cornea and are the source of the wandering cells mentioned earlier. The blood only when there is stasis in the venous system.

THE UVEA (THE VASCULAR TUNIC)

Choroid Membrane. The choroid is a thin, soft, brown membrane adjacent to the inner surface of the sclera (Fig. 540). Between the sclera and the choroid is a potential cleft, the perichoroidal space; it is trav-

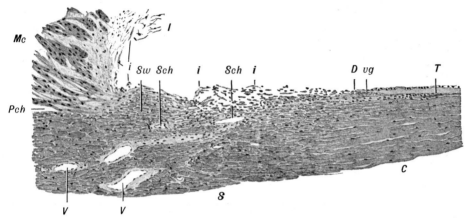

Fig. 542. Meridional section through scleral furrow. C, Cornea; D, border of Descemet's membrane; I, iris root; i, uveal framework; Mc, ciliary muscle; Pch, beginning of perichoroidal space; Sch, canals of Schlemm, with their veins, V; Sw, scleral roll; T, deep root of the scleral framework; vg, anterior marginal ring. 96 ×. (After Salzmann.)

blood vessels which invade the substantia propria in chronic inflammation also arise from these loops.

On the inner surface of the wall of the eyeball, the sclerocorneal junction is marked by a shallow, ring-shaped furrow, the *internal scleral furrow* or *sulcus*. Its posterior lip forms a small, centrally projecting ridge, the *scleral roll*, to which the ciliary body is fastened (Fig. 542). At the bottom of the internal scleral furrow the scleral tissue contains one or several cavities lined with endothelium. They are the cross sections of a circular canal which parallels the border of the cornea and in many places breaks up into several irregular branches which then fuse again. It is the *canal of Schlemm*, or the "venous sinus" of the sclera (Fig. 542). It communicates with the venous system and is believed to drain the aqueous humor from the anterior chamber (see p. 568). It is usually filled with clear liquid, and contains

ersed by thin lamellae which run obliquely from the choroid to the sclera and form a loose, pigmented tissue layer—the *suprachoroid layer*. This is composed of fine, transparent membranes with fibroblasts on their surface and with a rich network of elastic fibers (Fig. 540). Everywhere between and in the lamellae large, flat melanoblasts are scattered. In the suprachoroid, as in the rest of the uvea, are scattered macrophages. The lamellae of the suprachoroid pass without a distinct boundary into the substance of the choroid. This tunic can be subdivided into three main layers. From outside inward they are: (1) the vessel layer, (2) the capillary layer, and (3) the glassy or Bruch's membrane.

Vessel Layer. This layer consists of a multitude of intercrossing large and medium-sized arteries and veins (v in lower part of *Choroid* in Fig. 540). The spaces between the vessels are filled with loose connective tissue rich in chromatophores. The lamellar arrangement here is much less distinct than in the suprachoroid. According to some, the vessel layer contains strands of smooth muscle independent of the arteries.

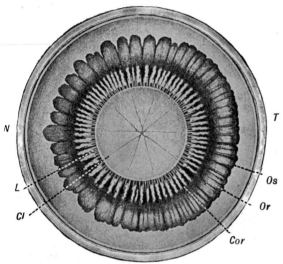

Fig. 543. Anterior half of the eye seen from within. N, Nasal and, T, temporal side; Os, ora serrata retinae; Or, ciliary ring; Cor, ciliary crown; Cl, circumlental space; L, posterior surface of the lens with the lens star. 3 ×. (After Salzmann.)

Choriocapillary Layer. This is formed by a capillary network arranged in one plane (see Fig. 540). In places this layer is connected with the vascular layer. The individual capillaries have a large and somewhat irregular caliber. The net is especially dense and the capillary layer much thicker in the region of the fovea. Anteriorly it ceases near the ora serrata. This layer contains flattened fibroblasts, which have been erroneously described as a separate endothelial layer.

Glassy or Bruch's Membrane. This is a brilliant, limiting line 1 to 4 microns thick between the choroid and the pigment epithelium of the retina. It can be divided into two lamellae. The outer one, facing the capillary layer, is a dense plexus of finest elastic fibers which are the continuation of the elastic nets of the capillary interstices. The inner, thicker lamella is homogeneous, and is produced by the pigment epithelium of the retina.

Ciliary Body. If the eyeball is cut across along its equator, and its anterior half, after removal of the vitreous, is inspected from within, a sharply outlined, dentate border is seen running around the inner surface of the wall in front of the equator. This is the *ora serrata* of the retina. The girdle between the ora and the edge of the lens is the *ciliary body*, a thickening of the vascular tunic. Its surface is covered by the darkly pigmented ciliary portion of the retina. In a meridional section through the eye bulb, the ciliary body appears as a thin triangle with its small base facing the anterior chamber of the eye and attached here by its outer angle to the scleral roll. The long narrow angle extends backward and passes into the choroidea (Fig. 544). The inner surface of the ciliary body is divided into a narrow anterior zone, the *ciliary crown*, and a broader posterior zone, the *ciliary ring* (Fig. 543). The inner surface of the ring has shallow grooves, *ciliary striae*, which run forward from the teeth of the ora. On its inner surface the ciliary crown has seventy radially arranged ridges, the *ciliary processes*.

Ciliary Muscle. The main mass of the ciliary body, exclusive of the ciliary processes, consists of the smooth *ciliary muscle*. It is composed of three portions. Closest to the sclera is the muscle of Brücke, whose bundles are stretched chiefly in the meridional direction. The outer part of the ciliary muscle stretches the choroidea and is also called *tensor muscle of the choroid*. Its role in accommodation is discussed in the section dealing with the lens. In the next inward portion of the ciliary muscle, the bundles of muscle cells radiate fanlike from the region of the scleral roll toward the cavity of the eyeball; this is the *radiated* or *reticular portion of the ciliary muscle*. The third or *circular portion of the ciliary muscle* (of Müller) is usually absent in the newborn, appearing in the course of the second or third year. The meshes between the muscular bundles are filled with a small amount of connective tissue with abundant elastic networks and chromatophores. The latter become especially numerous toward the sclera and where the connective tissue gradually passes into the lamellae of the suprachoroid.

The inner, *vascular layer of the ciliary body* consists of connective tissue with numerous blood vessels. In the ciliary ring it is the direct continuation of the same layer of the choroid. In the region of the ciliary

Next to the connective tissue of the vascular layer of the ciliary body is the thin, dense *elastic lamella.* Inwardly it is followed by a dense collagenous sheet with a few fibroblasts. The inner surface of the uveal portion of the ciliary body is coated with the cuticular lamella.

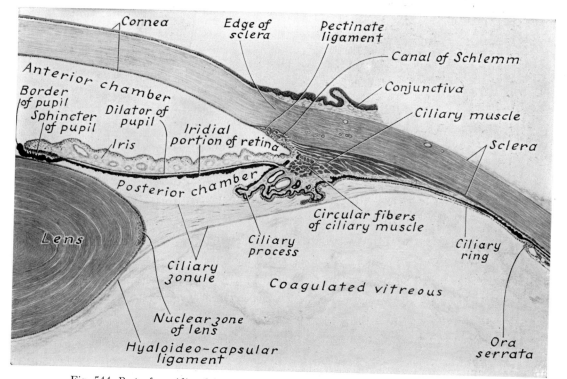

Fig. 544. Part of meridional section of human eye. 14 ×. (Modified after Schaffer.)

crown it covers the inner surface of the ciliary muscle and forms the core of the ciliary processes. The vessels are almost exclusively capillaries and veins of varying caliber. The corresponding arteries branch in the peripheral layers of the ciliary body. The connective tissue is dense, especially near the root of the iris, and contains abundant elastic networks. In old age it often shows hyaline degeneration. Chromatophores are usually found only near the surface of the muscle. The inner surface of the vascular layer of the ciliary body is lined by the continuation of the *glassy membrane* of the choroid. In the region of the ciliary body this membrane splits into three distinct lamellae.

The *ciliary portion of the retina* continues forward beyond the ora serrata and covers the inner surface of the ciliary body. It consists of an outer pigmented layer and of a nonpigmented inner layer and does not receive light stimuli. This deeply pigmented epithelium consists of one layer of columnar cells and continues upon the posterior surface of the iris, where it partly undergoes a muscular differentiation. The inner, colorless layer is a simple columnar epithelium. The height of its cells decreases from behind forward. Its inner surface is lined with a distinct glassy membrane—the *ciliary inner limiting membrane*—considered to be a continuation of the inner limiting membrane of the optical portion of the retina.

Toward the root of the iris, on the anterior surface of the ciliary processes, the cells of the inner epithelial layer gradually accumulate pigment granules. On the posterior surface of the iris they are as heavily pigmented as the outer layer. This is the *iridial portion of the retina.*

loose, pigmented, highly vascular connective tissue and some smooth muscles. The anterior surface of the stroma is said to be lined with epithelium, which continues here from the posterior surface of the cornea. A thin layer of the stroma immediately beneath the mesenchymal epithelium, the anterior

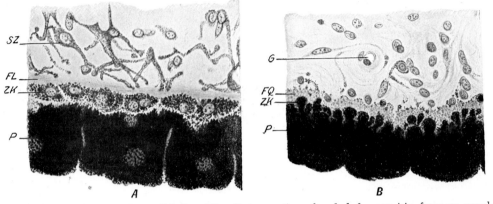

Fig. 545. A, Posterior part of a radial (meridional) transection of a dark human iris, from an enucleated eyeball. *FL,* Fibrillae of the dilator muscle in longitudinal section; *P,* pigment epithelium of the inner (posterior) layer of the pars iridica retinae; *SZ,* pigment containing connective tissue cells (melanophores) of the vascular layer; *ZK,* pigment containing cellbodies of the dilator muscle (outer or anterior layer of the iridial portion of the retina). *B,* Tangential section of a light human iris. The fibers of the dilator muscle in cross section (*FQ*); *G,* blood vessels in the stroma. 380 ×. (After Schaffer.)

Iris. The posterior surface of the iris near the pupil rests upon the anterior surface of the lens; in this way the iris separates the anterior chamber from the posterior chamber. The margin of the iris connected with the ciliary body is called the *ciliary margin,* or the root of the iris. The pupil is surrounded by the *pupillary margin of the iris.* The iris diminishes in thickness toward both margins.

The anterior surface of the iris presents, besides its individually varying color, certain distinct markings. About 1.5 mm. from the pupillary margin a concentric, jagged line separates the anterior surface into a pupillary and a wider, ciliary zone. Near the pupillary and the ciliary margins the anterior surface has many irregular excavations, the *crypts,* which may extend deep into the tissue. In addition, there are oblique, irregularly arranged contraction furrows which are especially marked when the pupil is dilated.

The main mass of the iris consists of a

stromal sheet or lamella, is devoid of blood vessels. Farther inward is the thick vessel layer. Its posterior surface is covered with a double layer of heavily pigmented epithelium, the iridial portion of the retina.

Anterior Stromal Sheet or Lamella. This contains, in a homogeneous ground substance, a few collagenous fibers and many fibroblasts and chromatophores. The color of the iris depends on the quantity, the color and the arrangement of the pigment and on the thickness of the lamella. If this layer is thin and its cells contain but little or no pigment, the black pigment epithelium on the posterior surface, as seen through the colorless tissue, gives the iris a blue color (Fig. 545). An increasing amount of pigment brings about the different shades of gray and greenish hues. Large amounts of dark pigment cause the brown color of the iris. In albinos the pigment is absent or scanty, and the iris is pink because of its blood vessels.

Vessel Layer. This layer contains numerous blood vessels. The spaces between them are filled with a loose connective tissue and some branched chromatophores.

Iridial Portion of the Retina. The epithelial pigment layer on the posterior surface of the iris is a direct continuation of the

fibrillated parts of the cells become a continuous, radially fibrillated membrane called the posterior stromal sheet or lamella. The rest of the cell bodies keep the elongated nucleus, accumulate pigment, are pushed backward, and form a layer of pigmented spindle cells (Fig. 545). These are only in-

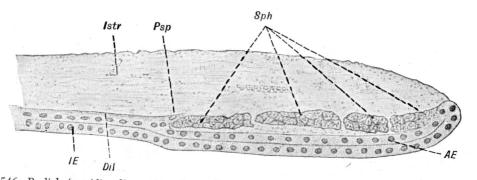

Fig. 546. Radial (meridional) section of pupillary border of the iris of a newborn infant. *IE,* Inner epithelial layer and, *AE,* outer epithelial layer of the optic cup; *Sph,* sphincter; *Dil,* dilator of the pupil; *Psp,* spurlike process of epithelium; *Istr,* stroma of the iris. (After von Szily, from Franz.)

ciliary portion of the retina and, like it, originally consists of two layers of epithelium. The inner, nonpigmented layer of the ciliary portion becomes heavily pigmented in the iridial region, and the outer, pigmented layer becomes less pigmented. In the iris the outer, less pigmented layer differentiates into smooth muscles.

Muscles of the Iris. Being an adjustable diaphragm, the iris contains two smooth muscles which keep the membrane stretched and press it against the surface of the lens. The contraction of the circular *sphincter of the pupil* reduces the pupil. It is a thin, flat ring whose breadth changes, according to the contraction of the iris, from 0.6 to 1.2 mm. It surrounds the margin of the pupil. Its smooth muscle fibers are arranged in thin circular bundles, and on the posterior surface often course obliquely to the *dilator of the pupil.* This muscle widens the pupil and consists of radially arranged myo-epithelial elements which form a thin membrane between the vessel layer and the pigment epithelium.

The elements of the dilator at first are spindle-shaped, fibrillated cells with moderately pigmented cytoplasm. In the adult the

distinctly set off from the posterior stromal lamella (*FL, FQ*), but are sharply separated from the pigment epithelium.

Numerous muscular connections can be found between the sphincter and the dilator. The innervation of both muscles, however, is quite different, although both are supplied by visceral nerve fibers. The postganglionic neurons for the dilator are located in the superior cervical ganglion and are sympathetic. Their axons pass to the gasserian ganglion, thence into the ophthalmic branch of the latter, and finally reach the dilatator through the long ciliary nerves. The postganglionic neurons for the sphincter lie in the ciliary ganglion, and their axons reach the sphincter with the short ciliary nerves which also innervate the ciliary muscles; these are parasympathetic. When the eye accommodates for a near object by the contraction of the ciliary muscle, there is always a simultaneous contraction of the pupillary sphincter.

Pigment Epithelium of the Iris. The large cells of the pigment epithelium are filled with coarse, dark brown melanin granules that obscure their outlines and their nuclei. The posterior (inner) surface of the pigment

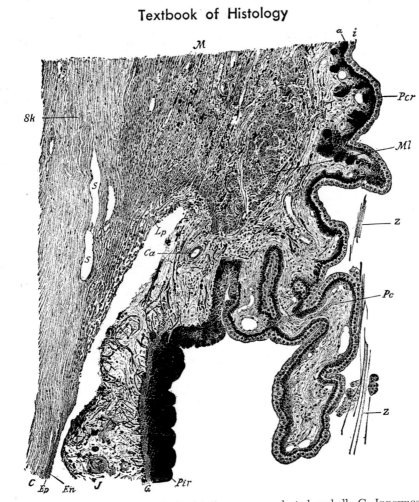

Fig. 547. Meridional section of angle of the iris from an enucleated eyeball. C, Innermost layers of the corneal substantia propria; Ca, major arterial ring of the iris; En, endothelium; Ep, membrane of Descemet; G, dilator of the pupil; J, stroma of the iris; Lp, pectinate ligament of the iris; M, ciliary muscle; Ml, circular fibers of the ciliary muscle; Pc, ciliary process; Pcr, ciliary portion of the retina; Pir, iridial portion of the retina; S, canal of Schlemm; Sk, innermost layers of the sclera; Z, fibers of the ciliary zonule: a, pigment epithelium of the ciliary portion of the retina; i, inner epithelial layer of the ciliary portion of the retina. 90 ×. (After Schaffer.)

layer is covered with the fine *limiting membrane of the iris*, a continuation of the inner limiting membrane of the ciliary portion of the retina.

Angle of the Iris. This circular recess at the periphery of the anterior chamber of the eye (where the posterior surface of the cornea and the anterior surface of the iris meet) plays an important role in the circulation of the intra-ocular liquid. The elements of the sclera and of the ciliary muscle also take part in the formation of this region.

The endothelial wall of the *canal of*

Schlemm at the corneoscleral junction is surrounded by loose connective tissue and is separated by connective tissue lined with mesenchymal epithelium from the anterior chamber. This meshwork is the *angle of the iris*. It extends from the edge of the membrane of Descemet to the scleral roll and to the root of the iris. Its meshes, the *spaces of Fontana*, are in direct communication with the anterior chamber. It is subdivided into a larger and coarser part, the *scleral framework* (Fig. 542), which is adjacent to the sclera, and into a smaller, more delicate part, connected with the iris, the *uveal frame-*

work, or the *pectinate ligament of the iris* (Figs. 542, 547). In the human eye the meshwork of the iris angle, especially its pectinate ligament, is much less developed than in some mammals.

REFRACTIVE MEDIA OF THE EYE

The cornea and the two chambers of the eye have been described.

Lens. The lens is a transparent, round, biconvex body placed behind the pupil. Its form changes during the process of accommodation. Its outer form varies somewhat in different persons and also with age. Its diameter is from 7 mm. in a newborn up to 10 mm. in an adult. Its thickness is approximately 3.7 to 4 mm., increasing during accommodation to 4.5 mm. and more. The posterior surface or pole is more convex than the anterior, the respective radii of curvature being 6.9 and 10 mm. The index of refraction is 1.36 in the peripheral layers and 1.42 in the inner zone or nucleus. The lens weighs 0.2 gm. and is slightly yellow.

The lens is covered with a homogeneous, highly refractive *capsule*, a cuticular membrane, 11 to 18 microns thick. Beneath it and covering the anterior face is a layer of flattened hexagonal cells, the epithelium of the lens. Toward the equator these cells approach a columnar form and become arranged in meridional rows. Becoming progressively elongated, the cells at the equator are transformed into *lens fibers* that constitute the tissue of the lens. In this transition or *nuclear zone* the cells have a characteristic arrangement. The epithelial cells are of prime importance for the normal metabolism of the lens. The surface of the capsule covering the posterior pole has no epithelium.

In the human lens each fiber is a six-sided prism, from 7 to 10 mm. long, 8 to 12 microns wide, and only 2 microns thick (Fig. 549). In the region of the nucleus the thickness may reach 5 microns. In younger fibers a firmer cortical and a semiliquid axial part can be distinguished. With advancing age the axial part becomes increasingly solid (sclerosis). The young fibers have smooth surfaces and join one another, so that their

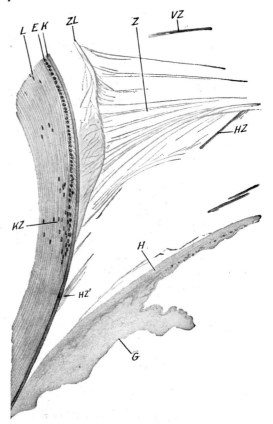

Fig. 548. From a meridional section of the anterior part of human eye. Attachment of the fibers of the zonula ciliaris to the equator of the lens. E, Epithelium of the lens; G, vitreous body; H, membrana hyaloidea; HZ, posterior fibers of the zonule; HZ', their connections with the capsule of the lens (K); KZ, nuclear zone of the lens; L, fibers of the lens substance in longitudinal section; VZ, anterior fibers of the zonule; Z, zonule; ZL, detached outer layer of the capsule of the lens. 110 ×. (After Schaffer.)

narrow edges interdigitate. They are kept together by thin layers of a cementing substance which has the same index of refraction as the fibers themselves. This substance is considered by some to be a lubricant enabling slight movements of the fibers during accommodation. In the older fibers, in the dense, inner portion of the lens, the nucleus is absent and the outlines of the cross sections often become irregular and serrated. At the two poles of the lens where the fibers join their ends, they form a figure of a star with three or more rays (Fig. 543).

The lens is held in position by a system of

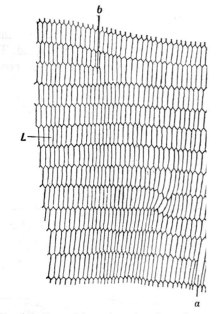

Fig. 549. Part of frontal section through equator of the human lens. The cross sections of the fibers are arranged in radial rows or lamellae (L): a, Fiber of double width; b, branching of a radial lamella. 500 ×. (After Schaffer.)

fibers—the *ciliary zonule*. The zonule fibers (Fig. 548, Z, VZ, HZ) are straight, homogeneous filaments varying in thickness (up to 22 microns or more) and having many branches. They seem to arise from the epithelium of the ciliary portion of the retina. Near the ciliary crown they fuse into thicker fibers and finally form about 140 bundles. At the anterior margin of the ciliary processes they leave the surface of the ciliary body and radiate freely toward the equator of the lens. The larger ones are straight and reach the capsule in front of the equator of the lens (*anterior sheet of the zonule*). The thinner fibers assume a slightly curved course and are attached to the posterior surface of the lens (*posterior zonular sheet*). All zonular fibers break up into a multitude of fine brushlike fibers which fuse with the substance of the outermost layer of the capsule. Where the vitreous touches the lens capsule it forms the *hyaloideocapsular ligament*.

The radii of curvature of the surfaces of the several dioptrical media of the *normal* eye, especially of the lens, and their indices

of refraction are such that light rays coming from a remote point form an inverted and real image of the object in the layer of the photoreceptive cones and rods in the retina. If the object is approaching, the light rays diverge more and more and the image moves backward. A change of position of object from infinite distance to about 5 meters causes the image to shift about 60 microns backward in the retina. Since this image is still within the outer segments of the rods and cones, accommodation is not needed. For nearer distances, accommodation is necessary.

In a photographic camera the focusing of objects which move nearer to the lens is effected by moving the ground glass plate away from the lens. In the higher vertebrates and in man, the curvature of the lens is changed. When the eye is at rest the lens is kept stretched in the plane vertical to the optic axis by the ciliary zonule. When the eye has to focus a near object, the ciliary muscle, especially its meridional fibers, contracts and pulls the choroid with the ciliary body forward. This relieves the tension exerted by the zonule, the lens gets thicker, and its surface, especially at the anterior pole, becomes more convex. This increases the refractive power of the lens and keeps the focus within the bacillary layer.

Vitreous Body. The vitreous body fills the space (vitreal cavity) between the lens and the retina. It adheres everywhere to the optical portion of the retina, and the connection is especially firm at the serrated margin. Farther forward it gradually recedes from the surface of the ciliary portion of the retina.

The fresh vitreous body has a gelatinous consistency, is colorless, structureless and of glasslike transparency. Its index of refraction is 1.334. When fixed, it shows a network of extremely fine fibrils with its meshes filled with clear liquid. Almost 99 per cent of the vitreous consists of water and dissolved substances.

From the papilla of the optic nerve to the posterior surface of the lens *the hyaloid canal* (Cloquet) extends through the vitreous body. It is a residue after the resorption of the embryonic hyaloid artery. It has a diameter of 1 mm. and is filled with aqueous liquid. In the living, especially in young persons, it is visible with the help of the slit lamp microscope. In the peripheral layers of the vitreous, free cells float in the liquid. They are probably hematogenous lymphoid cells.

connected with the choroid. About 2.5 mm. from the border of the optic papilla the inner surface of the retina appears excavated. This shallow, round depression is the *central fovea* (Figs. 539, 550, *f*; 553).

When detached from the pigment epithelium, the fresh retina is almost perfectly transparent. It has a distinctly red color due to the presence in its rod cells of *visual*

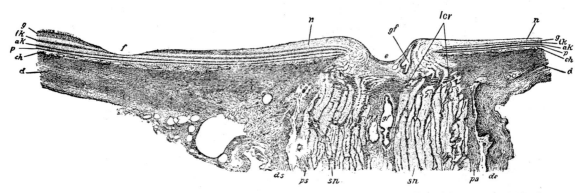

Fig. 550. Place of entrance of the optic nerve and the central fovea of an enucleated human eye in horizontal meridional section. *ak*, Outer nuclear layer; *ch*, choroid; *d*, sclera; *ds*, dural sheath of optic nerve; *e*, physiological excavation; *f*, central fovea; *g*, layer of ganglion cells; *gf*, blood vessels; *ik*, inner nuclear layer; *lcr*, lamina cribrosa; *n*, layer of nerve fibers; *p*, pigment layer of retina; *ps*, pial sheath of the optic nerve; *sn*, bundles of fibers of the optic nerve. 17 ×. (After Schaffer.)

THE RETINA

The retina is the innermost of the three coats of the eyeball and is the photoreceptor organ. It arises in early embryonic development through a bilateral evagination of the prosencephalon, the *primary optic vesicle*. Later it is transformed into the *secondary optic vesicle* (Fig. 562). Each optic cup remains connected with the brain by a stalk, the *future optic nerve*. In the adult this tunic consists of an outer, pigmented epithelial layer (Fig. 552) and an inner sheet, the *retina proper*. It contains elements similar to those of the brain, and it may be considered to be a specially differentiated part of the brain.

The *optical* or *functioning portion of the retina* lines the inner surface of the choroid and extends from the papilla of the optic nerve to the serrated margin anteriorly (Figs. 539, 543). At the papilla, where the retina continues into the tissue of the nerve, and at the serrated margin, the retina is firmly

purple or rhodopsin. Light rapidly bleaches the visual purple; in darkness the color gradually reappears. The fovea and its immediate vicinity contain yellow pigment, and are called the *macula lutea*. Large blood vessels circle above and below the central fovea, whereas only fine arteries and veins, and capillaries, are present in it (Fig. 556). In the very center of the fovea, in a territory measuring 0.5 mm. across, even the capillaries are absent, greatly increasing its transparency.

Only that portion of the image of an external object which falls upon the fovea is seen sharply. Accordingly, the eyes are moved so as to bring the object of special attention into this central part of the visual field. Photoreceptors are absent from the optic papilla. This is the "blind spot" of the visual field.

Layers of Retina. In the retina, exclusive of the fovea, the papilla, and the serrated margin, ten parallel layers can be distinguished from outside inward (Fig. 552): (1) the pigment epithelium; (2) the layer of rods and cones (bacillary layer); (3) the outer limiting membrane; (4) the outer nuclear layer; (5) the outer plexiform layer; (6) the inner nuclear layer; (7) the inner plexiform layer; (8) the layer of ganglion cells; (9) the layer of optic nerve fibers; and (10) the inner limiting membrane. The numbers 1 to 10 correspond with those in Figures 552–555, 557.

Regions of the Retina. The distribution of the cellular and fibrous elements varies considerably in detail from the center of the retina in the fovea to its anterior limit at the serrated margin. Thus seven circular *regions* can be distinguished (Fig. 553). The inner three (*I* to *III*) compose the *central area*, distinguished by the great number of ganglion cells in the eighth layer, and by the general refinement and even distribution of the structural elements, especially of the rods and cones. The most delicate elements are in the fovea (region *I*), where they are accumulated in greatest numbers. The regions outside the central area (*IV* to *VI*), including the ora serrata (*VII*), constitute the *extra-areal periphery*. Here the elements are fewer, larger, less differentiated and less evenly distributed. (Note that Roman numerals refer in text and legends to regions of the retina, while the Arabic refer to the layers.)

Pigment Epithelium. This layer consists of one row of low prismatic cells. When seen from the surface, they usually appear as fairly regular hexagons of an average diameter of 16 microns. In cross section the same cells appear as rectangles 8 microns high. The inner surface of the cells sends out thin protoplasmic processes (ten to forty to a cell) filled with pigment (fuscin), which surround the rods and cones and separate them from one another. The outer part of the protoplasm adjacent to the choroid is free of pigment and contains an oval nucleus.

With changes of illumination these pigment inclusions change their position. In an eye which has been exposed to light the rod-shaped pigment granules move into the processes, thus providing each rod and cone with a pigment sheath. This is supposed to prevent the diffusion of light from one rod or cone to another. In an eye protected from light the pigment leaves the fringes and is massed in the cell body.

Visual Cells. These elements are the receptors of the light stimuli or photoreceptors (2 and 4 in Figs. 552, 553, 554, 557). The light rays, before reaching them, must first penetrate most of the retina. The outer portions of the visual cells are believed to be

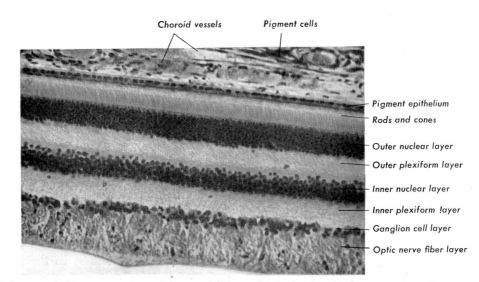

Choroid vessels   Pigment cells

Pigment epithelium
Rods and cones
Outer nuclear layer
Outer plexiform layer
Inner nuclear layer
Inner plexiform layer
Ganglion cell layer
Optic nerve fiber layer

Fig. 551. Photomicrograph of human retina. H + E. 240 ×. (After von Herrath and Abramow.)

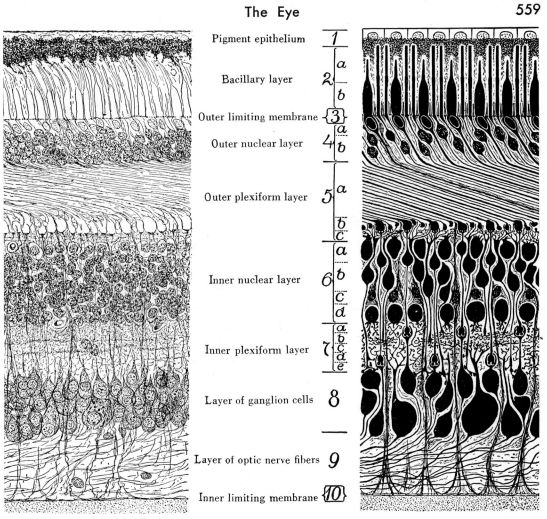

Pigment epithelium — 1

Bacillary layer — 2 {a, b}

Outer limiting membrane — {3}

Outer nuclear layer — 4 {a, b}

Outer plexiform layer — 5 {a, b, c}

Inner nuclear layer — 6 {a, b, c, d}

Inner plexiform layer — 7 {a, b, c, d, e}

Layer of ganglion cells — 8

Layer of optic nerve fibers — 9

Inner limiting membrane — {10}

Fig. 552. Layers of adult human retina (region III). Left figure stained routinely, about 400 ×; the right figure is a schematic reconstruction from sections stained with Golgi's method. (Slightly modified after Polyak.)

the parts sensitive to light. There are two kinds of visual cells: (a) the rod cells and (b) the cone cells.

Rod Cells. The rod cell is a filamentous element arranged with its outer portion vertical to the surface of the retina (Fig. 554, a). This causes the regular striation of layer 2. The scleral part of the rod cell, the *rod proper*, is situated between the outer limiting membrane and the pigment epithelium, its outward third being embedded between the pigmented fringes. The vitreal end of the rod proper extends through the outer limiting membrane into layer 4. Each rod proper consists of an outer and inner segment. The outer segment is a smooth cylinder of uniform thickness with a rounded outer end. Its substance has a peculiar brilliancy, is homogeneous in life, and is positively birefringent. With the electronmicroscope the outer rod is seen to be composed of thin disks oriented perpendicular to the long axis of the rod. The inner segment is a trifle stouter and larger than the outer segment.

At its junction with the outer segment the inner rod segment contains a darkly staining "fiber apparatus" and a diplosome. In fishes and in birds the inner rod segment is contractile. When illuminated, it lengthens and pushes the photosensitive outer segment

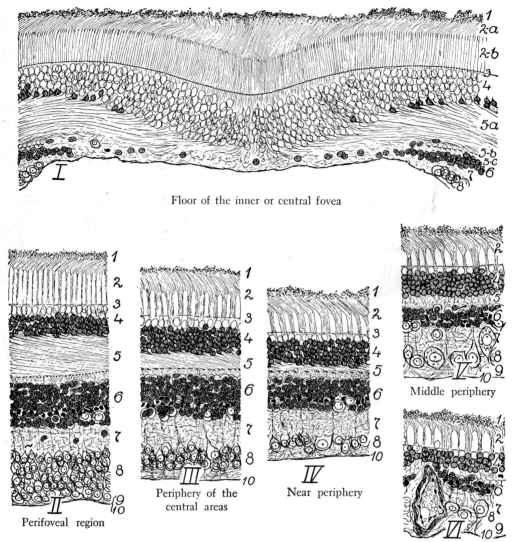

Fig. 553. Samples from various regions of the retina of a rhesus monkey. (Slightly modified after Polyak.)

deeper into the pigment epithelium toward the sclera. In dim light the inner rod segment contracts, moving the outer segment closer to the outer limiting membrane and thus exposing it to more light. Little is known of the contractility of the inner rod segment in primates.

The rods are fairly uniform in appearance, although their dimensions vary somewhat from region to region. Their thickness in the central area (regions *I* to *III*) is 1 to 1.5 microns, gradually increasing to 2.5 or 3 microns near the ora (region *VII*). Their

length decreases from approximately 60 microns in the fovea to 40 microns in the far periphery.

The rest of the rod cell is made of the *rod fiber* and the *rod body*. It extends from the lower end of the rod proper through layer *4* to layer *5-b*, where it terminates with a tiny, round swelling, the *rod spherule*, smaller than the analogous cone pedicle. The rod fiber is a protoplasmic thread of smooth appearance and uniform thickness which does not exceed 1 micron; its length varies considerably. In the central area the course of the rod fibers assumes a slanting to horizontal position, while in the extra-areal regions it is vertical.

Along the rod fiber is the *rod body* containing a nucleus, smaller and more intensively stained than the cone nucleus, and surrounded by scant protoplasm. The rod proper with the outer fiber is the homologue of the receptive dendritic expansions of a neuron, the inner rod fiber of the emissive axis cylinder. In the central area the inner rod and cone fibers, and the corresponding portions of Müller's fibers (p. 563) which envelop them, form a thick fiber layer, the outer fiber layer of Henle (zone 5-*a*).

The rod nuclei represent the majority of the nuclei of the fourth layer (4) in all regions except in the fovea, where rods are few, and in its center, where they are absent.

In all rod cells, except those of a zone 3 to 4 mm. wide at the serrated margin, the rods contain visual purple. To this is due the red color of the retina during life. As there are only a few rods in the periphery of the fovea and none in its center, this area appears devoid of rhodopsin. When the retina is exposed to light, rhodopsin disintegrates, but is constantly produced anew. This regeneration occurs only as long as the connection of the rods with the pigment epithelium is preserved.

The number of rods in the human retina, according to Krause, is 130 millions.

Cone Cells. These neurons (Fig. 554) are made up of essentially the same parts as the rod cells, but differ in detail. On the whole, they are bulkier. The outward portion, instead of being a slender rod, is a thick, flask-shaped structure.

The part situated outside the outer limiting membrane is the *cone*, or cone proper. It, too, is divided into two parts. The highly refractive and fragile outer segment is a long, slender cone. It rests upon the stout inner segment and tapers toward its blunt tip (the swollen tip often seen is an autolytic artefact). The inner cone segment varies in shape and size from place to place. In the central region and close to it, it is cylin-

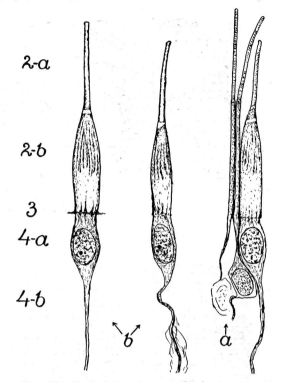

Fig. 554. Rods (*a*) and cones (*b*) from an osmic acid-fixed, unstained, teased preparation of retina of a rhesus monkey (preparation of G. W. Bartelmez). Designation of layers as in Figure 552. Outer rod and cone segments in zone 2-*a*, inner segments in 2-*b*, rod bodies with their nuclei in zone 4-*b*, cone bodies with nuclei in 4-*a*; 3, outer limiting membrane; fiber apparatus visible in the upper portion of the inner cone segments. Some of the outer segments slightly bent. (Courtesy S. Polyak.)

drical, gradually becoming flask-shaped in the periphery. Like the rod, it contains a "fiber apparatus" and a diplosome. It is much more resistant to physical and chemical agents than the outer segment. There is no visual purple in the cones.

The cones vary considerably in different regions of the retina. In the central fovea the cones measure 75 microns or more in length and from 1 to 1.5 microns in thickness. Their length gradually decreases to 45 microns in the extra-areal periphery. The relative length of the outer and the inner segments is usually as three to four. In the fovea the two are approximately the same length. The lower end of the inner cone segment slips through an opening in the outer limiting membrane (3), and protrudes slightly into the fourth layer.

In teleostean fishes and amphibians the inner cone segment is contractile. It shortens in bright light and stretches in dim light or darkness. The displacement of these cones is, accordingly, opposite in direction to that of the rods. It is not certain whether human cones have the same property.

Passing the outer limiting membrane, the inner cone segment merges with its *body* containing a nucleus, which is larger and paler staining than the rod nucleus. The bodies and nuclei of the cones, as distinct from those of the rods, are placed in a single row (4-*a*) immediately beneath the outer limiting membrane. The exceptions are the cones in the outer fovea whose nuclei are accumulated in several rows (Fig. 553, *I*). Only here the cones have an *outer fiber*. From the body of all cones a stout, smooth *inner fiber* descends to the middle zone of the outer plexiform layer (5-*b*), where it terminates with a thick triangular or club-shaped swelling, the *cone pedicle*. Up to a dozen short, barblike filaments emanate from the base of each pedicle, except in the fovea, where there are usually none. These filamentous outgrowths spread horizontally in zone 5-*c*. The length and course of the inner cone fibers vary considerably, depending on the region, the longest (600 microns) and almost horizontally placed being those in the outer fiber layer of Henle (5-*a*) in the central area. The inner cone fibers have all the earmarks of an axis cylinder, the cone pedicle those of a teledendron of a neuron.

The number of cones in the human retina is estimated at 6,000,000 to 7,000,000 (Østerberg). The ratio of the nerve fibers of the optic nerve (438,000) to the number of cones of one eye is as 1:6 or 1:7.

The relative number and distribution of the rods and cones in different vertebrates present great variations depending on the mode of life. In diurnal birds the cones are more numerous than the rods. In most diurnal reptiles there are only cones and no rods. In many nocturnal vertebrates only rods are present, although in others a few rudimentary cones can be found among numerous rods. On similar comparative data M. Schultze (1866) assumed a difference in the function of the two kinds of photoreceptors (duplicity theory).

The cones in the adult primate retina, including those of the fovea, are quite distinct from the rods. The opinion that there is more than one variety of cone cell in mammals (including primates) and that this is related to certain theories of color perception, has not been verified. The evidence indicates that the cone cells throughout the primate retina are of one variety, although they vary in detail from place to place. This is also true of the rods, though in a lesser degree.

Horizontal Cells. These cells are typical neurons whose bodies form the uppermost one or two rows of the inner nuclear layer (zone 6-*a* in Figs. 552, 557). From the upper end of the body arise short dendritic twigs producing several tufts spreading in the lower zone of the outer plexiform layer (5-*c*), where each tuft comes in contact with the vitreal face of one cone pedicle. The axis cylinder takes a horizontal course chiefly in zone 5-*c*, and its terminal twigs come in contact with both rod spherules and cone pedicles. The horizontal cells, accordingly, receive impulses from a group of cone cells of one locality and transmit them to a group of rod and cone cells of another locality (Fig. 557, *c*).

Bipolar Cells. These neurons connect the rods and cones with the ganglion cells of the retina, and through these with the visual centers of the brain. The bipolar cells stand approximately upright with respect to the retinal layers, except in the central fovea, where their position is oblique. Their nuclei are in the sixth layer, with a few in the fifth. Each bipolar has one or several outward expansions that spread into the outer plexiform layer (5), where they synapse with the photoreceptors. There is usually a single inward expansion that spreads into the seventh layer, where it is synaptically related to the ganglion cells and other adjoining cells. Two groups of bipolars can be distinguished: centripetal bipolars, which transmit impulses from rods and cones to ganglion cells (*d, e, f, h*), and centrifugal bipolars, which transmit impulses in the opposite direction (*i*).

The bipolar cells apparently play an essential role in distributing and rearranging the impulses received from the rods and cones before transmitting them to the third category of retinal neurons, the ganglion cells.

Ganglion Cells. These cells (*m, n, o, p, s* in Fig. 557, and layer 8 in Fig. 552) represent the third link, the last in the retina, of the chain of neurons that form the afferent visual pathway. These cells are larger than those of the two nuclear layers, and closely resemble neurons of the brain. The bodies are in the ganglion layer, with a few displaced into the lowermost zone of the inner nuclear layer. Their dentrites spread in the inner plexiform layer. Chromophile substance is present in all. From the body or the chief dendritic trunk of each ganglion cell arises one axis cylinder that leaves the retina and becomes an optic nerve fiber terminating in the subcortical visual centers of the brain.

Optic Nerve Fibers in the Primate Retina. Because of the presence of the central fovea, the optic nerve fibers have a special course (Fig. 556). In general they converge radially toward the optic papilla. However, those originating in the upper temporal quadrant of the retina circle above the central area, while those originating in the lower temporal quadrant circle below the central area on their way to the papilla. They follow the larger retinal vessels fairly closely. A line connecting the fovea with the temporal circumference of the retina separates the optic nerve fibers of the upper from those of the lower temporal quadrant. This separation is preserved along the central visual pathway as far as the cortical visual center.

In primates each retina is divided into two halves along the vertical meridian passing through the center of the fovea. The fibers from the nasal half cross in the optic chiasma and pass to the optic tract of the opposite side; those from the temporal half enter the tract of the same side. Each optic tract is, therefore, composed of fibers from the temporal half of the same side and from the nasal half of the retina of the opposite eye. This arrangement remains in the visual radiation in the occipital lobes of the brain.

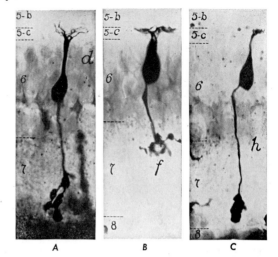

Fig. 555. Photomicrographs of centripetal bipolar cells: variety *d* (A), variety *f* (in B), variety *h* (in C). Method of Golgi. Rhesus monkey. Designation of layers as in Figure 552. (Courtesy of S. Polyak.)

It accounts for the blindness in the opposite halves of the two fields of view (homonymous hemianopia) when the optic tract or the visual radiation of one side is interrupted.

Supporting or Neuroglial Elements of the Retina. The retina, a modified part of the brain, contains supporting elements of neuroglial character. The most important are the radial fibers of Müller (*u* in Fig. 557). These are present throughout the central area, including the fovea, as well as in the periphery.

Their oval nuclei lie in the middle zone of the inner nuclear layer (*6-c*, Fig. 552). The cell body is a slender fiber or pillar which extends radially from the outer (3) to the inner limiting membrane (10). Their inner ends expand conically and form the *inner limiting membrane.* In the two plexiform layers the radial fibers give off many branches, which form a dense neuroglial network in whose meshes are lodged the ramifications of the neurons described earlier.

The cell bodies of the radial fibers are beset with excavations which envelop bodies of the ganglion cells, bipolars, horizontal cells and the cone and rod cells. The bodies of the nervous elements appear to be completely enveloped in thin husks of supporting structures which perhaps serve as insulators. The rod and cone fibers are likewise encased in

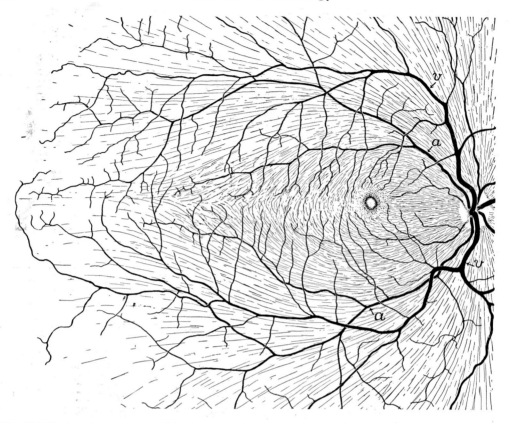

Fig. 556. Retina of right eye of adult rhesus monkey as seen in a total preparation. Intravital staining with methylene blue (Ehrlich). The elliptic papilla of the optic nerve is near the right side of the figure. Fine lines radiating from the papilla in all directions represent bundles of optic nerve fibers. The stippled circular area almost free from fibers is the central fovea. Within it a small white circle is the floor of the fovea; the dark ring surrounding it is the foveal slope. Note the direction of some of the foveal fibers straight to the fovea, of others more or less circling to it or around it, encircling the foveal region from above and below, and forming on the temporal side to it (left) the horizontally placed "raphe" or retinal seam. *a*, Arteries; *v*, veins. Camera lucida. 8 ×. (Courtesy of S. Polyak.)

thin, tubelike sheaths produced by Müller's fibers.

At the limit between the outer nuclear layer and the layer of the rods and cones the radial fibers fuse and form the *outer limiting membrane*. This is pierced by numerous openings through which the rods and cones are connected with their inner parts, their bodies.

Central Area and Fovea ("Macula"). Slightly lateral to the papilla is the place of most distinct vision. This region, the *central area*, is characterized by the agglomeration of cones and other nervous elements in numbers greater than outside it and by their structural refinement and synaptic perfection.

In the center of this area, the layers inward to zone *5-a* are displaced laterally, producing a shallow depression on the vitreal surface of the retina called the *central fovea*. This permits an almost free passage of rays of light to the layer of photoreceptors, and it is here that the visual axis touches the retina.

The central fovea is a shallow bowl with its concavity toward the vitreous (Fig. 558). It is in the center of the central area 2 to 2.5 mm. on the temporal side of the papilla. In its center a *floor* or *fundus* can be distinguished, with the *slopes* and a *margin of the fovea*. The width of the entire foveal depression measures 1.5 mm.

In the fundus of the central fovea, the

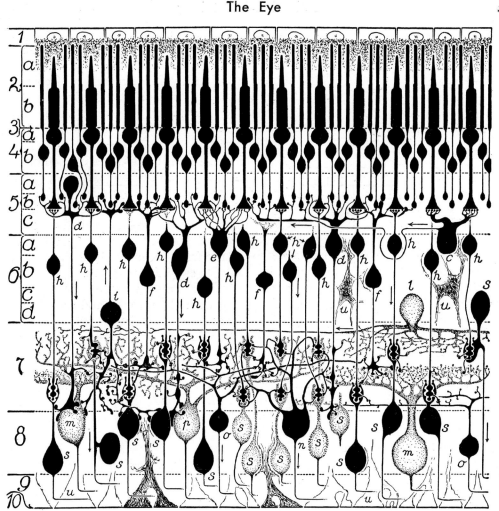

Fig. 557. Diagram representing the structures of the primate retina composed from numerous Golgi-stained preparations of man, chimpanzee and macaque. The designation of layers and zones on the left side as in Figure 552. In the upper part the slender structures are the rod cells (*a*), the thicker ones the cone cells (*b*); *c*, horizontal cell; *d, e, f, h*, centripetal bipolar cells; *i*, centrifugal bipolar cells; *l*, inner horizontal or association cell; *m, n, o, p, s*, ganglion cells; *u*, parts of the radial fibers of Müller, with their nuclei in 6, and their lower or inner ends forming the inner limiting membrane (*10*). Note the various synaptic relations between different neurons, reciprocal overlapping of expansions or its absence, the probable direction of the nervous impulses indicated by arrows, and other details. The indicated termination of the l-axon is not completely proved. The rods and the cones are not designated by letters *a* and *b* as in Figure 554. (After Polyak.)

cones are most numerous and are thinner and longer than elsewhere in the retina. This formation, the *outer fovea*, contains 20,000 to 25,000 cones. This region, measuring about 400 microns across, probably corresponds to the portion of the field of view where vision is most discriminating. The *rod-free area*, where only cones are present, measures 500 to 550 microns in diameter and contains up to 30,000 cones.

Capillaries are present in the ventral layers

of the foveal slopes to the very edge of the foveal floor, or 275 microns from the very center. The *avascular central territory* is almost as large as the rodless area (500 to 550 microns).

Function of the Eye. Synapses and Function of the Retina. The eye is essentially a camera obscura provided with dioptric media: the cornea with the aqueous humor and the adjustable crystalline lens are optically active. The inner surface of this dark

Fig. 558. Diagram of the fovea. The layers are represented alternately in black and white in the right and left halves. The line dividing them is in the foveal center. Asterisks indicate the margins of the central or inner fovea (region I of the retina). The outer fovea is indicated by arrows. Ch, Choroid membrane. The numbers of the layers correspond with those in Figure 552. (Slightly modified after Polyak.)

chamber is lined by the photosensitive retina. The rays of light emanating from each point of an illuminated object which impinge on the cornea are refracted by it and converge on the lens. In the lens the rays are further refracted and focused in the photosensitive layer of the retina (2 in the figures). The sum of the foci that correspond with the points on the surface of the object seen constitutes the retinal image of this object. In relation to the object the retinal image is inverted (because of the crossing of the rays in the pupil's aperture), real (since the foci are actually on the retina and not behind or in front of it) and very much reduced in size.

Stripped of many important details, the complex story of the interneuronic relationships in the retina is as follows: In the photosensitive rods and cones, light initiates a nervous process which in turn produces nervous impulses to be forwarded along the nervous pathways to the brain. Subjectively, this is interpreted as light, colors, shapes, sizes, position and movement of the objects seen. The *synaptic mechanism* of the retina is composed of the following systems of neurons (Fig. 557): The rod cells (a) transmit impulses to two or three varieties of bipolars (d, e-f) and through these to all varieties of the ganglion cells (m, n, o, p, s). The cones (b), on the contrary, discharge impulses to three or four bipolar varieties (d, e-f, h), and through these to all varieties of ganglion cells (m, n, o, p, s); the cones also stimulate the horizontal cells (c) and thus may influence distant rods (a) and cones (b).

The rods, it is believed, are responsive to

weak light stimuli, thus being adapted for seeing in dim light. They do not respond selectively to lights of different wavelengths associated with the sensation of colors. Conversely, color sensations are initiated through the stimulation of cones which are less responsive to weak "colorless" light. This makes the cones especially suitable for vision in bright light. At the third neuronal level, in the ganglion cells (m, n, o, p, s) since all three bipolar varieties (d, e-f, h) are synaptically connected with each of the several ganglion varieties—the rod and cone impulses apparently merge with one another. The fate of the impulses in the brain is unknown.

The synaptic relations suggest that the cones react in a more territorially restricted way than the rods. In and near the central fovea, each cone is linked to one h-bipolar, which in turn is related to a single s-ganglion cell (Fig. 191, B). This implies that the visual system here is made up of a great number of anatomical and functional units, each of which responds independently to a minute photic stimulus. This may be the structural basis for visual space perception or visual acuity.

The rods, being connected in groups to bipolars, always respond in groups, no matter how restricted the photic stimulus may be. Thus the smallest receptive rod territory is larger than the cone territory of the same region. Such grouplike connections might well result in reinforcement of the intensity of excitation generated in the rods (Fig. 191, D).

In the central area the size of the receptor-conductor units corresponds roughly with that of the individual cones. This agrees with the difference in retinal acuity in different localities, the acuity being at its peak in the very center of the field of view (corresponding with the foveal center) and at first rapidly, then more slowly, decreasing toward the periphery of the field of view.

In the primate retina at least fifteen distinct varieties of neurons are present; these form at least thirty-eight kinds of synapses with one another. In the retina, in addition to photoreception, many other processes usually associated with the central nervous system,

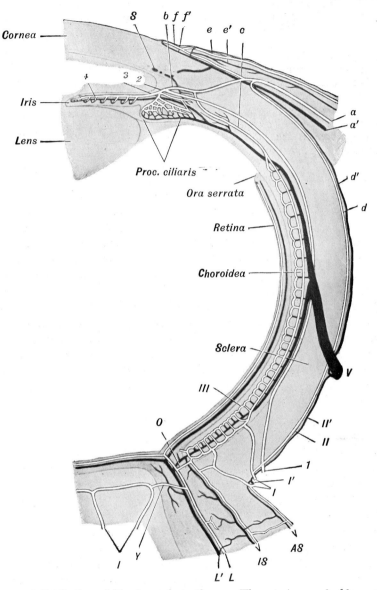

Fig. 559. Diagram of distribution of blood vessels in the eye. The arteries are double-contoured, the veins are solid black. *L* and *L'*, Central retinal artery and vein; *Y*, anastomosis with the branches of the short posterior ciliary arteries; *O*, anastomosis with the vessels of the choroid; *IS*, vessels of the inner and, *AS*, of the outer sheath of the optic nerve; *I* and *I'*, short posterior ciliary arteries and veins; *II* and *II'*, their arterial and venous episcleral branches; *III*, capillaries of the choriocapillary lamina; *1*, posterior long ciliary artery; *2*, cross section of the major circle of the iris; *3*, its branches to the ciliary body; *4*, its branches for the iris; *a* and *a'*, anterior ciliary artery and vein; *b*, their connection with the major circle of the iris; *c*, their connection with the choriocapillary lamina; *d* and *d'*, their arterial and venous episcleral branches; *e* and *e'*, their arterial and venous branches to the scleral conjunctiva; *f* and *f'*, their arterial and venous branches to the margin of the cornea; *V*, vena vorticosa; *S*, cross section of the canal of Schlemm. Note: The anastomoses *O* and *Y* are usually capillaries or precapillaries; the central artery is functionally a terminal artery. (After Leber and Stöhr, slightly modified.)

such as selection, facilitation, inhibition, summation of excitations, take place. The retina is thus essentially a *receptor-integrator* organ. (For further details see Polyak, *The Retina*, and the Symposium on "Visual Mechanisms," edited by Klüver.) The metabolism of the retina is reviewed by Krause and Sibley.

Blood Vessels of the Eye. These arise from the ophthalmic artery and can be subdivided into two groups which are almost completely independent and anastomose with each other only in the region of the entrance of the optic nerve. The first group, the *retinal system,* represented by the central artery and vein, supplies a part of the optic nerve and the retina. The second, the *ciliary system,* is destined mainly for the uveal tunic.

Lymph Spaces of the Eye. True lymph capillaries and lymph vessels are present only in the scleral conjunctiva. In the eyeball they are absent.

A mass injected into the space between the choroid and sclera penetrates along the walls of the vortex veins into the *space of Tenon.* The latter continues as the *supravaginal space* along the outer surface of the dural sheath of the optic nerve to the optic foramen. Again, it is possible to inject Tenon's space from the subarachnoid space of the brain. From the *anterior chamber* the injected liquid passes into the *posterior chamber,* and also into Schlemm's canal. All these spaces cannot, however, be regarded as belonging to the lymphatic system. The space of Tenon is more like a joint cavity and facilitates the movements of the eyeball.

The *aqueous humor* is believed to originate through secretion or transudation from the ciliary processes. This is a clear, watery fluid of slightly alkaline reaction with an index of refraction of 1.33. It contains 0.77 per cent sodium chloride, traces of urea and glucose, and practically no proteins, and few or no wandering cells. It is much like the cerebrospinal fluid. From the posterior chamber it permeates the vitreous. It also penetrates between the lens and the iris and through the pupil into the anterior chamber. The drainage of the aqueous humor from the anterior chamber is effected mainly through the spaces of Fontana and the canal of Schlemm. The normal intra-ocular pressure (28 mm. of mercury), which causes the spherical form of the eyeball, is the resultant of the rates of transudation and of drainage of the aqueous humor. In glaucoma the intra-ocular pressure may increase considerably. Drainage through the canal of Schlemm seems doubtful, and it is possible that the liquid from the anterior chamber is resorbed by the crypts, by the blood vessels of the iris, and by the perivascular spaces of the episcleral and vortex veins.

Nerves of the Eye. These are the optic nerve, supplying the retina, and the ciliary nerves supplying the eyeball with motor, sensory and sympathetic fibers.

The *optic nerve,* an evagination of the prosencephalon, the optic vesicle, is not a peripheral nerve like the other cranial nerves, but is a tract of the central nervous system, as found in any part of the white substance. It consists of about 1200 bundles of myelinated fibers without neurolemma. The nerve fibers are kept together by the same kind of neuroglia as in the white substance of the central nervous system. On the surface of each bundle the glia forms a thin membrane which separates the nervous elements from the connective tissue. A similar layer is also found at the periphery of the optic nerve.

The meninges and the intermeningeal spaces of the brain continue upon the optic nerve. The outer sheath of the nerve is formed by the dura, which continues toward the eyeball and fuses with the sclera. The pia mater forms a connective tissue layer which is closely adherent to the surface of the nerve and fuses with the sclera at the entrance of the optic nerve. This pial layer sends connective tissue partitions with blood vessels into the nerve. Inflammatory processes can extend from the eyeball toward the meningeal spaces of the brain through the spaces between the sheaths.

The optic nerve leaves the posterior pole of the eyeball in a slightly oblique direction and continues into the entrance canal of the optic nerve. Just after leaving the eye through the openings in the lamina cribrosa, the fibers get their myelin sheaths. The central artery and the central vein reach the eyeball through the optic nerve; they penetrate the nerve on the lower side at a distance from the eyeball varying from 5 to 20 mm., usually 6 to 8 mm.

ACCESSORY ORGANS OF THE EYE

In an early stage of embryonic development the anterior segment of the eyeball projects freely on the surface. Later a circular fold of integument encircles the cornea. From its upper and lower parts the upper and the lower lids grow toward each other over the surface of the cornea. In this way the conjunctival sac is formed, which protects and moistens the free surface of the eye and especially the cornea. The part lining the inner surface of the lids is the *palpebral conjunctiva,* that covering the eyeball is the *bulbar conjunctiva.* The reflection of the palpebral on the bulbar conjunctiva forms deep recesses between the lids and the eyeball, the superior and the inferior fornices.

Eyelids. The outermost layer is the skin. It is thin and provided with a few papillae and many small hairs with sebaceous and small sweat glands. The derma contains a varying number of pigment cells with yellow or brown granules. The loose subcutaneous layer is rich in fine elastic networks, and in Caucasians is almost completely devoid of fat. Toward the edge of the lid the derma becomes denser and has higher papillae.

The *eyelashes* are large hairs obliquely inserted in three or four rows along the edge of the lid. With their follicles they penetrate deeply into the tissue. The sebaceous glands connected with the eyelashes are small; arrector muscles are missing. The eyelashes are replaced every hundred to 150 days.

Between and behind the follicles of the eyelashes are peculiar sweat glands, the *glands of Moll*. Unlike ordinary sweat glands, the terminal portion here is generally straight or only slightly coiled. The excretory ducts open, as a rule, into the follicles. The epithelium of the terminal portions consists of an indistinct, outer myo-epithelial layer and an inner layer of pyramidal, apocrine glandular elements. The lumen is often considerably dilated, and the glandular cells are flattened. In the ducts the epithelium consists of two distinct cell layers. The nature of the secretion of these glands is not known.

The next layer inward consists of the thin, pale, stri-

ated fibers of the palpebral portion of the *ring muscle of the eye* (orbicular muscle). The part behind the follicles of the eyelashes or behind the ducts of the meibomian glands is the ciliary muscle of Riolan.

Behind the orbicular muscle is a layer of connective tissue, the palpebral fascia, a continuation of the tendon of the palpebral levator (or depressor) muscle. It contains the arterial arc (tarsal arc). In the upper part of the upper lid, strands of smooth muscle, the *superior tarsal muscle of Müller*, are attached to the edge of the tarsus. This plate of dense connective tissue forms the skeleton of the lid. In the upper lid its breadth is about 10 mm., in the lower only 5 mm. In its substance the *glands of Meibom* are embedded. They are elongated and arranged in one layer, parallel to one another and perpendicular to the length of the tarsal plate. Their openings form a single row imme-

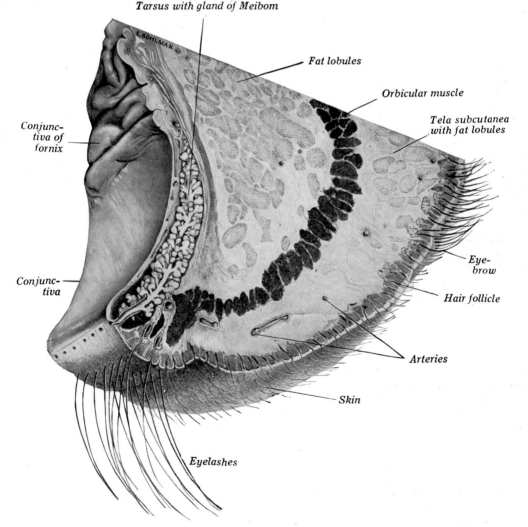

Tarsus with gland of Meibom

Fat lobules

Orbicular muscle

Tela subcutanea with fat lobules

Conjunctiva of fornix

Eyebrow

Conjunctiva

Hair follicle

Arteries

Skin

Eyelashes

Fig. 560. Camera lucida drawing of a slice of the upper eyelid of a newborn infant. Stained with hematoxylin, 12×. (Drawn by Miss Esther Bohlman.)

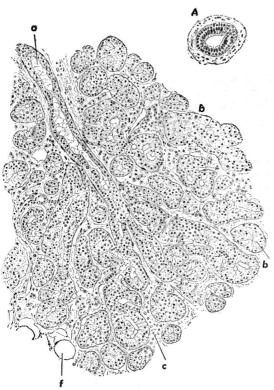

Fig. 561. A small lobule of human lacrimal gland. *a*, Small intralobular excretory duct; *b*, terminal portions; *c*, intralobular interstitial connective tissue with blood vessels; *f*, fat cells. A, Cross section of a larger interlobular excretory duct with pseudostratified epithelium. 112 ×. (After Schaffer.)

diately in front of the inner free edge of the lid, where the skin passes into the conjunctiva.

The meibomian glands are sebaceous, but have lobated alveolar terminal portions. They are connected by short lateral ducts with a long central excretory duct lined with stratified squamous epithelium.

The innermost layer of the lid is the *conjunctiva*. At the inner edge of the margin of the lid the epidermis continues as the narrow admarginal zone to the inner surface of the lid. Here the superficial cells become thicker, the number of layers decreases, mucous cells appear, and the epithelium assumes a stratified columnar character which is typical for the whole conjunctiva and varies only in thickness in different places. The superficial cells have a short prismatic form and are provided with a thin cuticle. Spherical goblet cells are scattered between them.

At the upper edge of the tarsus the epithelium is sometimes reduced to two cell layers, and its surface presents many irregular invaginations. Some of them are lined with mucous cells and described as glands. In the conjunctiva of the fornix the epithelium is thicker.

The lamina propria of the conjunctiva is dense connective tissue. In the region of the fornix it is loosely

attached to the intra-orbital fat tissue; this permits the free motion of the eyeball in the conjunctival sac.

In the region of the corneal limbus the epithelium of the conjunctiva assumes a stratified squamous character and continues as such on the surface of the cornea. It may still contain a few scattered mucous cells.

The rudimentary *third eyelid* or *semilunar fold* (the homologue of the nictitating membrane of the lower vertebrates) is formed by the scleral conjunctiva at the inner palpebral commissure, lateral to the lacrimal caruncle. It consists of connective tissue which contains smooth muscle fibers; it is covered with conjunctival epithelium which, on the outer surface, contains many mucous cells.

Lacrimal Gland. In connection with the conjunctival space there is a system of glands, the secretion of which moistens, lubricates and flushes the surface of the eyeball and of the lids. Of these glands, only the lacrimal gland reaches a high development. It has the size and shape of an almond and is lodged beneath the conjunctiva at the lateral upper side of the eyeball. It consists of a group of separate glandular bodies and sends out six to twelve excretory ducts which open along the upper and lateral surfaces of the superior conjunctival fornix.

The lacrimal gland is of the tubulo-alveolar type. Its terminal portions are provided with a relatively large lumen and with irregular, saccular outpocketings. The basement membrane is lined with glandular cells resembling those of the serous salivary type. They have, however, a narrower columnar shape and contain, besides small fat droplets, large, pale secretion granules whose number changes with the volume of the cells, according to the functional conditions.

These cells are provided with secretory capillaries; between their bases and the basement membrane well-developed basket (myo-epithelial) cells are present. The smallest intralobular excretory ducts are lined with a layer of low columnar or cuboidal cells and have a few myo-epithelial cells. The larger intralobular ducts have a two-layered epithelium.

On the inner surface of the lids, especially the upper one, near the upper edge of the tarsus, a varying number of small accessory lacrimal glands—the *tarsal lacrimal glands*—are scattered.

After having washed the conjunctival cavity, the secretion of the lacrimal gland (the tears, a sterile liquid) reaches the region of the inner palpebral commissure (internal canthus). Here the two eyelids are separated by a triangular space, the *lacrimal lake*, in which the secretion accumulates temporarily. From here it passes through two tiny orifices called *lacrimal points*, one on the margin of each eyelid, into the *lacrimal ducts*. The latter converge medially into the *lacrimal sac*, whence the *nasolacrimal duct* leads into the inferior meatus of the nose.

The wall of the excretory lacrimal passages is formed by connective tissue lined with epithelium. The epithelium of the lacrimal ducts is stratified

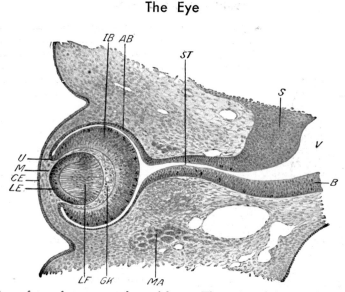

Fig. 562. Primordium of eye of a mouse embryo of 8 mm. The cavity of the primary optic vesicle is reduced to a thin cleft. *AB*, outer layer of secondary optic vesicle; *B*, bottom of anterior brain vesicle; *CE*, epithelium of cornea; *GK*, vitreous body; *IB*, inner layer of secondary optic vesicle; *LE*, epithelium of the lens; *LF*, lens fibers with nuclear zone; *M*, mesenchyme; *MA*, primordium of muscle; *S*, side of anterior brain vesicle; *ST*, stalk of optic vesicle; *U*, border of the optic cup; *V*, ventricle of brain. 70 ×. (After Schaffer.)

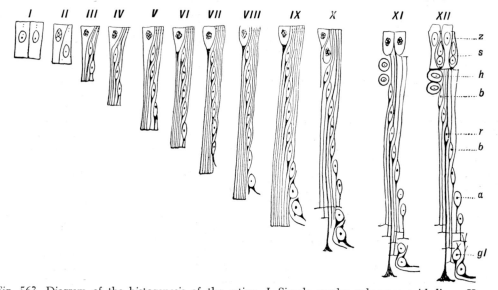

Fig. 563. Diagram of the histogenesis of the retina. *I*, Simple regular columnar epithelium; *II*, pseudo-stratified epithelium with two and, *III*, with three rows of nuclei; the number of nuclear rows increases in *IV–VII*; *VII*, the lowermost cell has developed an axon; *VIII*, the first (lower) ganglion cell has separated from the other elements; *IX*, the second ganglionic cell becomes separated; *X*, all cells except the radial fibers are separated from the inner surface; the ganglion cells and the amacrines have also severed their connections with the outer surface; *XI*, all cells except the indifferent stem cells, the visual cells and the radial fibers are separated from the outer surface; the horizontal cells also are free; *XII*, the rod cells (*s*) form a double layer between the cone cells; the cones have protoplasmic outgrowths; *z*, cone cells; *h*, horizontal cells; *r*, radial fibers; *b*, bipolars; *a*, amacrines; *gl*, ganglion cells. (After Fürst from Franz.)

squamous. The lacrimal sac and the nasolacrimal duct are lined with a pseudostratified, tall columnar epithelium.

From the bottom of the lacrimal lake, between the two lacrimal ducts, there bulges a small, soft mass of tissue, the *lacrimal caruncle*. The top is covered with a thick, squamous epithelium in which only the uppermost layers are flattened, although not cornified. It contains mucous cells, and gradually merges into the conjunctival epithelium. The lamina propria contains bundles of striated muscles, sweat and abortive lacrimal glands, and tiny hairs with sebaceous glands. These are the source of the whitish secretion which often collects in the region of the inner palpebral commissure.

Blood and Lymph Vessels of the Eyelids. The arteries in each lid form two archlike anastomoses, which run in front of the tarsus, one near the free margin of the lid, the other near the upper (or lower) margin of the tarsus. The palpebral conjunctiva is provided with dense, subepithelial capillary networks which can be easily studied in living condition with the aid of the slit-lamp microscope. Branches of the blood vessels in the scleral conjunctiva anastomose with the marginal blood vessels of the cornea and with the branches of the anterior ciliary arteries.

The lymphatics form dense nets in the conjunctiva behind the tarsus. In front of the latter there is another, thinner, pretarsal net. A third net can be distinguished in the skin and the subcutis. All these nets communicate with one another. The lymphatic capillaries of the scleral conjunctiva end blindly near the corneal margin.

The abundant supply of the conjunctiva with blood and lymph capillaries explains the rapid absorption of solutions introduced into the conjunctival sac.

Histogenesis of the Eye. The stalk of the optic vesicle growing out of the brain is transformed into the optic nerve; the double-walled vesicle gives rise to the retina. Where the optic vesicle touches the ectoderm, the latter forms an invagination with a greatly thickened bottom, the *primordium of the lens*. It apparently develops as the result of stimulation of the ectoderm by the optic vesicle. In amphibian larvae, after excision of the optic vesicle, the lens is not formed. The lens primordium comes to lie in the invagination of the optic vesicle. Simultaneously, mesenchyme and blood vessels grow into the choroidal fissure, which splits the lower periphery of the vesicle and continues upon the optic stalk. These vessels give rise to the hyaloid and retinal vascular systems. The opposite margins of the fissure, which received the vessels, soon grow together, and the secondary optic vesicle assumes the form of a double-walled cup, while the stalk is transformed into a solid strand, the optic nerve.

The lens primordium soon becomes detached from the ectoderm, and the space between the two is filled by the layer of mesenchyme: the primordium of the substantia propria of the cornea and of the connective tissue of the iris. The lens, surrounded by vascular mesenchyme, acquires a solid, spherical form, while the original cavity disappears. The inner, thicker sheet of the double wall of the optic cup differentiates into the *retina proper;* it remains permanently in direct continuation with the optic nerve. The outer sheet of the cup is transformed into the pigment epithelium. The surrounding mesenchyme comes into close relation with the optic cup and gives rise to the two outer tunics of the eyeball, the *uveal* and *fibrous tunics*. The structural differentiation of the retina proceeds in a way similar to that of the wall of the neural tube. It is characterized by proliferation, by shifting of the cells and by the establishment of complex synaptic relationships. The eyeball attains full size toward the end of the first decade, whereas the structure of the retina, including the central fovea, matures toward the end of the first year.

REFERENCES

Arey, L. B.: Visual Cells and Retinal Pigment, in Cowdry's Special Cytology, (2), 887, 1932, and in Penfield's Cytology and Cellular Pathology, (2), 743, 1932.

Berliner, M. L.: Biomicroscopy of the Eye. New York, Paul B. Hoeber, Inc., 1949.

Duke-Elder, W. S.: Textbook of Ophthalmology. The Development, Form, and Function of the Visual Apparatus. London, 1932, Vol. I.

Hecht, S.: Rods, Cones, and the Chemical Basis of Vision. Physiol. Rev., 17:239, 1937.

Klüver, H. (ed.): Visual Mechanisms. Biol. Symposia, (7). Lancaster, Pa., Jaques Cattell Press, 1942.

Kolmer, W., and Lauber, H.: Haut und Sinnesorgane, 2nd part, Auge, in v. Möllendorff's Handb. d. mikroskop. Anat. (3/2), 1936.

Krause, A. C., and Sibley, J. A.: Metabolism of the Retina. Arch. Ophthalmol., 36:328, 1946.

Mann, J.: The Development of the Human Eye. London, 1928; Developmental Abnormalities of the Eye. London, 1937.

Polyak, S.: The Retina. Chicago, 1941.

Salzmann, M.: The Anatomy and Physiology of the Human Eyeball in the Normal State. Transl. by E. V. L. Brown, 1912.

Sjostrand, F. S.: An Electron Microscope Study of the Retinal Rods of the Guinea Pig Eye. J. Cell. & Comp. Physiol., 33:383, 1949.

Walls, G. L.: The Vertebrate Eye and Its Adaptive Radiation. Bloomfield Mills, Mich., Cranbrook Press, 1943.

XXXIII. THE EAR

The organ of hearing consists of three parts. The first part, the *external ear*, receives the sound waves; the second, the *middle ear*, transmits the vibrations to the third part, the *internal ear* or labyrinth, where the sound waves elicit specific nervous impulses. These are conveyed by the acoustic nerve to the central nervous system. The internal ear also contains the vestibular organs, highly specialized end organs of the proprioceptive sense concerned chiefly with the function of equilibration.

EXTERNAL EAR

The external ear includes the auricle, the external acoustic meatus and the tympanic membrane.

Auricle. The complicated form of the auricle is due to its irregular plate of cellular elastic cartilage, 0.5 to 1 mm. thick. Its flexible perichondrium contains abundant elastic networks. The skin covering the auricle has a distinct subcutaneous layer only on the posterior surface. It carries a few small hairs with sebaceous glands, sometimes of considerable size; in old age, especially in men, large stiff hairs develop on the dorsal edge and the ear lobe. The sweat glands are scarce and small.

External Auditory Meatus. The external auditory meatus is oval in cross section and extends from the bottom of the auricle to the tympanic membrane, which separates it from the tympanic cavity. Its outer wall is formed by a continuation of the cartilage of the auricle and its inner wall by the temporal bone. The skin lining it is thin, devoid of papillae, firmly attached to the perichondrium and periosteum, and has no subcutaneous layer. The numerous hairs in the cartilaginous portion protect the meatus against the entrance of foreign bodies. In old age they enlarge considerably in the same way as those of the auricle. The sebaceous glands connected with the hair follicles are exceptionally large. In the inner, osseous portion, small hairs and sebaceous glands are found only along the upper wall.

The external meatus contains *cerumen*, a brown, waxy secretion with a bitter taste, which protects the skin from desiccation and from invasion by insects. It is a mixture of the secretion of the sebaceous and *ceruminous* glands of the skin in the meatus. These are tubular, coiled glands and are a variety of the apocrine sweat glands. The ducts of the ceruminous glands open either on the free surface of the skin or, together with the sebaceous glands, into the necks of the hair follicles.

Tympanic Membrane. The oval tympanic membrane is thin and semitransparent. One of the auditory ossicles, the *malleus*, is attached by its *manubrium* to the inner surface of the membrane and reaches its center. Two layers of collagenous bundles and fibroblasts similar to those of a tendon form the mass of the membrane. The fibers in the outer layer have a radial arrangement; those in the inner layer are circular. There are also thin networks of elastic fibers, mainly in the central part of the membrane and at its periphery. The membrane is covered by a thin layer of skin (50 to 60 microns) and is lined on its inner surface by the mucous membrane of the tympanic cavity, here only 20 to 40 microns thick. The epidermis has a thin, horny layer. Along the handle of the malleus is a layer of connective tissue, through which vessels and nerves reach the center of the membrane. The lamina propria of the mucosa consists of a few collagenous fibers and capillaries and is covered by a simple squamous epithelium.

MIDDLE EAR

The middle ear comprises the tympanic cavity and the auditory or eustachian tube.

Tympanic Cavity. The tympanic cavity is an irregular, air-containing space in the temporal bone. Its lateral wall is largely formed by the tympanic membrane, its medial wall by the lateral side of the *osseous labyrinth*.

On the medial wall of the tympanic cavity, formed by the ossseous labyrinth, are two "windows," the fenestrae. One of these, the *vestibular fenestra*, is an oval opening closed by the base of the stapes; this is attached to the cartilaginous edges of the opening by a circular fibroblastic ligament. This demarcates the tympanic cavity from the scala vestibuli

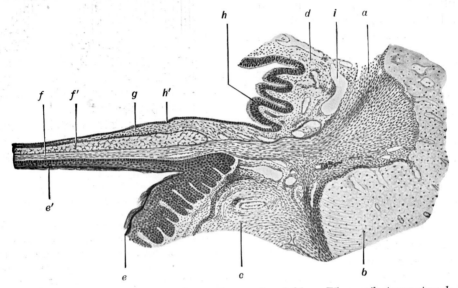

Fig. 564. Cross section of edge of tympanic membrane of a child. *a*, Fibrocartilaginous ring; *b*, bone; *c*, derma with papillae; *d*, mucous membrane of tympanic cavity; *e*, epidermis of the external meatus; *e'*, epidermis of the tympanic membrane; *f*, radial fibers; *f'*, circular fibers of the tympanic membrane; *g;* mucosa of the tympanic membrane; *h'*, its squamous epithelium; *h*, ciliated columnar epithelium of tympanic cavity; *i*, vessels. (Redrawn from von Ebner.)

The cavity contains the ear bones (*auditory ossicles*), two small muscles connected with the ossicles (tensor tympani and stapedius), the chorda tympani nerve, and connective tissue trabeculae. The cavity continues into the auditory tube, which opens into the nasal part of the pharynx. In the adult, the posterior part of the tympanic cavity is connected, through the large tympanic antrum, with air-filled cavities, or "cells," in the mastoid process of the temporal bone.

The epithelium of the tympanic cavity is generally of the simple squamous type, although near the opening of the auditory tube and near the edge of the tympanic membrane, it is cuboidal or columnar and provided with cilia. The presence of glands is generally denied.

of the cochlea. The other opening is round— the *fenestra tympanica* or *rotunda*. It is situated below and behind the oval fenestra and is closed by a fibrous membrane, the secondary tympanic membrane. It separates the tympanic cavity from the scala tympani of the cochlea.

Auditory Ossicles. These three bones— the malleus, the incus, and the stapes—extend from the tympanic membrane (to which the malleus is attached) to the oval fenestra, which is closed by the base of the stapes; they are connected with one another by tiny articulations. They contain small cavities with vascular connective tissue. On the handle of the malleus and the base of the stapes are small patches of hyaline cartilage. The periosteum covering the ossicles fuses with the lamina propria of the mucous membrane into a thin layer of connective tissue covered by simple squamous epithelium.

Auditory or Eustachian Tube. The auditory tube has a flattened lumen (1 to 2 mm.) which in the portion nearest to the tympanic cavity is surrounded by bone. In the next part the wall is supported by a plate of hyaline cartilage. The mucous membrane lining the lumen in the bony portion has a low columnar ciliated epithelium; nearer the pharynx a taller, pseudostratified ciliated epithelium is found; at the pharyngeal opening numerous goblet cells appear. The tympanic cavity regulates the air pressure on the inner side of the tympanic membrane. By the act of swallowing, the lumen of the tube is opened for a short interval, and the pressure in the middle ear is equalized with the outside pressure.

INNER EAR OR LABYRINTH

The inner ear, called the labyrinth because of its complex structure, comprises a series of canals and cavities hollowed out of the petrous part of the temporal bone. As the layer of bone immediately surrounding the cavities is harder than the rest of the petrous portion, it is possible by careful dissection to isolate an *osseous labyrinth* from the mass of the bone. It must be kept in mind, however, that a *free* osseous labyrinth is entirely artificial. In it a central part of irregular, oval shape, the *vestibule*, can be distinguished medial to the tympanic cavity. Its wall facing the tympanic cavity has the two fenestrae mentioned earlier.

Three *semicircular canals* arise from above and behind the vestibule and return to it. According to their position they are distinguished as the superior, the posterior and the lateral canals. The lateral canal is the shortest (12 to 15 mm.) and the posterior the longest (18 to 22 mm.). The lateral canals of both ears are in nearly the same plane. The superior canal of one side is approximately parallel to the posterior canal of the other.

The superior and the lateral canals have dilatations, called *ampullae*, which open near each other into the upper part of the vesti-

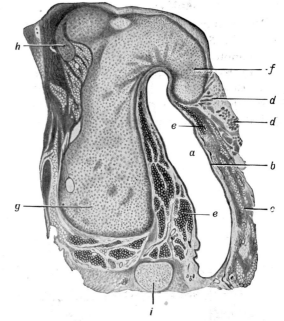

Fig. 565. Transection of cartilaginous portion of the auditory tube near its opening into the pharynx. *a*, Lumen of the tube in dilated condition; *b*, ciliated epithelium; *c*, membranous lateral wall with fat tissue; *d*, muscle bundles; *e*, mixed glands; *f*, lateral cartilaginous plate forming hook; *g*, medial cartilaginous plate with darker spots caused by patches of elastic cartilage; *h* and *i*, accessory cartilages. 11 ×. (Redrawn from von Ebner.)

bule above the oval fenestra. The ampullated end of the posterior canal opens into the posterior part of the vestibule. The upper end of this canal fuses with the medial end of the superior canal to form the *crus commune*, which opens into the medial part of the vestibule. The lateral canal opens independently into the upper part of the vestibule. From the medial wall of the vestibule a thin canal extends to the posterior surface of the *pars petrosa* of the temporal bone—the *vestibular aqueduct*.

The vestibule continues into the *bony cochlea*—a spirally coiled tube which forms a conical body resembling a snail shell. It measures about 5 mm. from base to apex, with a diameter of about 9 mm. at the base.

Membranous Labyrinth. The interior of the osseous cavities is lined with periosteum and encloses a system of vesicles and canals with a fibrous wall—the membranous labyrinth. All its parts communicate with one another and are filled with *endolymph*. The inner surface of their wall is lined with an epithelium of ectodermal origin. In some places the fibrous wall of the membranous labyrinth adheres to the periosteum of the osseous labyrinth. In general, however, it is separated from this periosteum by irregular

ous vestibule consists, not of one, but of two separate sacs—the *utricle* and the *saccule*.

It is relatively easy to isolate the membranous labyrinth from its osseous container. The central part is occupied by the utricle and the saccule (Fig. 566). The oblong *utricle* communicates by five orifices with the three membranous semicircular canals, which cor-

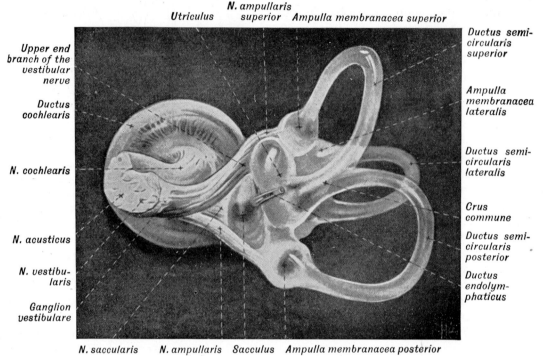

Fig. 566. Right membranous labyrinth of an adult; medial and posterior aspects. 5 ×. (After Spalteholz.)

cavities filled with *perilymph*. Thin strands of connective tissue (trabeculae) arise from the periosteum, penetrate the perilymphatic spaces, and reach the wall of the membranous labyrinth, together with the blood vessels. Thus the membranous labyrinth is suspended within the osseous labyrinth by these trabeculae. The perilymphatic spaces are homologous to the subarachnoid spaces of the meninges; the perilymph corresponds to the cerebrospinal fluid.

The form and arrangement of the various parts of the membranous labyrinth generally correspond to those of the osseous labyrinth in which they are enclosed. However, the membranous part contained in the osse-

respond in form and position to the osseous canals containing them. The three ampullar enlargements are much more pronounced in the membranous canals. Each ampulla has a flattened floor which forms part of the convex surface of its canal and a hemispherical roof bulging on the concave side. The superior and lateral ampullae open close to each other into the upper end of the utricle, the posterior ampulla into its lower end. The *crus commune*, formed by the superior and inferior canals, joins the middle part of the utricle near the second orifice of the lateral canal.

The roughly spherical saccule lies in front of the utricle and is connected with it by the *utriculosaccular duct*. Their junction continues as the slender *endolymphatic duct*, which runs through the vestibular aqueduct to the posterior surface of the petrous part of the temporal bone, where it ends with an enlargement, the *endolymphatic sac*. From the lower part of the saccule the short, narrow *ductus reuniens* (Fig. 567), leads to the *cochlear duct*.

The wall of the membranous labyrinth becomes extremely complex in six sensory epithelial areas containing the endings of the acoustic nerve (Fig. 567). They are the *macula utriculi* and *macula sacculi*, the three *cristae ampullaries* (one in the ampulla of each semicircular canal) and the *organ of Corti*, running along the cochlear canal.

Utricle and Saccule. The connective tissue layer of the wall of the utricle and saccule, like the other parts of the membranous labyrinth, has a finely fibrillated substance with fibroblasts and often with melanophores. Its outer surface, the trabeculae which run through the perilymphatic spaces, and the inner surface of the periosteum, are lined with mesenchymal epithelium. The connective tissue is separated from the epithelium by a basement membrane. Except in the neuroepithelial areas, the epithelium is a layer of squamous cells, 3 to 4 microns thick and usually provided with a diplosome and a flagellum.

The spoon-shaped *macula utriculi* occupies the lateral wall of the utricle and measures 2 by 3 mm. The *macula sacculi*, occupying the medial wall of the saccule, is of similar size and is heart-shaped. The surfaces of the maculae are perpendicular to each other. The epithelium is the same in both maculae. It is 30 to 35 microns thick and consists of *supporting cells* and *hair cells*. The first are slender columnar structures containing a bundle of tonofibrils and a round nucleus at the lower end. The free surface, provided with cuticular plates, are interconnected by terminal bars. Under each plate lies a diplosome with a minute protruding flagellum and, farther down, a Golgi net and sometimes granular or fatty inclusions.

The *hair cells* are lodged between the

supporting cells, but occupy only the upper half of the epithelial layer. They have the form of short flasks with a rounded bottom which contains the nucleus; their free surface is covered by a round, cuticular plate, connected with the cuticles of the supporting cells. From the center of the cuticle rises a

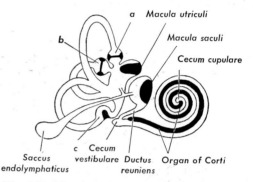

Fig. 567. Diagram of membranous labyrinth with neuro-epithelial areas in black. *a*, Superior; *b*, lateral; *c*, posterior ampullae of respective semicircular canals. (Modified after von Ebner.)

tuft of long (20 to 25 microns), nonmotile cilia, held together by a cement substance and forming a long, tapering brush. The diplosome sends out a flagellum which adheres to the surface of the tuft of cilia and is believed to beat during life. The spaces between the supporting cells and the hair cells are filled with a semifluid substance.

The surface of the maculae is covered by the *otolithic membrane*—a thick (22 microns) layer of a gelatinous substance into which the hair tufts penetrate. Each tuft is surrounded by a narrow space filled with endolymph. Between these spaces the gelatinous substance is connected with the terminal bars of the epithelium by thin partitions. The jelly, beyond the hairs, contains a multitude of minute (3 by 5 microns) crystalline bodies, the *otoconia* or *otoliths* (Fig. 568, *St*). These are prisms ending in pyramids and are a mixture of calcium carbonate (aragonite) and a protein. After the calcium is dissolved, their outlines remain visible.

At the edge of the macula the hair cells end abruptly, and the supporting cells gradually pass into the simple squamous epithelium of the rest of the wall.

The connective tissue of the wall is thickened in the area of the macula and is firmly attached to the endosteum. Here the intercellular substance is especially firm, and the basement membrane is distinct. Most of the myelinated nerve fibers which supply the macula lose their myelin sheaths close to the basement membrane. Naked axis cylinders

In a longitudinal section of the ampulla, the *crista* appears in cross section as a rounded prominence occupying about one third of the lumen. When cut longitudinally, the crista is seen to be highest in its middle part and to slope down toward the side walls of the ampulla. Seen from the surface, the ends of the crista are rounded and edged by a cre-

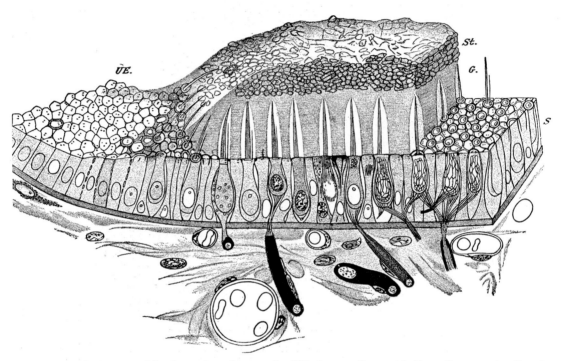

Fig. 568. Plastic diagram of border region of a macula. *UE*, Intermediate epithelium; *St*, otoconia; *G*, gelatinous layer; *S*, supporting elements. (After Kolmer.)

pierce the membrane and branch in the spaces between the epithelial cells. The terminal arborizations of the thicker fibers form basket-like nests closely surrounding the hair cells and almost reaching the free epithelial surface. The thinner fibers end with branches between the supporting cells.

Semicircular Canals. The membranous semicircular canals are slightly oval in cross section. Their convex surface is close to the periosteum, and the opening surface is surrounded by a large perilymphatic space (Fig. 569, *pr*) with numerous trabeculae (Fig. 569, *b*). The wall of the membranous canals has the same structure as that of the utricle and saccule.

scentic area, the *planum semilunatum*. The latter is covered by columnar epithelium which contains inclusions and has, perhaps, a glandular function.

When fixatives are applied to the living crista of fishes, the hairs are seen to shorten slowly, and the space in the lumen formerly occupied by them is filled with a coagulum which shrinks to the form of a cupula. The cupula of fixed preparations is therefore an artefact.

The neuro-epithelium of the human crista has much in common with that of the maculae, with similar supporting elements and hair cells. Near the surface of each hair cell a flagellum, arising from a diplosome, is continuous with what appears to be a tuft of matted cilia. In fixed preparations the crista is covered by a gelatinous cap, the cupula, which seems to rest on the hairs. The relations of the nerve fibers to the hair cells are essentially the same as in the maculae.

of spongy bone, the *modiolus*. Its base forms the bottom of the internal acoustic meatus. Blood vessels, surrounded by connective tissue and bundles of the cochlear divisions of the acoustic nerve, penetrate through numerous openings into the bony substance of the

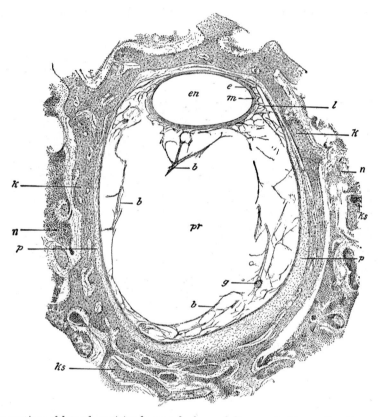

Fig. 569. Cross section of lateral semicircular canal of an adult man. *b*, Connective tissue trabeculae in the perilymphatic space: *e*, epithelium; *en*, endolymphatic space; *g*, blood vessel; *k*, bone of the bony labyrinth; *ks*, bone trabeculae of the spongiosa; *l*, ligamentum canaliculi; *m*, membrana propria of the membranous semicircular canal; *n*, bone marrow; *p*, periosteum; *pr*, perilymphatic space. 46 ×. (After von Ebner, from Schaffer.)

Cochlea. The canal of the cochlea makes two and a half spiral turns around the axis of this structure. The direction parallel to the course of the canal may be designated "spiral," a plane parallel to the axis, but not passing through it, as "tangential." The radial direction from the axis to the surface of the cochlea is called "outward." The most informative sections of the cochlea are radial ones which pass through the plane of the axis and perpendicular to the cochlear canal.

The *axis of the cochlea* is a conical pillar

modiolus. The nerve fibers run upward and turn outward to reach the spiral ganglion, which extends along the inner wall of the cochlear canal.

The lumen of the canal of the osseous cochlea (about 3 mm. in diameter) is divided along its whole course (about 35 mm. in man) into an upper and a lower section by the *spiral lamina*. Its inner zone contains bone and is called the *osseous spiral lamina* (Fig. 571, *Lo*). The fibrous outer zone is the *basilar membrane* (*membranous spiral*

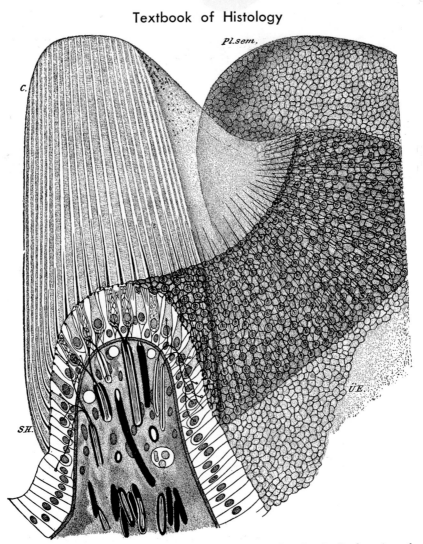

Fig. 570. Plastic diagram of one half of an ampullar crista as seen in a longitudinal section of a semicircular canal, passing across the crista. *SH.*, Hair tufts; *C.*, gelatinous mass of the cupula; *UE.*, intermediate epithelium; *Pl. sem.*, planum semilunatum. (After Kolmer.)

lamina) (Fig. 571, *Mb*). The extent of ossification is greatest in the lowest coil. At the attachment of the basilar membrane to the outer wall of the cochlea the periosteum is thickened and forms the *spiral ligament*. The *vestibular membrane* extends obliquely from the spiral lamina to the outer wall of the osseous cochlea. Thus a cross section of the osseous cochlear canal will show three cavities: the upper cavity, or *scala vestibuli*, a lower cavity, *scala tympani*, and the *ductus cochlearis*, or scala media.

The scala tympani and scala vestibuli are perilymphatic spaces whose walls have the same structure as the other perilymphatic spaces in the labyrinth. The bone is lined by a thin layer of connective tissue covered with mesenchymal epithelium. The scala vestibuli extends into and through the perilymphatic space of the vestibule and reaches the inner surface of the fenestra ovalis. At the apex of the cochlea the two scalae communicate through a small opening—the *helicotrema*.

The lower, vestibular end of the cochlear duct is a small outpocketing, the *cecum vestibulare*, separated from the fenestra ovalis by the enlarged perilymphatic space. Into it opens the canalis reuniens, which connects it with the saccule; in adults it is almost

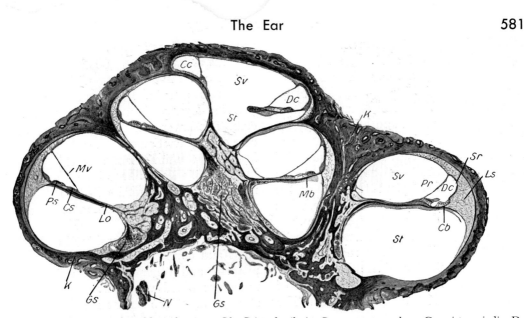

Fig. 571. Axial section of cochlea of a man. *Cb*, Crista basilaris; *Cc*, cecum cupulare; *Cs*, crista spiralis; *Dc*, ductus cochlearis; *Gs*, ganglion spirale; *K*, bony wall of the cochlea; *Lo*, lamina spiralis ossea; *Ls*, ligamentum spirale; *Mb*, membrana basilaris; *Mv*, membrana vestibularis; *N*, cochlear nerve; *Pr*, prominentia spiralis; *Ps*, organ of Corti; *Sr*, stria vascularis; *St*, scala tympani; *Sv*, scala vestibuli. 16 ×. (After Schaffer.)

obliterated. The upper end of the cochlear duct ends blindly with the *cecum cupulare*.

The functions of the structures in the cochlea are so imperfectly known that no consistent theory has been formulated.

Osseous Spiral Lamina and the Basilar Membrane. The spiral ganglion extends along the line of attachment of the osseous spiral lamina to the modiolus. It is lodged in an irregular cavity of the bone, the *spiral canal of the modiolus*. From the ganglion, along its whole length, bundles of nerves arise and run through radial canals in the osseous spiral lamina toward the organ of Corti.

In the inner corner of the cochlear duct, the periosteum of the upper surface of the spiral lamina bulges into the duct as the *limbus spiralis*. Its edge overhangs the *internal spiral sulcus*, with its two margins, the *vestibular* and *tympanic lips* (Fig. 572). The connective tissue of the limbus has a firm, intercellular substance and, especially in its deeper layers, stellate connective tissue cells. On the surface the connective tissue forms small ridges which protrude over the edge of the vestibular lip as the *auditory teeth of Huschke*.

The periosteum on the lower surface of the spiral osseous lamina continues outward beyond the tympanic lip of the limbus. It contains the radial bundles of myelinated fibers which come from the spiral ganglion (Fig. 573). In the lower coil of the cochlea, the osseous lamina extends outward as far as the tympanic lip.

A little beyond the vestibular lip, the nerve bundles enter the epithelium of the organ of Corti. In doing so, they emerge from the connective tissue (or from the bone) through a series of small radial slits, the *foramina nervosa*. When seen from above, they form a row of holes in the tympanic lip; hence the name *habenula perforata*.

The tympanic lip continues outward into the *basilar membrane* (Fig. 573), which is tightly stretched between it and the crest of the spiral ligament. The basilar membrane can be subdivided into the zona arcuata, extending from the foramina nervosa to the base of the external pillars, and the zona pectinata, between the external pillars and the crest of the spiral ligament.

The middle layer in both zones is formed by the *auditory strings* or *basilar fibers*. In the zona arcuata they are thin and arranged in the fashion of a net; in the zona pectinata they are thicker (1 to 2 microns), straight, and smooth, and do not branch. In fresh condition they are soft and flexible and can be isolated easily. Acetic acid dissolves them; after fixation they become hard and brittle. They are birefringent, but differ from collagenous as well as from elastic fibers. They are embedded in a small amount of ground substance. On reaching the spiral ligament, some of the strings penetrate fanlike into its tissue, while others run upward under the epithelium.

The length of the strings increases considerably from the base of the cochlea to its apex. In the beginning of the first coil they measure 64 to 128 microns, at the end of the membrane, 352 to 480 microns. The number of strings in the human basilar membrane is estimated at 24,000.

Above the middle layer with its auditory strings is a thin, homogeneous *vestibular covering layer* with a few connective tissue cells. The lower surface is lined with a delicate connective tissue, the *tympanic covering layer*. In the inner zone of this layer are blood capillaries connected with a vein running under the tunnel of Corti. The pars pectinata of the basilar membrane lacks blood vessels.

The spiral ligament consists of collagenous fibers and connective tissue cells filled with pigment and other inclusions; it also has numerous blood vessels. Slightly above the attachment of the basilar membrane to the

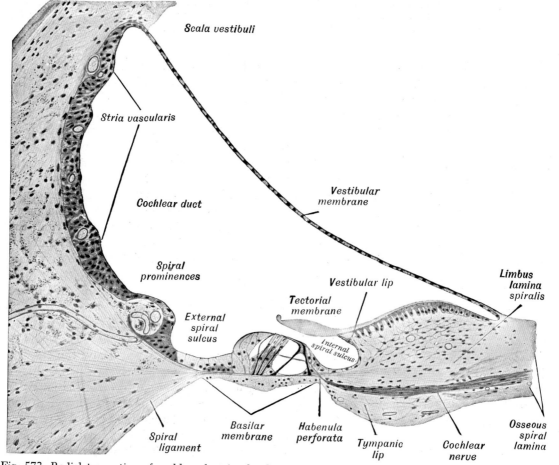

Fig. 572. Radial transection of cochlear duct in the first coil of human cochlea. The separation of the free end of the tectorial membrane from the organ of Corti is due to improper fixation. (After Held.)

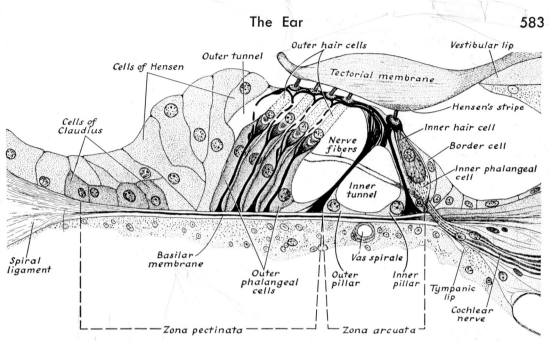

Fig. 573. Radial transection of the human organ of Corti, from the upper part of the first coil. (Slightly modified after Held.)

spiral ligament, the connective tissue forms a small ridge extending through the whole cochlea—the *prominentia spiralis*. It contains large capillary loops—the *vas prominens*. The groove between the ridge and the crest of the spiral ligament is the *external spiral sulcus*.

The *vestibular membrane* is a thin (3 microns) connective tissue layer which in man lacks blood vessels, but may contain pigment cells and fine elastic networks. On the vestibular surface it is covered with the mesenchymal epithelium of the perilymphatic spaces.

Epithelium of the Cochlear Duct. The ectodermal epithelium lining the cochlear duct presents great differences in its various regions. The inner surface of the vestibular membrane is covered with a simple squamous epithelium often containing pigment. The surface of the limbus is a mosaic of cuticular plates belonging to epithelial cells whose bodies are deep in the subjacent connective tissue. They are arranged in rows along the furrows on the limbus, between the auditory teeth. The internal spiral sulcus is lined with a layer of epithelial cells of medium thickness.

Outwardly they are followed by the inner border cells of the organ of Corti.

The thick epithelium covering the outer wall of the cochlear duct extends to the external spiral sulcus and is called the *stria vascularis* (Fig. 572). It is a low stratified columnar epithelium. Many of its cells send processes into the connective tissue, and some of them come in contact with the blood vessels. The abundant capillaries run for the most part in the spiral direction, forming loops which penetrate the epithelium, and sometimes accompanied by connective tissue cells.

It is believed that the stria vascularis secretes the endolymph of the cochlear canal. As the organ of Corti has no blood vessels, its elements must receive their nutritive materials and oxygen from the endolymph. Since the organ of Corti does not display *peripheral fatigue*, it is probable that the endolymph is constantly renewed.

In the external spiral sulcus the epithelium is cuboidal; its cells also have processes penetrating deep into the connective tissue. Approaching the basilar membrane, the epithelium becomes more regular and continues

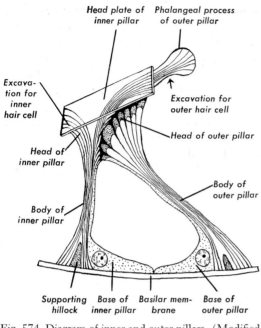

Fig. 574. Diagram of inner and outer pillars. (Modified after Kolmer.)

upon the pars pectinata as the *cells of Claudius* (Fig. 573). In parts of the basal coil, small groups of polyhedral cells (*of Boettcher*) are scattered between the basilar membrane and the cells of Claudius.

The Organ of Corti, or the Papilla Basilaris. The basilar membrane carries an exceedingly complex epithelial ridge—the organ of Corti, or the *papilla basilaris*. It bulges into the cochlear duct and extends throughout its length (Figs. 571, 572, 573). Among its elements two types may be distinguished: (1) *supporting cells* which form a rigid but flexible framework and (2) *hair cells*—neuro-epithelial receptors of the stimuli produced by the sound waves. These elements are arranged in regular, longitudinal (spiral) rows.

Supporting Cells. The several types of supporting cells have certain characteristics in common. They contain tonofibrils and are tall elements extending from the basilar membrane through the epithelium, and end as cuticular plates on the free surface of the organ of Corti. Although the cells are separated from one another by large intercellular spaces, their cuticles form a continuous membrane covering the organ. This membrane has

many round holes; hence the name *reticular membrane*. These holes are filled with the round cuticular plates of the hair cells. The supporting cells include (1) inner and outer pillars, (2) inner and outer phalangeal cells, (3) border cells, (4) cells of Hensen.

Within the organ of Corti is the *inner tunnel*, a canal extending the length of the cochlea and bounded by the basilar membrane and the inner and outer pillar cells. The bodies of the pillars are separated by cleftlike spaces through which the tunnel communicates with the other intercellular cavities in the organ of Corti.

Inner Pillars. The inner pillars have a broad base which rests on the basilar membrane, and a cell body rising conically upward. The cytoplasm at the inner corner of the tunnel contains a round nucleus and a conical condensation surrounded by a cone of darkly staining tonofibrils. These rise into a cylindrical bundle forming the body of the pillar (2 to 3 microns thick) sheathed by a trace of protoplasm. Approaching the surface, the pillar again becomes thicker and ends with a head, covered by a rectangular cuticular plate (Fig. 574). Its long sides are connected with those of the neighboring inner pillars. The inner margin fits the edge of the cuticle of an inner hair cell. The outer margin overlies the cuticular plate of the outer pillars.

Outer Pillars. The outer pillars are longer than the inner ones. Their base is attached to the basilar membrane at the junction of the zona arcuata with the pectinata. Like the base of the inner pillars, it also consists of a small amount of cytoplasm surrounding a nucleus; it too continues into a long slender body with a bundle of tonofibrils (Fig. 574). The head of the outer pillar fits an excavation in the head of the inner pillar to which it is firmly attached. The cuticular plate projects from under the cuticle of the inner pillar and has a shovel-like shape. The cuticular plates of the outer pillars form the first row of phalanges. Into the holes between their excavated edges fit the cuticles of the first row of the outer hair cells.

The inner pillars number 5600, the outer

ones 3800. On an average, three inner pillars are connected with two outer pillars.

Inner Phalangeal Cells. These cells form a row on the inner surface of the inner pillars. Their bases occupy the narrow space between the bases of the inner pillars and the foramina nervosa on the basilar membrane. The cell body contains a nucleus in its lower part, a slender bundle of tonofibrils, and ends at the surface with a small cuticular plate. The plate is elongated in the radial direction, and both its long edges are excavated; hence the name *phalanges*. The outer ends of the phalanges are connected with the cuticles of the inner pillars. Their sides, together with those of the plates of the inner pillars and of the border cells, surround the cuticular plates of the inner hair cells.

Outer Phalangeal Cells (Deiters). The three rows of outer phalangeal cells are adapted to the three rows of outer hair cells. In the second coil are four rows of each cell type. In the third coil a fifth, interrupted row of hair cells and atypical phalangeal cells is added.

The bases of the cells of Deiters rest on the basilar membrane. The cell body is prism-shaped, and through its axis runs a bundle of fibers starting in the middle of the base. The body tapers abruptly toward the surface and continues as a thin stalk formed by the fibrillar bundle. It mounts to the surface and expands into a phalanx with a semicircular excavation on each long side. Into these excavations fit the cuticles of the hair cells of the corresponding row. The phalanges of one row interdigitate with those of the next. The joined phalanges of the different orders constitute the *reticular membrane* with its regular mosaic pattern and alternating rows of round openings containing the cuticles of the hair cells (Fig. 575). The outermost phalanges have a polygonal shape and form the outer edge of the reticular membrane.

Where the body of the outer phalangeal cell begins to taper into the thin stalk, its protoplasm lodges the lower, rounded end of a hair cell (Fig. 576).

In a radial section of the cochlea, the cells of Deiters are never seen in their full length, since the cell body is cut off at the level where it begins to taper. A full view of a cell of Deiters can be had only in a tangential section parallel to the axis of the modiolus. Here it is seen that the slender phalangeal process of each cell is bent toward the apex of the cochlea and that it passes three hair cells before reaching the surface and ending with its phalanx.

Whereas the basal parts of the phalangeal cells are close to one another, there are large spaces (*of Nuel*) between their processes. An especially conspicuous space is found between the outer pillars and the first row of phalangeal cells. Through the clefts between the outer pillars the spaces of Nuel communicate with the tunnel. All these spaces are believed to be filled with a gelatinous substance.

Border Cells. These slender elements stand in a row beside the inner hair cells (Fig. 573). Their narrow cuticles are also arranged in a row which forms the inner margin of the openings containing the cuticles of the inner hair cells. The basal part of these cells sends out processes which accompany the nerve fibers in the organ of Corti. Toward the in-

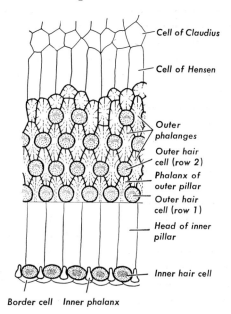

Fig. 575. Diagram of papilla spiralis viewed from above, showing cuticles of hair and supporting cells. (Modified after Retzius, Kolmer, Schaffer.)

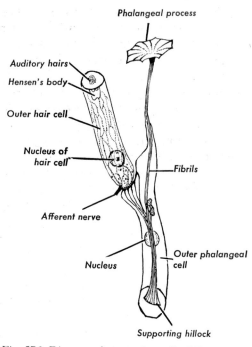

Fig. 576. Diagram of supporting cell of Deiters and the associated outer hair cell. (Modified after Kolmer.)

ner spiral sulcus the border cells are succeeded by cells which rapidly diminish in size and pass into squamous cells.

Cells of Hensen. The cells of Deiters are succeeded in the outward direction by the tall cells of Hensen (Fig. 573). These are arranged in several rows, decrease rapidly in height, and pass into the *cells of Claudius*.

Hair Cells. The free surface of the hair cells, fastened in the holes of the reticular membrane, is provided with short, bristle-like outgrowths. The *inner hair cells* are arranged in a single row between the inner phalangeal and the border cells on the one hand and the inner pillars on the other (Fig. 573). The *outer hair cells* form three rows and are suspended between the outer pillars and the outer phalangeal cells. In the second coil a fourth, in the upper coil a fifth row of outer cells is added. All the hair cells are short cylinders with a rounded lower end containing the nucleus and with an oval cuticular plate on the free surface. Immediately under the cuticle is a modified Golgi net—the *body of Hensen*. At the lower end

of the cell is a condensed protoplasmic mass with pigment granules, the *body of Retzius*. The cuticle of the inner hair cells is surmounted by forty-one to sixty-four hairs arranged in two or more straight, parallel rows in the longitudinal (spiral) direction. At the outer edge of the cuticle lies the diplosome with a minute flagellum. The hairs of the outer cells (eighty-three to one hundred hairs to a cell) form several parallel, horseshoe-shaped lines, with the convexity directed outward. The length of these hairs decreases from outside inward. The outer edge of the cuticle contains the diplosome.

Tectorial Membrane. The surface of the organ of Corti is covered by a ribbon-like, gelatinous structure, the tectorial membrane. After fixation its outer free edge is usually curled, or the whole membrane is detached from the epithelium (Figs. 572, 573). The width of the membrane increases toward the apex of the cochlea. It begins in the inner angle of the cochlear canal as a thin layer attached to the epithelial surface of the limbus. Farther outward, where the membrane overhangs the inner spiral sulcus and touches the organ of Corti, its lower surface remains even, while the upper one bulges considerably upward. Here its thickness reaches 25 microns. Passing over the organ of Corti, it again becomes thinner and after reaching the cells of Hensen it ends with a fringed edge.

The tectorial membrane is composed of a homogeneous ground substance with numerous fibrils, most conspicuous at the upper surface, where they form networks. In the deeper layers they are more or less parallel; their general direction is radial, but with a marked deviation from this plane toward the apex of the cochlea. Along the lower surface of the membrane, opposite the row of inner hair cells, the *stripe of Hensen* extends in the spiral direction. In the living condition and in well-fixed preparations the lower surface of the tectorial membrane rests upon the ends of the hairs which protrude from the hair cells.

Nerve Endings in the Organ of Corti. Except for the possible presence of vasomotor nerves in the labyrinth, the end branches of the cochlear nerve are the only nerve fibers in the cochlea. The presence of centrifugal fibers of unknown origin ending in the organ of Corti is doubtful, although such fibers are present in the modiolus and osseous spiral lamina and are probably sympathetic.

The nerve cells of the spiral ganglion are of the bipolar type; their central processes are myelinated and continue into the acoustic nerve. The peripheral, dendritic processes run through the canals of the osseous lamina and lose their myelin sheaths as they pass through the foramina nervosa on their way to the hair cells. A thin layer of myelin is also found on the surface of the cell body.

There are two kinds of nerve fibers in the organ of Corti. The first, thin and numerous, radiate from the spiral ganglion in parallel bundles to the nearest segments of the organ of Corti. Here each fiber divides into small branches which terminate with buttons attached to the surface of the hair cells. Because of their straight course they are called *direct acoustic nerve fibers* (orthoneurons of von Ebner). Each of them is stimulated by a compact group of hair cells.

Nerve fibers of the second type, usually thicker and fewer than the first, are also at first arranged radially. But after reaching the organ of Corti they turn sharply, follow a longitudinal (i.e., spiral) course and form parallel bundles beneath and between the several rows of hair cells and the supporting structures. Here they form so-called "plexuses," one beneath the inner hair cells, one in the inner tunnel, and several between the outer phalangeal cells. Because of their course these fibers are called *spiral fibers* (spironeurons of von Ebner). They, too, terminate with branches larger than in the direct fibers, each spiral fiber being related to a compact group of hair cells. The group of cells is always at a definite distance along the basilar papilla from the point where the fiber changes from the radial to the spiral course. The spiral fibers, while in the organ of Corti, as a rule turn toward the basal coil of the cochlea.

The presence of the two varieties of acoustic nerve fibers in the organ of Corti

is well established, but the interpretation of such an arrangement in terms of function is less certain. Although the relations between the peripheral receptors (hair cells) and the acoustic neurons are not as individualized as the monosynaptic relationships of the foveal cones, they are sufficiently restricted to permit the reception of localized stimuli impinging upon small segments of the cochlea. This applies to both direct and spiral fibers. The significance of the spiral fibers is unknown. Possibly, in collaboration with the groups of direct fibers, the spiral fibers serve in the reception of complex sounds, whereas the system of direct fibers alone is instrumental in the perception of simple tones.

In any event, the cochlea, like the retina, must have a receptor surface whose different points have different functional value. This view agrees with the fact that the basilar membrane is represented topically, or point for point, in the brain (Polyak, Lewi and Kobrak, Walker).

Nerves of the Labyrinth. The eighth cranial nerve supplies the sensory areas of the labyrinth. It consists of two parts of quite different functional nature and central connections—the *vestibular* and the *cochlear* nerves. The first divides into a superior and an inferior branch. The fibers of all these nerves are the central processes (axons) of bipolar ganglionic cells which form two ganglia. Of these, the spiral or cochlear ganglion is incorporated in the cochlear nerve and located in the modiolus of the cochlea, while the vestibular ganglion belongs to the vestibular nerve and is situated in the inner auditory meatus of the temporal bone. Corresponding with the subdivision of the vestibular nerve into a superior and an inferior branch, the vestibular ganglion can also be separated into a superior and an inferior part. The peripheral branches (dendrites) of the bipolar ganglionic cells run to the sensory areas. The superior vestibular ganglion sends out four branches which supply (1) the horizontal or lateral ampulla; (2) the frontal or superior ampulla; (3) the utricular macula; and (4) a small part of the

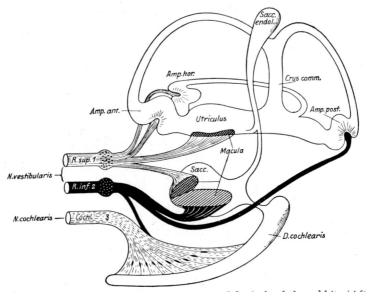

Fig. 577. Diagram of distribution of nerves in the membranous labyrinth of the rabbit. (After de Burlet, from Kolmer.)

saccular macula. From the inferior vestibular ganglion three branches arise. The first supplies the larger part of the saccula macula; the second, the sagittal or posterior ampulla; the third, the smallest, joins the fibers of the cochlear nerve. This last connection needs further study.

The vestibular nerve terminates centrally in the reflex centers of the medulla oblongata and the cerebellum. Its cortical connections are unknown. The cochlear nerve also has reflex connections in the medulla oblongata and the midbrain; but most of its fibers run in the lateral lemniscus to the medial geniculate body of the thalamus and thence to the sylvian fossa of the brain center for hearing.

Blood Vessels of the Labyrinth. The labyrinthine artery is a branch of the inferior cerebellar artery. It enters the internal meatus and divides into two branches, the *vestibular artery* and the *common cochlear artery*. The latter divides into the *vestibulocochlear artery* and the *cochlear artery proper*.

The vestibular artery supplies the upper and lateral parts of the utricle and saccule and parts of the superior and lateral semicircular canals. It forms dense networks of capillaries in the region of the maculae; in the thin connective tissue layer of these structures the capillary networks are loose.

The vestibulocochlear artery supplies the lower and medial parts of the utricle and saccule, the crus com-

mune, and the posterior semicircular canal with its vestibular branch. Its cochlear branch supplies the lowest part of the first cochlear coil.

The cochlear artery proper penetrates the cavities of the modiolus, where its branches form many zigzags and coils and run spirally to the apex; this is the so-called "spiral tract." From it, branches go to the spiral ganglion and, through the periosteum of the scala vestibuli and the spiral osseous lamina, to the inner parts of the basilar membrane. Here the capillaries are arranged in arcades in the tympanic covering layer under the tunnel and the limbus; from them arises the *vas spirale*. The vascular stria and the spiral ligament receive their blood through branches of the spiral arterial tract which run in the roof of the scala vestibuli. They do not form connections with the vessels of the basilar membrane. The lower wall of the scala tympani receives its own small arteries from the same source.

The course of the veins of the labyrinth is quite different from that of the arteries. There are three draining venous systems. In the cochlea, veins originate in the region of the prominentia spiralis and run downward and inward through the periosteum of the scala tympani to the spiral vein, which is found under the spiral ganglion. Upper and lower spiral veins, belonging to the corresponding coils of the cochlea, receive branches from the osseous spiral lamina and from the spiral ganglion. Above the spiral vein is the small vein of the spiral lamina which receives a part of the blood from the spiral lamina and from the spiral ganglion and is connected by anastomoses with the spiral vein. These cochlear veins form a plexus in the modiolus which empties the blood partly into the vena auditiva interna, which leaves the labyrinth along the labyrin-

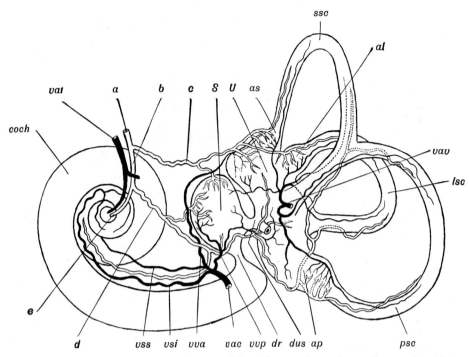

Fig. 578. Diagram of right human membranous labyrinth, seen from the medioposterior side, to show distribution of blood vessels; the endolymphatic saccule cut off. *a*, Arteria labyrinthica; *al*, lateral ampulla; *ap*, posterior ampulla; *as*, superior ampulla; *b*, arteria cochlearis communis; *c*, arteria vestibularis; *coch*, cochlea; *d*, arteria vestibulocochlearis; *dr*, ductus reuniens; *dus*, ductus utriculosaccularis; *e*, arteria cochlearis propria; *lsc*, lateral semicircular canal; *psc*, posterior semicircular canal; *S*, saccule; *ssc*, superior semicircular canal; *U*, utricle; *vac*, vena aquaeductus cochleae; *vai*, vena auditiva interna; *vav*, vena aquaeductus vestibuli; *vsi*, vena spiralis inferior; *vss*, vena spiralis superior; *vva*, vena vestibularis anterior; *vvp*, vena vestibularis posterior. (Redrawn and modified from Stöhr.)

thine artery, and partly into the vein of the cochlear aqueduct, which drains into the jugular vein. The veins of the vestibular apparatus and the semicircular canals empty into the veins of the vestibular and of the cochlear aqueducts.

This arrangement of the vessels in the internal ear seems to insure the best possible protection of the sound receptors from concussions caused by the pulsating waves. The arteries are arranged, for the most part, in the wall of the scala vestibuli, while the wall of the scala tympani contains the veins. The zona pectinata of the basilar membrane and the vestibular membrane are devoid of blood vessels. The course of the spiral arteries in the modiolus probably also contributes to the damping of pulsations. In certain mammals the coils of these arteries are so prominent that they suggest glomeruli.

True lymphatics are absent from the labyrinth. Instead, the excess of the tissue liquid is drained into the perilymphatic spaces, which are connected through the cochlear aqueduct with the subarachnoid spaces. A certain amount of drainage may be effected through the perivascular and perineural connective tissue sheaths.

Histophysiological Remarks. The tympanic membrane, besides protecting the middle ear, receives the sound waves and transmits them to the auditory ossicles.

Function of the Cochlea. The vibrations of the tympanic membrane are transmitted through the chain of auditory ossicles to the fenestra ovalis and hence to the perilymph filling the scala tympani. The organ of Corti is the receptor for sound stimuli. It is generally believed that the analysis of the sound waves is accomplished in the organ of Corti and that this depends upon the basilar membrane, a mechanism for *sympathetic vibration* or *resonance*.

Function of the Vestibule. The nervous impulses elicited by the stimulation of the maculae and the cristae play an important role in the regulation and coordination of the movements of equilibrium and locomotion. These impulses exert their influence upon coordinated muscular contractions, upon muscular tonus, and upon the eyes through the brain stem and the cerebellum.

Histogenetic Remarks. External and Middle Ears. The tympanic cavity and the auditory tube are derivatives of the first branchial pouch. The external auditory meatus develops through an invagination of the integument directed toward the tympanic cavity. The tissue layer remaining between this invagination and the tympanic cavity becomes the tympanic membrane.

Otic Vesicle. The primordium of the labyrinth develops as a shallow groove of thickened ectoderm, dorsally to the first branchial groove, on both sides of

the brain, between the myelencephalon and the metencephalon (human embryo of eight somites). The groove is invaginated into the subjacent mesenchyme and becomes the *otic vesicle*. In a human embryo of 2.8 mm. it separates through constriction from the ectoderm and is surrounded by mesenchyme. The vesicle is lined by tall, pseudostratified epithelium which secretes the endolymph filling it. From its earliest stages the otic vesicle comes into intimate contact with the large acoustic ganglion, which later divides into the vestibular and cochlear ganglia. Unequal proliferation in places in the wall of the otic vesicle transforms it into an extremely complex system of saclike and tubelike cavities. Soon after its isolation from the ectoderm, the dorsal periphery of the vesicle sends out an evagination which is the primordium of the endo-

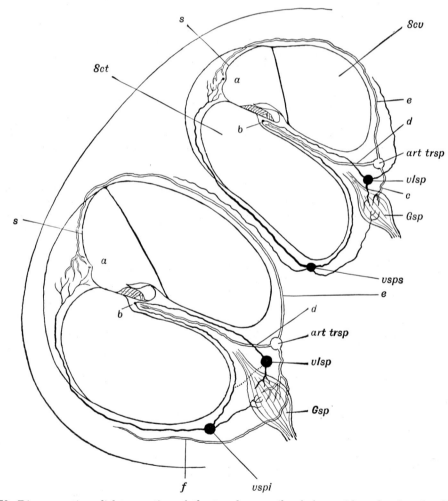

Fig. 579. Diagrammatic radial transection of the two lower coils of the cochlea, showing the distribution of blood vessels; arteries with double contours, veins black. *art trsp,* Artery of spiral tract; *a,* prominentia spiralis; *b,* vas spirale; *c,* artery supplying the spiral ganglion; *d,* artery supplying the spiral lamina; *e,* artery circling the upper wall of the scala; *f,* artery supplying partition between two coils of the cochlea; *Gsp,* ganglion spirale; *s,* stria vascularis; *Sct,* scala tympani; *Scv,* scala vestibuli; *vlsp,* vein of the spiral lamina; *vspi,* inferior spiral vein; *vsps,* superior spiral vein. (Redrawn and modified from Stohr.)

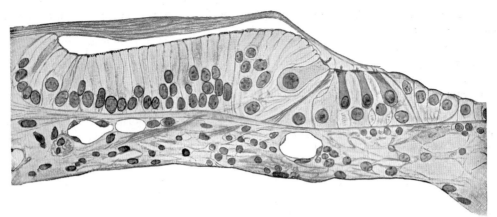

Fig. 580. Histogenesis of the organ of Corti in a human fetus of six months. The tectorial membrane has become detached from the large epithelial ridge and remains connected only at the periphery with the surface of the smaller ridge (the future organ of Corti); hair cells make their appearance. 311 ×. (After Kolmer.)

lymphatic duct. Then a larger dorsal part of the vesicle becomes distinct from a smaller ventral part. The first —the vestibular part—gives rise to the semicircular canals and the utricles. The second, the cochlear part, forms the saccule and the cochlea.

On the wall of the vestibular part three evaginations appear and develop into the three semicircular canals, each with an ampulla. What remains of the vestibular part is now the utricle. The cochlear part sends out a curved outpocketing—the primordium of the cochlea. It gradually gains in length, coils as it grows, and becomes separated from the saccule by a deep constriction. In a human embryo of 22 mm. the form of the labyrinth corresponds to that of the adult.

Maculae and Cristae. The maculae and cristae develop earlier than the organ of Corti. On its medial side, where the acoustic ganglion is located, the epithelium of the wall of the otic vesicle develops a thickened area, the *macula communis*, which later divides into an upper and a lower epithelial pad. The first gives rise to the macula of the utricle and to the upper and lateral cristae. A small part of the second thickening forms the crista of the posterior ampulla; the rest of the second pad divides into the macula sacculi and the primordium of the organ of Corti, which gradually extends into the growing cochlea.

In the maculae and cristae of a human embryo of 15 mm. the plumper and darker neuro-epithelial cells and the more slender supporting cells can be distinguished. In an embryo of 18.5 mm. the hair cells have developed a small tuft of hairs.

The cupula and the otolithic membrane arise in the center of the respective epithelial surfaces, when the two cell types just begin to differentiate, while at their edge the maculae or cristae are still growing. The membrane and the cupula appear first as a thin homogeneous layer on the epithelial surface. Then, new layers of jelly-like substance are added; above the hair cells free spaces remain, into which the growing hairs expand. The otoconia first arise as tiny, granular pre-

cipitates. They are believed to be secreted by the epithelium as soluble calcium salts and to diffuse into the gelatinous layer; when they reach its surface they precipitate as crystals.

Histogenesis of the Organ of Corti. The differentiation of the organ of Corti proceeds gradually from the basal coil of the growing cochlea to its apex. The epithelium extends along the basal wall of the canal as a long ridge which divides longitudinally into a large, inner ridge and a small, outer one. In the former, connective tissue penetrates the epithelium and separates it into radial rows of flask-shaped cells embedded in connective tissue, while their cuticles form a mosaic pavement on the surface. This region develops into the limbus spiralis. In the outer part of this ridge, the tall epithelial cells gradually involute, leaving a squamous epithelium which lines the internal spiral sulcus.

The small, outer ridge, the primordium of the organ of Corti, at first consists of uniform cells. Then, flask-shaped, inner and outer hair cells appear among them. The remaining elements elaborate tonofibrils and differentiate into the supporting cells. On the surface their cuticles form a continuous membrane.

The surface of both epithelial ridges is covered from the beginning by a fibrillated, jelly-like substance, the future tectorial membrane.

The connections between the sensory areas of the labyrinth and the nerve fibers of the vestibular and cochlear ganglia are established in early stages. The free ends of the fibers find their way into the thickened epithelial patches and form the endings described earlier.

Histogenesis of the Perilymphatic Space. While the otic vesicle grows and differentiates, the mesenchyme surrounding the growing labyrinth develops into a layer of cartilage, which remains separated from the epithelium by a layer of mesenchyme. This later condenses into a fibrous layer and, with the epithelium, forms the wall of the membranous labyrinth. Between the wall and the cartilaginous capsule, the mesenchyme loosens and its meshes enlarge into the perilymphatic spaces, around the membranous labyrinth. These spaces are traversed by strands of connective tissue, which connect the cartilaginous capsule with the wall of the membranous labyrinth. The mesenchyme remains dense where the epithelium forms the sensory areas. The mesenchymal cells which remain on the surface of the trabeculae and of the labyrinthine wall and perichondrium become mesenchymal epithelium.

In tadpoles of the anura, if the otic vesicle is transplanted into another area, it becomes surrounded by cartilage arising from local mesenchyme.

The cochlea receives its perilymphatic spaces, the two scalae, through extension of the perilymphatic cisterna. In embryos of 43 mm. the scala tympani appears in the region of the cochlear fenestra and the scala vestibuli at the 50-mm. stage. They gradually grow and coil with the cochlear duct, remaining attached to its upper and lower walls. At the outer periphery of the cochlear duct, as well as at its inner edge, the wall of the duct remains connected with the cartilaginous capsule. Later, ossification occurs and gives rise to the modiolus and the osseous cochlea.

REFERENCES

Alexander, G., and Marburg, O.: Handbuch der Neurologie des Ohres. Vienna, Berlin, 1921–26.

Bast, T. H.: Development of the Optic Capsule. I. Resorption of the Cartilage in the Canal Portion of the Optic Capsule in Human Fetuses and Its Relation to the Growth of the Semicircular Canals. Arch. Otolaryngol., 16:19, 1932.

Bast, T. H., and Anson, B. J.: The Temporal Bone and The Ear. Springfield, Illinois.

Bowen, R. E.: The Cupula of the Membranous Labyrinth. J. Comp. Neurol., 58:517, 1933.

Guild, S. R.: Correlation of Differences in the Density of Innervation of the Organ of Corti with Differences in Acuity of Hearing. Acta Otolaryngol., 15: 1931.

Hamberger, C. A., and Hydén, H.: Cytochemical Changes in the Cochlear Ganglion Caused by Acoustic Stimulation and Trauma. Acta Otolaryngol., Suppl. 61, 1945.

Held, H.: Die Cochlea der Säugetiere, etc. In Bethe et al., Handb. d. Norm. u. Pathol. Physiol., (11/1), 1926.

Kolmer, W.: Gehörorgan, in v. Möllendorff's Handb. d. mikroskop. Anat., (3/1), 250, 1927.

Lorente de Nó, R.: Études sur l'anatomie et la physiologie du labyrinthe de l'oreille et du VIIIe nerf. Trabajos (Travaux) Invest. Biol. Madrid, 24:53, 1926; Anatomy of the Eighth Nerve. Laryngoscope, 43:3, 1933.

Polyak, S.: Ueber den allgemeinen Bauplan des Gehörsystems, etc. Ztschr. f. d. g. Neurol. u. Ps., 110:1, 1927.

Polyak, S., McHugh, G., and Judd, D. K., Jr.: The Human Ear in Anatomical Transparencies. New York, 1946.

Ramón y Cajal, S.: Histologie du système nerveux. Paris, 2 vols., 1909–11.

Shambaugh, G. E.: Cytology of the Internal Ear, in Cowdry's Special Cytology, (2), 927, 1932.

Tello, J. F.: Le réticule des cellules ciliées du labyrinthe chez la souris et son indépendence des terminaisons nerveuses de la VIIIe paire. Trabajos (Travaux) Invest. Biol. Madrid, 27:151, 1931–32.

INDEX